Major Geological, Climatic, and Biological Events

Approximate time since beginning of interval in millions of years before the present.

Time	Events
0.01 1.7	There were extensive and repeated periods of glaciation in the Northern Hemisphere. The Neogene midlatitude savanna faunas became extinct, and hominids expanded throughout the Old World. Near the end of the interval hominids reached the New World and there was an extinction of many large mammals, especially in the New World and in Australia. The remaining carnivorous flightless birds also became extinct
5.2 23	Cooler and more arid climates persisted, resulting from mountain uplift and the formation of the Isthmus of Panama near the end of the interval. The Arctic ice cap formed by the end of the interval. The first grasslands spread in the middle latitudes. Modern families of mammals and birds radiated, and marine mammals and birds diversified in the oceans. The first hominids were seen near the end of the interval.
33.4 55 **65**	Global climate was warm in the early part of the interval, with forests above the arctic circle, but later in the interval temperatures fell in the higher latitudes, with the formation of the Antarctic ice cap. Mammals diversified into larger body sizes and a greater variety of adaptive types, including predators and herbivores. Mammal radiations included archaic forms, now extinct, and the earliest members of living orders. Giant carnivorous flightless birds common as predators.
145.5	Further separation of the continents occurred, including the breakup of the southern continent, Godwanaland. Teleost fishes radiated, but marine reptiles flourished. Angiosperms first appeared, and rapidly diversified to become the dominant land plants by the end of the period. Dinosaurs remained the dominant tetrapods, but small mammals diversified. Air space and shorelines were shared by birds and pterosaurs, and the first snakes appeared. A major mass extinction at the end of the period, defining the end of the Mesozoic, claimed dinosaurs, pterosaurs and marine reptiles, as well as many marine invertebrates.
208	The world continent began to break up, with the formation of the Atlantic ocean. Marine invertebrates began to take on a modern aspect with the diversification of predators, modern sharks and rays appeared, and marine reptiles diversified. Conifers and other gymnosperms were the dominant terrestrial vegetation, and insects diversified. Dinosaurs diversified while mammals remained small and relatively inconspicuous. The first birds, lizards, and salamanders were seen at the end of the period.
245	The world continent was relatively high, with few shallow seas. No evidence of glaciation existed, and the interior of the continent was arid. Seed fern terrestrial vegetation was replaced by conifers in the later part of the period. Mammallike reptiles declined, while archosaurian reptiles (including dinosaur ancestors) diversified. Remaining large nonamniote tetrapods now all specialized aquatic forms. First appearances by the end of the period included: true mammals, dinosaurs, pterosaurs, marine reptiles, crocodiles, lepidosaurs, froglike amphibians, and teleost fishes.
290	A single world continent, Pangea, was formed at the end of the period. Glaciation ceased early in the period. The large terrestrial nonamniote tetrapods declined and the amniotes radiated. Amniote diversification included the ancestors of modern reptiles and the ancestors of mammals, the mammallike reptiles, which were the dominant large terrestrial tetrapods. The first herbivorous tetrapods were known. The largest known mass extinction event occurred on both land and sea the end of the period, defining the end of the Paleozoic.
363	There was a major glaciation in the second half of the period, with low atmospheric levels of CO_2. Coal swamps were prevalent in the then tropical areas of North America and Europe. Major radiation of insects, including flying forms. Diversification of jawed fishes, including sharklike forms and primitive bony fishes, and first appearance of modern types of jawless fishes. Extensive radiation of nonamniote tetrapods, with the appearance of the first amniotes (including the earliest mammallike reptiles) by the late part of the period.
409	There was major mountain building in North America and Europe. Major fresh water basins preserved, containing the first tetrapods at the end of the period in equatorial regions. About the same time there were the first forests with tall trees on land, and terrestrial arthropods diversified. Both jawed and jawless fishes diversified, but both experienced major extinctions toward the end of the period, with the disappearance of the ostracoderms, the armored jawless fishes.
439	The extensive shallow seas continued, but on dry land there was the first evidence of vascular plants and arthropods. Jawless fishes radiated and jawed fishes (sharklike forms) were now definitely known.
490	There were widespread shallow seas over the continents, and the global climate was equable until a sharp glaciation at the end of the period. First evidence of complex plants on land. Major radiation of marine animals, including the first well-known jawless fishes and fragmentary evidence of jawed fishes.
545	Continental masses of the Late Proterozoic now broken up in to smaller blocks, covered by shallow seas. Explosive radiation of animals at the beginning of the period, with first appearance of forms with shells or other hard coverings. First appearance of chordates and great diversification of arthropods, including trilobites. Possible first vertebrates at the end of the period.
2,500	Formation of large continental masses. Oxygen first appears in the atmosphere. First eukaryotic organisms appeared around 2 billion years ago. Major diversification of life at 1 billion years ago, with multicellular organisms, including algae. First animals appeared around 600 million years ago, just after a major glaciation.
4,600	Formation of the earth. Major bombardment of the earth by extraterrestrial bodies, precluding formation of life until 4 billion years ago (first fossils known at 3.5 billion years ago). Small continents. Hydrosphere definite at 3.8 billion years, atmosphere without free oxygen.

Vertebrate Life

Fifth Edition

Vertebrate Life

F. Harvey Pough
Arizona State University West

Christine M. Janis
Brown University

John B. Heiser
Cornell University

Prentice Hall International, Inc.

Senior Editor: Teresa Ryu
Executive Editor: Sheri L. Snavely
Editor in Chief: Paul F. Corey
Editorial Director: Tim Bozik
Assistant Vice President of Production and Manufacturing: David W. Riccardi
Executive Managing Editor: Kathleen Schiaparelli
Project Management: J. Carey Publishing Service
Senior Marketing Manager: Jennifer Welchans
Manufacturing Manager: Trudy Pisciotti
Manufacturing Buyer: Ben Smith
Director of Creative Services: Paula Maylahn
Associate Creative Director: Amy Rosen
Art Director: Heather Scott
Assistant to Art Director: John Christiana
Art Manager: Gus Vibal
Art Editor: Karen Branson
Text Designer: Anne Flanagan
Cover Designer: Bruce Kenselaar
Cover Photograph: © Ulrich Doring
Photo Editor: Lorinda Morris-Nantz
Photo Researcher: Mary Teresa Giancoli
Editorial Assitants: Lisa Tarabokjia and Nancy Bauer
Art Studio: Laura Schuett and Academy Artworks
Text Composition: Preparé/Emilcomp

© 1999, 1996 by Prentice-Hall, Inc.
Simon & Schuster / A Viacom Company
Upper Saddle River, New Jersey 07458

Printed in the United States of America

10 9 8 7 6 5 4 3 2

ISBN 0-13-020047-6

Prentice-Hall International (UK) Limited, *London*
Prentice-Hall of Australia Pty. Limited, *Sydney*
Prentice-Hall of Canada, Inc., *Toronto*
Prentice-Hall Hispanoamericana, S. A., *Mexico*
Prentice-Hall of India Private Limited, *New Delhi*
Prentice-Hall of Japan, Inc., *Tokyo*
Simon & Schuster Asia Pte. Ltd., *Singapore*
Editora Prentice-Hall do Brasil, Ltda., *Rio de Janeiro*
Prentice Hall, *Upper Saddle River, New Jersey*

About the Authors

F. Harvey Pough began his biological career at the age of fourteen when he conducted his first research project on the ecology of turtles in Rhode Island. His reserarch now focuses on organismal biology, blending physiology, morphology, behavior, and ecology in an evolutionary context. He greatly enjoys teaching undergraduates and has taught courses in vertebrate zoology, functional ecology, herpetology, and the ecology, environmental physiology, and evolution of humans. After 23 years at Cornell University, he moved to Arizona State University West as Chair of the Department of Life Sciences to focus on the challenges of teaching undergraduates at a university that emphasizes community involvement. When not slaving over a hot computer revising *Vertebrate Life*, he enjoys walking in the desert with his labrador retriever, Martha.

Christine M. Janis is an Associate Professor of Biology at Brown University where she teaches comparative anatomy and vertebrate evolution. A British citizen, she obtained her bachelor's degree at Cambridge University and then crossed the pond to get her Ph.D. at Harvard University. She is a vertebrate paleontologist with a particular interest in mammalian evolution (especially hoofed mammals) and faunal responses to climatic change. She first became interested in vertebrate evolution after seeing the movie *Fantasia* at the impressionable age of seven. That critical year was also the year that she began riding lessons, and she has owned at least one horse since the age of 12. She is still an active rider, although no longer as aggressive a competitor (she used to do combined training events). She attributes her lifestyle to the fact that she has failed to outgrow either the dinosaur phase or the horse phase.

John B. Heiser was born and raised in Indiana and completed his undergraduate degree in biology at Purdue University. He earned his Ph.D. in ichthyology from Cornell University for studies of the behavior, evolution and ecology of coral reef fishes, research which he continues today with molecular colleagues. For fifteen years he was Director of the Shoals Marine Laboratory operated by Cornell University and the University of New Hampshire on the Isles of Shoals in the Gulf of Maine. While at the Isles of Shoals his research interests focused on opposite ends of the vertebrate spectrum–hagfish and baleen whales. J.B. enjoys teaching vertebrate morphology, evolution, and ecology both in the campus classroom and in the field and is recipient of the Clark Distinguished Teaching Award from Cornell University. His hobbies are natural history, travel and nature photography and videography, especially underwater using scuba. He has pursued his natural history interests on every continent and all the world's major ocean regions. Because of his experience he is a popular ecotourism leader having led Cornell Adult University groups to the Caribbean, Sea of Cortez, French Polynesia, Central America, the Amazon, Borneo, Antartica, and Spitsbergen in the High Arctic.

Brief Contents

Contents

16   Ectothermy: A Low-Cost Approach to Life   468

PART 4   Terrestrial Endotherms: Birds and Mammals   486

17   Characteristics of Birds: Specializations for Flight   487

18   The Ecology and Behavior of Birds   516

19   The Synapsida and the Evolution of Mammals   552

24 Humans as Vertebrates

Preface

The fifth edition of *Vertebrate Life* continues to reflect extraordinary activity in vertebrate biology. The most pervasive innovations have resulted from the widespread adoption of phylogenetic systematics (cladistics) as the basis for determining the evolutionary relationships of organisms. The emphasis that this system of classification places on the importance of monophyletic groupings has ramifications in many areas of biology. As an objective (albeit frequently controversial) method that reflects information about the sequence of changes during evolution, cladistics provides an evolutionary framework in which ideas from other biological specialties can be accommodated. As a result, studies of behavior, physiology, and ecology are increasingly being placed in an explicitly evolutionary context, and this common ground has fostered increased interaction among those specialties.

In this edition we have expanded the cladistic classification originally introduced in the third edition, especially in our treatment of anatomy and physiology. As in previous editions, we have included cladograms illustrating the postulated relationships of vertebrates. In doing so, we have tried to reconcile the views of various authorities and point out major areas of disagreement. We pruned excessive detail from the cladograms in this edition while retaining information about the geologic time span for the lineages illustrated. The cladograms include synopses of the character states on which they are based and citations of the primary sources used. This information will facilitate exploration of different views, and will help faculty and students to modify the phylogenies presented here as new interpretations are published.

Literature citations have been brought up to date, with many references from 1997 and later. As before, we have chosen citations on the basis of their helpfulness to students attempting to enter the literature of the subject; review articles are cited when possible, and recent references are used because students can trace earlier work through them.

■ Acknowledgments

The ability of our editor, Teresa Ryu, to combine support and decisiveness was critical to keeping the project on schedule, and it has been a pleasure working with her. Jennifer Carey, our production manager, worked tirelessly to pull the various parts of the book together. Without her organizational ability and command of the intricacies of publishing the manuscript would still be spread in pieces across the floors of the authors' houses. Laura Schuett's extraordinary ability to capture the essence of an animal or a structure has enriched the illustrations immeasurably. We are grateful to Carol Abrazincas whose thumbnail sketches make the revised cladograms more informative and more attractive than previous versions.

Writing a book with a scope as broad as this one requires the assistance of many people, and we are grateful to the following colleagues for their generous responses to our requests for information and their comments and suggestions:

William E. Bemis, *University of Massachusetts*
Beth Brainerd, *University of Massachusetts*
Matthew Carrano, *University of Chicago*
Robert Carroll, *McGill University*
Fuzz Crompton, *Harvard University*
M. J. Fouquette, Jr., *Arizona State University*
Margaret H. Fusari, *University of California, Santa Cruz*
Erik W. A. Gergus, *Arizona State University West*
H. T. Hendrickson, *University of North Carolina at Greensboro*
Fritz Hertel, *University of California, Los Angeles*
James A. Hopson, *University of Chicago*
Karel Liem, *Harvard University*
Jon Mallatt, *Washington State University*
Keith B. Malmos, *Arizona State University West*
John Maisey, *American Museum of Natural History*
Betty McGuire, *Smith College*
Richard R. Montanucci, *Clemson University*
Marion Preest, *University of Miami*
John Ruben, *Oregon State University*
David F. Russell, *University of Missouri-St. Louis*
Gordon W. Schuett, *Arizona State University West*
J. John Sepkoski, Jr., *University of Chicago*
Ellen M. Smith, *Arizona State University West*
Moya Smith, *Guys Hospital, London*
Jessica Theodor, *Brown University*
Blaire Van Valkenburgh, *University of California, Los Angeles*
Paul Verrell, *Washington State University*
Fred Wasserman, *Boston University*
Bruce A. Wunder, *Colorado State University*

F. Harvey Pough
Christine M. Janis
John B. Heiser

Vertebrate Life

PART 1 Vertebrate Diversity, Function, and Evolution

The 45,000 living species of vertebrates inhabit nearly every part of the Earth, and other kinds of vertebrates that are now extinct lived in habitats that no longer exist. Increasing knowledge of the diversity of vertebrates was one of the products of European exploration and expansion that began in the fifteenth and sixteenth centuries. In the middle of the eighteenth century, the Swedish naturalist Carolus Linnaeus developed a binominal classification to catalog the varieties of animals and plants. The Linnean system remains the basis for naming living organisms today.

A century later Charles Darwin explained the diversity of plants and animals as the product of natural selection and evolution, and in the early twentieth century Darwin's work was coupled with the burgeoning information about mechanisms of genetic inheritance. This combination of genetics and evolutionary biology is known as the New Synthesis or Neo-Darwinism, and continues to be the basis for understanding the mechanics of evolution. Recent work has broadened our view of evolutionary mechanisms by suggesting, on the one hand, that some major events in evolution may be the result of chance rather than selection, and, on the other hand, that natural selection can sometimes extend beyond individuals to related individuals, populations, or even entire species. The emphasis on methods of classifying animals has also changed during the twentieth century, and classification, which began as a way of trying to organize the diversity of organisms, has become a way of generating testable hypotheses about evolution.

Vertebrate biology and the fossil record of vertebrates have been at the center of these changes in our view of life. Comparative studies of the anatomy, embryology, and physiology of living vertebrates have often supplemented the fossil record. These studies reveal that evolution acts by changing existing structures. All vertebrates have basic characteristics in common that are the products of their common ancestry, and progressive modifications of these characters can trace the progress of evolution. Thus, an understanding of vertebrate form and function is basic to understanding the evolution of vertebrates and the ecology and behavior of living species.

CHAPTER
1

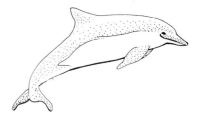

The Diversity, Evolution, and Classification of Vertebrates

Evolution is central to vertebrate biology because it provides a principle that organizes the diversity we see among living vertebrates and helps to fit extinct forms into the context of living species. Classification, initially a process of attaching names to organisms, has become a method of understanding evolution. Current views of evolution stress natural selection operating at the level of individuals as a predominant mechanism that produces change over time. The processes and events of evolution are intimately linked to the changes that have occurred on Earth during the history of vertebrates. These changes have resulted from the movements of continents and the effects of those movements on climates and geography. In this chapter we present an overview of the scene, the participants, and the rules governing the events that have shaped the biology of vertebrates.

■ The Vertebrate Story

Mention "animal" and most people will think of a vertebrate. Vertebrates are often abundant and conspicuous parts of people's experience of the natural world. Vertebrates are also very diverse: The approximately 50,000 extant (= currently living) species of vertebrates range in size from fishes that weigh as little as 0.1 gram when they are fully mature to whales that weigh nearly 100,000 kilograms. Vertebrates live in virtually all the habitats on Earth: Bizarre fishes, some with mouths so large they can swallow prey larger than their own bodies, cruise through the depths of the sea, sometimes luring prey to them with glowing lights. Some 15 kilometers above the fishes, migrating birds fly over the crest of the Himalayas, the highest mountains on Earth.

The behaviors of vertebrates are as diverse and complex as their body forms. Vertebrate life is ener-

getically expensive, and vertebrates get the energy they need from food they eat. Carnivores eat the flesh of other animals and show a wide range of methods of capturing prey: Some predators search the environment to find prey, whereas others wait in one place for prey to come to them. Some carnivores pursue their prey at high speeds, others pull prey into their mouths by suction. In some cases the foraging behaviors that vertebrates use appear to be exactly the ones that maximize the amount of energy they obtain for the time they spend hunting; in other cases vertebrates can appear to be remarkably inept predators. Many vertebrates swallow their prey intact, sometimes while it is alive and struggling, but other vertebrates have very specific methods of dispatching prey: Venomous snakes inject complex mixtures of toxins, and cats (of all sizes from house cats to tigers) kill their prey with a distinctive bite on the neck. Herbivores eat plants. Plants cannot run away when an animal approaches, but they are hard to digest and they frequently contain toxic compounds. Herbivorous vertebrates show an array of specializations to deal with the difficulties of eating plants. These specializations include elaborately sculptured teeth and digestive tracts that provide sites in which symbiotic microorganisms digest compounds that are impervious to the digestive systems of vertebrates.

Reproduction is a critical factor in the evolutionary success of an organism, and vertebrates show an astonishing range of behaviors associated with mating and reproduction. In general, males court females and females care for the young, but these roles are reversed in many species of vertebrates. The forms of reproduction employed by vertebrates range from laying eggs to giving birth to babies that are largely or entirely independent of their parents (precocial young). These variations range across almost all kinds of vertebrates: Many fishes and amphibians produce precocial young and a few mammals lay eggs. At the time of birth or hatching some vertebrates are entirely self-sufficient and never see their parents, whereas other vertebrates (including humans) have extended periods of obligatory parental care. Extensive parental care is found in seemingly unlikely groups of vertebrates—fishes that incubate eggs in their mouths, frogs that incubate eggs in their stomachs, and birds that feed their nestlings a fluid called crop milk that is very similar in composition to mammalian milk.

The diversity of living vertebrates is fascinating, but the species now living are only a small proportion of the species of vertebrates that have existed. For each living species there may be as many as ten extinct species, and some of these have no counterparts among living forms. The dinosaurs, for example, that dominated the Earth for 180 million years are so entirely different from any living animals that it is hard to reconstruct the lives they led. Even mammals were once more diverse than they are now: The Pleistocene saw giants of many kinds—ground sloths as big as modern rhinoceroses, and raccoons and rodents as large as bears. Humans are great apes, close relatives of chimpanzees and gorillas, and much of the biology of humans is best understood in the context of our vertebrate heritage. The number of species of vertebrates probably reached its maximum in the Pliocene and Pleistocene, and has been declining since then. Some parts of that decline can probably be attrib-

uted to the effects of humans on species they used for food or viewed as competitors, although changes in climate and vegetation have also been instrumental. In the modern world, however, the effects of human activities are paramount, and the fate of other species of vertebrates is very much affected, for good or ill, by human decisions. Our responsibilities to other vertebrates cannot be ignored.

The story of vertebrates is fascinating: Where they originated, how they evolved, what they do, and how they work provide endless intriguing details. In preparing to tell this story we must introduce some basic information: what the different kinds of vertebrates are called and how they are classified, how evolution works, and what the world within which the story of vertebrates unfolded was like. In this chapter we provide an overview of the vertebrates and the processes of evolution and environmental change that have shaped them.

■ The Different Kinds of Vertebrates

The modern approach to biological classification, which is popularly known as cladistics, recognizes only groups of organisms that are related by common descent, or **phylogeny** (*phyla* = tribe, *genesis* = origin). The application of cladistic methods is making the study of evolution more rigorous than it has been heretofore. The natural groups recognized by cladistics are easier to understand than the artificial groups we are used to, except that we are familiar with the names of the artificial groups and the names of the new groups are sometimes strange. At this point we need to establish a basis for talking about particular animals by naming them, and to relate the old, familiar names to the new, less familiar ones. Figure 1–1 shows the major kinds of vertebrates and the relative numbers of living species. In the following sections we describe briefly the different kinds of living vertebrates.

Hagfishes and Lampreys (Myxinoidea and Petromyzontoidea)

Lampreys and hagfishes are elongate, scaleless, and slimy and have no internal hard tissues. They are scavengers and parasites and are specialized for those roles. Hagfishes (about 40 species) are marine and occur on the continental shelf and open ocean at depths around 100 meters, whereas many of the

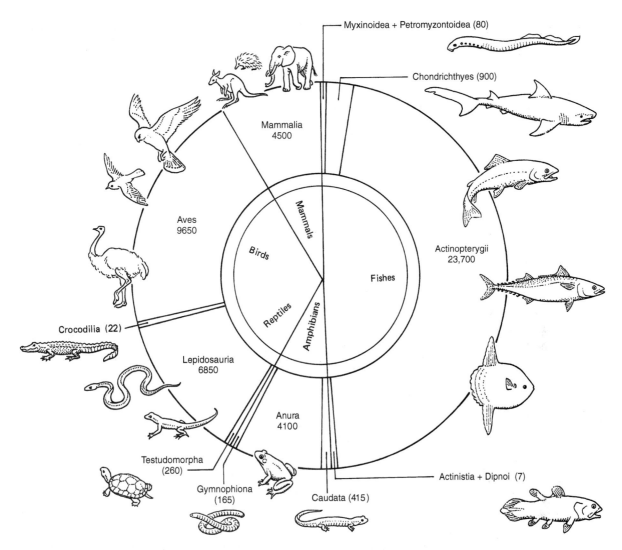

Figure 1–1   Diversity of vertebrates. The areas within the diagram correspond to the approximate numbers of living species in each group. Common names appear within the inner circle, and the formal names for the groups are on the outer parts of the diagram.

41 species of lampreys are migratory forms that live in oceans and spawn in rivers.

Hagfishes and lampreys are unique among living vertebrates because they lack jaws, and they occupy an important position in the study of vertebrate evolution. Hagfishes and lampreys have traditionally been grouped as agnathans (*a* = without, *gnath* = jaw) or cyclostomes (*cyclo* = round, *stoma* = mouth), but they probably represent two independent evolutionary lineages. Hagfishes lack many of the features that characterize most vertebrates; for example, they have no trace of vertebrae. In contrast, lampreys share many derived characters with jawed vertebrates. The jawless condition of both lampreys and hagfishes, however, is ancestral.

Sharks, Rays, and Ratfishes (Elasmobranchii and Holocephali)

Sharks have a reputation for ferocity that most of the 350 to 400 species would have difficulty living up to. Many sharks are small (15 centimeters or less), and the largest species, the whale shark, which grows to 10 meters, is a filter feeder that subsists on plankton it strains from the water. The 450 species of rays are dorsoventrally flattened, frequently bottom dwellers that swim with undulations of their extremely broad pectoral fins. Ratfish are bizarre marine fishes with long, slender tails and buck-toothed faces that look rather like rabbits. The name Chondrichthyes (*chondro* = cartilage, *ichthyes* = fish) refers to the cartilaginous skeletons of these fishes.

Bowfin, Gars, and Others (Actinopterygii)

Bony fishes are so diverse that any attempt to characterize them briefly is doomed to failure. Two broad categories can be recognized, the ray-finned fishes (actinopterygians; *actino* = ray, *ptero* = wing or fin) and the lobe-finned or fleshy-finned fishes (sarcopterygians; *sarco* = lobe).

The actinopterygian fishes we have included in this category are called polypterids, holosteans, and neopterygians in various systems of classification. Most have cylindrical bodies, thick scales, and jaws armed with sharp teeth. These fishes seize prey in their mouths with a sudden rush or gulp; they lack the specializations of the jaw apparatus that allow derived bony fishes to use more complex feeding modes.

Teleost Fishes (Actinopterygii)

More than 20,000 species of fishes fall into this category and they cover every imaginable range of body sizes, habitats, and habits, from seahorses to the giant ocean sunfish. Most of the familiar fishes are in this category—the bass and panfish you have fished for in fresh water, and the sole (a kind of flounder) and redfish you have eaten in restaurants. Modifications of the jaw apparatus have allowed many teleosts to be highly specialized in their feeding habits.

Lungfishes and the Coelacanth (Dipnoi and Actinistia)

These are the sarcopterygian (lobe-finned) fishes. They are the living fishes most closely related to terrestrial vertebrates. The lobe-finned fishes are heavy-bodied and slow-moving. The four species of lungfishes live in fresh water, and the coelacanth is marine.

Salamanders, Frogs, and Caecilians (Urodela, Anura, and Gymnophiona)

These three groups of vertebrates are popularly known as amphibians (*amphi* = double, *bios* = life) in recognition of their complex life histories, which often include an aquatic larval form (the larva of a salamander or caecilian and the tadpole of a frog) and a terrestrial adult. All amphibians have bare skins (that is, lacking scales, hair, or feathers) that are important in the exchange of water, ions, and gases with their environment. Salamanders are elongate animals, mostly terrestrial and usually with four legs; anurans (frogs, toads, treefrogs) are short bodied with large heads and large hind legs used for walking, jumping, and climbing; and caecilians are legless aquatic or burrowing animals.

Turtles (Chelonia)

Turtles are probably the most immediately recognizable of all vertebrates. The shell that encloses a turtle has no exact duplicate among other vertebrates, and the morphological modifications associated with the shell make turtles extremely peculiar animals. They are, for example, the only vertebrates with the shoulders (pectoral girdle) and hips (pelvic girdle) inside the ribs.

Tuatara, Lizards, and Snakes (Lepidosauria)

These three kinds of vertebrates can be recognized by their scale-covered skin as well as by characteristics of the skull. The two species of tuatara, stocky-bodied animals found only on some islands near New Zealand, are the sole living remnant of a lineage of animals called Sphenodontida that were more diverse in the Mesozoic. In contrast, lizards and especially snakes are now at the peak of their diversity.

Alligators and Crocodiles (Crocodilia)

These impressive animals (the saltwater crocodile has the potential to grow to a length of 7 meters) are in the same lineage (the Archosauria) as dinosaurs and birds. Crocodilians, as they are known collectively, are semiaquatic predators with long snouts armed with numerous teeth. Their skin contains many bones (osteoderms; *osteo* = bone, *derm* = skin) that lie beneath the scales and provide a kind of armor plating. Crocodilians are noted for the parental care they provide for their eggs and young.

Birds (Aves)

The birds are a lineage of dinosaurs that evolved flight in the Mesozoic. Feathers are the distinguishing characteristic of birds. Indeed, some fossils of *Archaeopteryx*, the earliest bird known, were originally classified as dinosaurs because no marks of the feathers were visible. Birds are conspicuous, often vocal, and active during the day (diurnal). As a result they have been studied extensively and much of our information about the behavior and ecology of terrestrial vertebrates is based on studies of birds.

Mammals (Mammalia)

The living mammals can be traced to an origin in the late Paleozoic from some of the earliest fully terrestrial vertebrates. Extant mammals include about 4500 species, most of which are placental (eutherian) mammals. Their name comes from the placenta, a structure that transfers nutrients from the mother to the embryo and removes the waste products of the embryo's metabolism. Most of the familiar animals of the world are placentals. Marsupials (mammals in which the young is born at a very small size and continues its development in an external pouch on the mother's abdomen) dominate the mammalian fauna only in Australia. Kangaroos, koalas, and wombats are familiar Australian marsupials. The strange monotremes, the duck-billed platypus and the echidnas, are mammals whose young are hatched from eggs.

■ Evolution

Evolution is the process that has shaped the vertebrate story, and it is the underlying principle of biology. An understanding of the principles and processes of evolution is essential to appreciating the diversity of vertebrates, because that diversity is the direct result of evolution.

Scientific ideas are shaped by the society and philosophical system in which they form, and in turn they may reshape society and philosophy. That process has been a conspicuous part of the development of evolutionary theory in western societies, most recently in the conflicts over teaching of evolution in schools. Many parts of western thought had their origin in Greek philosophy, but evolution was not among them. The Greek concept of nature was a static one, and the idea of evolutionary change in species of plants and animals was foreign to Greek thought. Platonic philosophy was based on the concept of an abstract ideal; earthly manifestations of that archetype (individual animals or plants, for example) were imperfect copies of its form. This attitude was incorporated into Christian theology as the view that an eternal, inviolable essence of every worldly object existed in the mind of God. A strict interpretation of the Bible insists that everything on Earth was created by God in its present form, and therefore nothing can change or has changed.

This view of life as unchanging was incorporated into biological thought and is still manifested in some biological practices. For example, the Rules of Zoological Nomenclature require that when a new species is named, one specimen of the new species must be designated the type specimen, or holotype of the species. The holotype is deposited in a museum, where it serves as a permanent record of the new species. The original role of the holotype was to show what the species was like. If you had another individual that you thought might be a member of the same species, you could compare it to the holotype and decide. Thus the holotype was a single example that was considered to define the essence of the new species. In effect, it was the designated representative of the Platonic ideal of the species.

Naming a new species still requires a holotype, but the role of the holotype has changed significantly, and in addition to the holotype it is usual to deposit several additional specimens called paratypes or the paratypic series. The paratypes are intended to show the range of variation of the species in such characteristics as body size, color, and pattern. The holotype now defines the species in those rare cases in which two unnamed species have been confused and both are represented in the paratypic series. The name remains with the species represented by the holotype, and the other species receives a new name.

The recognition that variation within species is biologically important is a major change from the idea that one specimen by itself could define a species, and it reflects the most significant change in biological thought that occurred between the writings of Plato (about 380 B.C.) and the work of Darwin and Wallace in the nineteenth century. In a Platonic view, the variations within a species are the imperfections of different copies of the archetype and they have no significance. To an evolutionary biologist, those variations are the raw material of evolution.

Biological Variation

The idea that no two people (except for identical twins) are exactly the same is a familiar one. Humans use individual variation every day in contexts that range from recognizing friends to fingerprinting criminal suspects. Individual variation is not confined to morphological variation like facial contours or fingerprints; it extends to any characteristic that can be measured.

These sorts of variation are examples of phenotypic variation. The phenotype of an organism means its form in a very broad sense. For example, phenotype can refer to color (pale skin versus dark skin), size or shape (tall versus short), or performance capacity (fast versus slow runners). Phenotypes can also be defined on the basis of molecular characteristics: Hemoglobin B is the normal form of the beta chain of the adult human hemoglobin molecule and hemoglobin S is the form of the beta chain that leads to sickle-cell anemia. The two forms differ in only one amino acid residue: A valine residue appears in hemoglobin S in place of a glutamine residue.

Behavioral phenotypes also can be defined: Guppies are most familiar as aquarium fish, but they occur wild in streams in the New World tropics. In Trinidad guppies occupy stream habitats with relatively few predators and other streams where predators are abundant. Populations in these habitats differ in male color and in the response of females to courtship by bright-colored and plain males (Breden and Stoner 1987). The bright colors of male guppies are part of the courtship display, but they also make males more visible to predators. In low-predation areas most male guppies are bright colored, but in areas of high predation they are plain. Experiments have shown a genetically determined difference in the responses of female guppies from streams with high and low predation to courtship by bright and plain males: Female guppies from low-predation habitats choose to mate with bright-colored males, whereas females from high-predation areas choose plain males. This response is apparently mediated by the chances that the offspring will survive. Bright-colored males sire bright-colored male offspring. In low-predation habitats, bright-colored male offspring are advantageous because they are attractive to females and run little risk of being eaten by a predator. However, in high-predation habitats bright-colored male offspring are vulnerable to predation, and females with the genetically determined behavioral trait of mating with plain males leave more surviving offspring than females that mate with bright-colored males.

These types of phenotypic variation are manifestations of genetic variation. Evolution is defined as change through time in the frequencies of different forms of a gene in the gene pool of a population. Different forms of a gene are called alleles and different alleles produce different phenotypes. The genotype of an individual is its genetic composition. Remember that in sexually reproducing organisms an individual receives one allele from its mother and one from its father. To use the example of sickle-cell anemia, there are three possible genotypes: If an individual receives the normal form of the beta-chain allele from both parents it will be Hb_BHb_B, that is, a homozygous genotype, and it produces the normal beta-chain phenotype. An individual that receives one allele from its mother and a different allele from its father would be Hb_BHb_S, that is, a heterozygote. Heterozygotes for the sickle-cell allele have an advantage in areas where malaria is endemic, apparently because red blood cells that contain hemoglobin S collapse (sickle) when a malaria parasite enters them. This sickling causes a decrease in the concentration of potassium inside the red cell and the eventual death of the parasite (Friedman 1978). An individual that receives the sickle-cell allele from both parents will have the genotype Hb_SHb_S: These homozygous individuals are at a disadvantage because the hemoglobin molecules sickle whenever the oxygen concentration in the blood drops, as it may, for example, during physical exercise.

Evolution depends on the existence of variation in genotypes among individuals that is (1) manifested in the phenotype, (2) inherited, and (3) associated with differences in reproductive success. Natural selection changes the relative frequency of different alleles in a population, and these changes in alleles are reflected in changes in the frequencies of different phenotypes. It is easier to think of phenotypes than of genotyopes in discussions of evolution because phenotypes are visible whereas alleles are not. However, it is alleles that are inherited.

Variation in genotypes results from the combined actions of several genetic processes in sexually reproducing organisms. During meiosis and the formation of gametes (sperm and ova) the pairs of chromosomes that make up the genome of an individual are first duplicated and then separated into gametes that contain only one of each pair of chromosomes. (This is the haploid chromosomal complement.) When two gametes unite to form a zygote (fertilized egg) the diploid chromosome number is regained: Two chromosomes of each pair are present, one from the father and one from the mother. Alleles are not entirely independent entities; their function is affected by other alleles present in the genotype. Consequently, the genetic rearrangement that accompanies sexual reproduction is an important source of phenotypic variation. Mutation is another source of variation, of smaller magnitude than rearrangement but nonetheless important. Mutation can result from errors in copying the genetic code during the initial duplication of chromosomes during meiosis, or it can be caused by events that precede meiosis, such as exposure of the sex cells to ionizing radiation. Other cellular events can cause changes in the linear sequence of genetic loci on chromosomes. Because the action of alleles is influenced by neighboring alleles, these changes in sequence can affect the phenotype.

Natural Selection

Evolution results from the action of natural selection on different phenotypes, and natural selection works through differential reproductive success, that is, the contribution of different phenotypes to the gene pool of succeeding generations. The term **fitness** is used to describe the relative contribution of different individuals to future generations. If individual A produces 100 offspring that survive to reproduce and individual B produces only 90 offspring, individual B is only 90 percent as successful as individual A. The fitness of the most successful individual (A in this example) is defined as 1.00, and other individuals are defined in relation to A. Thus the fitness of B would be 0.90. That means that the alleles represented in the genotype of indi-

vidual B would be underrepresented in the next generation by 10 percent compared with alleles in the genotype of A. In this example, selection would be said to select against B and the selection coefficient would be 0.10.

Modes of Selection

Natural selection can affect the distribution of phenotypes in a population in three different ways (Figure 1–2). **Directional selection** discriminates against individuals at one extreme of the variation in a phenotypic character. For example, small individuals might be at a disadvantage compared with individuals of normal or larger-than-normal size. The effect of directional selection is to move the mean value of the character in the direction of the most fit phenotypes from generation to generation.

Stabilizing selection discriminates against individuals that have extreme variation in the phenotypic character in either direction. It favors individuals that have values that lie close to the mean, and it can result in a reduction of the amount of variation within a population, but it does not change the mean value.

Disruptive selection is the reverse of stabilizing selection. That is, individuals at both extremes of the range of variation are favored and individuals near the mean are at a disadvantage. Disruptive selection increases the variation but does not change the mean value.

Note that these descriptions have assumed that only one mode of selection affects the trait being considered. In fact, more than one mode of selection can

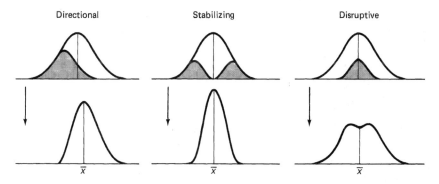

Figure 1–2   Three kinds of selection: directional, stabilizing, and disruptive. In each case the vertical axis is the proportion of individuals and the horizontal axis shows the range of variation. The outlines of the upper diagrams show the initial variation within the population. The individuals in the shaded areas are at a disadvantage relative to the rest of the population. The lower diagram shows the variation in the populations after selection ($\bar{x}$, average value).

occur simultaneously, and both the mean value of the trait and the amount of variation can change simultaneously. Natural selection is difficult to demonstrate under natural conditions because many different and sometimes conflicting selective forces operate simultaneously. Nonetheless, some examples are known, and John Endler (1986) has reviewed the evidence for natural selection in the wild.

Evolution of Complex Systems

Organisms are extraordinarily complicated entities, and that complexity is one of the principal reasons they are so fascinating. We try to illustrate that perspective throughout this book by emphasizing the ways in which ecology, behavior, morphology, and physiology interact in living vertebrates, and by considering how similar interactions in the past may have influenced the evolution of vertebrates.

How do such complex systems evolve? Three general explanations have been proposed: saltation, mosaic evolution, and correlated progression. The **saltation** hypothesis suggested that the mixture of characters that distinguish a mammal from a reptile, for example, could have been acquired all at once as a result of the random effects of genetic mutation and recombination. This hypothesis, which is associated with the early part of the twentieth century, is not supported by either our current understanding of developmental mechanisms or the fossil record.

The hypothesis of **mosaic evolution** and the related hypothesis of **correlated progression** are more consistent with what we see during the embryonic development of vertebrates and in the fossil record. It is a commonplace observation that organisms are mosaics of ancestral and derived characters. For example, your hand (= forefoot) is very much like the forefoot of a lizard, but your foot (= hindfoot) is quite different from a lizard's. Similarly, your eyes are essentially the same as those of a lizard, but your brain shows tremendous elaboration of some regions compared with the brain of a lizard. The distinction between mosaic evolution and correlated progression focuses on how much interaction occurred among the blocks (i.e., forefoot, hindfoot, eye, brain) during evolution. Independent evolution of the blocks because of coincidental response to the same new environment is mosaic evolution, whereas an interaction in which changes in one block influence changes in other blocks is correlated progression.

Mosaic evolution and correlated progression are two ends of a continuum rather than being mutually exclusive alternatives, and particular examples may fall at various points along the line. A particularly good example, and one that is treated in more detail later in this book, is the evolution of mammals from early reptilelike animals. That transition involved a host of changes among interdependent systems. Endothermy (i.e., the regulation of body temperature by heat produced by an animal's metabolism), for example, requires a physiological mechanism for heat production (high metabolic rate) and a morphological mechanism for retaining heat (an insulating covering of hair), and neither feature is advantageous unless the other one is already present. This catch-22 situation is discussed in Chapter 4, and the sequence of appearance of the changes in skeletal structure, dentition, maternal care, and brain development that distinguish mammals from reptiles is described in Chapter 19. In the case of mammals, we clearly see a process of correlated progression, in which changes in skeletal structure were associated with changes in locomotion, physiology, reproduction, and parental care.

Inclusive Fitness

We have defined fitness as the relative genetic contribution of different individuals to future generations, and described it in terms of the number of offspring produced by an individual. That is an oversimplification, however, because different individuals of a species have alleles in common, and the more closely related two individuals are the higher will be the proportion of their shared alleles. Siblings, for example, have an average of 50 percent of their alleles in common and half-siblings (one parent the same and one different) share 25 percent of their alleles. Remember that it is alleles that are transmitted from generation to generation, and you can see that it is possible for an individual to increase its own fitness (that is, to transmit alleles identical to its own) by assisting a related individual to reproduce successfully. For example, when your sibling reproduces, he or she transmits half the alleles you share to that offspring (which is your niece or nephew), and 25 percent of the alleles in the genotype of the offspring are the same as alleles in your genotype (50 percent of alleles shared between siblings times 50 percent of the genotype contributed by each parent = 25 percent of the alleles in the genotype of the offspring).

Your own offspring has 50 percent of the alleles in your genotype, twice as many as your niece or nephew. All else being equal, then, two nieces or nephews are the equivalent of one offspring of your own in terms of transmitting your alleles to future generations. The same calculations can be applied to increasingly distant genetic relationships. The important point is that reproduction of relatives contributes to the fitness of an individual. In some situations helping relatives to reproduce successfully may be the best way for an individual to increase its own fitness. This principle of inclusive fitness is believed to underlie many of the altruistic behaviors of birds and mammals (Chapters 18 and 23).

■ Variation and Evolution

Phenotypic and genotypic variation is the material on which natural selection operates, but not all kinds of variation are subject to selection, and characteristics of the biology of certain species can increase or decrease the importance of selection. In the first place, variation must be heritable if selection is to act on it. That is, variation in phenotypic characters must have an underlying genetic basis, and parents that manifest a particular character must produce offspring that also show that character. Not all variation does have a genetic basis, and many characters that do have a genetic basis are also affected by the environment. The body size of turtles at hatching is an example of this interaction between genetic and environmentally induced variation. Newly hatched turtles receive no parental care: They must dig their way out of nests in the soil, find their way to water, and begin to catch their own food entirely by their own efforts. Probably it is desirable for a female turtle to produce the largest hatchlings she can, because larger hatchlings can dig more strongly, move to water faster, and capture a wider variety of prey than can small individuals. The size of a hatchling turtle is correlated with the size of the egg it came from, and some female turtles lay larger eggs than others. All else being equal, female turtles that lay large eggs should produce larger hatchlings and be more fit than females that lay smaller eggs. However, the availability of water in the nest also affects the body size of hatchlings—nests in moist soil give rise to larger hatchlings than do nests in dry soil (Figure 1–3). Furthermore, hatchlings from moist nests can also crawl and swim faster than hatch-lings from dry nests. This component of variation in body size of hatchlings has no genetic basis and cannot be acted on directly by natural selection. If selection does act on this type of variation (and this sort of selection has not been demonstrated) it would have to be indirect, via a reduction in the fitness of female turtles that chose to nest in dry sites.

Variation That Is Subject to Natural Selection

Individual variation is the type of variation one usually thinks of in terms of natural selection—some individuals are larger than others, or faster, or more colorful, or more aggressive than others. The list of characters by which individuals differ can be extended indefinitely, and these differences result from the luck of the draw when gametes combine to form a zygote. The effects of genetic recombination and mutation lead to different genotypes and different phenotypes, and selection can act on those differences.

Individual variation is usually continuous. That is, some animals are small, others are large, and most are somewhere between those extremes. Continuous variation is the situation illustrated in Figure 1–2. A second type of variation is discontinuous: Instead of having a bell-shaped curve of frequencies of different forms, discontinuous variation can be sorted out into discrete categories. **Polymorphism** (*poly* = many, *morph* = form) is a common type of discontinuous variation. Figure 1–4 illustrates pattern polymorphism in a Puerto Rican frog, the coquí. Some individuals are uniformly colored, some have stripes along the sides of the body, and some have a mottled pattern of dark blotches. These different patterns are genetically determined and offspring inherit the patterns of their parents. One can find individuals with all these patterns in any population of the frogs, but some patterns are more common in one kind of habitat than another, probably because certain patterns are especially cryptic (hard for predators to detect) in particular habitats. In grasslands, for example, the striped patterns occur in high frequency, whereas in forests the unicolored and mottled patterns are more common. In grassy areas predators see the frogs against a background of grass stems, and the striped pattern may blend well with the straight, light-colored stems. In forests predators often see the frogs on a background of fallen leaves. There are few sharp, straight lines in a forest and mottled and solid patterns are probably more cryptic than stripes. The

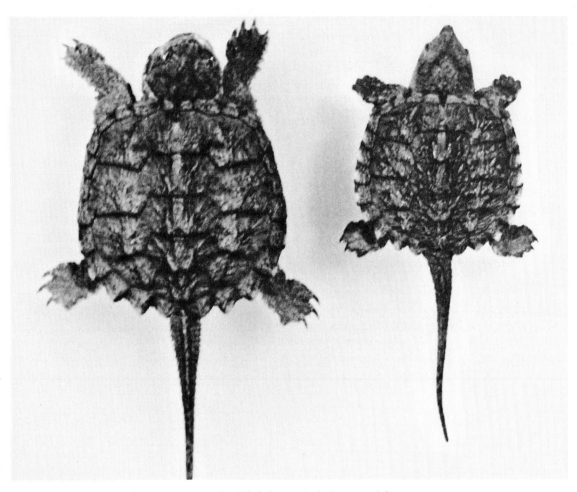

Figure 1–3   These two hatchling snapping turtles (*Chelydra serpentina*) emerged from eggs laid by the same female turtle. The eggs were the same size when they were deposited, and the difference in the size of the hatchlings represents an environmental effect. The turtle on the left hatched from an egg that was incubated in moist substrate, whereas the one on the right is from an egg incubated in dry substrate. (Photograph courtesy of Gary C. Packard.)

differences in frequencies of the patterns in different habitats indicate that natural selection has acted on the gene pool to change the frequencies of alleles producing the patterns.

Sexual dimorphism (*di* = two) is a special case of polymorphism in which males and females of a species differ in secondary sexual characters such as size or color (Figure 1–5). Sexual dimorphism results from the different roles that males and females play in reproduction and the differences in the selective pressures that affect the fitness of individuals of the two sexes. The difference in sexual roles begins with the investment of males and females in gametes: Males produce sperm, females produce ova. Sperm are small, energetically cheap, and quick to produce, whereas ova may contain large quantities of yolk and require a substantial investment of time and energy by the female.

As a result of this asymmetry of investment, the reproductive strategies that increase the fitness of males and females can be quite different. Because a male can readily produce more sperm he can usually increase his fitness by mating with as many females as possible—each mating has only a small cost and he can mate repeatedly with little delay between matings. The situation for the female is quite different: By the time she is ready to mate she has invested time and energy in producing mature ova. Furthermore, in many species the female provides most of the parental care. As a result, it is costly in time and energy for a female to breed repeatedly. Instead, her fitness is increased by mating with the best possible male.

Sexual dimorphism often reflects these differences in the selective forces acting on males and females: In *The Descent of Man and Selection in Relation*

(a)   (b)

(c)   (d)

Figure 1–4   Polymorphic patterns of the Puerto Rican coquí. These are four of the more than 20 different patterns that have been described: (a) mottled; (b) unicolor; (c) broad lateral stripes; and (d) broad dorsal stripe. Striped patterns (such as c and d) are more common in grassland habitats than they are in the forest. (Photographs: [a, b, c, d] Margaret M. Stewart, State University of New York at Albany.)

to Sex Darwin pointed out that males are often larger than females and more aggressive. They may engage in ritualized or actual combat with other males, and may form dominance hierarchies in which high-ranking males have opportunities to court females and low-ranking males do not. Darwin noted that females often must be courted repeatedly by a male before they will mate. Many secondary sexual characteristics of males, such as bright colors, the presence of horns or antlers, and vocalization, are examples of sexual dimorphism that are employed in combat or courtship. The role of female choice in determining the reproductive success of individual males has received increased attention recently. The bright-colored and plain-colored Trinidad guppies discussed in the preceding section provide an example of female choice in determining the reproductive

success of males, and additional examples are found in subsequent chapters.

Factors Promoting Speciation

Evolution consists of changes in frequencies of alleles within populations. If two populations of a species accumulate more and more differences in allelic frequencies over time, they become more and more distinct. Some alleles may be lost from one population but retained in the other population, and mutation may introduce new alleles into each population that are not represented in the other. How long can this process continue before the populations are no longer one species but two?

To answer that question we need a definition of a species, and that is a contentious issue among

Figure 1–5 Examples of sexual dimorphism. (a) A mating pair of European toads (Bufo bufo). Males of this species, and of many other amphibians, are substantially smaller than females. (b) African lions (*Panthera leo*). Among mammals, males are usually larger than females. (Photographs: [a] K. G. Vock/Okapia, Photo Researchers, Inc. [b] David Hosking, Photo Researchers, Inc.)

(a)

(b)

biologists. For sexually reproducing organisms, which include the overwhelming majority of vertebrates, the definition of a **biological species** that was formulated by Ernst Mayr (1942) has been remarkably durable: "Species are groups of interbreeding natural populations that are reproductively isolated from other such groups." Critics of Mayr's biological species definition have pointed out that it does not encompass unisexual organisms, or geographically isolated populations that are prevented from interbreeding by a barrier such as a river or a mountain range. Also, the biological

species definition does not include the idea of evolutionary continuity over time.

The **evolutionary species** concept, first defined by George Gaylord Simpson in 1961 and modified by E. O. Wiley in 1978, defines a species as "a single lineage of ancestral-descendant populations which maintains its identity from other such lineages and which has its own evolutionary tendencies and historical fate." All of these definitions of species emphasize that a species is the expression of a genetic system that evolves independently from other species. This view of species stresses the fact that members of a species not only evolve independently of other species but also must be able to survive in the face of competition from members of other species.

The Role of Isolation in Speciation   As long as populations are in contact, alleles can move among them. Even in species with large geographic ranges, gene flow maintains genetic continuity between populations at the extremes of the range of the species via intervening populations. A new allele created by a mutation in one part of the species range can spread through the entire species, and an allele that is lost in one part of the range will eventually be replaced by gene flow from the gene pool of the species. Gene flow is both a constraining and a creative force in evolution. On one hand, gene flow prevents local populations from accumulating enough genetic differences to evolve into different species, but at the same time gene flow allows superior alleles and combinations of alleles to spread through an entire species.

Allopatric speciation describes a situation in which a physical barrier such as a river or a mountain range prevents gene flow and allows two populations to diverge. Sympatric speciation describes the separation of a single population into two species without such a physical barrier. In this situation, ecological or behavioral differences between subdivisions of the population restrict or eliminate gene flow.

The Importance of Population Size in Evolution   How speciation might proceed in large interbreeding populations has perennially puzzled evolutionists. A large population that occupies extensive areas can usually be divided into subpopulations, or demes. Large continental areas are seldom homogeneous, but rather are a series of patchy habitats because of variation in geology and vegetation. Members of a deme are more likely to breed with members of their own deme than with members of adjacent demes, if for no other reason than proximity. The result is restricted gene flow within the species and, presumably, a reduction in heterozygosity or genetic variation in the deme. If the deme is large the effect of interbreeding will be slight, but if it is small the reduction in genetic variation may be significant. Occasional outbreeding with individuals from other demes will tend to maintain heterozygosity within the deme: An average of one individual exchanged between populations per generation is sufficient to prevent divergence.

Superimposed on this concept of semi-isolated demes with limited outbreeding is the amount or the intensity of natural selection. If, for example, environmental change, predation, or competition for resources is intense within a deme, individuals with the most appropriate phenotypes for the local conditions will be favored and their genotypes will increase within the population. If gene flow between demes remains low, genetic divergence of demes can occur.

The rate of evolution is most likely to be rapid in small populations, and small breeding populations can result from various circumstances including dispersal of a few adults to a new location, the sudden local isolation of a new deme by some environmental event, or a sudden reduction in the size of a population (a population crash). These periods of diminished population size are called bottlenecks, and they potentially stimulate rapid changes in the frequencies of alleles in the population. Furthermore, the small population resulting from the bottleneck will contain only those alleles present in the individuals that pass through the bottleneck, and these are the only alleles that will be represented in the descendant population. A similar phenomenon, called the founder effect, describes a situation in which a new isolated population is founded by a few individuals. For example, a flock of birds might be blown out to sea by a storm and ultimately land on an island. If conditions on the island are suitable, the waifs could breed and establish a new population that will contain only the alleles represented in the genotypes of the founding individuals. This is the sequence of events that is thought to have produced the bird faunas of many oceanic islands, including Hawaii and the Galápagos Islands.

A Classic Example of Evolution: The Galápagos Finches   How geographic isolation promotes speciation is emphasized on oceanic islands, as Darwin himself observed in his examination of the endemic forms of animal life in the Galápagos Islands, which lie about 1000 kilometers off the coast of Ecuador. Darwin's finches (subfamily Geospizinae) have become the classic example of evolution at the species level (Figure 1–6). These 14 species have evolved rapidly from a single, ancestral population of seed-eating birds that arrived from South America in relatively recent geological time—perhaps less than 500,000 years ago.

From time to time individuals spread to other islands in the Galápagos from the original, founding population. In these new environments, with

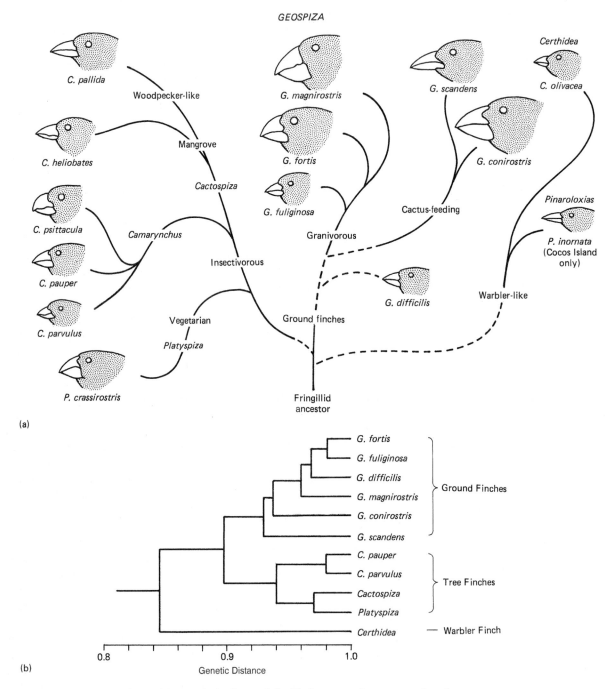

Figure 1–6 Differences among Darwin's finches and the likely rate and sequence of evolution. (a) The evolutionary sequence postulated by David Lack (1947, *Darwin's Finches*, Cambridge University Press, Cambridge, UK) was based mostly on morphological criteria. It is very similar to the phylogeny for 10 of those species based on a genetic analysis of similarity (S. Y. Yang and J. L. Patton, 1981, *Auk* 98:230–242) as shown in (b). Differences occur only within the ground finches.

ecological opportunities for which no competition from other species existed, these new founders were able to repeat the process of establishment and eventual adaptation to local conditions. In time many of these isolated populations accumulated sufficient genetic differences so that, when secondary contact was established on islands that had already been colonized, they proved to be reproductively isolated from one another and could coexist as sympatric species, each with an ecological niche of its own (Grant 1986). Today, each island has three to ten species, depending on the diversity of the vegetation and ecological opportunities.

Studies of diversity among the finches reveal that morphological variation has emphasized change in body size and the shape of the bill. Three primary subgroups are recognized: the warbler-like finches, the tree finches, and the ground finches. Differences in beak size and shape represent specialization for different diets and ways of obtaining food.

Investigations of genetic differences among the finches produce species relationships that are basically similar to the arrangement proposed by David Lack in 1947. Although evolution has been rapid, allopatric speciation seems the simplest explanation for the diversity of Darwin's finches, especially when one considers the relatively high chances of dispersal of a founder population to a nearby island. A study by Gibbs and Grant (1987) revealed how rapidly the morphology of a species of finch can change in response to changes in the environment. The Galápagos Islands are characterized each year by wet and dry seasons. In exceptional years, however, the wet season can be prolonged and bring heavy rain. When that happens the plants flourish and food becomes abundant. These exceptional years are the result of climatic effects that reach far beyond the Galápagos—they are El Niño years, the name given to the periodic invasion of the eastern South Pacific by warm water masses. In 1982–83, a decade-long drought in the Galápagos was broken by a record El Niño year. Gibbs and Grant had been monitoring a population of the medium-size ground finch *Geospiza fortis* on the small island of Daphne Major. The morphology of the birds changed between 1976–77 and 1984–85. Before the El Niño event, the population consisted of large-bodied and heavy-billed birds, but during and following the wet season both body size and bill size diminished. The differences in body and bill size have a genetic basis, and they also relate directly to success in feeding. In a drought, when

food is scarce, the larger birds apparently are favored because they can crack the large, hard seeds that are the most abundant food for the finches. During wetter times the small birds are apparently successful because small, soft seeds are abundant. Here is a clear example of changing environmental conditions leading to the selection of genetically controlled morphologies that favor survival. The genotype of these finches must carry enough heterozygosity to express either phenotype.

For land-based animals such as finches, oceanic islands are obvious geographic features for the isolation and speciation of populations. The ocean is a barrier to dispersal from a continental source, but it is not an absolute barrier. Habitats on mountaintops are isolated from each other in much the same way as islands. It is easy to see how a surrounding lowland forest or desert may be an effective barrier to frequent dispersal of animals that are adapted to live only in the highland situation.

Isolation on Continents   It has not been so easy to explain how speciation has occurred on continents, particularly in regions where environmental conditions remain uniform over vast areas, such as in the tundra and boreal forests of the Northern Hemisphere or the Amazonian forest of South America. It now appears that a mechanism similar to isolation on islands has been at work repeatedly and that much speciation of land vertebrates on continents can be accounted for by geographic isolation.

The Pleistocene epoch—approximately the last 2 million years of geological history—has been characterized by changes in mean annual temperature and rainfall. Geological and biogeographic evidence supports the conclusion that islandlike refugia of the tundra and taiga ecosystems persisted in northern latitudes even during maximum glaciations, whereas during interglacials these refugia have merged as continuous habitats of great expanse. Thus, species populations that were widely distributed in these uniform habitats during interglacials became fragmented and isolated in refugia during glaciations. This is precisely the sequence of events needed for speciation, and the present distributions of a number of bird and mammal species in boreal North America indicate that they have evolved in this way.

The changes in temperature and precipitation during the Pleistocene have been great enough to have effected changes in most biomes of the world, including those in the tropics (Connor 1986). The

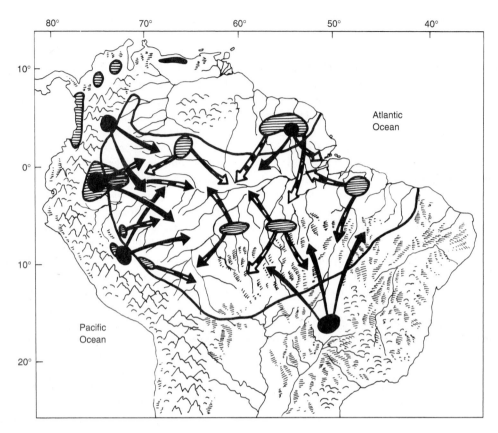

Figure 1–7   Proposed effects of changes during the Pleistocene on lowland forest vertebrates of the Amazon Basin. The black line shows the area within which forests are thought to have been fragmented. Within this region birds (black areas) and lizards (shaded areas) are thought to have been isolated in forest remnants. The arrows show postulated paths of reinvasion as the forests returned. (Based on P. E. Vanzolini, 1972, in *Tropical Forest Ecosystems in Africa and South America: A Comparative Review*, edited by B. J. Meggers et al., Smithsonian Institution Press, Washington, DC.)

Amazonian forest has apparently been broken up repeatedly into patches that persisted for a time as isolated forests and then coalesced to form a continuous biome again (Figure 1–7). Periods of drought have long been considered the cause of this disruption of continuous forest, and a recent interpretation suggests that floods were another factor in the evolution of the Amazonian forest (Räsänen et al. 1987). Similar shifts in the distribution of savanna and forest biomes in Australia, also associated with long-term climatic changes, may account for much recent speciation among birds on that continent. Most biogeographers and paleoclimatologists now agree that climate and the major biotic associations of plants and animals have fluctuated repeatedly on a worldwide scale during the Pleistocene. The result has been the repeated fragmentation of biomes, alternating with re-formation of more continuous, continental distributions, plus some change in species composition of the biomes. A few years ago ornithologists thought that most bird species had evolved in the Pliocene and were several million years old. Now most ornithologists feel that speciation has been very rapid during the Pleistocene, especially among small birds with limited dispersal abilities.

■ Earth History and Vertebrate Evolution

The phenomena of isolation and secondary contact that are important in the evolution of individual species like Galápagos finches and eastern warblers have also been important in the larger story of vertebrate evolution. The world in which vertebrates have been evolving has changed enormously and repeatedly since the origin of vertebrates in the early Paleozoic, and these changes have affected vertebrate evolution directly and indirectly. An understanding of the sequence of changes in the positions of the continents and the significance of those positions in terms of climates and interchange of faunas is a central part of understanding the vertebrate story. A summary table of these events is presented in the front of the book, and details are given in Chapters 5, 9, 14, and 20. The history of the Earth has occupied four geological **eons**: the Hadean, Archean, Proterozoic, and Phanerozoic. Only the Phanerozoic contains vertebrate life, and it is divided into three geological **eras**: the Paleozoic, Mesozoic, and Cenozoic. These eras are divided into **periods**, which can be further subdivided in a variety of ways. Here we will be considering only the subdivisions called **epochs** within the Cenozoic period.

Movements of land masses have been a feature of Earth's history, at least since the Proterozoic. The direction of vertebrate evolution has been molded in large part by continental drift. By the early Paleozoic a recognizable scene had appeared: The seas had formed, continents floated atop the Earth's mantle, life had become complex, and an atmosphere of oxygen had formed, signifying that the photosynthetic production of food resources had become a central phenomenon of life.

The continents still drift today—North America is moving westward and Australia northward at approximately 4 centimeters per year. Because the movements are so complex, their sequence, their varied directions, and the precise timing of the changes are difficult to summarize. By viewing the movements broadly, however, a simple pattern unfolds during vertebrate history: *fragmentation–coalescence–fragmentation* (Figure 1–8).

Continents existed as separate entities over 2000 million years ago. Some 300 million years ago all of these separate continents combined to form Pangaea, birthplace of the terrestrial vertebrates. Persisting and drifting northward as an entity, this single huge continent began to break apart about 150 million years ago. Its separation occurred in two stages: first into Laurasia and Gondwana, then into a series of units that have drifted and become the continents we know today.

The complex movements of the continents through time have had major effects on many phenomena significant to the evolution of vertebrates. The most obvious is the relationship between the location of land masses and their climates. At the start of the Paleozoic much of Pangaea was located on the equator and this situation persisted through the middle of the Mesozoic. Solar radiation is most intense at the equator, and climates at the equator are correspondingly warm. During the Paleozoic and much of the Mesozoic large areas of land enjoyed tropical conditions, and terrestrial vertebrates evolved and spread in these tropical regions. By the late Mesozoic much of the land mass of the Earth had moved out of equatorial regions, and most climates in the Northern and Southern Hemispheres are now temperate instead of tropical. The mechanisms and consequences of continental drift are considered in more detail in Chapter 5.

A less obvious effect of the position of continents on terrestrial climates comes about through changes in patterns of ocean circulation. For example, the Arctic Ocean is now largely isolated from the other oceans and it does not receive warm water via currents flowing from more equatorial regions. High latitudes are cold because they receive less solar radiation than do areas closer to the equator, and the Arctic Basin does not receive enough warm water to offset the lack of solar radiation. As a result, the Arctic Ocean is permanently frozen and cold climates extend well southward across the continents. The cooling of climates in the Northern Hemisphere at the end of the Mesozoic that may have been one

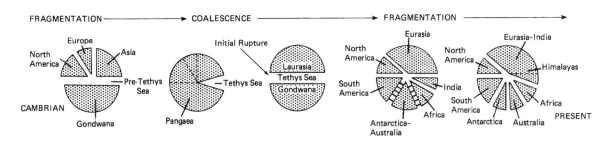

Figure 1–8 A summary of continental drift from the Cambrian to the present.

of the factors leading to the extinction of dinosaurs is partly the result of the changes in oceanic circulation at that time. (Additional effects of an Arctic ice cap are discussed in Chapter 5.)

Another factor that influences climates is the relative level of the continents and the seas. At some periods of the history of the Earth, most recently in the late Mesozoic and again in the first part of the Cenozoic, large parts of the continents have been flooded by shallow seas. These **epicontinental seas** extended across the middle of North America and the middle of Eurasia in the Cretaceous and early Cenozoic. Water has a great capacity to absorb heat as environmental temperatures rise and to release that heat as temperatures fall. The heat capacity of water buffers temperature change in areas of land near bodies of water. Areas with **maritime climates** do not get very hot in summer or very cold in winter, and they are usually moist because water that evaporates from the sea falls as rain on the land. **Continental climates**, which characterize areas of land far from the sea, are usually dry with cold winters and hot summers. The draining of the epicontinental seas at the end of the Cretaceous was a second factor that probably contributed to the demise of the dinosaurs by making climates in the Northern Hemisphere more continental.

In addition to changing climates, continental drift has formed and broken land connections between the continents. Isolation of different lineages of vertebrates on different land masses has produced dramatic examples of the independent evolution of similar types of organisms. These are well shown by mammals in the Cenozoic, a period when the Earth's continents were more widely separated than they ever have been before or since. Saber-tooth carnivores evolved among placental mammals in the Northern Hemisphere and among marsupials in South America, and grazing animals were represented by entirely different lineages of placental mammals in North America and South America and by kangaroos and wombats (both marsupials) in Australia.

Much of evolutionary history appears to depend on whether or not a particular lineage was in the right place at the right time. This stochastic (random, chance) element of evolution is assuming increasing prominence as more detailed information about the times of extinction of old groups and radiation of new groups is suggesting that competitive replacement of one group by another is not the usual mechanism of large-scale evolutionary change. The movements of continents and their effects on climates and the isolation or dispersal of animals are taking an increasingly central role in our understanding of vertebrate evolution.

■ Classification of Vertebrates

The diversity of vertebrates (50,000 living species and at least ten times that number of species now extinct) combines with the prevalence of convergent and parallel evolution to make the classification of vertebrates an extraordinarily difficult undertaking. Yet classification has long been at the heart of evolutionary biology. Initially, classification of species was seen as a way of managing the diversity of organisms, much as an office filing system manages the paperwork of the office. Each species could be placed in a pigeonhole marked with its name, and when all species were in their pigeonholes, one could comprehend the diversity of vertebrates. This approach to classification was satisfactory as long as species were regarded as static and immutable: Once a species was placed in the filing system it was there to stay.

Acceptance of the fact of evolution has made that kind of classification inadequate. Now it is necessary to express evolutionary relationships among species by incorporating evolutionary information in the system of classification (de Queiroz 1988). Ideally, a classification system should not only attach a label to each species, it should also encode the evolutionary relationship between that species and other species. Modern techniques of systematics (the phylogenetic classification of organisms) are moving beyond filing systems and have become methods for generating testable hypotheses about evolution.

Classification and Evolution

Our system of classifying organisms is pre-Darwinian. It traces back to methods established by the naturalists of the seventeenth and eighteenth centuries, especially those of Carl von Linné, a Swedish naturalist, better known by his Latin pen name, Carolus Linnaeus. The Linnaean system employs **binominal nomenclature** to designate species, and arranges species into hierarchical categories (**taxa**, singular **taxon**) for classification. This system is incompatible in some respects with evolutionary biology (de Queiroz and Gauthier 1992), but it is still widely used. Thus, you must understand the traditional classification because it forms the basis for much of the literature of vertebrate biology, but you should also understand the shortcomings of the traditional system to appreciate how dramatically our view of systematics has changed.

Binominal Nomenclature   The scientific naming of species became standardized when Linnaeus's monumental work, *Systema Naturae*, was published in sections between 1735 and 1758. He attempted to give an identifying name to every known species of plant and animal. His method involves assigning a generic name, which is a Latin noun, Latinized Greek, or a Latinized vernacular word, and a second species name, usually a Latin adjective, or similar derivative. Some familiar examples include *Homo sapiens* for human beings (*homo* = human, *sapiens* = wise), *Passer domesticus* for the house sparrow (*passer* = sparrow, *domesticus* = belonging to the house), and *Canis familiaris* for the domestic dog (*canis* = dog, *familiaris* = of the family).

Why use Latin words? Aside from the historical fact that Latin was the early universal language of European scholars and scientists, it has provided a uniform usage that has continued to be recognized worldwide by scientists regardless of their vernacular language. The same species may have different colloquial names, even in the same language. For example, *Felis concolor* ("the uniformly colored cat") is known in various parts of North America as cougar, puma, mountain lion, American panther, painter, and catamount. In Central and South America it is called león colorado, onça-vermelha, poema, guasura, or yaguá-pitá, but mammalogists of all nationalities recognize the name *Felis concolor* as referring to a specific kind of cat.

Hierarchical Groups: The Higher Taxa   Linnaeus and other naturalists of his time developed what they called a natural system of classification in which all similar species are grouped together in one **genus** (plural **genera**), based on characters that define the genus. The most commonly used characters were anatomical, because they are the ones most easily preserved in museum specimens. Thus all doglike species—various wolves, coyotes, and jackals— were grouped together in the genus *Canis* because they all share certain anatomical features, such as an erectile mane on the neck and a skull with a long, prominent sagittal crest on which massive temporal muscles originate for closure of the jaws. Linnaeus's method of grouping species was func-

tional because it was based on anatomical (and to some extent on physiological and behavioral) similarities and differences. Although Linnaeus lived before there was any knowledge of genetics and the mechanisms of inheritance, he used taxonomic characters that we understand today are genetically determined biological traits that, within limits, express the degree of genetic similarity or difference among groups of organisms.

Subsequent development of biological classification has employed seven basic taxonomic categories, listed below in decreasing order of inclusiveness:

> Kingdom
>   Phylum (= Division in plants)
>   Class
>   Order
>   Family
>   Genus
>   Species

These are the taxonomic levels (categories) that are employed in most of the primary and secondary literature of vertebrate biology.

■ Traditional and Cladistic Classifications

All methods of classifying organisms are based on similarities among the included species, whether or not the similarities reflect common ancestry. **Phenetic** methods, such as classical numerical taxonomy, do not explicitly address evolutionary relationships. Pheneticists group organisms strictly by the number of characters they have in common. Characters are not weighted to reflect their relative importance, and as a result the presence of two arches in the skulls of lizards and birds would be treated equally to the presence of the oxygen-transport pigment hemoglobin in both groups. Phenetic classification is ideal for some types of data, such as biochemical information about the similarities and differences in the proteins or DNA sequences of species. With these sorts of data there is no basis for assuming that one difference is more important than another and assigning greater weight to it.

Morphological, behavioral, and physiological characteristics of organisms provide a different sort of information: It is possible to make a judgment that some differences are more significant than others. For example, only a few kinds of vertebrates have skulls with a pattern of two arches, but nearly all vertebrates have paired limbs. Consequently, knowing that the species in question share the two-arched skull pattern tells you more about the closeness of their relationship than knowing that they have paired limbs, and you would give more weight to the skull characters than to paired limbs. Today, two major classification systems are in use for these sorts of data: the older systematics, which we will refer to as traditional or evolutionary systematics following Charig's (1982) terminology, and the newer phylogenetic systematics, also known as cladistics. The goal of each of these approaches to systematics is to establish the pattern of evolutionary descent of organisms, but the methods differ.

Phylogenetic Systematics

In 1966, Willi Hennig introduced phylogenetic systematics by forcefully emphasizing that a phylogeny can be reconstructed only on the basis of shared derived characters. Derived in this sense means "different from the ancestral condition." For example, the feet of terrestrial vertebrates have distinctive bones, the carpals, tarsals, and digits. This arrangement of foot bones is different from the ancestral pattern seen in lobe-finned fishes, and is a shared derived character of terrestrial vertebrates. In cladistic terminology, shared derived characters

are called **synapomorphies** (*syn* or *sym* = together, *apo* = away from, i.e., derived from, *morph* = form).

Of course, organisms also have shared characters that they have inherited from their ancestors. These are called **plesiomorphies** (*plesi* = near). Terrestrial vertebrates have a vertebral column, for example, that was inherited essentially unchanged from lobe-finned fishes. Hennig called shared ancestral characters **symplesiomorphies**. Plesiomorphies tell us nothing about degrees of relatedness. They are useful only in highlighting what characters are apomorphies. It is the insistence that only shared derived characters can be used to determine genealogies that particularly characterizes cladistics.

The jargon associated with cladistics makes it hard for newcomers to appreciate its importance. To clarify the meaning of the major terms, consider the examples presented in Figure 1–9. Any one of the three cladograms represents a possible evolutionary relationship (i.e., phylogeny) for the three taxa identified as 1, 2, and 3. The letters A/a, B/b, and C/c represent characters—morphological structures, enzymes, physiological processes, or behaviors for example. To make the example a bit more concrete, we can say that A/a represents the toes on the front foot, B/b represents the skin covering, and C/c represents the tail. A, B, and C are the ancestral character states, that is, the conditions

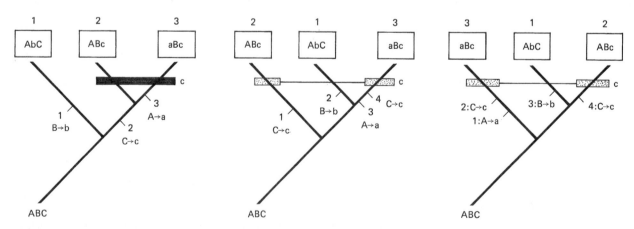

Figure 1–9   Cladograms showing the hypothetical distribution of three character states in three taxa (1, 2, and 3). The three ancestral states are represented by the capital letters A, B, and C, and the derived conditions by a, b, and c. Bars connect derived characters (apomorphies). The dark bar shows a shared derived character (a synapomorphy) of the lineage that includes taxa 2 + 3. The stippled bars represent the two independent origins of the same derived character state that must be assumed to have occurred if the apomorphy was not present in the most recent common ancestor of taxa 2 and 3. The numbers identify changes from the ancestral character state to the derived condition.

of each character that was inherited from the most recent common ancestor of the lineages we are examining, and a, b, and c are the derived character states. For the purpose of this example, let's say that the ancestral character state for A/a is to have five toes on the front foot (= A) and the derived state is four toes (= a). We'll say that the ancestral state of character B/b is a scaly skin (= B), and the derived state is lacking scales (= b). And for C/c, the ancestral state is tail present (= C) and the derived state is tail absent (= c).

Figure 1–9 shows the distribution of those three character states in the three groups. The animals in group 1 have five toes on the front feet (A), lack scales (b), and have a tail (C). Animals in group 2 have five toes, scaly skins, and no tails, and animals in group 3 have four toes, scaly skins, and no tails.

How can you use this information to decipher the evolutionary relationships of the three groups of animals? Notice that the ancestral character state C occurs only in taxon 1 and the derived condition c is found in both taxa 2 and 3. The most parsimonious phylogeny (i.e., the phylogeny that requires the fewest number of evolutionary changes) is represented by the left diagram in Figure 1–9. Only three changes are needed to produce the derived character states a, b, and c from the a starting point with the ancestral character states A, B, and C:

1. In the evolution of group 1, scales are lost (B → b).
2. In the evolution of group 2 + group 3, the tail is lost (C → c).
3. In the evolution of group 3, a toe is lost from the front foot (A → a).

The other two phylogenies are possible, but they would require that tail loss (the derived condition c) originated independently in taxon 2 and in taxon 3. Both of these phylogenies require four evolutionary changes, so they are less parsimonious than the first phylogeny we considered. Usually we consider that the most parsimonious phylogeny is most likely to be correct, and that's the one we would use.

A phylogeny of this sort (called a **cladogram**) is a hypothesis about the evolutionary relationships of the groups included. Like any scientific hypothesis, it can be tested with new data, and if it fails that test it is rejected and a different hypothesis (cladogram) takes its place.

So far we have avoided one of the central issues of phylogenetic systematics: How do you know which character state is ancestral (plesiomorphic) and which is derived (apomorphic)? That is, how do you determine the polarity (direction) of evolutionary transformation of the characters? For that, you need additional information. Increasing the number of characters you are considering can help, but comparing the characters you are using with an outgroup that consist of the closest relatives of the ingroup (i.e., the organisms you are studying) is the preferred method. A well-chosen outgroup will consistently possess unequivocal ancestral character states compared to the ingroup. For example, lobe-finned fishes are an appropriate outgroup for terrestrial vertebrates.

Cladists establish and name taxonomic groups within a cladogram solely on the basis of **monophyly** (single origin). For example, every vertebrate depicted in Figure 1–10 that is ascendant from a chosen branch point (i.e., each clade or lineage) along the cladogram is related by the shared derived characters that diagnose that lineage. The name assigned to this lineage identifies all members in the clade. The cladogram depicted in Figure 1–10 is our hypothesis of the evolutionary relationships of the major living groupings of vertebrates. There are 13 dichotomous branches leading from the origin of the vertebrates from other chordates to the mammals. A cladist ranks the organisms by sequencing the cladogram from ancestral to derived dichotomies, and assigning names to the lineages originating at each branch point. This process produces a nested series of groups, starting with the most inclusive. Thus, the name Gnathostomata includes all vertebrate animals that have jaws; that is, every taxon to the right of the number 3 in Figure 1–10 is included in the Gnathostomata, every taxon to the right of number 4 is included in the Teleostomii, and so on.

Evolutionary Hypotheses

Phylogenetic systematics is based on the assumption that organisms that are grouped together share a common heritage that accounts for their similarity. If that assumption is correct, we can use cladograms to ask questions and draw conclusions about evolution. We can examine the historical origin and functional significance of characters of living animals, and make inferences about the biology of extinct organisms. For example, the phylogenetic relationship of crocodilians, dinosaurs, and birds is shown in Figure 1–11. We know that crocodilians and birds care for their eggs and young.

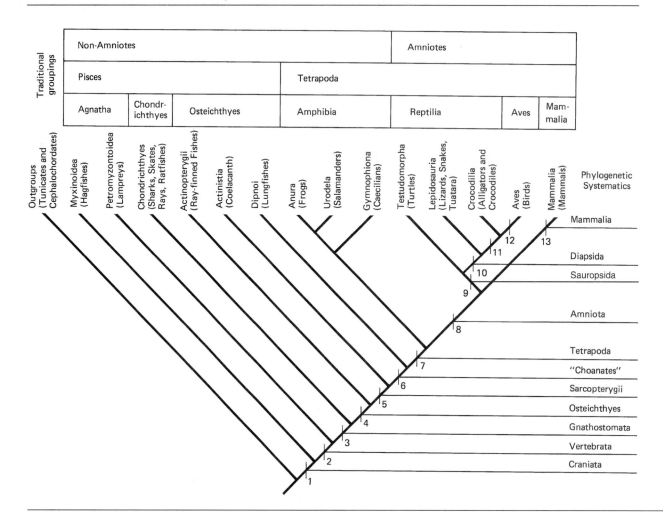

Fossilized dinosaur nests, some of which contain remains of baby dinosaurs, suggest that at least some dinosaurs cared for their young. Is that a plausible inference?

The intermediate lineages in the cladogram are extinct, so we cannot hope to observe their reproductive behavior, but the phylogenetic diagram in Figure 1–11 provides another way to approach the question. Both of the closest living relatives of the dinosaurs, crocodilians and birds, do have parental care. Looking at living representatives of more distantly related lineages, we see that parental care is not universal among fishes, amphibians, or reptiles other than crocodilians. With that information, we can conclude that parental care is a derived character of the evolutionary lineage that contains crocodilians + dinosaurs + birds (Archosauria). The most parsimonious explanation of the occurrence of parental care in both crocodilians and birds is that it had

evolved in that lineage before the crocodilians separated from dinosaurs + birds. (We could postulate that parental care evolved separately in crocodilians and in birds, but that would be a less parsimonious hypothesis.) So we are probably correct when we interpret the fossil evidence as showing that dinosaurs had parental care.

Figure 1–11 also illustrates one of the ways that cladistics has made talking about restricted groups of animals more complicated than it used to be. Suppose you wanted to refer to just the two lineages of animals that are popularly known as dinosaurs—what could you call them? Well, if you call them dinosaurs, you're not being PC (phylogenetically correct), because the taxon Dinosauria includes birds. So if you speak of dinosaurs, you are including ornithischians + saurischians + birds, even though any seven-year-old would understand that you are trying to restrict the conversation to extinct Mesozoic animals.

1. Distinct head region skeleton incorporating anterior end of notochord, one or more semicircular canals, brain consisting of three regions, paired kidneys, gill bars, neural crest tissue. **2.** Arcualia or their derivatives form vertebrae, two or three semicircular canals. **3.** Jaws formed from mandibular arch, teeth containing dentine, three semicircular canals, branchial skeleton internal to gill membranes, branchial arches containing four elements on each side plus one unpaired ventral median element, paired fins with internal skeleton and muscles supported by girdles in the body wall. **4.** Presence of lung or swimbladder derived from the gut, unique pattern of dermal bones of shoulder, unique characters of jaw and branchial muscles. **5.** Unique supporting skeleton in fins. **6.** Choanae* present, derived paired appendage structure, conus arteriosus of heart partly divided, unique dermal bone pattern of braincase, loss of interhyal bone. **7.** Limbs with carpals, tarsals, and digits; vertebrae with zygapophyses. **8.** A distinctive arrangement of extraembryonic membranes (the amnion, chorion, and allantois). **9.** Tabular and supratemporal bones small or absent, simple coronoid, centrum of atlas and intercentrum of axis fused, medial centrale of ankle absent. **10.** Skull with a dorsal temporal fenestra, upper temporal arch formed by triradiate postorbital and triradiate squamosal bones. **11.** Presence of a fenestra anterior to the orbit of the eye, orbit shaped like an inverted triangle. **12.** Feathers, loss of teeth, metabolic heat production used to regulate body temperature (endothermy). **13.** Hair, lower jaw formed only by dentary bone, mammary glands, independent development of endothermy.

*The homology of the choanae of dipnoans with those of tetrapods is questioned by many authorities, thus the name "Choanates" may not be appropriate but the grouping appears to be valid.

Figure 1–10 Phylogenetic relationships of extant vertebrates. This diagram shows the probable relationships among the major groups of vertebrates. The boxes across the top of the diagram show the traditional groupings of the taxa, and the names along the right side show how the lineages are grouped by phylogenetic systematics. Note that these groupings are nested progressively; that is, all sarcopterygians are osteichthyans, all osteichthyans are gnathostomes, all gnathostomes are vertebrates, all vertebrates are craniates, and so on. The numbers indicate derived characters that distinguish the lineages.

In fact, in cladistic terminology there *is* no correct taxonomic name for just the animals popularly known as dinosaurs. That's because cladistics recognizes only monophyletic lineages, and a monophyletic lineage, or clade, includes an ancestral form *and all its descendants*. The most recent common ancestor of ornithischians, saurischians, and birds in Figure 1–11 lies at the intersection of the lineage of ornithischians with saurischians + birds, so Dinosauria is a monophyletic lineage. But if birds are omitted, all the descendants of the common ancestor are no longer included, so ornithischians + saurischians minus birds does not fit the definition of a monophyletic lineage. (It would be called a **paraphyletic** group by cladists.)

Biologists who are interested in how organisms live often want to talk about paraphyletic groups. After all, the dinosaurs (in the popular sense of the word) differed from birds in many ways. The only correct way to refer to the animals popularly know as dinosaurs is to call them nonavian dinosaurs, and you will find that and other examples of paraphyletic groups later in the book. Sometimes even this construction does not work because there is no appropriate name for the part of the lineage you want to distinguish. In this situation we will use quotation marks (e.g., "ostracoderms") to indicate that the group is paraphyletic.

One other useful bit of terminology is **sister group**. The sister group is the monophyletic lineage that is most closely related to the monophyletic lineage being discussed. In Figure 1–11, for example, the lineage that includes crocodilians and phytosaurs is the sister group of the lineage that includes pterosaurs + ornithischians + saurischians + birds. Similarly, pterosaurs are the sister group of ornithischians + saurischians + birds, ornithischians are the sister group of saurischians + birds, and saurischians are the sister group of birds.

Figure 1–11   Using a cladogram to make inferences about behavior. (a) The cladogram shows the relationships of the Archosauria, the evolutionary lineage that includes living crocodilians and birds. (The symbol † indicates lineages that are entirely extinct. Phytosaurs were crocodilelike animals that disappeared at the end of the Triassic, and pterosaurs were the flying reptiles of the Jurassic and Cretaceous.) The two extant groups, crocodilians and birds, both display extensive parental care of eggs and young. The most parsimonious explanation of this situation assumes that parental care is an ancestral character of the archosaur lineage. (b) The phylogenetic taxonomy of the Archosauria shows the same nested arrangement of taxa as the cladogram. ([1] "Other groups" in this example refers to phytosaurs and pterosaurs.) (c) Traditional taxonomy provides no information about the evolutionary relationships of the taxa, and suggests that birds have a status equivalent to that of all the other archosaurians. ([2] "Other groups" in this example includes turtles, lizards, snakes, and tuatara as well as the crocodilians and dinosaurs listed as orders of reptiles.)

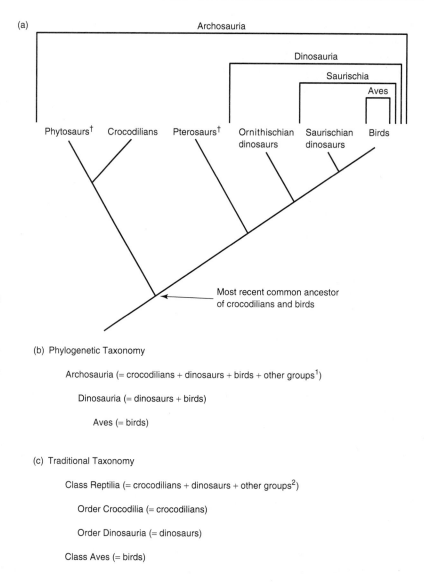

(a)

Archosauria

Dinosauria

Saurischia

Aves

Phytosaurs†   Crocodilians   Pterosaurs†   Ornithischian dinosaurs   Saurischian dinosaurs   Birds

Most recent common ancestor of crocodilians and birds

(b) Phylogenetic Taxonomy

Archosauria (= crocodilians + dinosaurs + birds + other groups[1])

Dinosauria (= dinosaurs + birds)

Aves (= birds)

(c) Traditional Taxonomy

Class Reptilia (= crocodilians + dinosaurs + other groups[2])

Order Crocodilia (= crocodilians)

Order Dinosauria (= dinosaurs)

Class Aves (= birds)

Determining Phylogenetic Relationships

We've established that the derived characters systematists used to group species into higher taxa must be inherited via common ancestry, that is, they must be **homologous** similarities. Unfortunately, the word "homologous" has at least three distinct meanings in evolutionary biology, only one of which is the same as its use in everyday speech, and these different meanings can cause confusion. (1) In the narrowest sense, homologous means "descended from the same derived structure." (2) In a slightly broader sense, homologous can mean "descended from the same ancestral structure." (3) In the form employed by molecular geneticists (most of whom are not familiar with evolutionary biology), homologous means "similar" without any implications of evolutionary descent. The first definition is the one employed by phylogenetic systematists, but the second definition is widespread in the literature of vertebrate biology. The third definition is not widely used in evolutionary biology, although it does appear in cases where DNA sequences are used to infer evolutionary relationships. A reader must be careful to determine which of the possible meanings of homology the author intended (Gould 1988).

We can turn to the limbs of terrestrial vertebrates again, this time to illustrate the difference between the first and second definitions of homologous: The forelimb of tetrapods consists of one bone (the humerus) in the upper limb and two bones (the radius and ulna) in the lower arm. This is the ancestral condition for terrestrial vertebrates, and all terrestrial vertebrates have forelimbs with this structure. By definition 2, all these forelimbs are homologous structures. That includes forelimbs as different as those of humans, horses, and birds. Birds have extensively modified the ancestral forelimb and hand to form wings. Wings are a derived character of birds, and no other vertebrates have exactly the same modifications of the forelimb bones. Different kinds of birds have wings of different shapes—short and broad, long and narrow, and so on. The wings of all species of bird are homologous by the most restrictive definition of homology (definition 1) because all descended from the wing (derived forelimb) of an ancestral bird.

Structures that perform the same function or have the same appearance without being homologous are called **homoplastic** (*plast* = form, shape). The wings of birds and bats are both forelimbs specialized for flight (Figure 1–12). By definition 1 they are not homologous because they are not derived from a common ancestor of birds and bats that had a forelimb specialized for flight; therefore, the wings of birds and bats would be called homoplastic. By definition 2, the wings of birds and bats would be considered homologous because they are derived from the ancestral vertebrate limb.

Homoplastic similarities include **convergence** and **parallelism**. It is well known that distantly related species with similar modes of life may have superficially very similar morphological structures and body shapes as the result of the same selective forces acting on different genotypes (convergence). Examples of convergence among vertebrates include the similarity in body shape of a pelagic fish (shark),

an aquatic lepidosauromorph (ichthyosaur), and an aquatic mammal (porpoise). The fusiform body shapes of these animals have been derived independently, beginning from very different ancestral body forms (fishlike, lizardlike, and mammalian, respectively). Parallelism describes the evolution of similar structures from a derived starting point. For example, some lineages of desert rodents, such as the jerboas of the Old World and the kangaroo rats of the New World, have long hind limbs, a long, bare tail with a tuft of hair on the end, and enlarged middle ears. Jerboas and kangaroo rats each originated from the rodent lineage (that is, from an already derived mammalian body form), and they have developed their specializations in parallel.

■ The Effect of Human Population Growth on Vertebrate Diversity

Starting from the appearance of the earliest vertebrates in the Late Cambrian or Ordovician, the diversity of vertebrates appears to have increased slowly through the Paleozoic and early Mesozoic, and then rapidly during the past hundred million years. This overall increase has been interrupted by eight periods of extinction for aquatic vertebrates and six for terrestrial forms (Benton 1990). The number of species of vertebrates reached a peak in the Pliocene or Pleistocene, and has declined since then (World Conservation Monitoring Centre 1992).

Extinction is as normal a part of evolution as species formation, and the duration of most species in the fossil record appears to be from one million to ten million years. Periods of major

Figure 1–12 Wing bones of a bird and a bat showing the similarities and differences.

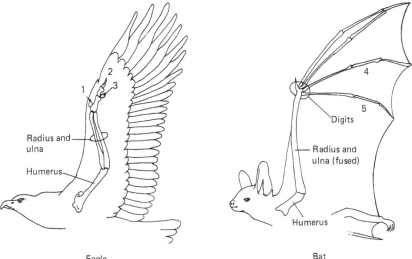

Eagle

Bat

extinction (a reduction in diversity of 10 percent or more) are associated with changes in climate and the consequent changes in vegetation. (Impacts of extraterrestrial objects have clearly occurred many times during the history of vertebrates, but they have probably played only minor roles in extinctions.)

Changes in that pattern of reasonably long-lived species and extinctions that are correlated with changes in climate and vegetation appear about the time that humans became a dominant factor in many parts of the world (Wilson 1992, Steadman 1995). Hawaii probably had more than 100 species of native birds when Polynesian colonists arrived about 300 A.D. (Olson and James 1991a,b). By the time European colonists reached Hawaii in the late eighteenth century, that number had been reduced by half, and in the past two centuries another third of the native Hawaiian birds have become extinct. The arrival of humans in Australia (between 100,000 and 40,000 years ago), North America (40,000 to 10,000 years ago), Madagascar (1500 years ago), and New Zealand (1000 years ago) coincided in every instance with waves of extinction. These extinctions were selective—large mammals and flightless birds disappeared,

whereas small mammals and most flying birds were not affected. Hunting was probably the principle cause of these extinctions, because the species that disappeared were those that human hunters concentrated on (Diamond 1989).

Animal species continue to become extinct today (Figure 1–13), and a worldwide survey of extinctions since the start of European colonization reveals two trends: Island extinctions began almost two centuries earlier than continental extinctions, and both island and continental extinctions have increased rapidly from the early or mid nineteenth century through the twentieth century (World Conservation Monitoring Centre 1992).

It is not easy to calculate the rate at which extinctions are occurring, and different assumptions can produce very different values. Recent estimates of the number of species of birds that would be committed to extinction by the year 2015 range from 450 to 1350 (Heywood et al. 1994). (Committed to extinction means that a species' populations in the wild are no longer viable, and the species will inevitably become extinct unless major conservation actions reverse the current trend.) What is clear is that destruction of habitat is the major threat, affecting more than 60 percent of threatened

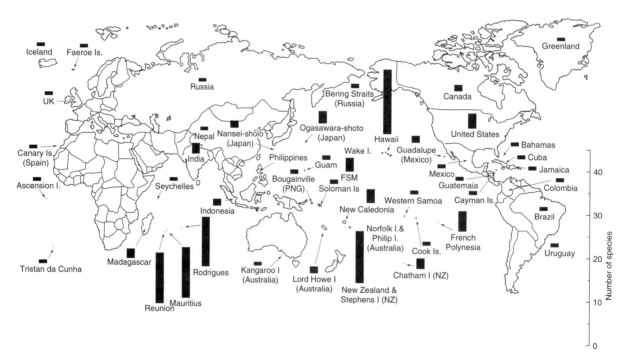

Figure 1–13   The numbers of confirmed extinctions of species of birds since 1600. Islands have suffered more extinctions than continental areas. (*Source:* World Conservation Monitoring Centre 1992.)

Figure 1–14 The major threats affecting birds (on a worldwide basis) and mammals (Australasia and the Americas). Habitat destruction is the single most important threat for both kinds of animals, affecting 60 percent of birds and 76 percent of mammals. Hunting (for food and sport) is a greater threat to mammals than to birds. Introduced species may be predators or competitors, and international trade refers to commercial exploitation for fur, feathers, and the pet trade. *Incidental take* is the term used to designate accidental mortality, such as dolphins that are drowned by boats fishing for tuna. (*Source:* World Conservation Monitoring Centre 1992.)

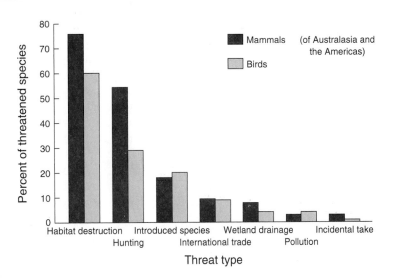

species of birds and nearly 80 percent of threatened species of mammals (Figure 1–14).

An especially ominous trend has become apparent recently: the decline of populations and the disappearance of species from causes that seem to be worldwide, indirect, and sometimes affect areas that appear pristine. Consider these examples:

1. Populations of frogs and salamanders are declining or disappearing entirely, and examples have been reported from all continents and from sites where human influence seems trivial or nonexistent (Wake 1991, Phillips 1994, Blaustein et al. 1994b). Ultraviolet B radiation, which kills the eggs and embryos of some species of amphibians, may be one cause of these declines, possibly activing in concert with other factors such as acidification of breeding pools by acid rain (Blaustein et al. 1994a; Long et al. 1995). The amount of ultraviolet B radiation reaching the Earth's surface is increasing as a result of depletion of ozone in the stratosphere by chlorofluorocarbons released by human activities, and this phenomenon is not confined to the well-known hole over the Antarctic. Measurements of ultraviolet B radiation at Toronto, Canada, since 1989 show an increase of 35 percent per year in winter and 7 percent per year in summer (Kerr and McElroy 1993).

2. Populations of migratory birds in North America declined 50 percent from the 1940s to the 1980s. Destruction of forest habitats in North America (where the species breed) and in Mexico, the West Indies, and Central and South America (where they spend the winter) appears to have been an important part of these declines (Terborgh 1989).

3. Some birds in European forests are producing eggs with thin, porous shells that break easily. The problem is a lack of calcium in the birds' diets because acid in rain and snow has dissolved calcium from the soil. These depleted soils no longer support the populations of snails that once supplied the calcium the birds need to form eggshells (Graveland et al. 1994).

4. An average of 82 percent of alligator eggs from Lake Apopka in Florida fail to hatch, and about half of the alligators that do emerge from these eggs die within two weeks. In testimony before the Subcommittee on Health and the Environment of the Committee on Energy and Commerce of the United States House of Representatives in October 1993, Louis Guillette of the University of Florida reported that examination of hatchlings and young alligators revealed that males had been feminized: They had estrogen concentrations typical of females and virtually no testosterone, the phallus was one-half to one-third the normal size, and their gonads had the structure of ovaries rather than testes (Committee on Energy and Commerce 1994). Female alligators from Lake Apopka had about twice the normal concentration of estrogen and the eggs in their ovaries were both abnormal and too numerous. The pesticide dicofol and its contaminants DDT, DDE, and

DDD are probably responsible for these abnormalities. When alligator eggs from uncontaminated sites were painted with dicofol, the hatchlings had hormone levels that were nearly identical to hatchlings from Lake Apopka. Dicofol is just one example of an environmental hormone that acts like a synthetic estrogen. Similar effects are produced by other pesticides, including kepone, heptachlor, dieldrin, mirex, and toxaphene, as well as by polychlorinated biphenyls (PCBs), dioxin (a compound that is a contaminant of some herbicides and is produced by incinerating some plastics), and alkylphenol polyethoxylates (APEs, a group of surfactants used in many dishwashing liquids). In addition to alligators, the list of vertebrates that have probably been feminized by these synthetic estrogens includes fishes (trout, carp, sturgeon), birds (gulls, birds of prey), and mammals (the Florida panther) (Raloff 1994). Humans are probably not immune from the effects of environmental estrogens. Between 1938 and 1991 the average sperm densities of human males in Europe and North America declined from 113 million per milliliter of seminal fluid to 66 million per milliliter, and the average volume of seminal fluid decreased from 3.40 milliliters to 2.75 milliliters. Feminization by environmental estrogens has been suggested as the cause of this phenomenon (Carlsen et al. 1992).

Human Population Growth and Conservation

The world's human population is currently about 6 billion people, double what it was only 50 years ago. A quarter of a million humans are added to the population each day, a population the size of New York City is added each month, and nearly 100 million additional people demand resources each year. The human population has been growing and an ever-increasing rate for thousands of years, a pattern of growth that cannot be sustained. An increase in the number of humans leads to exponential increases in the rate of use of resources—food, fiber, fuel—and in the production of wastes that pollute ecosystems around the globe. Any conservation issue untimately rests directly on finding a solution to the problems of the human population explosion.

It is important to understand that consumption of resources and pollution of the environment increase at rates far greater than the rate of population growth. This differential is increasing as global communication (especially television) exposes the overwhelming majority of humans to a Western life style, raising expectations and aspirations worldwide. Per capita energy use has nearly tripled since 1850, and most of the increase has occurred in the past few decades (Vitousek 1994). Typically the use of materials in a modern technological society increases four to five times faster than population growth, a rate far faster than in pretechnological societies.

The magnitude and complexity of the problems facing conservation biologists are daunting, and the scale on which remedial efforts must be attempted is nearly beyond comprehension. The growth of human populations is at the root of the crisis in biodiversity. The United Nations Population Fund estimated that the human population of the Earth will reach 8.3 billion by 2025 and 9.8 billion by 2050. These increases will occur despite the fact that the total fertility rate (births per woman) is declining because the base population (number of women of child-bearing age) keeps growing (Bongaarts 1994).

It has been estimated that no more than 2 billion humans can be indefinitely sustained on Earth (Pimentel et al. 1994). At that population, a reasonable quality of life could be sustainably provided for all. If these estimates are even vaguely correct, then human population restraint and action towards a sustainable future must begin now. Allison Jolly (1985) has calculated that the total world population of all wild primates combined is less than that of any of the Earth's major cities. The entire extant populations of many species are no larger than that of a small town. Conditions are equally critical for many other vertebrates. Almost two decades ago Jolly (1980) expressed the problems we face even more painfully as biologists today.

> This realization has been painful. It began for me in Madagascar, where the tragedy of forest felling, erosion, and desertification is a tragedy without villains. Malagasy peasant farmers are only trying to change wild environments to feed their own families, as mankind has done everywhere since the Neolithic Revolution. The realization grew in Mauritius, where I watched the world's last five echo parakeets land on one tree and knew they will soon be no more. It has come through an equally painful intellectual change. I became a biologist through wonder at the diversity of nature. I became a field biologist because I preferred watching nature go its own way to messing it about

with experiments. At last I understood that biology, as the study of nature apart from man, is a historical exercise. From the Neolithic Revolution to its logical sequels of twentieth-century population growth, biochemical engineering of life forms, and nuclear mutual assured destruction, human mind has become the chief factor in biology. . . . the urgent need in [vertebrate] studies is conservation. It is sheer self-indulgence to write books to increase understanding if there will soon be nothing left to understand.

Reviews of the biodiversity crisis agree that an essential first step in coming to grips with the problem is a clear understanding of what species exist, where they are, and what are the critical elements in their survival (Wilson 1992, World Conservation Monitoring Centre 1992). This is an enterprise that must enlist biologists from specialties as diverse as systematics, ecology, behavior, physiology, genetics, nutrition, and animal husbandry. Academic biologists have sometimes stood aloof from colleagues who work in applied areas of biology, but that kind of elitism hinders progress toward the synthesis we need. Throughout this book, we have noted areas in which a combination of basic and applied information about vertebrates has the potential to contribute to conservation of biodiversity.

■ Summary

The 50,000 species of living vertebrates span a size range from less than a gram to more than 100,000 kilograms and live in habitats from the bottom of the sea to the tops of mountains. This extraordinary diversity is the product of 500 million years of evolution. Evolution means a change in the relative frequencies of alleles in the gene pool of a species. Heritable variation among the individuals of a species is the raw material of evolution, and natural selection is the mechanism that produces evolutionary change. Natural selection works by differential reproduction, and fitness describes the relative contribution of different individuals to future generations.

In addition to individual variation, species often exhibit sexual dimorphism and geographic variation. Sexual dimorphism reflects the different selective forces that act on males and females of a species as a result of the asymmetry of reproductive investment by the two species. In most cases males can maximize their fitness by mating with as many females as possible, whereas females should attempt to choose the best possible mate. When a local population of a species is isolated from the rest of the species, genetic differences accumulate. If genetic differences become extensive, individuals of the isolated population may be unable to breed with individuals of the main population when they reestablish contact. This process is called allopatric speciation.

The Earth has changed dramatically during the half billion years of vertebrate history. Continents were fragmented when vertebrates first appeared; coalesced into one enormous continent, Pangaea, about 300 million years ago; and began to fragment again about 100 million years ago. This pattern of fragmentation–coalescence–fragmentation has resulted in isolation and recontact of major groups of vertebrates on a worldwide basis. On a continental scale the advance and retreat of glaciers in the Pleistocene caused homogeneous habitats to split and merge repeatedly, isolating populations of widespread species and leading to the evolution of new species.

Phylogenetic systematics, usually called cladistics, classifies animals on the basis of shared derived character states. Natural evolutionary groups can be defined only on the basis of these derived characters; retention of ancestral characters does not provide information about evolutionary lineages. Application of this principle produces groupings of animals that reflect evolutionary history as accurately as we can discern it, and forms a basis for making hypotheses about evolution.

The diversity of vertebrates has increased steadily (albeit with several episodes of extinction) for the past 500 million years, and peaked in the Pliocene or Pleistocene. Much of the decline in diversity of vertebrates (and other forms of life) since then can be traced to the direct and indirect effects of humans on the other species with which we share the planet. The major threats to the continued survival of species of vertebrates include habitat destruction, pollution, and hunting. At the base of all these phenomena is the enormous increase in human population size. Knowledge of vertebrates and other organisms is an essential part of the conservation of biodiversity, but control of human population growth is the only solution to the biodiversity crisis.

■ References

Benton, M. J. 1990. Patterns of evolution and extinction in vertebrates. Pages 218–241 in *Evolution and the Fossil Record*, edited by K. Allen and D. Briggs. Smithsonian Institution Press, Washington, DC.

Blaustein, A. R., P. D. Hoffman, D. G. Hokit, J. M. Kiesecker, S. C. Walls, and J. B. Hays. 1994a. UV repair and resistance to solar UV-B in amphibian eggs: a link to population declines. *Proceedings of the National Academy of Sciences, USA* 91:179.

Blaustein, A. R., D. B. Wake, and W. P. Sousa. 1994b. Amphibian declines: judging stability, persistence, and susceptibility of populations to local and global extinctions. *Conservation Biology* 8:60–71.

Bongaarts, J. 1994. Population policy options in the developing world. *Science* 263:771–776.

Breden, F., and G. Stoner. 1987. Male predation risk determining female preference in the Trinidad guppy. *Nature* 329:831–833.

Carlsen, E., A. Giwercman, N. Keiding, and N. E. Skakkebaek. 1992. Evidence for decreasing quality of semen during the past 50 years. *British Medical Journal* 305:609–619.

Charig, A. 1982. Systematics in biology: a fundamental comparison of some major schools of thought. Pages 363–440 in *Problems of Phylogenetic Reconstruction*, edited by K. A. Joysey and A. E. Friday. Academic, New York, NY.

Committee on Energy and Commerce, U. S. House of Representatives. 1994. *Health Effects of Estrogenic Pesticides*. Serial No. 103-87. U. S. Government Printing Office, Washington, DC.

Connor, E. F. 1986. The role of Pleistocene forest refugia in the evolution and biogeography of tropical biotas. *Trends in Ecology and Evolution* 1:164–168.

de Queiroz, K. 1988. Systematics and the Darwinian revolution. *Philosophy of Science* 55:238–259.

de Queiroz, K., and J. Gauthier. 1992. Phylogenetic taxonomy. *Annual Review of Ecology and Systematics* 23:449–480.

Diamond, J. 1989. Quaternary megafaunal extinctions: variations on a theme by Paganini. *Journal of Archaeological Science* 16:167–175.

Endler, J. A. 1986. *Natural Selection in the Wild*. Monographs in Population Biology, No. 21. Princeton University Press, Princeton, NJ.

Friedman, M. J. 1978. Erythrocyte mechanism of sickle cell resistance to malaria. *Proceedings of the National Academy of Sciences* ([Symbol]U[Geneva]SA) 75:1994–1997.

Gibbs, H. L., and P. R. Grant. 1987. Oscillating selection on Darwin's finches. *Nature* 327:511–513.

Gould, S. J. 1988. The heart of terminology. *Natural History* 97(2):24–31.

Grant, P. R. 1986. *Ecology and Evolution of Darwin's Finches*. Princeton University Press, Princeton, NJ.

Graveland, J., R. van der Wal, J. H. van Balen, and A. J. van Noordwijk. 1994. Poor reproduction in forest passerines from decline of snail abundance on acidified soils. *Nature* 368:446–448.

Hennig, W. 1966. *Phylogenetic Systematics*. University of Illinois Press, Urbana, IL.

Heywood, V. H., G. M. Mace, R. M. May, and S. N. Stuart. 1994. Uncertainties in extinction rates. *Nature* 368:105.

Jolly, A. 1980. *A World Like Our Own: Man and Nature in Madagascar*. Yale University Press, New Haven, CT.

Jolly, A. 1985. *The Evolution of Primate Behavior*, 2nd edition. Macmillan, New York, NY.

Kerr, J. B., and C. T. McElroy. 1993. Evidence for large upward trends of ultraviolet-B radiation linked to ozone depeletion. *Science* 262:1032–1034.

Lack, D. 1947. *Darwin's Finches*. Cambridge University Press, Cambridge, MA.

Long, L. E., L. S. Saylor, and M. E. Soulé. 1995. A pH/UVB synergism in amphibians. *Conservation Biology* 9:1301–1303.

Mayr, E. 1942. *Systematics and the Origin of Species*. Columbia University Press, New York, NY.

Olson, S. L., and H. F. James. 1991a. Descriptions of thirty-two new species of birds from the Hawaiian Islands. Part 1: Non-passeriformes. *Ornithological Monographs* 45:1–88.

Olson, S. L., and H. F. James. 1991b. Descriptions of thirty-two new species of birds from the Hawaiian Islands. Part 2: Passeriformes. *Ornithological Monographs* 46:1–88.

Phillips, K. 1994. *Tracking the Vanishing Frogs*. St. Martin's Press, New York, NY.

Pimentel, D., R. Harman, and M. Pacenza. 1994. Natural resources and an optimum human population. *Population and Environment* 15:347–369.

Raloff, J. 1994. The gender benders. *Science News* 145(2): 24–27.

Räsänen, M. E., J. S. Salo, and R. J. Kalliola. 1987. Fluvial perturbance in the western Amazon Basin: regulation by long-term sub-Andean tectonics. *Science* 238:1398–1401.

Simpson, G. G. 1961. *Principles of Animal Taxonomy*. Columbia University Press, New York, NY.

Steadman, D. W. 1995. Prehistoric extinctions of Pacific island birds: biodiversity meets zooarchaeology. *Science* 267:1123–1131.

Terborgh, J. 1989. *Where Have All the Birds Gone?* Princeton University Press, Princeton, NJ.

Vitousek, P. M. 1994. Beyond global warming: ecology and global change. *Ecology* 75:1861–1876.

Wake, D. B. 1991. Declining amphibian populations. *Science* 253:860.

Wiley, E. O. 1978. The evolutionary species concept reconsidered. *Systematic Zoology* 27:17–26.

Wilson, E. O. 1992. *The Diversity of Life*. Norton, New York, NY.

World Conservation Monitoring Centre. 1992. *Global Biodiversity: Status of the Earth's Living Resources*. Chapman & Hall, London, UK.

CHAPTER

2

The Origin of Vertebrates

The principles of evolution and natural selection that we described in the preceding chapter apply to all forms of life, not just to vertebrates. In this chapter we explain what characteristics are necessary to diagnose a vertebrate and describe the systems that make a vertebrate a functional animal in the context of its life-style. We also address the question of the origin of vertebrates: What characters are unique to vertebrates, and what characters are shared with other, less derived, animals? If we could identify the sister group (i.e., the most closely related evolutionary lineage) of vertebrates, would that information help us to explain the process by which vertebrates arose from invertebrate ancestors? We compare the most widely accepted view of the origin of vertebrates with several alternatives that may provide different insights about the events and mechanisms responsible for early vertebrate evolution.

■ Points to Consider in Discussions of Classification and Adaptation

Each group of vertebrates differs from all others in some fundamental way, but all share some common definitive characters at least at some point in their lifetime. What is the meaning of the underlying similarity? Since Darwin's *Origin of Species* we have understood that the sharing of fundamental similarities (those that can be determined to be of identical genetic and evolutionary origin), or homologies, among widely different groups of species indicates that they evolved from a common ancestor that possessed the same features. In general, the more homologies two species (or other taxonomic groups) share, the more closely the groups are related.

A relationship between different taxonomic groups can be established only on the basis of shared derived characters (synapomorphies, see Chapter 1). However an important, although some-

times confusing, point is that whether or not a character is considered primitive or ancestral (and hence not suitable for determining relationships) depends on the level that is being examined. For example, mammals are usually thought of being distinguished from other vertebrates by their shared derived features of hair and mammary glands. Yet while these features *do* distinguish mammals as a group (and hence are derived features within the vertebrates as a whole), *within* the mammals they are of no use in telling if one mammal is more closely related to one than to any other. Thus hair and mammary glands are then considered to be primitive characters at the level of the class Mammalia. Hair is a feature that can be used to link you as more closely related to a horse than to a lizard, but it cannot be used to link you as more closely related to a horse than to any other mammal.

The diversity of body form and ecology among vertebrates, as among any group of organisms, reflects their diverse evolutionary histories. However, the ways in which different vertebrates might respond (in an evolutionary adaptive fashion) to various environmental circumstances also depends on their evolutionary history up to that point in time. For example, a lineage of fishes beginning to forage for food on land would improve its chances of success at this venture if its members were better able to walk on land and to breathe air. Thus we would predict that, over time, selection would favor change in morphology to suit this new environment (i.e., adaptational change), with the acquisition of legs and lungs. However, fishes that forage on land today (such as mudskippers) have adapted their bodies in a different fashion from those fishes originally ancestral to tetrapods (land vertebrates). Mudskippers come from a derived lineage of fishes (teleosts) that have lost primitive features possessed by our own fishy ancestors, such as lunglike air sacs and fins with robust bones. Thus mudskippers have solved the problem of life on land in a different fashion from tetrapods, using their hind fins as struts rather than as propulsive limbs and breathing air via an expanded opercular chamber rather than with lungs.

Evolution and adaptation are major themes of this book. We shall therefore direct attention to the following sorts of questions. What were the ancestral precursors of any structure or behavior under consideration? How does the structure or behavior promote survival and reproduction of the organism in its natural environment? Was the original function of the structure or behavior the same as its current function?

We must be wary of traps when talking about evolution or considering the evolutionary history of a group. It is common to talk about adaptation and evolution as if they were in some way purposeful: for example, "fishes coming onto land need lungs to breathe air." Interpreting adaptations as purposeful in this fashion is to fall prey to *teleology:* Such examples of teleological reasoning are erroneous because evolution cannot work with foresight. Biologists often have been accused of presenting teleological arguments, even though there was no intention to present a predeterministic view of evolutionary processes. But as with the popular aphorism, "Life must be lived forward, but can only be understood in retrospect," from our present vantage point, evolutionary patterns and trends appear to unfold over time. In describing evolutionary trends, we must be explicit about the processes that must have hap-

pened at the time, irrespective of later events. A lineage of fishes spending time out of water might encounter selection pressures for immediate changes that would increase their ability to obtain oxygen from the air. Improved blood circulation (vascularization) of existing pharyngeal pouches would improve extraction of oxygen from gulped air and benefit those animals at the time, without implying any evolutionary foresight that those pouches might some day, in a distant descendant, form fully fledged lungs, although in retrospect one might determine that these pharyngeal pouches were an essential preliminary step in the evolution of lungs.

■ Definition of a Vertebrate

Vertebrates belong in the phylum **Chordata**, in the subphylum **Vertebrata**. Other members of the Chordata are the tunicates (subphylum Urochordata) and the cephalochordates (subphylum Cephalochordata). The shared derived features of chordates, seen in all members of the phylum in at least some point of their lives, are commonly listed as follows: **notochord, muscular postanal tail, dorsal hollow nerve cord,** and **pharyngeal slits** (or pouches). The slits in the pharynx (the throat region), although characteristic of chordates, may not be a uniquely derived chordate feature because similar structures are seen in members of the related phylum Hemichordata, and may even be present in some fossil echinoderms. Another shared derived feature of chordates is the **endostyle**. In larval lampreys (primitive jawless vertebrates) and the adults of nonvertebrate chordates this structure is a ciliated, glandular groove on the floor of the pharynx that secretes mucus and is used to trap food in filter feeding. The endostyle is homologous with the thyroid gland of vertebrates (indeed, the metamorphosis from endostyle to thyroid gland can be seen in lampreys when the filter-feeding larva changes to the suction-feeding adult). Both the endostyle and the thyroid concentrate iodine (from the surrounding seawater in more primitive chordates, and from the blood in more derived vertebrates).

Chordates also share the features of bilateral symmetry, distinct head and tail ends, and a basic internal organization of a tube-within-a-tube, that is, with the gut and the major internal organs (the inner tube) lying within a body cavity or coelom with the body wall forming the outer tube. However, these are not uniquely derived chordate features, but rather are shared with many other groups of animals (see Figure 2–2). Insects, for example, are superficially rather like chordates in these features, but differ profoundly in other aspects of internal design (for example, their nerve cord is ventral in position).

The term *Vertebrate* is obviously derived from the vertebrae that are serially arranged to make up the spinal column, or backbone (Figure 2–1). In ourselves, as in other tetrapods, the vertebrae form around the notochord during development, also encircling the nerve cord, and the bony vertebral column replaces the original notochord after the embryonic period. In many fishes the vertebrae are made of cartilage rather than of bone. However,

not all animals included within the traditional subphylum Vertebrata possess vertebrae. Among living jawless vertebrates hagfishes lack vertebral elements entirely, and lampreys possess only cartilaginous rudiments that flank the nerve cord. Fully formed vertebrae, with a centrum surrounding the notochord, are found only in jawed vertebrates among the array of living forms. Many jawed fishes retain a functional notochord as adults, with centra composed of a number of separate elements rather than a single block of bone. The condition in extinct jawless vertebrates is unlikely to be known for certain, because if any vertebrae were present they would probably have been cartilaginous and hence

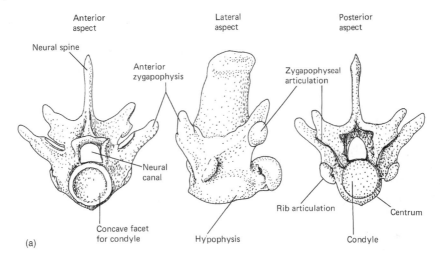

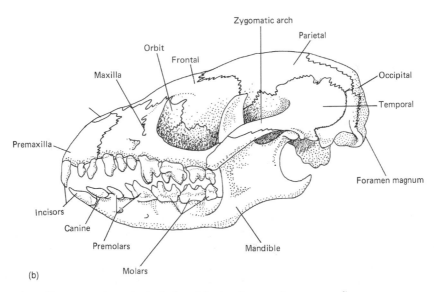

Figure 2–1   Examples of bony structures typical of vertebrates (as seen in a mammal): (a) vertebra; (b) skull.

not preserved. Note, however, that Janvier and Blieck (1979) interpret some impressions on the underside of the dermal head shield of an early vertebrate (a heterostracan) as representing vertebral elements. This interpretation implies that all vertebrates except for hagfishes possessed at least some vertebral rudiments (see Figure 6–1).

However, all vertebrates do possess the uniquely derived feature of a **cranium**, or skull of some sort—a bony, cartilaginous, or fibrous structure surrounding the brain. Thus many people prefer the older term for the group, Craniata, based on the reasoning that all animals that fall in the subphylum currently termed Vertebrata have a cranium, but not all have vertebrae. (The use of the term Vertebrata also reflects the fashion of a century or so ago, to consider the living jawless vertebrates to be degenerate rather than merely primitive, with the assumption that they had somehow rather carelessly lost their vertebrae.) Many researchers currently consider that the term *craniate* should properly be substituted for the traditional term *vertebrate*, with the latter term restricted to mean only those vertebrates that actually possess vertebrae of some sort (i.e., all living forms with the exception of hagfishes: see Maisey 1986). However, we continue to use the traditional term *vertebrate* in this book, including hagfishes with other vertebrates.

What other features distinguish vertebrates from nonvertebrate chordates? Two critical embryological features may account for many of the differences. The first is the duplication of the **Hox gene complex** (= homeobox genes) that characterizes most animals, vertebrate and invertebrate (Marx 1992, Garcia-Fernandez and Holland 1994, Gee 1994, Monastersky 1996). The second is the development of a type of embryonic tissue called **neural crest** that forms many new structures in vertebrates, especially in the head region (Le Douarin 1982, Northcutt and Gans 1983) (see further discussion in Chapter 3). Embryonic tissue possibly related to neural crest forms the **epidermal placodes**, which are the source of the complex sensory organs in vertebrates, including the inner ear, the lateral line, and the cranial nerves that innervate it. The brain of vertebrates is additionally enlarged over the condition in more primitive chordates and is tripartite (three parted) in structure (see Chapter 3).

The origin of this so-called new head of vertebrates (Northcutt and Gans 1983) is controversial. Classical embryology holds that this is an add-on, consisting of three new segments anterior to the original tip of the chordate head. However, recent molecular genetic studies find the same segmental series of genes in amphioxus and vertebrates, suggesting that the head may have been expanded anteriorly, but that the elaborated front portion is not a new addition.

At the whole-body level all the features that distinguish vertebrates from more primitive chordates (see later discussion in this chapter and in Chapter 3) can be summarized as resulting from two evolutionary advances of vertebrates: an increase in body size and an increase in the level of activity (Gans 1989). With regard to body size, vertebrates are in general an order of magnitude larger than nonvertebrate chordates. Living cephalochordates are about 1 to 5 cm in length, while living jawless vertebrates (and their extinct relatives) are/were at least 10 cm long, with lengths of 100 cm not being uncommon (although this was not true of conodonts, extinct possible vertebrates, see later). Because of the relatively large size of vertebrates many of the biological processes that can be carried out by diffusion (e.g., respiration) or ciliary action (e.g., movement of water over the gills) in the smaller, nonvertebrate chordates, must be conducted by specialized systems in vertebrates. Likewise, an increase in the level of activity also necessitates specialized organ systems that can carry out processes at a high rate.

We can simply observe the size differences between vertebrates and other chordates, but where is the evidence for the higher levels of activity in vertebrates, except for the rather circular argument that the presence of more specialized organ systems must reflect high levels of activity? For a start, the basal metabolic rate of living vertebrates is considerably greater than that of nonvertebrate chordates. Ruben and Bennett (1980) also showed that vertebrates differ from other animals in their ability to decouple the primitive anaerobic part of the respiratory cycle, where glucose is broken down to yield some energy in the absence of oxygen, from the more derived, oxidative part of the cycle typical of eukaryotic organisms (the Krebs cycle—see Chapter 4). Vertebrates have the capacity to jump-start muscular activity by means of anaerobic burst metabolism, producing energy initially by this rather inefficient method, before the oxidative part of the cycle, which requires oxygen to be delivered to the tissues by the circulatory system, kicks in. This metabolic trick allows rapid movement for brief periods at very short notice, perhaps for catching prey or escaping from predators.

Where Vertebrates Fit in the Animal Kingdom

The fossil record preserves no direct evidence of intermediate forms between chordates and other animals, but we can use the diversity of living animals and features they share to infer where vertebrates must belong in the animal kingdom (see Figure 2–2). Almost every invertebrate phylum has been suggested at some time as the closest relative of the chordate line. Affinities have been postulated with annelids, arachnids, and arthropods—animals that share with chordates the features of bilateral symmetry and a distinct head end. However, developmental patterns within the various animal phyla reveal a different and rather surprising conclusion. The Chordata are in fact more closely related to the Echinodermata (starfishes, sea urchins, and the like), marine forms without distinct heads and with pentaradial (fivefold and circular) symmetry as adults.

Figure 2–2 shows in diagrammatic form the interrelationships of some of the major animal phyla. All animals are multicellular, and possess **collagen** as a structural protein. Above the level of sponges, all animals possess a nervous system and distinct layers of cells (at least an outer ectoderm layer and an inner endoderm layer). Animals above the level of jellyfishes and their kin add an additional, middle cell layer of mesoderm and are bilaterally symmetrical with a distinct head end (at least at some point in their life history). Another derived feature within animals is the acquisition of a **coelom**, or inner body cavity, formed as a split within the mesoderm (although the coelom may not be homologous in all coelomate animals).

There are two basic divisions within coelomate animals, involving two different developmental patterns for forming the early embryonic and larval stages (Nielsen 1985, Schaeffer 1987). The Mollusca (snails, clams, octopi, etc.), Arthropoda (insects, crabs, spiders, etc.), and Annelida (earthworms,

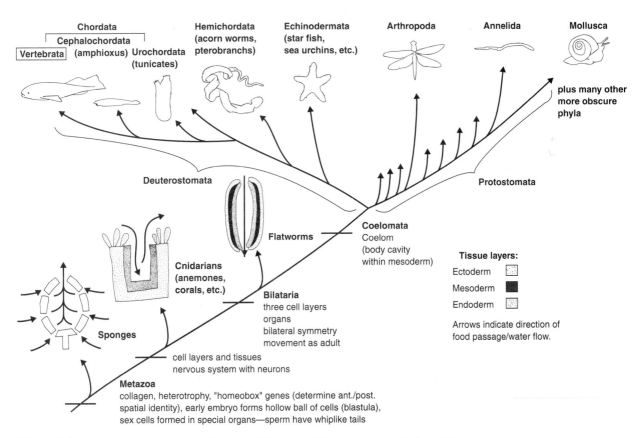

Figure 2–2 Simplified phylogeny of the animal kingdom. There are a total of about 30 phyla today (Chordata, Echinodermata, Annelida, etc. all represent phyla). Approximately 15 additional phyla are known from the early Paleozoic, and became extinct at the end of the Cambrian Period.

etc.), plus some other, less commonly known phyla, are grouped as the **protostomes** (*proto* = first, *stoma* = mouth). Other phyla, which also share a distinctive embryology, are placed in the **deuterostomes** (*deutero* = second). The blastopore (the original infolding of the ball of embryonic cells) of protostomes ultimately forms the mouth of the organism, whereas the blastopore of deuterostomes forms the anus.

Table 2.1 summarizes the main embryological differences between these divisions of coelomate animals. More recent phylogenies based on molecular evidence also have confirmed the reality of these two groups, the existence of protostomes and deuterostomes. However, the current data tend to support few closely related deuterostome phyla, in contrast with a large clumping of various protostome phyla.

The majority of present-day researchers would support the relationships of the deuterostomes shown in Figure 2–2: echinoderms as the most primitive, hemichordates (the rather annelidlike acorn worms and the sea-lilylike pterobranchs) as the sister group to chordates (linked by the shared derived character of pharyngeal gill slits), and the tunicates being the most primitive group within the chordates (Northcutt and Gans 1983, Schaeffer 1987). However, some dissension exists. Some people still maintain a protostome affinity for chordates on physiological and biochemical characters (Lovtrup 1977). Within the deuterostomes, the basal position of the echinoderms remains problematical. Part of the problem is that the living echinoderms (starfishes, sea urchins, sea lilies, sea cucumbers, and brittle stars), while seemingly quite diverse today, in fact represent only the tip of the iceberg of echinoderm diversity when fossil forms are taken into account. Not all fossil echinoderms had pentaradial symmetry (which, if one considers the phylogeny in Figure 2–2, is best

inferred to be a derived echinoderm feature, as bilateral symmetry was initially evolved in the common ancestry of protostomes and deuterostomes). In fact, the diversity of the earliest fossil echinoderms is such that it has been suggested that, if the entire group was displayed on the phylogeny, it would actually represent a paraphyletic assemblage of primitive deuterostomes rather than the discrete group, united by pentaradial symmetry, seen today (see Gee 1996). Another alternative interpretation of deuterostome relationships places echinoderms and hemichordates as *derived* members of the clade, with the chordate body form being the more primitive deuterostome condition (Gutmann 1981).

Some fossil deuterostomes, the **calcichordates**, had a more bilateral, fishlike shape (see Figure 2–3), and there has been a long-standing claim by Richard Jefferies (1986) that these animals were in fact basal chordates. He interprets their internal anatomy to contain chordate features such as a notochord, a segmented brain, and pharyngeal gill slits (although gill slits may be a primitive deuterostome feature, lost in derived, living echinoderms [Gee 1996]). Jefferies's interpretation of chordate phylogeny would place different genera of calcichordates as either sister taxa to the chordates as a whole, or as more closely related to particular groups of chordates (some related to urochordates, some to cephalochordates, and some to vertebrates). Because of the distribution of characters in the calcichordates his phylogeny ends up with urochordates (rather than cephalochordates) as the sister group of vertebrates among living chordates.

It is perhaps this final conclusion about the interrelationships of living chordates that other workers have found the most problematical about Jefferies's scheme. As is detailed later, many characteristics suggest that cephalochordates are more closely related to vertebrates than are urochordates (see

TABLE 2.1	Embryological differences between protostomes and deuterostomes	
Feature Compared	*Protostomes*	*Deuterostomes*
Cleavage	Spiral and determinate	Radial and indeterminate
Blastopore	Forms the mouth	Forms the anus
Coelom formation	Schizocoelous (a rift or split within the mesoderm)	Enterocoelous (outpocketing from the dorsolateral gut wall); *except vertebrates*
Type of larva	Trochophore	Tornaria or bipinnaria *except chordates*

Figure 2–3   A calichordate.

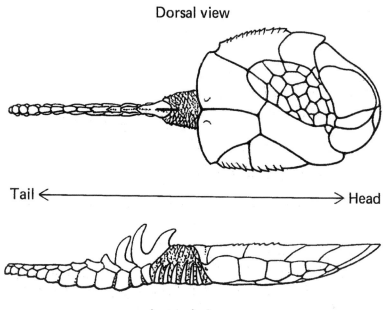

Maisey 1986, Gans 1989). A comprehensive phylogenetic analysis by Peterson (1994) suggested that calcichordates are better considered as specialized echinoderms, even if they are assigned the supposed chordate features of their soft anatomy that Jefferies proposes (although note that Jefferies [1997] refuted Peterson's claims).

The Middle Cambrian Burgess Shale in British Columbia, a spectacular fossil deposit preserving soft as well as hard parts and providing evidence of early members of many other animal phyla, has yielded about 60 specimens of what has been called the world's first known chordate, the 40-millimeter *Pikaia* (Gould 1989). Although details of its anatomy remain to be described, and its chordate status is not fully assured (Conway Morris 1997), it has frequently been compared to the cephalochordates (Figure 2–4). More recently another chordatelike animal, *Cathaymyrus*, has been reported from sediments 10 million years earlier, from the Early Cambrian of

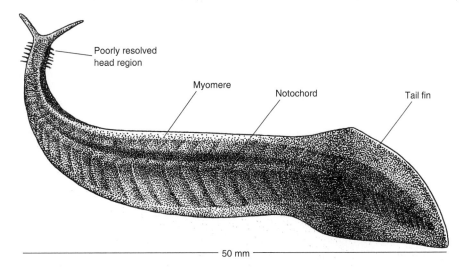

Figure 2–4   *Pikaia*, a possible early chordate from the Middle Cambrian Burgess Shale of British Columbia. (Illustration by Marianne Collins from Stephen Jay Gould, 1989, *Wonderful Life: The Burgess Shale and the Nature of History*, Norton, NY. Reproduced with the permission of Marianne Collins and W. W. Norton & Company, Inc., copyright © 1989 by Stephen Jay Gould.)

China (Shu et al. 1996). The most obvious chordate features of *Pikaia* are a notochord running along the posterior two-thirds of the body and segmental, V-shaped muscle bands (myomeres). In addition, it had a small bilobed head with a pair of short, slender tentacles, and bilaterally paired rows of about 12 tufts behind the head may represent exterior evidence of gill slits. The only other fossilized evidence of cephalochordates is the amphioxus-related *Palaeobranchiostoma* from the Early Permian of South Africa (Blieck 1992). The obvious swimming adaptations of this animal, with large dorsal and ventral fins, suggest that burrowing by modern amphioxus is a derived feature.

■ Nonvertebrate Chordates

The two groups of extant nonvertebrate chordates are both small, marine animals. The larval forms of the urochordates may represent a starting point for the evolution of vertebrates, and cephalochordates may have life-styles similar in some respects to those of the earliest vertebrates.

Urochordates

Present-day tunicates (subphylum Urochordata), are filter-feeding marine animals obtaining their food by filtering the surrounding water with a basketlike, perforated pharynx. There are about 2000 living species, and the great majority of these (all but 100 or so) are sedentary as adults, attached to the substrate either in a solitary fashion or in colonies. There are three classes of tunicates: The ascideans (or sea squirts) are all sedentary as adults with a tadpolelike planktonic larva, whereas the larvaceans and the thaliaceans are free-living as adults. Larvaceans are apparently derived from the larval form of their ancestor (as the name suggests), and thaliaceans are derived from the adult ancestral form.

Most adult tunicates appear to bear little similarity to cephalochordates and vertebrates (Figure 2–5c). Their pharyngeal gill slits, comprising the pharyngeal basket, appear to be their only chordate feature. However, their tadpolelike larvae look more promising than the adults as forms that belong within the phylum Chordata. In addition to pharyngeal slits, these larvae have a notochord, a dorsal hollow nerve cord, and a muscular postanal tail, which moves in a fishlike swimming pattern (Figure 2–5a). The larvae use these features for dispersal. However, in most species after a brief free-

swimming existence, generally of no more than a few minutes to a few days, the larvae metamorphose into adult animals that bear almost no resemblance to the larvae or to other adult chordates.

A popular and long-held theory is that cephalochordates and vertebrates evolved from a tunicatelike ancestor. By what evolutionary means could this have occurred? A scenario was proposed by Walter Garstang in 1928. He suggested that vertebrates originated from a tunicatelike lineage in which the larvae failed to metamorphose but instead developed functional gonads and reproduced. As previously mentioned, a few living tunicates do demonstrate this type of life-style, where the adult stage has apparently been suppressed, and the juvenile morph is retained into the adult reproductive phase. Garstang termed this evolutionary process **paedomorphosis** (*paedo* = child, *morph* = form) (see Box 2–1). In contrast other researchers (e.g., Ruben and Parrish 1990) have suggested that it is the tunicates with the sessile adult stage that are the derived forms, and that those tunicates that remain in permanent larval form more closely resemble the ancestral type of chordate.

The fossil record is unlikely to provide evidence about whether the sessile adult tunicate stage is a primitive or derived chordate feature, but evidence from other sources suggests that a sessile form may be the primitive chordate type, and that most typical chordate features were originally larval adaptations. The first line of evidence comes from the strange, dual nature of the nervous system and segmentation of vertebrates (the "dual animal" notion of Alfred Romer). Vertebrates and cephalochordates are unique among animals in having a double system of innervation, comprising a somatic system for innervating segmented structures, and a visceral system for innervating non-segmented structures (see Chapter 3). Romer proposed an explanation for this strange arrangement by suggesting that, in the course of evolution, an originally unsegmented tunicatelike body (with its visceral nervous system) had been overrun by a retained segmented larval tail (with its somatic nervous system), with segmentation then imposed on the main body.

The second line of evidence comes, rather surprisingly, from the vertebrate immune system. The same immune system that allows vertebrates to recognize invading bacteria as foreign cells also results in the recognition of tissue from other individuals of the same species as foreign, which is why transplants and tissue grafts are often unsuccessful in human medicine. But this phenomenon of allorecogni-

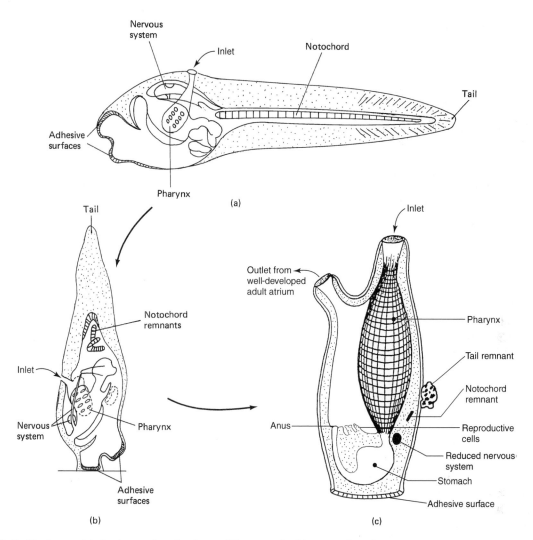

Figure 2–5   Tunicates: (a) the free-swimming larva, (b) an attached larva undergoing meta-morphosis, (c) and the sessile adult.

tion is not common in the animal kingdom. In fact, apart from being present in echinoderms it is otherwise seen only in colonial organisms, where it acts to prevent one colony of closely related individuals from accidentally fusing with another, less related, colony (Buss 1987). Allorecognition among echinoderms has been related to the fact that ancestors of living echinoderms were apparently sedentary, potentially colonial organisms. We may have inherited our immune system from a primitive deuterostome stock, or more directly from an originally sessile, colonial ancestral type of chordate.

Cephalochordates

The subphylum Cephalochordata contains some 22 species, all of which are small, fusiform, superfi-cially fishlike, marine animals usually less than 5 centimeters long. The best known is the lancelet (*Branchiostoma lanceolatum*), more commonly known as **amphioxus**. Lancelets are widely distributed in marine waters of the continental shelves and are usually burrowing, sedentary animals as adults (some paedomorphic pelagic species also exist).

A notable characteristic of amphioxus is its fish-like locomotion, resulting from the contraction of segmented **myomeres**, blocks of striated muscle fibers arranged along both sides of the body and separated by sheets of connective tissue. These myomeres, found in vertebrates as well as in cephalochordates, are apparently homologous with the series of muscle bands of the tail of the tunicate larva, but tunicates are too small to possess the complexity typical of true myomeres, with their

BOX 2–1   Heterochrony

The attainment of sexual maturity in an arrested larval animal has been called paedomorphosis, paedogenesis, progenesis, and neoteny, with the result that confusion exists about two rather different evolutionary–developmental processes (Gould 1977). **Neoteny** (*neo* = new, i.e., juvenile; *ten* = hold) is the retention of one or more larval or embryonic traits in the adult body. Neoteny results from slowing down or stopping the development of the young traits affected. Some familiar neotenic traits include the external gills of certain adult aquatic salamanders in which the larval gills are only slightly modified, and the flat face and expanded brain case of human beings, traits that are widespread in mammalian embryos but are retained in the postfetal stages of humans. Although neoteny is characterized by the retention of embryonic or larval characteristics in an otherwise typically adult body, **progenesis** (*pro* = forward, i.e., early; *genesis* = birth, i.e., reproduction) describes the early development of the gonads in an otherwise larval body. The developmental process that leads to progenesis is thus the opposite of the one leading to neoteny, but both processes are a part of the process of paedomorphosis, whereby ancestral juvenile, larval, or embryonic traits are incorporated in the reproductive stage of the species.

Both neoteny and progenesis are examples of a process called **heterochrony** (*hetero* = different, *chron* = time); that is, a change in the timing of events during development. For example, a vertebrate lineage that retained juvenile characteristics when it was sexually mature would have a proportionally larger head and eyes than normal for its sister group. Modifications of growth and ontogenetic development are usually not so exaggerated, but over evolutionary time heterochronic changes can have spectacular effects. Paedomorphosis in a tunicatelike organism in which the larval morphology was retained in the adult, for example, may have initiated the entire vertebrate lineage.

---

infolded shape. The myomeres contract in sequence, bending the body in a way that causes forward propulsion. (For a discussion of swimming, see Chapter 8.) The notochord here acts as an incompressible, elastic rod, which extends the full length of the body and prevents the body from shortening when the myomeres contract. The notochord of amphioxus extends from the tip of the snout to the end of the tail, projecting well beyond the region of the myomeres at both ends. The anterior elongation of the notochord apparently is a specialization and it aids in burrowing.

Figure 2–6 shows some details of the internal structure of amphioxus. A difference between amphioxus and vertebrates is in the use of the pharynx and gill slits in amphioxus for filter feeding rather than for respiration. Amphioxus is small enough so that respiration (oxygen uptake and carbon dioxide loss) can occur by diffusion over the body surface. Specializations of the head end of amphioxus for filter feeding include the buccal cirri attached to the margin of the oral hood that filter out large particles, the velum, which also helps in screening particles, and the wheel organ, a complex set of ciliated tracts where some food particles are entrapped and sent back to the pharynx.

The circulatory system of amphioxus has the same basic design as that of vertebrates, with a ventral-to-dorsal circulation through the gill arches powered by a ventral pump behind the gill slits and a major artery running dorsally (the aorta), with its blood circulation moving both headward and tailward from the area above the gill slits. But with little need to transport respiratory gases, amphioxus has no need for the rapid movement of blood. The features of the circulatory system that distinguish vertebrates from cephalochordates (a single, large, multichambered ventral heart and a closed circulatory system) probably reflect the switch in the use of the gill slits from filter feeding to respiration. (Vertebrates are not only more active than cephalochordates, but also are too large for diffusion to be an effective mode of gas exchange.) In addition, the excretory system of amphioxus differs from that of vertebrates in lacking a discrete kidney. However, the cells that comprise these excretory structures are

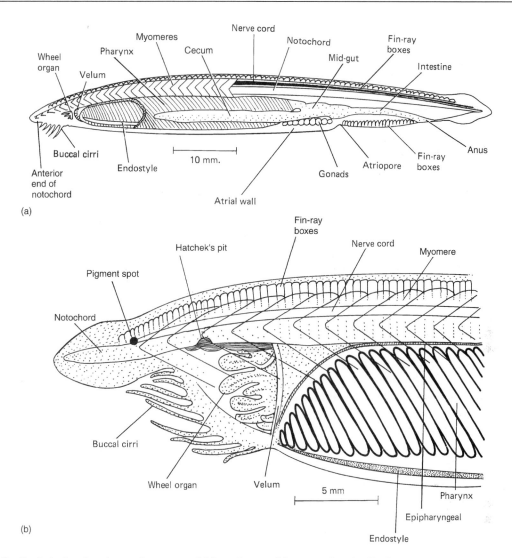

Figure 2–6 Cephalochordate internal anatomy: (a) lancelet, amphioxus—a longitudinal parasagittal section with the posterior myomeres removed; (b) detail of the anterior end of amphioxus showing the structures involved in filter feeding.

of a type known as podocytes, as are the cells in the excretory structures (nephrons) of vertebrates, suggesting a homology between these two systems at a fundamental level (Gans 1989).

Although these differences probably reflect only the more primitive nature of amphioxus (lamprey larvae also use the gills for filter feeding, but they rely on the muscular pharynx, rather than on cilia, to pump water), some other differences between amphioxus and vertebrates may reflect independent evolution in the cephalochordates. Of course, it must be remembered that cephalochordates have been evolving separately from vertebrates for at least 500 million years. However much amphioxus

might look like our idea of a generalized protovertebrate, it cannot possibly be the ancestor to vertebrates itself.

Cephalochordates have an atrium, or extra-body cavity, formed by the metapleural folds and opening to the outside world by the atriopore (Figure 2–7a). Tunicates also have a structure called an atrium surrounding the pharynx (Figure 2–5c), which may or may not be homologous with the atrium of cephalochordates. The atrium appears to control passage of substances through the pharynx (in combination with the beating of the cilia on the gill bars and in the wheel organ in the head). If the atriopore is closed, contraction of the atrium can produce a coughing action, flushing water backward through the pharynx for cleaning. The walls of the atrium also protect the fragile gill bars from the sharp sand particles in which amphioxus burrows. It may be possible that, rather than being a derived feature of amphioxus, the atrium was a primitive feature of all chordates, perhaps lost by the process of neotony in vertebrates.

Cephalochordates also have profound asymmetry during development. The left gill slits appear first in development, but form initially on the right side of the animal. Later, they move across the median ventral line over to the left side, while the true right side gill slits develop in place. This asymmetric development also involves the mouth and the formation of the hood and buccal cirri. It is not clear if this type of asymmetric development is unique to cephalochordates or perhaps, at some level, is a primitive deuterostome feature.

Despite these differences, most researchers would hold that cephalochordates and vertebrates are more closely related to each other than either is to tunicates. They share a number of derived characters: true somites (segmented muscle blocks or myotomes) throughout the trunk region as well as in the tail; lateral plate mesoderm (body tissue derived from the ventral, unsegmented portion of the mesoderm, as will be explained in Chapter 3); embryological induction of various neural tissues by the notochord in development; a caudal (tail) fin fold; a ventral to dorsal pattern of blood circulation through the gills; and excretory tissue formed from specialized cells called podocytes (Gans 1989).

■ Probable Steps in the Origin of the First Vertebrates

The evolution of the first true vertebrates, larger, more active animals with a distinct enlarged head end (containing an enlarged brain protected by a cranium and specialized sense organs), would represent an entirely new level of chordate organization. These new sense organs reflected an evolutionary change to a more active mode of life, with a more predatory mode of feeding replacing the original chordate habit of filter feeding (Northcutt and Gans 1983, Gans 1989, Forey and Janvier 1994). The differences between a hypothetically typical nonvertebrate chordate, based on amphioxus, and a true vertebrate are listed in Table 2.2, and also illustrated in Figure 2–7.

The Nature of the Earliest Vertebrates and the "Conodont Animals"

Curious microfossils known as conodont elements are widespread and abundant in marine deposits from the Late Cambrian to the Late Triassic. These are small (generally less than 1 millimeter long) spine- or comblike structures composed of apatite (the particular mineralized structure of calcium carbonate and calcium phosphate that is characteristic of vertebrate hard tissues). They were originally variously described as skeletal parts of marine algae, as phosphatic annelid jaws, fish teeth, gill rakers, gastropod radulae, nematode copulatory spicules, arthropod spines, and denticles of free-swimming lophophorate animals (Higgins 1983). However, recent studies of conodont mineralized tissues interpret them as histologically similar to dentine and enamel, uniquely vertebrate tissues (Sansom et al. 1994, 1994). Thus conodont elements have been claimed to be the toothlike elements of true vertebrates, an interpretation confirmed by the discovery of impressions of complete conodont animals with conodont elements arranged within the pharynx in a complex apparatus (Figure 2–8) (Briggs et al. 1983, Mikulic et al. 1985, Benton 1987).

A close relationship between the conodonts and vertebrates has been suggested (Sansom et al. 1992, Briggs 1992), although exactly where they lie in relation to known vertebrates remains an area of active debate. They appear to have had a notochord, myomeres, and perhaps even fin rays and two eyes protected by sclerotic rings composed of cartilage. Although the pharynx may have been muscular (to operate the conodont apparatus), there are no signs of pharyngeal slits, and at this very small size (40 millimeters in length) respiration could have been accomplished by diffusion alone. Some workers (e.g., Janvier 1996) would go so far as to place conodonts as more derived than living jawless vertebrates, based on their possession of mineralized tissues. Others would deny them full vertebrate status: Pridmore et al. (1997) pointed out that they appear to have cephalochordate-like V-shaped myomeres (trunk muscles) rather than vertebrate-like W-shaped ones, and Schultz (1996) claimed that conodont mineralized tissues are not homologous with vertebrate ones. However, whether conodonts are eventually accepted as true vertebrates or as the sister group of vertebrates, they now seem firmly planted in the vertebrate ancestry (Gabbott et al. 1995, Purnell 1995, Smith et al. 1996).

TABLE 2.2	Comparison of features in nonvertebrate chordates and in primitive vertebrates

Generalized Nonvertebrate Chordate	*Primitive Vertebrate*
(Based on features of the living cephalochordate amphioxus)	(Based on features of the living jawless vertebrates—hagfishes and lampreys)
A. Brain and Head End	
Notochord extends to tip of head.	Head extends beyond tip of notochord.
No cranium (skull).	Cranium—skeletal supports around brain, consisting of capsules surrounding the main parts of the brain and their sensory components.
No true brain (has cerebral vesicle) or specialized sense organs (except photoreceptive frontal organ, possibly homologous with the vertebrate eye).	Tripartite brain and multicellular sense organs (eye, nose, inner ear).
Poor distance sensation (although the skin is sensitive).	Improved distance sensation: in addition to the eyes and nose, also have a lateral line system along the head and body that can detect water movements (poorly developed lateral line system on the head only in hagfishes).
No electroreception.	Electroreception may be a primitive vertebrate feature (but absent in hagfishes).
B. Pharynx and Respiration	
Gill bars used for filter feeding (respiration is by diffusion over the body surface).	Gill bars support gills used for respiration.
Numerous gill slits and bars (up to 100 on each side).	Fewer gills (6–10 on each side), individual gills with highly complex internal structure (gill filaments).
Pharynx not muscularized (except in wall of atrium).	Pharynx with specialized (branchiomeric) musculature.
Water moved through pharynx and over gill bars by ciliary action.	Water moved through pharynx and over gills by active muscular pumping.
Gill bars made of collagen.	Gill bars made of cartilage (allows for elastic recoil—aids in pumping).
C. Feeding and Digestion	
Gut not muscularized: food passage by means of ciliary action.	Gut muscularized: food passage by means of peristalsis.
Digestion of food is intracellular: (individual food particles taken into cells lining gut).	Digestion of food is extracellular: enzymes poured onto food in gut lumen, then breakdown products absorbed by cells lining gut.
No discrete liver and pancreas: (structure called the midgut cecum or diverticulum is probably homologous to both).	Discrete liver and pancreatic tissue.

(continued)

| TABLE 2.2 | *(continued)* Comparison of features in nonvertebrate chordates and in primitive vertebrates |

D. Heart and Circulation

Ventral pumping structure (no true heart, just contracting regions of vessels, = sinus venosus of vertebrates). Also accessory pumping regions elsewhere in the system.	Ventral pumping heart only (but accessory pumping regions retained in hagfishes). Three-chambered heart: (in order of blood flow) sinus venosus, atrium, and ventricle.
No neural control of the heart to regulate pumping.	Neural control of the heart (except in hagfishes).
Circulatory system open: large blood sinuses, capillary system not extensive.	Circulatory system closed: without blood blood sinuses (some remain in hagfishes and lampreys) and with an extensive capillary system.
Blood not specifically involved in the transport of respiratory gases (O_2 and CO_2 mainly transported via diffusion). No red blood red blood cells or respiratory pigment.	Blood specifically involved in the transport of respiratory gases. Have red blood cells containing the respiratory pigment hemoglobin (binds with O_2 and CO_2 and aids in their transport).

E. Excretion and Osmoregulation

No specialized kidney. Coelom filtered by flame cells or solenocytes, work by creating negative pressure within cell. Cells empty into the atrium (false body cavity) and then to the outside world via the atriopore.	Specialized glomerular kidney, segmental structure along dorsal body wall, works by ultrafiltration of blood. Empties to the outside via the archinephric ducts leading to the cloaca.
Body fluids same concentration and ionic composition as seawater. No need for volume control or ionic regulation.	Body fluids more dilute than seawater (except for hagfishes). Kidney important in volume regulation, especially in freshwater environment. Monovalent ions regulated by the gills (also the site of nitrogen excretion), divalent ions regulated by the kidney.

F. Support and Locomotion

Notochord provides main support for body muscles.	Notochord provides main support for body muscles, vertebral elements around nerve cord at least in all vertebrates except hagfishes.
Myomeres with simple V-shape.	Myomeres with more complex W-shape.
No lateral fins, or median fins besides tail fin.	Primitively, no lateral fins. Dorsal fins present in all except hagfishes.

The Origin of Bone and other Mineralized Tissues

Bone is a tissue unique to vertebrates, although not all vertebrates have it. Living jawless vertebrates lack bone entirely, perhaps a secondary condition. However bone was a characteristic feature of the fossil jawless vertebrates, the **ostracoderms**, many of which had extensive bony head shields and hefty bony scales covering the rest of the body (see Figure 2–9 and Chapter 6). Of course, a claim could also be made that, necessarily, we would only be able to recognize those ancient vertebrates that did possess bone, as the nonbony ones would not fossilize! Bone is only one type of mineralized tissue in vertebrates: enamel and dentine, tissues more highly mineralized than bone, seen in living vertebrates primarily in the teeth, are at least as old as

Figure 2–7 Design of a generalized nonvertebrate chordate compared with that of a primitive vertebrate: (a) amphioxuslike nonvertebrate chordate; (b) hypothetical primitive vertebrate.

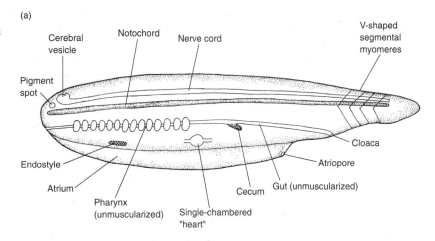

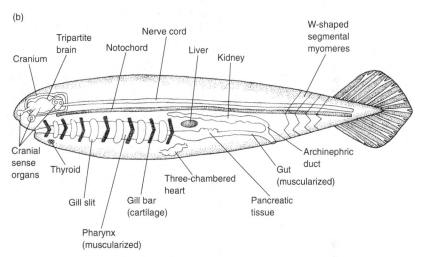

The Nature of Early Bone

The origin of vertebrate mineralized tissues remains a puzzle. Bone (including other calcified tissues such as enamel and dentine) cannot easily be homologized with any tissues in invertebrate phyla. Like the exoskeletons of arthropods, shells of mollusks, and hard parts of other animals, bone results from the deposition of minerals in an organic matrix produced by special cells, laid down in a supporting framework of the fibrous protein collagen. The cells involved in the formation of calcified tissues derive from embryonic ectoderm and mesoderm, and the

bone, and were originally found in intimate association with it. The skeletal system of vertebrates, including the differences between the exoskeleton (outer structures such as the bony head shield and scales) and the originally cartilaginous endoskeleton, is described further in Chapter 3.

matrices produced usually contain complex sugars and protein. The minerals deposited generally consist of crystals of calcium carbonate or calcium phosphate. Vertebrate bone is unique in its combination of characteristic cells, matrices, and minerals.

The earliest known mineralized vertebrate tissues already comprised several different tissue types, and were certainly no more simple in structure than the mineralized tissues of living vertebrates. The basic units of mineralized tissue in most early vertebrates appear to be **odontodes**, little toothlike elements formed in the skin (Schaeffer 1977, Smith and Hall 1990, 1993). They consist of projections of dentine, covered in some cases with an outer layer of enameloid (an enamellike tissue), with a base of bone; indeed, our own teeth are very similar to these structures, and are probably homologous with them. Odontodes occur in almost unmodified from as the sharp denticles in the skin of sharks, and the larger scales, plates and shields

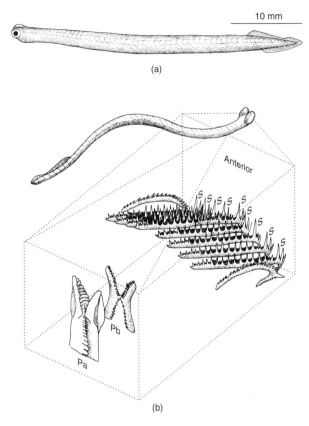

10 mm

(a)

Anterior

Pb

Pa

(b)

Figure 2–8   Conodonts. (a) The conodont *Clydagnathus* in lateral view. (Modified from M. A. Purnell, 1995, *Lethaia* 28, 187–188.) (b) Close-up of the feeding apparatus (conodont elements) inside the head of the conodont *Idiognathus*. The anterior S and M elements appear to be designed for grasping, and the posterior P elements appear to be designed for crushing. (Modified from M. A. Purnell, 1994, *Lethaia* 27, 129–138.)

on the heads of many ostracoderms and early bony fishes are interpreted as aggregations of these units. A body covering of small odontode elements may the primitive vertebrate condition, as seen in the well-studied latest Cambrian dermal bone fragments from North America, termed *Anatolepis*. A similar type of construction of dermal armor is found in the Ordovician *Arandaspis* from Australia (Smith et al. 1995). However, newly discovered vertebrate material from the Late Cambrian of Australia comprises a more sheetlike continuous armor, lacking odontodes, and formed from enamellike tissue (Young et al. 1996).

The evidence from ostracoderms suggests that the primitive disposition of vertebrate mineralized tissue is of odontode elements in the skin. But this hypothesis appears to be contradicted by the pres-

ence of teeth in conodonts in the absence of dermal armor. Conodont teeth may represent an early experiment in tissue mineralization prior to the evolution of the dermal skeleton in other vertebrates (Smith et al. 1996). However, pharyngeal toothlike structures have also been reported in thelodonts, poorly known ostracoderms that lack a well-mineralized skeleton (van der Brugghen and Janvier 1993). The resolution of the primitive vertebrate distribution of mineralized tissues awaits a better understanding of the relationship of conodonts to other vertebrates (Smith et al. 1986, Smith and Hall 1993).

When Did Bone First Appear in Vertebrates?   An understanding of the nature of the earliest vertebrate hard tissues is one evolutionary puzzle. Another is figuring out in what level of vertebrate evolution bone first appeared, especially because living primitive vertebrates (the jawless hagfishes and lampreys) lack bone or other mineralized tissues. How could we deduce if this absence of bone in these vertebrates represents the primary condition or secondary loss? One approach to this problem is via phylogenetic analysis, that is, to see how these vertebrates are related to other vertebrates possessing bone. Hagfishes are most likely more primitive than any known vertebrate, living or fossil (see Chapter 6). Thus the absence of bone in these animals might well represent the primary condition (although the possibility of secondary loss cannot be ruled out). However, most workers would agree that the relationships of lampreys lie within the cluster of ostracoderms (e.g., Forey and Janvier 1994, see Figure 6–1). If this represents their true phylogenetic position then we would have to infer that they had lost bone from an originally bony ancestral condition. (Note, however, that a later opinion of Janvier [1996] places lampreys as more primitive than ostracoderms, with the implication that absence of bone is a primary condition in both living jawless vertebrates.)

Another approach to this issue of when bone first appeared is to examine other clues about the physiology of living jawless vertebrates. Bone serves as a store of calcium and phosphorus, thus features indicating the monitoring and regulation of these minerals might suggest the original possession of bone. Hagfishes, like all other vertebrates, possess the hormone calcitonin, which regulates blood calcium levels (Maisey 1988). This could suggest the ancestral possession of bone. Another suggestive feature is the typically verte-

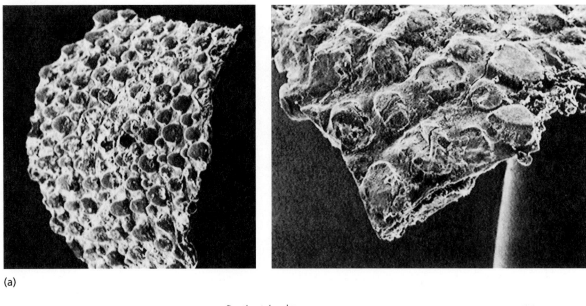

(a)

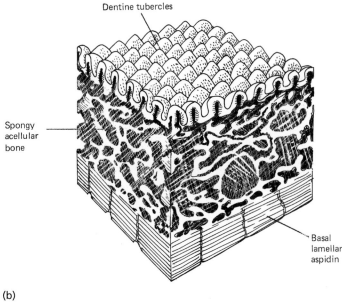

(b)

Figure 2–9   Remains of early vertebrates. (a) Earliest known remains believed to be of vertebrate origin: Scales of *Anatolepis* from the Late Cambrian have been found in Oklahoma, Washington, and Wyoming, and by the Early Ordovician; *Anatolepis* was widely distributed in North America and Spitzbergen. Remains of other early vertebrates are known from the Late Cambrian and Early Ordovician in Australia. Two views of the same specimen show (left) tonguelike surface ornaments (odontodes), which probably pointed posteriorly and (right) an edge showing a break through the plate revealing the solid surface layer, the cavity-rich middle layer, and the thick internal lamellar layer. (Scanning electron micrographs at approximately 220× courtesy of J. E. Repetski, U.S. National Museum.) (b) Three-dimensional block diagram of heterostracan dermal bone. (Based on B. Stahl, 1974, *Vertebrate History*, McGraw-Hill, New York, NY; and L. Halstead, 1969, *The Pattern of Vertebrate Evolution*, Oliver & Boyd, Edinburgh, UK.) (c) *Astraspis*, an Ordovician vertebrate from North America (about 20 centimeters long), showing the body form of the earliest known vertebrates, lacking paired fins, and with a head shield and body armor made from dermal bone. (Modified from I. J. Sansom, M. P Smith, M. M. Smith, and P. Turner, 1997, *Palaeontology* 40(3): 625–643.)

Figure 2–9 *(continued)*

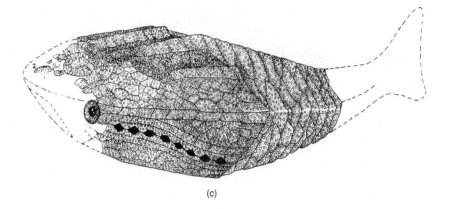

(c)

brate glomerular kidney, present in both hagfishes and lampreys, which possesses the new ability (for chordates) to regulate calcium and phosphate ions (see next section). However, it has also been proposed, on physiological grounds, that bone could not be deposited in a medium of high body fluid ionic concentration (Moss 1968). If this feature of bone physiology were proved true, it would seem likely that hagfishes, which alone among living vertebrates have body fluids matching the concentration of seawater, were primitively without bone.

Anatomical features also suggest that living jawless vertebrates are capable of laying down mineralized tissues of some sort. Both hagfishes and lampreys possess dense bodies of calcium carbonate in their inner ears (otoliths, used in balance and orientation, see Chapter 3) (Pridmore et al., 1997), and X-ray images show that lampreys have some calcification within their internal skeleton (Bardack and Zangerl 1971). At the moment the evidence for where bone first appeared in vertebrates is conflicting and contradictory; we simply don't have sufficient information to determine whether bone was an initial feature of all vertebrates or whether the most primitive vertebrates were primarily without bone. New fossil evidence, perhaps of an armored form definitely more primitive than hagfishes, might help to resolve the issue.

Reasons for the Evolution of Bone   What selective advantage could mineralized tissues have had? The head shields of ostracoderms were originally thought to be defensive structures against attack from predators, in particular large, scorpionlike creatures known as eurypterids. However, fossil evidence shows that at least in some species this armor was made of plates that could grow, with bone resorbed and redeposited during the animals' lifetime. If this is the case, then the shields could not have been external to the skin, like a turtle's shell. Rather, they must have been covered with a layer of skin, like the bones of our skull, which makes it less likely that they functioned primarily as an antipredator defense system.

The dentine of the head shield of early vertebrates has a characteristic system of pores and tubercules, suggestive of a sensory function of the tissue (Smith and Hall 1990). The bony head shield may have originated as a protective and electrically insulating coating around the electroreceptors in the head of early vertebrates that enhanced electrosensitive detection of prey (Northcutt and Gans 1983, Gans 1989).

Subsequently, the need for phosphorus, which is a relatively rare element in natural environments, may have been one of the early selective forces involved in the evolution of bone. Although we think of bone as primarily supportive or protective, it also serves as a store of calcium and phosphorus. Mineral regulation involves deposition and mobilization of calcium and phosphorus ions. Vertebrates rely on anaerobic metabolism during activity, producing lactic acid as a metabolic product, resulting in low blood pH following extended bursts of activity. A skeleton made of hydroxyapatite (rather than of calcite, as in many invertebrates) may resist acidity of the blood during anaerobic metabolism (Ruben and Bennett 1987).

Thus, a variety of explanations have been proposed for the origin of bone: protection, electroreception, and mineral storage. None of these explanations are mutually exclusive, and all may have been involved in the evolutionary origins of this complex tissue.

■ The Environment of Early Vertebrate Evolution

By the Late Silurian armored ostracoderms and early jawed fishes were abundant in both freshwater and marine environments. For years students of evolution have argued whether the vertebrates had a freshwater origin or a marine one. Under what conditions did the first vertebrates evolve?

For many years it was believed that vertebrates had a freshwater origin. A main proponent of this idea was the paleontologist Alfred Romer (Romer, 1967). Although all known Ordovician vertebrate remains are found in marine sediments, and there are very few fossil localities that represent freshwater environments prior to the Silurian, Romer speculated that the Ordovician bone fragments might have been washed downstream into the sea from as yet unknown freshwater habitats. However, the more extensive fossil record accumulated in more recent years fails to demonstrate the presence of vertebrates in anything but marine sediments prior to the Silurian (Repetski 1978, Boucot and Janis 1983, Smith et al. 1996, Young 1997).

A second line of argument came from a physiologist, Homer Smith (Smith 1953). Smith's studies of vertebrate kidney structure and function also led him to support a freshwater origin hypothesis. Among living vertebrates the glomerular kidney is seen to function par excellence in the case of freshwater bony fishes. These fishes, like all vertebrates except for hagfishes, have body fluids that are dilute in comparison with seawater, but that are still more concentrated than fresh water, and hence water tends to enter the body by the process of osmosis. A prime role of the kidney is to produce copious quantities of dilute urine to rid the body of the excess water. (In contrast, marine bony fishes face the opposite osmotic problem. Here the kidney is no longer involved in volume control, and the glomerulus may even become nonfunctional; see Chapter 4.) The example from living vertebrates was clear to Smith: Since all vertebrates possess a glomerular kidney, but this kidney shows its true function only in fresh water, then vertebrates must have originated in fresh water.

In spite of Romer's and Smith's arguments, however, a marine origin of vertebrates is now widely accepted. The first line of evidence is paleontological—the earliest vertebrate fossils are found in marine sediments. The second line of evidence comes from comparative physiology: All nonvertebrate chordates and deuterostome invertebrate phyla are exclusively marine forms with body fluids the same concentration as their surroundings, and so are hagfishes, the most primitive of all known vertebrates in this respect. The condition in hagfishes was not unknown to these earlier workers, but in the nineteenth century the living jawless vertebrates were thought to be degenerate rather than merely primitive, and the fact that hagfishes did not fit the overall scheme was not deemed important. Now we interpret many features of these primitive jawless vertebrates as the real primitive conditions. If the primitive vertebrate condition is to possess a glomerular kidney in association with a marine habitat and body fluids of a concentration similar to seawater, then the origin of the kidney must be explained in that context, however useful the structure may happen to be in more derived vertebrates living in freshwater habitats (this brings us back to the kind of problem with teleological arguments addressed at the start of this chapter).

So, what *was* the likely primitive function of the vertebrate kidney? The major difference in excretory function between cephalochordates and vertebrates is in the regulation of divalent ions like calcium and phosphorus (although in hagfishes a considerable amount of divalent ion regulation is also carried out by the skin). These minerals provide the proper cellular environment for muscle function, and the control of their levels in the body may have been an essential component in the evolutionary transition to a more active life-style in the early vertebrates (Robertson 1957, Boucot and Janis 1983, Gans 1989). In this view, the glomerular kidney would be a stellar example of a preadaptation, a structure evolved for one purpose (divalent ion regulation in a marine environment) but which was serendipitously co-opted for an entirely different function (volume control in a freshwater environment).

An alternative viewpoint has been advanced by Griffith (1994). He considered that vertebrates evolved from esturine forms that bred in fresh water and lived in more salty water as adults (although there is no support in the fossil record for this scenario). Griffith contended that the presence of chloride cells on the gills of hagfishes supports his hypothesis that the high ionic concentration of their body fluids is a secondary condition, associated with an evolutionary return, from earlier freshwater habits, to a fully committed marine mode of life. In extant fishes chloride cells are important in controlling salt levels, and in marine bony fishes they excrete excess salt (see Chapter 4). But hagfishes *do* regulate their internal ion concentrations, perhaps via these chloride cells, even though their body fluids have the same osmolality as seawater.

It also seems strange that that hagfishes should be the *only* evolutionary lineage of marine fishes to revert to having concentrated body fluids to solve the osmotic problem faced by an animal with dilute body fluids when it moves back into seawater (see Chapter 4). If hagfishes could do that, why did other lineages not adopt the same method? Probably vertebrates cannot revert from dilute body fluids to body fluids as concentrated as seawater. The evidence from invertebrates also suggests that body fluids cannot be reconcentrated in evolution once they have been diluted. Thus, the current view is that vertebrates had a marine origin, and that the concentrated body fluids of hagfishes represent the primitive vertebrate condition.

■ Summary

Vertebrates are members of the phylum Chordata, a group of animals whose other members (tunicates and lancelets) are not especially like most modern vertebrates, being small, marine, and sluggish in their activity, if not entirely sessile as adults. Chordates share with many derived animal phyla the features of being bilaterally symmetrical, with a distinct head and tail end, and a tube-within-a-tube internal design. Within this range of more complex animals, both embryological and molecular evidence shows that the affinities of chordates lies with echinoderms rather than with superficially more similar animals like arthropods. Chordates are generally distinguished from other animals by the possession of pharyngeal gill slits, a notochord, a dorsal hollow nerve chord, and a muscular postanal tail. Vertebrates have the unique features of an expanded head with multicellular sense organs and a cranium (or skull) housing an enlarged, tripartite brain. The features that distinguish vertebrates from other chordates appear to be related to two critical embryological innovations: a doubling of the Hox gene complex and the development of neural crest tissue. Vertebrates appear to be most closely related to lancelets (cephalochordates) among the nonvertebrate chordates, and most of the differences in structural design and physiology between lancelets and primitive vertebrates can be explained by an evolutionary change to an animal of larger body size with a greater level of activity, and a switch from filter feeding to predation.

The history of vertebrates covers a span of more than 500 million years. The earliest probable chordates are Early Cambrian in age, and the earliest definite vertebrates, the jawless ostracoderms with a covering of dermal bone, are known with certainty from the Ordovician (and possibly from the Late Cambrian). New contenders for the status of early vertebrates, the conodonts, originally known only from phosphatic toothed feeding structures, are now known from whole-body impressions. If these animals truly are vertebrates, they would push back the origin of vertebrates to a definite Late Cambrian date.

Speculation exists about both the origin of bone, a tissue unique to vertebrates, and the environment of early vertebrate evolution. Bone is first found with accompanying external layers of dentine and enamellike tissue in the dermal armor of early fishes, either as complete sheets or as separate small elements with their own bone of attachment. Current explanations for its original evolutionary use include protection, a store for calcium and phosphorus, and as a housing for electroreceptive sense organs. Vertebrates were formerly thought to have originated in fresh water, in part because many early fossils were originally found in freshwater deposits, and also because their glomerular kidney was thought to be an adaptation to osmoregulation in a fresh water environment. New paleontological materials and interpretations of the physiology of primitive vertebrates now lead most workers to believe that the earliest vertebrates were marine.

■ References

Bardack, D., and R. Zangerl. 1971. Lampreys in the fossil record. Pages 67–84 in *The Biology of Lampreys*, volume 1, edited by M. W. Hardisty and I. C. Potter. Academic Press, London.

Benton, M. J. 1987. Conodonts classified at last. *Nature* 325:482–483.

Blieck, A. 1992. At the origin of chordates. *Geobios* (Lyons) 25(1):101–103.

Boucot, A. J., and C. M. Janis. 1983. The environment of early Paleozoic vertebrates. *Palaeogeography, Palaeoclimatology, Palaeoecology* 41:251–287.

Briggs, D. E. G. 1992. Conodonts: a major extinct group added to the vertebrates. *Science* 256:1285–1286.

Briggs, D. E. G., E. N. K. Clarkson, and R. J. Aldridge. 1983. The conodont animal. *Lethaia* 26:275–287.

Buss, L. W. 1987. *The Evolution of Individuality.* Princeton University Press, Princeton, NJ.

Conway Morris, S. 1997. The first chordates: evidence from the Cambrian. *Journal of Morphology* 232(3):243.

Forey, P., and P. Janvier. 1994. Evolution of the early vertebrates. *American Scientist* 82:554–565.

Gabbott, S. E., R. J. Aldridge, and J. N. Theron. 1995. A giant conodont with preserved muscle tissue from the Upper Ordovician of South Africa. *Nature* 374:800–803.

Gans, C. 1989. Stages in the origin of vertebrates: analysis by means of scenarios. *Biological Reviews* 64:221–268.

Garcia-Fernandez, J., and P. W. H. Holland. 1994. Archetypal organization of the amphioxus Hox gene cluster. *Nature* 370:504–505.

Garstang, W. 1928. The morphology of the Tunicata and its bearing on the phylogeny of the Chordata. *Quarterly Journal of the Microscopical Society* 72:51–87.

Gee, H. 1994. Return of the amphioxus. *Nature* 370:504–505.

Gee, H. 1996. *Before the Backbone.* Chapman & Hall, London, UK.

Gould, S. J. 1977. *Ontogeny and Phylogeny.* Belknap, Cambridge, MA. (But see B. A. Pierce and H. M. Smith, 1979, Neoteny or paedogenesis? *Journal of Herpetology* 13(I):119–121, for continuing problems with terminology.)

Gould, S. J. 1989. *Wonderful Life.* Norton, New York, NY.

Griffith, R. W. 1994. The life of the first vertebrates. *Bioscience* 44(6): 408–417.

Gutmann, W. F. 1981. Relationships between invertebrate phyla based on a functional–mechanical analysis of the hydrostatic skeleton. *American Zoologist* 21:63–81.

Higgins, A. 1983. The conodont animal. *Nature* 302(5904):107.

Janvier, P. 1996. *Early Vertebrates.* Oxford Monographs on Geology and Geophysics–33. Clarendon Press, Oxford, UK.

Janvier, P., and A. Blieck. 1979. New data on the internal anatomy of the Heterostraci (Agnatha), with general remarks on the phylogeny of the Craniota. *Zoological Scripta* 8:287–296.

Jefferies, R. P. S. 1986. *The Ancestry of the Vertebrates.* British Museum of Natural History, Dorset Press, Dorchester, UK.

Jefferies, R. P. S. 1997. A defence of the calcichordates. *Lethaia* 30:1–10.

Le Douarin, N. 1982. *The Neural Crest.* Cambridge University Press, Cambridge, UK.

Lovtrup, S. 1977. *The Phylogeny of the Vertebrates.* Wiley, London, UK.

Maisey, J. G. 1986. Heads and tails: a chordate phylogeny. *Cladistics* 2:201–256.

Maisey, J. G. 1988. Phylogeny of early vertebrate skeletal induction and ossification patterns. *Evolutionary Biology* 22:1–36.

Marx, J. 1992. Homeobox genes go evolutionary. *Science* 255:399–401.

Mikulic, D. G., D. E. G. Briggs, and J. Kluessendorf. 1985. A Silurian soft-bodied biota. *Science* 228:715–717.

Monastersky, R. 1996. Jump-start for the vertebrates: new clues to how our ancestors got a head. *Science News* 149:74–75.

Moss, M. K. 1968. The origin of vertebrate calcified tissues. *Nobel Symposium* 4:359–371.

Nielsen, C. 1985. Animal phylogeny in the light of the trochlea theory. *Biological Journal of the Linnean Society* 25:243–249.

Northcutt, R. G., and C. Gans. 1983. The genesis of neural crest and epidermal placodes: a reinterpretation of vertebrate origins. *Quarterly Review of Biology* 58:1–28.

Peterson, K. J. 1994. The origin and early evolution of the Craniata. Pages 14–37 in *Major Features of Vertebrate Evolution,* edited by D. R. Prothero and R. M. Schoch. *Short Courses in Paleontology,* no. 7. The University of Tennessee and the Paleontological Society, Knoxville, TN.

Pridmore, P. A., R. E. Bardwick, and R. S. Nicholl. 1997. Soft anatomy and the affinities of conodonts. *Lethaia* 29:317–328.

Purnell, M. A. 1995. Microwear on conodont elements and macrophagy in the first vertebrates. *Nature* 374:798–800.

Repetski, J. E. 1978. A fish from the Upper Cambrian of North America. *Science* 200:259–531.

Robertson, J. D. 1957. The habitat of the earliest vertebrates. *Biological Reviews* 32:156–187.

Romer, A. S. 1967. Major steps in vertebrate evolution. *Science* 158:1629–1637.

Ruben, J. A., and A. F. Bennett. 1980. Antiquity of the vertebrate pattern of activity metabolism and its possible relation to vertebrate origins. *Nature* 286:886–888.

Ruben, J. A., and A. F. Bennett. 1987. The evolution of bone. *Evolution* 41:1187–1197.

Ruben, J. A., and J. K. Parrish. 1990. Antiquity of the chordate pattern of exercise metabolism. *Paleobiology* 16:355–359.

Sansom, I. J., M. P. Smith, H. A. Armstrong, and M. M. Smith. 1992. Presence of the earliest vertebrate hard tissues in conodonts. *Science* 256:1308–1311.

Sansom, I. J., M. P. Smith, and M. M. Smith. 1994. Dentine in conodonts. *Nature* 368:591.

Schaeffer, B. 1977. The dermal skeleton in fishes. Pages 25–52 in *Problems in Vertebrate Evolution,* edited by S. M. Andrews, R. S. Miles, and A. D. Walker. Academic Press, London, UK.

Schaeffer, B. 1987. Deuterostome monophyly and phylogeny. *Evolutionary Biology* 21:179–235.

Schultz, H.-P. 1996. Conodont histology: an indicator of vertebrate relationships? *Modern Geology* 20:275–285.

Shu, D.-G., S. Conway Morris, and X.-L. Xang. 1996. A *Pikaia*-like chordate from the Lower Cambrian of China. *Nature* 384:157–158.

Smith, H. 1953. *From Fish to Philosopher.* Little, Brown, Boston, MA.

Smith, M. M., and B. K. Hall. 1990. Development and evolutionary origins of vertebrate skeletogenic and odontogenic tissues. *Biological Reviews* 65:277–373.

Smith, M. M., and B. K. Hall. 1993. A developmental model for evolution of the vertebrate exoskeleton and teeth: the role of cranial and trunk neural crest. *Evolutionary Biology* 27: 387–448.

Smith, M. M., I. J. Sansom, and P. Smith. 1995. Diversity of the dermal skeleton in Ordovician to Silurian vertebrate taxa from North America: histology, skeletogenesis and relationships. *Geobios* 19:65–70.

Smith, M. M., I. J. Sansom, and M. P. Smith. 1996. "Teeth" before armour: the earliest vertebrate mineralized tissues. *Modern Geology* 20:303–319.

Van der Brugghen, W., and P. Janvier. 1993. Denticles in thelodonts. *Nature* 364:107.

Young, G. C. 1997. Ordovician microvertebrate remains from the Amadeus Basin, central Australia. *Journal of Vertebrate Paleontology* 17(1):1–25.

Young, G. C., V. N. Karatajute-Talimma, and M. M. Smith. 1996. A possible Late Cambrian vertebrate from Australia. *Nature* 383:810–812.

CHAPTER
3

Vertebrate Organ Systems and Their Evolution

We saw in the first chapter that evolution is a process of change in the frequencies of alleles in the gene pool of a species. This relationship of gene to structure is expressed during development. New structures in adult vertebrates are produced by modifications of ancestral patterns of embryonic development. We need an understanding of the fundamentals of vertebrate design to appreciate the changes that have occurred during the evolution of vertebrates, and to trace homologies in the systems between more primitive vertebrates and more derived ones. Van Valen (1973) noted that "A plausible argument could be made that evolution is the control of development by ecology." In this chapter we consider the basic functions and organ systems of vertebrates, and consider how evolutionary changes have accompanied changes in ecology; that is, in the lifestyles and habitats of the animals.

■ The Unity of Vertebrate Structure: Basic Vertebrate Design

The well-known physiologist Homer Smith summed up a century of accumulation of detailed morphological and physiological research by scores of biologists with the title of his 1953 book, *From Fish to Philosopher*. All vertebrates can be seen to have a fundamentally similar design plan in organ systems and in the functional attributes of these systems: the condition in a human can be understood in terms of the condition present in primitive fishes, and even in terms of lowly nonvertebrate chordates such as amphioxus.

All organisms have functions that they must perform in order to survive. This chapter considers vertebrate structure, while Chapter 4 considers aspects of vertebrate physiology. An appreciation of the vertebrate organ systems requires basic knowledge of their development in the individual from the **zygote** (fertilized egg) to the adult form by the processes of **embryogenesis** and **organogenesis**. Next must come an understanding of the basic functions of these systems and how the associated organs carry them out. To investigate this we will attempt to reconstruct the probable ancestral vertebrate condition from a consideration of primitive living vertebrates and nonvertebrate chordates. Finally, we will address the evolutionary changes in the systems over the course of vertebrate history. Understanding the way in which the vertebrate systems have evolved to assume their current forms in different animals is a bit like unraveling a detective story. The forms of evidence at our disposal are comparative anatomy, embryology, and the fossil record.

Occasionally the fossil record can provide direct evidence of the evolutionary history of vertebrate systems, especially the history of hard parts such as the skeleton. In Chapter 10 we will see how recent discoveries of early tetrapods (land vertebrates) showed us something that no one has previously suspected, that the earliest land vertebrates had up to eight fingers and toes, rather than the five digits long assumed to be the primitive condition. But in many instances, for example, the history of the heart and vascular system, there is no direct fossil evidence. Here we must rely on living organisms, using the tools of embryology and comparative anatomy.

Embryology provides a window into how systems develop. Modern scientists no longer adhere rigidly to the biogenetic law that "ontogeny recapitulates phylogeny" proposed by nineteenth-century embryologists such as von Baer and Haeckel—i.e., that the embryo faithfully passes through its ancestral evolutionary stages in the course of its development. Nevertheless embryology can provide many clues about the ancestral condition and about homologies between structures in different animals (Northcutt 1990). An example of the use of embryology in this fashion is provided in Chapter 19, in considering the evolution of the mammalian middle ear, showing how the embryonic mammalian condition resembles that of more primitive vertebrates, and the fossil record also lends direct evidence in this example.

Comparative anatomy uses the structures of adults rather than those of embryos. For this information to be useful in reconstructing evolutionary events we must have a good phylogeny of living animals on which to base our hypotheses (see Chapter 1). An example of the use of comparative anatomy comes later in this chapter in the discussion of the evolution of lungs. Here the distribution of lungs among living vertebrates leads us to deduce that lungs are actually a primitive feature for tetrapods, inherited from their fish ancestors rather than evolved for the purpose of breathing air on land. Here a good phylogeny is essential—had a mistaken phylogeny placed lungfish as closely related to sharks, or even to most living bony fish, rather than to tetrapods, we might have reached a different conclusion.

Vertebrate Embryology and Basic Cell Layers

The embryogenesis of vertebrates, from a single fertilized cell (the zygote) through various developmental stages to the adult condition, will not be considered in detail here. This is important background information for many studies, but a detailed treatment is not crucial for the topics covered in this book. Good summaries of vertebrate embryogenesis can be found in textbooks dealing specifically with vertebrate anatomy, such as Romer and Parsons (1986), Walker and Liem (1994), Hildebrand (1995), and Kardong (1998). An excellent review for more advanced students of the recent work integrating genetic evolutionary studies with traditional morphological ones is Hall (1992).

Almost all animals, with the exception of some very primitive ones like sponges and jellyfishes, have bodies made of three layers of cells termed **germ layers**, which are laid down early in embryogenesis at a stage termed **gastrulation**. The fates of germ layers have been very conservative throughout vertebrate evolution. In vertebrates the outermost germ layer, the **ectoderm** (*ecto* = outside; *derm* = skin), forms the adult superficial layers of skin (the epidermis), the linings of the most anterior and most posterior parts of the digestive tract, and the nervous system, including most of the sense organs, such as the eye and the ear. The innermost layer, the **endoderm** (*endo* = within), forms the rest of the lining of the digestive tract, as well as the lining of the glands associated with the gut, including the liver and the pancreas, and most respiratory surfaces of vertebrate gills and lungs. A middle layer, the **mesoderm** (*mesos* = middle), which is usually the last of the three layers to appear in development, forms everything else: the muscles, skeleton (including the notochord), connective tissues, and circulatory and urogenital systems. A little later in development a split develops within the originally solid mesoderm layer, forming a **coelom** or body cavity. The coelom is the cavity containing the internal organs, and is divided into the pleuroperitoneal cavity (around the viscera) and the pericardial cavity (around the heart).

A later stage of development than gastrulation is the **pharyngula** stage, when the ancestral vertebrate feature of pharyngeal pouches in the head region makes at least a fleeting appearance in the embryos of all vertebrates (see Figure 3–1). In fish the grooves between the pouches (the pharyngeal clefts) perforate to become the gill slits, whereas in tetrapods these clefts are transient and are obliterated in the adult form. The linings of the pharyngeal pouches give rise to half a dozen or more glandular structures often associated with the lymphatic system, including the thymus gland, parathyroid glands, carotid bodies, and tonsils.

The Ectoderm: the Nervous System and the Fate of the Neural Crest Cells

The typical dorsal hollow nerve cord of vertebrates (Chapter 2) is formed by the infolding and subsequent pinching off and isolation of a long ridge of the ectoderm running dorsal to the developing notochord. The notochord itself appears to contain the developmental instructions for this critical embryological event, which is probably why the notochord is retained in the embryos of vertebrates such as ourselves that have lost the original structure in the adult. The cells that will form the neural crest (mesectoderm cells) arise from cells adjacent to the developing nerve cord (the neural tube) at this stage.

From their originally dorsal position, neural crest cells disperse laterally and ventrally, ultimately settling and differentiating in locations throughout the embryo. Derivatives of the neural crest form almost all of the peripheral nervous system (including the autonomic system and the Schwann cells, which make the myelin sheaths of peripheral nerves), portions of the central nervous system (including the cranial nerve ganglia and portions of the brain), several endocrine glands, pigment cells, portions of the circulatory system, and perhaps most remarkably, many of the skeletal and connective tissues of the head, including the entire visceral skeleton forming the gill arches, and later the teeth and the jaws. We saw in Chapter 2 that vertebrates can be considered as having a new front part to the head, and the components of this new head are mainly composed of this uniquely vertebrate tissue, the neural crest.

Another new vertebrate feature is epidermal thickenings in the head region called **placodes**. Although the placodes are not part of the neural crest, it has been suggested that they and the neural crest cells evolved from a common ancestral cell line present in a prevertebrate ancestor (Gans 1989). The cells of the placodes contribute to the sense organs of the head (nose, eye, ear, lateral-line mechano- and electroreceptors, and taste buds), and some migrate caudally to participate (along with neural crest cells) in the formation of the lateral line system (a sensory system of aquatic vertebrates—see later discussion).

The Mesoderm: Segmented and Unsegmented Portions of the Vertebrate Body

Embryonic mesoderm becomes divided into three distinct portions, as shown in Figure 3–1. The dorsal (upper) part of the mesoderm, lying above the gut and adjacent to the nerve cord, forms a series of thick-walled segmental buds, or **somites**, running from the head end to the tail end. This somitic portion is sometimes termed the epimere. The ventral (lower) part of the mesoderm, surrounding the gut, is thin-walled and unsegmented, and is termed the **lateral plate** (sometimes known as the hypomere). Small segmental buds linking the somites and the lateral plate are termed **nephrotomes** (this middle portion is also sometimes termed the mesomere or the intermediate mesoderm). We discussed in Chapter 2 how Alfred Romer proposed that this strange system of segmental overlaying nonsegmental pattern of vertebrate design may reflect vertebrate origins.

The segmental somites will eventually form the dermis of the skin, the axial and limb muscles of the body, and the axial skeleton (vertebral column and portions of the back of the skull). Some of these segmental muscles later migrate ventrally from their originally dorsal (epaxial) position to form the layer of striated muscles on the underside of the body (the hypaxial muscles), and from there they can develop the muscles of the limbs in more derived vertebrates. The lateral plate forms all the internal, nonsegmented portions of the body, such as the connective tissue, the blood vascular system, the mesenteries (tissue connecting the gut and other structures to the body wall), the peritoneal and pericardial linings of the coelomic cavities, and the reproductive system. It also forms the smooth muscle of the gut and the cardiac muscle. The nephrotomes form the kidney, an elongated segmental structure in the primitive vertebrate condition, and the kidney drainage duct (the archinephric duct).

Some anomalous exceptions exist to this segmented versus nonsegmented division of the vertebrate body. Although the locomotory muscles, both axial (body) and appendicular (limbs) and the axial skeleton are derived from the somites, the appendicular skeleton is derived from the lateral plate, as are the tendons and ligaments of the appendicular muscles. The explanation for this may lie in the fact that limbs are add-ons to the basic vertebrate design (see Chapters 2 and 6). Other peculiarities are found in the new head of vertebrates.

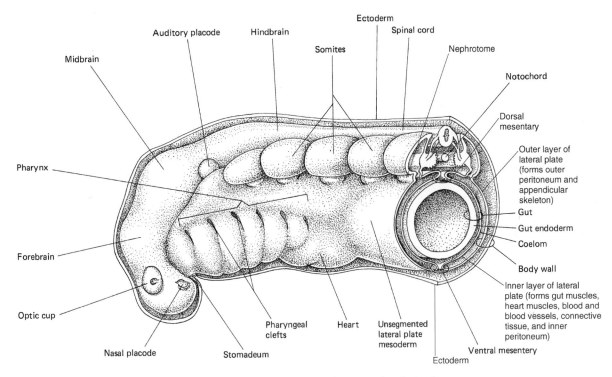

Figure 3–1   Diagrammatic three-dimensional view of a portion of a generalized vertebrate embryo. The ectoderm is stripped off, showing segmentation of the mesoderm in the trunk region and pharyngeal development. (After E. S. Goodrich, 1930, *Studies on the Structure and Development of Vertebrates*, Macmillan, London, UK.)

The vertebrate head does not follow the strict pattern of development and segmentation seen in the body. The head appears to be composed of eight segments, the posterior four segments containing true somites, and the anterior four composed of seven somitelike structures called somitomeres (Northcutt 1990). These somitomeres lie anterior to the otic capsule, the landmark division between the so-called new head and the rest of the body. The head mesoderm is not divided into somites and lateral plate, but instead comprises undifferentiated paraxial mesoderm, which gives rise to the eye muscles and to the brachiomeric muscles powering the visceral arches (gills and jaws). The pattern of innervation of these muscles is a little peculiar, as we discuss later. Within the brain, the forebrain and midbrain do not appear to be segmented, but the hindbrain can be divided into segmental structures termed rhombomeres.

Basic Adult Tissue Types

There are five basic tissues in vertebrates: *epithelial, connective, blood (= vascular), muscular,* and *nervous.*

These tissues are combined in a wide assortment of permutations to form larger units called **organs**. Organs often contain most or all of the five basic tissues. The basic functions of vertebrate life are supported by groups of organs united into one of the ten vertebrate organ systems (see later).

A fundamental component of most animal tissues is the fibrous protein **collagen**. In vertebrates, collagen also makes up the organic matrix of bone, and the tough tissue of tendons (that link muscles to bone) and ligaments (that link bones to other bones), as well as the softer tissues of organs. The collagen molecule is made up of three strands of polypeptide chains (tropocollagen macromolecules), that form a three-dimensional structure of twisted strands with hydrogen cross-linkages that allows the molecule to plastically deform (for example, in the stretching of the uterus of mammals during birth). Collagen is stiff and does not stretch easily for energy storage. In some tissues collagen can be incorporated with the protein **elastin** that is less stiff, and so can provide a greater capacity to stretch and recoil. Another important fibrous protein, seen only in vertebrates among animals, is **keratin**. Keratin is mainly found in tetrapods; that is, four-legged terrestrial vertebrates (basically all vertebrates that are not fishes). Keratin is found in epidermal structures (making features of the skin such as hair, scales, feathers, claws, horns, beaks, etc.), whereas collagen is primarily mesodermal. Keratin, like collagen, can become calcified to a certain extent (for example in baleen or whalebone, which forms the filtering apparatus in filter-feeding whales).

■ Protection, Support, and Movement

There are two basic differences between vertebrates and other chordates that lie behind our understanding of the differences in their structural design (Gans 1989). Vertebrates are much bigger than nonvertebrate chordates, so can no longer carry out bodily processes by diffusion or by ciliary action, and they are more active, with higher metabolic rates and more specialized organs that carry out metabolic processes at a greater rate. Vertebrates are characterized by exceptional mobility, and the ability to move requires muscles and an endoskeleton. Mobility brings vertebrates into contact with a wide range of environments and objects in those

environments, and a vertebrate's external protective covering must be tough but flexible. Bone and other mineralized tissues that we consider characteristic of vertebrates had their origins in this protective integument.

The Integument

The external covering of vertebrates, the integument, is a single organ, making up 15 to 20 percent of the body weight of many vertebrates and much more in armored forms. It includes the skin and a series of its derivatives, such as glands, scales, dermal armor, and hair. The skin protects the body and receives information from the outside world (Bereiter–Hahn et al. 1986). The major divisions of the vertebrate skin (Figure 3–2) are the **epidermis** (the superficial cell layer derived from embryonic ectoderm) and the unique vertebrate **dermis** (the deeper cell layer of mesodermal and neural crest origin). The dermis extends deeper into a purely mesodermally derived subcutaneous tissue (**hypodermis**) that overlies the muscles and bones.

Epidermis   The epidermis forms the boundary between a vertebrate and the environment, and is

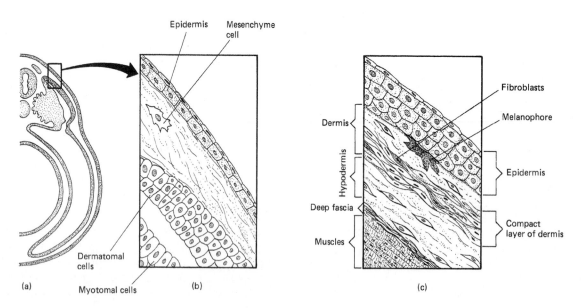

Figure 3–2   Development and differentiation of the vertebrate integument. (a) The ectoderm and somite contribute to the adult skin. (b) In addition, wandering cells from the neural crest and later the mesenchyme cells contribute to the differentiation of the integument. (c) The differentiated skin as described in the text. (After M. H. Wake, editor, 1979, *Hyman's Comparative Vertebrate Anatomy*, 3d edition, University of Chicago Press, Chicago, IL.)

of paramount importance in protection, exchange, and sensation. Nonetheless, the epidermis may be only a few cells thick in fishes. In fishes and aquatic amphibians the entire epidermis is alive and metabolically active. It often contains secretory glands, and may play a significant role in osmotic and volume regulation (see Chapter 4).

In most tetrapods (including adult terrestrial amphibians) the skin acts as a barrier to water loss. The epidermis is thick, with the superficial layer of dead, avascular (without circulation) cells forming a barrier and with the deeper active cells (the stratum germinativum) obtaining nutrients from the underlying vascular dermis. The protein keratin is now an important component of the epidermis, forming a horny layer. Keratin is especially important in amniotes; that is, those vertebrates who lay (or whose ancestors laid) shelled eggs. This includes reptiles, birds, and mammals (i.e., all tetrapods except for amphibians). In amniotes keratin forms such epidermal structures as scales, feathers, hair, horn, and hooves (see Chapters 11, 17, and Chapter 21). The fact that the molecular structure of the keratin in mammalian hair (alpha keratin) and in reptile scales and bird feathers (mainly beta keratin) is rather different suggests that the elaboration of a horny integument must have happened at least twice independently in amniotes.

Dermis   The dermis is the main structural layer of the skin in vertebrates, with a prominent component of collagen fibers that provide elasticity and help to maintain its strength and shape. It is thin in some regions (over joints, for example) and thicker in others (e.g., on the soles of the feet in humans). The dermis is vascular (containing blood vessels), and the amount and rate of blood flow within these vessels is sometimes under neural and hormonal control and sometimes controlled by the external temperature. Thus the vessels may contract in cold temperature, conserving body heat, or dilate in the warmth, helping to dissipate heat. Hormonal control of the blood flow can be illustrated by human emotional responses, such as blushing, where the vessels are dilated and blood rushes to the skin. Smooth muscle fibers may also occur in the dermis, such as the ones in mammals that produce skin wrinkling around the nipples.

In tetrapods the dermis houses the majority of the sensory structures and nerves associated with sensations of temperature, pressure, and pain. The dermis also houses **melanocytes**, cells derived from the neural crest that actually come to rest between the dermis and epidermis. Melanocytes are also known as pigment cells, as they contain granules of the pigment melanin that can also be injected into adjacent cells. These cells cause the coloration of the skin: different amounts and types of melanin will produce different degrees of coloration. This can be seen in the differences in skin pigmentation between the human races, or within an individual whose skin becomes darker (suntanned) in summer and lighter in winter. Additional structures termed chromatophores and the degree of vascularization of the skin can also affect color. In some animals the ability of the cells to concentrate or disperse pigment is under neural influences, so the animal can rapidly appear to change color; this capacity is seen in many fishes, and in some amphibians and lizards (such as the legendary chameleon).

Hypodermis   The hypodermis, or subcutaneous tissue layer, is not functionally a part of the skin but lies between the dermis and the fascia overlying the muscles. This region contains collagenous and elastic fibers, and is the area where subcutaneous fat may be stored (primarily in birds and mammals). The subcutaneous striated muscles of mammals, such as those that enable them to make facial expressions or to flick the skin to get rid of a fly, are found in this area.

Mineralization   In Chapter 2 we discussed the notion that the original mineralized tissues of vertebrates were found in the skin, as **dermal ossifications**. We still retain this type of mineralization in our teeth and as the dermal roofing bones of our skull. Bony fishes and their descendants, the tetrapods, do something unusual from the perspective of the primitive vertebrate condition—they extend tissue mineralization to the internal portions of the endoskeleton as **endochondral ossification** ("within cartilage bone formation"). Endochondral bone has a complex developmental history. The endoskeleton is initially formed of cartilage, which allows growth. During development the cartilage is gradually replaced by mineralized bone. Vertebrates can also have **perichondral ossification**, in which the internal bone is ossified around the edge but not all the way through.

There are four types of tissues that can become mineralized in vertebrates. Three of them, **enamel**, **dentine**, and **bone**, are found only in the mineralized condition in the adult. The fourth, **cartilage**, is usually unmineralized in tetrapods, but is the main mineralized endoskeletal tissue in sharks (sharks appear to have lost true bone). Enamel and dentine are the most mineralized of the tissues (about 99 percent and 90 percent mineralized, respectively), and are found only in teeth or in the dermal skeleton of primitive fishes. This high degree of mineralization is the reason why teeth are more likely to be found as fossils than are bones (which are only about 50 percent mineralized), the rest of the tissue consisting of collagen. Indeed, much of the fossil history of sharks is known from their teeth alone; unmineralized cartilage rarely fossilizes. A fifth type of vertebrate hard tissue, **enameloid**, is found in fishes with the exception of the lobe-finned fish ancestral to tetrapods; this tissue appears similar to enamel, being hard and glassy, and has an outer position in the layers of dermal bones like enamel. But in terms of the cell lineages that it is derived from enameloid is actually more closely related to dentine. The final type of hard tissue is **cementum**, a bonelike substance which fastens the teeth in their sockets, and which may grow to become part of the tooth structure itself (see Chapter 21).

In the primitive vertebrate condition dermal bone was composed of external layers of enamel and dentine, as well as of underlying true bone. This type of dermal bone was seen in the head shield of ostracoderms and in the body scales of primitive bony fishes, and is retained in certain living fishes such as reed fishes and gars (see Chapter 8). Although the dermal bone in mammalian skulls has a different type of embryonic origin from endochondral bone (it forms in a membrane, rather than in cartilage), it is for all intents and purposes just like endochondral bone, and can remodel itself (see later).

The basic structure of the teeth of gnathostomes (jawed vertebrates) is like that of the odontode components of primitive vertebrate dermal armor, with an outer layer of enamel (or enameloid). Shark scales (dermal denticles) have a similar structure, and both elements are probably homologous with ancient vertebrate odontodes (see Chapter 2). Teeth form within the dermis of the skin (see Figure 3–3a). Enamel is formed from cells called **ameloblasts**, which have an ectodermal origin. Ameloblasts migrate downward from the epidermis to form the **enamel organ** and induce the underlying **odontoblasts**, which have a neural crest origin in the dermis, to make the underlying dentine. Teeth always form in the skin like this where there is a juxtaposition of epidermal and dermal tissues to make the

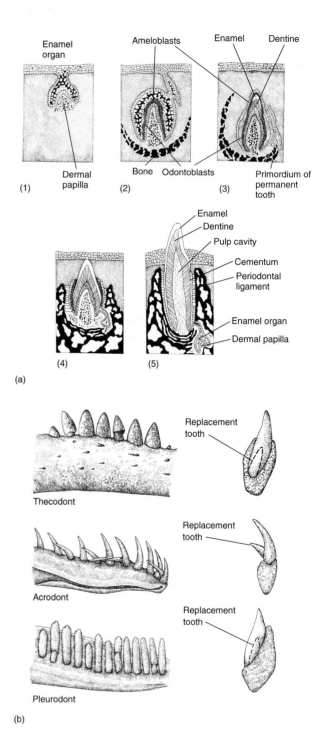

Figure 3–3 Vertebrate mineralized tissues. (a) Development of a mammalian tooth. (b) Types of rooted teeth found in vertebrates. (After K. V. Kardong 1998, *Vertebrates-Comparative Anatomy, Function, Evolution*, 2nd Ed., Wm. C. Brown Publishers. Reprinted by permission of the McGraw-Hill Companies.)

two types of dental tissues. For a similar reason, when teeth are found fused to bones (as opposed to the tooth whorls of cartilaginous fishes, see Chapter 7) they are found only on dermal bones.

When the tooth is fully formed it erupts through the gum line where it can become functional. Replacement teeth may start to develop off to one side of the main tooth even before its eruption. Once the tooth erupts growth can continue to occur from below if the roots have not yet been formed, but no more enamel can be added to the functional surface on the top of the tooth, as the tissues are no longer there to add further material. Even though all bony fishes and tetrapods had teeth set in the dermal bone of the jaws, only mammals and some reptiles (archosaurs—crocodiles and extinct relatives, such as dinosaurs) have truly rooted teeth, termed **thecodont** teeth, which are set in sockets and held in place by periodontal ligaments. Other types of teeth can be termed **acrodont** (fused to the jaw bone), or **pleurodont** (set in a little shelf in the jaw bone) (see Figure 3–3b).

Bone tissue is composed of a complex matrix of collagenous fibers, bone cells (osteocytes) that secrete a protinaceous tissue matrix, and crystals of calcium phosphate in the form of hydroxyapatite. Bone remains a highly vascular tissue even when ossified, and calcium and phosphate in bone are in dynamic turnover with calcium and phosphate ions in the blood. The calcium phosphate crystals are aligned on the matrix of collagenous fibers in layers with alternating directions, much like the structure of plywood (see Figure 3–4a). This combination of cells, fibers and minerals gives bone its complex, latticework appearance that not only combines strength with relative lightness, but also helps in preventing crack propagation, much as a knot in a piece of wood will halt a spreading crack.

Long bones grow by replacing the original cartilage with bone. Once the bone has been ossified, it can no longer elongate from within by expansion, but can only be thickened by adding bone around the rim (perichondral ossification). Bones can grow in length because they retain a zone of cartilage where growth can occur, found in mammals between the shaft of the bone (the **diaphysis**) and the joints at the ends (the **epiphyses**) (see Figure 3–4b). In the bones of juvenile mammals clear lines can be seen between the bone shaft and the ends, whereas in adults these lines have vanished due to **epiphyseal fusion**. A unique capacity of bone is the ability to **remodel** itself. Old bone is eaten away by specialized blood cells (osteoclasts), which are derived from the same cell lines as the macrophage white blood cells. New osteoblasts enter behind the osteoclasts and redeposit new bone, bit by bit, in the wake of the destruction of the old. In this way, bone can mend itself from within, and can also change its internal structure to suit the mechanical stress imposed on the animal (see later). Calcified cartilage, as seen in the endoskeleton of sharks, is unable to remodel itself in this fashion because it does not contain blood vessels.

Endochondral bone is not of uniform thickness throughout: if it were, animals would be very heavy. The external layers are formed of dense, compact or lamellar bone, but the internal layers are of spongy or cancellous bone. The bony trabeculae that form the cancellous bone can be remodeled to meet the stress demands of the animal (this is why exercise builds up bone and why astronauts lose bone in the zero gravity of space). The joints at the ends of the bone are covered by a layer of **articular cartilage**, presumably for better joint mobility (arthritis occurs if this cartilage is damaged or worn), and the bone within the joint is comprised of cancellous bone rather than dense bone. The entire joint is enclosed in a **joint capsule**, containing **synovial fluid** for lubrication (see Figure 3–4b). The characteristic form of lamellar bone in amniotes is arranged in concentric layers around blood vessels within the bone to form cylindrical units called **Haversian systems** (see Figure 3–4a).

The evolution of endochondral ossification remains a bit of a puzzle. Remember, its evolution entails the replacement of the tissue that originally formed the internal bones (cartilage) with another tissue (bone) that had previously been found only in the skin. What type of selection pressures might have been involved in this evolutionary event? Endochondral bone, with its capacity to remodel and to continually adapt to gravitational stresses (not to mention the ability to mend itself if broken), is a key feature of tetrapods. It might have been impossible to evolve large-size tetrapods without this remodeling capacity of the internal supportive skeleton. Yet endochondral bone first appears in the bony fishes, aquatic animals for whom these considerations would not have been an issue! Calcified cartilage, as seen in larger sharks, appears to be a perfectly adequate internal supportive device for an aquatic vertebrate. Perhaps the endochondral bone of bony fishes is related to metabolic

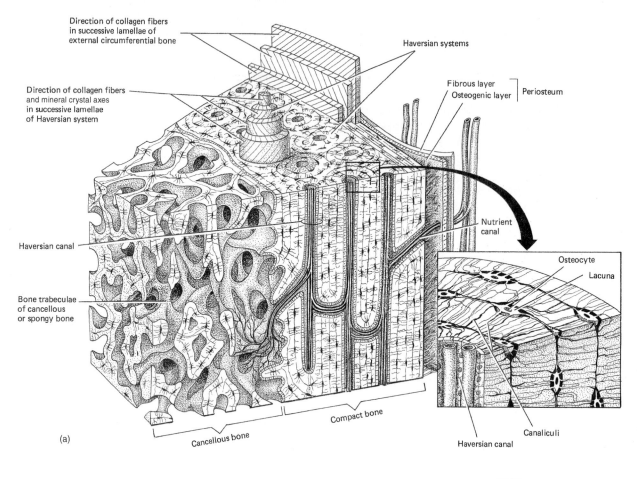

Direction of collagen fibers in successive lamellae of external circumferential bone

Direction of collagen fibers and mineral crystal axes in successive lamellae of Haversian system

Haversian systems

Fibrous layer
Osteogenic layer] Periosteum

Nutrient canal

Haversian canal

Bone trabeculae of cancellous or spongy bone

Compact bone

Cancellous bone

Osteocyte

Lacuna

Canaliculi

Haversian canal

(a)

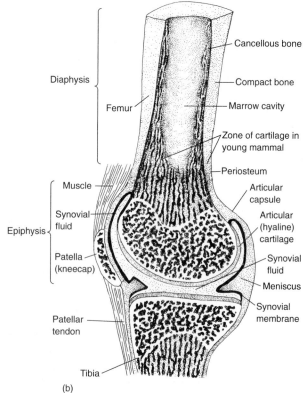

Cancellous bone

Compact bone

Marrow cavity

Diaphysis

Femur

Zone of cartilage in young mammal

Periosteum

Muscle

Articular capsule

Synovial fluid

Articular (hyaline) cartilage

Epiphysis

Synovial fluid

Patella (kneecap)

Meniscus

Synovial membrane

Patellar tendon

Tibia

(b)

Figure 3–4 Organization of vertebrate bone. (a) Bone from a section of the shaft of a long bone of a mammal, showing Haversian canal systems. (b) Section through a human knee joint, showing the gross internal structure of a long bone and the structure of a joint capsule. Note that the patella (kneecap) is an example of a sesamoid bone (a bone formed within a tendon).

requirements, as its vascular nature allows it to act as a reserve store of minerals that can be reclaimed by the body. But certainly the remodeling capacity of bone is a critical preadaptation in the later evolution of tetrapods from bony fishes.

The Endoskeleton

The basic structural feature of chordates is the **notochord**, acting as a dorsal stiffening rod running along the length of the body. Note that the more familiar vertebrate features of a vertebral column (made of cartilage or bone) replacing the notochord, and paired limbs, are not a feature of the most primitive vertebrates, although lampreys do possess small precursors of segmental vertebral elements, or **arcualia**, flanking the nerve cord (see Chapter 6). However, all vertebrates differ from nonvertebrate chordates in their possession of a **cranium**, or skull, a series of initially cartilaginous elements housing the brain and the sense organs. The **visceral (pharyngeal) skeleton** of the gill arches and their derivatives appeared at the same time as the cranium. It is not until gnathostomes that there is the appearance of true vertebrae and ribs, and the skeleton of the appendages. The cranium, visceral skeleton, notochord, vertebrae, and ribs, plus the median fin supports of fishes, are together called the **axial skeleton**. The paired fin or limb skeletons and girdles make up the **appendicular skeleton**.

Skull   The skull or cranium, which houses the brain and sense organs, is the most complicated portion of the skeleton and the most informative with respect to vertebrate phylogeny and functional adaptations (Hanken and Hall 1993). The skull is formed by three basic components: the chondrocranium, the visceral arches or splanchnocranium, and the dermatocranium (see Figure 3–5).

The **chondrocranium** is the deepest lying and probably phylogenetically the oldest portion of the skull. As its name implies, the entire structure forms initially as cartilage, and is cartilaginous in the adults of agnathans (jawless fish) and chondrichthyans (cartilaginous fish). The chondrocranium may be partly or entirely replaced by endochondral ossification in more derived vertebrates such as bony fishes and tetrapods. The chondrocranium (also known as the neurocranium in the human condition) (Figure 3–6) is made up of portions of the floor of the cranial cavity that begin as a pair of cartilages flanking the anterior tip of the notochord (the **parachordals**). Other contributions come from the posterior wall of the brain cavity surrounding the spinal cord and from a pair of longitudinal cartilaginous bars (the **trabeculae**) located anteriorly and derived from the neural crest. The chondrocranium is completed by the cartilaginous **sensory capsules** (also derived from the neural crest) that form around the sense organs: the olfactory (nasal) capsules (around the nose in the region of the forebrain), the optic capsules (around the eyes) plus the orbital cartilages (between the eyes in the region of the midbrain), and the otic capsules (around the inner ear regions of the hindbrain). The main part of the adult braincase is made by the eventual fusion of these elements around and under the brain, except for the optic capsules which must remain free in order for the eyes to rotate.

The **splanchnocranium** comprises the visceral arches or gill supports, derived from neural crest, and relating to the basic series of fleshy septa between pharyngeal gill slits or pouches. Visceral arches also form initially in cartilage, and may be replaced by bone in bony fishes and tetrapods. Each of these skeletal visceral arches is made up of several elements, usually five in each arch on each side of the head. In gnathostomes the anterior two pairs of arches become the jaws and their supporting structures, including the support of the tongue in tetrapods (Figure 3–5a; see also Chapter 6). Where functional gills exist in adult vertebrates, as in fishes, they are supported by the more posterior arches. When gills are lost and respiration is via lungs, as in tetrapods, the posterior arches contribute to the larynx and trachea.

The **dermatocranium** is the portion of the skull derived from dermal bones. In many ways it is the simplest of the skull's components, made up of dermal bones of the head integument, covering the other portions of the skull. Dermal bones are not preformed in cartilage, and an unmineralized dermatocranium is seen only as a highly derived condition in secondarily cartilaginous bony fishes such as sturgeons (Chapter 8). The dermatocranium appears to have been secondarily lost in living jawless fish and in chondrichthyans, but in other vertebrates it surrounds, unites with, or replaces portions of the other components of the skull so closely as to have usurped many of the functions of chondrocranial and visceral elements.

A dermatocranium of sorts was obviously present in the extinct vertebrate groups of ostracoderms and placoderms, but today it is seen only in

Figure 3–5 Basic form of the vertebrate skull. (a) Chondrocranium and splanchnocranium of a shark. (b) Dermatocranium of a primitive bony fish, lateral view. (c) Palatal view of a primitive bony fish, left-hand side showing dermal bones, right-hand side showing the underlying chondrocranium and splanchnocranium. (After W. F. Walker, Jr., and K. F. Liem 1994, *Functional Anatomy of Vertebrates*, 2nd Ed., copyright © by Saunders College Publishing, reproduced by permission of the publisher.)

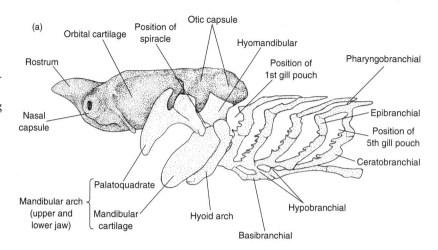

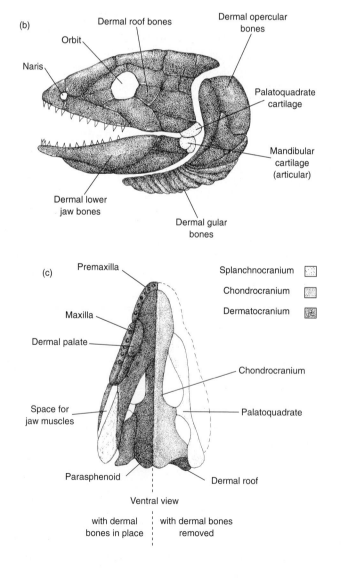

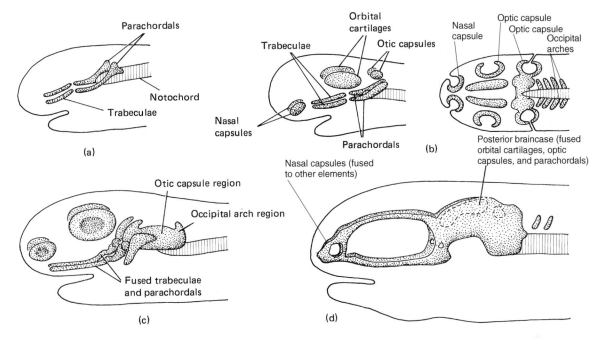

Figure 3–6 Early development of the chondrocranium. (a) through (d) are progressively more advanced stages of development. (b) Lateral view on left, dorsal view on right. The trabecular and parachordal cartilages are usually formed first, followed by the sensory capsules, the orbital cartilages, and the occipital arches. These centers of chondrification fuse to form the braincase. (Modified after W. W. Ballard, 1964, *Comparative Anatomy and Embryology*, Ronald, New York, NY.)

bony fishes and their descendants, tetrapods. At some level the dermal skull bones of all vertebrates must be homologous, but the patterning and distribution of the dermal elements in living vertebrates are unique. The inception of this pattern of dermal bones was probably coincident with the evolution of the first bony fishes. The dermatocranium of bony fishes and tetrapods includes the roof of the skull, the superficial area around the orbits, the gill covers (opercula) when they are present, and the roof of the mouth (the palate and portions of the floor of the skull) (see Figure 3–5b, c). It also contributes to the jaws, which in their most derived character state are formed primarily (in birds) or entirely (in mammals) by dermal bones.

Notochord The notochord is made up of a core of large, closely packed cells distended with fluid-filled vacuoles, wrapped in a complex fibrous sheath that also acts as a site of attachment for segmental muscle and connective tissues. Its rigidity results from the incompressible nature of the fluids bound within the fibrous sheath. In amphioxus and in primitive vertebrates the notochord may have contractile properties in addition to its supportive

role. The notochord of all vertebrates ends anteriorly just posterior to the bud of the pituitary gland and continues posteriorly to the tip of the fleshy portion of the tail.

In many fossil and extant fishes a notochord as just described (called an unrestricted notochord) appears as the endoskeletal body axis in the adult. In other fishes and in all tetrapods the sheath of the notochord and the adjacent skeletogenous septa become involved in the development of structures that pinch and otherwise distort the notochord. In several clades of vertebrates the notochord becomes segmentally constricted into an axial series of nubbins (portions of the intervertebral disks in mammals) or obliterated altogether by derived axial endoskeletal elements, the vertebrae.

Vertebrae and Ribs In gnathostomes the axial skeleton is made up of a series of intersegmentally arranged **vertebrae**, which offer more strength and a greater number and variety of attachment points for muscles than does the simple sheath of the notochord. The series of vertebrae from the skull to the tip of the tail constitutes the **vertebral column** or **spine**, which provides rigidity to the body and postural support on land. In swimming vertebrates the vertebral column retains the ancestral function of resisting body shortening during lateral undulation. Flexibility of the spine is allowed by the alternation of the rigid vertebrae with flexible cartilaginous **intervertebral disks**. These disks, which are partly remnants of the notochord, are bound between vertebrae by muscle and ligament attachments running from vertebra to vertebra.

The formation of the vertebral column in gnathostomes represents the migration and differentiation of mesodermal cells into a system of **skeletogenous septa**, which surrounding the notochord during development and provide landmark points for many of the key elements of the axial skeleton (Figure 3–7). The axial musculature consists of segmental muscle blocks, or **myomeres**, derived from the somites. Each myomere is divided from its neighbor by a sheet of tissue called the **myoseptum**. During development the mesoderm condenses around the notochord and forms a vertebra at the intersection (intersegmental) of every myoseptum with the horizontal and dorsal/ventral septa. Thus, intersegmental vertebrae alternate with developing segmental muscle masses. The muscles eventually insert on the vertebrae and form the flexible spinomuscular basis of lateral undulatory locomotion.

Vertebrae possess a variable number of bilaterally symmetrical projections (apophyses) that are used for the attachment of muscles and ligaments, for locomotion or to link the vertebrae to other skeletal elements. They also possess a dorsal neural arch, enclosing the nerve cord, and the tail vertebrae may also possess a hemal arch, enclosing the caudal artery and vein. **Ribs** are functionally and anatomically related to the vertebral apophyses. They provide sites for muscle attachment and strengthen the body wall. The vertebrae and ribs of fishes usually have a purely locomotory function, although occasionally some elements may be uniquely modified for specialized functions such as hearing in catfish and their relatives (Chapter 8).

The tetrapod function of the axial skeleton, for support on land and for lung ventilation, is very much the derived vertebrate condition. The vertebrae of tetrapods now interlock by means of processes termed **zygapophyses** (see Chapter 10), which allow the vertebral column to act as an analogue of a suspension bridge to supporting the weight of the viscera on land. (Note that tetrapods that have permanently returned to the water, such as whales and many of the extinct Mesozoic marine

reptiles, have secondarily lost the zygapophyses.) Ribs are confined to the anterior trunk (thoracic) vertebrae in the mammalian skeleton (Chapter 19), and the trunk ribs tend to be the most prominent ones in tetrapods in general, but many primitive tetrapods have smaller ribs throughout the entire vertebral column. The ribs of early tetrapods were fairly stout, more prominently developed than in fishes (see Chapter 10), and may have served primarily to stiffen the trunk in these primitive animals that would not yet have developed postural support from the axial musculature. Modern amphibians have almost entirely lost their ribs. The use of the ribs as devices to ventilate the lungs was probably an amniote invention (see discussion in Chapter 10).

The trend in the axial skeleton of tetrapods has been toward differentiation into five regions from anterior to posterior (see Chapter 10). With the loss of the operculum of the bony fishes, which connected the head to the pectoral girdle, tetrapods now have a distinct neck region. Enhancing mobility of the head while continuing protection of the spinal cord is the function of the neck or **cervical** vertebrae. The two most anterior cervical vertebrae are the **atlas** and **axis**, of highly differentiated form in mammals. The middle region of the body comprises the **trunk** vertebrae: In mammals these are further differentiated into the **thoracic** vertebrae (that bear ribs) and the **lumbar** vertebrae (that have lost ribs—see Chapter 19). The **sacral** vertebrae, derived from the trunk vertebrae, fuse with the pelvic girdle and transfer force to the appendicular skeleton. The number of sacral vertebrae varies from a single one in early tetrapods and living amphibians, to a dozen or more in some dinosaurs (mammals have between three and five). The tail, or **caudal**, vertebrae are usually simpler in structure than the trunk vertebrate. The **sternum** is a midventral, usually segmental structure, common to all tetrapods, which links the lower ends of right and left thoracic ribs. It is extensively ossified only in birds and mammals, and its evolutionary origins are obscure.

Thus in tetrapods the axial skeleton and its musculature assume a very different role from their original function in aquatic vertebrates. As well as aiding in locomotion the skeleton now must assume the roles of postural support and ventilation of the lungs. Not all of these different functions are compatible with one another. For example, when lizards run, the bending of their trunk means that they

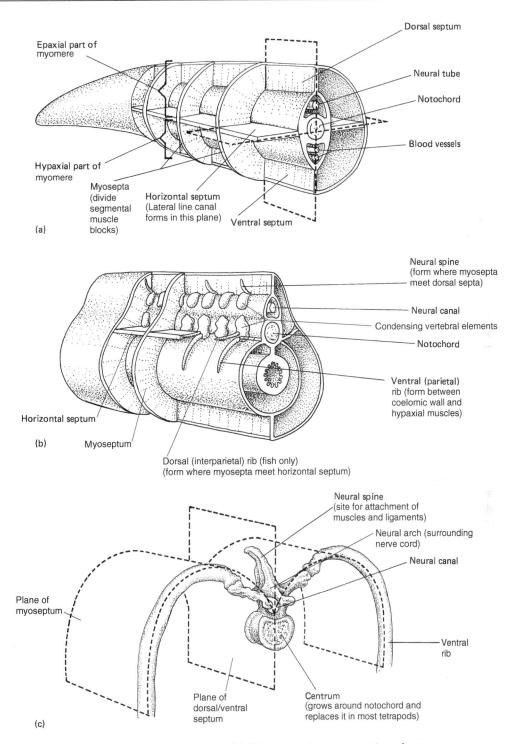

Figure 3–7   The skeletogenous septa of gnathostomes. (a) Diagrammatic representation of the orientation of the various mesenchymal septa in the tail of a generalized gnathostome. (b) Differentiation of the septa and the endoskeletal elements that grow at the various intersections in the trunk region of a generalized fishlike vertebrate. (c) Human thoracic vertebra and rib, which develop in the same skeletogenous septa intersections. Note that in the tail of some tetrapods (but not in mammals) there is also a hemal arch and spine on the ventral side of the centrum, encircling the caudal artery and vein and additionally acting as an area for muscle attachment.

have difficulty in using their ribs for lung ventilation, creating a conflict between locomotory and respiratory functions of the axial skeleton and muscles. More derived tetrapods such as mammals and birds that are more metabolically active, have addressed this conflict by the development of an **upright posture**, so that the animal is propelled by limb movements rather than by trunk bending (see Chapters 10 and 19).

Appendicular Skeleton   Fishes have a number of median fins in addition to the paired pectoral and pelvic fins, including an anal fin, one or two dorsal fins, and a tail (caudal) fin (Chapter 7). Tetrapods have lost these median fins (although remnants of a tail fin are seen in the earliest tetrapods, see Chapter 10). The pelvic fins are not directly attached to the vertebral column in any fish. In many teleosts (derived bony fishes) the pelvic fins move forward in position and may even become fused to the pectoral girdle (Chapter 8). In tetrapods the pelvic girdle becomes fused directly to modified sacral vertebrae and the hindlimbs function as the primary propulsive mechanism. In bony fishes the pectoral girdle is attached to the opercular bones that form the posterior portion of the dermal skull roof. The tetrapod pectoral girdle becomes freed from the dermal skull roof with the loss of the operculum and the opercular series of bones (although the clavicle, retained in most tetrapods including ourselves, is a remnant of that old dermal bone series). The pectoral girdle does articulate directly with the vertebral column; there is no equivalent of a sacrum in the anterior vertebral column (the only exception being seen in pterosaurs, extinct flying reptiles). The connection in all other vertebrates, if present, is indirect via the sternum and the ribs.

The ancestral form of the endoskeletal elements of the paired fins of most fishes is a semicircular girdle embedded in the ventral musculature providing articulation for a small number of fanlike **basal elements**. The basals support one or more ranks of cylindrical **radials**, which usually articulate with raylike structures that support most of the surface of the fin web (Figure 3–8a). The primitive gnathostome condition is represented by a shark, where the basals and radials are robust, but

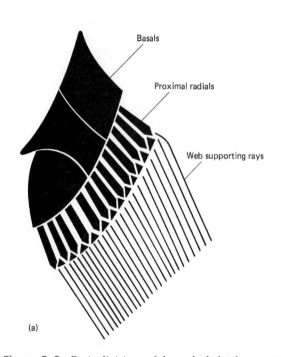

APPENDICULAR SEGMENTS		PECTORAL	PELVIC
GIRDLE		Scapula (shoulder blade)	Pelvis (hip bone)
PROPODIUM		Humerus (upper arm)	Femur (thigh)
EPIPODIUM		Ulna/Radius (forearm)	Tibia/Fibula (lower leg)
MESOPODIUM		Carpus (wrist)	Tarsus (ankle)
METAPODIUM		Metacarpus (hand)	Metatarsus (foot)
PHALANGES		Phalanges (fingers)	Phalanges (toes)

(a)

(b)

Figure 3–8   Basic divisions of the endoskeletal supports of vertebrate paired appendages. (a) Most fishes. (b) Tetrapods as exemplified by the primitive mammalian condition with common and anatomical terminology compared.

are restricted to the proximal (close to the body) part of the fin. Bony fishes diverge from this pattern in two different ways. Primitive ray-finned fishes (actinopterygians), such as *Polypterus*, have an internal fin structure that is rather sharklike, but more derived ones reduce the basals and radials so that the fin is almost entirely comprised of the fin rays (see Chapter 8). Lobe-finned fishes (sarcopterygians) extend the basals and radials out into the body of the fin itself, and the extent of the fin rays may be rather reduced (see Chapter 10). The basic tetrapod limb is made up of the limb girdle and five segments articulating end to end (Figure 3–8b). The evolution of the tetrapod limb from the fish fin is discussed in more detail in Chapter 10.

The Muscular System

The skeleton's functions of support and locomotion would be impossible without the muscular system with which the endoskeleton has so intimately coevolved. Box 3–1 describes the structure of muscle tissue and briefly explains how muscles work. Here we will discuss primarily the muscles that power the trunk, or the **axial** muscles. The **appendicular** muscles, which power the limbs, were not a feature of the earliest vertebrates (which lacked paired limbs entirely) and are not present in the living jawless vertebrates. The **cranial** muscles, which are used primarily in respiration and feeding, reflect the complex nature of the skull.

Axial Muscles   Vertebrates and cephalochordates (amphioxus) share a pattern of axially segmented muscle blocks (myomeres). These muscle blocks are complexly folded in three dimensions, so that each myomere extends anteriorly and posteriorly over several body segments, and thus over several vertebrae in gnathostomes (see Figure 3–10). This folding is functional for locomotion in that the sequential muscle blocks now overlap, and so can better act in concert to produce undulation of the body. An important difference between vertebrates and cephalochordates is that in amphioxus these myomeres have a simple V shape, while in vertebrates they have a more complex W shape. The shape in gnathostomes is even more complex than in agnathans, with the addition of the horizontal septum along the axial skeleton (Figure 3–7), and the distinctive division of the axial blocks into **epaxial** (upper) and **hypaxial** (lower) portions.

This segmental patterning of the axial muscles is clearly visible in fishes: The next time you happen to see a cooked fillet of fish notice how the flesh falls apart in little zigzag blocks. This pattern is also similar to the herringbone fabric pattern, a series of interlocking Vs that would perhaps be better termed herring muscle. In tetrapods this segmental pattern is less obvious; in ourselves the axial muscles are used more for support and ventilation than for locomotion. However, a segmental pattern can still sometimes be observed, for example on the washboard stomach of body builders (each ridge of the washboard represents a segmental component of the rectus abdominus muscle).

In tetrapods the axial muscles assume new roles—postural support of the body and ventilation of the lungs—and become increasingly differentiated in anatomical structure and function. Muscles are important for maintaining posture on land because the body is no longer buoyed up by surrounding water, and without muscular action the skeleton would buckle and collapse. Likewise the process of ventilating the lungs is very different if the chest is surrounded by air rather than by water. The axial muscles still function in locomotion in more primitive tetrapods, producing the lateral flexion of the backbone during movement in many amphibians and reptiles. However, in birds and mammals their locomotory role has been largely superseded by limb movements (see later).

In modern amphibians (and hence, most likely, in the earliest tetrapods) the epaxial muscles still form an undifferentiated single mass, as in fishes, but the hypaxials now show a more complex pattern of differentiation into layers. The hypaxials form two layers in bony fishes (the external and internal obliques), but in tetrapods a third inner layer is added, the transversus abdominus. This muscle is responsible for exhalation of air from the lungs of modern amphibians (which do not use their ribs to breathe), and may have been an essential acquisition for respiration on land by early tetrapods (Brainerd et al. 1993). Air-breathing fish can use the pressure of the water column on the body to force air from the lungs when the mouth is opened at the surface, but land-dwelling tetrapods need muscular action to force air out of their lungs. Another new muscle in tetrapods is the rectus abdominus (mentioned earlier in connection with washboard stomachs), which runs along the ventral surface from the pectoral girdle to the pelvic girdle; its role appears to be primarily postural. In amniotes all three layers of the

BOX 3–1   Structure and Design of Muscles

A muscle (i.e., the gross fleshy structure linking bone to bone in ourselves) is composed of increasingly finer units, all running in the same direction as the main muscle itself. (The description below best applies to vertebrate striated, skeletal muscle, as shown in the picture: however all muscle types in all animals are formed in this same basic way.)

The muscle as a whole is formed of a bunch of bundles of **muscle fibers**. Each fiber is in turn comprised of bunches of **muscle fibrils**. Each muscle fibril is comprised of a long, multinucleated cells, packed with long units (**myofibrils**), in turn composed of repeating units, the **sarcomeres**. It is the lining up of the myofibrils, and their repeating units, within the structure of the muscle cells, that gives vertebrate skeletal muscle its "striated" appearance, but *all* types of muscles have sarcomeres (in all animals), whether lined up or not, as their basic microstructural elements. Sarcomeres in turn are composed of filaments; thick central filaments (**myosin**) and thinner filaments at each end (**actin**); sarcomeres are separated by structures called **Z bands**.

Muscle contraction, at the molecular level, is produced within each sarcomere, with the actin bands sliding in between the myosin bands, forming cross bridges and shortening the length of each sarcomere. It may be this microscopic relationship that underlies a basic feature of muscles, in that they cannot be stretched more than one-third of their resting length (without damaging the muscle—perhaps the microfila-ments are pulled out of alignment). This is an important concept of muscle design, as we see in later chapters. In designing a functional system of skeletal structures as levers moved by muscles in more derived animals, this fundamental feature of the stretchability of muscle is an important constraint.

Because muscle action involves the shortening of the sarcomere, muscles only act by shortening—hence they only act by pulling, never by pushing. In skeletal systems, muscles tend to be arranged in **antagonistic pairs**, one pulling to close the joint, the other to open it (e.g., the biceps and triceps around the human elbow joint). In smooth muscle systems, a muscle constricting a sphincter (for example) will be accompanied by a dilator.

The functional unit of muscle action, at the gross level, is the **motor unit** (the unit of the innervation of the muscle fibers supplies by a single motor neuron from the spinal chord). The impulse of a nerve to a muscle, signaling it to action, is an all-or-nothing event (either the nerve fires, or it doesn't). The amount (force/strength) of the reaction of the muscle depends on the number of motor units activated by the nervous system. Note that the particular innervation of muscles by particular nerves appears to be a highly conservative feature in evolution (used for tracing muscle homologies, etc.).

Three types of muscles are found in vertebrates. **Striated muscle** (= "voluntary" muscle) is usually associated with the skeletal system (as the axial and the appendicular musculature). The striated muscles of the body are derived

hypaxial muscles form the costal muscles in the region of the rib cage, and are responsible for inhalation as well as for exhalation. Amniote epaxial muscles are also distinctly differentiated into three major components, and their primary role is now postural rather than locomotory (Ritter 1995).

Appendicular Muscles   The paired fins of fishes are not usually used for propulsion. Some specialized cases where pectoral fins are used in this manner include certain coral reef teleosts, such as wrasses, and skates and rays, which have winglike projections formed from the pectoral fins. Propulsion comes from the trunk and tail and the actions of the axial winglike projections muscles. The original function of appendicular muscles (which are derived from the hypaxial muscles) was to move the fins for steering, braking, and providing lift. Thus the original form of the appendicular muscles, as seen today in sharks, for example, is fairly simple: a basic mass of muscle to lift up the fins and draw them outward and backward (pectoral and pelvic levators) and a

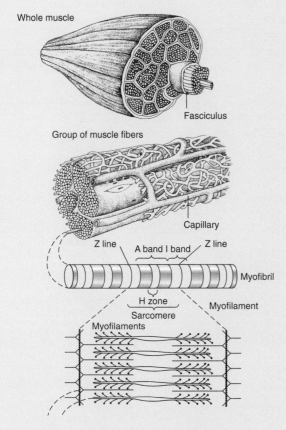

Whole muscle

Fasciculus

Group of muscle fibers

Capillary

Z line   A band I band   Z line

Myofibril

H zone   Myofilament

Sarcomere
Myofilaments

Figure 3–9 Diagrammatic structure of a muscle. (After W. F. Walker, Jr. and K. F. Liem 1994.)

from the somites and are innervated by somatic motor nerves. The striated branchiomeric muscles in the head are a little different: they are derived from the paraxial mesoderm in front of the true somites, and are innervated by the special branchial fibers of the cranial nerves. Striated muscle typically has strong, rapid contractions in the active state generating tensile force, fairly rapid return to the resting state once the nerves have stopped firing. **Smooth muscle** (= "involuntary" muscle) is so called because appears to lack striations; instead it consists of short muscle cells joined together in sheets. It is derived from the lateral plate mesoderm, and is found in the visceral components of the body (digestive tract, blood vessels, lungs), innervated by visceral motor nerves. In contrast with striated muscle it has slow, sustained (tonic) contractions. **Cardiac muscle** is a type of smooth muscle; it is found only in the heart and looks rather like striated muscle (but the individual cells are shorter).

Muscles rarely attach directly to a bone, but instead attach via **tendons** (tightly packed bundles of collagenous fibers). **Ligaments** are similar structures but join one bone to another, and may also contain elastic material so that they can store energy when stretched and return the bone to its original position without additional energy when muscular contraction ceases.

Skeletal striated muscles can be arranged in a parallel fiber arrangement, or a pinnate fiber arrangement. **Pinnate muscles** have fibers oriented oblique to the line of action: more fibers can be backed in to a given space (although each fiber is shorter), and the muscle as a whole can provide greater force. The force that a muscle can generate is proportional to its cross sectional area: thus bigger animals must have relatively bigger muscles to maintain the same proportional strength as smaller ones.

muscle mass to move the fin back down, in, and forward (pectoral and pelvic depressors).

In tetrapods the limbs are used for propulsion, increasingly so in more derived forms. Correspondingly, the appendicular muscles have become increasingly complicated and differentiated. The old pattern of a major levator and a major depressor is still present. In our arms (= pectoral fins) the levator corresponds to the deltoids (running from the scapular over the shoulder down to the upper arm), and the depressor corresponds to the pectoralis (running from the upper arm to the chest). But we also possess many additional muscles in the shoulder region alone, not to mention the ones that move the elbow, the wrist, and the multitude of complex muscles in the hand. A detailed description of tetrapod appendicular muscle structure and function is beyond the scope of this chapter, but several examples of the modification of appendicular muscles in specialized tetrapods are discussed later: for example, changes in the hip muscles for bipedal locomotion in dinosaurs (Chapter 13),

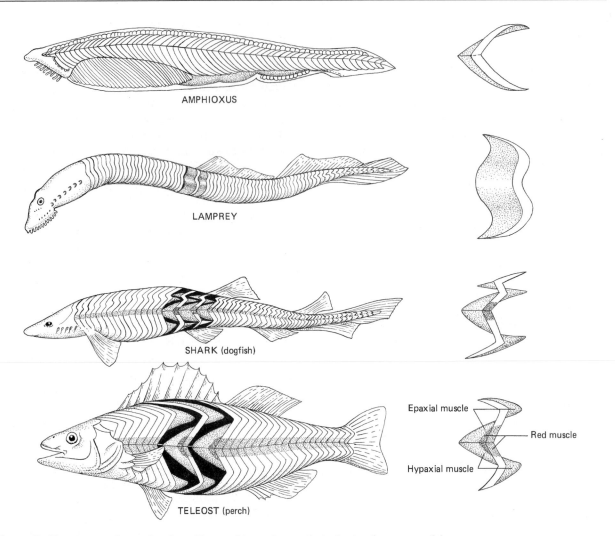

Figure 3–10   Nonvertebrate chordates like amphioxus have relatively simple myomeral form that is only slightly more complex in jawless fishes such as the lamprey. The myomeres are more complexly folded in advanced chondrichthyans and osteichthyans. Unshaded: surface appearance below skin; light shading: deep portions of myomere associated with axial skeleton but not visible from the surface; dark shading: areas of concentration of red muscle fibers. (Modified from A. G. Kluge et al., 1977, *Chordate Structure and Function*, 2d edition, Macmillan, New York, NY; and Q. Bone and N. B. Marshall, 1982, *Biology of Fishes*, Blackie, Glasgow, UK.)

modifications of the shoulder muscles for flight in birds (Chapter 17), modifications of the hindlimb muscles for upright locomotion in the ancestors of mammals (Chapter 19), and modification of the shoulder muscles to form a scapular sling in conjunction with a mobile shoulder girdle in more derived mammals (Chapter 21).

Cranial Muscles   There are two main types of striated muscles in the head of vertebrates, both derived from the paraxial mesoderm of the somitomeres and postotic head somites, but with different patterns of innervation. The first type is the extrinsic eye muscles that rotate the eyeball. There are six of these to each eye in all vertebrates except hagfishes, where their absence may represent secondary loss. These muscles are innervated by somatic motor nerves in a fashion similar to the striated muscles of the body. The second type is the **branchiomeric** muscles, the muscles associated with the splanchnocranium and involved with feeding and respiration. Their innervation is peculiar in that it comes from a special component of what appear to be visceral motor nerves that normally innervate only smooth and cardiac muscles. The section on cranial nerves, later in this chapter, further details the innervation of branchiomeric muscles.

The form of the branchiomeric muscles is best understood in conjunction with the form of the underlying splanchnocranium. In the primitive jawed fish condition (seen in sharks) two anterior visceral arches, the mandibular and the hyoid arches, form the jaws and the jaw supports, respectively. The branchiomeric muscles associated with these two arches (the major muscle being the **adductor mandibularis** that closes the jaws) are primarily involved in feeding, but also aid ventilation by sucking water into the mouth (Mallatt 1996). The muscles associated with the posterior arches that support the gills form a characteristic series of levators, adductors, and constrictors in association with each arch. Their action aids in forcing water through the gills (see Figure 3–11). Jawless vertebrates have a similar system of branchiomeric muscles powering the gill arches, although their organization is not precisely like that of gnathostomes (see Chapter 6).

For a long time it was supposed that the earliest vertebrate would have involved all of the visceral arches in some system of respiration, and that the primary function of all the branchiomeric muscles was originally for gill ventilation. However, recent reinvestigation of the anatomy of both living and fossil primitive vertebrates suggests that the mandibular and hyoid arches and their branchiomeric musculature may have always had a role in feeding, even before the evolution of jaws (Mallatt 1996). Another new feature in gnathostomes is the addition of **hypobranchial** muscles to the system, which run from the mandibular and hyoid arches to the pectoral girdle, and aid in opening the mouth. These muscles are derived from trunk somites that migrate forward in development and have a normal spinal innervation of somatic motor nerves like that of the axial muscles from which they are derived.

In tetrapods the gills are lost, and with them is lost much, but not all, of the associated branchiomeric musculature. A prominent retention is the gill levators. In fishes these muscles are combined into a single unit, the **cucullaris**; this muscle in tetrapods becomes the **trapezius**, running from the top of the neck and shoulders to the shoulder girdle. In mammals this muscle helps to rotate and stabilize the scapula in locomotion, and we use it when we shrug our shoulders. An interesting fact about human spinal injuries can be explained from understanding the original homologies of the trapezius muscle: People paralyzed from the neck down by a spinal injury can still shrug their shoulders because the trapezius, being an old branchiomeric muscle, is innervated directly from the brain by cranial nerves, not from the nerves exiting from the spinal cord in the neck. Other remnants of the gill arch associated branchiomeric muscles remain in small muscles in the throat; for example, those powering the larynx and the vocal cords. Ingenious biomedical engineering allows paraplegic individuals to use this remaining muscular function to activate a substantial range of prostheses.

The major branchiomeric muscles in tetrapods are those associated with the mandibular and hyoid arches, now solely involved in feeding. The adductor mandibularis remains the major jaw-closing muscle, and it becomes increasingly complex in more derived tetrapods. The various specialties of the adductor mandibulae muscle complex can be found elsewhere in this book, for example, specializations in the ray-finned bony fishes (Chapter 8) and in turtles (Chapter 12), the evolution of the condition in early tetrapods (Chapter 10) and mammallike reptiles and mammals (Chapter 19), and the form of the jaw muscles in mammals of different feeding specialties (Chapter 21).

The hyoid musculature forms two new important muscles in tetrapods. One is the **depressor mandibulae**, running from the back of the jaw to the skull and helping the hypobranchials to open the mouth. The other is the **constrictor colli** (also known as the sphincter colli) that surrounds the neck (as its name suggests) and acts primarily in swallowing food (Smith 1992). In mammals, where there is a specialized swallowing reflex of a small food bolus rather than the use of the constrictor colli, this muscle is no longer present in this form. Rather, it has migrated forward to become the muscles of facial expression seen only in mammals among vertebrates (see Chapter 21). (We can be sure of the homologies of these different muscles among vertebrates because of the characteristic pattern of cranial nerve innervation, as discussed later in this chapter.)

Locomotion

Many small aquatic animals (especially larval forms) move by using cilia on their surfaces to beat against the water, but ciliary propulsion works only at very small body sizes. Some protochordates may

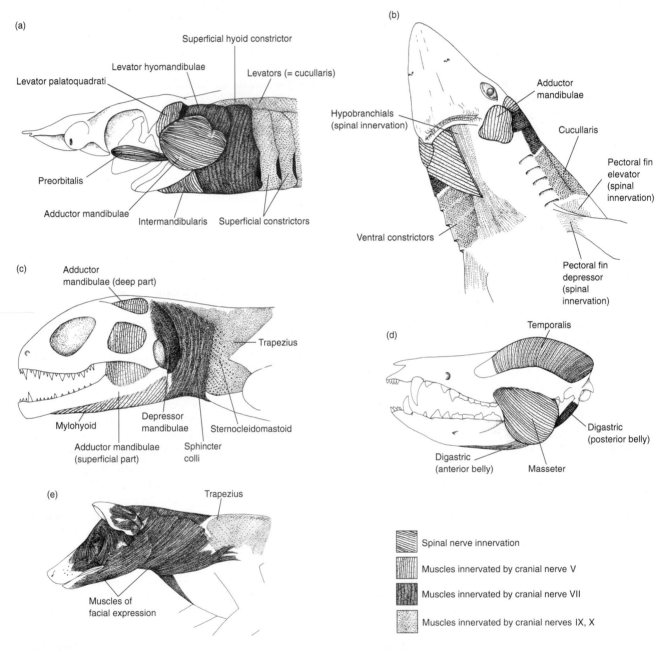

Figure 3–11 Form of head and neck musculature in vertebrates. (a) Primitive gnathostome condition (shark). (b) Shark in ventral view. (c) Generalized tetrapod condition (the reptile *Sphenodon*). (d) Mammal, deeper view. The digastric muscle is a new feature in mammals, a jaw-opening muscle replacing the depressor mandibulae of other tetrapods. (e) Mammal, more superficial view showing overlying facial musculature. ([a, c-e] After W. F. Walker, Jr., and K. F. Liem 1994; [b] After from L. B. Radinsky in M. H. Wake, 1979, *Hyman's Comparative Vertebrate Anatomy*, University of Chicago Press, Chicago, IL.)

have used cilia for locomotion, as do echinoderm larvae, but adult chordates are in general too big to use ciliary locomotion. The chordate feature of the postanal tail (possibly first evolved for a startle response in larval forms) is the basis of their locomotion. This mechanism works by the serial contraction of segmental muscle bands in conjunction with the notochord, which acts as a dorsal stiffening rod for the muscles to work against (otherwise the contraction of these muscles would just result in shortening of the body, not in forward propulsion). The basic vertebrate mode of locomotion, as seen in most present-day fishes, is still the use of the tail and, to a lesser extent, the trunk, in a series of axial undulations for swimming in the water (see further description in Chapter 8).

A fishlike mode of swimming will, of course, work only in a dense medium. Although flying through the air resembles swimming through the water to a certain extent, lift is much more important in air, and propulsion must now come from the movements of the wings (ultimately equaling modified pectoral fins), not from oscillation of the tail (see Chapter 8). When the first tetrapods emerged onto land there were new problems in supporting the body. Overcoming drag from the surrounding medium is not a problem in air, but friction must be generated between the feet and the ground for propulsion. As previously discussed, the axial musculature has a new role in providing postural support for the body and the appendicular musculature has a new role in providing propulsion.

The basic form of tetrapod limb movement is to move diagonal pairs of legs together. The right front and left hind move as one unit, and the left front and right hind move as another, in a type of gait known as the walking trot. Even though humans are bipedal, relying entirely on the hind legs for locomotion, we retain this primitive coupling of the limbs in walking in our tendency to swing the right arm forward when striding with the left leg and vice versa. This type of coupled, diagonally paired limb movement is probably a primitive feature for gnathostomes, as sharks also move their fins in this fashion when locomoting over the submerged substrate (Pridmore 1994/95). The initial mode of tetrapod locomotion, as seen today in salamanders, probably involved axial flexion of the body with the limbs moving in this walking trot fashion, but with the feet acting primarily as holdfasts on the substrate rather than for propulsion of the body. Lizards retain a modified version

of this mode of locomotion, although their limbs are important for propulsion (Ritter 1995). In addition, it should not be forgotten that while frogs are amphibians, their jumping mode of locomotion is highly specialized (Chapter 11).

A new specialization of amniotes is the gait of the **walk**, where each leg is moved in succession, rather than diagonally opposite legs being used together in a pairwise fashion (see Figure 3–12C) (Hildebrand 1980) The quadrupedal amniote walk, identified by a characteristic pattern of footfall sequences, involves the movement of each leg independently, usually with three feet being on the ground at any one time. However, it is possible for mammals to employ a speeded-up walk where only one foot or two feet may be on the ground at any time, as seen in the **amble** of elephants and some horses (Figure 3–12O). All amniotes can also use a form of the trot, where diagonal pairs of limbs are moved together, as in the primitive tetrapod condition.

More derived amniotes, such as mammals and archosaurs (birds, dinosaurs, and crocodiles) are specialized with respect to the primitive sprawling tetrapod condition in having an upright posture, with the limbs held more directly underneath the body (Chapters 10 and 19). While archosaurs tended toward bipedality, mammals devised some new modes of locomotion with the evolution of the **dorsoventral flexion** of the vertebral column. The characteristic new gait of mammals is the **bound**, which involves jumping off from the hind legs and landing on the fore legs, with the flexion of the back contributing to the length of the stride (Hildebrand 1980). In larger mammals, such as horses and cows, whose size dictates that they must move more cautiously to avoid injury, the bound is modified into the **gallop**, where the period of suspension in the air is not with legs stretched out in mid leap, but in the bunched up recovery phase where the hind legs move forward for the next stride, and there is less movement in the back (see Figure 3–12L). (The canter of horses is really just a slow version of the gallop.) If you watch domestic pets you can see that cats usually bound and dogs usually gallop, although many animals larger than dogs (such as cheetahs and antelope) use the bound.

Another gait that is typical of mammals is the **trot**, which is the old version of the diagonal pairs of limbs acting in sequence but with the new twist that there is now a distinct jump from one pair of legs to the other with a period where all four legs

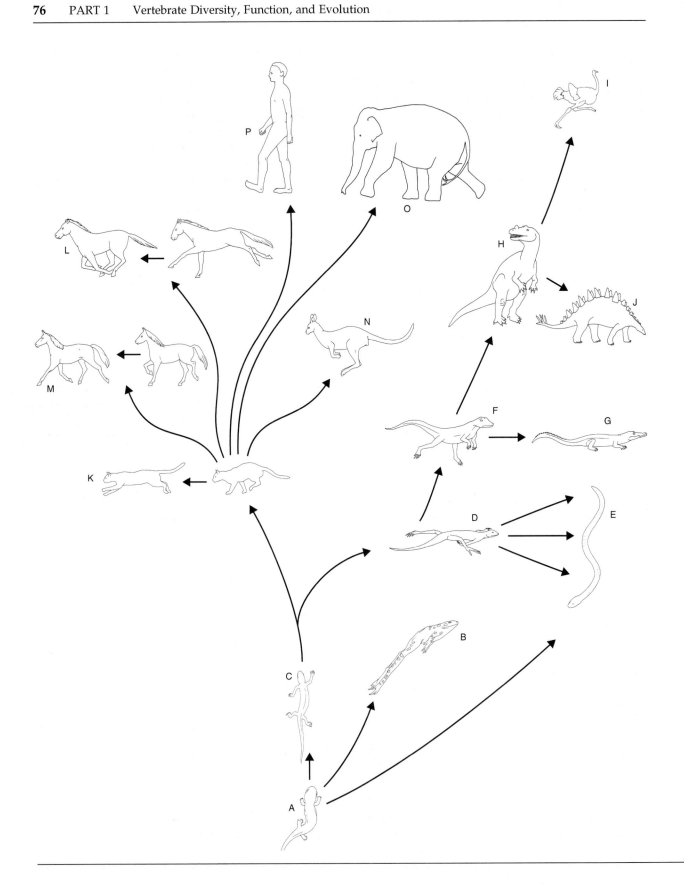

are off the ground (see Figure 3–12M). A more specialized type of mammalian locomotion is the **ricochet**, or bipedal hopping, probably derived from the bound at some evolutionary point. Although kangaroos are famous for this type of gait, a number of placental rodents (e.g., kangaroo rats, jerboas, and spring hares) have also, independently of one another, evolved this locomotory mode. Other specializations of mammals for locomotion are discussed in Chapter 21. Note that the mode of human locomotion, bipedal striding with an upright trunk, is unique among vertebrates.

Quadrupedal dinosaurs (note that all such dinosaurs are *secondarily* quadrupedal from a bipedal ancestor) are often portrayed in popular illustrations as trotting and galloping like mammals. The upright posture and stiff trunk of these beasts make it probable that they could have a mammallike trot. But dinosaurs have not lost their lumbar ribs, as mammals have done in association with evolving a respiratory diaphragm (Chapter 19), and so would have had limited ability for dorsoventral flexion of the spine. This makes it unlikely that dinosaurs would have had a mammallike gallop, which had its origins in the gait of a small bounding form. An alternative fast dinosaurian gait might have been an elephantlike speeded-up walk or amble.

Finally, the most specialized mode of amniote locomotion might be powered flight. Many different types of tetrapods can glide, including not only mammals like flying squirrels and flying possums, but also frogs, lizards, and even a snake! But powered (flapping) flight appears to have evolved only three times among amniotes: in birds (see Chapter 17), in bats among mammals, and in pterosaurs among extinct archosaurian reptiles (see Chapter 13). Quite apart from the fact that the phylogenetic relationships of vertebrates tells us beyond a doubt that flight had arisen independently in these three groups, the wing structure of each clearly demonstrates that each case was an independent modification of the basic plan of the tetrapod forelimb (see Chapter 1).

■ Energy Acquisition and Support of Metabolism

Vertebrates are among the most intensive consumers of energy on Earth. The energy vertebrates use is gleaned from the environment as food that must be processed to release energy and nutrients. This processing is the primary function of the digestive system.

Figure 3–12   Phylogenetic view of tetrapod terrestrial stance and locomotion. (a) Primitive tetrapod condition, retained today in salamanders: movement mainly via axial movements of the body, limbs act more as holdfasts, moved in diagonal pairs (basic walk-trot gait). (b) Derived jumping form of locomotion in a modern amphibian, the frog. (c) Primitive amniote condition: limbs used more for propulsion, with development of the walk gait (limbs moved one at a time independently). (d) Diapsid amniote condition with hindlimbs longer than forelimbs, tendency for bipedal running. (e) Derived limbless condition with anguilliform (eellike) locomotion. Evolved convergently several times among primitive tetrapods (e.g., several types of lepospondyls), amphibians (caecilians and limb-reduced salamanders), and squamates (snakes, amphisbaenids, and limb-reduced or limbless lizards). (f) Primitive archosaur condition, with upright posture and tendency to bipedalism. (g) Secondary return to sprawling posture and quadrupedalism in crocodiles. (h) Obligate bipedality in early dinosaurs and (i) birds. (j) Return to quadrupedality several times within dinosaurs. (k) Primitive mammalian condition: upright posture and the use of the bound as a fast gait with dorsoventral flexion of the vertebral column (all mammals use the walk as a slow gait). (l) Condition in larger mammals where the bound is turned into the gallop, where the period of suspension (off the ground) is in the bunched up phase rather than in the stretched out phase. (m) The true trot, also seen in larger mammals, where the use of diagonal pairs of legs involves a jump from one pair to the other, with an intervening period of suspension. (n) The ricochet, a derived hopping gait of kangaroos and some rodents. (o) The amble, a speeded up walk gait seen as the fast gait of elephants, who are too big to trot or gallop. (p) The human condition of upright bipedality, unique among vertebrates.

After food has been digested and assimilated into the body, it must be transported to the tissues where the energy it contains is released and where some of its chemical constituents may be incorporated into the body tissues of the animal. Oxygen is required for the process of energy release, and the functions of gas exchange surfaces and the circulatory system are closely intertwined with those of the digestive system.

Feeding and Digestion

The trophic process of vertebrates is divisible into feeding and digestion. Feeding includes getting food into the oral chamber, some oral or pharyngeal processing (i.e., chewing in the broad sense, although today only mammals truly chew their food; see Crompton 1995), and swallowing. Digestion includes the breakdown of complex compounds into small molecules that are absorbed

across the wall of the gut. Both feeding and digestion are two-part processes; each has a physical component and a chemical component, although the physical components dominate in vertebrate feeding, and the chemical ones dominate in digestion. A description follows of the derived mode of digestion in humans, presented here as an example because it is the one most familiar to most people (see also Figure 3–13).

First, we take in large particles of food (a general gnathostome trait), and reduce the particle size of the food in our mouth by mastication using our teeth, tongue, and cheeks (both mammalian traits), while our salivary glands start the process of carbohydrate digestion by releasing amylase enzymes. Swallowing, and the movement of food through the gut in general, occurs by the peristaltic action of smooth muscles lining the esophagus and intestine.

Food passes down the esophagus to the stomach, which is lined with glandular epithelium and acts

Figure 3–13 Basic plan of the mammalian digestive system.

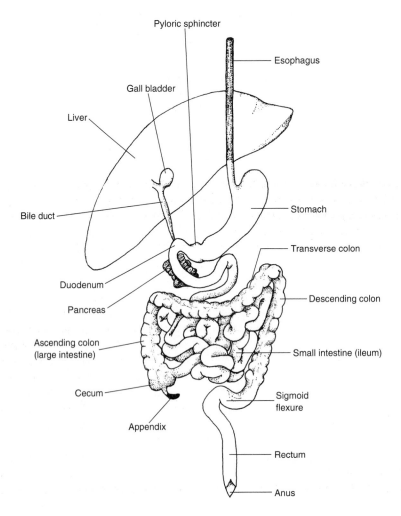

as a containment area. The glands in the stomach lining secrete hydrochloric acid (an acid stomach is a derived character of vertebrates) and the proteolytic enzyme pepsin, which acts only in an acid medium. The acid may also be important for killing accidentally ingested organisms. The muscles of the stomach wall churn and mix the food, forming a particle-laden solution known as chyme. There is little absorption of breakdown products in the stomach, but some fluids and salts are taken up there. Chyme passes to the small intestine through the pyloric sphincter (a valve) for further digestion and absorption. In the upper portion of the small intestine, the duodenum, enzymes that digest carbohydrates are released from the pancreas, and bile is released from the liver to emulsify fats. In the rest of the small intestine (jejunum and ileum) digestive enzymes for all food types are added, and the food breakdown products (amino acids, volatile fatty acids, and carbohydrates) are absorbed. Microvilli (projections from the surfaces of cells lining the intestine) increase the surface area for absorption.

The liver and the pancreas are extremely important digestive glands. The liver is the largest gland in the body of any vertebrate. It produces digestive secretions, processes absorbed nutrients and metabolites, and detoxifies harmful substances. These functions are facilitated by the position of the liver in the circulatory system. It receives blood coming from intestinal walls carrying the molecules absorbed from the digestate. The secretory function of the liver is twofold: It produces endocrine secretions for release into the blood and exocrine secretions (defined as those carried to the outside of the body—in this case to the lumen of the gut). The exocrine secretions are combined in the bile, which is part waste (neutralized toxins) and part digestive juice. The digestive components are not enzymatic, but rather fat-emulsifying organic molecules that act like detergents on entering the gut. They form submicroscopic droplets of fats a few molecules in size, allowing fats to be absorbed by the intestinal epithelium. Without these bile secretions, fats and oils in foods cannot be absorbed and would simply pass through the tract. Bile enters the intestine via the bile duct just posterior to the pyloric valve. A gallbladder may or may not occur as a blind storage sac along the bile duct. The distribution of the gallbladder among vertebrates, its size, and the overall rate of bile secretion correlate positively with the amount of fat consumed in a species' natural diet.

Although the pancreas is not involved in as many complex biochemical processes as the liver, it also has both endocrine and exocrine functions segregated quite sharply by cell type. Pancreatic enzyme secretions are essential for the final breakdown of carbohydrates to simple sugars and fats to glycerol and fatty acids. Most important are as many as five potent pancreatic protease and nuclease enzymes that complete the digestion begun in the stomach. These enzymes would, of course, digest the pancreas if they were not secreted as inactive precursor molecules that are activated on mixing with the lumenal contents. The bile and pancreatic juice are also rich in bicarbonate that neutralizes the stomach acid; thus, digestion in the gut (in contrast to that in the stomach) occurs at neutral pH. A final suite of digestive enzymes is incorporated in the membranes of the microvilli of the intestinal epithelial cells. Digestion occurs on the surfaces of these microvilli, which also possess the carrier molecules necessary for active transport of glucose and amino acids into the cells and eventually to the circulatory system of the gut. The products of fat digestion are biochemically reconfigured and shunted to the lacteals, specialized branches of the lymphatic system of the gut wall. From there fats are introduced to the general circulation, bypassing the liver.

The large intestine, or colon, serves mainly as an area for water absorption, although some mucus secretion also occurs there. Feces are stored in the rectum, that generally has an involuntary sphincter formed by smooth muscle and a voluntary sphincter formed by striated muscle, and then passed out through the anus (which, in humans, as in most placental mammals, is separate from the duct for the passage of urine). Feces are the result of removal of water, ions, and many of the digested organic molecules from the chyme. The remaining undigested food residue, bile secretions, microorganisms, and actively secreted wastes such as heavy metals are passed to the outside of the body by the action of the muscles of the rectum.

The process of digestion in humans represents a very derived condition in comparison with the primitive vertebrates. Amphioxus serves as an example of the probable prevertebrate chordate condition. This animal is a filter feeder, using ciliary action to pass water over the pharyngeal gill slits and entrapping small particles of suspended food. There is no true stomach, and no separate distinct liver or pancreas, just a digestive gland termed the cecum (not homologous with the mammalian gut structure of the same name). No gut muscles are present: Food passage down the intestine is by ciliary action rather than by peristalsis. Digestion is intracellular: Particles of food are taken into the gut cells themselves, and digested within the cell.

Vertebrates are particulate feeders rather than filter feeders (Mallatt 1996, but note that the lamprey larva still uses the gill slits for filter feeding). The visceral mass of vertebrates is proportionately greater than in amphioxus, and digestion is extracellular. All vertebrates have a true liver with a gallbladder and a bile duct, but there is no separate pancreas in living jawless vertebrates (although diffuse pancreatic tissue is found in the duodenal region). Pancreatic tissue in all vertebrates is separated into exocrine (secreting the gut enzymes into the gut) and endocrine (secreting the hormone insulin into the blood) portions. There is no true stomach in living jawless vertebrates, but this may be a secondary condition associated with their diet of blood, body fluids, and decaying tissues; a stomach has been identified in fossils of some jawless vertebrates, the thelodonts (see Chapter 6). Gut muscles move the food via peristaltic action. The ciliary mode of food transport in amphioxus would be ineffective for the transport of large particles; extracellular digestion and muscularization of the gut are significant vertebrate advances. Vertebrate branchiomeric muscles, used primarily for respiration, could also aid in particulate feeding. They could be used to push the mouth over the prey, then by contraction they could push food from the pharynx into the gut. The intestine (no distinct large intestine or rectum is present in primitive vertebrates) opens to the **cloaca**, a common opening in most vertebrates for the urinary, reproductive, and alimentary systems.

The prevertebrate mode of feeding was probably the filtering of very small particles, as in amphioxus. Although many living bony fishes feed on small planktonic organisms, vertebrates in general appear to be primarily designed to take in larger food particles than their filter-feeding relatives. In aquatic environments suction feeders take advantage of the dense and viscous properties of water by creating a flow of water that carries food into the mouth. No similar mechanism can exist among terrestrial vertebrates, as air is much less dense than the food particles. You can envisage this for yourself by thinking about particles suspended in soup. You can imbibe particles like noodles in soup by putting your mouth to the edge of the bowl and sucking with pursed lips, but no amount of sucking would create a movement of the same noodles if taken out of the soup and simply placed on the side of the plate. Terrestrial vertebrates must devise other mechanisms for helping to draw the food into the mouth. The **muscular tongue** of tetrapods is probably a key innovation for feeding on land, both in terms of food capture and in terms of food transport through the mouth to the gullet. The tetrapod tongue is operated in concert with the hyoid apparatus, the lower part of the hyoid arch, that was integrated with the gill arches in fishes (Bramble and Wake 1985). Some tetrapods, such as frogs, salamanders, and chameleon lizards, have evolved a projectile tongue to capture food (see Chapter 11).

The anterior teeth or the beaks of most vertebrates are used to capture prey and to sever pieces of food. In mammals a battery of specialized posterior teeth acts in concert with jaws, cheeks, and tongue to chew food (**mastication**, see Chapter 21). Certain herbivorous dinosaurs may have had a similar type of oral food preparation. Most non-mammalian vertebrates do little or no mechanical processing of food in the mouth before swallowing. Only mammals have a distinct swallowing reflex processing a discrete small bolus of food; other vertebrates ingest large food items by a process of pharyngeal emptying rather than discrete swallowing (Smith 1992, Crompton 1995).

Salivary glands are known only in terrestrial vertebrates, probably because some lubrication is required to swallow food on land. Some oral chemical processing may take place via the products of salivary glands, especially in mammals. Insectivorous mammals, certain lizards, and several lineages of snakes have elaborated these secretions into venoms that kill prey. A variety of venoms are known in fishes from many evolutionary lineages, but they all appear to be used defensively. None is known to be used in subduing potential prey, and venoms are rarely associated with the teeth of fishes, perhaps because fishes do not have salivary glands.

The stomach of most vertebrates is capable of considerable distention. This is carried to an extreme in some deep-sea fishes. The swallowers (Elopomorpha) have a pharynx, esophagus, and stomach of such distensibility that they can swallow fishes twice their own length (Chapter 8). The size and structure of the stomach is related to dietary habits. Vertebrates that feed on fluids have reduced or nonexistent stomachs; these include blood-sucking jawless fishes such as lampreys and nectar-feeding birds and mammals. Herbivores, which feed primarily on the digestion-resistant leaves and stems of plants, often have greatly enlarged and frequently multichambered stomachs (see Chapter 21). As a rule, herbivores also have elongate intestines that accommodate the slow release of nutrients from plant digestion. The liver of sharks is extremely large, reaching a maximum of 25 percent of the body mass in some species. In these fishes it is a storage reservoir for oils in addition to its normal functions; these light oils, with a specific density lower than water, may help to make sharks more buoyant in the water (Chapter 7).

The intestine is straight only in jawless fishes. The intestines of most vertebrates are many times longer than the body and are coiled or folded. Herbivores have especially long intestines. Sharks, skates, primitive bony fishes (including lungfishes), and at least one fossil jawed fish (a placoderm) illustrate an alternative method of increasing the area of intestinal surface in contact with the chyme—the **spiral valvular intestine**. This distinctive structure is apparently a primitive gnathostome feature. The spiral valve consists of a broad sheet of the secretory and absorptive lining of the intestine that protrudes into the lumen (cavity) of the gut; the base of the fold extends from near the pylorus to near the end of the gut in a tight spiral path along the wall of the intestine. Both long intestines and spiral valves increase the surface area of the intestine, augmenting its function of absorption. Additional specializations, especially well developed in mammals, further increase the surface area of the intestine by large- and small-scale foldings of the lining. In birds and mammals finger- or leaflike projections composed of epithelial cells around a core of mesoderm form **villi**. The gut epithelial cells themselves have closely packed **microvilli** on the lumenal surface of each cell. These structures increase the surface area of the intestine greatly: The total surface area of the human intestine is about 300 square meters, about the size of a regulation basketball court.

In most mammals a sac, the **cecum** (plural ceca) which leads to the blind-ending **appendix** is found at the junction of the large and small intestine. Birds have a pair of ceca in this position. Some bony fishes have similar ceca in the region of the pyloric valve. Ceca appear to be fermentation chambers for gut microorganisms that digest cellulose, and thus are larger in herbivorous species (see Chapter 21). These symbiotic microorganisms break down plant cell components, especially carbohydrates, which may then be available for absorption. A large intestine, distinct from the small intestine, is found only in tetrapods (aquatic vertebrates would have less need of resorbing water from their food). Anal glands in mammals frequently add lubricants as well as pheromones to the numerous volatile substances already present in the feces. Thus, feces can be used in communication, especially to mark territorial boundaries.

Respiration and Ventilation

We are used to thinking of respiration as meaning breathing oxygen in and carbon dioxide out via our lungs. Technically, the term respiration should be reserved for the cellular process of respiration, using oxygen to break down carbohydrates via the Krebs cycle to produce adenosine 5'-triphosphate (ATP), with carbon dioxide as the waste product. Getting air in and out of the lungs (or pumping water over the gills) is *ventilation*.

Ancestral chordates probably relied on cutaneous respiration—oxygen absorption and carbon dioxide loss by diffusion directly into the blood and body tissues across a thin skin. This is the mode of respiration of amphioxus, an animal that is still small and sluggish enough that it does not require specialized respiratory organs; while it has gill slits, these are employed in filter feeding rather than in respiration (as is also true for lamprey larvae). Cutaneous respiration is still an important component of respiration in many vertebrates, especially the loss of carbon dioxide in an aquatic environment. Don't forget that, ultimately, all vertebrates acquire oxygen by diffusion. Diffusion is the universal mechanism whereby oxygen moves from the medium in which it is being carried (water or air) into the blood system and by which carbon dioxide moves in the opposite direction. Thus the epithelium of the respiratory tissue (e.g., in the lung alveoli in mammals) and the lining of the blood capillaries in the gills or the lung must be thin, to minimize the diffusion distance and hence speed up the rate of diffusion.

Vertebrates are characterized by the acquisition of gills on the pharyngeal arches, with a complex highly folded surface, comprising the gill lamellae, richly invested with blood vessels, and by the acquisition of red blood cells containing the respiratory pigment hemoglobin that aids in the transport of the respiratory gases. The structure and function of fish gills is described in Chapter 8. The gill bars of vertebrates are made of cartilage tissue, which is less stiff than the collagen that forms the gill bars in amphioxus. Cartilaginous gills bars are better able to stretch and recoil, aiding in propelling water over gill slits. Active inspiratory suction ventilation is a derived character of gnathostomes (Mallatt 1996; see Chapter 6). The unique design of the dermatocranium of bony fishes includes the bony **operculum**, which takes over much of the action of pumping water over the gills. Bony fishes are in general more efficient at extracting oxygen from the water than are cartilaginous ones, and because of the presence of the operculum have been able to reduce much of the skeletal and musculature components of the gills themselves.

In addition to functional gills, many bony fishes have accessory respiratory organs that are derived from the gut. The most common and phylogenetically oldest of these structures appears to be a form of lungs—blind-ended, thin-walled vascular sacs arising from outpocketings of the gut just posterior to the pharyngeal pouches. Paired lungs of this nature, with a ventral glottis (combined opening to the two lungs), are seen in primitive living ray-finned fishes (polypterids), in lungfishes among lobe-finned fishes, and in tetrapods. A single, dorsal lung is seen in primitive neopterygian ray-finned fishes, such as garpike and bowfins. Conversion of the primitive lung into a nonrespiratory swimbladder, now used as a buoyancy device, has occurred at least three times in the bony fishes: in the chondrosteans (sturgeon and paddlefish) and the teleosts among the ray-fins, and in the coelacanth (where it is fat filled and has ossified walls) among the lobefins. The teleost swimbladder is described in more detail in Chapter 8.

It is important to note that the lung is a primitive feature of bony fishes. Thus although lungs are obviously of critical importance to tetrapods, they were not evolved for the express purpose of breathing on land. For many years it was assumed lungs evolved in fishes in order to breathe air in stagnant, oxygen-depleted water where gulping oxygen-rich air would help in supplying the body tissues. However, although some lungfishes are found in stagnant, anoxic environments, other air-breathing fishes (e.g., the bowfin) are active animals found in oxygen-rich habitats. Recent work by Colleen Farmer (Farmer 1997) provided an alternative explanation for the evolution of lungs. She suggested that air breathing could have evolved in well-aerated waters, in active fishes where the additional oxygen is needed primarily to supply the heart muscle itself, rather than the body tissues.

One consequence of the anatomy of the circulatory system of fishes is that the heart receives and pumps only deoxygenated (venous) blood. Blood is oxygenated in the gills, after it leaves the heart. Most fishes lack coronary arteries to bring oxygenated blood to the heart. Coronary vessels appear to have been evolved convergently in mammals and archosaurs, and also in sharks, but the heart of most ray-finned fishes must extract the oxygen it needs from blood that has already been depleted of oxygen as it traveled through the body.

Farmer suggested that the lung may have evolved as a way to provide oxygenated blood directly to the heart to meet the metabolic needs of activity. The bowfin, a primitive ray-finned fish, does not use its lungs to get additional oxygen in stagnant water, but *does* become distressed if it is prevented from gulping air from the surface when it is active, even when the water is well aerated. Teleosts (derived ray-finned fishes) have all converted their lungs to swimbladders, perhaps because the buoyancy provided by this device was more important for this group than a respiratory lung. However, certain active teleosts, such as tuna, have also evolved a coronary circulatory system (Farmer 1997). These facts are consistent with the hypothesis that lungs evolved initially to provide oxygen to the heart muscle itself. We will see later, when discussing vertebrate hearts, that oxygenated blood returning from the lungs may still be important for supplying the heart muscle directly in many tetrapods.

Fishes and amphibians use the hyoid apparatus to ventilate the lungs. The oral cavity is expanded, sucking air into the mouth, and then the floor of the mouth is raised, squeezing the air into the lungs. This method of lung ventilation is called a pulse pump or positive pressure mechanism, also known as **buccal pumping**. A new feature in tetrapods is the transversus abdominus layer of the hypaxial muscles that forces air out of the lungs. Amniotes use an aspiration pump or negative pressure mechanism of lung ventilation via the ribs (**costal aspiration**). Expansion of the ribcage by the intercostal hypaxial muscles creates a negative pressure (that is, below atmospheric pressure) in the pleuroperitoneal (abdominal) cavity and sucks air into the lungs. Air is expelled (exhaled) by compressing the abdominal cavity, primarily through an elastic return of the rib cage to a resting position of smaller volume and a contraction of the elastic lungs, as well as by contraction of the transversus abdominus. Simple movement of the ribs alone is probably the primitive amniote condition, as seen in lizards and snakes. Mammals have restricted the ribs to the anterior (thoracic) trunk vertebrae, and have a muscular sheet, the diaphragm, which aids the ribs in inspiration, and divides the original pleuroperitoneal cavity into a **peritoneal cavity**, surrounding the viscera, and paired **pleural cavities**, surrounding the lungs. In crocodiles a piston-like motion of the liver acts in a fashion analogous to the mammalian diaphragm to aid the ribs. Turtles cannot use their ribs at all as they have fused them with their shell; they use movements of the forelimbs to ventilate the lungs (see Chapter 12). Birds have perhaps the most derived amniote condition. They have a one-way perfusion of the lungs via a series of air sacs, powered by movements of the ribs and the sternum (see Chapter 17).

The lungs of many modern amphibians are simple sacs with few internal divisions. This morphology must represent the primitive tetrapod condition, because the lungs of mammals are partitioned in a fashion different from those of other amniotes, suggesting the existence of a common amniote ancestor without internally complicated lungs. In addition, modern amphibians have only a simple short orobranchial chamber leading directly into the lungs, with little or minimal development of a distinct trachea. In contrast, amniotes have a long **trachea** (windpipe), strengthened by cartilage rings, branching into a series of bronchi in each lung. The short neck of fossil nonamniote tetrapods suggests that a long trachea was also an amniote invention. Amniotes also possess a **larynx** (derived from pharyngeal arch elements) at the junction of the pharynx and the trachea, used for sound production. Mammals have a finely branching system of bronchioles in each lung, terminating in tiny thin-walled blind-ending chambers (the sites of gas exchange) called **alveoli**. In contrast reptiles and birds have subdivided their lungs by a series of internal septa, in which further subdivisions (faveoli) provide the area for gas exchange.

John Ruben (Ruben et al. 1997) suggested that these differences in lung design may have profound consequences for amniote evolution. For ectothermic amniotes either lung design would work equally well, but the consequences would be different in an endothermic animal requiring a greater amount of gas exchange in the lung. In the mammalian type of alveolar lung, the alveoli themselves actively participate in the ventilation process. They expand passively during inhalation and facilitate exhalation via elastic rebound, and their extremely thin walls aid in the rapid diffusion of gases to and from the blood. But in the reptile/bird-type of septate lung, the faveoli are not only less well vascularized than alveoli, but also are not active participants in the movement of air. Large amounts of the lung volume represent non-vascularized portions that assist in air ventilation within the lung. Increase in lung volume in reptiles, in contrast to the situation in mammals, may not greatly increase the amount of vascularized tissue available for gas exchange. Ruben suggests that the only way in which a septate lung could accommodate the demands of an endotherm would be to have the complex efficient flow-through mechanism of a bird.

Cardiovascular System

The cardiovascular system of vertebrates transports oxygen and nutrients to the living cells of the body, removes carbon dioxide and other metabolic waste products from the cells, and participates in maintaining the internal environment. In addition, it carries hormones from their sites of release to their target tissues and is a second line of defense against pathogens and other foreign substances.

In amphioxus, where oxygen and carbon dioxide exchange take place primarily by diffusion across the body surface, the blood carries only substances that do not need to be transported at a high rate, such as food and hormones. While amphioxus possesses the basic vertebrate circulatory pattern (see later), vertebrate innovations include red blood cells, hemoglobin as a respiratory pigment, a true heart with higher blood pressure to effect a rapid rate of transport, and a closed circulatory systems with capillary beds.

Blood   Blood is a fluid tissue composed of liquid plasma and cellular constituents known as red blood cells (**erythrocytes**) and white blood cells (**leucocytes**). **Plasma** is the water-based fluid that remains when all cellular components are removed from the blood. Blood plasma contributes to other important fluids. The **interstitial fluid** is essentially blood plasma minus the large proteins, which do not pass through the capillary endothelium. **Lymph** is derived from interstitial fluid and is augmented by the addition of some of the larger proteins characteristic of circulating plasma and by certain white blood cells from the lymph nodes (lymphocytes).

From 20 percent to nearly half of the volume of the blood (depending on the species) is made up of erythrocytes. These red blood cells owe their red color to high concentrations of **hemoglobin**, the iron-containing globin protein that acts as a carrier for oxygen. The structure of erythrocytes varies among vertebrates. Mammals have eliminated the nucleus and many other cell organelles from mature erythrocytes, so that technically they are not living cells and are incapable of replication or self-repair. Some fishes (e.g., the Antarctic crocodile ice fishes, Chaenichthyidae) have eliminated erythrocytes altogether, transporting oxygen exclusively in plasma. The sites of erythrocyte formation differ interspecifically and also change during the ontogeny of an individual. Adult sites of **hematopoiesis** (blood-cell formation) include the blood vessels of fishes, the gut wall, kidneys, and liver of most vertebrates, and a few specialized organs especially characteristic of tetrapods: the **spleen**, the **thymus**, the **lymph nodes**, and the **red bone marrow**. In adult mammals erythrocytes are produced almost exclusively in the red bone marrow.

Cells specialized to promote clotting of blood (**thrombocytes**) are present in all vertebrates except mammals, where they are replaced by noncellular **platelets**. These blood elements react to surfaces they do not normally encounter by adhering to the unfamiliar surface and to one another. Specific blood proteins react to damaged tissues as well, polymerizing as a network of fibers that enmesh cellular components of blood to form a wound-plugging clot.

White blood cells (**leucocytes**) are less abundant than erythrocytes. There are at least five types of white blood cells in humans. Leucocytes form the first line of defense against invasion by pathogenic bacteria and other foreign particles, they are involved in inflammation responses, and they support antigen–antibody activities of the immune system. Unlike erythrocytes, which normally remain entirely within the vascular channels, leucocytes squeeze between the endothelial cells of capillaries and venules and spend most of their lives moving freely through the loose connective tissues.

Blood Vessels   The blood of vertebrates is contained within specialized vessels and organs in a **closed circulatory system** (Figure 3–14). Arteries carry blood away from the heart in a ramifying series of vessels of progressively decreasing diameter, and blood returns to the heart in veins. Arteries have thicker walls than veins, with a layer of smooth muscle and an outer layer of fibrous connective tissue. Blood pressure drops as the blood continues around the body, and thus the blood pressure in the veins is less than in the arteries, and the blood moves more slowly (blood spurts out if you cut an artery, but merely seeps if you cut a vein). There are more veins in the body than arteries, and more of the total blood volume is in the veins than in the arteries at any one time. In tetrapods, which are subjected to the effects of gravity on land, the veins returning the blood from the limbs contain valves to prevent back flow.

Interposed between the smallest arteries (arterioles) and the smallest veins (venules) are the **capillaries**, which are the sites of exchange between the blood and tissues. Capillaries pass close to every living cell and provide an enormous surface area for the exchange of gases, nutrients, and waste products. Capillaries are very thin walled, made up of only one layer of the **endothelial** cells that line the interior of the circulatory system. The surface area of the capillaries of a human is about 700 square meters, or nearly the area enclosed by the bases of a regulation baseball diamond. Capillaries form dense beds in metabolically active tissues and are sparsely distributed in tissues with low metabolic activity. Blood flow through a capillary bed is regulated by the opening and closing of precapillary sphincter muscles. Normally at any given time, only a fraction of the capillaries in a tissue have blood flowing in them; the rest are stagnant or empty. **Arteriovenous anastomoses** connect some arterioles directly to venules, allowing blood to bypass a capillary bed. When the metabolic activity of a tissue increases—when a muscle becomes active, for example—waste products of metabolism stimulate precapillary sphincters to dilate, increasing blood flow to that tissue.

The *rete mirabile* (marvelous net, plural *retia mirabilia*) is a widely occurring vascular structure in vertebrates. In a rete mirabile the afferent vessel (an artery carrying blood from the heart to an organ or to a structure such as a limb) breaks down into a network of small, parallel vessels. The corresponding efferent vessel (a vein carrying blood from the organ back toward the heart) forms a similar series of small vessels. These vessels have thin walls and lie side by side, facilitating the transfer of heat or dissolved substances between them. Because the blood flows in opposite directions in the afferent

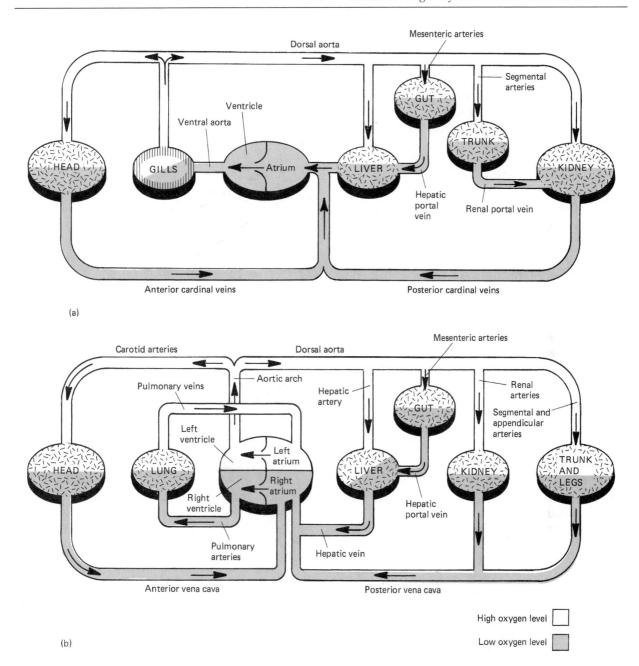

Figure 3–14   Basic plans of vertebrate cardiovascular circuits. (a) Single-circuit fishlike pattern. (b) Double-circuit tetrapodlike pattern exemplified by that of a bird or mammal. Dark shading: venous blood.

and efferent vessels, a rete is a countercurrent exchange system. Retia are commonly found in the limbs of tetrapods, where they help to conserve heat. They are also used to retain metabolic heat in the swimming muscles, sense organs, and/or parts of the brain of warm-bodied fishes such as tunas and some sharks, and to retain high concentrations of substances in restricted parts of the body, such as high concentrations of oxygen in the swim bladders of bony fishes (see Chapter 8), and the high concentrations of sodium and chloride in mammalian kidneys (see Chapter 4).

Some vessels, known as **portal vessels**, are interposed between two capillary beds. Portal vessels promote sequential processing of blood. The **hepatic portal vein**, seen in all vertebrates, is interposed between the capillary bed of the gut and the sinusoids of the liver (see Figure 3–14). Substances absorbed from the gut are transported directly to the liver where toxins are rendered harmless and some nutrients are further processed or removed for storage. Most portal systems are venous, but an hypophyseal portal artery system exists between the brain and the pituitary (see Figure 3–24).

Gnathostomes show a number of features of the circulation that indicate a more derived condition, correlated with a higher blood pressure, than the more primitive vertebrate one. For a start, they have an additional heart chamber in front of the ventricle, the conus arteriosus, which dampens the pulsatile nature of the blood flow (see later section on hearts). Their arteries also contain the protein **elastin** in their walls (Sage and Gray 1979). As its name suggests, elastin has elastic properties, and also helps damp the pulsatile nature of the blood flow by allowing the arteries to expand during ventricular contraction (systole) and elastically recoil during ventricular refilling (diastole). Gnathostomes also have a **renal portal system** between the kidneys and the veins returning from the posterior trunk and the tail (see Figure 3–14a) that presumably helps in processing the waste metabolites returning from the axial muscles that are used in locomotion. This system is lost in mammals, and greatly reduced in birds; as previously discussed, these tetrapods no longer rely on the axial muscles for locomotion.

A final derived system of gnathostomes, best developed in tetrapods and in teleosts, is the presence of a **lymphatic system**. In the closed circulatory system of vertebrates, fluid is squeezed out into the tissues from the small capillaries forming a closed link between the arteries and veins. With the higher blood pressure seen in gnathostomes, there is then the need to develop another system to return fluid to the heart that does not find its way back into the veins. The lymphatic system is a one-way system of blind-ending veinlike vessels that parallel the trackways of the veins, and drain back the excess tissue fluid into the venous system at the base of the neck. Specialized lymph vessels (lacteals) also help in picking up large chain fatty acids from the digestive tract. Valves in the tubes prevent backflow and, in some vertebrates (e.g., teleost bony fishes) lymph hearts help pump the fluid; in tetrapods lymph is kept moving by the action of the contraction of muscles and tissues (which is why fluid tends to pool in your feet if you just stand around without moving). **Lymph nodes**, concentrations of lymphatic tissues, are found in mammals and some birds at intervals along the lymph channels. Lymphatic tissue is also involved in the immune system; white blood cells (macrophages) travel along this route, and the lymph tissue can intercept foreign or unwanted material, such as migrating cancer cells.

Basic Vascular Circuits   The basic vertebrate circulatory plan consists of midline vessels with the major arteries in a dorsal position and the veins slightly ventral to them (Figure 3–14a). The heart pumps blood anteriorly in the **ventral aorta** to the gill capillaries, where it is oxygenated. The primitive vertebrate plan appears to be six pairs of vessels, or **aortic arches**, that split off from the ventral aorta to supply the gills, presumably supplying an original system of six gill slits. This is the number seen primitively and in the embryonic development of all vertebrates, but a first aortic arch is not seen in any living adult. In gnathostomes, the original first gill slit has been lost or converted into a spiracle. In sharks the spiracular artery is probably the homologue of the original first aortic arch (see Figure 3–15a). Living jawless vertebrates have also modified the front part of their head so that the original first arch is lost; however, they also add some extra arches onto the back of the basic pattern of six. Additional arches are never seen in the embryology of gnathostomes, suggesting that the condition in hagfishes and lampreys is a derived one rather than a primitive holdover.

The blood leaving the gills (again in a series of paired vessels) collects on either side into paired **dorsal aortae** (see Figure 3–15a). From this point, two different circuits derive. Blood collected from the more anterior gill arches flows forward to the head, in what now becomes the paired **carotid arteries**. The blood from the head returns to the heart via the paired **anterior cardinal veins** (= **jugular veins**). Blood collected from the more posterior gill slits flows tailward, and the paired dorsal aortae above the gill region unite to form the single dorsal aorta seen in the trunk. Blood returns from the body to the heart via the paired **posterior cardinal veins**. The anterior and posterior cardinal veins unite in a common cardinal vein to enter the heart.

This primitive vertebrate condition of a **single circulation** is an inherently low-pressure system because of the drop in blood pressure across the resistance provided by the gill capillaries. With the

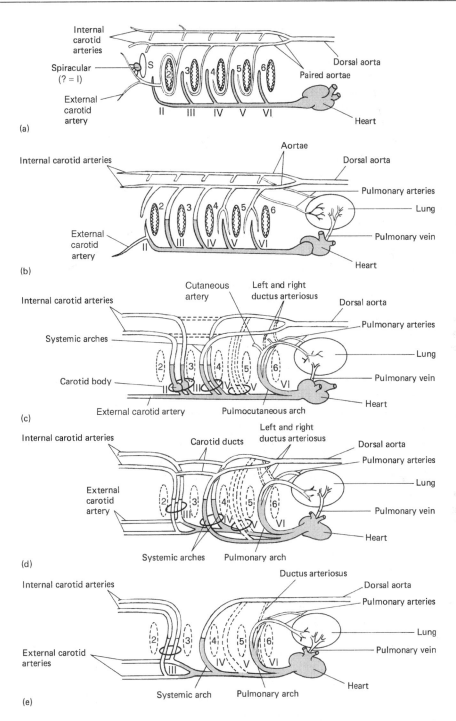

Figure 3–15   Evolution of the aortic arches. (a) Generalized scheme for a gill-breathing primitive gnathostome, retained by most chondrichthyans. Actinopterygians have numerous independently derived specializations that do not depart drastically from this basic plan. (b) The lungfish and (c) the adult frog demonstrate variations on the double circulation and dual respiratory adaptations of these vertebrates. (d) Primitive amniote condition as found in a lizard. (e) Derived amniote condition as found in a mammal. The ductus arteriosus is the remains of the dorsal part of the pulmonary arch, and is present and functional in the amniote fetus where it is used as a bypass shunt for the lungs. Arabic numbers: gill slits/visceral pouches (S = the spiracle, the presumptive original first gill slit); Roman numerals: aortic arches. Numberings represent presumptive primitive condition for vertebrates. (See R. Lawson in M. H. Wake, 1979, *Hyman's Comparative Vertebrate Anatomy*, University of Chicago Press, Chicago, IL.)

advent of lungs vertebrates evolved a **double circulation** in which the **pulmonary** circuit supplies the lungs with deoxygenated blood and the **systemic** circuit supplies oxygenated blood to the body. The single heart is the pump for both circuits, and is divided into right (pulmonary) and left (systemic) halves. The division of the heart into right and left sides is an actual morphological separation in archosaurs (crocodilians and birds) and mammals. In lungfishes, amphibians, and reptiles other than crocodiles there is no permanent morphological separation, but complex interactions between heart morphology and flow patterns maintain the separation of oxygenated and deoxygenated blood (see Chapter 11). The double circulation of tetrapods can be pictured as a figure eight with the heart at the intersection of the loops (see Figure 3–14b). One loop is the pulmonary circuit, and the other is the systemic circuit. The completely divided heart of birds and mammals permits the blood pressure to be low in the pulmonary circuit (where the blood flows through delicate capillaries during gas exchange) and high in the systemic circuit (where blood must be pumped long distances and through muscles that are contracting and squeezing the blood vessels). A completely divided double circuit of this type would be important for an endotherm, where the blood pressure needs to be considerably higher than for an ectotherm (see Chapter 4).

The Heart   The heart of fishes is a muscular tube folded on itself and constricted into four sequential chambers: the sinus venosus, the atrium, the ventricle, and the conus arteriosus (this latter chamber being seen in gnathostomes only). Blood enters the tubular fish heart via the common cardinal veins, and also by a hepatic vein from the liver (see Figure 3–14a). The **sinus venosus** is a thin-walled sac with few cardiac muscle fibers. It is filled by pressure in the veins and pulsatile drops in pressure in the pericardial cavity as the heart beats. Suction produced by muscular contraction draws blood anteriorly into the **atrium**, which has valves at each end that prevent backflow. It thus acts as a one-way pre-pump that fills the main pump, the **ventricle**. The ventricle is thick walled, and the muscular walls have an intrinsic pulsatile rhythm, which can be speeded up or slowed down by the autonomic nervous system. Contraction of the ventricle forces the blood into the **conus arteriosus**. Teleosts lack a conus arteriosus formed by cardiac muscle, but have an elastic bulbus cordis that is formed by smooth muscle. Either

the conus or the bulbus serves as an elastic reservoir that dampens the pulses of blood pressure that are produced by contractions of the ventricle, and they have a valvular construction that prevents blood from flowing back into the ventricle.

The sinus venosus and conus arteriosus are reduced or absent in the hearts of tetrapods. Lungfish and tetrapods have a heart that is at least partially divided. The right side of the heart receives blood from the systemic veins, returning from the body (usually deoxygenated) and the left side of the heart receives blood from the pulmonary veins, returning from the lungs (oxygenated) (see Figure 3–14b). The atrium is always completely subdivided in lungfish and tetrapods, and the ventricle is at least partially subdivided in lungfish and amniotes. The lack of any ventricular division in living amphibians may be a secondary feature related to their possession of a pulmocutaneous artery and vein, returning oxygenated blood from the skin via the systemic circuit (see later discussion). The functioning of the tetrapod heart is discussed in more detail in Chapters 11 and 12.

Evolution of Vertebrate Cardiovascular Systems   In more derived vertebrates the circulatory system is modified in a variety of ways. An obvious important addition to the original system (as shown in Figure 3–16b), with the addition of paired limbs, is of a **subclavian** artery and vein to supply the front limb (pectoral fin) and an **iliac** artery and vein to supply the hindlimb (pelvic fin). As the pectoral fin appeared earlier in vertebrate evolution than the pelvic one (see Chapter 6), the subclavian circulatory system must also predate the iliac one. The subclavian artery branches off from the anterior part of the dorsal aorta (where it is still paired), and the subclavian vein feeds back into the paired anterior cardinal veins. The iliac arteries branch off from the end of the dorsal aorta, but the venous return from the pelvic fin is rather different in cartilaginous fishes and bony fishes. In sharks, the iliac veins feed independently into paired **lateral abdominal veins** running along the lateral body wall, which then feed into the subclavian veins returning from the pectoral fin (Figure 3–16b). Teleosts lack abdominal veins, perhaps in association with the reduction of their fins. But in lungfish and tetrapods (perhaps representing the ancestral bony fish condition), the iliac veins combine to form a midline **ventral abdominal vein**, which then drains into the liver (some returning blood is also routed into the posterior cardinals) (Figure 3–16c). Adult mammals have lost all trace of the ventral abdominal vein: This vessel has now become the **umbilical vein**, feeding blood back from the placenta in the fetus.

Profound changes in the general system of venous return have also occurred in more derived vertebrates (see Figure 3–16). Unlike the system of paired anterior and posterior cardinal veins returning the blood to the heart, mammals have a single vein in each case on the right hand side of the body; the **anterior (superior) vena cava** returning blood from the head, and the **posterior (inferior) vena cava** returning blood from the body. The derivation of the single anterior vena cava is easy to understand. Mammals have two jugular veins (the homologues of the anterior cardinals), draining blood from either side of the head. In the neck the left one crosses over to join the right one, and the combined vessel is then the anterior vena cava (Figure 3–16e). Other vertebrates all retain a double system of anterior cardinal veins.

The acquisition of the posterior vena cava is a more complex story. This vessel is first apparent in lungfishes, where a single midline vessel, dipping ventrally in its return to the right side of the heart, arises from the paired posterior cardinals (Figure 3–16c). Lungfishes and salamanders possess posterior cardinals and a posterior vena cava; however in amniotes and frogs (presumably in a convergent evolutionary fashion) the posterior vena cava is the sole main vessel, and the posterior cardinals have been reduced to blind-ending **azygous veins** draining the dorsal body wall (Figure 3–16e).

The aortic arches also undergo considerable changes in the more derived vertebrates, especially with the loss of the gills in tetrapods (see Figure 3–15). Note however that the complex pattern of the aortic arches (even in adult tetrapods) with the ventral origin, the branching into two, and the dorsal final position, is reflective of their original function as gill-supplying arteries. Arch number two, retained in sharks, is lost in tetrapods and also in derived bony fishes that have lost the spiracle, such as teleosts. Arch five is also lost in the adults of all tetrapods except salamanders. The major arches to be retained are the third (the **carotid arch**, going to the head), the fourth (the **systemic arch**, going to the body), and the sixth (**pulmonary arch**, going to the lungs).

Variants on this condition exist in different tetrapods. In birds and mammals there is only a single systemic arch (although the original doubled state is apparent in development). This condition clearly arose convergently in the two groups, as it is the left arch that is retained (as the single **aorta**) in mammals, and the right arch in birds. The historical double condition of the arch can be further observed in the detailed vascular anatomy. For example, in mammals, a blind-ending portion of the right systemic arch is retained to serve as the point of origination of the right subclavian artery leading to the right arm. The loss of one side of the double arch may be related to higher blood pressure of the endothermic condition: A pressure drop could occur where the two arches separated, and then turbulence might present a problem when they reunited.

In amphibians, where the skin is of prime importance in the exchange of oxygen and carbon dioxide, the pulmonary arch is actually a **pulmo-cutaneous arch**, with a major **cutaneous artery** branching off the pulmonary artery to supply the skin (Figure 3–15c). The **cutaneous vein**, now carrying oxygenated blood, feeds back into general systemic system and hence into the right atrium. Thus oxygenated blood feeds into the amphibian ventricle from both the left atrium (supplied by the pulmonary vein), and the right atrium (see Chapter 11). This type of heart in modern amphibians, with the absence of any ventricular division, is most likely a derived condition, adapted for using the skin as well as the lungs for respiration.

In amniotes the conus region is absent in adults and the aortic arches arise directly from the heart. A small sinus venosus supplies the right atrium in the more primitive amniote condition, but has been lost entirely in birds and in therian mammals (marsupials and placentals). A ventricular septum of some sort is present in all amniotes, but the form is different in different amniote lineages (primarily vertical in position in mammals and in archosaurs, primarily horizontal in position in turtles, lizards, and snakes), which suggests independent origins of a complex septum in different amniote groups.

Several decades ago the incomplete ventricular septum of reptiles (excluding crocodiles) was interpreted as the hallmark of an inefficient design, because of the potential for mixing of the oxygenated and deoxygenated blood from the left and right atria. At that time reptiles were considered as little more than an evolutionary intermediate between amphibians and mammals in this context. If you think about it for a minute, it would be

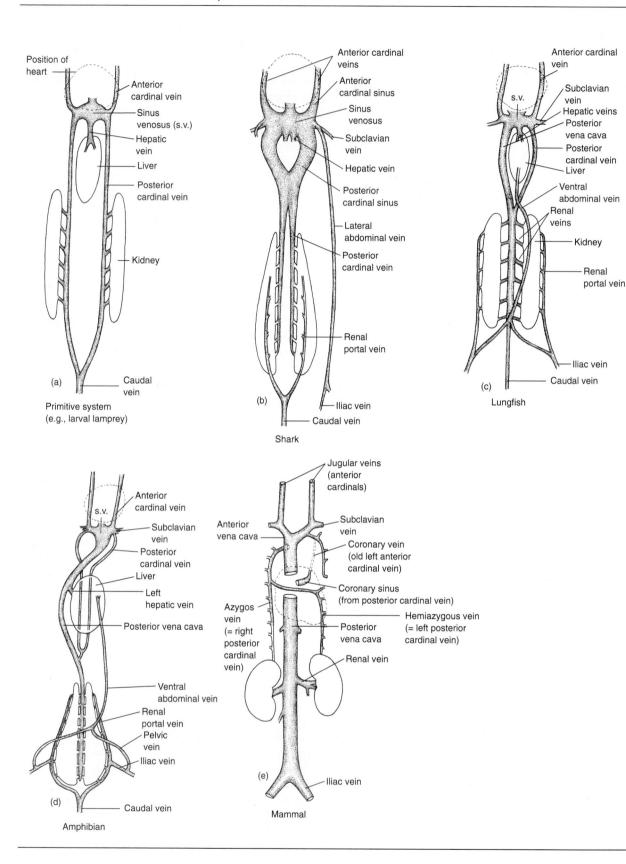

absurd to suppose that reptiles could manage to evolve features as specialized as a turtle's shell and yet be unable to devise an extra inch of so of ventricular septum. Reasoning of this nature, not entirely absent from many present-day evolutionary interpretations, falls into the trap of seeing mammalian (especially human) design as superior, within the old-fashioned idea of humans as the pinnacle of evolution. However, no animal that has survived to the present day (or even that survived for long enough to be recorded as a fossil) can possibly be considered an evolutionary failure. Nor can humans be considered as examples of evolutionary perfection. For example, our tendency to have problems with our backs and feet show that our adaptations to bipedality are far from perfect! One of the major themes of this book is to illustrate how the various vertebrates, living and fossil, are adaptively suited, albeit with compromises and shortcomings, for their life-style and surroundings.

The function of a ventricular septum is to separate the flow of oxygenated and deoxygenated blood within the heart, so that oxygenated blood is sent preferentially to the head and body, and deoxygenated blood is sent to the lungs. However, considering the phylogeny of vertebrates, an incomplete ventricular septum is clearly the primitive condition. Thus the evolutionary question that needs to be posed is not "why do reptiles have an incomplete septum?" but rather, "why do birds and mammals need to have a complete septum?" Another way of phrasing this question would be "why should an incomplete septum be retained in ectothermic amniotes?" A more recent way of interpreting the function of amniote hearts is to have an appreciation of the flexibility afforded by an incomplete ventricular septum. In birds and mammals, the heart is constrained to always send the same amount of blood to the lungs as to the body with each contraction. This situation may not be disadvantageous for a endotherm with high levels of oxygen requirement, but could prove disadvantageous for an ectotherm. Reptiles can choose (by means of activating vascular sphincters on the pulmonary arteries) to shunt most of their blood away from the lungs and out to the body in conditions where the lungs are being used less, such as when they are resting, or when they are diving, an ability that may have a number of physiological advantages (Burggren 1987). Details of the functioning of this type of reptile heart are discussed in Chapter 12.

However in endotherms, with their need for a higher blood pressure, a complete ventricular septum may be mandated: The high pressure at which blood is sent by the left ventricle to the systemic circuit might be dangerously high for the delicate capillaries lining the lungs. In mammals and birds the right ventricle is less muscular than the left, and blood pressure in the pulmonary circuit is considerably less than in the systemic one. Crocodiles have a design rather similar to that of birds, but with a few of their own specializations (see Chapter 13). It might be preferable to view the heart design of birds and mammals as an evolutionary compromise, rather than as an evolutionary pinnacle, with the need for protecting the lungs from a high systemic blood pressure meaning the sacrifice of the flexibility afforded by the incomplete ventricular septum.

A more recent addition to the adaptive story comes from the work of Colleen Farmer (Farmer 1997), which we discussed previously in connection with the reason for lung evolution in fishes. She suggested that, as in fishes, the blood returning

Figure 3–16 Basic plans of vertebrate systemic venous return circuits (hepatic portal system not shown). (a) Primitive vertebrate condition as seen in the larval lamprey. (b) Chondrichthyan pattern, as seen in the shark. Illustrates the generalized gnathostome condition of a renal portal system and blood returning from the forelimbs via the subclavian vein, plus blood from the hindlimbs returning via lateral abdominal veins. (c) Probable primitive bony fish pattern, as seen in the lungfish, with blood from the hindlimbs returning via the ventral abdominal vein. Formation of a posterior vena cava is seen in sarcopterygians and tetrapods only. (d) Primitive tetrapod pattern, as seen in the salamander, showing the reduction of the posterior cardinal veins. (e) Mammalian pattern, showing the loss of the renal portal system, the conversion of the posterior veins to azygous veins, and the conjoining of the anterior cardinal veins into an anterior vena cava. (Modified from R. Lawson in M. H. Wake, 1979, *Hyman's Comparative Vertebrate Anatomy*, University of Chicago Press, Chicago, IL.)

from the lungs in most tetrapods also has an important function to play in oxygenating the heart muscle itself. While other workers have emphasized the possibility of a right-to-left shunt within the reptile heart (directing deoxygenated blood from the right atrium away from the lungs), she emphasized the potential importance of a left-to-right shunt (sending oxygenated blood from the left atrium across to the musculature of the wall of the right ventricle). A corollary of this hypothesis is that the evolution of a complete ventricular septum would mandate an improved system of coronary blood vessels supplying the heart muscle from the outside, as is indeed the case in birds and mammals.

■ Excretory and Reproductive Systems

The excretory and reproductive systems are linked anatomically in vertebrates, as they share ducts for exit of products (metabolic wastes and gametes) to the outside world. However, they have different developmental origins: The kidneys are segmental in origin, derived from the nephrotome or intermediate mesoderm, which forms the embryonic nephric ridge; the gonads form from the genital ridge, which, although it lies adjacent to the nephric ridge, is nonsegmental in origin, derived from the outer layer of the lateral plate.

Excretory System

Excretion entails the disposal of the body's waste products, primarily nitrogenous waste from protein metabolism and carbon dioxide from cellular respiration. Excretory organs also maintain the body's internal environment (the process of homeostasis) by additionally regulating the levels of substances such as water (osmoregulation) and minerals (especially sodium, chloride, calcium, magnesium, potassium, and phosphate). In tetrapods it is the kidneys that are responsible for almost all these functions (with the exception of the excretion of carbon dioxide, carried out by the lungs or the skin). But in more primitive vertebrates the skin and the gills play important roles, and the role of the kidney is less extensive. The original role of the kidney in vertebrates may have been primarily for the regulation of divalent ions such as calcium and phosphate (see Chapter 2). Chapter 4 covers the physiology of excretion and osmoregulation in more detail.

Kidneys   The familiar compact, bean-shaped kidney of mammals represents a very derived form of kidney shape. The kidney in fishes is a long, segmental structure, running along the entire length of the dorsal body wall, as is seen in all vertebrate embryos (see Figure 3–17a). The more discrete, compact kidney seen in adult amniotes (the metanephric kidney) is homologous only to the posterior portion of this original kidney.

Amphioxus has no true kidney and no specialized kidney ducts. Instead it possesses cells associated with the pharyngeal blood vessels called **solenocytes** (= flame cells or nephridia), that work by creating a negative pressure inside the cell (by flagellum inside the cell) rather than by the vertebrate method of ultrafiltration. (Ultrafiltration is probably functionally dependent on the higher blood pressure afforded by a closed circulatory system.) The solenocytes empty individually into the false body cavity (atrium), rather than joining together into a common collecting duct, and the effluent is finally discharged to the outside via the atriopore. It was originally thought that solenocytes had no homology with the kidney of vertebrates, even though they are in a similar anatomical position in the body cavity. However, more recent work suggests that the cells themselves (podocytes) may be homologous with the cells of the kidney nephrons (Gans 1989, Ruppert 1994).

Early in vertebrate development (and possibly representing some early stage in vertebrate evolution), the kidney tubules are segmentally arranged and open through funnellike ciliated mouths to the coelom, from which they drain fluid derived from the interstitial fluid (Figure 3–17c). This fluid is conveyed along an **archinephric duct**, which connects each segment's tubule to the region of the cloaca. Here the ducts from each side open to release the urine to the exterior. Later in development the individual tubules lose their direct connection to the coelom, and derive their filtrate directly from the capillary system. In the metanephric kidney of adult amniotes the tubules become highly compacted and numerous, achieving the capacity to concentrate the urine. The mammalian kidney is further specialized in having acquired an organized structure permitting an exceptionally dynamic range of urine concentrations. In spite of these evolutionary changes, the basic unit of all adult vertebrate kidneys is essentially the same—the tubular **nephrons** (Figures 3–17c and Chapter 4).

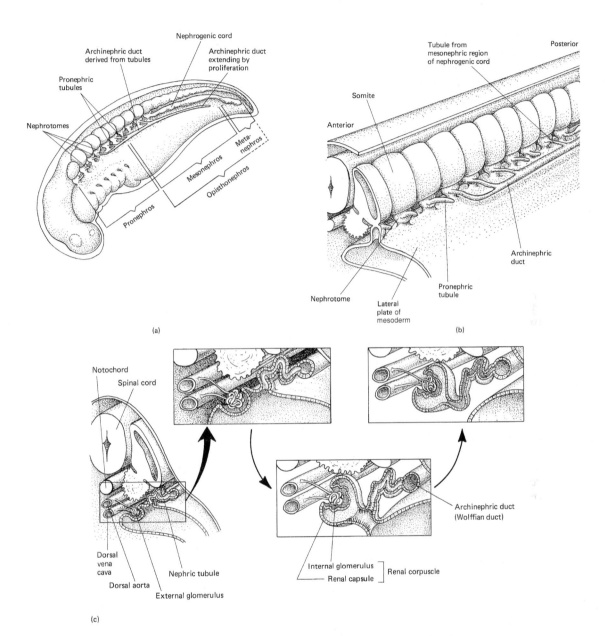

Figure 3–17   Kidney and nephron development. (a) Nephrotome regions in a generalized vertebrate embryo. The pronephros is functional only in embryonic forms. The mesonephros is functional in adult nonamniotic vertebrates and in embryonic amniotes. Adult nonamniotes have a kidney composed of the mesonephros plus metanephros, the opisthonephric kidney, drained by the archinephric duct. Adult amniotes have a metanephric kidney only, drained by the ureter (new). The archinephric duct now drains the testis alone in the adult. (b) The relationship of the nephrotome and its developing tubules and archinephric duct to the somites, lateral plate of mesoderm, and coelom. (c) Details of the development of the adult structure of the isolated renal corpuscle and its tubule from the earlier condition where the corpuscle is attached to the coelomic cavity.

A urinary bladder for the storage of urine is seen only in tetrapods, although some bony fishes have a bladderlike extension of the kidney duct. The bladder of modern amphibians has the capacity for water resorption, but in amniotes this regulation is carried out solely within the kidney itself. The kidney in amniotes acquires a new drainage duct, the **ureter** (the archinephric duct is taken over by the testes; see the next section). The amniote bladder, and the duct that links it to the cloaca (the **urethra**), is homologous with the allantoic membrane of the amniote egg (see Chapter 10). The ureters empty into the base of bladder in therian mammals (marsupials and placentals), but this represents a highly derived condition (see the discussion of the evolution of the mammalian condition in Chapter 21). In other amniotes the ureters empty directly into the cloaca (from which the urine backwashes into the bladder) (the same is true for the archinephric ducts in amphibians) (Figure 3–18b, c). The bladder is lost in many amniotes which excrete a semisolid paste of uric acid rather than liquid urine (see Chapter 4), especially in snakes and in most birds. Note that the use of the penis in males as a conduit for urine, as well as for sperm, is seen only in therian mammals.

In most vertebrates the urinary, reproductive, and alimentary systems reach the outside via a single common opening, the **cloaca** (see Figure 3–18). There may be some division within the cloaca to separate the different functions, but there is still only one common opening. In therian mammals the cloaca is replaced by separate openings for the urinogenital and alimentary systems. Primates and some rodents are unique among mammals in having separate openings for the urinary and genital systems in the females; other mammals conjoin the urethra and the vagina into a single **urogenital** sinus leading to the outside. Primates also are unusual in having a pendulous penis that cannot be retracted back into the body.

Figure 3–18   Anatomy of the cloaca and urogenital ducts in vertebrates. (a) Probable primitive condition, seen in lampreys and bony fishes. (b) Condition in most vertebrates, including nonmammalian amniotes. (c) Male monotreme, illustrating more derived amniote condition. (d) Condition in male placental mammals. (e) Condition in most female placental mammals. (f) Specialized condition in female primates. (After M. Hildebrand 1995.)

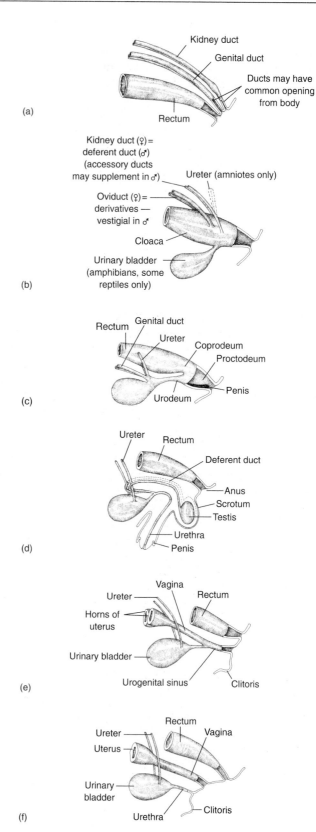

Reproduction

Reproduction is the means by which the gametes are produced, released, and combined with those belonging to a member of the opposite sex to produce a fertilized zygote. Vertebrates, like most animals, usually have two separate sexes, and sexual reproduction is the normal mode (although not the invariant one in all vertebrates). Other considerations of reproduction include the mode of development of the offspring, whether in an egg left to fend for itself (probably the primitive vertebrate condition), in an egg protected by the parents (as in birds), or as an embryo retained within the mother's body until development is complete (as in mammals, but also in other vertebrates such as many sharks and lizards).

Sex Determination and Sex Chromosomes   The mechanisms of sex determination in vertebrates are not as obvious as one might at first imagine. In all vertebrates the gonad is initially indifferent and capable of producing either an ovary or a testis. Individuals with both types of gonads present and functional are called **hermaphrodites**. Hermaphroditism is common in nonamniotic vertebrates, especially fishes, but virtually absent among amniotes (Chapter 8). The gender of most mammals is generally obvious from birth, expressed by genitalia and other secondary sex characteristics, but in other classes of vertebrates genitalia and sexually dimorphic structures are absent or not expressed until maturity is achieved (van Tienhoven 1983). For example, we can tell male and female birds apart if they are sexually dimorphic in coloration (e.g., ducks), but it is very hard to determine the sex if both genders look the same (e.g., crows).

Sex determination in therian mammals is by distinctive sex chromosomes, the X and Y chromosomes: females have two X chromosomes and males have an XY combination. Sex chromosomes are a derived feature among vertebrates. They are absent from amphibians and fishes, and breeding experiments indicate that sex-determining genes are distributed over several chromosomes (Bull 1983). As a result, intersexuality and several types of hermaphroditism, including functional sex reversal (where a female changes from female to male, or vice versa, during its lifetime), are widespread in nonamniotic vertebrates (van Tienhoven 1983).

Birds also have sex chromosomes, but here the chromosomal designation is different: ZZ produces a male and ZW a female (Jablonka and Lamb 1990). This difference alone is an indication that the sex chromosomes evolved independently in birds and mammals. Ecothermic amniotes (reptiles) do not have sex chromosomes, although, in contrast with nonamniote tetrapods, sex reversals are atypical. Sex determination in living reptiles is often affected by environmental temperature during development (Chapter 12). If this represents the primitive amniote condition, it seems obvious that both types of endothermic amniotes (birds and mammals) would have to devise a different method of sex determination, as their young develop at a constant high temperature.

It appears that a gene located on the Y chromosome in mammals initiates male gonadal development, and female gonadal development results from its absence. Once a gonad has had its primary sex declared as female or male, the sex hormone estrogen or testosterone is produced. These hormones affect the development of the secondary sex characters (Ehrhardt and Meyer–Bahlburg 1981, Wilson et al. 1981). In humans the genitalia, breasts, hair patterns, and differential growth patterns are secondary sex characteristics. Horns, antlers, differences in plumage length, and dimorphic color patterns are familiar differences that we associate with sex in other vertebrates.

An evolutionary explanation for the female being the homogametic (XX) sex in mammals has been advanced by Ursula Mittwoch (1973). The heterogametic sex is physiologically dominant. During pregnancy in mammals maternal estrogens can cross the maternal–fetal barrier. For a female fetus (XX) this presents no problem, but a male (XY) would be swamped by estrogenic effects (femaleness) unless a strong masculinizing agent existed. Mittwoch has suggested that this crossing of the placental barrier by maternal hormones explains the dominance of XY masculinizing effect in directing the secondary sex differentiation of therian mammals. This explanation also accounts for the absence of a Y chromosome in the egg-laying monotremes. In birds the egg isolates the embryo, whether male or female, from direct maternal influence and female heteromorphy in birds is quite possibly a matter of evolutionary chance. Although there are some unique selective pressures associated with the evolution of female sex chromosome heteromorphy (Jablonka and Lamb 1990), they may not be as potent as those operating in the mammalian situation.

Female and Male Reproductive Organs   Ovaries differentiate as relatively simple organs with an undifferentiated connective tissue, **stroma**, in which are embedded many large primary sex cells called **follicles**. As they mature the follicular cell layer becomes much larger, often forming a spherical, sometimes fluid-filled organ within the ovary nurturing the developing egg and producing the hormone estrogen. The follicle stimulates the development of yolk in the egg. Egg yolk constitutes a major energy investment in reproduction for many vertebrates, either because of the number of eggs produced or because of the amount of yolk in each egg. When the eggs mature the follicle ruptures, releasing the completed egg (**ovulation**). In most vertebrates the eggs are released into the coelomic cavity. The epithelial cells of the collapsed follicle remain in the stroma of the ovary after ovulation. In many vertebrates these cells form a second hormone-producing gland, the **corpus luteum** (plural *corpora lutea*). The corpus luteum produces the hormone progesterone, which in mammals stimulates changes in the relevant portions of the female for retention of the developing young. In birds where no retention of ova occurs, corpora lutea do not develop. The production of eggs by the ovary may be almost continuous (humans), seasonal (the vast majority of vertebrates), or occur only once in a lifetime (fishes, such as the eel, and some mammals, such as marsupial mice).

The testes differentiate as compact organs made up of interconnecting **seminiferous tubules** where sperm develop. Sperm are among the most highly specialized of animal cells. No cytoplasm in the conventional sense remains in a sperm cell; it is specialized to deliver nuclear information to the ovum. Sperm differentiate from prolifically dividing sex cells and are supported, nourished, and conditioned by cells that remain permanently attached to the tubule walls, the **supporting** or **Sertoli** cells. Unlike the follicular cells of the ovary, the testicular supporting cells are not endocrine but strictly sperm-nurturing cells. The hormone testosterone is produced by clusters of **interstitial cells** between the seminiferous tubules in tetrapods.

The reproductive tracts of vertebrates are the gamete conduits to the external environment. Lampreys and hagfishes lack any conduits; sperm or eggs erupt from the gonad and move through the coelom to pores that open to the outside near the cloaca. In gnathostomes, the gametes are always transported to the cloaca via specialized ducts. In the males, this usually involves a degree of takeover of the archinephric duct that originally drained the kidney. The oviducts of gnathostomes not only act for the conduction of ova, but can also produce coatings for the egg (such as the jelly of amphibian eggs, or the shells of shark, reptile, and bird eggs), and also the albumen that surrounds the embryo and the yolk in amniotes. The oviducts can become enlarged and fused in a variety of ways to form a **uterus** or paired uteri in which eggs can be stored, or young can develop.

Modes of Reproduction and Reproductive Strategies
Living jawless vertebrates reproduce by means of external fertilization, which is assumed to be the primitive mode among vertebrates. The two types of living agnathans differ, however, in what we might term reproductive strategy. Given that a female has a certain amount of resources to devote to her eggs, the resources (yolk in this case) can be divided in a couple of major ways: she can either lay many small eggs, each with a little yolk (as in lampreys), or she can produce a smaller number of larger eggs, each with a greater amount of yolk and with a greater degree of maternal care, perhaps bypassing the larval stage in the egg (as in hagfishes, see Chapter 6) or retaining the young for development in the uterus. Simple laying of eggs is termed **oviparity**, while retention of the young in the uterus, bypassing the laying of a distinct egg altogether, is termed **viviparity**. Oviparous vertebrates are called **matrotrophic** when the nutrients for the young are derived from maternal secretions, or **lecithotrophic** when the eggs are retained in the uterus but embryonic nourishment is still via the yolk (intermediate conditions also exist) (see Chapters 7 and 15). In order for viviparity to occur, the egg must obviously be fertilized while it is still within the reproductive tract, and viviparous vertebrates usually have some sort of **intromittent organ** for the ending of the sperm ducts (such as the amniote penis) by which this internal fertilization can be accomplished.

Among fishes, the cartilaginous fish possess **pelvic claspers** situated on the pelvic fins in the males (as did some extinct placoderms), which form intromittent organs. Thus all of these fishes are (or were) capable of internal fertilization of the eggs. Living cartilaginous fishes are predominately viviparous, and the few oviparous species lay a small number of large, yolky, well-protected eggs (see Chapter 7). In contrast, the majority of bony fishes lay large numbers of small eggs. Where the development of an intromittent organ (from the anal fin) and internal fertilization and viviparity are seen (as in familiar aquarium fishes such as guppies), the condition has clearly been evolved independently in different groups. Viviparity is seen in some types of teleosts, and in the lobe-finned coelacanth (Wake 1989) (see Chapter 8).

The primitive tetrapod mode of reproduction was probably to lay a large number of unshelled eggs in the water with external fertilization, as seen today in many frogs. However, living amphibians have devised a wide variety of different reproductive strategies, including various forms of internal fertilization and viviparity, and even the evolution of an intromittent organ in caecilians (limbless amphibians) and one species of frog (see Chapter 11). Amniotes are characterized by the **amniote egg**, a shelled egg laid on land in which the larval stage of the young is bypassed entirely (see Chapter 10). As the shell must be put on the egg before it leaves the mother's reproductive tract all amniotes have internal fertilization. Most amniotes have an intromittent organ in the males for this purpose, the **penis**. (The penis has been secondarily lost in many birds.)

All therian mammals are viviparous (see Chapter 21). Among nonmammalian amniotes viviparity occurs only in lepidosaurs (at least in living animals), where it has evolved many times among lizards and snakes (see Chapter 15). Because the gilled larval form is lost in amniotes, amniotic eggs are not designed to be laid in the water. If an amniote returns to the water and is fully aquatic, it must have some means of viviparity. Whales, dolphins, and sea snakes are viviparous fully aquatic tetrapods today, but the fossil record also shows (by means of the preservation of individuals containing well-developed embryos) that certain extinct marine reptiles, such as ichthyosaurs (see Chapter 13) were also viviparous. In contrast, no marine turtle has become so extensively modified for swimming that it cannot return to land to lay its eggs. It is of interest to note that no living archosaur (bird or crocodile) is viviparous, even though birds show a wide variety of reproductive strategies. There are a number of evolutionary hypotheses for the absence of viviparity in birds (see Chapter 18).

■ Coordination and Integration

The nervous system provides an organism with information about the outside world, in addition to controlling the actions and functions of the various organs and muscles. Organ functions must be coordinated to work in concert if the action of one is not to cancel the action of another. Signals transmitted by the nervous system and endocrine secretions distributed to target organs by the cardiovascular system are significant coordinators in this regard.

The Nervous System: General Features

The basic unit of neuroanatomy is the **neuron**. Neurons are made up of nerve cell bodies with long, thin processes, the **dendrites** and **axons**, which extend from the cell body and transmit electrical impulses. Dendrites (usually shorter and branched) carry impulses into the cell body, and axons (usually longer and unbranched) carry them out to the target organs or tissues. In gnathostomes the axons are encased in a fatty insulating coat, the **myelin sheath**, which increases the conduction velocity of the nerve impulse. Generally, axons in transit from one population of cells to another are collected together like wires in a cable. Such collections of axons in the **peripheral nervous system (PNS)** are called nerves; within the **central nervous system (CNS)** they are called tracts and compose most of the white matter (so called because of the color of the myelin). Nerve cell bodies are often clustered together, usually in groups with similar connections or functions, and are called ganglia (in the PNS) and nuclei (not to be confused with the nucleus inside of the cell) that make up most of the gray matter (in the CNS). Nerve cells are embedded in generally nonconducting but physically and physiologically significant glial cells of a variety of distinct types.

The **spinal cord** is composed of a hollow tube with an inner core of gray matter (cell bodies) and an outer layer of white matter (axons). The spinal cord receives sensory inputs, transmits and integrates them with other portions of the CNS, and sends motor output as appropriate. Ancestrally, the spinal cord had considerable autonomy, even in such complex movements as swimming. Fishes can continue to produce coordinated swimming movements when the brain is severed from the spinal cord. The trend in vertebrate evolution has been toward more complex circuits within the spinal cord and between the spinal cord and the brain (although our familiar knee jerk reaction, following the application of the doctor's hammer to our kneecap, can be mediated by the spinal cord alone as a *reflex arc*).

The nerves of the PNS are segmentally arranged, exiting from the spinal cord between the vertebrae. Each spinal nerve complex is made up of four types of fibers: somatic sensory fibers from the body wall (conveying sensory information from skin, such as temperature and pressure, and in frogs and amniotes, positional information from the appendicular muscles and joints); visceral sensory fibers from the gut wall and blood vessels (conveying information about things that we are usually unaware of, such as gut activities and blood pressure); visceral motor fibers to the muscles and glands of the gut and to the blood vessels (supplying the smooth muscles of the gut and the vascular system); and somatic motor fibers to the body wall (supplying the striated axial and appendicular muscles). The nerve cell bodies of both types of sensory fibers are collected in a segmental series of spinal ganglia adjacent to the spinal cord. They too are derived from neural crest cells and thus are absent from the segmental nerves of amphioxus.

Bony fishes and tetrapods divide up these nerves so that the sensory (somatic and visceral) fibers enter the spinal cord dorsally (via the dorsal root), and the motor fibers exit the spinal cord ventrally (via the ventral root). Both roots combine outside of the spinal cord to form a single spinal nerve (one per segment on either side) (Figure 3–19a). This arrangement is obviously the derived condition. In chondrichthyans some visceral motor fibers also exit via the dorsal root (Figure 3–19b), and in jawless fishes all of the visceral motor fibers exit via the dorsal root (Figure 3–19c). In the primitive vertebrate condition (as seen in lampreys) and in amphioxus the dorsal and ventral roots are arrayed in a staggered fashion down the spinal column, and do not combine to form a single segmental nerve (Figure 3–19d). The arrangement in amphioxus and primitive vertebrates makes some functional sense for an animal with only axial musculature: the ventral roots emerge within each segment to supply the underlying block of musculature, while the other nerves emerge between segments to make their way out to the gut and the body wall (Figure 3–19d).

The visceral motor fibers emerging from the spinal column form the **autonomic nervous system**. In mammals there is a clear division of this system into the **sympathetic** and **parasympathetic** divisions. The sympathetic nervous system generally stimulates an organ to react in a manner appropriate to a stressful set of circumstances (e.g., to prepare for rapid energy expenditures, such as speeding up the

Figure 3–19 Anatomy of the spinal chord and segmental nerves in vertebrates. (a) Condition in bony fishes and tetrapods, where the dorsal root is completely sensory in nature and the ventral root is completely motor, and dorsal and ventral roots combine to form a single segmental nerve. (b) Primitive jawed vertebrate condition, seen in cartilaginous fishes, where the dorsal nerve root also carries some visceral motor fibers. (c) Condition in lampreys (probably primitive vertebrate condition), where all the visceral motor fibers are carried in the dorsal root. (d) Lateral view of a lamprey, showing staggering down the spinal chord of the exit of dorsal ventral nerve roots (After A. S. Romer and T. S. Parsons 1986, *The Vertebrate Body*, 6th Ed., copyright © by Saunders College Publishing, reproduced by permission of the publisher.)

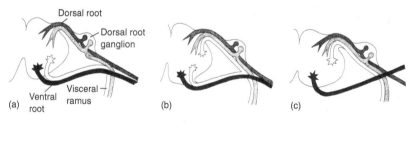

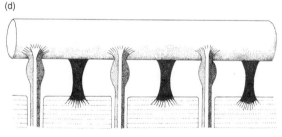

Somatic sensory   Visceral motor
Visceral sensory   Somatic motor

heart rate). The parasympathetic nervous system is antagonistic to the sympathetic system in its effect, causing the organs innervated to function appropriately for peaceful conditions (e.g., rest or digestion, such as slowing down the heart rate). The two systems are distinct in terms of their anatomy: Sympathetic nerves exits from spinal column in the trunk and neck region, while the parasympathetic nerves exit from the skull (via the cranial nerves) or from the sacral region. They are also different in their neurology, having differences in the way the nerves synapse within ganglia prior to reaching the target organ, and in the neurotransmitter used at the target. Nonmammalian vertebrates have a less distinct separation of the autonomic system into discrete sympathetic and parasympathetic components.

Mammals have twelve **cranial nerves**, numbered with Roman numerals in the order in which they exit the brain through the skull. This numbering system is applied to all other vertebrates, even though the number of nerves may vary. In contrast to the spinal nerves, the cranial nerves of vertebrates appear to retain an amphioxuslike pattern, where dorsal and ventral roots are separate and ventral roots contain somatic motor fibers only. An additional peculiarity of cranial nerves is that the nerves interpreted as dorsal root nerves (V, VII, IX, and X) contain, in addition to the regular (parasympathetic) visceral motor fibers, motor fibers that supply the branchiomeric striated muscles associated with the splanchnocranium (i.e., the muscles that power the gills and the gill derivatives, such as the jaws). These have been termed **special visceral branchial motor** nerves, mainly because of their position exiting through the dorsal roots. However, we now know that the branchiomeric musculature is indeed true somatic muscle, derived from paraxial mesoderm (visceral motor nerves in the body supply only the smooth and cardiac muscle derived from the lateral plate). New evidence suggests that these special branchial nerves may really be peculiarly placed forms of somatic motor nerves (Northcutt 1990). Nerves VII, IX, and X also contain the unusual **special visceral sensory nerves**, conveying information to the brain from the taste buds (we are usually unaware of visceral sensory sensations, but taste is definitely a conscious phenomenon!). Some new evidence suggests that these visceral sensory components may in fact be separate cranial nerves in their own right, traveling along with the more regular nerves. The same has been suggested of the special sensory nerves that supply the lateral line in fishes, usually also considered as components of nerves VII, IX, and X (Northcutt 1990).

The most important cranial nerves to concern us for the purposes of this book are the dorsal root equivalents mentioned above (V, VII, IX, and X), which carry the motor nerves that supply the branchiomeric musculature (Figure 3–11 illustrates the difference in innervation of the major muscles), as they help us to understand homologous muscles in evolutionary history. For example, we know that mammalian facial muscles are derived from the old constrictor colli of reptiles (and hence from the hyoid arch constrictors of fishes) because of their innervation by cranial nerve VII. We know that they are not of the same origin as the adjacent muscles operating the jaw, as these are innervated by cranial nerve V, in its original association with the mandibular arch. The vagus (cranial nerve X) is also very important in its ramification throughout all but the most posterior part of the trunk, carrying the parasympathetic nerve supply to various organs. This is why people who break their necks may lose the function of their skeletal muscles, but can still retain their visceral functions (workings of the gut, heart, etc.) as the supply from the vagus is entirely independent of the spinal cord.

Other nerves that innervate muscles appear to be homologues of the primitive vertebrate style of ventral roots, as they carry only somatic motor nerves. These are the three nerves (III, IV, and VI) that innervate the muscles that move the eyes. The other cranial nerves cannot be homologized with spinal nerve equivalents. They are either outgrowths of brain, such as the olfactory (I) and optic (II) nerves, or they represent various evolutionary splits or add-ons. For example, nerves VIII and XI are actually portions of nerves VII and X, respectively, and not really individual nerves in their own right.

Brain Anatomy and Evolution

The brain of all vertebrates is basically a tripartite structure (Figure 3–20). In the most simple condition the forebrain relates to olfaction, the midbrain to vision, and the hindbrain to balance/vibration detection (the inner ear). These portions of the brain are associated with the nasal, optic, and otic capsules of the chondrocranium, respectively (see Figure 3–6). During later development the brain differentiates into five distinct regions, containing

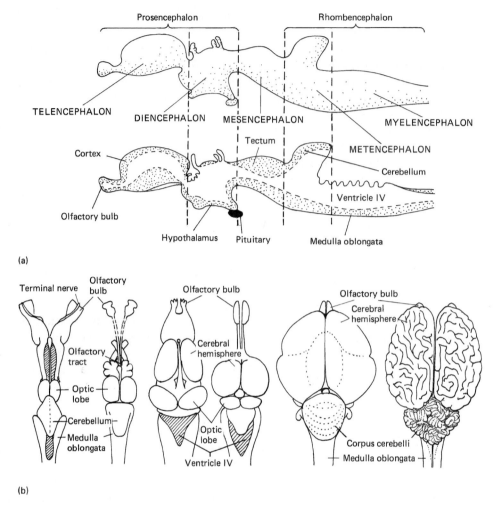

Figure 3–20   The vertebrate brain. (a) Diagrammatic developmental stage in generalized vertebrate brain showing principal divisions and structures described in the text. Lateral view above; sectioned view below. The forebrain (= the prosencephalon) is comprised of the telencephalon and the diencephalon. The stalk sticking up from the anterior part of the midbrain is the pineal organ, or epithalamus. The midbrain is comprised of the mesencephalon. The hindbrain (= rhombencephalon) is comprised of the metencephalon and the myelencephalon. (b) Representative vertebrate brains seen in dorsal view (the cerebellum and the corpus cerebelli are the same structures). All brains are drawn to approximately the same total length, which emphasizes relative differences in regional development. From left to right: *Scymnus*, a shark; *Gadus*, a teleost; *Rana*, a frog; *Alligator*, a crocodilian; *Anser*, a goose; and *Equus*, a horse, as an example of a derived modern mammal.

both gray and white matter, each region serving a different basic function. The brain of amphioxus appears to be only a simple swelling, the cerebral vesicle, originally thought to be homologous only with the vertebrate hindbrain, but in fact has been shown to have an area homologous with the diencephalon, the posterior portion of the vertebrate forebrain (Lacalli et al. 1994).

Posteriorly, two regions differentiate from the embryonic hindbrain region associated with the developing ear. The most posterior, the **myelencephalon** or **medulla oblongata**, is primarily an enlarged anterior extension of the spinal cord. The nuclei of the medulla oblongata form synapses primarily with the sensory organs of the muscles and skin of the head plus a distinctive set of nuclei, those associated with the sense organs of the inner ear. All impulses from the receptor cells of the balance (vestibular) and the hearing (cochlear) regions of the mammalian ear synapse first in these medulla oblongata nuclei.

The anterior portion of the posterior region of the embryonic brain, called the **metencephalon**, develops an important dorsal outgrowth, the **cerebellum** (present as a distinct structure in gnathostomes only; Northcutt 1996). The cerebellum coordinates and regulates motor activities whether they are reflexive, such as maintenance of posture, or directed, such as escape movements. The nuclear or gray matter of the cerebellum receives nerve impulses from the vestibular area of the myelencephalon (in particular, impulses relayed from the vestibular nuclei), impulses from the complex system of muscle and tendon stretch receptors (amniotes and frogs only), and indirectly, impulses from the skin, optic centers, and other coordinating brain centers.

The central embryonic brain region, the midbrain or **mesencephalon**, develops in conjunction with the eye. The roof of the mesencephalon is known as the **tectum** and receives input from the optic nerve. The floor of this region contains fiber tracts that pass anteriorly and posteriorly to other regions of the brain as well as to nuclei concerned with eye movements.

A rather small region, the **diencephalon**, is one of the areas that develops from the embryonic forebrain. In amniotes it is a major relay station between sensory areas and the higher brain centers. The eyes develop from stalklike outgrowths of the diencephalon, the stalks remaining as the optic nerves (cranial nerve II). A ventral outgrowth of the diencephalon contributes to the formation of the dominant endocrine organ, the **pituitary gland**, or hypophysis, which, together with the floor of the diencephalon (**hypothalamus**), forms the primary center for neural–hormonal coordination and integration (see next section). Another endocrine gland, the **pineal organ**, is a dorsal outgrowth of the diencephalon. Originally it was a median photoreceptor (light-sensitive organ) in primitive vertebrates.

Finally, the most anterior region of the adult forebrain, the **telencephalon**, develops in association with the olfactory capsules and as the first nuclei of olfactory synapse, and also coordinates inputs from other sensory modalities. The telencephalon becomes enlarged (in which condition it is also known as the **cerebrum** or cerebral hemi-spheres) in various different ways in different vertebrate groups. Tetrapods develop an area termed the **neocortex** or **neopallium**: In mammals this becomes the primary seat of sensory integration and nervous control. On a different branch of the vertebrate evolutionary lineage, bony fishes also evolved a larger, more complex telencephalon, but by a completely different mechanism (see Chapter 8). Sharks and, perhaps surprisingly, hagfishes (Northcutt 1996) have also evolved relatively large forebrains in an independent fashion, although a large cerebrum in general is primarily a feature of tetrapods (Figure 3–21).

An understanding of the evolution of the cerebrum in tetrapods (see Figure 3–21), and the homologies of various portions of the cerebrum in different tetrapod groups, has been hampered in the past by interpretation of the brain of reptiles as some sort of intermediate evolutionary condition from which the more complex forebrains of both mammals and birds can be derived (Striedter 1997). However, given our current understanding of tetrapod phylogeny, mammals and sauropsids (reptiles plus birds) have been independent offshoots from early in the history of amniote evolution (see Chapter 10). Thus the brains of living reptiles provide clues to the brain of birds, but have little to tell us about the ancestral mammalian condition. New analyses of homologies suggest that the area of the neocortex that is enlarged, and that receives the major projections from the underlying integration center in the diencephalon (the thalamus), is rather different in mammals and in sauropsids. Mammals enlarge the dorsal part of the cortex, while sauropsids enlarge the lateral portion, but the mammalian condition appears to represent the dorsal migration of areas of neural tissue present in the lateral brain regions of sauropsids (Karten 1997). Mammals derived a complex laminated structure to the neocortex, but the bird neocortex is also complicated in a somewhat convergent fashion. In more derived mammals the neocortex dominates the entire telencephalon and becomes highly folded (Figure 3–20b). Sauropsids also show a dramatic reduction in the projection of the olfactory bulbs to the neocortex, especially in contrast with the mammalian condition. (Striedter 1997).

Traditional wisdom holds that the mammalian way of forming a neocortex results in an increased capacity for learned, complex behavior, an ability less developed in birds. While it is true that birds

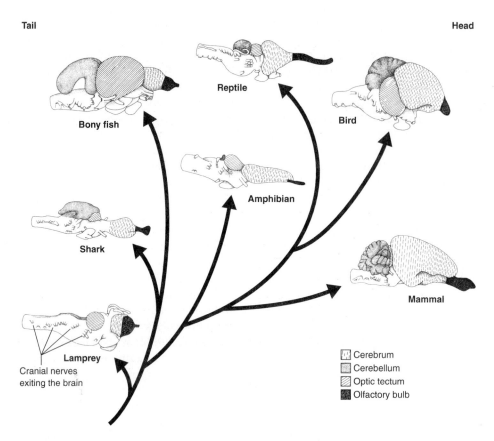

Figure 3–21 Phylogeny of vertebrate brains, showing the relative contributions of different major portions in different vertebrate groups. (After K. V. Kardong 1997.)

do not have the type of intelligence that some (but by no means all) mammals exhibit, there seems to be little experimental evidence to support the idea that the reason lies in the detailed differences between the neocortices. This notion may just be another example of the mammal equals better type of bias that we have encountered before.

The Sense Organs

We traditionally think of mammals as having five senses: taste, touch, sight, smell, and hearing; however, this array does not reflect the primitive vertebrate condition. For example, hearing of airborne sound waves is not a general feature of primarily aquatic vertebrates. Likewise a major means of sensation in fish, the lateral line system, is not functional on land, and is entirely absent from amniotes. Complex, multicellular sense organs are a derived feature of vertebrates, formed from the epi-

dermal placodes in development. Amphioxus possesses only single-celled receptors in the skin, plus a light-sensitive pigment spot that may be homologous with the vertebrate eye (Northcutt 1996).

Chemoreception The senses of smell and taste both involve the direct detection of dissolved molecules on specialized receptors. We think of these two senses as being closely interlinked; for example, our sense of taste is poorer if our sense of smell is blocked by having a cold. But the two senses are actually very different in terms of embryological origin. Smell is a somatic sensory system, with the sensations projecting to the forebrain. Taste is a visceral sensory system, with the sensations projecting initially to the hindbrain.

Taste buds, made up of specialized sensory epithelial cells, are restricted to the moist membranes of the walls of the mouth, the throat, and especially the tongue of tetrapods, but many bony fishes have taste buds on their heads, fins, or specialized facial structures called barbels (e.g., the whiskers of catfishes). The olfactory receptor apparatus is basically the same in all vertebrates. In fishes olfactory organs are usually independent of the mouth area and pharynx; separate incurrent and excurrent canals open on the exterior of the snout. The nasal epithelium is folded into a complex rosette of great surface area but does not have bony support. In tetrapods a choana (internal nostril) links the nose with mouth, and the nasal cavity and pharynx are confluent, at least at some point. In mammals the sensory cells reside on specialized epithelium on thin, scrolllike bones within the nasal cavity (turbinate bones). There are actually several different types of turbinate bones in mammals. The nasoturbinates and ethmoturbinates, containing the olfactory epithelium, are situated high in the nasal cavity; more ventral maxilloturbinate bones and nasal epithelium are concerned with temperature and water regulation (Chapter 19).

The total area of the olfactory surfaces may exceed that of the entire body surface in some vertebrates. A single molecule can excite a receptor cell, and only a few molecules are needed to elicit a behavioral response. The subtle differences in odor that mammals can detect are probably due to an ability to distinguish the hundreds of combinations possible from no more than a dozen basic odors. Such combinations would produce the individual differences in body odor that are important in maintenance of many mammalian social groups. **Pheromones** are chemical signals produced by an individual that affect the behavior and/or physiology of conspecifics. The physiological state of an individual can often be determined from the odors it produces, especially in the feces and urine. Excretions are used by a wide variety of vertebrates to mark their territories or home ranges. One large group of freshwater fishes, the Ostariophysi (minnows and their 6000 relatives, Chapter 8) have a unique type of epidermal cell that exudes an alarm substance when the skin is abraded. Other fishes smell the substance and scatter, diving for the bottom in apparent antipredator behavior in direct response to the chemical signal.

Tetrapods possess an additional organ of olfaction in the anterior roof of the mouth, the **vomeronasal organ** or **Jacobson's organ**. This organ appears to serve as a more direct means of almost tasting smells, possibly evolved with the difference in perceiving airborne molecules on land as opposed to molecules already dissolved in water. When snakes flicker their tongue in and out of their mouth they are directly transferring molecules from the air to this organ. Many male ungulates (hoofed mammals) sniff or taste the urine of females, a behavior that permits them to determine the stage of her reproductive cycle. This sniffing is usually followed by *flehmen*, a behavior in which the male curls the upper lip and often holds his head high, probably inhaling molecules of pheromones into the vomeronasal organ. Primates, with their relatively flat faces, were thought to have lost their vomeronasal organs, but some recent work suggests the presence of a remnant of this structure in humans, used for pheromone detection.

Mechanoreception   There are least four different kinds of epithelial receptors in the skin of tetrapods sensitive to stimuli ranging from light touch to heavy pressure. In mammals touch receptors may also be combined with specialized hairs, the **vibrissae** (whiskers), which grow on the muzzle, around the eyes, or on the lower legs. A specialized set of mechanoreceptors, the lateral line system, occurs in aquatic nonamniotes (discussed later in conjunction with the acousticolateralis system).

Related to mechanoreception is the **proprioception** of the appendicular muscles of amniotes and frogs (presumably evolved convergently). Amniote proprioceptors include muscle spindles, which detect the amount of stretch in the muscle, and tendon organs, which convey information about the position of the joints. Proprioception provides information about where your limbs are in space relative to your body: It's the proprioceptors in your arm that enable you to touch your finger to your nose when your eyes are closed. As proprioceptors are found only in the limbs of tetrapods, they must be of importance for determination of posture and balance on land. (A fish, buoyed up by the water, has little need to worry about posture.)

Vision   Visual systems are considered the distance sense par excellence, sensitive to those wavelengths of electromagnetic radiation (light) that reach the surface of the Earth with the least interference by intervening air and water. Light of different wavelengths is differentially absorbed, transmitted, and reflected so that the spectral (wavelength) distribution of light reflected from an object is altered. These properties of light give nearly unambiguous cues about the structure and texture of an object. Another significant attribute of light is its speed, which is instantaneous compared to the speed of transmission and action of the vertebrate neuromuscular system.

The receptor field of the vertebrate eye is arrayed in a hemispherical sheet, the **retina**, which originates as an outgrowth of the diencephalon of the brain. Nerves from the retina project to the visual cortex of the telencephalon. The retina contains two types of light-sensitive cells, **cones** and **rods**, which are distinguished from each other by morphology, photochemistry, and neural connections. Each point on the retina corresponds to specific neural connections and a different visual axis in space. Thus, a vertebrate can determine where a target is in at least two-dimensional space and whether it is stationary or moving. Because of neuronal interactions, vertebrate eyes can also detect sharp beginnings and endings of visual stimuli (ons, offs, and edges) with great precision.

The eyes of vertebrates (Figure 3–22) consist of a light-shielding container, the sclera, and choroid coats. These prevent stimulation of the eye by light from multiple directions. The eye has a variable entrance aperture, the pupil surrounded by the iris, to control the amount of light that enters. A focusing system—the cornea, lens, and ciliary body—converges the rays of light on the photosensitive cells of the retina.

Figure 3–22 The vertebrate eye as illustrated by mammals. (a) The eye sectioned horizontally in the plane of the optic axis and optic nerve. In addition to the structures discussed in the text, (b) details structures of the anterior portion of the eye primarily responsible for image focus (cornea, lens, ciliary body) and quantitative control of light (iris). (c) Enlargement of the fundus of the eye showing the specialized sensory and neural regions found there. Note especially the continuity of the brain covering meninges (pia mater, arachnoid, and dura mater) to the protective and nutritive coats of the eye (sclera and choroid). (Modified after J. E. Crouch, 1969, *Text-Atlas of Cat Anatomy*, Lea & Febiger, Philadelphia, PA.)

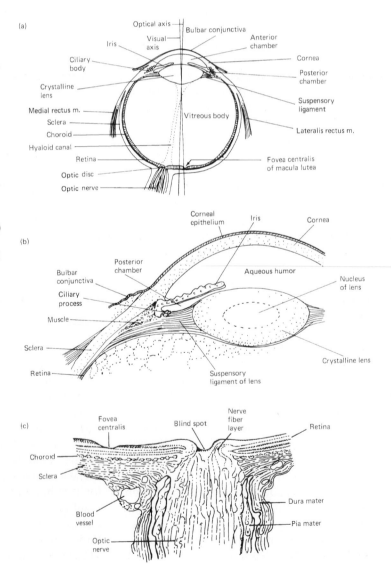

Lizards and birds have better visual acuity than most fishes and mammals, probably because of their nearly pure cone retinas. Mammals approach this acuity only in one small region of the retina, the all cone **fovea**. In addition to high visual acuity, cones are the basis for color vision. Cones have relatively low photosensitivity, however; they are at least two orders of magnitude less sensitive than rods and thus fail to function at night and in other dim-light conditions. Thus while reptiles and birds have superior color vision to mammals, mammals have superior night vision.

Anthropoid primates (monkeys and apes) are unusual among mammals in having good visual acuity and good color vision, perhaps serving to compensate for their relatively poor sense of olfaction. In addition, these primates, unlike most mammals, are primarily diurnal (daytime) animals. It is popularly supposed that most mammals cannot perceive color, and older text books depict dogs and horses seeing the world as if on a black and white television set. However, more recent investigations show that nonprimate mammals can indeed perceive some color, although they may not attach to it the sensory significance that humans do. Our sense of color vision palls besides that of birds (see Chapter 21). We have receptors for three primary colors (red, green, and blue), while birds have receptors for four colors, and can also see into the regions of ultraviolet. Colorful as birds' plumage appears to us, we must see only a pale subset of the colors with which they perceive one another.

Electroreception   The capacity to perceive the electrical impulses generated by the muscles of other organisms is also a form of distance reception, like vision, but one that is entirely foreign to us. Electroreception was probably an important feature of early vertebrates, although this sense appears to be lacking in hagfishes. One of the hypotheses of bone evolution was that it was initially formed in the skin of the head in conjunction with housing electroreceptive organs (Gans 1989; see Chapter 2). Related to electroreception is the ability to produce electric discharge, seen in many fishes today. These senses are further discussed in Chapter 8.

Electroreception appears to be primarily a feature of fishes. Yet it was recently discovered that the specialized beaklike snouts of monotremes contain electroreceptive organs: The platypus uses its peak to detect invertebrates underwater, and the echidna uses its beak to detect invertebrates in leaf litter.

The Acousticolateralis System   The structure that we call the inner ear in mammals has a long phylogenetic history. The original function of the inner ear was as an organ of detection of position in space, used in conjunction with the lateral line system along the body. The fundamental sensory cell in this system is the **hair cell**, which functions as a mechanoreceptor to detect the movement of fluid. In the lateral line system of fishes and aquatic amphibians the hair cells are aggregated into **neuromast organs** in canal systems and detect the movement of water around the body (see Chapter 8). Used in conjunction with the **vestibular apparatus** in the inner ear (see later) a fish can determine whether the movement of water represents the movement of its own body or the movement of something approaching it.

The vestibular apparatus is comprised of the **membranous labyrinth**, a series of sacs and tubules containing the fluid endolymph (which resembles intracellular fluid), and its housing within the otic capsule of the skull, surrounded by the fluid perilymph (which resembles extracellular fluid). The sensory cells within the membranous labyrinth are variants on the basic hair cell. The lower parts of the labyrinth, the sacculus and utriculus, house sensory organs called macculae. These contain minute crystals of calcium carbonate (the hair cells embedded in the membrane below these crystals detect which way up the animal is), and also linear acceleration, by detecting the displacement of these crystals. The upper part of the membranous labyrinth contains the **semicircular canals**. Sensory areas in these canals (in the ampullae) detect angular acceleration by means of cristae, hair cells embedded in a cupola of jellylike substance, by monitoring the movement of the endolymph during motion. Gnathostomes have three semicircular canals on each side of the head, hagfishes have one, and lampreys and all fossil agnathans (where this can be determined) have two (Figure 3–23).

We often fail to realize the importance of the vestibular senses in ourselves, as we are usually dependent on vision for determination of spatial position. However, we can sometimes be fooled by vision, as when sitting in a stationary train or car and thinking that we are moving, only to realize when the vestibular apparatus kicks in that it is the

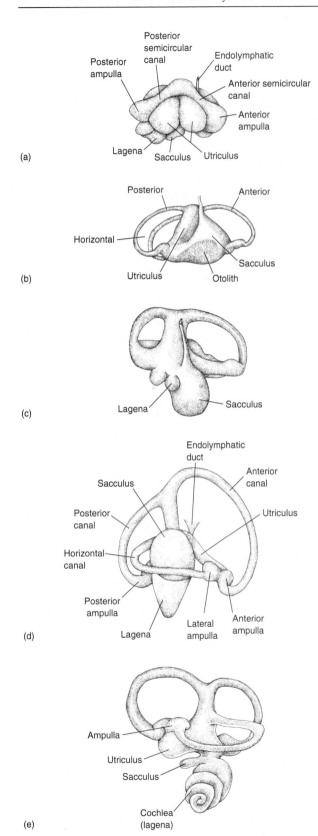

(a)

(b)

(c)

(d)

(e)

vehicle *next* to us that is moving. The inertia of the endolymph in the semicircular canals is what makes you feel that you're still moving after you've stopped spinning around on a rotating stool.

The inner ear assumes the function of hearing airborne sounds in tetrapods, with the transmission of sound waves through a bone (or a chain of bones) in a middle ear. It requires considerably more energy to set the fluids of the inner ear in motion than most airborne sounds could impart directly. The middle ear receives the relatively low energy of airborne sound waves on its outer membranous end, the **tympanic membrane** or **eardrum**, and produces corresponding vibrations in the fluids of the inner ear. Tetrapods have a new structure in the inner ear, the **lagena** (= the **cochlea** in mammals), which discriminates the frequency and intensity of vibrations it receives (again by a sensory system based on the hair cell, the **organ of Corti**), and transmits this information to the central nervous system in the form of neurally encoded firing patterns.

The middle ear of tetrapods has clearly evolved convergently several times. although in each case the **stapes** (= the old fish hyomandibula, often called the **columella** in nonmammalian tetrapods) is used as an auditory ossicle. Modern amphibians have an organization of the inner ear that is different from that of amniotes, indicating a completely independent evolution of hearing (Lombard and Hetherington 1993). Among amniotes, a functional middle ear with an eardrum has clearly been evolved independently in mammals and sauropsids (the reptile/bird lineage) (see Chapter 10). Detailed studies suggest that independent evolution of the middle ear occurred numerous times within sauropsids; turtles, lizards, and derived archosaurs (crocodiles, dinosaurs and birds) may

Figure 3–23 Design of the vestibular apparatus in different vertebrates. (a) Lamprey, note only two semicircular canals. (b) Generalized gnathostome condition, as illustrated by a shark. Note the addition of a third (horizontal) semicircular canal. (c) Generalized tetrapod condition, as illustrated by a frog. Note the acquisition of a small lagena for hearing airborne sounds. (d) Generalized amniote condition, as illustrated by a lizard. Note the increase in size of the lagena. (e) Therian mammalian condition, with the cochlea (= lagena) now lengthened and coiled. (After K. V. Kardong 1998, Reprinted by permission of the McGraw-Hill Companies.)

have obtained their more sophisticated ears, capable of hearing high frequency sound, in a parallel fashion (Clack 1997). Some bony fishes have quite independently evolved a system for hearing airborne sounds that is analogous with the tetrapod middle ear (the Weberian ossicles in ostariophysan teleosts; see Chapter 8).

The middle ear is not an airtight cavity; if it were, pressure differentials between the cavity and the middle ear could result in problematical pressures on the eardrum. The **eustachian tube**, derived from the first embryonic visceral pouch (= the spiracle of fishes), connects the mouth with the middle ear. Air flows in or out of the middle ear as air pressure changes. (These tubes sometimes become blocked, and when that happens changes in external air pressure can produce a painful sensation in addition to reduced auditory sensitivity. Anyone who has flown in an airplane while they had a bad cold knows all about this.)

Mammals have a middle ear that is more complex than that of other tetrapods, containing a chain of three bones (with the addition of the **malleus** and the **incus**), rather than just one. It may be true that this auditory design provides mammals with a greater acuity of hearing than other tetrapods, as this ossicle chain seems to have a mechanical advantage that boosts the force of vibration on the inner ear and provides a much broader range of frequency sensitivity than a single transducing element. But the incorporation of three bones (rather than one) into the middle ear was evidently an evolutionary accident rather than any design plan for increased auditory capacity (see Chapter 19). Several other features of therian mammals also increase auditory acuity. These include a longer cochlea, capable of a greater degree of pitch discrimination, that must now be coiled to fit inside the otic capsule, and an external ear, or **pinna**, which helps to determine sound direction. The pinna and the narrowing of the external auditory meatus of mammals concentrate sound from the relatively large area encompassed by the external opening of the pinna to the small, thin, tympanic membrane. The pinna is unique to mammals, although it has a feathery analog in certain owls (see Chapter 17). Most mammals can move their pinnae to pick up sound, although higher primates lack this capacity. The auditory sensitivity of a terrestrial mammal is reduced if the pinnae are removed. Pinnae are reduced or lost in aquatic

mammals as sound direction cannot be easily sensed underwater, and the pinnae can serve as a source of heat loss.

Endocrine System

The responses of vertebrates to their surroundings and to their internal needs are controlled by the nervous systems and the endocrine system. Both neurobiology and endocrinology deal with the study of the generation and reception of stimuli, their transmission, and transfer from one area of the body to another. In nerve cells this process is achieved by electrical discharges that propagate along the nerve cell axon and are transferred to adjacent cells, generally by diffusion of chemical signals, for further neural processing. The neural transmission of stimuli from sensory receptor cells to effector cells (e.g., muscle) is very rapid, usually measured in fractions of a second.

The endocrine system transfers information from one area to another via the release from a cell or organ complex (endocrine gland) of a chemical messenger, a **hormone**, that produces a response in the target cells, but in a slower time frame than in neural transmission (measured in minutes to hours—the distance of the target organ from the site of the release of the hormone obviously being a factor). Hormones can be produced either in discrete endocrine glands, whose primary function is hormone production and excretion (e.g., the thyroid, thymus, and the adrenals), or by organs with other major bodily functions (such as the gonads, the kidney, and the gastrointestinal tract). The trend in the evolution of vertebrate endocrine glands has been consolidation from scattered clusters of cells or small organs in fishes to larger, more definitive organs in amniotes. Endocrine secretions are predominantly involved in the control and regulation of energy use, storage, and release, as well as energy allocation to special functions at critical times (Table 3.1).

Neurobiology and endocrinology have merged considerably in recent decades, however, with the discovery of **neurohormones**, hormones that act as chemical intermediates in the transfer of electrical activity from cell to cell. The classic example is acetylcholine, which is released from many nerve cell axonal terminals into a synapse (the junction between two nerve cells or a nerve cell and a muscle cell), and diffuses across the synapse (a slow process relative to nerve conduction) to produce a

TABLE 3.1	Some examples of functions of the vertebrate endocrine system

Source of Hormone and Abbreviation	Effects
Hypothalamus	
Thyrotropin releasing hormone, TRH	Stimulates TSH secretion
Prolactin inhibiting factor, PIF	Suppresses prolactin secretion
Pituitary gland	
Posterior lobe	
Oxytocin	Stimulates milk secretion, uterine contraction
Vasopressin (arginine vasopressin), AVP (antidiuretic hormone), ADH	Stimulates renal water absorption
Distal lobe	
Follicle stimulating hormone, FSH	Female: Stimulates ovarian follicle growth, estradiol synthesis
	Male: Stimulates spermatogenesis
Prolactin, PRL	Stimulates milk synthesis, synthesis of progesterone by the corpus luteum in some species
Thyrotropin, TSH	Stimulates synthesis and release of thyroid hormone
Thyroid gland	
Thyroxine, T4	Stimulates growth, differentiation, metabolism, heat production
Adrenal Glands	
Adrenal steroidogenic tissue	
Cortisol, corticosterone	Stimulates carbohydrate metabolism
Aldosterone	Stimulates sodium retention by kidney
Adrenal chromaffin tissue	
Epinephrine, E, and Norepinephrine, NE	Multiple stimulatory and inhibitory effects on nerves, muscles, cellular secretions, and metabolism
Ovary	
Estradiol (estrogen)	Stimulates female sexual development and behavior
Testes	
Testosterone (Leydig cells)	Stimulates male sexual development and behavior
Thymus Gland	
Thymic hormones	Stimulates proliferation and differentiation of lymphocytes
Pancreatic Islets	
Insulin	Lowers blood glucose; increases synthesis of protein, fat, and glycogen
Glucagon	Increases blood glucose

response, usually a depolarization or hyperpolarization in the next nerve cell. Thus, in most cases neural activity involves both electrical transmission and the release of a neurohormone, or neurotransmitter substance, to pass information from cell to cell.

The **pituitary gland** and **hypothalamus**, often called the **pituitary axis**, are present in all vertebrates (Figure 3–24). This complex acts as a major central regulator between input from the nervous system and output of hormones by the endocrine organs. Nerve activity directed into the hypothalamus causes the release of peptides (releasing factors) that are transported by the blood to distinct regions of the pituitary. They cause pituitary secretion of **tropins** (hormones that induce the release of the unique hormones of other endocrine glands). The release of thyroid hormone is a model of a negative feedback loop, that is common in hormonal systems.

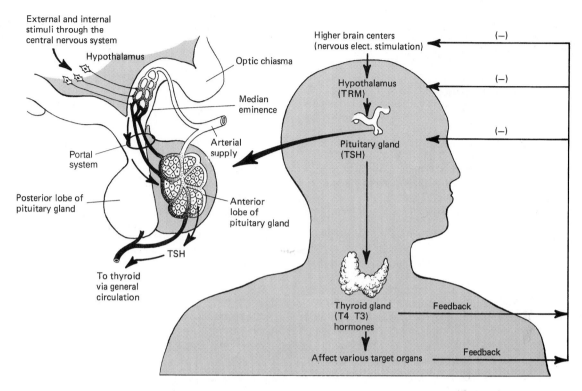

Figure 3–24   Pituitary axis and the release of thyroid hormones as an example of negative feedback to control hormonal release. High circulating levels of thyroid hormones in blood inhibit the release of thyroid releasing hormone from the hypothalamus and inhibit the release of thyroid stimulating hormone from the anterior lobe of the pituitary gland (indicated by minus signs), thereby lowering the rate of secretion of thyroid hormones from the thyroid gland.

■ Summary

The complex activities of vertebrates are supported by an equally complex morphology. Patterns of embryonic development are generally phylogenetically conservative, and many of the shared derived characters of vertebrates can be traced to their origins in the early embryo. In particular, the neural crest cells, which are unique to vertebrates, form many of the new derived characters of vertebrates, predominately those of the new anterior portion of the head.

An adult vertebrate can be viewed as a number of interacting systems. Here we have considered the systems involved in protection, support and movement, in the acquisition of energy and the support of metabolism, in excretion and reproduction, and in coordination and integration. Viewed in a phylogenetic context, there can be seen to be several key points in vertebrate evolution where

these systems can undergo profound functional and structural changes. The most important transition to consider is from the prevertebrate condition, as exemplified today by amphioxus, to the true vertebrate one, as exemplified by the living jawless vertebrates. Other important transitions include the ones from jawless to jawed vertebrates, involving many changes reflecting a more active mode of life, and from fish to tetrapod, involving changes reflecting the change in habitat from water to land. Within the jawed fishes, the teleost bony fishes, a major present-day radiation, frequently demonstrate very derived evolutionary features. Within the tetrapods, important transitions included the one from anamniote (amphibian) to amniote, and then within the amniotes the change from ectotherm to endotherm, convergently in birds and mammals.

■ References

Bereiter–Hahn, J., A. G. Matoltsy, and K. S. Richards (editors). 1986. *Biology of the Integument 2: Vertebrates.* Springer, New York, NY.

Brainerd, E. L., J. S. Ditelberg, and D. M. Bramble. 1993. Lung ventilation in salamanders and the evolution of vertebrate air-breathing mechanisms. *Biological Journal of the Linnean Society* 49:163–183.

Bramble, D. M., and D. B. Wake. 1985. Feeding mechanisms of lower vertebrates. Pages 230–261 in *Functional Vertebrate Morphology*, edited by M. Hildebrand, D. M. Bramble, K. F. Liem, and D. B. Wake. Harvard University Press, Cambridge, MA.

Bull, J. J. 1983. *Evolution of Sex Determining Mechanisms.* Benjamin-Cummings, Menlo Park, CA.

Burggren, W. W. 1987. Form and function in reptilian circulations. *American Zoologist* 27:5–19.

Clack, J. A. 1997. The evolution of tetrapod ears and the fossil record. *Brain, Behavior and Evolution* 50:198–212.

Crompton, A. W. 1995. Masticatory function in nonmammalian cynodonts and early mammals. Pages 55–75 in *Functional Morphology in Vertebrate Paleontology*, edited by J. J. Thomason. Cambridge University Press, Cambridge, UK.

Ehrhardt, A. A., and H. F. L. Meyer–Bahlburg. 1981. Effects of prenatal sex hormones on gender related behavior. *Science* 211:1312–1318.

Farmer, C. 1997. Did the lungs and intracardiac shunt evolve to oxygenate the heart in vertebrates? *Paleobiology* 23:358–372.

Gans, C. 1989. Stages in the origin of vertebrates: analysis by means of scenarios. *Biological Reviews* 64:221–268.

Hall, B. K. 1992. *Evolutionary Developmental Biology.* Chapman & Hall, UK.

Hanken, J., and B. K. Hall (editors). 1993. *The Skull*, volumes 1, 2, and 3. University of Chicago Press, Chicago, IL.

Hildebrand, M. 1980. The adaptive significance of tetrapod gait selection. *American Zoologist* 20:255–267.

Hildebrand, M. 1995. *Analysis of Vertebrate Structure*, 4th edition. Wiley, New York, NY.

Jablonka, E., and M. J. Lamb. 1990. The evolution of heteromorphic sex chromosomes. *Biological Reviews* 65(3):249–276.

Kardong, K. V. 1998. *Vertebrates—Comparative Anatomy, Function, Evolution*, 2nd edition. Wm. C. Brown Publishers, Dubuque, IA.

Karten, H. J. 1997. Evolutionary developmental biology meets the brain: the origins of mammalian cortex. *Proceedings of the National Academy of Science* 94:2800–2804.

Lacalli, T. C., N. D. Holland, and J. E. West. 1994. Landmarks in the anterior nervous central nervous system of amphioxus larvae. *Philosophical Transactions of the Royal Society, London*, B 344:165–185.

Lombard, R. E., and T. E. Hetherington. 1993. Structural basis of hearing and sound transmission. Pages 241–302 in *The Skull*, volume 3, edited by J. Hanken and B. K. Hall. University of Chicago Press, Chicago, IL.

Mallatt, J. 1996. Ventilation and the origin of jawed vertebrates: a new mouth. *Zoological Journal of the Linnean Society* 117:329–404.

Mittwoch, U. 1973. *Genetics of Sex Determination.* Academic, New York, NY.

Northcutt, R. G. 1990. Ontogeny and Phylogeny: A re-evaluation of conceptual relationships and some applications. *Brain, Behavior and Evolution* 36:116–140.

Northcutt, R. G. 1996. The agnathan ark: the origin of craniate brains. *Brain, Behavior and Evolution* 48:237–247.

Pridmore, P. A. 1994/95. Submerged walking in the epaulette shark *Hemiscyllium ocellatum* (Hemiscyllidae) and its implications for locomotion in rhipidistean fishes and early tetrapods. *ZACS (Zoology—Analyses of Complex Systems)* 98:278–297.

Ritter, D. 1995. Epaxial muscle function during locomotion in a lizard (*Varanus salvator*) and the proposal of a key innovation in the vertebrate axial musculoskeletal system. *Journal of Experimental Biology* 198:2477–2490.

Romer, A. S., and T. S. Parsons 1986. *The Vertebrate Body*, 6th edition. Saunders College Publishing, Philadelphia, PA.

Ruben, J. A., T. D. Jones, N. R. Geist, and W. J. Hillenius. 1997. Lung structure in theropod dinosaurs and early birds. *Science* 278:1267–1270.

Ruppert, E. E. 1994. Evolutionary origin of the vertebrate nephron. *American Zoologist* 34(4): 542–553.

Sage, H., and W. R. Gray. 1979. Studies on the evolution of elastin, I: phylogenetic distribution. *Comparative Biochemistry and Physiology* 64B:313–327.

Smith, H. W. 1953. *From Fish to Philosopher.* Little, Brown, Boston, MA.

Smith, K. K. 1992. The evolution of the mammalian pharynx. *Zoological Journal of the Linnean Society* 104:313–349.

Striedter, G.F. 1977. The telencephalon of tetrapods. *Brain, Behavior and Evolution* 49:179–213.

van Tienhoven, A. 1983. *Reproductive Physiology of Vertebrates*, 2d edition. Cornell University Press, Ithaca, NY.

Van Valen, L. 1973. Festschrift. *Science* 180:488.

Wake, M. H. 1989. Phylogenesis of direct development and viviparity in vertebrates. Pages 235–250 in *Dahlem Workshop Reports: Complex Organismal Functions: Integration and Evolution in Vertebrates.* Wiley, New York, NY.

Walker, W. F., Jr., and K. F. Liem. 1994. *Functional Anatomy of the Vertebrates—an Evolutionary Perspective*, 2nd edition. Saunders College Publishing, Philadelphia, PA.

Wilson, J. D., F. W. George, and J. E. Griffin. 1981. The hormonal control of sexual development. *Science* 211:1278–1284.

CHAPTER
4

Homeostasis and Energetics: Water Balance, Temperature Regulation, and Energy Use

In the preceding chapter we described some of the structural complexities of vertebrates, and here we consider the way those structures work. Vertebrates are complicated organisms: In particular they maintain very different conditions inside their bodies from the conditions in the environment immediately external to them. The concentrations of water, ions, and molecules inside the body of a vertebrate have profound effects on biochemical and physiological mechanisms, and they must be regulated within specific limits. Temperature affects both the biochemical processes of life and the cellular environment within which those processes take place. Regulation of their internal conditions (homeostasis) is a central part of the biology of vertebrates. Structure and function are usually tightly coupled—changing the form of a structure is likely to change its function as well. Thus, the evolution of vertebrate morphology has been accompanied by changes in the ways that vertebrates work. Some kinds of specializations of vertebrates are mutually exclusive, whereas others are mutually compatible and can be combined in the same organism. The relationships between structure and function are often reflected in broad aspects of the biology of vertebrates and directly affect their ecology and behavior. These relationships are also intimately related to the characteristics of the environments in which vertebrates live; for example, many of the problems faced by terrestrial and aquatic vertebrates are quite different. In this chapter we describe the basic aspects of homeostasis of vertebrates and how they have changed in major evolutionary steps, including the transition from aquatic to terrestrial life or from ectothermy to endothermy.

■ The Internal Environment of Vertebrates

Seventy to eighty percent of the body mass of most vertebrates is water, and many of the chemical reactions that release energy or synthesize new compounds take place in an aqueous environment containing a complex mixture of ions and other solutes. Some ions are cofactors that control the rates of metabolic processes; others are involved in the regulation of pH, the stability of cell membranes, or the electrical activity of nerves. Metabolic substrates and products must move from sites of synthesis to the sites of utilization. Almost everything that happens in the body tissues of vertebrates involves water, and maintaining the concentrations of water and solutes within narrow limits is a vital activity.

Temperature, too, is critical in the function of organisms. Biochemical reactions are temperature sensitive. In general, the rates of reactions increase as temperature increases, but not all reactions have the same sensitivity to temperature. Furthermore, the permeability of cell membranes and other features of the cellular environment are sensitive to temperature. A metabolic pathway is a series of chemical reactions in which the product of one reaction is the substrate for the next, yet each of these reactions may have a different sensitivity to temperature, so a change in temperature can mean that too much or too little substrate is produced to sustain the next reaction in the series. To complicate the process of regulation of substrates and products even more, the chemical reactions take place in a cellular milieu that itself is changed by temperature. Clearly, the smooth functioning of metabolic pathways is greatly simplified if an organism can limit the range of temperatures its tissues experience.

From the perspective of environmental physiology, an organism can be described as a complex of self-sustaining exchanges with the environment. Energy is the basis of these exchanges. Vertebrates gain energy from the environment as food and as heat; they use energy for activity, growth, and reproduction; and they release energy as waste products and as heat.

In this chapter we describe some of the mechanisms that vertebrates use to regulate their exchanges of water and heat with the environment, and the significance of those mechanisms in the use of energy by vertebrates.

■ Exchange of Water and Ions

In a sense, an organism can be thought of as an aqueous solution of organic and inorganic substances contained within a leaky membrane, the body surface. Exchange of material and energy with the environment is essential to the survival of the organism, and much of that exchange is regulated by the body surface. The significance of differential permeability of the skin to various compounds is particularly conspicuous in the case of aquatic vertebrates, but it applies to terrestrial vertebrates as well. Both active and passive processes of exchange are used by vertebrates to regulate their internal concentrations in the face of varying external conditions.

The Vertebrate Kidney

The cells of an organism can exist over only a narrow range of solute concentrations of the body fluids. Another area of narrow tolerance is in the accumulation of wastes. The small nitrogen-containing molecules that result from protein catabolism are toxic and are an especially important category of wastes. The vertebrate kidney has evolved superb capacities for homeostatic control of water balance and waste excretion.

The adult vertebrate kidney consists of hundreds to millions of tubular **nephrons**, each of which produces urine. The primary function of the nephron is removing excess water, salts, waste metabolites, and foreign substances from the blood. In this process, the blood is first filtered through the **glomerulus**, a structure unique to vertebrates (Figure 4–1). Each glomerulus is composed of a leaky arterial capillary tuft encapsulated within a sievelike filter. Arterial blood pressure forces fluid into the nephron to form an **ultrafiltrate**, composed of blood minus blood cells and larger molecules. The ultrafiltrate is then processed to return essential metabolites (glucose, amino acids, and so on) and water to the general circulation. When necessary, the walls of the nephron actively excrete toxins. These actions take place in the **proximal convoluted tubules** (PCT) and **distal convoluted tubules** (DCT) of the nephron (Figure 4–2). Finally, wastes are excreted as urine to the exterior.

Regulation of Ions and Body Fluids

The first vertebrates, the ostracoderms, probably had ion levels like those of their marine invertebrate ancestors, which, presumably, were like those of most living marine invertebrates. The solute concentrations in the body fluids of many marine invertebrates are similar to those in seawater, as are those of hagfishes (Tables 4.1 and 4.2). In contrast, solute levels are greatly reduced in the blood of all other vertebrates, a characteristic shared only with invertebrates that have penetrated estuaries, fresh waters, or the terrestrial environment.

The presence of solutes in seawater or blood plasma lowers the kinetic activity of water. Therefore, water flows from a dilute solution (high kinetic activity of water) to a more concentrated solution (low kinetic activity), a phenomenon called **osmosis**. The osmotic concentrations of various animals and of seawater are shown in Table 4.1. In most marine invertebrates and the hagfishes, the body

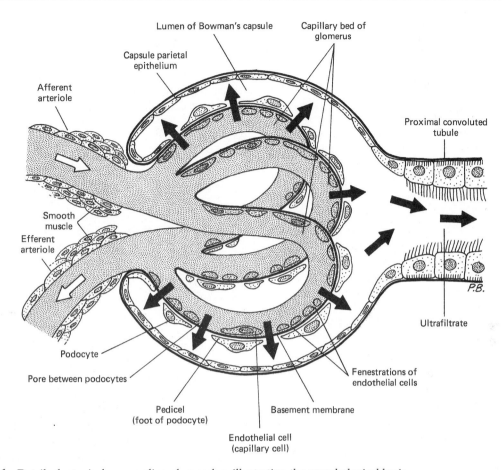

Figure 4–1   Detail of a typical mammalian glomerulus, illustrating the morphological basis for its function.

fluids are in osmotic equilibrium with seawater; that is, they are **isosmolal** to seawater (approximately 1000 millimoles per kg of water [mmoles·kg^{-1}]). Body fluid concentrations in marine teleosts and lampreys are between 350 and 450 mmoles·kg^{-1}. Therefore, water flows outward from their blood to the sea. In chondrichthyans the osmolality of the blood is slightly higher than that of seawater, and water flows from sea to blood. These osmolal differences are specified by the terms **hyposmolal** (marine teleosts and lampreys) and **hyperosmolal** (coelacanth and chondrichthyans). Freshwater fishes are hyperosmolal to the medium, but through reduction in NaCl their blood osmolality is lower than that of their marine counterparts (Table 4.1). The water and salt balance of teleosts is constantly threatened by either (1) osmotic loss of water and salt gain when in seawater, or (2) osmotic gain of water and loss of salts when in fresh water. [For additional details see Evans (1980) and Nishimura and Imai (1982).]

Most fishes are **stenohaline** (*steno* = narrow, *haline* = salt): They inhabit either fresh water or seawater and survive only modest changes in salinity. Because they remain in one environment, the magnitude and direction of the osmotic gradient to which they are exposed is stable. Some fishes, however, are **euryhaline** (*eury* = wide): They inhabit both fresh water and seawater and tolerate large changes in salinity. In euryhaline species the water and salt gradients are reversed as they move from one medium to the other.

Freshwater Organisms: Teleosts and Amphibians   Several mechanisms are involved in the salt and water regulation of vertebrates that live in fresh water (Figure 4–2). The body surface of fishes has low permeability to water and to ions. However, fishes cannot entirely prevent osmotic exchange. Gills, which are permeable to gases, are also permeable to water. As a result, most water and ion movements take place across the gill surfaces. Water is

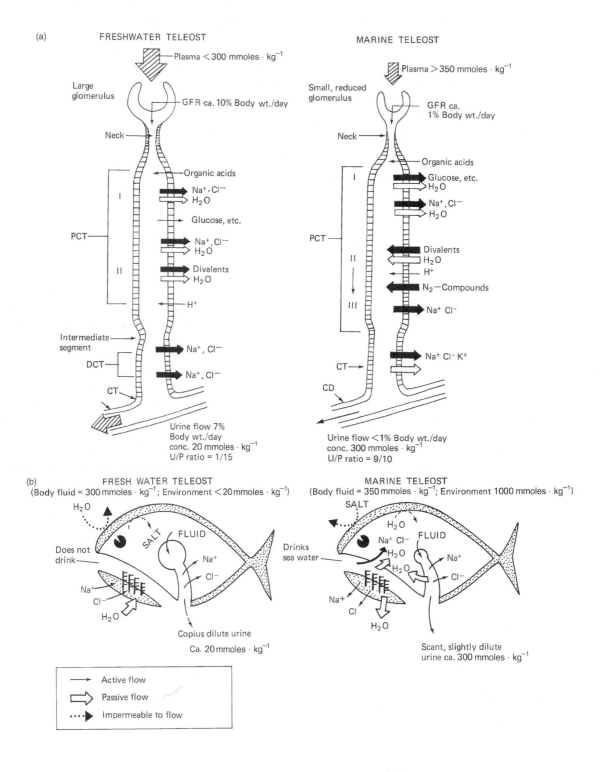

(a)

FRESHWATER TELEOST

Plasma < 300 mmoles · kg⁻¹

Large glomerulus

GFR ca. 10% Body wt./day

Neck

Organic acids
Na⁺, Cl⁻
H₂O
Glucose, etc.
Na⁺, Cl⁻
H₂O
Divalents
H₂O
H⁺

PCT

I

II

Intermediate segment
DCT
Na⁺, Cl⁻
Na⁺, Cl⁻
CT

Urine flow 7% Body wt./day
conc. 20 mmoles · kg⁻¹
U/P ratio = 1/15

MARINE TELEOST

Plasma > 350 mmoles · kg⁻¹

Small, reduced glomerulus

GFR ca. 1% Body wt./day

Neck

Organic acids
Glucose, etc.
H₂O
Na⁺, Cl⁻
H₂O
Divalents
H₂O
H⁺
N₂—Compounds
Na⁺ Cl⁻

PCT

I

II

III

Na⁺ Cl⁻ K⁺

CT
CD

Urine flow < 1% Body wt./day
conc. 300 mmoles · kg⁻¹
U/P ratio = 9/10

(b)

FRESH WATER TELEOST
(Body fluid = 300 mmoles · kg⁻¹; Environment < 20 mmoles · kg⁻¹)

H₂O
SALT
FLUID
Does not drink
Na⁺
Cl⁻
H₂O
Na⁺
Cl⁻

Copius dilute urine
Ca. 20 mmoles · kg⁻¹

MARINE TELEOST
(Body fluid = 350 mmoles · kg⁻¹; Environment 1000 mmoles · kg⁻¹)

SALT
H₂O
Na⁺ Cl⁻
H₂O
H₂O
FLUID
Drinks sea water
Na⁺
Cl⁻
H₂O
Na⁺
Cl⁻

Scant, slightly dilute urine ca. 300 mmoles · kg⁻¹

→ Active flow
⇒ Passive flow
····▶ Impermeable to flow

gained by osmosis, and ions are lost by diffusion. To compensate for this influx of water, the kidney produces a large volume of urine. To reduce salt loss, the urine is diluted by actively reabsorbing salts. Indeed, urine processing in a freshwater teleost provides a simple model of vertebrate kidney function. A freshwater teleost does not drink water, because osmotic water movement is already providing more water intake than it needs—drinking would only increase the amount of water it had to excrete via the kidneys.

The large glomeruli of freshwater teleosts produce a copious flow of urine, but the glomerular ultrafiltrate is isosmolal to the blood and contains essential blood salts. To conserve salt, ions are reabsorbed across the proximal and distal convoluted tubules. Because the distal convoluted tubule is impermeable to water, the urine becomes less concentrated as ions are removed from it. Ultimately, the urine becomes hyposmolal to the blood. In this way the water that was absorbed across the gills is removed and ions are conserved. Nonetheless, some ions are lost in the urine in addition to those lost by diffusion across the gills. Salts from food compensate for some of this loss. In addition, freshwater teleosts have special cells located in the gills that absorb sodium and chloride ions from fresh water. These ions must be moved by active transport against a concentration gradient, and this requires energy (Kirschner 1995).

Freshwater amphibians face similar osmotic problems. The entire body surface of amphibians is involved in the active uptake of ions from the water. Like freshwater fishes, aquatic amphibians do not drink. Acidity inhibits this active transport of ions in both amphibians and fishes, and inability to maintain internal ion concentrations is one of the causes of death of these animals in habitats acidified by acid precipitation.

Marine Organisms: Teleosts and Other Fishes   The osmotic and ionic gradients of vertebrates in seawater are largely the reverse of those experienced by freshwater vertebrates. Seawater is more concentrated than the body fluids of vertebrates, so there is a net outflow of water by osmosis and a net inward diffusion of ions.

Teleosts   The integument of marine fishes, like that of freshwater teleosts, is highly impermeable, so that most osmotic and ion movements occur across the gills (Figure 4–2). The kidney glomeruli are small and the glomerular filtration rate is low. Less urine is formed, and the water lost in urine is reduced. Marine teleosts lack a water-impermeable distal convoluted tubule. As a result, urine leaving the nephron is less copious but more concentrated than that of freshwater teleosts, although it is always hyposmolal to blood. To compensate for osmotic dehydration, marine teleosts do something unusual—they drink seawater. Sodium and chloride ions are actively absorbed across the lining of the gut, and water flows by osmosis into the blood. Estimates of seawater consumption vary, but many species drink in excess of 25 percent of their body weight per day and absorb 80 percent of this ingested water. Of course, drinking seawater to compensate for osmotic water loss increases the influx of sodium and chloride ions. To compensate for this salt loading, discrete cells, called **chloride**

Figure 4–2   Kidney structure and function of marine and freshwater teleosts. (a) Schematic comparison of nephron structure and functions in a freshwater and marine teleost fish. GFR is the glomerular filtration rate at which the ultrafiltrate is formed, expressed in percentage of body weight per day. PCT is the proximal convoluted tubule (in fishes sometimes referred to as the proximal tubule). Two segments (I and II) of the PCT are recognized in both freshwater and marine teleosts. Segment III of the PCT of marine teleosts is sometimes equated with the DCT (distal convoluted tubule) of freshwater teleosts. Darkened arrows represent active movements of substances, open arrows passive movement, and hatched arrows indicate by their size the relative magnitude of fluid flow. Note that Na^+ and Cl^- are reabsorbed in the PCT segment I and in the CT (collecting tubule) in both freshwater and marine teleosts; water flows osmolally across the PCT in both freshwater and marine teleosts but only across the CT of marine teleosts. Water permeability of the CT (and also the DCT) is therefore low in freshwater teleosts. U/P, ultrafiltrate to blood plasma concentration ratio—is a measure of the concentrating power of a nephron. (b) General scheme of the osmolal and ionic gradients encountered by freshwater and marine teleosts.

TABLE 4.1	Representative concentrations of sodium and chloride and osmolality of the blood in vertebrates and marine invertebrates. Concentrations are expressed in millimoles per kilogram of water; all values are reported to the nearest 5 units

Type of Animal	$mmole \cdot kg^{-1}$	Na^+	Cl^-	Other Major Osmotic Factor	Source
Seawater	~1000	475	550		
Fresh water	<10	~5	~5		
Marine invertebrates					
Coelenterates, mollusks, etc.	~1000	470	545		1
Crustacea	~1000	460	500		1
Marine vertebrates					
Hagfishes	~1000	535	540		2
Lamprey	~300	120	95		2
Teleosts	<350	180	150		3
Coelacanth	<1000 to 1180	180	200	Urea 375	4, 10
Elasmobranch (bull shark)	1050	290	290	Urea 360	5
Holocephalian	~1000	340	345	Urea 280	9
Freshwater vertebrates					
Polypterids	200	100	90		3
Acipenserids	250	130	105		3
Primitive neopterygians	280	150	130		3
Dipnoans	240	110	90		3
Teleosts	<300	140	120		3
Elasmobranch (bull shark)	680	245	220	Urea 170	5
Elasmobranch (freshwater rays)	310	150	150		6
Amphibians*	~250	~100	~80		7
Terrestrial vertebrates					
Reptiles	350	160	130		8
Birds	320	150	120		8
Mammals	300	145	105		8

*Ion levels and osmolality highly variable, but tend toward 200 $mmole \cdot kg^{-1}$ in fresh water.

Sources: 1. W. T. W. Potts and G. J. Parry, 1964, Osmotic and Ionic Regulation in Animals, Macmillan, New York, NY. 2. J. D. Robertson, 1954, Journal of Experimental Biology 31:424–442. 3. M. R. Urist et al., 1972, Comparative Biochemistry and Physiology 42:393–408. 4. G. E. Pickford and F. G. Grant, 1964, Science 155:568–570. R. W. Griffith et al., 1975, Journal of Experimental Zoology 192:165–171. 5. T. B. Thorson et al., 1973, Physiological Zoology 46:29–42. 6. T. B. Thorson et al., 1967, Science 158:375–377. 7. P. J. Bentley, 1971, Endocrines and Osmoregulation, Zoophysiology and Ecology Series, volume 1, Springer, New York, NY. 8. C. L. Prosser, 1973, Comparative Animal Physiology, 3d edition, Saunders College Publishing, Philadelphia, PA. 9. L. J. Read, 1971, Comparative Biochemistry and Physiology, 39A:185–192. 10. D. H. Evans, 1979, Comparative Physiology of Osmoregulation in Animals, edited by G. M. O. Maloiy, Academic, New York, NY.

TABLE 4.2	Intracellular concentration of major inorganic ions in marine invertebrates. (Concentration values are in millimoles per liter; compare with Table 4.1.)*

	Na^{++}	Cl^-	K^+	Ca^{2+}	Mg^{2+}
Seawater	475	550	10	10	53
Marine invertebrates	54–325	54–380	48–175	3–89	8–96
Vertebrates					
Hagfishes	122	107	117	2	13
All others	8–45	11–30	83–185	2–9	7–11

*Note that the monovalent ions Na^+ and Cl^- are reduced relative to seawater, and K^+ increased in all animals. For divalent cations, especially Mg^{2+}, a reduction is found in all vertebrates but not in all marine invertebrates.

cells, located in the gills, actively pump sodium and chloride ions outward against a large concentration gradient.

Hagfishes and Chondrichthyans   Hagfishes minimize their problems with ion balance by regulating only divalent ions and reduce osmotic water movement by being nearly isosmolal to seawater. Chondrichthyans and coelacanths also minimize osmotic flow by maintaining the internal concentration of the body fluid close to that of seawater. These animals retain nitrogen-containing compounds (primarily urea and trimethylamine oxide) to produce osmolalities that are usually slightly hyperosmolal to seawater (Table 4.1). As a result, chondrichthyans gain water by osmotic diffusion across the gills and need not drink seawater. This net influx of water permits large kidney glomeruli, as in freshwater teleosts, to produce high filtration rates and therefore rapid cleansing of the blood. Urea is very soluble and diffuses through most biological membranes, but the gills of chondrichthyans are nearly impermeable to urea and the kidney tubules actively reabsorb it. With internal ion concentrations that are low relative to seawater, chondrichthyans experience ion influxes across the gills as do marine teleosts. Unlike the gills of marine teleosts, those of chondrichthyans have low ion permeabilities (less than 1 percent that of teleosts). Chondrichthyans generally do not have highly developed salt-excreting cells in the gills. Rather, they achieve ion balance by secreting from the rectal gland a fluid that is approximately isosmolal to body fluids and seawater, but contains higher concentrations of sodium and chloride ions.

The urea and trimethylamine oxide in the blood of chondrichthyans also contribute to buoyancy. Chondrichthyans are more dense than seawater, so they sink when they are motionless. Sharks and rays lack the gas-filled swim bladders that bony fishes use to adjust their buoyancy, but many sharks have large, oil-filled livers. The oil is lighter than water, and the large size of the liver helps to make a shark buoyant. The Port Jackson shark (*Heterodontus portjacksoni*), however, has a small liver with a low oil content that does not contribute significantly to its buoyancy. Urea and trimethylamine oxide in the blood and muscle tissue of Port Jackson sharks provide positive buoyancy because they are less dense than an equal volume of water (Withers et al. 1994). Chloride ions also provide positive buoyancy, whereas sodium and protein are denser than water and are negatively buoyant.

The net effect of these solutes is a significant positive buoyancy.

Freshwater Elasmobranchs and Marine Amphibians
Some elasmobranchs are euryhaline—sawfishes, some sting rays, and bull sharks are examples. In seawater bull sharks retain high levels of urea, but in fresh water their blood urea levels decline. Sting rays in the family Potamotrygonidae spend their entire lives in fresh water and have very low blood urea concentrations. Their blood sodium and chloride ion concentrations are 35 to 40 percent below those in sharks that enter fresh water, and only slightly above levels typical of freshwater teleosts (Table 4.1). The potamotrygonids may have existed in the Amazon basin for tens of millions of years, and their reduced salt and water gradients may reflect long adaptation to fresh water. When exposed to increased salinity, potamotrygonids do not increase the concentration of urea in the blood as euryhaline elasmobranchs do, even though the enzymes required to produce urea are present. Apparently their long evolution in fresh water has led to an increase in the permeability of their gills to urea and reduced the ability of their kidney tubules to reabsorb it.

Most amphibians are found in freshwater or terrestrial habitats. One of the few species that occurs in salt water is the crab-eating frog, *Rana cancrivora*. This frog inhabits intertidal mudflats in southeast Asia and is exposed to 80 percent seawater at each high tide. During seawater exposure, the frog allows its blood ion concentrations to rise and thus reduces the ionic gradient. In addition, proteins are deaminated and the ammonia is rapidly converted to urea, which is released into the blood. Blood urea rises from 20 to 30 mmoles·kg^{-1}, and the frogs become hyperosmolal to the surrounding water. In this sense *Rana cancrivora* functions like an elasmobranch and absorbs water osmotically. Frog skin, unlike that of elasmobranchs, is permeable to urea and urea is rapidly lost. To compensate for this loss, the activity of the urea-synthesizing enzymes is very high. The tadpoles of *Rana cancrivora*, like most tadpoles, lack urea-synthesizing enzymes until late in their development. Thus, tadpoles of crab-eating frogs must use a method of osmoregulation different from that of adults. The tadpoles have extrarenal salt-excreting cells in the gills, and by pumping ions outward as they diffuse inward, the tadpoles maintain their blood hyposmolal to seawater in the same manner as marine teleosts.

Nitrogen Excretion by Vertebrates

Vertebrates require food in proportion to their activity. Metabolism of carbohydrates and fats (composed of carbon, hydrogen, and oxygen) produces carbon dioxide and water, which are easily voided. Proteins and nucleic acids are another matter, for they contain nitrogen. When protein is metabolized, the nitrogen is enzymatically reduced to ammonia through a process called deamination. Ammonia is very diffusible and soluble in water but also extremely toxic. Rapid excretion of ammonia is therefore crucial. Differences in how ammonia is excreted are partly a matter of the availability of water and partly the result of phylogeny. Nitrogen is eliminated by most vertebrates as ammonia, as urea, or as uric acid. Most vertebrates excrete all three of these substances, but the proportions of the three compounds differ among the groups of vertebrates (Figure 4–3).

Fishes and Amphibians   Many aquatic invertebrates excrete ammonia directly, as do vertebrates with gills, permeable skins, or other permeable membranes that contact water. Excretion of nitrogenous wastes as ammonia is termed **ammonotelism**, excretion as urea is **ureotelism**, and excretion as uric acid is **uricotelism**. Urea is synthesized from ammonia in

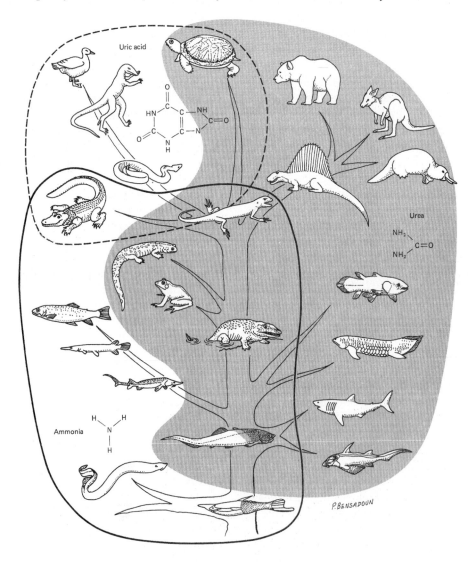

Figure 4–3   Phylogenetic distribution of the three major nitrogenous wastes in vertebrates. The types of wastes excreted by extinct vertebrates are unknown; examples merely provide visual continuity to the phylogeny. (Modified from B. Schmidt–Nielsen, 1972, pages 79–103 in *Nitrogen Metabolism and the Environment*, edited by J. W. Campbell and L. Goldstein, Academic, London, UK.)

a cellular enzymatic process called the **urea cycle**. Urea synthesis requires greater expenditure of energy than does ammonia production. The value of ureotelism, therefore, lies in the benefits derived from urea itself, not in energy economy.

Urea has two advantages. First, it is retained by some marine vertebrates to counter osmotic dehydration. A second function of urea synthesis is the detoxification of ammonia under environmental circumstances that prevent its rapid elimination. The less toxic urea can be concentrated in urine, thus conserving water.

Ureotelism probably evolved independently several times. Perhaps ureotelism developed in early freshwater fishes to avoid osmotic dehydration as they reinvaded the sea, as exemplified by chondrichthyans and coelacanths. In other instances ureotelism may have evolved in response to desiccation. Ureotelism was preadaptive for invasion of the land, because it allowed nitrogen to be retained in a detoxified state until sufficient water was available for excretion.

A fascinating example of this preadaptation was discovered in the ammonotelic African lungfish, *Protopterus*, by the late Homer Smith. During drought lungfishes estivate and slowly oxidize their carbohydrate, fat, and protein stores. The ammonia is detoxified and urea accumulates, increasing body fluid osmolality. This reduces the vapor pressure across the lung surface and water loss through evaporation. When rains return, the lungfishes rapidly take up water and excrete the accumulated urea. An analogous process takes place in some spadefoot toads that inhabit arid environments (see Chapter 16). Ureotelism may have been similarly advantageous to the first Devonian tetrapods.

Mammals The capacity of the mammalian kidney to conserve water, rid the body of nitrogenous and other wastes, and maintain a narrow ion and acid–base variation is essential to mammalian life. Only with the concentrating powers of the mammalian kidney could mammals have invaded so many diverse and severe environments. Understanding the mammalian kidney is a key factor in understanding the success of mammals.

The mammalian kidney is a highly derived organ composed of millions of nephrons, the basic microanatomical units of kidney structure that are recognizable in all vertebrates. Each nephron is composed of a glomerulus that filters the blood and a long tubular conduit in which the chemical composition of the filtrate is altered. The mammalian kidney is capable of producing a urine more concentrated than that of any nonamniote and, in most cases, more concentrated than that of birds as well (Table 4.3).

TABLE 4.3	Maximum urine concentrations of tetrapods		
Species		**Maximum Observed Urine Concentration (mmole·kg⁻¹)**	**Approximate Urine: Plasma Concentration Ratio**
Shingle-back lizard (*Trachydosaurus rugosus*)		300	0.95
Pelican (*Pelecanus erythrorhynchos*)		700	approx. 2
Savanna sparrow (*Passerculus sandwichensis*)		2000	4.4
Human (*Homo sapiens*)		1430	4
Bottlenose porpoise (*Tursiops truncatus*)		1600–1800	approx. 5
Hill kangaroo (*Macropus robustus*)		2730	7–8
Camel (*Camelus dromedarius*)		2800	8
White rat (*Rattus norvegicus*)		2900	8.9
Cat (*Felis domesticus*)		3250	9.9
Pack rat (*Neotoma albigula*)		4250	11 (est.)
Marsupial mouse (*Dasycercus cristicauda*)		approx. 4000	12 (est.)
Kangaroo rat (*Dipodomys merriami*)		approx. 4650	12 (est.)
Vampire bat (*Desmodus rotundus*)		4650	14
Australian hopping mouse (*Notomys alexis*)		9370	22

Source: P. J. Bentley, 1959, *Journal of Physiology* 145:37–47; M. S. Gordon et al., 1982, *Animal Physiology*, 4th edition, Macmillan, New York, NY; R. L. Malvin and M. Rayner, 1958, *American Journal of Physiology*, 214:187–191; R. E. MacMillen, 1972, *Symposium of the Zoological Society of London* 31:147–174; W. N. McFarland and W. A. Wimsatt, 1976, *Comparative Biochemistry and Physiology* 28:985–1007; and K. Schmidt-Nielsen, 1964, *Desert Animals*, Oxford University Press, Oxford, UK.

This ability greatly reduces water loss and the need for water, and is important for several lineages of mammals that live in arid habitats.

The basic mechanism of urine concentration is removal of water from an ultrafiltrate, leaving behind the concentrated excretory residue. Because cells are unable to transport water directly, they use osmotic gradients to manipulate movements of water molecules. In addition, the cells lining the nephron actively reabsorb substances important to the body's economy from the ultrafiltrate and secrete toxic substances into it. The cells lining the nephron differ in permeability, molecular and ion transport activity, and reaction to the hormonal and osmotic environments in the surrounding body fluids.

The cells of the proximal convoluted tubule (PCT) have an enormous luminal surface area produced by long, closely spaced microvilli, and the cells contain many adenosine 5'-triphosphate (ATP) producing mitochondria (Figure 4–4). These struc-

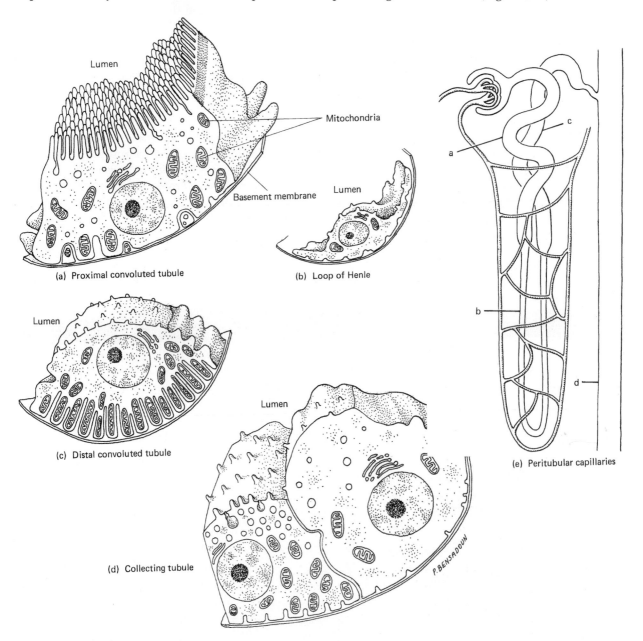

Figure 4–4 The structure of the cells lining the walls of the mammalian nephron: (a) proximal convoluted tubule; (b) loop of Henle; (c) distal convoluted tubule; (d) collecting tubule. In part (e) the letters correspond to the detailed drawings.

tural features reflect the function of the PCT in rapid, massive transport of sodium from the lumen of the tubule to the peritubular space and capillaries; sodium transport is followed by passive movement of chloride to the peritubular space to neutralize electric charge (Figure 4–5). Water then flows osmotically in the same direction. Farther

down the nephron, the cells of the thin segment of the loop of Henle are waferlike and contain fewer mitochondria. The descending limb permits passive flow of sodium and water, and the ascending limb actively removes sodium from the ultrafiltrate. Finally, cells of the collecting tubule appear to be of two kinds. Most seem to be suited to the relatively

(a) BODY HYDRATED — ADH ABSENT — COPIOUS, DILUTE URINE

Figure 4–5 Diagram showing how the mammalian kidney produces dilute urine when the body is hydrated and concentrated urine when the body is dehydrated. Black arrows indicate active transport and white arrows indicate passive flow. The numbers represent the approximate osmolality of the fluids in the indicated regions. Percentages are the volumes of the forming urine relative to the volume of the initial ultrafiltrate. (a) When blood osmolality drops below normal concentration (about 300 mmole·kg^{-1}), excess body water is excreted. (b) When osmolality rises above normal, water is conserved. (Based on F. H. Netter, 1973, *The CIBA Collection of Medical Illustrations*, volume 6, CIBA Publications, Summit, NJ.)

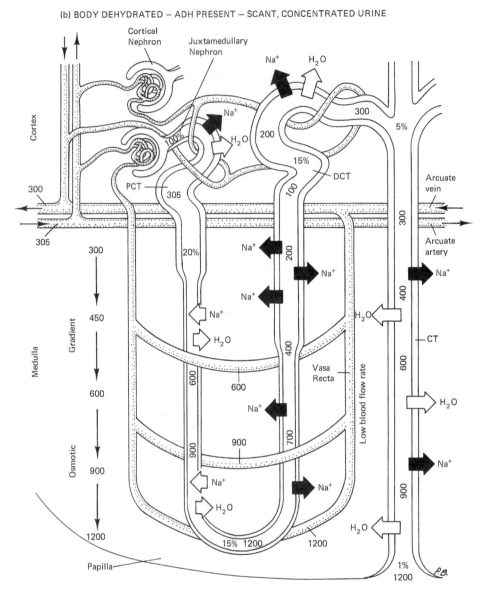

Figure 4–5 *(continued)*

impermeable state characteristic of periods of suffi-cient body water. Other cells are mitochondria rich and have a greater surface area. They are probably the cells that respond to the presence of antidiuretic hormone (ADH) from the pituitary gland, triggered by insufficient body fluid. Under the influence of ADH, the collecting tubule actively exchanges ions, pumps urea, and becomes permeable to water, which flows from the lumen of the tubule into the concentrated peritubular fluids.

The nephron's activity may be considered a six-step sequential process, each step localized in regions having special cell characteristics and dis-

tinctive variations in the osmotic environment. The first step is production of an ultrafiltrate at the glomerulus (Figure 4–5). The ultrafiltrate is isos-molal with blood plasma and resembles whole blood after the removal of (1) cellular elements, (2) substances with a molecular weight of 70,000 or greater (primarily proteins), and (3) substances with molecular weights between 15,000 and 70,000, depending on the shapes of the molecules. An average filtration rate for resting humans approxi-mates 120 milliliters of ultrafiltrate per minute. Obviously, a primary function of the nephron is reduction of the ultrafiltrate volume—to excrete

170 liters (45 gallons) of glomerular filtrate per day is impossible.

The second step in the production of the urine is the action of the **proximal convoluted tubule** (PCT, Figure 4–5) in decreasing the volume of the ultrafiltrate. The PCT cells have greatly enlarged lumenal surfaces that actively transport sodium and perhaps chloride ions from the lumen to the exterior of the nephron. Water flows osmotically through the PCT cells in response to the removal of sodium chloride. By this process about two-thirds of the salt is reabsorbed in the PCT, and the volume of the ultrafiltrate is reduced by the same amount. Although it is still very nearly isosmolal with blood, the substances contributing to the osmolality of the urine after it has passed through the PCT are at different concentrations than in the blood.

The next alteration occurs in the descending limb of the **loop of Henle**, which is a derived structure forund only in mammals. The thin, smooth-surfaced cells in the loop of Henle freely permit diffusion of sodium and water. Because the descending limb of the loop passes through tissues of increasing osmolality as it plunges into the medulla, water is lost from the urine and it becomes more concentrated. In humans the osmolality of the fluid in the descending limb may reach 1200 mmoles·kg^{-1}. Other mammals can achieve considerably higher concentrations. By this mechanism the volume of the forming urine is reduced to 25 percent of the initial filtrate volume, but it is still large. In an adult human, for example, 25 to 40 liters of fluid per day reach this stage, yet only a few liters will be urinated.

The fourth step takes place in the ascending limb of the loop of Henle, which possesses cells with large, numerous, densely packed mitochondria. The ATP produced by these organelles is utilized in actively removing sodium from the forming urine. Because these cells are impermeable to water, the volume of urine does not decrease and it enters the next segment of the nephron hyposmolal to the body fluids. Although this sodium-pumping, water-impermeable, ascending limb does not concentrate or reduce the volume of the forming urine, it sets the stage for these important processes.

The very last portion of the nephron changes in physiological character, but the cells closely resemble those of the ascending loop of Henle. This region, the **distal convoluted tubule** (DCT), is permeable to water. The osmolality surrounding the DCT is that of the body fluids, and water in the entering hyposmolal fluid flows outward and equilibrates osmotically. This process reduces the fluid volume to 5 to 20 percent of the original ultrafiltrate.

The final touch in the formation of a scant, highly concentrated mammalian urine occurs in the **collecting tubules**. Like the descending limb of the loop of Henle, the collecting ducts course through tissues of increasing osmolality, which withdraw water from the urine. The significant phenomenon associated with the collecting duct, and to a lesser extent with the DCT, is its conditional permeability to water. During excess fluid intake, the collecting duct demonstrates low water permeability: Only half of the water entering it may be reabsorbed and the remainder excreted. In this way a copious, dilute urine can be produced. When a mammal is dehydrated the collecting ducts and the DCT become very permeable to water and the final urine volume may be less than 1 percent of the original ultrafiltrate volume. In certain desert rodents so little water is contained in the urine that it crystallizes almost immediately on micturition.

A polypeptide called **antidiuretic hormone** (ADH; also known as **vasopressin**), is produced by specialized neurons in the hypothalamus, stored in the posterior pituitary, and released into the circulation whenever blood osmolality is elevated or blood volume drops. When present in the kidney, ADH increases the permeability of the collecting duct to water and facilitates water reabsorption to produce a scant, concentrated urine. The absence of ADH has the opposite effects. Alcohol inhibits the release of human ADH, induces a copious urine flow, and this frequently results in dehydrated misery the following morning.

The key to concentrated urine production clearly depends on the passage of the loops of Henle and collecting ducts through tissues with increasing osmolality. These osmotic gradients are formed and maintained within the mammalian kidney as a result of its structure (Figure 4–6), which sets it apart from the kidneys of other vertebrates. Particularly important are the structural arrangements within the kidney medulla of the descending and ascending segments of the loop of Henle and its blood supply, the **vasa recta**. These elements create a series of parallel tubes with flow passing in opposite directions in adjacent vessels (countercurrent flow). As a result, sodium secreted from the ascending limb of the loop of Henle diffuses into the medullary tissues to increase their osmolality, and this excess salt is distributed by the countercurrent flow to create a steep osmotic gradient within the medulla (see Fig-

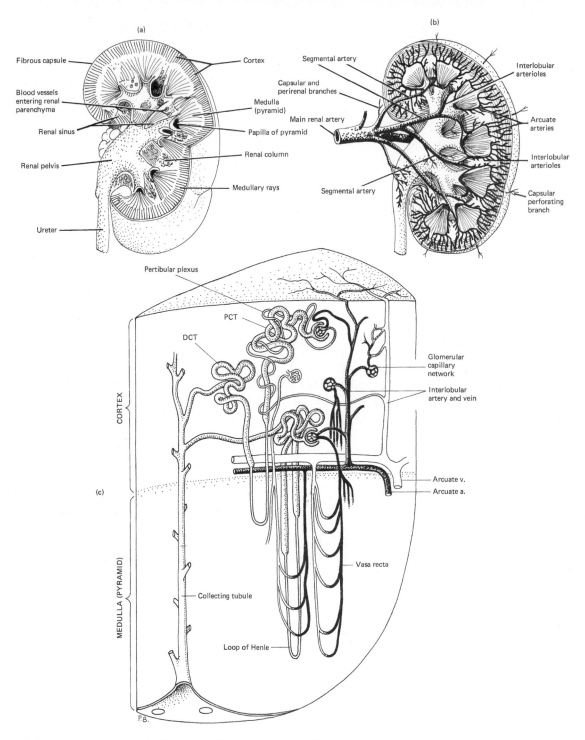

Figure 4–6 Gross morphology of the mammalian kidney exemplified by that of a human. (a) Structural divisions of the kidney and proximal end of the ureter; (b) the renal artery and its subdivisions in relation to the structural components of the kidney. The renal vein (not shown) and its branches parallel those of the artery; (c) enlarged diagram of a section extending from the outer cortical surface of the apex of a renal pyramid, the renal papilla. The general relationship of the nephrons and blood vessels to the gross structure of the kidney can be visualized by comparing these diagrams. (Based on F. H. Netter, 1973, *The CIBA Collection of Medical Illustrations*, volume 6, CIBA Publications, Summit, NJ; and H. W. Smith, 1956, *Principles of Renal Physiology*, Oxford University Press, New York, NY.)

ure 4–5b). The final concentration of a mammal's urine is determined by the amount of sodium accumulated in the fluids of the medulla. Physiological alterations in the concentration in the medulla result primarily from the effect of ADH on the rate of blood flushing the medulla. When ADH is present, blood flow into the medulla is retarded and salt accumulates to create a steep osmotic gradient. Another hormone, aldosterone, from the adrenal gland increases the rate of sodium secretion into the medulla to promote an increase in medullary salt concentration.

In addition to these physiological means of concentrating urine, a variety of mammals have morphological alterations of the medulla. Most mammals have two types of nephrons: those with a cortical glomerulus and abbreviated loops of Henle that do not penetrate far into the medulla, and those with juxtamedullary glomeruli, deep within the cortex, with loops that penetrate as far as the papilla of the renal pyramid (Figure 4–6c). Obviously, the longer, deeper loops of Henle experience large osmotic gradients along their lengths. The flow of blood to these two populations of nephrons seems to be independently controlled. Juxtamedullary glomeruli are more active in regulating water excretion; cortical glomeruli function in ion regulation. Finally, some desert rodents have exceptionally long renal pyramids. Thus, the loops of Henle and the vasa recta are extended and can produce large differences in osmolality from the cortical to the papillary ends. The maximum concentrations of urine measured from a given species of mammal correlate well with the length of its renal pyramids.

Fossils of early mammals suggest that they were primarily insectivores and carnivores with a high energy demand. This diet would be rich in protein, which, when metabolized, would produce large amounts of urea. Considerable water would be required to void this nitrogenous waste unless a means of concentrating urea was available. The unique concentrating power of the mammalian kidney may have been an early response to the accumulation of metabolic wastes from high-protein diets.

Diapsids and Turtles   All living representatives of the diapsid lineage are uricotelic, and uric acid and its salts account for 80 to 90 percent of urinary nitrogen in most species. Turtles also excrete a variable proportion of their nitrogenous wastes as salts of uric acid (Table 4.4).

The kidneys of diapsids and turtles lack the long loops of Henle that allow mammals to reduce the volume of urine and raise its osmotic concentration to several times the osmotic concentration of the blood plasma. Urine from the kidneys of diapsids and turtles consists of a moderately dilute solution of uric acid and ions. It is isosmolal with the blood plasma, or even somewhat hyposmolal to the blood. However, uric acid differs from urea in being only slightly soluble in water. It will precipitate from a dilute solution, and that is what happens when urine from the ureters enters the cloaca or bladder. (Many diapsids lack a urinary bladder entirely; others have an ephemeral bladder that is lost shortly after they hatch; and some diapsids and probably all turtles have a functional bladder throughout life.) The uric acid combines with ions

TABLE 4.4	Distribution of nitrogenous end products among diapsids and turtles		
	Percentage of Total Urinary Nitrogen		
Group	*Ammonia*	*Urea*	*Salts of Uric Acid*
Squamates			
Tuatara	3–4	10–28	65–80
Lizards and snakes	Small	0–8	90–98
Archosaurs			
Crocodilians	25	0–5	70
Birds	6–17	5–10	60–82
Turtles			
Aquatic	4–44	45–95	1–24
Desert	3–8	15–50	20–50

in the urine and precipitates as a light-colored mass that includes sodium, potassium, and ammonium salts of uric acid and also contains ions held by complex physical forces. When the uric acid and ions precipitate from solution, the urine becomes less concentrated. In effect, water is released and reabsorbed into the blood. In this respect, excretion of nitrogenous wastes as uric acid is even more economical of water than is excretion of urea, because the water used to produce urine is reabsorbed and reused.

Water is not the only substance that is reabsorbed from the cloaca, however. Many diapsids and turtles also reabsorb sodium ions and return them to the bloodstream. At first glance, that seems a remarkably inefficient thing to do. After all, energy was used to create the blood pressure that forced the ions through the walls of the glomerulus into the urine in the first place, and now more energy is being used in the cloaca to drive the active transport that returns the ions to the blood. The animal has used two energy-consuming processes and it is back where it started, with an excess of sodium ions in the blood. Why do that?

The solution of the paradox lies in a third water-conserving mechanism that is present in many diapsids and turtles, salt-secreting glands that provide an extrarenal pathway that disposes of salt with less water than the urine. In at least four groups of diapsids (lizards, snakes, crocodilians, and birds) some species possess glands specialized for the elective transport of ions out of the body (Peaker and Linzell 1975, Minnich 1982). Salt glands are widespread among lizards. In all cases it is the lateral nasal glands that excrete salt. The secretions of the glands empty into the nasal passages, and a lizard expels them by sneezing or by shaking its head. In birds, also, the lateral nasal gland has become specialized for salt excretion. The glands are situated in or around the orbit, usually above the eye. Marine birds (pelicans, albatrosses, penguins) have well-developed salt glands, as do many freshwater birds (ducks, loons, grebes), shorebirds (plovers, sandpipers), storks, flamingos, carnivorous birds (hawks, eagles, vultures), upland game birds, the ostrich, and the roadrunner. Depressions in the supraorbital region of the skull of the extinct aquatic birds *Hesperornis* and *Ichthyornis* suggest that salt glands were present in these forms as well.

In sea snakes (Hydrophiidae) and elephant-trunk snakes (Acrochordidae), the posterior sublingual gland secretes a salty fluid into the tongue sheath, from which it is expelled when the tongue is extended. In some species of homalopsines (a group of rear-fanged aquatic snakes from the Indoaustralian region) the premaxillary gland secretes salt. Salt-secreting glands on the dorsal surface of the tongue have been identified in several species of crocodiles, in a caiman, and in the American alligator.

The diversity of glands involved in salt excretion among diapsids indicates that this specialization has evolved independently in various groups. At least four different glands are used for salt secretion by diapsids, indicating that a salt gland is not an ancestral character for the group, and the differences between crocodilians and birds and between snakes and lizards suggest that salt glands are not ancestral either for archosaurs or for squamates.

Finally, in sea turtles and in the diamondback terrapin, a turtle that inhabits estuaries, the lachrymal gland secretes a salty fluid around the orbits of the eyes. Photographs of nesting sea turtles frequently show clear paths streaked by tears through the sand that adheres to the turtle's head. Those tears are the secretions of the salt glands.

Despite their different origins and locations, the functional properties of salt glands are quite similar. They secrete fluid containing primarily sodium or potassium cations and chloride or bicarbonate anions in high concentrations (Table 4.5). Sodium is the predominant cation in the salt gland secretions of marine vertebrates, and potassium is present in the secretions of terrestrial lizards, especially herbivorous species such as the desert iguana. Chloride is the major anion, and herbivorous lizards may also excrete bicarbonate ions.

The total osmolal concentration of the salt gland secretion may reach 2000 mmoles·kg^{-1}—more than six times the osmolal concentration of urine that can be produced by the kidney. This efficiency of excretion is the explanation of the paradox of active uptake of salt from the urine. As ions are actively reabsorbed, water follows passively, so an animal recovers both water and ions from the urine. The ions can then be excreted via the salt gland at much higher concentrations, with a proportional reduction in the amount of water needed to dispose of the salt. Thus, by investing energy in recovering ions from urine, diapsids and turtles with salt glands can conserve water by excreting ions through the more efficient extrarenal route.

Uricotelic Frogs   Terrestrial amphibians have long been considered ureotelic, aquatic forms ammonotelic. However, J. P. Loveridge (1970) discovered that, during the dry season, a period when

TABLE 4.5	Salt gland secretions from diapsids and turtles			
		Ion Concentration (mmole·kg^{-1})		
Species and Condition		Na^+	K^+	Cl^-
Lizards				
Desert iguana (*Dipsosaurus dorsalis*), estimated field conditions		180	1700	1000
Fringe-toed lizard (*Uma scoparia*), estimated field conditions		639	734	465
Snakes				
Sea snake (*Pelamis platurus*), salt loaded		620	28	635
Homalopsine snake (*Cerberus rhynchops*), salt loaded		414	56	—
Crocodilian				
Saltwater crocodile (*Crocodylus porosus*), natural diet		663	21	632
Birds				
Blackfooted albatross (*Diomeda nigripes*), salt loaded		800–900	—	—
Herring gull (*Larus argentatus*), salt loaded		718	24	—
Turtles				
Loggerhead sea turtle (*Caretta caretta*), seawater		732–878	18–31	810–992
Diamondback terrapin (*Malaclemys terrapin*), seawater		322–908	26–40	—

most frogs retire to a burrow and estivate, a South African frog, *Chiromantis xerampelina*, remains above ground. Even more surprising, its excretions contain uric acid; biochemically, *Chiromantis* is like a lizard. It has subsequently been shown that the South American frog *Phyllomedusa sauvagei* responds in the same way to aridity (Shoemaker et al. 1972). There is a lesson in these unusual findings: Evolutionary convergence works on all levels of biological organization—anatomical, behavioral, physiological, and biochemical—and its direction is determined by interactions with the environment.

■ Responses to Temperature

Vertebrates occupy habitats from cold polar latitudes to hot deserts. To appreciate this adaptability, we must consider how temperature affects a vertebrate such as a fish that has little capacity to maintain a difference between its body temperature and the temperature of the water around it (a poikilotherm). Organisms have been described as "bags of chemicals catalyzed by enzymes." This view, although narrow, emphasizes that organisms are subject to the laws of physics and chemistry. Because temperature influences the rates at which chemical reactions proceed, temperature vitally affects the life processes of organisms. Most chem-

ical reactions double or triple in rate for every rise of 10°C. We describe this change in rate by saying that the reaction has a Q_{10} of 2 or 3, respectively. A reaction that does not change rate with temperature has a Q_{10} equal to 1 (Figure 4–7).

The **standard metabolic rate** (SMR) of an organism is the minimum rate of oxygen consumption needed to sustain life. That is, the SMR includes the costs of ventilating the lungs or gills, of pumping blood through the circulatory system, of transporting ions across membranes, and of all the other activities that are necessary to maintain the integrity of an organism. The SMR does not include the costs of activities like locomotion or the cost of growth. The SMR is temperature sensitive, and that means that the energy cost of living is affected by changes in body temperature. If the SMR of a fish is 2 milliliters of oxygen per minute at 10°C and the Q_{10} response is 2, the fish will consume 4 milliliters of oxygen per minute at 20°C and 8 mL/min at 30°C.

Control of Body Temperature: Ectothermy and Endothermy

Because the rates of many biological processes are affected by temperature, it would probably be advantageous for any animal to be able to control its body temperature. However, the high heat capacity and heat conductivity of water make it dif-

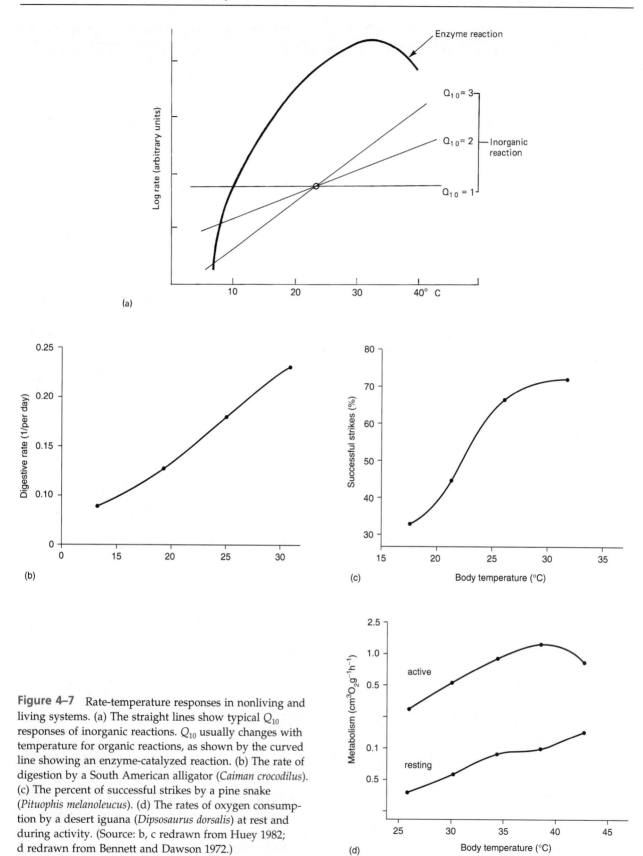

Figure 4–7 Rate-temperature responses in nonliving and living systems. (a) The straight lines show typical Q_{10} responses of inorganic reactions. Q_{10} usually changes with temperature for organic reactions, as shown by the curved line showing an enzyme-catalyzed reaction. (b) The rate of digestion by a South American alligator (*Caiman crocodilus*). (c) The percent of successful strikes by a pine snake (*Pituophis melanoleucus*). (d) The rates of oxygen consumption by a desert iguana (*Dipsosaurus dorsalis*) at rest and during activity. (Source: b, c redrawn from Huey 1982; d redrawn from Bennett and Dawson 1972.)

ficult for most fishes or aquatic amphibians to maintain a temperature differential between their bodies and their surroundings. Air has both a lower heat capacity and a lower conductivity than water, and the body temperatures of most terrestrial vertebrates are at least partly independent of the air temperature. Some aquatic vertebrates also have body temperatures substantially above the temperature of the water around them. Maintaining these temperature differentials requires thermoregulatory mechanisms, and these are well developed among vertebrates.

The classification of vertebrates as poikilotherms (*poikilo* = variable, *therm* = heat) and homeotherms (*homeo* = the same) was widely used through the middle of the twentieth century, but this terminology has become less appropriate as our knowledge of the temperature-regulating capacities of a wide variety of animals has become more sophisticated. Poikilothermy and homeothermy describe the variability of body temperature, and they cannot readily be applied to groups of animals. For example, mammals have been called homeotherms and fishes poikilotherms, but some mammals become torpid at night or in the winter and allow their body temperatures to drop 20°C or more from their normal levels, whereas many fishes live in water that changes temperature less than 2°C in an entire year. That example presents the contradictory situation of a homeotherm that experiences 10 times as much variation in body temperature as a poikilotherm.

Because of complications of that sort, it is very hard to use the words "homeotherm" and "poikilotherm" rigorously. Some mammalogists and ornithologists still retain those terms, but most biologists concerned with temperature regulation prefer the terms **ectotherm** and **endotherm**. They are *not* synonymous with poikilotherm and homeotherm because, instead of referring to the variability of body temperature, they refer to the sources of energy used in thermoregulation. Ectotherms (*ecto* = outside) gain their heat largely from external sources—by basking in the sun, for example, or by resting on a warm rock. Endotherms (*endo* = inside) largely depend on metabolic production of heat to raise their body temperatures. The source of the heat used to maintain body temperatures is the major difference between ectotherms and endotherms. Terrestrial ectotherms like squamates and turtles and endotherms like birds and mammals all have activity temperatures in the range 30 to 40°C (Table 4.6).

Endothermy and ectothermy are not mutually exclusive mechanisms of temperature regulation, and many animals use them in combination. In general, birds and mammals are endothermal, but some species make extensive use of external sources of heat. For example, roadrunners are predatory birds that live in the deserts of the southwestern United States and adjacent Mexico. On cold nights roadrunners become hypothermic, allowing their body temperatures to fall from the normal level of 38 to 39°C down to 33 to 35°C. In the morning they bask in the sun, raising the feathers on the back to expose an area of black skin in the interscapular region. Calculations indicate that a roadrunner can save 132 joules per hour by using solar energy instead of metabolism to raise its body temperature. Snakes are normally ectothermal, but the females of several species of python coil around their eggs and produce heat by rhythmic contraction of their trunk muscles. The rate of contraction increases as air temperature falls, and a female Indian python is able to maintain her eggs close to 30°C at air temperatures as low as 23°C. This heat production entails a substantial increase in the python's metabolic rate—at 23°C, a female python uses about 20 times as much energy when she is brooding as she does normally. Thus, generalizations about the body temperatures and thermoregulatory capacities of vertebrates must be made cautiously, and the actual mechanisms used to regulate body temperature must be studied carefully.

Ectothermal Thermoregulation

From the time of Aristotle onward, lizards, snakes, and amphibians have paradoxically been called cold blooded while they were thought to be able to tolerate extremely high temperatures. Salamanders frequently seek shelter in logs, and when a log is put on a fire, the salamanders it contains may come rushing out. Observations of this phenomenon gave rise to the belief that salamanders live in fire. In the first part of the twentieth century biologists were using similar lines of reasoning. In the desert lizards often sit on rocks. If you approach a lizard it runs away but the rock stays put, and touching the rock shows that it is painfully hot. Clearly, the reasoning went, the lizard must have been equally hot. Biologists marveled at the heat tolerance of lizards, and statements to this effect are found in authoritative textbooks of the period.

TABLE 4.6	Representative body temperatures of vertebrates. Body temperatures are those that the animals maintain when they are able to thermoregulate normally	
Group	*Body Temperature*	
	Primarily Ectothermal Groups	
Fishes		
Most fishes	Little different from water temperature	
Warm-bodied fishes (tunas, some sharks)	About 30°C in water of 20°C	
Amphibians		
Aquatic	Little different from water temperature	
Terrestrial	Usually slightly below air temperature because of evaporative cooling; some amphibians raise their body temperatures 5–10°C above air temperature by basking	
Amniotic ectotherms		
Turtles and crocodilians	From close to water temperature to about 35°C while thermoregulating	
Squamates	From 20–25°C for forest-dwelling tropical species, to 35–42°C for thermoregulating desert lizards	
	Primarily Endothermal Groups	
Birds	40–41°C	
Mammals		
Monotremes*	28–30°C	
Marsupials	33–36°C	
Placentals	36–38°C	

*Sloths, which are placentals, have body temperatures in this range.

A study of thermoregulation of lizards by Raymond Cowles and Charles Bogert (1944) demonstrated the falsity of earlier observations and conclusions. They showed that reptiles can regulate their body temperatures with considerable precision, and that the level at which the temperature is regulated is characteristic of a species. The implications of this discovery in terms of the biology of amphibians and reptiles are still being explored.

Energy Exchange Between an Organism and Its Environment A brief discussion of the pathways by which thermal energy is exchanged between a living organism and its environment is necessary to understand the thermoregulatory mechanisms employed by terrestrial animals. An organism can gain or lose energy by several pathways, and by adjusting the relative flow through various pathways an animal can warm, cool, or maintain a stable body temperature (Tracy 1982).

Figure 4–8 illustrates pathways of thermal energy exchange. Solar energy can reach an animal in several ways. Direct **solar radiation** impinges on an animal when it is standing in a sunny spot. In addition, solar energy is reflected from clouds and dust particles in the atmosphere, and from other objects in the environment, and reaches the animal by these circuitous routes. The wavelength distribution of the energy in all these routes is the same—the portion of the solar spectrum that penetrates the Earth's atmosphere. About half this energy is contained in the visible wavelengths of the solar spectrum (400 to 700 nanometers) and most of the rest is in the infrared region of the spectrum (> 700 nanometers).

Energy exchange in the **infrared** is an important part of the radiative heat balance. All objects, animate or inanimate, radiate energy at wavelengths determined by their absolute temperatures. Objects in the temperature range of animals and the Earth's surface (roughly −20 to +50°C) radiate in the infrared portion of the spectrum. Animals continuously radiate heat to the environment and receive infrared radiation from the environment. Thus, infrared radiation can lead to either heat gain or loss, depending on the relative temperature of the animal's body surface and the environmental sur-

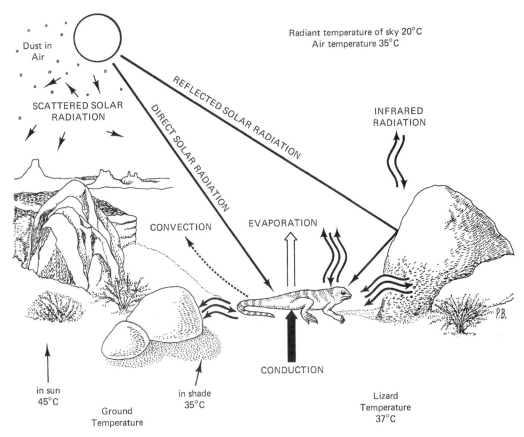

Figure 4–8 Energy is exchanged between a terrestrial organism and its environment by many pathways. These are illustrated in simplified form by a lizard resting on the floor of a desert arroyo. Small adjustments of posture or position can change the magnitude of the various routes of energy exchange and give a lizard considerable control over its body temperature.

faces and on the radiation characteristics of the surfaces themselves. In the example in Figure 4–8 the lizard is cooler than the sunlit rock in front of it and receives more energy from the rock than it loses to the rock. However, the lizard is warmer than the shaded side of the rock behind it and has a net loss of energy in that exchange. The radiative temperature of the clear sky is about 20°C, so the lizard loses energy by radiation to the sky.

Heat is exchanged between objects in the environment and the air via **convection**. If an animal's surface temperature is higher than air temperature, convection leads to heat loss; if the air is warmer than the animal, convection is a route of heat gain. In still air, convective heat exchange is accomplished by convective currents formed by local heating; but in moving air, forced convection replaces natural convection and the rate of heat exchange is greatly increased. In the example shown, the lizard is warmer than the air and loses heat by convection.

Conductive heat exchange resembles convection in that its direction depends on the relative temperatures of the animal and environment. Conductive loss occurs between the body and the substrate where they are in contact. It can be modified by changing the surface area of the animal in contact with the substrate and by changing the rate of heat conduction in the parts of the animal's body that are in contact with the substrate. In this example the lizard gains heat by conduction from the warm ground.

Evaporation of water occurs from the body surface and from the pulmonary system. Each gram of water evaporated represents a loss of about 2450 joules (the exact value changes slightly with temperature). Evaporation of water transfers heat from the animal to the environment, and thus represents a loss of heat. The inverse situation, condensation of water vapor on an animal, would produce heat gain, but it rarely occurs under natural conditions.

Metabolic heat production is the final pathway by which an animal can gain heat. Among ectotherms metabolic heat gain is usually trivial in relation to the heat derived directly or indirectly from solar energy. There are a few exceptions to that generalization, and some of them are discussed later. Endotherms, by definition, derive most of their heat energy from metabolism, but their routes of energy exchange with the environment are the same as those of ectotherms and must be balanced to maintain a stable body temperature.

Behavioral Control of Body Temperatures by Ectotherms
The behavioral mechanisms involved in ectothermal temperature regulation are quite straightforward and are employed by insects, birds, and mammals (including humans) as well as by ectothermal vertebrates (Avery 1979). Lizards, especially desert species, are particularly good at behavioral thermoregulation. Movement back and forth between sun and shade is the most obvious thermoregulatory mechanism they use. Early in the morning or on a cool day, lizards bask in the sun, whereas in the middle of a hot day they retreat to shade and make only brief excursions into the sun. Sheltered or exposed microhabitats may be sought out. In the morning when a lizard is attempting to raise its body temperature, it is likely to be in a spot protected from the wind. Later in the day when it is getting too hot it may climb into a bush or onto a rock outcrop where it is exposed to the breeze and its convective heat loss is increased.

The amount of solar radiation absorbed by an animal can be altered by changing the orientation of its body with respect to the sun, the body contour, and the skin color. All of these mechanisms are used by lizards. An animal oriented perpendicular to the sun's rays intercepts the maximum amount of solar radiation, and one oriented parallel to the sun's rays intercepts minimum radiation. Lizards adjust their orientation to control heat gained by direct solar radiation. Many lizards are capable of spreading or folding the ribs to change the shape of the trunk. When the body is oriented perpendicular to the sun's rays and the ribs are spread, the surface area exposed to the sun is maximized and heat gain is increased. Compressing the ribs decreases the surface exposed to the sun and can be combined with orientation parallel to the rays to minimize heat gain. Horned lizards provide a good example of this type of control (Heath 1965). If the surface area that a horned lizard exposes to

the sun directly overhead when it sits flat on the ground with its ribs held in a resting position is considered to be 100 percent, the maximum surface area the lizard can expose by orientation and change in body contour is 173 percent and the minimum is 28 percent. That is, the lizard can change its radiant heat gain more than sixfold solely by changing its position and body shape.

Color change can further increase a lizard's control of radiative exchange. (See the color insert.) Lizards darken by dispersing melanin in melanophore cells in the skin and lighten by drawing the melanin into the base of the melanophores. The lightness of a lizard affects the amount of solar radiation it absorbs in the visible part of the spectrum, and changes in heating rate (in the darkest color phase compared with the lightest) are from 10 to 75 percent.

Lizards can achieve a remarkable independence of air temperature as a result of their thermoregulatory capacities (Avery 1982). Lizards occur above the timberline in many mountain ranges, and during their periods of activity on sunny days they are capable of maintaining body temperatures 30°C or more above air temperature. While air temperatures are near freezing, these lizards scamper about with body temperatures as high as those species that inhabit lowland deserts.

The repertoire of thermoregulatory mechanisms seen in lizards is greater than that of many other ectothermal vertebrates. Turtles, for example, cannot change their body contour or color, and their behavioral thermoregulation is limited to movements between sun and shade and in and out of water. Crocodilians are very like turtles, although young individuals may be able to make minor changes in body contour and color. Most snakes cannot change color, but some rattlesnakes lighten and darken as they warm and cool.

During the parts of a day when they are active, desert lizards maintain their body temperatures in a zone called the **activity temperature range**. This is the region of temperature within which a lizard carries out its full repertoire of activities—feeding, courtship, territorial defense, and so on. For many species of desert lizards the activity temperature range is as narrow as 4°C, but for other ectotherms it may be as broad as 10°C. Different species of lizards have different activity temperature ranges. The thermoregulatory activities of a lizard are directed toward keeping it within its activity temperature range, but the precise temperature it maintains within this range depends on a variety of internal and external conditions. For example, many ectotherms maintain higher body temperatures when they are digesting food than when they are fasting. Female lizards when they are carrying young may maintain different body temperatures than at other times, and ectotherms with experimentally induced bacterial infections show a fever that is achieved by maintaining a higher-than-normal body temperature by behavioral means (Kluger 1979).

Not all lizards regulate their body temperatures closely. Some lizards that live in the understory vegetation of tropical forests where sunlight does not penetrate do not raise their body temperatures above air temperatures. Differences in the intensity and availability of solar radiation in different seasons, different habitats, or even at different times of day can alter the balance of costs and benefits of thermoregulatory behavior (Huey 1982). These ecological aspects of thermoregulation are discussed in Chapter 15.

Physiological Control of the Rate of Change of Body Temperature by Ectotherms

A new dimension was added to studies of ectothermal thermoregulation in the 1960s by the discovery that ectotherms can use physiological mechanisms to adjust their rate of temperature change (Bartholomew 1982). The original observations, made by George Bartholomew and his associates, showed that several different kinds of large lizards were able to heat faster than they cooled when exposed to the same differential between body and ambient temperatures. Subsequent studies by other investigators extended these observations to turtles and snakes. From the animal's viewpoint, heating rapidly and cooling slowly prolongs the time it can spend in the normal activity range.

Fred White and his colleagues have demonstrated that the basis of this control of heating and cooling rates lies in changes in peripheral circulation. Heating the skin of a lizard causes a localized vasodilation of dermal blood vessels in the warm area. Dilation of the blood vessels, in turn, increases the blood flow through them, and the blood is warmed in the skin and carries the heat into the core of the body. Thus, in the morning, when a cold lizard orients its body perpendicular to the sun's rays and the sun warms its back, local vasodilation

in that region speeds transfer of the heat to the rest of the body.

The same mechanism can be used to avoid overheating. The Galápagos marine iguana is a good example (White 1973). Marine iguanas live on the bare lava flows on the coasts of the islands. In midday, beneath the equatorial sun, the black lava becomes extremely hot—uncomfortably if not lethally hot for a lizard. Retreat to shade of the scanty vegetation or into rock cracks would be one way the iguanas could avoid overheating, but the males are territorial and those behaviors would mean abandoning their territories and probably having to fight for them again later in the day. Instead, the marine iguana stays where it is and uses physiological control of circulation and the cool breeze blowing off the ocean to form a heat shunt that absorbs solar energy on the dorsal surface and carries it through the body and dumps it out the ventral surface.

The process is as follows: In the morning the lizard is chilled from the preceding night and basks to bring its body temperature to the normal activity range. When its temperature reaches this level the lizard uses postural adjustments to slow the increase in body temperature, finally facing directly into the sun to minimize its heat load. In this posture the forepart of the body is held off the ground (Figure 4–9). The ventral surface is exposed to the cool wind blowing off the ocean, and a patch of lava under the animal is shaded by its body. This lava is soon cooled by the wind. Local vasodilation is produced by warming the blood vessels: It does not matter whether the heat comes from the outside (from the sun) or from inside (from warm blood). Warm blood circulating from the core of the body to the ventral skin warms it and produces vasodilation, increasing the flow to the ventral surface. The lizard's ventral skin is cooler than the rest of its body—it is shaded and cooled by the wind, and in addition it loses heat by radiation to the cool lava in the shade created by the lizard's body. In this way the same mechanism that earlier in the day allowed the lizard to warm rapidly is converted to a regulated heat shunt that rapidly transports solar energy from the dorsal to the ventral surface and keeps the lizard from overheating. In combination with postural adjustments and other behavioral mechanisms, such as the choice of a site where the breeze is strong, these physiological adjustments allow a male iguana to remain on station in its territory all day.

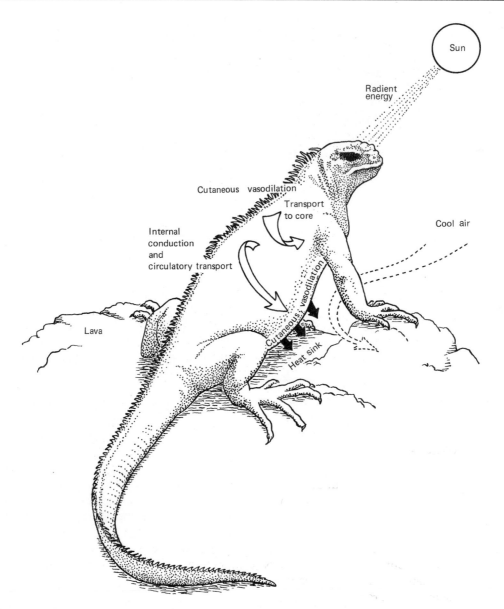

Figure 4–9   The Galápagos marine iguana uses a combination of behavioral and physiological thermoregulatory mechanisms to shunt heat absorbed by its dorsal surface out its ventral surface. (Modified from White, 1973, *Comparative Biochemistry and Physiology* 45A:503–513.)

The behavioral and physiological thermoregulatory mechanisms of ectotherms are intimately intertwined. Although we have tried to simplify our presentation by discussing them separately, it is essential to realize that neither behavioral, nor physiological, nor morphological thermoregulatory mechanisms function by themselves. They are used in combination, and they have evolved in combination. The thermoregulation of a lizard (and, as we will see, of a bird or mammal) involves all these mechanisms simultaneously.

Endothermal Thermoregulation

Birds and mammals are endotherms that regulate their high body temperatures by mechanisms that precisely balance metabolic heat production and heat loss to the environment. An endotherm can change the intensity of its heat production by varying metabolic rate over a wide range. In this way, an endotherm maintains a constant high body temperature by adjusting heat production to equal heat loss from its body under different environmental conditions.

Endotherms produce metabolic heat in several ways. Besides the obligatory heat production derived from the basal or resting metabolic rate, there is the heat increment of feeding, often called the **specific dynamic action** or **effect** of the food. This added heat production after ingestion of food apparently results from the energy used to assimilate molecules and synthesize protein, and varies in amount depending on the type of foodstuff being processed. It is highest for a meat diet and lowest for a carbohydrate diet.

Activity of skeletal muscle produces large amounts of heat, especially during locomotion, which can result in a heat production exceeding the basal metabolic rate by 10- to 15-fold. This muscular heat can be advantageous for balancing heat loss in a cold environment, or it can be a problem requiring special mechanisms of dissipation in hot environments that approach or exceed the body temperature of the animal. Cheetahs, for example, show a rapid increase in body temperature when they chase prey, and it is usually overheating that causes a cheetah to break off a pursuit. **Shivering**, the generation of heat by muscle fiber contractions in an asynchronous pattern that does not result in gross movement of the whole muscles, is an important mechanism of heat production. Birds and mammals also possess mechanisms for nonshivering thermogenesis.

Because endotherms usually live under conditions in which ambient temperatures are lower than the regulated body temperatures of the animals themselves, heat loss to the environment is a more usual circumstance than heat gain, although heat gain from the environment can be a major problem in deserts. Balancing of heat loss is therefore one of the most important regulatory functions of an endotherm, and birds and mammals employ their plumage or hair in a very effective way as insulation against heat loss.

Any material that traps air is an insulator against conductive heat transfer. Hair and feathers provide insulation by trapping air, and the depth of the layer of trapped air can be adjusted by raising and lowering the hair or feathers. We humans have goose bumps on our arms and legs when we are cold because our few remaining hairs rise to a vertical position in an ancestral mammalian attempt to increase our insulation.

These physiological responses to temperature are controlled from neurons located in the hypothalamus of the brain. In some mammals, as in hibernators, the hypothalamic thermostat can be reset for a lower control temperature. In ectotherms the hypothalamic thermostat controls behaviors that place the animal in favorable circumstances (e.g., moving to a preferred ambient temperature away from excess heat, or orienting to maximize heat loss or gain).

Mechanisms of Endothermal Thermoregulation   Body temperature and metabolic rate must be considered simultaneously to understand how endotherms maintain their body temperatures at a stable level in the face of environmental temperatures that may range from −70 to +40°C. Most birds and mammals conform to the generalized diagram in Figure 4–10.

Each species of endotherm has a definable range of ambient temperatures $(t_1$ to $t_4)$ over which the body temperature can be kept stable by using physiological and postural adjustments of heat loss and heat production. This ambient temperature range is called the **zone of tolerance**. Above this range the animal's ability to dissipate heat is inadequate, and both the body temperature and metabolic rate increase as ambient temperature increases until the animal dies. At ambient temperatures below the zone of tolerance the animal's ability to generate heat to balance heat loss is exceeded, body temperature falls, metabolic rate declines, and cold death results. Large animals usually have lower values for t_1 and t_2 than small animals because heat is lost from the body surface, and large animals have smaller surface-to-mass ratios than those of small animals. Similarly, well-insulated species have lower values for t_1 and t_2 than those of poorly insulated ones, but thinly insulated species usually have higher values for t_3 than those of heavily insulated ones.

The **thermoneutral zone** $(t_2$ to $t_3)$ is the range of ambient temperatures within which the metabolic rate of an endotherm is at its basal level and thermoregulation is accomplished by changing the rate of heat loss. The thermoneutral zone is also called the zone of physical thermoregulation because an animal uses processes such as fluffing or sleeking its hair or feathers, postural changes such as huddling or stretching out, and changes in blood flow (vasoconstriction or vasodilation) to exposed parts of the body (feet, legs, face) to adjust its loss of heat.

The larger an animal is and the thicker its insulation, the lower will be the temperature it can withstand before physical processes become inadequate to balance its heat loss. The **lower critical tempera-**

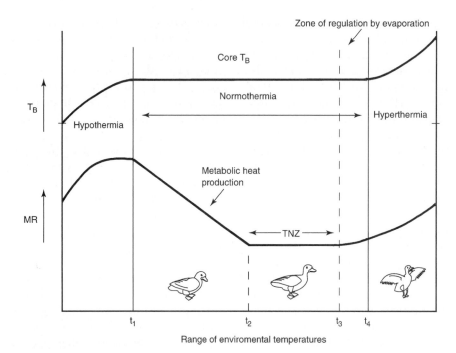

Figure 4–10 Generalized pattern of changes in body temperature and metabolic heat production of an endothermic homeotherm in relation to environmental temperature. Core T_B is the normal body temperature and varies somewhat for different mammals and birds. t_1, incipient lower lethal temperature; t_2, lower critical temperature; t_3, upper critical temperature; t_4, incipient upper lethal temperature; TNZ, thermoneutral zone.

ture (t_2) is the point at which an animal must increase metabolic heat production to maintain a stable body temperature. In the **zone of chemical thermogenesis**, the metabolic rate increases as the ambient temperature falls. The quality of the insulation determines how much additional metabolic heat production is required to offset a change in ambient temperature. That is, well-insulated animals have relatively shallow slopes for the graph of increasing metabolism below the lower critical temperature, and poorly insulated animals have steeper slopes (see Figure 22–3). Many birds and mammals from the Arctic and Antarctic are so well insulated that they can withstand the lowest temperatures on earth (about −70°C) by increasing their basal metabolism only threefold. Less well-insulated animals may be exposed to temperatures below their **lower lethal temperature** (t_1). At that point metabolic heat production has reached its maximum rate and is still insufficient to balance heat loss to the environment. Under those conditions the body temperature falls, and the Q_{10} effect of temperature on chemical reactions causes the metabolic rate to fall as well. A positive-feedback condition is initiated in which falling body temperature reduces heat production, causing a further reduction in body temperature. Death from hypothermia (low body temperature) follows.

Endotherms are remarkably good at maintaining stable body temperatures in cool environments, but they have difficulty at high ambient temperatures. The **upper critical temperature** (t_3) represents the point at which nonevaporative heat loss has been maximized by using all of the physical processes that are available to an animal—exposing the poorly insulated areas of the body and maximizing cutaneous blood flow. If these mechanisms are insufficient to balance heat gain, the only option vertebrates have is to use evaporation of water by panting, sweating, or gular flutter. The temperature range from t_3 to t_4 is the **zone of evaporative cooling**. Many mammals sweat, a process in which water is released from sweat glands on the surface of the body. Evaporation of the sweat cools the body surface. Other animals pant, breathing rapidly and shallowly so that evaporation of water from the respiratory system provides a cooling effect. Many birds use a rapid fluttering movement of the gular region to evaporate water for thermoregulation.

Panting and gular flutter require muscular activity, and some of the evaporative cooling they achieve is used to offset the increased metabolic heat production they require.

At the **upper lethal temperature** (t_4) evaporative cooling cannot balance the heat flow from a hot environment, and body temperature rises. The Q_{10} effect of temperature produces an increase in the rate of metabolism, and metabolic heat production raises the body temperature, increasing the metabolic rate still further. This process can lead to death from hyperthermia (high body temperature).

The difficulty that endotherms experience in regulating body temperature in high environmental temperatures may be one of the reasons that the body temperatures of most endotherms are in the range 35 to 40°C. Most habitats seldom have air temperatures that exceed 35°C. Even the tropics have average yearly temperatures below 30°C. Thus the high body temperatures maintained by mammals ensure that in most situations the heat gradient is from animal to environment. Still higher body temperatures, around 50°C, for example, could ensure that mammals were always warmer than their environment. There are upper limits to the body temperatures that are feasible, however. Many proteins denature near 50°C. During heat stress, some birds and mammals may tolerate body temperatures of 45 to 46°C for a few hours, but only some bacteria, algae, and a few invertebrates exist at higher temperatures. This is another case in which the direction of vertebrate evolution has been established by a balance between biotic needs and physiochemical realities.

Advantages of a High Body Temperature   Mammals and birds have high resting metabolic rates, at least six times the SMR of ectotherms. Although it is energetically expensive, there are benefits to regulating body temperature at a high rather than a low level that are independent of the mechanisms of thermoregulation discussed in the preceding section.

We have already noted that the biochemistry of vertebrates involves thousands of interacting enzyme-catalyzed reactions, most of which are temperature sensitive. A constant internal temperature is required to obtain maximum chemical coordination among these reactions. In addition, the higher the body temperature, the more rapid the response of cells to organismal needs. Although it is capable of acting at very cold temperatures (as in arctic fishes), the CNS functions more rapidly at high temperatures. As one example, neurotransmitters such as acetylcholine and norepinephrine act by diffusing from their site of release across the synaptic junction to the postsynaptic receptor surface. Because diffusion is a physical process, its rate increases as temperature increases. A high body temperature enhances the rate of information processing, a competitive advantage often neglected when considering the success of mammals and birds. Very rapid responses can be vital in catching prey and avoiding predators. Some ectotherms enjoy the same neurological benefits when they are warm, but very rapid responses on cool nights can occur only in endothermal homeotherms. In addition, muscle viscosity declines at high temperatures. This reduction in internal friction may result in more rapid, forceful contraction and faster response times.

Thus, endothermal homeothermy has some obvious advantages over ectothermy. (Ectothermy has its own advantages, which are discussed in Chapter 16.) Ectothermy is the ancestral condition for vertebrates. How did endothermy evolve?

The Evolution of Endothermy   Endothermy has evolved from an ancestral ectothermal condition at least twice in the history of vertebrates—in birds and in mammals. Some evidence suggests that pterosaurs (flying archosaurs of the Mesozoic) might also have been endothermal, and if this is true, it would represent a third independent origin of endothermy. How would that transition occur?

The difference in the sources of heat used by ectotherms and endotherms creates a paradox when one tries to understand how an evolutionary lineage shifts from ectothermy to endothermy. Ectotherms rely on heat from outside their bodies, and the major specializations of ectothermal thermoregulation facilitate exchange of heat with the environment. The body surfaces of ectotherms have little insulation, probably because insulation would interfere with the gain and loss of heat. Metabolic rates of ectotherms are low, and ectotherms normally do not obtain sufficient heat from metabolism to warm the body significantly. (The warm-bodied tunas and sharks described in the next section and the sea turtles discussed in Chapter 13 are exceptions to this generalization because of their large body sizes, high levels of activity, and specializations of the circulatory system.) Thus, the thermoregulatory mechanisms of ectotherms are based on low metabolic rates, little insulation, and rapid exchange of heat with the environment.

Endothermal thermoregulation has exactly the opposite characteristics. The high metabolic rates of endotherms produce large quantities of heat, and that heat is retained in their bodies by the insulation provided by hair or feathers. Endothermal thermoregulation consists largely of adjusting the layer of insulation so that heat loss balances the heat produced by high rates of metabolism.

An evolutionary shift from ectothermy to endothermy appears to encounter a catch-22 situation: A high metabolic rate is of no use unless an animal has insulation to retain metabolically produced heat, because without insulation the heat is rapidly lost to the environment. However, insulation serves no purpose for an animal without a high rate of metabolism because there is little internally produced heat for the insulation to conserve. Indeed, insulation can be a handicap for an ectotherm, because it prevents it from warming up. Raymond Cowles demonstrated that fact in the 1930s when he made small fur coats for lizards and measured their rates of warming and cooling. The potential benefit of a fur coat for a lizard is, of course, its effect of keeping the lizard warm as the environment cools off. However, the lizards in Cowles' experiments never achieved that benefit of insulation, because when they were wearing fur coats they were unable to get warm in the first place.

Those well-dressed lizards illustrate the paradox of the evolution of endothermy: Insulation is ineffective without a high metabolic rate, and the heat produced by a high metabolic rate is wasted without insulation. By this line of reasoning, neither one of the two essential features of endothermy would be selectively advantageous for an ectotherm without the previous development of the other. So how did endothermy evolve?

Probably endothermy evolved as a by-product of selection for one or more other activities that involved some of the same characteristics that are needed by endotherms. Ideas about the evolution of endothermy are unavoidably speculative, but they can be tested to some extent by examining the fine anatomy of fossils (Ruben 1996).

Feathers, which provide the insulating layer that permits birds to be endotherms, are derived from the scales that covered the bodies of Mesozoic archosaurs. One hypothesis for the origin of feathers suggests that an intermediate stage in their evolution consisted of elongate scales. An animal with scales of this type could orient its body while it was warming so that sunlight penetrated between the scales. When it was warm enough, a change of orientation would convert the scales to a series of parasols, blocking heat uptake (Regal 1975). This sort of scale probably would be suitable for the sort of ectothermal thermoregulation exemplified by the Galápagos marine iguana, and it might also have the basic features needed to provide insulation if the scales trapped a layer of air when they were lowered to press against each other. An animal with a body covering that had achieved some insulating capacity would be able to retain metabolically produced heat and might derive some benefit from a high metabolic rate (Regal 1985).

A different sequence of events, called the aerobic capacity model, has been suggested to account for the origin of mammalian endothermy. The synapsid lineage from which mammals are derived shows skeletal changes that seem to indicate a progressive increase in locomotor capacity (Chapter 19). If the animals were indeed becoming more active, it is plausible that the morphological changes were accompanied by an increasing aerobic metabolic capacity needed to sustain that activity, and that heat production by muscles during activity raised the body temperature (Bennett and Ruben 1979). In that situation, hair that provided insulation could help to maintain the elevated body temperature for some period after activity ceased.

Thus, in the evolution of mammalian endothermy metabolic heat production (as a by-product of locomotor activity) might have preceded insulation, whereas in birds insulation (a by-product of ectothermal thermoregulation) might have preceded high rates of metabolism. Other plausible evolutionary scenarios can be proposed to explain how endothermy could evolve in birds or mammals, and the ones suggested here may be incorrect. However, they do have the merit of illustrating an important point: The selective pressures that were responsible for the origin of a trait are not necessarily the ones that are responsible for its present value. In the case of the evolution of endotherms from ectotherms, the conflicting requirements of the two modes of thermoregulation are so different that some factors other than thermoregulation were almost certainly involved in the initial stages.

Regional Heterothermy: Warm Fishes

Endothermy and regulation of body temperature are not all-or-nothing phenomena for vertebrates. Regional heterothermy is a general term used to refer to different temperatures in different parts of an animal's body. Dramatic examples of regional

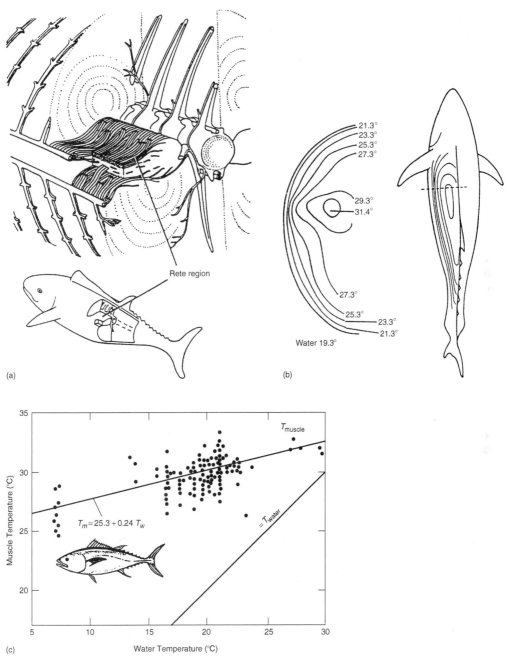

Figure 4–11 Details of body temperature regulation by the bluefin tuna. (a) The red muscle and retia are located adjacent to the vertebral column. (b) Cross-sectional views showing the temperature gradient between the core (at 31.4°C) and water temperature (19.3°C). (c) Core muscle temperatures of bluefins compared to water temperature. (Modified from F. G. Carey and J. M. Teal, 1966, *Proceedings of the National Academy of Sciences U.S.A.* 56:1464–1469.)

heterothermy are found in several fishes that maintain some parts of their bodies at temperatures 15°C warmer than the water they are swimming in. That's a remarkable accomplishment for a fish, because each time the blood passes through the gills it comes into temperature equilibrium with the water. Thus, to raise its body temperature by using endothermal heat production, a fish must prevent the loss of heat to the water via the gills.

The mechanism used, as you will guess, is a countercurrent system of blood flow in retia mirabilia (Chapter 3). As cold arterial blood from the gills enters the warm part of the body, it flows through a rete and is warmed by heat from the warm venous blood that is leaving the tissue. This arrangement is found in some sharks, especially species in the family Lamnidae (including the mako, great white shark, and porbeagle), which have retia mirabilia in the trunk. These retia retain the heat produced by the activity of the swimming muscles, with the result that those muscles are kept 5 to 10°C warmer than water temperature.

Scombroid fishes, a group of teleosts that includes the mackerels, tunas, and billfishes (swordfish, sailfish, spearfish, and marlin), have also evolved endothermal heat production. Tuna have an arrangement of retia that retains the heat produced by myoglobin-rich swimming muscles located close to the vertebral column (Figure 4–11). The temperature of these muscles is held near 30°C at water temperatures from 7 to 23°C. Additional heat exchangers are found in the brains and eyes of tunas and sharks, and these organs are warmer than water temperature, but somewhat cooler than the swimming muscles (Carey 1982).

The billfishes have a somewhat different arrangement in which only the brain and eyes are warmed, and the source of heat is a muscle that has changed its function from contraction to heat production (Block 1991). The superior rectus eye muscle of these billfishes has been extensively modified. Mitochondria occupy more than 60 percent of the volume of the cells, and changes in cell structure and biochemistry result in the release of heat by the calcium-cycling mechanism that is usually associated with contraction of muscles. A related scombroid, the butterfly mackerel, has a thermogenic organ with the same structural and biochemical characteristics found in billfishes, but in the mackerel it is the lateral rectus eye muscle that has been modified.

An analysis of the phylogenetic relationships of scombroid fishes by Barbara Block and her colleagues (Block et al. 1993) suggests that endother-

mal heat production has arisen independently three times in the lineage—once in the common ancestor of the living billfishes (by modification of the superior rectus eye muscle), once in the butterfly mackerel lineage (modification of the lateral rectus eye muscle), and a third time in the common ancestor of tunas and bonitos (involving the development of countercurrent heat exchangers in muscle, viscera, and brain, and development of red muscle along the horizontal septum of the body).

The ability of these fishes to keep parts of the body warm may allow them to venture into cold water that would otherwise interfere with body functions. Block has pointed out that modification of the eye muscles and the capacity for heat production among scombroids is related to the temperature of the water in which they swim and capture prey. The oxidative capacity of the heater cells of the butterfly mackerel, which is the species that occurs in the coldest water, is the highest of all vertebrates. Swordfishes, which dive to great depths and spend several hours in water temperatures of 10°C or less, have better developed heater organs than do marlins, sailfishes, and spearfishes, which spend less time in cold water.

■ Energy Utilization: Patterns among Vertebrates

Vertebrates usually require more energy than most metazoan animals of similar size, and those vertebrates that physiologically regulate their body temperature at high levels require much more energy. As a result, vertebrates expend much of their active time in the search for food. As a consequence, the impact of vertebrates on the environment (that is, their demand for resources) is great in proportion to their abundance.

Aerobic and Anaerobic Metabolism

Most vertebrates require oxygen to live and oxidize their basic foods (carbohydrates, fats, and proteins) to carbon dioxide and water. To accomplish this task, oxygen must be supplied to the mitochondria of each cell, where the final stages of oxidation and ATP formation take place. All vertebrates accomplish the initial steps of the cellular breakdown of foods anaerobically (Figure 4–12). Thus, glucose is ultimately converted to pyruvate, and the energy released by this glycolytic process is converted in part into ATP. Generally, the pyruvate is decarboxylated and oxidized to carbon dioxide and

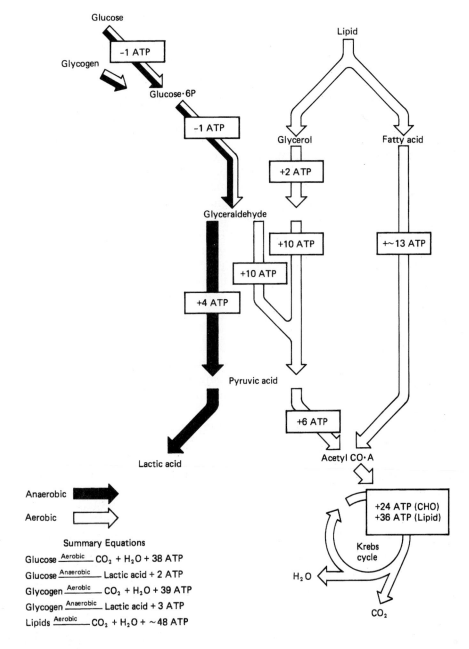

Figure 4–12   Schematic diagram of the main elements in aerobic and anaerobic energy metabolism. (From M. S. Gordon, G. A. Bartholomew, A. D. Grinnell, C. B. Jorgensen, and F. N. White, 1982, *Animal Physiology: Principles and Adaptations*, Macmillan, New York, NY.)

water to yield additional ATP if oxygen is available. In active skeletal (striated) muscle, the pyruvate may accumulate faster than oxygen can be supplied for its complete oxidation. As a result, the tissue becomes anoxic (devoid of oxygen) and the accumulation of pyruvate inhibits further breakdown of glucose and thus slows ATP generation. By converting pyruvate to lactic acid, however, glycolysis can proceed until depletion of cellular energy stores causes fatigue. This process is called anaerobic metabolism because oxygen is not used as an electron acceptor.

A vertebrate can swim, fly, or run at maximum rate only for a limited time until it drops from fatigue. This is an important ecological point: There is a time limit as well as a mechanical limit placed on vertebrate mobility. Most behaviors take place at levels of energy expenditure only two to four times resting metabolic levels. For example, the lengthy migrations that many vertebrates undertake require much energy, but they are performed at speeds that do not exceed the limits of aerobic metabolism. In contrast, the brief pursuits of prey by predator, territorial defense, and nuptial gyrations between mates may drive oxygen consumption to ten times the resting rate and still require more ATP than can be synthesized by those aerobic metabolic pathways alone.

All vertebrates have the capacity for both aerobic and anaerobic metabolism, and the balance between the pathways differs in various species and situations. In general, endotherms have greater capacity for aerobic metabolism than do ectotherms, but even endotherms use anaerobic pathways to supplement aerobic production of ATP during intense activity. High levels of aerobic metabolism require high rates of transport of oxygen to active tissues, and animals with high aerobic metabolic capacities have large hearts, high rates of blood flow, high hematocrits, and high concentrations of hemoglobin in the blood (Table 4.7).

Physiological characteristics of muscles specialized for aerobic and anaerobic metabolism also differ. Red muscle takes its color from the myoglobin it contains. Myoglobin is a protein that binds oxygen and speeds its diffusion from blood to mitochondria, and muscles with high concentrations of myoglobin are well vascularized and have high activities of the enzymes associated with aerobic metabolic pathways. White muscle lacks myoglobin, is poorly vascularized, and has high activities of enzymes associated with anaerobic metabolic pathways. The distribution of red and white muscle in many vertebrates tells much about the sorts of activities those muscles support. For example, gallinaceous birds (a group that includes domestic chickens) walk around all day, but they fly only if they are startled, and then for only a few seconds. The leg muscles of these birds are composed of red muscle (the dark meat) with high aerobic capacity. The flight (breast) muscles are white and are largely anaerobic. In tunas the swimming muscles are red (dark meat tuna), and other trunk muscles are white (light meat tuna).

The metabolic capacity of an animal is the sum of its aerobic and anaerobic energy production. A lizard (the desert iguana) and a mammal (the kangaroo rat) are both able to produce about 0.015 millimole of ATP per gram during 30 seconds of activity, but about 70 percent of that ATP comes from aerobic pathways in the mammal compared with 76 percent from anaerobic pathways for the lizard (Table 4.8). The ecological significance of that difference lies in the ability of the two animals to sustain activity. The oxygen and metabolic substrates used for anaerobic metabolism are carried to the muscles by the circulatory system. For anaerobic metabolism the substrate is glycogen, which is stored in the cell, and when that glycogen has been used up, anaerobic metabolism must stop. Thus, aerobic metabolism can continue nearly indefinitely, whereas anaerobic metabolism can produce

TABLE 4.7	Representative values of the heart and blood for vertebrates					
Species	Body Mass (kg)	Heart Mass (percentage of body mass)	Cardiac Output (mL/kg · min)	Blood Pressure (mm Hg)	Hematocrit (percent)	Hemoglobin (g/100 mL blood)
Fishes: carp	1	0.15	9	43	31	10.5
Lizards: iguana	1	0.19	58	75	31	8.4
Mammals: dog	14	0.65	150	134	46	14.8

TABLE 4.8	Estimated aerobic and anaerobic contributions to 30 seconds of activity for a mammal (the kangaroo rat, *Dipodomys merriami*) and a lizard (the desert iguana, *Dipsosaurus dorsalis*)		
	Millimoles ATP per Gram Body Mass		
Species	*Aerobic*	*Anaerobic*	*Total*
Dipodomys	0.0098 (70%)	0.0043 (30%)	0.0141
Dipsosaurus	0.0044 (24%)	0.0142 (76%)	0.0186

Source: J. A. Ruben and D. E. Battalia, 1979, *Journal of Experimental Zoology* 208:73–76.

large quantities of ATP, but for only a brief time before the substrate is depleted and the animal is exhausted. Animals with high aerobic capacities can be seen as specialized for sustained activity, whereas animals with low aerobic capacities are specialized for burst activity.

Metabolic Levels Among Vertebrates

The amount of energy that vertebrates use is reflected by the amount of oxygen they consume. In general, the minimum rate at which animals consume oxygen is set by the level necessary to support life. The maximum rate may be determined by the capacity of the respiratory and circulatory systems—that is, the rate at which oxygen and nutrients can be supplied to cells (Weibel 1984). The lower aerobic limit, often referred to as the **standard metabolic rate** (SMR), is set by the minimum energy required to maintain life in an organized state. As a rule, vertebrates seldom operate at their SMR. Therefore, it is necessary to define the conditions under which the SMR is measured. When the resting oxygen consumption is measured following a meal, the metabolism will be at least 5 to 30 percent higher than the SMR because of the costs of digestion. Other factors, such as visual or mechanical disturbance, cause significant increases in oxygen uptake by inducing stress, and low oxygen or high carbon dioxide levels have pronounced effects on energy metabolism. Because increasing temperature usually increases the rates of chemical reactions, including aerobic metabolism, it can have an overriding influence on organisms.

The Effect of Body Size   SMR is reported in terms of the volume of oxygen consumed per unit of time at standard pressure and temperature (STP). Obviously, large animals consume more oxygen than small animals (Figure 4–13). To allow comparisons of animals of different sizes, the SMR is adjusted

for body size to yield a mass-specific SMR (rate of oxygen consumption/body mass). It is immediately apparent that within vertebrates the mass-specific SMR decreases as body size increases. The slope of the regression of SMR on body mass is roughly similar for different kinds of vertebrates and also for a wide variety of invertebrates. This relationship has intrigued biologists for over 100 years, but a clear, unambiguous explanation has proved elusive.

Several biologists have pointed out that the increase in mass-specific SMR with decreased size might result from the relatively larger body surface area of small animals. Surface area is proportional to the two-thirds power (0.67) of the body mass. About 100 years ago Max Rubner showed that the heat loss across each unit of body surface of small and large dogs was the same (about 420 kilojoules per square meter), even though the mass-specific SMR was higher in smaller dogs. To explain this paradox he reasoned that small dogs must lose heat more rapidly than larger dogs because of their relatively high surface area. To maintain body temperatures small dogs compensate for their increased heat loss by an increase in mass-specific SMR. Rubner felt the regression of SMR on mass was sufficiently close to a slope of 0.67 that the phenomenon was explained by body geometry.

For many vertebrates this slope has a value near 0.75, that is, the SMR varies as the three-fourths power and not the two-thirds power of body mass (Kleiber 1961). Subsequently, theoretical arguments have been advanced to support Kleiber's rule. A mass exponent of 0.75 can be derived from the mechanics of locomotion (McMahon 1973) and from the geometry of four dimensions (Blum 1977). Recently the mass exponent of 0.67 has reemerged as the predicted value for comparisons of different-size individuals of a single species (Heusner 1982). Feldman and McMahon (1983) have suggested that both 0.75 and 0.67 are valid exponents, the first

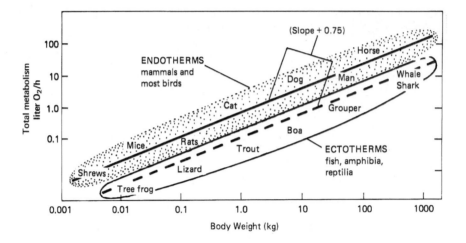

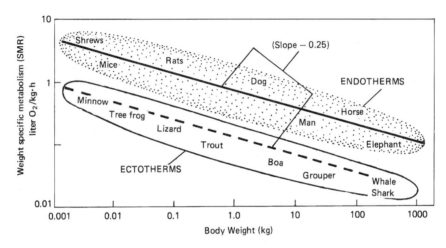

Figure 4–13 Comparison of body size and metabolic rate of ectotherms and endotherms. Upper graph: The total metabolism per hour plotted against the body mass (both on logarithmic scales) yields a straight line with a slope that usually lies between 0.65 and 0.85 and is conventionally considered to be equal to 0.75. Lower graph: Total metabolism converted to oxygen consumption per unit of body mass per hour to give a mass-specific metabolic rate (SMR). The plot of SMR against body mass (both on logarithmic scales) yields a slope that is conventionally considered to be −0.25.

applying to comparisons of different species and the second being appropriate for comparisons of individuals within species. Although the mechanistic basis of the phenomenon remains unexplained, two points are clear: Metabolic rate is related to body size in all vertebrates, and that relationship has profound ecological and evolutionary consequences.

Although the exact values of the slopes relating metabolism to body mass are still subject to debate, it is clear that the slopes are less than 1. The metabolic rate can be thought of as the energy requirement of an animal. Because the slope of metabolism versus mass is less than 1, doubling the size of an animal does not double its energy requirement. To understand that relationship, assume that the mass exponent for metabolism is 0.75 and consider an animal weighing 2.5 kilograms and another animal of the same kind that weighs 5 kilograms. The metabolic rates of the two animals will be proportional to their body masses raised to the 0.75 power. Thus,

$$\text{MR of animal 1} = (2.5 \text{ kg})0.75 = 1.99$$

and

$$\text{MR of animal 2} = (5 \text{ kg})0.75 = 3.34$$

The energy requirements of the larger animal are only 1.68 times greater than those of the small animal. In ecological terms, that means that a small animal has a greater energy requirement *for its size* than does a large animal, although a large animal needs more energy *in total* than does a small animal.

At least two regression lines are required to fit the SMR data for all vertebrates (Figure 4–13). The lower SMRs of ectotherms result partly from their lack of internal heat generation to maintain a high body temperature. The SMR of an ectotherm averages one-sixth that of an endotherm of the same size. The cost of maintaining a high body temperature demands that birds and mammals consume more food than ectotherms of similar size. But vertebrates are mobile animals and, whether ectothermic or endothermic, all require more energy when active.

■ Summary

Vertebrates, like other organisms, are composed mostly of water. Inorganic and organic solutes are dissolved in the water, and the complex biochemical processes that make organisms self-sustaining require regulation of the water content and solute concentrations of their tissues and cells. Most vertebrates have osmolal concentrations between 250 and 350 mmoles·kg^{-1} of water, whereas fresh water is usually below 10 mmoles·kg^{-1} and seawater is about 1000 mmoles·kg^{-1}. Sodium and chloride are the major osmotically active compounds in seawater and in most vertebrates. The gills of fishes and skin of amphibians are permeable to water.

Freshwater teleosts and amphibians have osmolal and ion concentrations higher than their surroundings. Consequently, they must cope with an inward osmotic flow of water and an outward diffusion of ions. They produce copious, dilute urine to excrete water and expend energy to take up ions from the external medium. Marine teleosts are less concentrated than seawater; they lose water by osmosis and gain salt by diffusion. These fishes drink seawater and use active transport to excrete ions. Hagfishes, elasmobranchs, and coelacanths have osmolal concentrations close to that of seawater, but ionic concentrations that are different from those of their environment. As a result, osmotic water movement is low, but energy is used to regulate solute concentrations.

Deamination of proteins during metabolism produces ammonia, which is toxic. Ammonia is very soluble in water, and aquatic vertebrates excrete ammonia as their main nitrogen-containing waste product (ammonotelism). Terrestrial animals do not have enough water available to be ammonotelic. Mammals convert ammonia to urea, which is nontoxic and very soluble. The capacity of the mammalian kidney to produce concentrated urine allows mammals to excrete urea (ureotelism) without an excessive loss of water. The kidneys of diapsids and turtles do not have the urine-concentrating capacity of mammalian kidneys, and these animals convert much of the ammonia to uric acid (uricotelism). Uric acid is not very soluble, and it combines with ions to form urate salts that precipitate in the cloaca. As the salt precipitates, water is released, and uricotely is very economical of water. Some uricoteles save even more water by using extrarenal routes of salt secretion (salt glands) to eliminate sodium and chloride in solutions that may exceed 2000 mmoles·kg^{-1}.

Temperature profoundly affects the biochemical processes that sustain vertebrates, and thermoregulatory mechanisms are widespread. Few fishes and amphibians can maintain a temperature difference between their bodies and the water around them, but some fast-swimming tunas and sharks have muscle temperatures that are 10°C or more above water temperature. Billfishes have specialized tissues that produce heat that warms the eyes and brain. Many terrestrial vertebrates have the capacity to regulate their body temperature. Ectotherms rely on sources of heat from outside the body for thermoregulation, balancing heat gained and lost by radiation, conduction, convection, and evaporation. This is a complex and effective process; many ectotherms maintain stable body temperatures substantially above ambient temperatures while they are thermoregulating. Endotherms use metabolically produced heat and manipulate insulation to balance the rates of heat production and loss. Endothermal thermoregulation confers considerable independence of environmental conditions but is energetically expensive. The mechanisms of ectothermal and endothermal thermoregulation are quite different, and an evolutionary transition from ectothermy to endothermy would be complex. Nonetheless, that transition occurred at least twice, once in the evolution of birds and once in the evolution of mammals. The evolutionary origins of the two essential components of endothermy—insulation and a high metabolic rate—were probably different from their current significance.

Vertebrates use two pathways of metabolic energy production: aerobic metabolism and anaerobic metabolism (glycolysis). Aerobic metabolism requires a circulatory system that can transport oxygen and metabolic substrates to active tissues, whereas anaerobic metabolism relies on the glycogen stores present in the cell. Both can produce ATP at high rates, but only aerobic metabolism can be sustained for long periods. Endotherms rely primarily on aerobic metabolism to sustain activity. As a result, they have high rates of oxygen consumption even when they are inactive. Ectotherms use anaerobic metabolism when they must produce ATP at high rates, and have low rates of oxygen consumption at rest—about one-seventh those of endotherms of the same body size. Large animals, whether endotherms or ectotherms, require more energy than small ones, but energy requirements increase more slowly than body mass. As a result, large animals require less energy per gram of body tissue than do small ones.

■ References

Avery, R. A. 1979. *Lizards: A Study in Thermoregulation*. University Park, Baltimore, MD.

Avery, R. A. 1982. Field studies of reptilian thermoregulation. Pages 93–166 in *Biology of the Reptilia*, volume 12, edited by C. Gans and F. H. Pough. Academic, London, UK.

Bartholomew, G. A. 1982. Physiological control of body temperature. Pages 167–211 in *Biology of the Reptilia*, volume 12, edited by C. Gans and F. H. Pough. Academic, London, UK.

Bennett, A.F. and W. R. Dawson. 1982. Metabolism. Pages 127–223 in *Biology of the Reptilia*, volume 5, edited by C. Gans and W. R. Dawson. Academic Press, London, UK.

Bennett, A. F., and J. A. Ruben. 1979. Endothermy and activity in vertebrates. *Science* 206:649–655.

Block, B. A. 1991. Evolutionary novelties: how fish have built a heater out of muscle. *American Zoologist* 31:726–742.

Block, B. A., J. R. Finnerty, A. F. R. Stewart, and J. Kidd. 1993. Evolution of endothermy in fish: mapping physiological traits on a molecular phylogeny. *Science* 260:210–214.

Blum, J. J. 1977. On the geometry of four dimensions and the relationship between metabolism and body mass. *Journal of Theoretical Biology* 64:599–601.

Carey, F. G. 1982. Warm fish. Pages 216–233 in *A Companion to Animal Physiology*, edited by C. R. Taylor, K. Johansen, and L. Bolis. Cambridge University Press, Cambridge, UK.

Cowles, R. B., and C. M. Bogert. 1944. A preliminary study of the thermal requirements of desert reptiles. *Bulletin of the American Museum of Natural History* 83:261–296.

Evans, D. H. 1980. Osmotic and ionic regulation by freshwater and marine fishes. Pages 93–122 in *Environmental Physiology of Fishes*, edited by M. A. Ali. Plenum, New York, NY.

Feldman, H. A., and T. A. McMahon. 1983. The 3/4 mass exponent for energy metabolism is not a statistical artifact. *Respiratory Physiology* 52:149–163.

Heath, J. E. 1965. Temperature regulation and diurnal activity in horned lizards. *University of California Publications in Zoology* 64:97–136.

Heusner, A. A. 1982. Energy metabolism and body size, I: Is the 0.75 mass exponent of Kleiber's equation a statistical artifact? *Respiration Physiology* 48:1–12.

Huey, R. B. 1982. Temperature, physiology, and the ecology of reptiles. Pages 25–91 in *Biology of the Reptilia*, volume 12, edited by C. Gans and F. H. Pough. Academic, London, UK.

Kirschner, L. B. 1995. Energetics of osmoregulation in fresh water vertebrates. *Journal of Experimental Zoology* 271:243–252.

Kleiber, M. 1961. *The Fire of Life: An Introduction to Animal Energetics*. Wiley, New York, NY.

Kluger, M. J. 1979. Fever in ectotherms: evolutionary implications. *American Zoologist* 19:295–304.

Loveridge, J. P. 1970. Observations on nitrogenous excretion and water relations of *Chiromantis xerampelina* (Amphibia, Anura). *Arnoldia* 5:1–6.

McMahon, T. 1973. Size and shape in biology. *Science* 179:1201–1204.

Minnich, J. E. 1982. The use of water. Pages 325–395 in *Biology of the Reptilia*, volume 12, edited by C. Gans and F. H. Pough. Academic, London, UK.

Nishimura, H., and M. Imai. 1982. Control of renal function in freshwater and marine teleosts. *Federation Proceedings* 41:2355–2360.

Peaker, M., and J. L. Linzell. 1975. *Salt Glands in Birds and Reptiles*. Cambridge University Press, Cambridge, UK.

Regal, P. J. 1975. The evolutionary origin of feathers. *Quarterly Review of Biology* 50:35–66.

Regal, P. J. 1985. Commonsense and reconstructions of the biology of fossils: *Archaeopteryx* and feathers. Pages 67–74 in *The Beginnings of Birds, Proceedings of the International Archaeopteryx Conference, Eichstatt 1984*, edited by M. K. Hecht, J. H. Ostrom, G. Viohl, and P. Wellnhofer. Jura Museum, Eichstatt, West Germany.

Ruben, J. 1996. Evolution of endothermy in mammals, birds and their ancestors. Pages 347–376 in *Animals and Temperature*, edited by I. A. Johnston and A. F. Bennett. Cambridge University Press, Cambridge, UK.

Shoemaker, V. H., D. Balding, and R. Ruibal. 1972. Uricotelism and low evaporative water loss in a South American frog. *Science* 175:1018–1020.

Tracy, C. R. 1982. Biophysical modeling in reptilian physiology and ecology. Pages 275–321 in *Biology of the Reptilia*, volume 12, edited by C. Gans and F. H. Pough. Academic, London, UK.

Weibel, E. R. 1984. *The Pathway for Oxygen*. Harvard University Press, Cambridge, MA.

White, F. N. 1973. Temperature and the Galápagos marine iguana: insights into reptilian thermoregulation. *Comparative Biochemistry and Physiology* 45A:503–513.

Withers, P. C., G. Morrison, and M. Guppy. 1994. Buoyancy role of urea and TMAO in an elasmobranch fish, the Port Jackson shark, *Heterodontus portjacksoni*. *Physiological Zoology* 67:693–705.

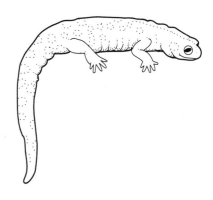

CHAPTER
5

Geography and Ecology from the Cambrian to the Mid-Devonian

I n this chapter we illustrate the role of the environment by considering the conditions that prevailed from the early Paleozoic through the middle of the Devonian. The world was very different then from the one we know—the continents were in different places, climates were different, and there was little structurally complex life on land. All these elements played a role in setting the stage for the origin and diversification of vertebrates.

■ Earth History, Changing Environments, and Vertebrate Evolution

To understand the patterns of vertebrate evolution, it is important to realize that the world of today is very different from the world of times past. Our particular pattern of global climates, including such features as ice at the poles and the directions of the major winds and water currents, results from the present position of the continents. The world today is in general rather cold and dry in comparison with many past times. It is also an unusual world because the continents are separated from one another, and the main continental land mass is in the Northern Hemisphere.

Continental Drift: History of Ideas and Effects on Global Climate

The Earth's climate results from the interaction of sunlight, temperature, rainfall, evaporation, and wind throughout a year. Because climate profoundly affects the kinds of plants and animals that occupy an area, knowledge of paleoclimates helps

us to understand the conditions under which plants and animals evolved. We discussed in Chapter 1 how the positions of the continents could influence global climates and oceanic circulation, and how mountain ranges could influence climate by exerting a rain shadow effect. The primary factors that determine terrestrial climates of large areas such as continents are latitudinal position (i.e., how far north or south of the equator, which affects the amount of solar energy received), proximity to an ocean (which buffers temperature change and provides water via evaporation and rainfall), and the presence of barriers like mountains that influence the movement of atmospheric moisture (Cox and Moore 1993).

The understanding of the dynamic nature of the Earth and the variable nature of the Earth's climate over time is a fairly recent occurrence (Hallam 1994). The notion of mobile continents, or **continental drift**, dates back to the middle of the nineteenth century. The botanist Joseph Hooker then proposed that the vegetation of the southern tip of South America, Australia, and New Zealand was so similar as to suggest that the continents must have been connected at some point in time. (Other researchers at that time proposed that the present-day distribution of plants and animals could be understood only in terms of rather elaborately concocted land bridges that once linked continents and now have conveniently sunk beneath the oceans.) The hypothesis of continental drift was formally proposed by Alfred Wegener in 1924. While this notion was accepted by some researchers, the majority held it to ridicule. Although the theory fit with some kinds of evidence (such as the distribution of living and fossil organisms), there was no mechanism to explain how continents might, in fact, move across the Earth's surface. It was not until the late 1960s, following new oceanographic research demonstrating the spreading of the seafloor as a plausible mechanism for continental movement, that the theory of **plate tectonics** (essentially the same as continental drift) became established. Even then, the theory was not universally accepted, and plate tectonics did not become accepted by mainstream science until the 1980s.

Continents move because they float. The soil, rock, and pavements you walk on may not seem light, but they are not as dense as the material far beneath them. The continents are formed of sedimentary and igneous rocks with an average density of 2.7 grams per cubic centimeter, whereas the mantle that lies beneath the continents consists of basaltic rocks with an average density of 3.0 grams per cubic centimeter. A continental block floats in the mantle, just as an ice cube floats in water. However, because mantle rock is far more viscous than water, continents move slowly compared with ice cubes.

Heat in the Earth's core produces slow convective currents in the mantle. Upwelling plumes of molten basalt rise toward the Earth's surface, forming midocean ridges where they reach the top of the lithosphere and spread horizontally (Figure 5–1). The seafloor is covered by a chain of midoceanic ridges that extend around the globe. The youngest seafloor crust is found in the centers of the ridges, and the seafloor becomes older as you move away from the axis of the ridge. Subduction zones form where the lithosphere sinks back down into the mantle. The continents drift on tectonic plates formed by these processes. As a result of the cycle of upwelling at midoceanic ridges and sinking back into the mantle at subduction zones, rocks

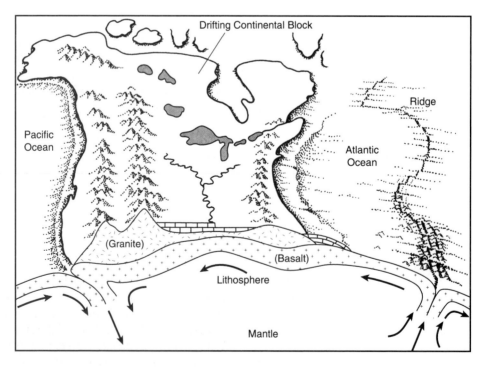

Figure 5–1 Generalized geological structure of a continent. The continental blocks float on a basaltic crust. Arrows show the movements of crustal elements and the interactions with the mantle that produce continental drift.

older than 200 million years do not occur anywhere on the ocean floor.

Movements of the tectonic plates are responsible for continental fragmentation, coalescence, and refragmentation that has occurred during the Earth's history. Plants and animals were carried along as continents slowly drifted, collided, and separated. When continents moved toward the poles, organisms they carried encountered cooler climates. As once-separate continents collided, terrestrial floras and faunas that had evolved in isolation mixed, while populations of marine organisms were often separated. A recent example (around 2.5 million years ago, recent in geological terms!) of this phenomenon is the joining of North and South America. The faunas and floras of the two continents mingled, which is why we now have armadillos in Texas and deer in Argentina (see Chapter 20). But the marine organisms on the east and west side of the Isthmus of Panama, which were essentially identical in the early Pliocene, have been evolving in isolation since the land bridge formed and are today different from each other.

The position of continents affects patterns of oceanic circulation, and because ocean currents transport enormous quantities of heat those changes in water flow affect climates worldwide. We saw in Chapter 1 how the breakup and northern movements of the continents in the late Mesozoic and Cenozoic eventually led to the isolation of the Arctic Ocean, with the formation of an ice cap by the start of the Pliocene epoch, around 5 million years ago.

The Arctic ice cap is not just a cold habitat in a more equable world, housing polar bears rather than tigers. The original appearance of the ice cap influenced global climatic conditions in a variety of ways, and the world today is colder and drier in general than it was prior to Pliocene times. The Arctic ice cap also plays some critical roles in the dynamic systems that influence today's global climates in rather unexpected ways. Some researchers have proposed that should the world become warmer, and the ice cap become smaller, parts of western Europe (such as England) might actually become *colder*. How could this be? It seems that cold Arctic waters are a determinant in the dynamic conveyer belt of global oceanic currents, which have as a component the Gulf Stream that transports warm water from the equatorial Atlantic and the Gulf of Mexico over the north Atlantic

Ocean and across to Europe. With a smaller ice cap this conveyer belt might be disrupted (Kunzig 1996). Without the Gulf Stream, England, which is at the same latitude as Newfoundland, would probably have a similarly cold climate. This example serves to illustrate how very labile the Earth's climate is, and how dependent it is on a particular configuration of continental masses influencing ice cover and oceanic currents. We can only hope that global warming won't make England's climate a test case in demonstrating the validity of this particular hypothesis.

The Earth's Time Scale and the Early History of the Continents

Vertebrates are known from the portion of Earth's history called the **Phanerozoic Eon** (*Phanerozoic* = visible life) in which we still live. The Phanerozoic began 545 million years ago, and contains the **Paleozoic** (ancient life), **Mesozoic** (middle life), and **Cenozoic** (new life) Eras. (Our own portion of time, the **Recent**, is contained within the Cenozoic Era.) Each era contains a number of periods, and each period contains a number of epochs (see the Frontispiece figure). The Phanerozoic contains at least 99 percent of described fossil species, although the oldest fossils are known from around 3.5 billion years ago, and the origin of life is estimated to be around 4 billion years ago.

The time before the Phanerozoic is often loosely referred to as the **Precambrian**, as the Cambrian is the first period in the Paleozoic Era. Hence the base of the Cambrian is the same as the base of the Phanerozoic, and the earlier part of Earth's history is indeed "before the Cambrian." This terminology is rather misleading as the Precambrian actually represents seven-eighths of the entire history of the Earth! Precambrian time is better perceived as a series of eons, comparable to the Phanerozoic Eon. The earliest eon is the Hadean, commencing with the formation of the Earth around 4.5 billion years ago. The start of the next, the Archean, is demarcated by the oldest recognized rocks at around 3.8 billion years ago. The final Precambrian Eon, the Proterozoic, began around 2.5 billion years ago. Although life dates from the early Archean, it is not until the Proterozoic that organisms more complex than bacteria are known, although multicellular organisms are not known until near the end of the eon about 1 billion years ago. The evolution of eukaryotic organisms, which depend on oxygen for respiration, followed shortly after the first appearance of atmospheric oxygen in the middle Proterozoic (around 2.2 billion years ago).

The start of the Proterozoic is demarcated by the appearance of large continental blocks as seen in today's world. (The pre-Proterozoic world would have looked rather like the South Pacific, lots of little volcanic islands separated by large tracts of ocean.) The formation of continents was accompanied by chemical changes that dramatically modified the composition of the oceans and the atmosphere (Holland 1984). The ocean and the atmosphere were probably chemically reducing, because of the absence of free oxygen (Kempe and Degens 1985). The evolution of oxygen-producing organisms during the 2 billion years of the Proterozoic resulted in the oceanic and atmospheric conditions we recognize today—chemically oxidative conditions and alkaline seas. By the end of the Proterozoic a major biotic shift occurred—the evolution from soft-bodied organisms of forms capable of secreting articulated skeletal parts (McMenamin and McMenamin 1989).

Continental Geography of the Early Paleozoic

The world of the early Phanerozoic contained at least six major continent blocks (Figure 5–2). A large block called **Laurentia** included most of modern North America, plus Greenland, Scotland, and part of northwestern Asia. Four smaller blocks contained other parts of what are now the Northern Hemisphere: Baltica—Scandinavia and much of central Europe; Kazakhstania—central southern Asia; Siberia—northeastern Asia; and China—Mongolia, North China, and Indochina. **Gondwana** included most of what is now the Southern Hemisphere (South America, Africa, Antarctica, and Australia) plus India, Tibet, South China, Iran, Saudi Arabia, Turkey, southern Europe, and part of the southeastern United States.

In the Late Cambrian, the time when vertebrates probably first appeared, Gondwana and Laurentia straddled the equator; Siberia, Kazakhstania, and China were slightly to the south of the equator; and Baltica was positioned far to the south (Figure 5–2a). Note that the position of the modern continents within Gondwana is different from today; for

example, Africa and South America appear to be upside down. Over the next hundred million years or so Gondwana drifted south and rotated in its position. By the Late Silurian the eastern portion of Gondwana was over the South Pole, and Africa and South America were in positions similar to those they assume today. Laurentia was still in approximately the same position, although it had rotated slightly counterclockwise. Baltica had by now moved north and collided with Laurentia, to form a united block called Laurussia. Kazakhstania, Siberia, and China had also moved north and were now situated in the Northern Hemisphere.

The most dramatic radiation of metazoan life had occurred by the start of the Cambrian. However, many of the groups known from the Cambrian were unique to that period and left no living descendants (Gould 1989). A more profound, although less dramatic, radiation of marine animals occurred in the Ordovician. No new phyla appeared, but there was a near tripling in the number of families, and many of the groups that were to dominate the ecosystem of the rest of the Paleozoic appeared and radiated at this time (Droser et al. 1996). The initial diversification of vertebrates, although sparsely documented in the fossil record from this period (see Chapter 2), was a component of this Ordovician radiation.

Early Paleozoic Terrestrial Ecosystems

The evolution of terrestrial ecosystems has been traced throughout the Phanerozoic (reviewed by Behrensmeyer et al. 1992). Photosynthesizing bacteria (cyanobacteria) probably existed in wet terrestrial habitats from their origin in the Archean (Horodyski and Knauth 1994), and algae, lichens, and fungi probably occurred on land since the late Proterozoic (Kenrick and Crane 1997). Fossilized soils from the Ordovician have mottled patterns that seem to indicate the presence of bacterial mats, and traces of erosion suggest that some of the soil surface was covered by algae, but there is no evidence of rooted plants (DiMichele and Hook 1992). Land plants appear to represent a single terrestrial invasion from a particular group of green algae (Kenrick and Crane 1997). The first major radiation of plants onto land probably took place in the Middle to Late Ordovician, although we have no direct evidence (i.e., macrofossils) of land plants until the Late Silurian. These pioneers included bryophytes,

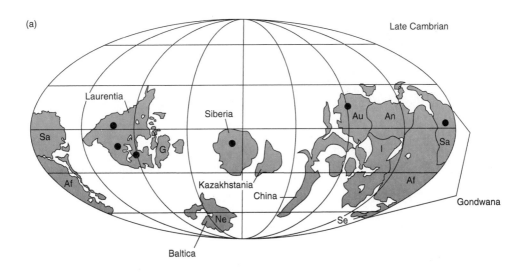

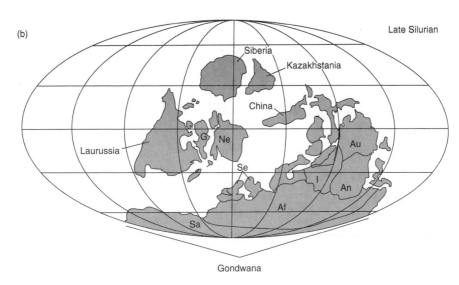

Figure 5–2   Location of continental blocks in (a) the Late Cambrian, (b) Late Silurian. The black dots in (a) indicate fossil localities where Ordovician vertebrates have been found. Positions of modern continents are indicated as follows: Af = Africa, An = Antarctica, Au = Australia, G = Greenland, I = India, Ne = northern Europe, Sa = South America, Se = southern Europe. (Modified from A. Hallam 1994, *An Outline of Phanerozoic Biography*, Oxford University Press, Oxford, UK.)

represented now by mosses, liverworts, and hornworts. The landscape would have looked bleak by our standards—mostly barren, with a few kinds of low-growing vegetation limited to moist areas.

As was the case with the evolution of land vertebrates, land plants had to cope with the transition from life in a watery medium to life in an airy one. The earliest land plants were small and simple, bearing a resemblance to the spore-producing phase of living primitive plants such as mosses. Adaptive responses to life on land included the evolution of an impenetrable outer surface (to prevent water loss), water-conducting internal tubes, and spore-bearing organs for reproduction (Kenrick and Crane 1997).

The diversity of terrestrial life increased during the Silurian, and a rootless, leafless plant called *Cooksonia* is abundant in Late Silurian fossil deposits. *Cooksonia*, which grew to a height of 10 to 15 millimeters, consisted of a group of unbranched stems topped by pinhead-size spore-producing structures. *Cooksonia* and other, similar Silurian plants were more primitive than the vascular plants that started to appear in the latest Silurian. The Silurian plant cover was probably fairly low, concentrated along river floodplains. Terrestrial fungi are also known among these plant assemblages, as are small arthropods which would have fed on these fungi, and some larger, probably predatory, arthropods. Thus by the latest Silurian there was a minimal terrestrial food web of primary producers (plants), decomposers (fungi), secondary consumers (fungus-eating arthropods), and predators (millipedes and scorpions) (DeMichele and Hook 1992).

The spread of land plants in the Devonian may have had profound effects on the Earth's atmosphere and climate. Fossil soils with deep-rooted plants first appear in the Devonian, and the formation of such soils would induce the dissolution of the underlying rocks by the process of weathering (the attacking of rock minerals by plant organic secretions, by roots obtaining nutrients, or by the decomposition of dead plant material). The chemical processes of weathering entrap atmospheric carbon dioxide. Other sources of evidence point to a sharp decrease in atmospheric carbon dioxide during the Devonian, and it is now thought that the spread of land plants was the cause (Berner 1997, Retallack 1997). Carbon dioxide levels reached an extreme low during the Late Carboniferous and Early Permian, resembling the levels of today's world. The reverse greenhouse effect of this low atmospheric carbon dioxide probably caused the extensive Permo-Carboniferous glaciations (see Chapter 9).

Terrestrial ecosystems increased in complexity through the Early and Middle Devonian, but food webs remained simple. The land would still have looked barren, although the changes that had occurred since the Silurian would be apparent. Plants were limited to stream banks and other areas of nearly continuous moisture, and occurred in patches composed of single species, but the diversity of plant species was greater than it had been in the Silurian. Still more dramatic would have been the increased height that was possible for vascular plants (which could transport water from the site of uptake to other locations). By the Middle Devonian, these plants probably attained heights of two meters, and the canopy they created would have modified microclimatic conditions on the ground. Treelike plants evolved independently among several ancient plant lineages, and by the Middle Devonian there were stratified forest communities (Kenrick and Crane 1997). However, these trees were not related to modern trees and were not really like modern trees in their structure. One would not be able to make furniture out of Devonian trees; they had narrow trunks and would not have provided enough woody tissue.

Today plants form the base of the terrestrial food chain, but there is no evidence that Devonian invertebrates were primary herbivores, feeding on living plants. Instead, they were probably detritivores, consuming dead plant material and fungi. This in turn would recycle the plant nutrients to the soil. Millipedes and scorpions were abundant, and springtails and mites were also present. The oldest insects known come from Early Devonian sediments in Canada, but they were nonflying forms; flying insects were not known until the Carboniferous (DeMichele and Hook 1992).

■ Early Paleozoic Climates

During the early Paleozoic sea levels were at or near an all-time high for the Phanerozoic, and atmospheric carbon dioxide levels were also apparently very high. There was a major glaciation in the Late Ordovician which would have created cool overall global conditions. Later in the Silurian the ice sheets retreated and the sea level fell, exposing more land and restricting oceanic circulation (Crowley and North 1991). These climatic ameliorations may have set the scene for the development of the Late Silurian terrestrial ecosystems.

■ Early Paleozoic Extinctions

There was a major extinction event among marine invertebrates in the Ordovician, but the record of vertebrates from that time is too poor to know if this event affected them as well. The next major extinction, in the Late Devonian, had severe effects on marine vertebrates. Thirty-five families of fish (= 76 percent) became extinct, including all of the remaining ostracoderms and placoderms, and many of the acanthodians and the lobe-finned fishes (Benton 1989, Janvier 1996).

■ References

Behrensmeyer, A. K., J. D. Damuth, W. A. DiMichele, R. Potts, H. Dieter-Sues, and S. L. Wing (editors). 1992. *Terrestrial Ecosystems Through Time*. University of Chicago Press, Chicago, IL.

Benton, M. J. 1989. Patterns of evolution and extinction in vertebrates. Pages 218–241 in *Evolution and the Fossil Record*, edited by K. C. Allen and D. E. G. Briggs. Belhaven Press, London, UK.

Berner, R. A. 1997. The rise of plants and their effect on weathering and atmospheric CO_2. *Science* 276:544–545.

Cox, C. B., and P. D. Moore. 1993. *Biogeography: An Ecological and Evolutionary Approach*, 5th edition. Blackwell Scientific, Oxford, UK.

Crowley, T. J., and G. R. North. 1991. *Paleoclimatology*. Oxford University Press, Oxford, UK.

DiMichele, W. A., and R. W. Hook (rapporteurs). 1992. Paleozoic terrestrial ecosystems. Pages 205–325 in *Terrestrial Ecosystems Through Time*, edited by A. K. Behrensmeyer, J. D. Damuth, W. A. DiMichele, R. Potts, H. Dieter-Sues, and S. L. Wing. University of Chicago Press, Chicago, IL.

Droser, M. L., R. A. Fortey, and X. Li. 1996. The Ordovician radiation. *American Scientist* 84:122–131.

Gould, S. J. 1989. *Wonderful Life: The Burgess Shale and the Nature of History*. Norton, New York, NY.

Hallam, A. 1994. *An Outline of Phanerozoic Biogeography*. Oxford University Press, Oxford, UK.

Holland, H. D. 1984. *The Chemical Evolution of the Atmosphere and Oceans*. Princeton University Press, Princeton, NJ.

Horodyski, R. J., and L. P. Knauth. 1994. Life on land in the Precambrian. *Science* 26:494–498.

Janvier, P. 1996. *Early Vertebrates*. Oxford Monographs on Geology and Geophysics—33. Clarendon Press, Oxford, UK.

Kempe, S., and E. T. Degens. 1985. An early sodic ocean? *Chemical Geology* 53:95–108.

Kenrick, P., and P. R. Crane. 1997. The origin and early evolution of plants on land. *Nature* 389:33–39.

Kunzig, R. 1996. In deep water. *Discover* 17(2):86–96.

McMenamin, M. A. S., and D. L. McMenamin. 1989. *The Emergence of Animals: The Cambrian Breakthrough*. Columbia University Press, New York, NY.

Retallack, G. J. 1997. Early forest soils and their role in Devonian climate change. *Science* 276:583–585.

PART 2 Aquatic Vertebrates: Cartilaginous and Bony Fishes

Vertebrates originated in the sea, and more than half of the species of living vertebrates are the products of evolutionary lineages that have never left an aquatic environment. Water now covers 73 percent of the Earth's surface (the percentage has been higher in the past) and provides habitats extending from deep oceans, lakes, and mighty rivers to fast-flowing streams and tiny pools in deserts. Fishes have adapted to all these habitats, and the nearly 24,000 species of living fishes currently described are the subject of this portion of the book.

Life in water poses challenges for vertebrates but offers many opportunities. Aquatic habitats are some of the most productive on Earth, and energy is plentifully available in many of them. Other aquatic habitats, such as the deep sea, have no in situ production of food and the animals that live in them depend on energy that flows from elsewhere. The physical structure of aquatic habitats has a similar range: Some aquatic habitats (coral reefs are an example) have enormous structural complexity, whereas others (like the open ocean) have virtually none. The diversity of fishes reflects specializations for this variety of habitats.

The diversity of fishes and the habitats in which they live have offered unparalleled scope for variations in life history. Some fishes produce millions of eggs that are released into the water to drift and develop on their own, other species of fishes produce a few eggs and guard both the eggs and the young, and numerous fishes give birth to precocial young. Males of some species of fishes are larger than females, in others the reverse is true; some species have no males at all, and a few species of fishes change sex partway through life. Feeding mechanisms have been a central element in the evolution of fishes, and the specializations of modern fishes range from species that swallow prey longer than their own bodies to species that rapidly extend their jaws like a tube to stick up minute invertebrates from tiny crevices. In this part of the book we consider the evolution of this extraordinary array of vertebrates and the ecological conditions in the Devonian that contributed to the next major step of evolution, the origin of terrestrial vertebrates.

CHAPTER
6

Early Vertebrates: Jawless Vertebrates and the Origin of Jawed Vertebrates

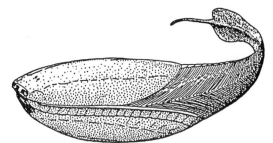

The earliest vertebrates represented an important advance over the nonvertebrate chordate filter feeders (Chapter 2). Their most distinctive and important new feature was a distinct head end, containing a tripartite brain enclosed by a cartilaginous cranium (brain box) and complex sense organs (eyes, nose, etc.). Instead of using cilia to move water over the gill bars, they used the newly acquired pharyngeal musculature. This water current was used for respiration, rather than for filter feeding, and gill tissue was elaborated on the gill bars. Early vertebrates were active predators rather than sessile filter feeders. They also possessed bone, a distinctive form of mineralized tissue, the acquisition of which may be related to their newly acquired sense organs and higher levels of activity (Chapter 2).

We know a remarkable amount about the anatomy of some of these vertebrates because the internal structure of their bony armor reveals the positions and shapes of many parts of their soft anatomy. The brains and cranial nerves of these jawless vertebrates were similar to those of living lampreys. Jawed vertebrates, contemporaneous with the more primitive jawless vertebrates but making their initial appearance somewhat later in time, represented a further advance in the vertebrate design for high levels of activity and predation. Jaws themselves, later used in seizing and holding prey, are homologous with the structures that form the gill arches, and probably first evolved as devices to improve the strength and effectiveness of gill ventilation. In this chapter we trace the earliest steps in the radiation of vertebrates beginning some 500 million years ago, and consider the transition to jawed vertebrates.

■ The Earliest Evidence of Vertebrates

A major new feature of vertebrates was mineralized tissues composed of calcium phosphate (bone, dentine, and enameloid; see Chapter 2). In early vertebrates these tissues were formed only in the skin, as a type of exoskeleton. Some form of internal cartilaginous skeleton was doubtless present (at least as the gill bars and the cranium surrounding the brain), but a fully bony, or ossified, internal skeleton is found only in bony fishes (osteichthyans) and their descendants, including ourselves (see Chapter 3). Mineralized tissues are more likely to fossilize than unmineralized, soft tissues. We do not know if there was a diversity of vertebrates prior to the acquisition of bone, but the fossil record of vertebrates subsequent to its evolution is extensive (Forey and Janvier 1994, Janvier 1996).

The oldest mineralized fragments believed to belong to vertebrates occur in the Late Cambrian of North America and Australia, around 100 million years prior to the time when whole body vertebrate fossils became abundant in the Silurian (Repetski 1978, Young et al. 1996). Recent histological examination of the North American material, termed *Anatolepis*, has shown it to have a strong resemblance to dentine, a unique vertebrate tissue (Smith et al. 1995) (see further discussion in Chapter 2).

Several Ordovician sites have yielded fragments of vertebrate fossils: Saaremaa, small island near Estonia in the Baltic Sea, and the adjacent coast as far as Leningrad; the North American Harding Sandstone Formation, extending from Arkansas to Montana; and the Amadeus Basin of central Australia (Sansom et al. 1996, Young 1997). The earliest vertebrates represented by complete articulated fossils are from the Late Ordovician of Bolivia. They are of an armored torpedo-shaped jawless fish, *Sacabambaspis*, about 35 cm long (Figure 6–2c). Better known are the more abundant forms that occur in the Late Silurian to Middle Devonian Old Red Sandstone in southwestern England and Wales, and in similar rocks in Scotland, Norway, and Spitzbergen, dating from around 400 million years ago. The more widespread Silurian fossils are similar to those of the Ordovician but are known from a greater variety of whole body fossils. The most diverse assemblages of Silurian fossils so far unearthed are in North America. Note, however, that the diversity of types of vertebrates in the Late Ordovician, as indicated by the diversities of mineralized tissues, is suggestive of a significant Ordovician radiation of vertebrates that is, as yet, barely documented (Smith et al. 1996, Young 1997). This early radiation involved both jawed and jawless groups. Based on the evidence provided by scales or denticles, jawed fish first occur in the Middle Ordovician, and definitive jawless fish a little earlier, in the Early Ordovician (Young 1997).

Many biologists conclude that vertebrates were the last major group of animals to evolve. Most of the other major metazoan groups appeared in the Early Cambrian, 20 to 30 million years before the first vertebrate fossils are known, and other chordates are also possibly known from this time (Shu et al. 1996). However, very early fragments of vertebrate mineralized tissue reveal a three-layered bony structure of considerable complexity—already as derived as that of much later vertebrates, even as complex as is seen in living vertebrates (see Chapter 2). If such histological complexity had evolved gradually, the anatomy of the earliest known vertebrates would suggest that the group had undergone considerable evolution *before* the time of earliest fossil evidence. But if unarmored vertebrates preceded armored ones, then why do we have no earlier fossil record of them?

The best guess is that early vertebrates were rather uncommon, soft-bodied marine forms whose existence was unlikely to be recorded by the rare circumstances that led to fossilization of soft parts. Perhaps the conditions for their fossilization simply did not exist during this presumptive early radiation. The absence of even soft-bodied vertebrates from the fossil record before the latest Cambrian is mysterious, because delicate organisms such as jellyfish medusae are known from the Early Cambrian, leaving such excellent impressions that their internal anatomy can be deciphered. Vertebrates are also conspicuously absent from the spectacular Middle Cambrian Burgess Shale Formation, which preserved many soft-bodied animals including the probable early chordate *Pikaia* (see Chapter 2). Perhaps early vertebrates lived in a habitat that was not conducive to the fossilization of soft tissues.

■ Reconstructing the Biology of the Earliest Vertebrates

The initial radiation of vertebrates was comprised of animals very different from any that survive today. They could basically be described as jawless fishes, but most were encased in bony armor, quite unlike the present-day jawless vertebrates (lampreys and hagfishes).

The Earliest Known Vertebrates

The earliest vertebrates (apart from the possibly vertebrate conodonts, see Chapter 2) were jawless animals collectively termed **"ostracoderms"** (*ostrac* = shell, *derm* = skin). The ostracoderms represent a paraphyletic assemblage because some more derived types are clearly more related to the gnathostomes (jawed vertebrates) than are others (see Figure 6–1), and thus this term is often put in quotation marks, as above. Ostracoderms encompass a number of distinct lineages, each with recognizable subdivisions, but our understanding of exactly how the different ostracoderm taxa are related to one another and to living vertebrates is in a considerable state of flux (Janvier 1996, Maisey 1996) (see later discussion).

Although Late Cambrian hydroxyapatite fragments are accepted as vertebrate remains, articulated pieces of early vertebrates that give us a basis for reconstructing the organisms are rare. No complete individuals are known until the Silurian/Devonian boundary. Only three geological formations, one each in Australia, North America, and South America, have yielded partial vertebrates of Ordovician age. The reasons seem clear. These early fishes were externally armored with a large number of small closely fitting, polygonal bony plates. Very special and rapid conditions of burial in beds destined to suffer minimal distortion in the subsequent 470 million years are required to keep such small plates articulated. These required conditions are understandably rare. It appears that a few shallow coastal marine, perhaps even tidal flat, environments provided the required conditions. Attempts at complete reconstructions of Middle and Late Ordovician vertebrates have been made (Ritchie in Rich and van Tets 1985, Elliott 1987, Gagnier 1989, Sansom et al. 1997). Both *Arandaspis* from central Australia and *Astraspis* from the eastern slopes of the Rocky Mountains were 13 to 14 centimeters long and had symmetrical tails (Figure 6–2). They were completely encased in small ornamented plates, each plate 3 to 5 millimeters in maximum dimension. Although the scales abut one another in the head and gill region, from about midbody posteriorly they may overlap as do scales in extant fishes. These bony plates show specializations for sensory canals, special protection around the eye, and in the reconstruction of the North American specimen, as many as eight gill openings on each side of the head. The numerous gill pouches have been hypothesized for other forms.

Full description of the gill region in the Australian and South American fossils and the rostral and mouth region of any of these Ordovician vertebrates will prove to be most interesting.

Later ostracoderms ranged in length from about 10 centimeters to more than 50 centimeters. Although they lacked jaws, some apparently had various types of movable mouth plates that lack analogues in any living vertebrates, positioned around a small circular mouth that appears to have been located further forward in the head than the larger, more gaping mouth of jawed vertebrates (Mallatt 1996). Although most ostracoderms possessed some sort of midline dorsal fin, only the more derived forms possessed any form of lateral paired appendages. Where lateral fins are preserved, only anterior (pectoral) fins are known, without evidence for endoskeletal support (this does not, of course, exclude the possibility of a cartilaginous internal fin skeleton). Their respiratory apparatus consisted of a variable number of separate pharyngeal gill pouches that opened along the side of the head, usually independently but opening through a common passage in one group (heterostracans). As in living jawless vertebrates, the notochord must have been the main axial support throughout adult life. Figure 6–3 depicts some typical ostracoderms.

While ostracoderms possessed bone and other mineralized tissues, analogy with living jawless vertebrates (see later) leaves us with little doubt that they must also have possessed another innovation, a muscular rather than a ciliary pump for ventilating the gills, and the use of the gills for respiration, rather than for filter feeding. Ciliary filter feeding is the mode of obtaining food (via the gill slits) of nonvertebrate chordates (see Chapter 2). In these animals (a great many of which are sessile or nearly so), water is wafted past food-snaring structures by the activity of great numbers of ciliated cells. Ciliary pumps are not appropriate for larger animals. An animal twice the length of amphioxus would require three times the number of cilia in order to maintain the same effective pumping, and with increasingly larger animals there would simply not be enough room in the pharynx to house the number of cilia that would be required. In contrast, muscular pumps are not disproportionately affected by body size increases. In addition, muscular pumping affords a more rapid and more forceful means of gill ventilation, appropriate for more active animals using the gills for gas exchange, and it also enables larger particles to be engulfed. The innovation of a muscular, pumping pharynx may have been a key factor in allowing the evolution of larger, more active vertebrates from the nonvertebrate chordates. Although most early vertebrates were less than 20 centimeters in length, this was still around an order of magnitude larger than the nonvertebrate chordate amphioxus.

It used to be assumed that, lacking jaws, early vertebrates also engaged in some form of filter feeding (e.g., Mallatt 1984a, 1984b). However, more recent interpretations of the anatomy of these animals (considering such features as the sophisticated

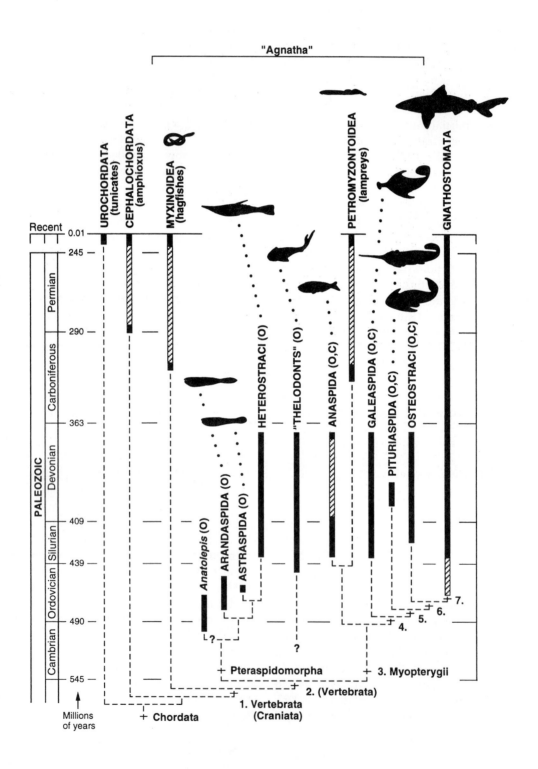

distance receptors in the head) have resulted in the conclusion that the adults, at least, must have been predators of some sort. They probably specialized on small, slow-moving, bottom-living prey (Northcutt and Gans 1983, Gans 1989, Mallatt 1996).

The Importance of Living Primitive Vertebrates in Understanding Ancient Ones

The fossil record of the first vertebrates reveals little about their pre-Silurian evolution; it provides no undisputed clues about the evolution of vertebrate organization from an invertebrate progenitor. How, then, can we have any knowledge of the form and features of these earliest vertebrates, or how can we make any confident determinations about the soft (nonbony) anatomy of the slightly later forms known from whole-body preservation? We are lucky enough to have two examples of surviving primitive vertebrates, representatives of the early agnathous (jawless) vertebrate radiation—hagfishes and lampreys. Although the biology and development of hagfishes is less well known than that of lampreys, they are especially important to our

understanding of the earliest vertebrate condition. Many biologists would regard hagfishes as retaining more primitive features than any known vertebrate, living or fossil, perhaps even predating the origin of bone (see Chapter 2). In contrast, some recent researchers would still prefer to link hagfishes and lampreys together as sister taxa, either on molecular (Stock and Whitt 1992) or morphological (Mallatt 1996) grounds. Mallatt (1996) especially notes the similarity in both hagfishes and lampreys of the elongated pharyngeal cavity, housing a powerful muscular tongue supported by a cartilaginous lingual apparatus. However, there are so many other features of hagfishes that suggest that they are more primitive than lampreys (see later and Table 6.1), that these oral features most likely evolved convergently, or perhaps represent a retained primitive feature inherited from the earliest vertebrates (Janvier 1996).

The issue of the supposed highly primitive nature of hagfishes is an important one; if it is true that they are more primitive than all known vertebrates, living or extinct, then we can have no doubt that features of anatomy and physiology that hag-

---

1. Vertebrata: Neural crest cells, highly differentiated somites, gills supported by a distinctive skeleton, a distinct head region with the following characters: tripartite division of brain with cranial nerves differentiated from neural tube, segmental nerves, paired optic, auditory, and probably olfactory organs, one or more semicircular canals, cranium incorporating the anterior end of the notochord and enclosing brain and paired sensory organs. In other regions of the body are a system of distinctive endocrine glands, lateral line system, probable electrosensors, well-developed heart, paired kidneys, and at least 15 additional derived characters. **2.** Presence of arcualia (vertebral rudiments surrounding the nerve cord), lateral line organs in a sensory canal, physiological capacity to form bone in the dermis, two or three semicircular canals, eyes well developed, and 20 additional derived characters. **3.** Myopterygii: True

dorsal and anal fins with fin rays and muscularization, asymmetrical tail shape, paired fins with fin rays and internal musculature developed from a lateral plate that extends from behind the gills to the region of the cloaca (subsequently lost in lampreys and galeaspids), large eyes with extrinsic musculature. Single dorsal median nostril (nasohypophysial opening). **4.** Perichondral bone (at least in head), large orbits, large head vein (dorsal jugular), externally open endolymphatic ducts. **5.** Pectoral fins with a narrow, concentrated base. **6.** Cellular dermal bone, heterocercal (epicercal) tail, two distinct dorsal fins, sclerotic ring, and scleral ossifications in the eye. **7.** Gnathostomata (many derived characters, see text and Table 6.2, including secondary loss of the dorsal nasohypophysial opening.) (Based primarily on J. G. Maisey 1986, with consideration of P. Forey and P. Janvier 1993, and P. Janvier 1996.)

Figure 6–1 Phylogenetic relationships of the vertebrates. This diagram depicts the probable relationships among primitive vertebrates, including living and extinct jawless vertebrates and the earliest jawed vertebrates. An (O) following the name of a taxon indicates an "ostracoderm", and a (C) indicates a "cephalaspid" (both paraphyletic groupings). Dotted lines show interrelationships only, and are not indicative of the times of divergence or the unrecorded presence of taxa in the fossil record. Crosshatched bars indicate ranges of time when the taxon is known to be present, but is unrecorded (or poorly recorded) in the fossil record. The numbers indicate derived characters that distinguish the lineages. Thelodonts are not assigned to a specific position as different species could fall anywhere between the numbers 2 and 6.

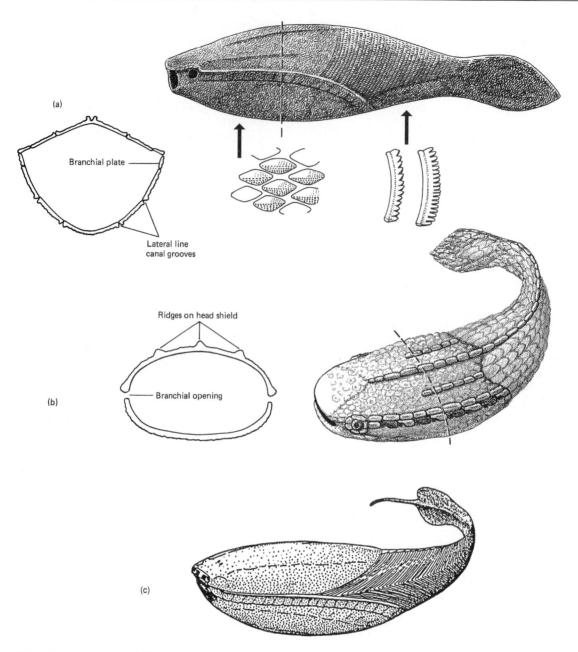

Figure 6–2 Reconstructions of Ordovician vertebrates: (a) *Arandaspis* from Australia;
(b) *Astraspis* from North America; (c) *Sacabambaspis* from Bolivia. *Sacabambaspis* was half again
as large as the others, averaging 25 centimeters. ([a] Modified from P. V. Rich and G. F. van
Tets 1985; [b] from D. K. Elliott 1987; [c] from P. Y. Gagnier 1989.)

fishes share with other vertebrates must have been
present in all extinct vertebrates (for example, the
muscular pharynx previously discussed). Should it
turn out that we are mistaken in our notion that
hagfishes are more primitive than all other vertebrates, this does not necessarily mean that conclusions about the earliest vertebrates drawn from the
biology of living primitive vertebrates would be

entirely misplaced. However, a primitive phylogenetic position of hagfishes certainly lends greater
confidence to our inferences about the biology of
extinct primitive forms.

Table 6.1 describes some features in which hagfishes are more primitive than other living vertebrates, including lampreys. In addition, several
other features lead to the conclusion that hagfishes

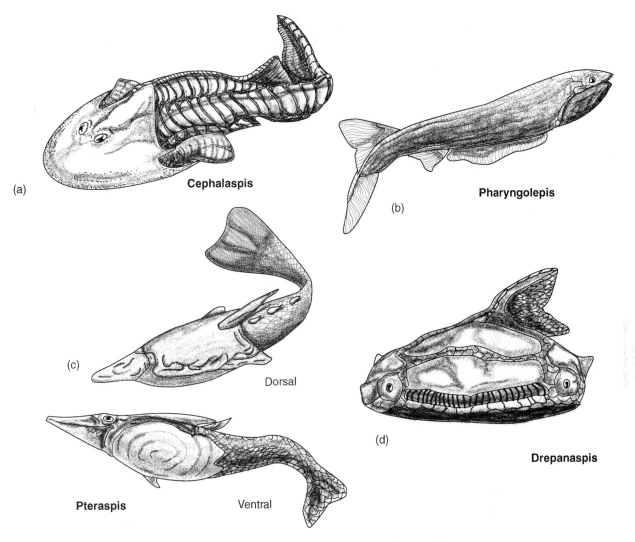

Figure 6–3   Four representative ostracoderms. Cephalaspids (= Monorhina, [a] and [b]); Heterostracans (= Diplorhina, [c] and [d]).

are more primitive than any known vertebrate, living or fossil. The absence of bone in hagfishes has been taken as one piece of evidence for their extremely primitive nature but, as discussed in Chapter 2, it is difficult to be certain as to whether their lack of bone is primary or secondary. However, claims that the keratinous teeth of hagfishes are homologous with the mineralized teeth of conodonts are probably incorrect (Smith et al. 1996). In addition, many apparently primitive features of hagfishes, such as their virtual lack of eyes and associated nerves and muscles, are probably secondary features associated with mud-burrowing habits. Hagfish eyes resemble the degenerate eyes of burrowing gnathostomes (Northcutt 1985).

However, two features of hagfishes are suggestive of a extremely primitive phylogenetic position. Firstly, hagfish body fluids are isosmolal with seawater, while other living vertebrates have dilute body fluids. Concentrated body fluids would preclude survival in freshwater habitats (see Chapter 4). However, all major groups of at least Silurian vertebrates have freshwater representatives. This would imply that hagfishes are at least more primitive than heterostracan ostracoderms. (Note, however, that conodonts were entirely marine.)

A second important feature is the anatomy of the hagfish taste sensory system. In other vertebrates the taste buds are situated in the dermis, innervated by cranial nerves IX and X (see Chapter 3).

TABLE 6.1	Features of hagfishes that are more primitive than the condition in lampreys and gnathostomes

1. Have very small paired eyes, extrinsic eye muscles and associated cranial nerves to move the eyes are lacking (but see discussion in text).
2. Cranium made of a sheath of fibrous tissue rather than of cartilage.
3. Lack a pineal eye.
4. Lack the facility of electroreception.
5. Apparent lack of lateral line sensory system (but canals, lacking neuromasts, are present in the head of some species [Wicht and Northcutt 1995]).
6. Have a single semicircular canal (organs of balance, one on each side of the head) in the inner ear (versus two in lampreys and ostracoderms, and three in gnathostomes).
7. Circulatory system retains accessory "hearts."
8. Have only one type of granular white blood cell (three types in lampreys and gnathostomes).
9. Lack autonomic innervation of the heart (but vagal innervation speeds, rather than slows, the heart in lampreys, may be evolved convergently with gnathostome condition).
10. Lack any type of spleen or splenic precursor.
11. Lack muscles in the midline fins.
12. Lack cartilaginous vertebral elements.
13. Lack renal collecting ducts in the kidney.
14. Have an open connection between the pericardial cavity and the coelom (closed in lampreys and gnathostomes).
15. Have body fluids isoosmolal with sea water (see text).

However, in hagfishes the sense of taste is via specialized sensory buds situated in the epidermis, innervated by cranial nerve V and spinal nerves; and in addition, the brain area that receives the nervous input is different (Braun 1996). This unique system of hagfishes must have evolved entirely independently from the sense of taste in lampreys and gnathostomes, suggesting an early divergence from the lineage leading to other vertebrates.

The most promising paths for understanding what is primitive and what is not about the many fascinating characteristics of hagfishes appear to be in comparative studies of hagfishes. With 40 to 60 species distributed in two distinct groups (Eptatretinae and Myxininae) variation in character states is more common than has usually been realized (Martini et al. 1997). Since *Myxine* and its relatives appear to be considerably more specialized (derived) than other hagfishes, comparative studies within the hagfishes may advance our understanding of which characteristics are those of the common ancestor of hagfishes and vertebrates.

■ The Radiation of Paleozoic Jawless Vertebrates

There were two main groups of ostracoderms. The heterostracans were the most primitive and were a monophyletic assemblage. The more derived "cephalaspids" were paraphyletic (and hence this name should properly be in quotes), because some of them were more closely related to the jawed vertebrates than others (see Figure 6–1). Lampreys also probably have their ancestry among the cephalaspids.

The Heterostracans and Other Primitive Vertebrates

The most primitive well-known group of ostracoderms, the **Heterostraci** (*hetero* = different, *ostrac* = shell), are known with certainty from the Early Silurian; had their major radiation in the Late Silurian and Early Devonian in North America, Europe, and Siberia; and survived into the Late Devonian. More poorly-known heterostracan relatives are known from the Ordovician and perhaps the Late Cambrian (Figure 6–1). Because of their curious shelled appearance, some have been called the **Pteraspida** (*ptera* = wing, *aspid* = shield) in various classifications. Impressions on the inside of the dorsal plate suggest that the brain had two separate olfactory bulbs. Because it is assumed that these bulbs were connected with two separate nasal openings, these primitive vertebrates are also called the **Diplorhina** (*diplo* = two, *rhin* = nostril) in some early classifications. (Note, however, that diplorhiny is evidently a primitive condition for vertebrates above the level

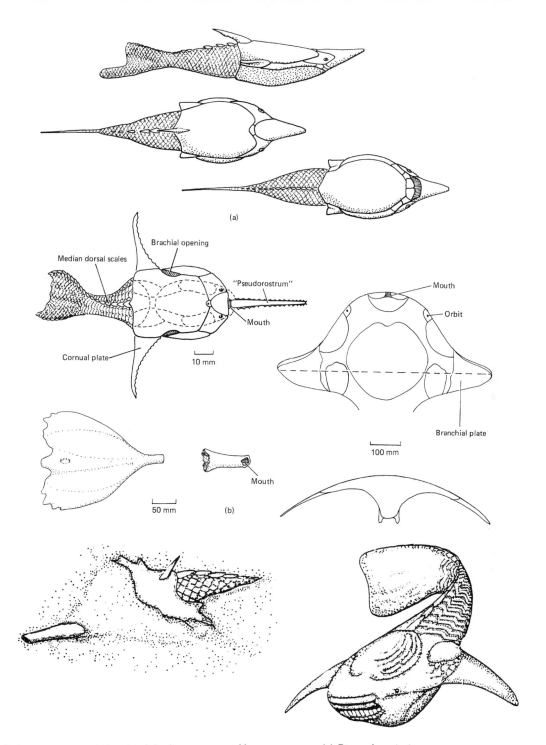

Figure 6–4 Diversity and details of the bony armor of heterostracans. (a) *Pteraspis rostrata*, a typical, relatively unspecialized species. Reconstruction of an 18-centimeter specimen from the Early Devonian. Lateral view above, dorsal surface left, ventral surface right. (b) Specialized heterostracans (in dorsal and life views). Clockwise from the upper left: a sawfishlike form *Doryaspis*, Early Devonian; form with enlarged down curved cornua (horns) and ventral runners (cross section of head region middle) and appearance in life, *Pycnosteus*, Middle Devonian; and eyeless, tube-mouthed form *Eglonaspis*, Early and Middle Devonian, which may have buried in the bottom, snout protruding. (Modified after J. A. Moy-Thomas and R. S. Miles 1971; and P. Janvier in J. Hanken and B. K. Hall, editors, 1993, *The Skull*, volume 2, University of Chicago Press, Chicago, IL.)

of hagfishes, and is shared with gnathostomes. The monorhinal condition of lampreys and other ostracoderms is secondarily derived from this one [Forey and Janvier 1993].) Thus "Heterostraci," "Pteraspida," and "Diplorhina" are variously used loosely as synonyms for this radiation of primitive vertebrates. Heterostracans can be grouped with some of the poorly known Ordovician taxa into the larger grouping Pteraspidomorpha (see Figure 6–1).

Heterostracans ranged in size from 10 centimeters to 2 meters and were encased anteriorly by bony articulating pieces that extended to the anus in some groups (Moy-Thomas and Miles 1971, Janvier 1996). Posterior to the anus was a short, probably mobile tail covered by smaller, protruding barblike plates. The head shell had an ornamented dorsal plate, one or more lateral plates, and several large ventral elements (see Figure 6–4). Thus heterostracans provide the earliest recorded solution to the growth-in-a-suit-of-armor problem, where either large articulating plates did not form until maximum size was attained, or numerous centers of bone formation enlarged circumferentially and fused into plates or a solid shield only as the animal reached maximum size. All these forms achieved an essentially solid carapace over the anterior one-third of their body, pierced by the mouth and a single pair each of eyes and external gill openings. No bone is known to have formed in endoskeletal structures and no bone cells are found within the osseous tissue, nor were true paired appendages or well-developed dorsal or anal fins present. The shell was composed of three distinct layers, and in all but two genera the shell appears to have continued to grow as the animal increased in size.

Openings for two eyes are lateral, one on each side of the head shield. In the middle of the dorsal plate is a small opening for a third, median eye, or **pineal organ**. The mouth is near the end of the body (terminal) but opens ventrally in many forms. Rimmed on its lower border by as many as two rows of small plates, the mouth is thought to have opened in a scooplike manner of V-shaped cross section in the species best preserved (Soehn and Wilson 1990). The lower lobe of the tail is disproportionately large. This lower lobe contains the axial support element (the notochord), a tail fin construction called **hypocercal**. The body is generally round in cross section, like that of a tadpole, and early heterostracans show little sign of stabilizing projections. Possibly these fishes were erratic swimmers and resembled some tadpoles by swimming with something less than precisely controlled locomotion. While feeding they may have oriented head down and plowed their jawless mouth through the bottom sediments.

As might be guessed, evolutionary trends in the heterostracans led to the improvement of locomotor capabilities. During their later history, the cross section of benthic species flattened ventrally but remained arched or rounded dorsally. The head shield developed solid, lateral, winglike stabilizing projections called **cornua** (= horns; Figure 6–4). The head shield shortened, and except for a dorsal ridge of plates, the bony covering became restricted to the anterior end. Although specialized edges around the mouth for biting and grasping did not evolve, some of the oral plates developed enlarged toothlike projections that may have been used for scraping.

The heterostracan lineage also gave rise to species of bizarre appearance. Some developed enormous cornua that may have acted as water-planing surfaces (hydrofoils), which produced lift for the heavy head when swimming. In addition, some had two narrow sledlike runners on the ventral surface, which presumably held the head above the substrate. Several forms developed dorsally directed mouths and a much reduced skeleton. Perhaps these species fed at the surface by filtering large quantities of plankton-rich water. Forms are also known with a long tooth-bearing projection extending from the edge of the mouth, rather like that of the living sawfish. The function of this rostrum is difficult to understand because the mouth was dorsal to the saw, just opposite to morphologically similar forms among today's vertebrates. Perhaps the saw was used to stir up organisms from the bottom.

About the middle of the Silurian, shortly after the diverse array of heterostracans entered the fossil record, another distinct but poorly known assemblage of jawless vertebrates appeared. Rather than large plates, these small fishes (Figure 6–5) were covered by numerous tiny **denticles**, small toothlike structures not unlike those of living sharks. Isolated denticles from the Ordovician may also belong to these fishes. No articulated specimens are known before the mid-Silurian, and by the end of Devonian they were extinct. On the assumption that they are all related, several names have been given to this group of fishes, all referring to characteristics of the scales: **Thelodonti** (*thelo* = nipple, *dont* = tooth) and **Coelolepida** (*coel* = hollow, *lepida* = scale) are the names most commonly

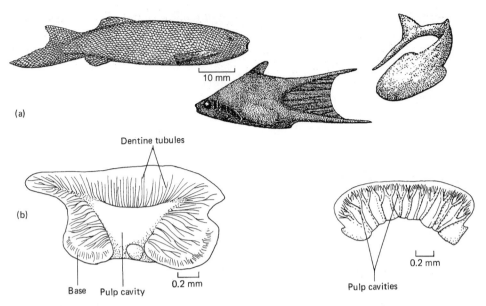

Figure 6–5 Thelodonts. (a) *Phlebolepis* (left), and *Loganellia* (middle), both from the Late Silurian, and (right) an unnamed Devonian species with deep body, forked tail, and a well-developed stomach; (b) cross sections of two types of thelodont scales. (Modified after J. A. Moy-Thomas and R. S. Miles 1971; P. Janvier in J. Hanken and B. K. Hall, 1993, *The Skull*, volume 2, University of Chicago Press, Chicago, IL; and M. V. H. Wilson and M. W. Caldwell 1993.)

used. The phylogenetic relationships of thelodonts are uncertain. The distinctive small separate scales, each with a pulp cavity like a tooth, and the other characters established by the fossils have been considered ancestral for vertebrates, and thus of no value in determining thelodont relationships. In fact, a body covered by small bony elements (*tesserae*) is just what has been hypothesized as the starting point (most primitive condition) for all the more heavily armored early vertebrate lineages. Perhaps "thelodonts" represent a polyphyletic collection of the remains of ostracoderms lacking heavy dermal armor. Some thelodont species appear to be very primitive, perhaps related to the heterostracans, while others have been proposed as the sister taxa to gnathostomes (Janvier 1996).

Thelodonts were between 10 and 20 centimeters long. Most were dorsoventrally flattened anteriorly and laterally compressed posteriorly. Some were fusiform (torpedo shaped), with ridges that correspond to the dorsal and anal fins in more derived fishes, and with a hypocercal tail. In addition, broad-based flanges projected from their sides where anterior paired appendages occur in later vertebrates. Like the heterostracans, thelodonts had the ancestral vertebrate characters of lateral eyes, a pineal opening, and a jawless mouth. Living fishes shaped like thelodonts feed by swimming along the bottom of the sea. Thelodonts may have skimmed organic deposits off the bottom into their small mouths with the aid of muscular suction. Some of the thelodonts had internal denticles thought to have crushed prey and trapped the fragments as pharyngeal teeth and gill rakers do in extant fishes (Van der Brugghen and Janvier 1993).

Recent discoveries of articulated fossils of marine thelodonts from the Silurian and Devonian of northwestern Canada have greatly broadened our perception of these animals (Wilson and Caldwell 1993). All the newly discovered forms have bodies covered in typical thelodont scales, but the bodies are deep and laterally compressed with symmetrical and deeply forked tails. Most interesting is evidence of a well-developed stomach, a feature previously thought to be a derived character of gnathostomes. Some very recently described forms from Scotland have evidence of pelvic and anal fins, again thought to only occur in jawed vertebrates (Märss and Ritchie 1997).

Apparently, thelodonts were most numerous in coastal estuaries, but eventually also radiated into fresh water. Where they occurred together, the small, lightly armored thelodonts were probably behaviorally very different from the larger, armored, and heavy-bodied heterostracans. Their phylogenetic relationship to other early vertebrates is unknown, but the recent discovery of characters previously thought to be found only in jawed vertebrates puts at least some of these enigmatic fishes in the ranks of possible jawed vertebrate ancestors.

The Appearance of the Cephalaspids and the Radiation of More Derived Vertebrates

A second group of vertebrates appeared at the same time as the thelodonts, and also had their major diversification in the Late Silurian and Early Devonian. Five distinct groups have sometimes been united as the **Cephalaspida** (*cephal* = head, *aspid* = shield) or Cephalaspidomorpha, although it currently seems more likely that this is a paraphyletic assemblage, and that these taxa represent the sister group to jawed vertebrates (see Figure 6–1). A single, large, solitary nasal opening that lies in the center of the head anterior to the eyes and is usually associated with the pineal gland has been used as a synapomorphy of the group. This structure has been the basis for another name widely used for these ancient vertebrates, the **Monorhina** (*mono* = one, *rhin* = nostril). A reversal of this feature of course would have to have occurred in the immediate ancestry of jawed vertebrates. This could have been accomplished by the process of heterochrony (see Chapter 2), as the dorsal migration of the nasal opening from a more ventral position is apparent during lamprey development.

A major group of cephalaspids is the **Osteostraci** (*osteo* = bone) from the mid-Silurian to Late Devonian of North America, Europe, and Siberia. A second is the **Galeaspida** (*gale* = helmet, *aspid* = shield) from the Early Silurian to Late Devonian of China and northern Vietnam. A third group is the recently described **Pituriaspida** (*pituri* is an Aboriginal word for an hallucinogenic plant, indicating how bizarre the shape of these animals is) from the Middle Devonian of Australia. And a fourth group is the **Anaspida** (*an* = without) primarily from the Silurian of North America, Europe, and China (although a few Late Devonian forms are known from Canada), which are thought to contain the ancestry of the extant lampreys (see Figure 6–1).

Like heterostracans, osteostracans were heavily armored (Figure 6–7). However, the bone contained lacunae or spaces for bone cells and their head

shield was a single, solid element devoid of sutures on its dorsal surface. In contrast, most heterostracans show evidence of periodic growth around the margins of their shield plates. The solid construction of the shield in osteostracans, however, and the absence of growth marks indicate that their head shield did not grow throughout life. Furthermore, all the individuals of a species of osteostracan are the same size. Perhaps osteostracans had a naked larval life, not unlike that of a lamprey ammocoete, and then metamorphosed into a stage where a head shield and other bony armor were deposited without further growth. Alternatively, all the different forms may not be species. They might represent stages in the life cycle of a few species. Between stages it would have been necessary for the dermal armor to be resorbed and the form changed before a new shield was laid down. Also like heterostracans, early osteostracans had extensive shields and no paired lateral stabilizers. Later types had short shields, movable paddlelike extensions of the body in the position of pectoral appendages, and hornlike extensions of the head shield just anterior to these paddles (Figures 6–3 and 6–7).

Unlike heterostracans, osteostracans had a **heterocercal** tail in which the lobe above the midline of the body was larger and stiffer than the lower lobe (a condition more precisely called **epicercal**). Their heterocercal tail may have resulted in a locomotor system that provided considerable lift, which increased their overall mobility. Apparently osteostracans, like many heterostracans, fed by expanding the pharynx and sucking material from the bottom.

The osteostracans are used as models of early jawless vertebrates even though they appear later in the fossil record than heterostracans. Two features have made osteostracans better known than other extinct jawless vertebrates. The first is their single-piece head shield, which resists disintegration better than a series of articulated plates. Second, within this shield the inner surface of the braincase and the channels are lined by thin layers of periosteal bone, a type of bone related to endochondral bone. (The presence of this derived character is one feature grouping osteostracans more closely with gnathostomes than with other ostracoderms.) The internal features of the braincase, with channels and foramina (small openings for the passage of nerves and blood vessels) are preserved in sufficient detail to allow reconstruction of the soft anatomy of the head. Eric Stensio and his collaborators in Sweden and England have patiently pol-

BOX 6–1   Interrelationships of Early Vertebrates

Our understanding of the early evolution and interrelationships of vertebrates is in a great deal of ferment. Two causes for argument are at the root of the many differing phylogenies proposed. First, the few extant forms are grossly different from the majority of known fossil forms, especially in their lack of bony tissues, the very basis for fossil remains. This problem is compounded by the fact that the oldest vertebrate fossils are fragmented, incomplete, and rare. Neither of these difficulties is likely to change in the foreseeable future; thus it is useful to examine a few of the differing phylogenies, the basis upon which their authors have proposed them, and why subsequent authors have disagreed. Very few authors have simultaneously treated all the major fossil and living jawless fishes. The names used for the taxa have not been identical even when precisely the same animals were being discussed. For ease of comparison, let us hold the names and number of principal taxa in each classification more nearly constant than did the original authors and look at some of the cladograms resulting from various hypotheses of jawless fish interrelationships. The reader should realize that the cladograms presented here contain editorial inclusions and deletions that were not part of the originals. Note that Figure 6–6 follows the recent convention, discussed in Chapter 2 but not adhered to in the rest of this volume, of substituting the term "Craniata" for the original use of the term Vertebrata, and restricting Vertebrata to mean vertebrates with the exclusion of hagfishes.

Although periodically proposed throughout this century, the hypothesis that hagfishes and gnathostomes are sister groups (Figure 6–6a) has little current support because of the lack of shared derived characters (Halstead 1982, Maisey 1986). A reexamination of the few hagfish embryos known (almost all of them were collected in 1896!) has found nothing consistent with a turn-of-the-century notion that the massive tonguelike structure in the floor of the hagfish oral cavity is homologous with the lower jaw of gnathostomes (Gorbman and Tamarin 1985). If other studies outlining extensive homologies in the feeding apparatus of hagfishes and lampreys (Yalden 1985, Mallatt 1996) prove to be correct, the concept of a valid taxon Cyclostomata would be supported (Figure 6–6b), a conclusion reached on other grounds by Schaeffer and Thomson (1980).

A very different view of the similarities between hagfishes and lampreys has been reached by workers concentrating on the character states of fossil jawless fishes and attempting to interpret the anatomy of living forms in reference to these ancient extinct fishes. One view proposed in the 1920s but now not widely accepted is that of hagfishes as the sister group of heterostracans, and lampreys as the sister group of Osteostracans (Figure 6–6c). This concept was based on extensive hypothetical reconstructions by Eric Stensio of the functional anatomy of heterostracans based on what was known of living hagfishes (Olson 1971). The circularity of this reasoning has given way in most recent phylogenies to viewing similarities between hagfishes and heterostracans as being due to the retention of numerous ancestral characters in each taxon.

Proponents of the validity of a close relationship between lampreys and hagfishes point to the differences between them as recent adaptations to anadromy by lampreys (e.g., osmoregulation) and to burrowing in the deep seafloor by hagfishes (e.g., degenerate, rather than plesiomorphic, structure of the eyes, inner ears, and lateral-line system). The majority of recent authors deny a close relationship on the grounds that there is little evidence that most hagfish characters are degenerate rather than ancestral. These authors derive hagfishes from the base of the evolution of vertebrates, sometimes expressly identifying them as the sister group of all other vertebrates (Figure 6–6d).

Focusing on the lamprey side of living jawless fish relationships, most authors accept an anaspid/lamprey sister group arrangement but differ on whether these two form a monophyletic group together with osteostracans (Figure 6–6d and e), based on the character of the single dorsal nostril (monorhiny), or whether the osteostracans are closest to the gnathos-

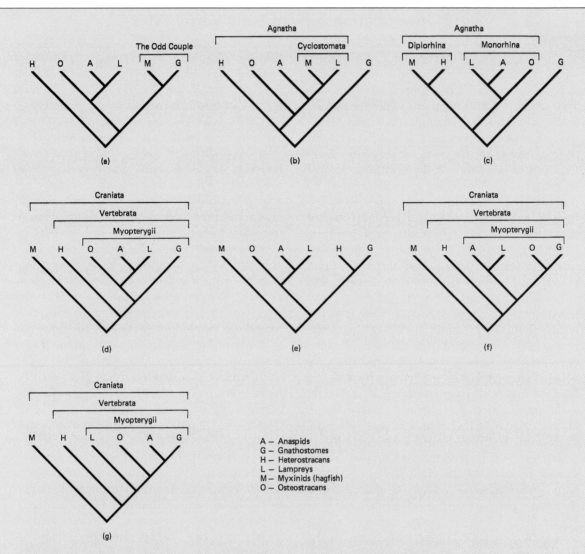

Figure 6–6 A few of the proposed interrelationships of the jawless fishes (past and present) and the gnathostomes.

A — Anaspids
G — Gnathostomes
H — Heterostracans
L — Lampreys
M — Myxinids (hagfish)
O — Osteostracans

tomes (Figure 6–6f, which is also the basis of Figure 6–1). This judgment depends entirely on which characters one values and which direction of the character state is considered to be derived in making interpretations. As an example, if acellular bone represented by gnathostome dentine is considered a condition derived from ancestral cellular bone, then, contrary to almost every other proposed arrangement, heterostracans become the sister group of gnathostomes since *all* their mineralized tissue is acellular. Another entry into the field of attempting to determine interrelationships of jawless fishes

and gnathostomes (Figure 6–6g; Maisey 1986) sees anaspid/lamprey relationships as equivocal but offers the possibility of an anaspid/gnathostome sister relationship. The most recently described groups of deep-bodied thelodonts, Chinese galeaspids and Australian pituriaspids, do nothing to clarify the picture.

In 1889, American paleontologist Edward Drinker Cope wrote, "We are embarrassed in the endeavor to present the relations of the earliest and lowest Vertebrata by want of knowledge of their structure" (see Forey 1984). The embarrassment continues (Forey and Janvier 1993, 1994).

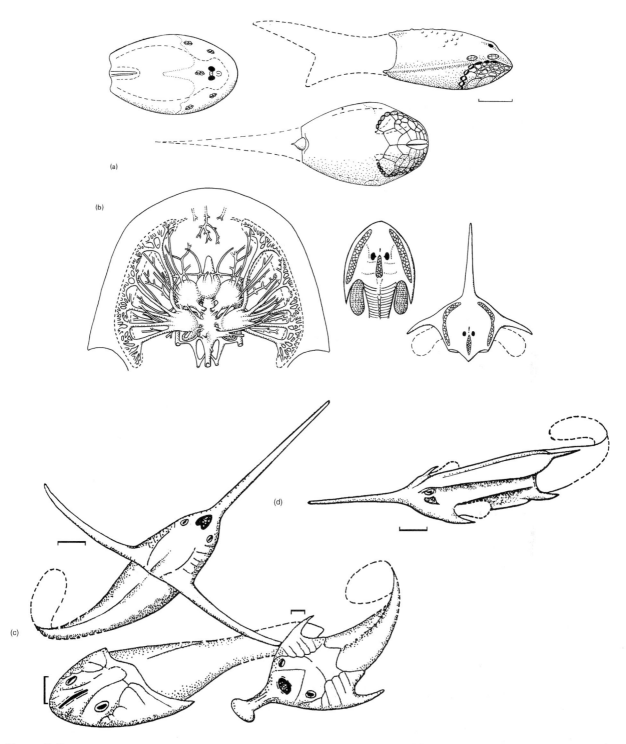

Figure 6–7 Details of osteostracans. (a) Primitive osteostracan, *Tremataspis*, Late Silurian, in lateral (right), dorsal (left), and ventral (below) reconstructions. (b) Derived osteostracans (l–r): reconstruction of the brain and cranial nerves of *Kiaeraspis*, Early Devonian, showing the detailed information obtainable from impressions left on the inner surface of the head shield; *Tyriaspis* of the Late Silurian; and the long rostrum *Boreaspis* of the Early Devonian. (c) Diversity of morphology in galeaspids from the Early Devonian of China. (d) Pituriaspid from the Early Devonian of Australia. All size bars one centimeter. (Modified primarily after [a, b] J. A. Moy–Thomas and R. S. Miles 1971; [c, d] P. Janvier in J. Hanken and B. K. Hall, 1993, *The Skull*, volume 2, University of Chicago Press, Chicago, IL.)

ished and ground away layer after layer of the precious fossils, taking photographs of each successive layer until they had serial photographs through the complete head shield. From these they could trace in three dimensions the canals and cavities that in life had been lined with bone (Figure 6–7b). Astonishingly, the internal anatomy of the brain and nervous system of osteostracans 400 million years old is very similar to that found in modern lampreys.

Along the dorsolateral edges of the head shield, and sometimes in the center behind the pineal opening, are peculiar fields of thin, irregular small plates (Figure 6–7). These fields form depressions connected to the inner ear cavity inside the braincase by huge canals that run through the shield. This combination of features has been interpreted as an electroreceptive system or as a sensory expansion of the membranous labyrinth of the inner ear. The osteostracans became abundant and diverse during the Devonian, even though they were competing with older groups and survived in the presence of jawed vertebrates. In part, their success may relate to these mysterious, unique adjuncts to their nervous system.

An apparently geographically isolated group of Early Devonian cephalaspids has come to light mostly during the past two decades in southern China and northern Vietnam. Many of these osteostracan look-alikes have been described as the galeaspids (Figure 6–7). They differed from the osteostracans in lacking paired fins and in having a large slit-, bean-, or even heart-shaped opening on the dorsal surface of their head shield. This opening was connected with the pharynx and may have been an inhalant canal. Galeaspids apparently had paired nasal cavities in this canal. Although the relationships of the galeaspids are not yet clear, some students of fossil fishes think they may have had muscularized median fins and that their lack of pectoral fins is the result of a secondary loss (Janvier 1984, 1996). If this is so, galeaspids must be considered relatively derived jawless fishes.

The most recently described major group of Paleozoic jawless fishes, the pituriaspids, has been found in the mid-Devonian of Australia (Figure 6–7). Superficially they resemble galeaspids and in addition are thought to have had paired pectoral appendages containing muscles like those of osteostracans. For this reason osteostracans are grouped by some paleontologists with the gnathostomes as the Myopterygii. Living lampreys have

muscles radiating into their median fins and have cranial nerve characters closely comparable to those of other myopterygians (Northcutt and Bemis 1993). If the lamprey lineage has secondarily lost muscular paired fins, as has been claimed for the galeaspids, then both of these groups also belong in the Myopterygii, and are closer to gnathostome (jawed vertebrate) ancestry than the heterostracans (see Figure 6–1).

In sediments from the Late Silurian through the Devonian a fourth group of cephalaspids, the anaspids, are found. All about 15 centimeters long, these freshwater fishes had minnowlike body proportions (Figure 6–8) resembling the probably unrelated thelodonts. Like their osteostracan relatives, the anaspids had a single median nasal opening anterior to the pineal foramen. Narrow scale rows (when they were present) covered the body in a manner similar to those along the posterior part of the osteostracans, but the flat scales were constructed of acellular layers. The head, however, was covered in most species by a complex of small plates or was naked. Anaspids also differed from osteostracans in having a hypocercal tail. They are considered to have been bottom-dwelling detritus feeders that fed in a head-down position reminiscent of that proposed for the heterostracans. Their stabilizing dorsal, anal, and lateral projections or folds, the spines and scutes associated with these projections, and the compressed shape of their fusiform bodies probably allowed an agility and locomotor capacity not known in the heterostracans or osteostracans. Anaspids are currently thought by many (e.g., Forey and Janvier 1993), but not all (e.g., Janvier, 1996) paleontologists to contain the ancestry of lampreys.

During the Late Silurian and Devonian most major known groups of extinct jawless vertebrates coexisted (Figure 6–1). Muscular filter feeding, increased mobility, and the protection that dermal bone afforded were important characters of these animals. Together, these features triggered a proliferation of variations on the vertebrate theme that spread into the waters of the world. Wherever photosynthesis produced small particulate matter capable of being sucked up and digested, vertebrates competed successfully with the established invertebrate lineages. This basic agnathous body plan also gave rise to eyeless, tube-snouted heterostracans, and nearly naked, sucker-mouthed anaspids that left their marks on other organisms.

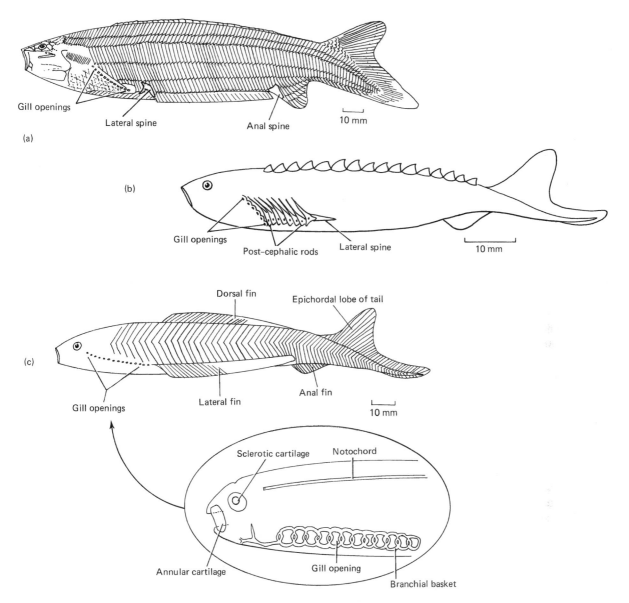

Figure 6–8   Reconstruction of Late Silurian fishes generally considered to be anaspids. (a) *Pharyngolepis*; (b) *Lasanius*; (c) *Jaymoytius* showing (inset) internal structures known from the head region. (Modified after J. A. Moy–Thomas and R. S. Miles 1971, *Paleozoic Fishes*, Saunders Philadelphia, PA.)

Here we observe for the first time a phenomenon repeated over and over again in the history of vertebrate life: A basic modification of the vertebrate framework appears, and a flood of forms using this new modification in conjunction with specializations explodes onto the scene. From a generalized form vertebrate life radiates in scores of directions to exploit the resources that this innovation has made available.

■ Extant Jawless Fishes

The living jawless vertebrates, hagfishes and lampreys, have long been placed with the ostracoderms in the "Class Agnatha", based on the fact that they share the lack of derived (gnathostome) features of jaws and two sets of paired fins. However, the new methods of phylogeny no longer allow grouping on the basis of shared primitive characters (see

Chapter 1), and besides it is now clear that the "Agnatha" is a paraphyletic assemblage. Not only are some ostracoderms more closely related to gnathostomes than are others, but even among the living vertebrates, lampreys appear to be more closely related to jawed vertebrates than are hagfishes. Because they possess round, jawless mouths living jawless fishes have often been combined in the Cyclostomata (*cyclo* = a circle, *stoma* = mouth), including lampreys in the Petromyzontoidea and hagfishes or slime-hags in the Myxinoidea, but this grouping is probably also a paraphyletic one. Figure 6–1 shows one possible interpretation of the interrelationships of early vertebrates (see also Box 6–1).

The fossil record of the modern types of jawless vertebrates is sparse. Lampreys are known from the Carboniferous—*Hardistiella* from Montana and *Mayomyzon* from Illinois. *Myxinikela*, an undisputed hagfish, and a second possible hagfish relative, *Gilpichthys* (Janvier 1981), have been found in the same deposits as *Mayomyzon* (Nelson 1994).

Hagfishes (Myxinoidea)

The hagfishes (Figure 6–9) are entirely marine. The sister group of all other Vertebrata, hagfishes lack vertebrae. Well over forty recognized species in five or six genera have nearly worldwide distribution, primarily on continental shelves (Brodal and Fange 1963). Hagfishes are never caught much above the bottom, often in deep regions of the shelf. Some live in colonies, each individual in a mud burrow marked in some species by a volcanolike mound at the entrance. Polychaete worms and shrimps are found in the guts of many species, and they probably live a molelike existence, finding their prey beneath the ooze or at its surface. They must be active when out of their burrows, for they are quickly attracted to bait and moribund fishes caught in gill nets. Small morphological differences between populations indicate that hagfishes are not wide ranging, but rather tend to live and breed locally (Martini et al. 1997).

Adult hagfishes are generally under a meter in length. Elongated, scaleless, and pinkish to purple in color, hagfishes have a single terminal nasal opening that connects with the pharynx via a broad tube. The eyes are degenerate or rudimentary and covered with a thick skin. The mouth is surrounded by six tentacles that can be spread and swept to and fro by movements of the head when the hagfish is searching for food. Within the mouth two multicusped, horny plates border the sides of a

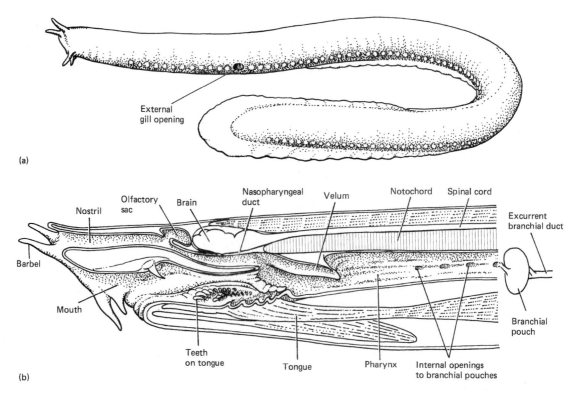

Figure 6–9 Hagfishes: (a) lateral view; (b) sagittal section of the head region. (Modified from D. Jensen, 1966, *Scientific American* 214[2]:82–90.)

protrusible tonguelike structure. These plates spread apart when protruded and fold together, the cusps interdigitating in a pincer-like action, when retracted. The feeding apparatus of hagfishes has been described as "extremely efficient at reeling in long worms, because the keratin plates alternately flick in and out of the oral cavity" (Mallatt 1985). When feeding on something the size and shape of another fish, hagfishes concentrate their pinching efforts on surface irregularities, such as the gills or the anus, where they can more easily grasp the flesh. Once attached, they can tie a knot in their tail and pass it forward along their body until they are braced against their prey and tear off the flesh in their pinching grasp. Hagfishes take only dead or dying vertebrate prey, and they often begin by eating only enough outer flesh to enter the prey's coelomic cavity, where they dine on soft parts. Once a food parcel reaches the hagfish's gut it is enfolded in a mucoid bag secreted by the gut wall. This membrane is permeable to digestive enzymes and digestate, and is excreted as a neat wrapper around the feces. The functional significance of this curious feature is unknown.

Different genera and species of hagfishes have variable numbers of external gill openings. From 1 to 15 openings occur on each side (Figure 6–9), but they do not correspond to the number of internal gills. The external openings occur as far back as the midbody, although the pouch-like gill chambers are just posterior to the head. The long tubes leading from the gills fuse to reduce the number of external openings to which they lead. The posterior position of the gill openings may be related to burrowing.

The internal anatomy of hagfishes is also peculiar. They have no vertebral anlage, the kidneys are extremely primitive, and there is only one semicircular canal on each side of the head. This last characteristic has been the subject of much technical debate. Northcutt (1985) pointed out that in spite of what the membranous structures look like, neurologically they are double sensory patches just as in lampreys, which have two semicircular canals. Hagfishes have long been thought to lack a lateral-line system. Recent work suggests that at least one genus has traces of the system (Wicht and Northcutt 1995), but whether this is an ancestral condition or a secondary reduction of ancestrally well-developed structures is not known.

Opening through the body wall to the outside are large mucous glands that secrete enormous quantities of mucus and tightly coiled proteinaceous threads. The latter straighten on contact with seawater to entrap the slimy mucus close to the hagfish's body. This obnoxious defense mechanism is apparently a deterrent to predators (Conniff 1991). When danger is past, the hagfish draws a knot in its body and scrapes off the mass of mucus, then sneezes sharply to blow its nasal passage clear. This mucus secretion also aids in the regulation of divalent ions.

In contrast to all other vertebrates, hagfishes have accessory hearts even in the caudal region in addition to the heart near the gills. They have capacious blood sinuses and very low blood pressure. The several hearts of hagfishes are aneural, meaning that their pumping rhythm is intrinsic to the hearts themselves rather than coordinated via the central nervous system. The blood vascular system demonstrates few of the immune reactions characteristic of other vertebrates, and its osmotic concentration is approximately the same as that of seawater (see Chapter 4). Examination of the gonads suggests that at least some species are hermaphroditic, but nothing is known of mating. The eggs are oval and over a centimeter long. Encased in a tough clear covering, the yolky eggs are secured to the sea bottom by hooks and are thought to hatch into small, completely formed hagfishes, bypassing a larval stage. Unfortunately, almost nothing is known of the embryology or early life history of any hagfish. Fertile eggs from which the development of hagfish anatomy can be studied have not been found since the last century!

An increased economic interaction between hagfishes and humans over the past two decades is but one example of how vertebrate species are becoming more and more frequently threatened by burgeoning, technological, highly consumptive human society. Fishermen using stationary gear such as gill nets have been retrieving catches damaged beyond sale by scavenging hagfishes. It is not surprising that they responded quickly when a commercial value equivalent to that of many food fishes was put on hagfishes from a most unusual source: the specialty leather industry. Almost all so-called eel skin leather products are made via a proprietary tanning process from hagfish skin. Worldwide demand for this leather specialty led to the eradication of economically harvestable hagfish populations, first in Asian waters, then in some sites along the west coast of North America. Current fishing efforts are focusing on South American and North Atlantic hagfishes. It is typical of human exploitation of natural resources, such as fisheries, which are held in common by society, that exploitation often depletes stocks because no attention is given to the biology of the resource and its renewable, sustainable characteristics. For example, we do not even know how long hagfishes live, how old they are when they first begin to reproduce, exactly how, when, or where they breed, where the youngest juveniles live, what the diets and energy requirements of free-living hagfishes are, or virtually any other of the prerequisite parameters for good management. As a result, eel skin wallets will probably become as rare as items made of whalebone (baleen), tortoise shell, or ivory.

Lampreys (Petromyzontoidea)

Although they are similar to hagfishes in size and shape, the 41 species of lampreys (Figure 6–10) are in other respects radically different from hagfishes. They possess vertebrae, although these cartilaginous skeletal elements are minute. Nearly all lampreys are anadromous; that is, they ascend rivers and streams to breed. Some of the most specialized species are known only from fresh water, where the adults neither feed nor migrate, and act solely as a reproductive stage in the life history of the species. Lampreys have a worldwide distribution except for

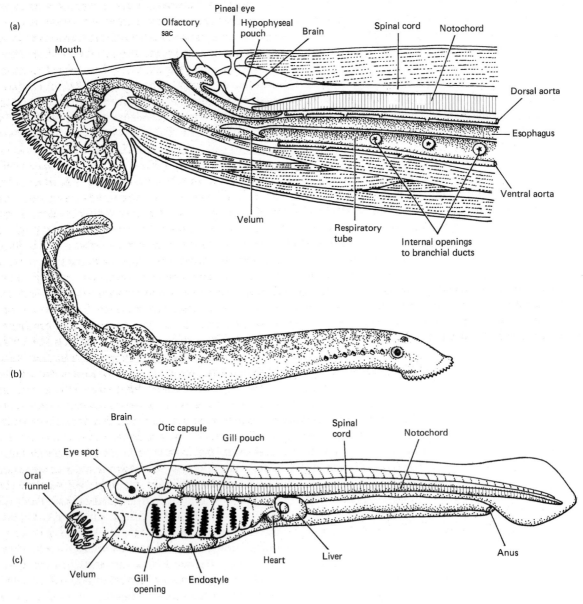

Figure 6–10 Lampreys: (a) sagittal section of the head region; (b) lateral view of an adult; (c) larval lamprey (ammocoete).

the tropics and high polar regions. Anadromous species that spend some of their life in the sea attain the greatest size, although 1 meter is about the upper limit. The smallest species are less than one-fourth of this size.

Little is known of the habits of adult lampreys because they are generally observed only during reproductive activities or when captured with their host. Despite their anatomically well-developed senses, no clear picture has emerged of how a lamprey locates or initially attaches to its prey. In captivity, lampreys swim sporadically with exaggerated, rather awkward lateral undulations. They attach to the body of another vertebrate by suction, and rasp a shallow, seeping wound through the integument of the host. The round mouth and tiny esophagus are located at the bottom of a large fleshy funnel, the inner surface of which is studded with horny conical spines. The protrusible tongue-like structure is covered with similar spines, and together these structures allow tight attachment and rapid abrasion of the host's integument. An oral gland secretes an anticoagulant. Feeding is probably continuous when a lamprey is attached to its host.

Lampreys generally do not kill their hosts, but detach, leaving a weakened animal with an open wound. At sea, lampreys have been found feeding on several species of whales and porpoises in addition to fishes. Swimmers in the Great Lakes, after having been in the water long enough for their skin temperature to drop, have reported initial attempts by lampreys to attach to their bodies. The bulk of an adult lamprey's diet consists of body fluids of fishes. The digestive tract is reduced, as is appropriate for an animal that feeds on such a rich and easily digested diet as blood and tissue fluids.

The single nasal opening is high on the head, and continues as a blind-end tube beneath the brain in close proximity to the pituitary gland. The eyes are large and well developed, as is the pineal body, which lies under a pale spot just posterior to the nasal opening. In contrast to hagfishes, lampreys have two semicircular canals on each side of the head—a condition shared with the extinct ostracoderms. The nerves, which exit segmentally along the length of the spinal cord, are completely separated into dorsal and ventral nerve roots. This probably represents the primitive vertebrate condition, similar to the condition in amphioxus. (Although hagfishes superficially resemble gnathostomes in having conjoined nerve roots, differences in detailed anatomy suggest convergence.) In addition, the heart is not aneural as in hagfishes, but is

innervated by the parasympathetic nervous system. In lampreys these nerves cause cardiac acceleration and not deceleration as do the neural regulators of heart rate in all other vertebrates.

Seven pairs of gills open to the outside just behind the head. Chloride cells in the gills and well-developed kidneys regulate ions, water, and nitrogenous wastes and maintain the osmolality of the body fluids, allowing the lamprey to exist in a variety of salinities. Female lampreys produce hundreds to thousands of eggs about a millimeter in diameter and devoid of any specialized covering such as that found in hagfishes. Like hagfishes, however, lampreys have no duct to transport the specialized products of the gonads to the outside of the body. Instead, the eggs or sperm fill the coelom, and contractions of the body wall expel them from pores located near the openings of the urinary ducts. Fertilization is external.

Lampreys spawn after a temperature-triggered migration to the upper reaches of streams where the current flow is moderate and the stream bed is composed of cobbles and gravel. They construct nests to receive the spawn. Males, later joined by females, select a site, attach themselves by their mouths to the largest rocks in the area, and thrash about violently. Smaller rocks are dislodged and carried a short distance by the current. The nest is complete when a pit is rimmed upstream by large stones and downstream by a mound of smaller stones and sand that produces eddies. Water in the nest is oxygenated by this turbulence, but does not flow strongly in a single direction. The weary nest builders spend the last of their energy depositing eggs and sperm, a process that may take two days. The female attaches to one of the upstream rocks laying eggs and the male wraps around her, fertilizing them as they are extruded. Adult lampreys die after breeding once.

The larvae hatch in about 2 weeks. Radically different from their parents, they were originally described as a distinct genus, *Ammocoetes* (Figure 6–10c). This name has been retained as a vernacular name for the larval form. A week to 10 days after hatching, the tiny 6- to 10-millimeter long ammocoetes leave the nest. They are pink, worm-like organisms with a large fleshy oral hood and nonfunctional eyes hidden deep beneath the skin. Currents carry the ammocoetes downstream to backwaters and quiet banks, where they burrow into the soft mud and spend 3 to 7 years as sedentary filter feeders. The protruding oral hood funnels water through the muscular pharynx where food particles are trapped in mucus and swallowed. An ammocoete may spend its entire larval life in the same burrow without any major morphological or behavioral change until it is 10 centimeters or more in length and several years old. Metamorphosis begins in midsummer, and produces a silver-gray juvenile ready to begin its life as a parasite. Downstream migration to a lake or the sea may not occur until the spring following metamorphosis. Adult life is usually no more than 2 years, and many lampreys return to spawn after 1 year. Some lamprey species lack parasitic adults. The larvae metamorphose and leave their burrows to spawn immediately and die.

During this century humans and lampreys have increasingly been at odds. Although the sea lamprey, *Petromyzon marinus*, seems to have been indigenous to Lake Ontario, it was unknown from the other Great Lakes of North America before 1921. The St. Lawrence River flowing from Lake Ontario to the Atlantic Ocean was no barrier to colonization by sea lampreys, and the rivers and streams that fed into Lake Ontario held landlocked populations. During their spawning migrations, lampreys negotiate waterfalls by slowly creeping upward using their sucking mouth, but the 50-meter height of Niagara Falls (between Lake Ontario and Lake Erie) was too much for the most amorous lampreys. Even after the Welland Canal connected Lakes Erie and Ontario in 1829, lampreys did not immediately invade Lake Erie; it took a century for lampreys to establish themselves in Lake Erie's drainage basin.

Since the 1920s lampreys have expanded rapidly across the entire Great Lakes basin. The surprising fact is not that they were able to invade the upper Great Lakes, but that it took them so long to initiate the invasion. Environmental conditions that vary between the lakes may provide the answer to this curious delay. Lake Erie is the most eutrophic and warmest of all the lakes and has the least appropriate feeder streams. Many of these streams run through flat agricultural lands that have been under intensive cultivation since early in the nineteenth century. The streams are silty and frequently have had their courses changed by human activities. Because of the terrain, flow is slow and few rocky or gravel bottoms occur. Perhaps lampreys simply could not find appropriate spawning sites in Lake Erie to develop a strong population.

Once they reached the upper end of Lake Erie, however, lampreys quickly gained access to the other lakes. By 1946 they were known from all the Great Lakes. There they found suitable conditions and were able to expand unchecked until sporting and commercial interests became alarmed at the reduction of economically important fish species, such as lake trout, turbot, and lake whitefish. Chemical lampricides and electrical barriers and mechanical weirs at the mouths of spawning streams have been employed to bring the Great Lakes lamprey populations down to their present level. Although the populations of large jawed fish species, including those of commercial value, are recovering, it may never be possible to discontinue these antilamprey measures, costly though they are. Human mismanagement (or initial lack of management) of lampreys has been to our own disadvantage. The story of the demise of the Great Lakes fishery is but one of hundreds in the recent history of vertebrate life where human failure to understand and appreciate the interlocking nature of the biology of our nearest relatives has led to gross changes in our environment. Introduction of exotic (= not indigenous) species is a primary cause for the decline of many vertebrate species worldwide, especially in aquatic habitats (Allan and Flecker 1993).

■ The Transition from Jawless to Jawed Vertebrates

Gnathostomes, or jawed vertebrates, were once considered as an entirely separate radiation from the agnathans, or jawless vertebrates. However, we now consider that they originated from within the agnathan radiation. Gnathostomes are considerably more derived than agnathans, not only in their possession of jaws, but also in a multitude of other ways.

The Basic Gnathostome Design

Gnathostomes (*gnath* = jaws, *stoma* = mouth) are first known with certainty from the Early Silurian, but isolated sharklike scales suggest that they date back to the Middle Ordovician (Sansom et al. 1996, Young 1997). Gnathostomes obviously differ from agnathans in their possession of jaws, which bear teeth in most, but not all, forms. (True teeth were apparently lacking in the extinct placoderms; see Chapter 7.) The details of how these jaws are formed is covered in Chapter 3. Here we will dwell more on the consideration of the evolutionary significance of the design of jawed vertebrates in general.

The traditional textbook definition of gnathostomes is the possession of jaws plus two sets of paired fins or limbs (pectoral and pelvic). However, we have already seen that pectoral fins were first acquired by some derived agnathans (osteostracans), even though they are lacking in living jawless vertebrates. The paired pelvic fins and a midline anal fin are traditionally taken to represent a gnathostome addition. However, pelvic and anal fins have recently been reported in some thelodonts (Märss and Ritchie 1997). A complete cartilaginous fin endoskeleton, with a characteristic pattern of basal and radial elements, and pectoral and pelvic limb girdles, is known only from gnathostomes (but osteostracans have evidence of an endoskeletal pectoral girdle).

The gnathostome body plan (see Figure 6–11) reveals that gnathostomes are more than just agnathans with the addition of jaws and pelvic fins. Many other anatomical features characterize the primitive gnathostome condition and suggest that gnathostomes represent a basic step-up in level of activity and complexity from the jawless vertebrates (Table 6.2). Just as the transition from non-vertebrate chordate to vertebrate was characterized by a duplication of the Hox gene complex (Chapter 2), the transition from jawless to jawed vertebrate

evidently involved a second duplication event (Monastersky 1996). The hypothesis that jaw evolution was related to increased efficiency of gill ventilation, as well as to more effective predation, is discussed in a later section. Other features of gnathostomes suggest improvements in locomotor, sensory, and circulatory systems.

An obvious change in the locomotor system is the acquisition of more complete vertebrae, with a vertebral centrum, or central elements (see Chapter 3). More complete vertebrae would better bolster the notochord, and eventually supplant its function, as a supporting rod for the action of the strengthened locomotory axial muscles. These vertebrae are now also attached ribs, which are positioned in the connective tissue between successive segmental muscles (myomeres), again providing greater anchorage for axial muscles. There is also now a clear distinction between the dorsal (epaxial) and ventral (hypaxial) blocks of the muscles, divided by a horizontal septum running the length of the animal. The lateral line canal, containing the neuromast organs that sense vibrations in the surrounding water, lies in the plane of this septum, perhaps reflecting improved integration between

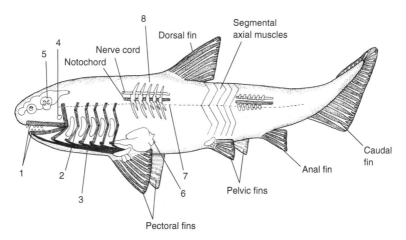

Figure 6–11   Generalized jawed vertebrate (gnathostome) showing derived features compared to the jawless vertebrate (agnathan) condition. Key to numbers on the figure: **1.** Jaws (containing teeth) formed from the mandibular gill arch. **2.** Gill skeleton consists of jointed branchial arches, and contains internal gill rakers that stop particulate food from entering the gills. Gill musculature is also more robust. **3.** Hypobranchial musculature allows strong suction in inhalation and suction feeding. **4.** Original first gill slit squeezed to form the spiracle, situated between mandibular and hyoid arches. **5.** Three semicircular canals in the inner ear (addition of horizontal canal). **6.** Addition of conus arteriosus to the heart, between the ventricle and the ventral aorta. (Note that the postion of the heart is actually more anterior, right behind the most posterior gill arch.) **7.** Horizontal septum divides trunk muscle into epaxial (dorsal) and hypaxial (ventral) portions. It also marks the position of the lateral line canal, containing the neuromast sensory organs. **8.** Vertebrae now possess centrum (surrounding the notochord) and ribs.

TABLE 6.2	Derived features of gnathostomes

Table lists additional characters to those shown on Figure 6–11.

Cranial Characters

1. Cranium enlarged anteriorly to end in a precerebral fontinelle.
2. Cranium elongated posteriorly, so that one or more occipital neural arches are incorporated in the rear of the skull.
3. Development of a postorbital process on the cranium, separating the functions of supporting the jaws and enclosing the eyes.
4. Intrinsic musculature in the eye for lens accommodation.

Internal Anatomical Characters

5. Atrium lies posterodorsally (versus laterally) to ventricle.
6. Renal portal vein present.
7. Spiral valve primitively formed within intestine.
8. Pancreas with both endocrine and exocrine functions.
9. Distinct spleen.
10. Kidneys formed only by more posterior sections in adult (mesonephros and metanephros).
11. Male gonads linked by ducts to excretory (archinephric) duct.
12. Female gonads with distinct oviducts and mesonephric ducts.
13. Two (versus one) contractile actin proteins (one specific to striated muscle and one specific to smooth muscle).

Sensory Characters

14. Nerves enclosed in myelinated sheaths.
15. Large, distinct cerebellum in the hind brain.
16. Two distinct olfactory tracts leading to widely separated olfactory bulbs.
17. Thicker spinal cord with "horns" of gray matter in section.
18. Dorsal and ventral spinal nerve roots linked to form compound spinal nerves.
19. Unique and evolutionarily conservative pattern of head lateral line canals (lost in adult amphibians and amniotes).
20. Lateral line on trunk region flanked or enclosed by specialized scales (lateral line lost in adult amphibians and amniotes).

Source: J. G. Maisey, 1986, *Cladistics* 2:201–256, and P. Janvier, 1996, *Early Vertebrates*, Clarendon Press, Oxford, UK.

locomotion and sensory feedback (Maisey 1986). (See Chapter 3 for more detail on the early gnathostome skeletomuscular system.)

In other parts of the nervous system the nerve fibers now have insulating sheaths of myelin, allowing for more rapid transmission of neuronal impulses. The neuromasts of the lateral line now lie in canals (in lampreys they merely lie in unconnected pits, although canals may be present in some ostracoderms). In the inner ear there is a third (horizontal) semicircular canal, which may reflect an improved ability to navigate and orientate in all three dimensions. (See Chapter 3 for more detail on these sensory systems.)

Finally the heart of gnathostomes has an additional small chamber in front of the pumping ventricle, the conus arteriosus, which acts as an elastic reservoir. Its presence is probably due to the stronger ventricular pumping and higher blood pressures in gnathostomes, with the concurrent need to dampen the pulsatile nature of the flow of blood. A true stomach is a new feature in gnathostomes among living vertebrates; however, as previously mentioned, some thelodont ostracoderms appear to have possessed a stomach.

The Problem Posed by the Gills of Early Vertebrates

For many years jawless and jawed vertebrates were seen as two separate evolutionary radiations. Before there was good knowledge of the extinct ostracoderms, lampreys and hagfishes were grouped together as sister taxa, both on primitive (plesiomorphic) features, such as the lack of jaws and paired fins, and on features that may be convergent, such as the elongated, eellike body, the pumping velum, and the muscular rasping tongue.

Ostracoderms were originally also perceived as very separate from jawed vertebrates. Features such as the pectoral fins of osteostracans, which we a consider to be a derived characteristic shared with gnathostomes, were interpreted as examples of convergent evolution. However, as shown in Figure 6–1 and discussed in Box 6–1, osteostracans and some thelodonts are now perceived as having numerous derived characteristics that link them closer to gnathostomes than to other ostracoderms. Lampreys are also interpreted as being closer to gnathostomes than are hagfishes. Thus the Agnatha is a paraphyletic assemblage, and any understanding of the origin of gnathostomes must encompass the view that at some point a jawless vertebrate was transformed into a jawed one.

The above narrative sounds like a simple, straightforward story of progress in our understanding of evolutionary events. Yet until quite recently many researchers perceived a major barrier to the notion that any jawless vertebrate could be ancestral to the jawed ones. This barrier was the structure of the gills and cartilaginous gill supports (branchial arches or visceral arches). Living jawless vertebrates possess what are termed pouched gills, as distinguished from the flatter, more lens-shaped spaces between the gills of gnathostomes. In the gills of lampreys and hagfishes the gill filaments themselves (the site of gas exchange) are situated *internal* to the branchial arches and their surface is formed from endodermal tissue, whereas in gnathostomes the filaments are *external* to the branchial arches and their surface is formed from ectodermal tissue. This difference in structure was seen as strong evidence that jawless and jawed vertebrates must represent divergent radiations from an original situation in which there were branchial arches but as yet no actual gill tissue (Sewertzoff 1928, Jarvik 1968, Schaeffer and Thomson 1980). Note that the situation in amphioxus cannot resolve the issue of what might be primitive and what derived with respect to the position of the gill supports. Amphioxus lacks gill filaments and has branchial arches made from collagen, which may not be homologous with the cartilaginous arches of vertebrates that are formed from the vertebrate innovation of neural crest tissue.

This issue was addressed by the studies of Jon Mallatt (e.g. Mallatt 1984a, 1984b, 1985, 1996). Much of the previous argument about the issue of agnathan/gnathostome interrelationships had been among paleontologists concerned about the phylogenetic position of the ostracoderms, but Mallatt focused on the anatomy and feeding behavior of living primitive vertebrates, using sharks as an example of primitive gnathostomes. He pointed out that the type of tissue forming the gills (endodermal versus ectodermal) was not a fixed aspect of inherited morphology, but more likely was related to exactly where in the pharynx the gills were developed, and easily could have changed during evolution. He also noted work of his own and others (e.g., Goodrich 1930) demonstrating that the internal structure of lamprey gills—in such features as position of the gill filaments, the entrance and exit of the blood vessels supplying the gills, the way in which the water passes through the gill itself, and numerous features of the microstructure—was very similar to the condition in the dogfish shark, in contrast to the rather different, possibly derived, condition in hagfishes.

Thus it seemed that the gills of lampreys were homologous with those of gnathostomes, but that the branchial arches (external versus internal) were not. But how could the difference in the position of the branchial supports be explained? Had they somehow moved from an original external position in jawless vertebrates to a new internal position in jawed ones (an unlikely scenario, at best)? Mallatt (1984a, 1996) resolved this issue with a consideration of the detailed anatomical structures of these primitive vertebrates. It appears that the original vertebrate condition, as seen in the anterior part of the pharynx in hagfishes, was to have both sets of branchial arches, one internal and one external. The internal set has been lost in lampreys, perhaps in association with their unique tidal mode of respiration entailing a small, tubular pharynx. Although there appears to be only an internal set in gnathostomes, small remnants of the external arches can be observed in sharks as extrabranchial cartilages (although these are lost entirely in more derived gnathostomes, such as bony fishes). Mallatt (1996) proposed that the enlargement of the internal support in gnathostomes was related to the strengthening of breathing muscles that move these arches back and forth during the strong inhalatory and exhalatory stages of gnathostome ventilation. Figure 6–12 illustrates Mallatt's evolutionary scenario.

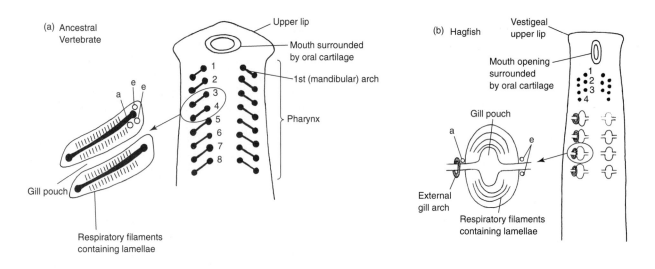

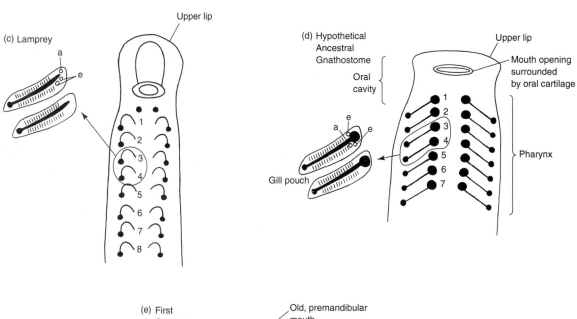

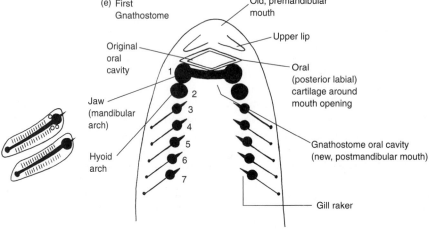

Stages in the Origin of Jaws

It has long been known that vertebrate jaws are made of the same material (neural crest derived cartilage) as the branchial arches, and they clearly develop as the first arch of this series in vertebrates (see Chapter 3). The arch that gives rise to the jaws (the mandibular arch) does not form functional gill arches in any living vertebrate (although it is presumed to have done so in at least some extinct forms) (see Maisey 1994 for a historical review of this idea). The notion that the more derived, predatory vertebrates should convert gill arches into toothed jaws has been more or less unquestioned. It is a common assumption that jaws are superior devices for feeding, and thus more derived vertebrates were somehow bound to obtain them. However, this simplistic approach does not address the issue of how the evolutionary event might actually have taken place: What use would a proto-jaw be prior to its full transformation? And even if early vertebrates had needed some sort of superior mouth design, why modify a pharyngeal gill arch for this purpose, which initially was located far behind the mouth opening? Why not just modify the existing cartilages and plates surrounding the mouth? Living agnathans possess specialized oral cartilages (Figure 6–12), and various ostracoderms apparently possessed oral plates (Mallatt 1996).

Mallatt has resolved this issue by suggesting that the initial enlargement of the mandibular arch into proto-jaws was for improved gill ventilation, not for feeding (Mallatt 1996). Numerous features of gnathostomes suggest that they are more active than ancestral vertebrates, with greater metabolic demands, as described earlier. One particular derived gnathostome feature is the more powerful mechanism for pumping water over the gills. Gnathostomes have a characteristic series of internal branchial muscles as well as new, external, ventral ones (the hypobranchials). These muscles not only push more water through the pharynx in exhalation but also draw (suck) more water into the pharynx in inhalation. Gnathostome fishes can generate much stronger suction than known agnathans, and thus powerful suction also forms the basis of drawing food into the mouth. Living agnathans derive a certain amount of suction from their pumping velum, but this mostly just *pushes* water, and its suction is weak.

Mallatt suggests that the original function of the mandibular arch (the proto-jaws) was to allow a rapid closing and opening of the entrance to the pharynx that had to accompany the strengthened ventilation. The enlargement of the branchial adductor muscle into a powerful adductor mandibularis (homologous with our own jaw-closing muscles)

Figure 6–12 Jon Mallatt's evolutionary scenario of the evolution of vertebrate gills and jaws. Animals are portrayed in ventral view. "a" = afferent artery (carrying deoxygenated blood to the gills); "e" = efferent artery (carrying oxygenated blood away from the gills). Black circles represent branchial arches. (a) Ancestral vertebrate condition (consistent with fossil heterostracans, osteostracans, and thelodonts): Both an internal and an external branchial arch are present in each gill. Respiratory filaments and lamellae are present. Afferent and efferent arteries are both internal. (b) Hagfishes: The first four branchial arches are modified to support a velum (a pumping flap), but parts of both external and internal arches remain. The first three gill pouches are lost, but other gills migrate posteriorly and only external arches form there. (Only four complete gills on each side are shown here; eight exist in total.) The gills are more highly pouched, and the arteries are rearranged in a complex way, probably to maximize oxygen extraction in oxygen-poor water of deep sea sediment. (c) Lamprey: The first branchial arch is modified to support the velum, and the first gill pouch is lost. On the other gills, the internal arches are lost in association with the new, tidal, ventilation. Only external arches remain. (d) Hypothetical gnathostome ancestor: The internal branchial arches enlarge to support strengthened breathing muscles that attach to these arches. (e) Early true gnathostome (condition retained in sharks): The first branchial arch is modified into a jaw, initially to improve ventilation, and later to improve feeding (gill internal details as in (d)). The mouth opening enlarges. The external arches are relatively small extrabranchial cartilages. (Drawing modified from one provided courtesy of Jon Mallatt.)

would act to bend the mandibular arch to prevent leakage of water out of the pharynx anteriorly during forceful expiration over the gills. The new gnathostome hypobranchial muscles would allow for rapid mouth opening, by pulling backward on the lower part of mandibular arch. The advantage of using the mandibular arch for this function, rather than the more anterior oral cartilages, would not just be the potential for more powerful muscle action, but might also relate to the fact that the muscles involved would be of the same functional series to the other ventilatory muscles, perhaps aiding in the neuronal wiring of the entire system.

Immediately upon evolving strong, ventilatory jaws, gnathostomes were able to suck in prey (during inhalation), and then grasp this prey with the jaws as the mouth closed (during exhalation). To hold such prey, the jaws experienced selection to grow larger still, and became feeding (as well as ventilatory) structures. Originally, the oral cavity in front of the mandibular arch had been large, but it became reduced in size so as not to interfere with the entry and grasping of prey by the jaw (see Figure 6–12). The original vertebrate oral cavity is so small in gnathostomes, in fact, that biologists have overlooked its importance. The gnathostome oral cavity has always been considered the region right behind the jaw, which is actually part of the pharynx (Mallatt 1996).

With the ability of the jaws to grasp prey as well as to aid in the production of powerful suction the stage was set for gnathostomes to enter a new realm of feeding ecology, with the new ability to prey on large, actively swimming mobile prey.

■ Summary

Fossil evidence indicates that vertebrates probably evolved in a marine environment during the Cambrian. We know nothing about the group prior to the evolution of dermal armor. The evolution of bone, a switch from filter feeding to more active predation, and a muscular pharyngeal pump for gill ventilation resulted in a radiation of distinct groups of jawless vertebrates: first the Pteraspidomorpha (best known from the heterostracans), and later a series of forms lumped as the "Cephalaspidomorpha." The extensive radiation of these forms demonstrates the numerous successful solutions to the problem of growing inside an armored skin. Only two types of very different and specialized survivors from these early radiations exist today: the hagfishes and the lampreys. Nevertheless, extant jawless fishes illustrate the extreme specialization of which the ancestral vertebrate body plan is capable.

Just as the evolution of vertebrates from nonvertebrate chordates represented a step up in anatomical and physiological design, so did the evolution of jawed vertebrates from jawless ones. While it used to be thought that the anatomy of the gills prevented the direct descent of jawed vertebrates from any jawless form, more recent work has shown that such a derivation was indeed likely. In addition to jaws, which may have been first evolved to improve gill ventilation rather than to bite prey directly, jawed vertebrates possess a number of derived anatomical features (such as true vertebrae, ribs, and a complete lateral line sensory system) suggestive of a more sophisticated and powerful mode of locomotion and sensory feedback.

■ References

Allan, J. D., and A. S. Flecker. 1993. Biodiversity conservation in running waters. *Bioscience* 43(1):32–43.

Braun, C. B. 1996. The sensory biology of the living jawless fishes: a phylogenetic assessment. *Brain, Behavior and Evolution* 48:262–276.

Brodal A., and R. Fange (editors). 1963. *The Biology of Myxine.* Universitetsforlaget, Oslo, Norway.

Conniff, R. 1991. The most disgusting fish in the sea. *Audubon* 93:100–118.

Elliott, D. K. 1987. A reassessment of *Astraspis desiderata,* the oldest North American vertebrate. *Science* 237:190–192.

Forey, P. L. 1984. Yet more reflections on agnathan–gnathostome relationships. *Journal of Vertebrate Paleontology* 4:330–343.

Forey, P., and P. Janvier. 1993. Agnathans and the origin of jawed vertebrates. *Nature* 361:129–134.

Forey, P., and P. Janvier. 1994. Evolution of the early vertebrates. *American Scientist* 82:554–565.

Gagnier, P. Y. 1989. A new image of *Sacabambaspis janvieri,* an Early Ordovician jawless vertebrate from Bolivia. *National Geographic Research* 5:250–253.

Gans, C. 1989. Stages in the origin of vertebrates: analysis by means of scenarios. *Biological Reviews* 64:221–268.

Goodrich, E. S. 1930. *Studies on the Structure and Development of Vertebrates.* Dover Publications, New York, NY.

Gorbman, A., and A. Tamarin. 1985. Early development of olfactory and adenohypophyseal structures of agnathans and its evolutionary implications. Pages 165–185 in *Evo-*

lutionary Biology of Primitive Fishes, edited by R. E. Foreman et al. Plenum, New York, NY.

Halstead, L. B. 1982. Evolutionary trends and the phylogeny of the Agnatha. Pages 159–196 in *Problems in Phylogenetic Reconstruction*, edited by K. A. Joysey and A. E. Friday, Systematics Association, Special Volume 21.

Janvier, P. 1981. The phylogeny of the Craniata, with particular reference to the significance of fossil agnathans. *Journal of Vertebrate Paleontology* 1:121–159.

Janvier, P. 1984. The relationships of the Osteostraci and Galeaspida. *Journal of Vertebrate Paleontology* 4:344–358.

Janvier, P. 1996. *Early Vertebrates*. Oxford Monographs on Geology and Geophysics—33. Clarendon Press, Oxford, UK.

Jarvik, E. 1968. Aspects of vertebrate phylogeny. Pages 497–527 in *Current Problems in Lower Vertebrate Phylogeny, Nobel Symposium* 4, edited by T. Orvig. Almqvist and Wiksell, Stockholm, Sweden.

Maisey, J. G. 1986. Heads and tails: a chordate phylogeny. *Cladistics* 2:201–256.

Maisey, J. G. 1994. Gnathostomes (jawed vertebrates). Pages 38–56 in *Major Features of Vertebrate Evolution*, edited by D. R. Prothero and R. M. Schoch. Short Courses in Paleontology, no. 7. The University of Tennessee and the Paleontological Society, Knoxville, TN.

Maisey, J. G. 1996. *Discovering Fossil Fishes*. Henry Holt and Company, New York, NY.

Mallatt, J. 1984a. Early vertebrate evolution: pharyngeal structure and the origin of gnathostomes. *Journal of Zoology*, London 204:169–183.

Mallatt, J. 1984b. Feeding ecology of the earliest vertebrates. *Zoological Journal of the Linnean Society* 82:261–272.

Mallatt, J. 1985. Reconstructing the life cycle and the feeding of ancestral vertebrates. Pages 59–68 in *Evolutionary Biology of Primitive Fishes*, edited by R. E. Foreman et al. Plenum, New York, NY.

Mallatt, J. 1996. Ventilation and the origin of jawed vertebrates: a new mouth. *Zoological Journal of the Linnean Society* 117:329–404.

Märss, T., and A. Ritchie. 1997. Articulated thelodonts of Scotland. *Journal of Morphology* 232(3):293.

Martini, F., J. B. Heiser, and M. P. Lesser. 1997. A population profile for Atlantic hagfish, *Myxine glutinosa* (L.), in the Gulf Of Maine. Part I: Morphometrics and reproductive state. *Fishery Bulletin*. 95:311–320.

Monastersky, R. 1996. Jump-start for the vertebrates: new clues to how our ancestors got a head. *Science News* 149:74–75.

Moy-Thomas, J. A., and R. S. Miles. 1971. *Paleozoic Fishes*. Saunders College Publishing, Philadelphia, PA.

Nelson, J. S. 1994. *Fishes of the World*, 3d edition. Wiley, New York, NY.

Northcutt, R. G. 1985. The brain and sense organs of the earliest vertebrates: reconstruction of a morphotype. Pages 81–112 In *Evolutionary Biology of Primitive Fishes*, edited by R. E. Foreman et al. Plenum, New York, NY.

Northcutt, R. G., and W. E. Bemis. 1993. Cranial nerves of the coelacanth *Latimeria chalumnae* (Osteichthyes: Sarcopterygii: Actinistia) and comparisons with other Craniata. *Brain, Behavior and Evolution* Supplement 1. 42:1–76.

Northcutt, R. G., and C. Gans. 1983. The genesis of neural crest and epidermal placodes: a reinterpretation of vertebrate origins. *Quarterly Review of Biology* 58:1–28.

Olson, E. C. 1971. *Vertebrate Paleozoology*. Wiley-Interscience, New York, NY.

Repetski, J. E. 1978. A fish from the upper Cambrian of North America. *Science* 200:529–531.

Rich, P. V., and G. F. van Tets. 1985. *Kadimakara, Extinct Vertebrates of Australia*. Pioneer Design Studio, Lilydale, Victoria, Australia.

Sansom, I. J., M. M. Smith, and M. P. Smith. 1996. Scales of thelodont and shark-like fishes from the Ordovician of Colorado. *Nature* 379:628–630.

Sansom, I. J., M. P. Smith, M. M. Smith, and P. Turner. 1997. *Astraspis*—the anatomy and histology of an Ordovician fish. *Palaeontology* 40(3):625–643.

Schaeffer, B., and K. S. Thomson 1980. Reflections on agnathan-gnathostome relationships. Pages 19–22 in *Aspects of Vertebrate History*, edited by L. L. Jacobs. Museum of Northern Arizona Press, Flagstaff, AZ.

Sewertzoff, A. N. 1928. Directions of evolution. *Acta Zoologica, Stockholm* 9:59–141.

Shu, D.-G., S. Conway Morris, and X.-L. Xang. 1996. A *Pikaia*-like chordate from the Lower Cambrian of China. *Nature* 384:157–158.

Soehn, K. L., and M. V. H. Wilson. 1990. A compete articulated heterostracan from Wenlockian (Silurian) beds of the Delorme Group, Makenzie Mountains, Northwest Territories, Canada. *Journal of Vertebrate Paleontology* 10:405–419.

Smith, M. P., I. J. Sansom, and M. P. Smith. 1995. Diversity of the dermal skeleton in Ordovician to Silurian vertebrate taxa from North America: histology, skeletogenesis and relationships. *Geobios*, Special Memoir 19:65–70.

Smith, M. M., I, J. Sansom, and M. P. Smith. 1996. "Teeth" before armour: the earliest vertebrate mineralized tissues. *Modern Geology* 20:303–319.

Stock, D. W., and G. S. Whitt. 1992. Evidence from 18S ribosomal RNA sequences that lampreys and hagfishes form a natural group. *Science* 257:787–789.

Van der Brugghen, W., and P. Janvier. 1993. Denticles in thelodonts. *Nature* 364:107.

Wicht, H., and R. G. Northcutt. 1995. Ontogeny of the head of the Pacific hagfish (*Eptatretus stouti*, Myxinoidea): development of the lateral line system. *Philosophical Transactions of the Royal Society, London, series B* 349:119–134.

Wilson, M. V. H., and M. W. Caldwell. 1993. New Silurian and Devonian fork-tailed "thelodonts" are jawless vertebrates with stomachs and deep bodies. *Nature* 361:442–444.

Yalden, P. W. 1985. Feeding mechanisms as evidence for cyclostome monophyly. *Zoological Journal of the Linnean Society* 84:291–300.

Young, G. C. 1997. Ordovician microvertebrate remains from the Amadeus Basin, Central Australia. *Journal of Vertebrate Paleontology* 17(1):1–25.

Young, G. C., V. N. Karatajute-Talimaa, and M. M. Smith. 1996. A possible Late Cambrian vertebrate from Australia. *Nature* 383:810–812.

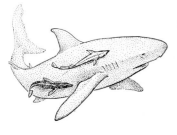

CHAPTER
7

The Rise of Jawed Vertebrates and the Radiation of the Chondrichthyes

Relatively soon after the first evidence of vertebrates in the fossil record, the next major step in vertebrate evolution appeared: jaws and internally supported paired appendages. Jaws play many roles in the biology of vertebrates, but their major use is in feeding. Paired fins with specialized internal skeletal and muscular components were a second important innovation because they gave a swimming vertebrate precise control of steering. The diversity of predatory specializations available to a vertebrate with jaws and precise steering is great, and the appearance of these characters signaled a new radiation of vertebrates. The cartilaginous fishes (sharks, rays, and ratfishes) are the descendants of one clade of this radiation, and they combine derived characters such as a cartilaginous skeleton with a generally plesiomorphic anatomy. Sharks have undergone three major radiations, which can be broadly associated with increasingly specialized feeding mechanisms, and extant sharks are a diverse and successful group of fishes. In this chapter we consider the origin of jaws and paired appendages and the roles that these two innovations have played in the success of extant cartilaginous fishes.

■ The First Appearance of Jaws and Unique Gnathostome Characters

Albert Sherwood Romer (1962) suggested that "perhaps the greatest of all advances in vertebrate history was the development of jaws and the consequent revolution in the mode of life of early fishes." Jaws allow behaviors that otherwise would be difficult, if not impossible, to perform. The presence of jaws manipulated by muscles allows an organism to grasp objects firmly. When the jaws are armed with teeth their grip becomes surer. Teeth with sharp cutting edges reduce food to particles of edible size and flat teeth grind hard foods. When vertebrates evolved jaws, therefore, new food resources became available. Jaws apparently placed the early gnathostomes in a commanding position, for many evolved an increase in size beyond that of other contemporary vertebrates and gnathostomes appear to have replaced many lineages of jawless vertebrates during the Devonian.

The functions of jaws are not limited to capturing and chewing prey. A grasping, movable jaw permits a new behavior—manipulation of objects—that enters many aspects of the life of vertebrates. Jaws can be used to dig holes, or to carry pebbles or vegetation to build nests, or to grasp mates during courtship and juveniles during parental care. No wonder Romer placed so much importance on jaws. The origin of jaws was discussed in Chapter 6.

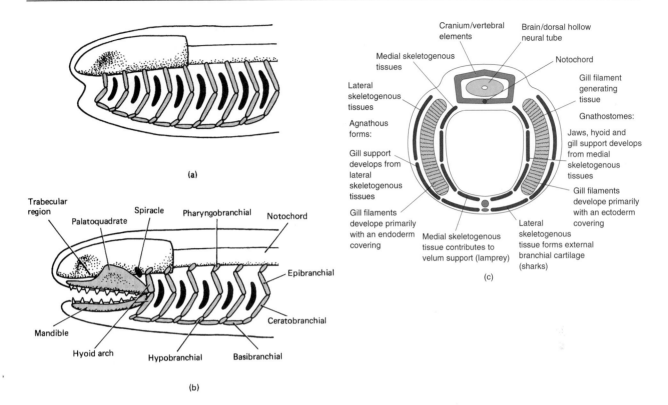

Figure 7–1 Evolution of the vertebrate jaw from anterior visceral arches. (a) Agnathous condition; (b) gnathostome condition; (c) diagrammatic cross section of a generalized vertebrate pharynx showing relationships between agnathous and gnathostome visceral arch components.

Figure 7–1 summarizes the differences in the visceral arches between jawed and jawless vertebrates, and illustrates the major components of the hinged gnathostome gill arches.

Locomotor function was improved by a well-developed heterocercal tail and fin webs supported by collagenous fin rays. Undoubtedly overshadowing these is a distinctive character of the gnathostomes—paired pectoral and pelvic appendages with internal supporting girdles and specialized musculature.

The Origin of Fins

Jaws are an advantage only when applied to an object. Suction can draw objects into the mouth over modest distances, but generally the body must be guided to the graspable object. This sounds simple, but guidance of a body in three-dimensional space is complicated. Yaw (swinging to the right or left) combines with pitch (tilting up or down) to make accurate contact with a target difficult. Roll (rotation around the body axis) must be countered for effective grasping. Especially if the target moves, perhaps evasively, quick adjustments of roll, pitch, and yaw are necessary. It is little wonder that sophisticated development of strong mobile fins was important in the functional evolution of jaws.

Fins act as hydrofoils, applying pressure to the surrounding water. Because water is practically incompressible, force applied by a fin in one direction against the water is opposed by an equal force in the opposite direction (Figure 7–2). Thus fins can resist roll if pressed on the water in the direction of the roll. Fins projecting horizontally near the anterior end of the body similarly counteract pitch. Yaw is controlled by vertical fins along the middorsal and midventral lines. Fins serve other functions as well. They increase the area of the tail for greater thrust during propulsion. Presented at angles to a flow of water, they produce lift. Spiny fins are used

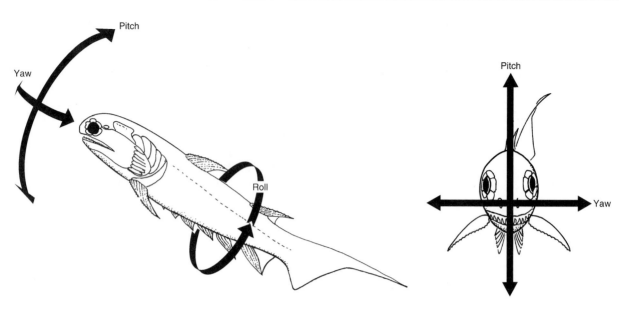

Figure 7–2 An acanthodian, *Climatius*. Shown in lateral and frontal views to illustrate pitch, yaw, and roll and the fins that counteract these movements.

in defense, and become systems to inject poison when combined with glandular secretions. Colorful fins are used to send visual signals to potential mates, rivals, and predators.

Fin structure of early fishes was variable. Although almost all academic attention has been given to the evolution of the paired fins, the median fins appear to have attained the structural complexity (fin rays, musculature) of paired fins much earlier than the appearance of gnathostome-like paired appendages. Agnathans had spines or enlarged scales derived from dermal armor that acted like fins. Osteostracans had paddlelike pectorally located structures, but they apparently lacked internal supports. Some anaspids had long finlike sheets of tissue running along the flanks. The earliest paired fins, although a universal feature of gnathostomes, were dissimilar in details of structure from one type of gnathostome to another, probably indicating separate evolutionary origins. Two early groups of gnathostomes, the **acanthodians** and the **placoderms**, illustrate this. Acanthodians had a variable number of spines, sometimes with attached membranes, extending along the ventrolateral aspects of the trunk. The internal skeleton of acanthodian fins (Figure 8–16) was composed of at least two rows of rod-shaped cartilages associated with horny, threadlike rays that did not protrude far into the fin. Placoderm pectoral appendages generally had more numerous rod-

shaped elements and horny fin rays extending far into the fin. Early fins, although always in approximately the same positions, were clearly different in internal and external construction and number.

There is little fossil evidence of the origin of fins, especially the paired pectoral and pelvic fins that were significant in later stages of vertebrate evolution. Although some early workers fancied a resemblance between the pectoral fins and the gill arches, a branchial origin is extremely doubtful. Fins are derived from mesoderm and have somatic (trunk-derived) musculature and innervation.

A fin-fold theory of the origin of paired appendages was based on the anatomy of certain anaspids, such as *Jaymoytius* (Figure 6–8), which had a pair of long-based lateral flaps extending from gills to anus. Early acanthodians had a series of bilaterally paired spines in the same region. By comparing these structures to the fin (metapleural) folds of amphioxus, discrete fins were pictured as originating from continuous fin folds. These fin folds were thought to be paired laterally but single dorsally and posteriorly. Broken into short segments and reduced in number, fin folds were said to have been the origin of the fins seen in today's fishes. But making a direct connection between the three constructions was merely an artificial assemblage of organisms with no direct phylogenetic relationship.

Because no fossil evidence to document these events has been uncovered, the fin-fold theory has become less appealing and it seems best to consider fins so beneficial that multiple evolutions have occurred. Multiple evolutionary origins with similar results (that is, convergent evolution) are to be expected when only a limited variety of fin positions and shapes provide the hydrodynamic advantages we attribute to fins. Thus, the fins of the jawless ostracoderms may be convergent with those of gnathostomes. Early fossil gnathostomes may or may not have had strictly homologous paired appendages. Nevertheless, the girdles and basal elements of the paired appendages of extant gnathostomes seem to be homologous.

A well-developed heterocercal caudal fin is almost as universal a feature of all early jawed fishes as are paired fins. Comparably developed caudal fins are found in some jawless fishes, although other jawless fishes had hypocercal or other shaped tails. An abruptly up- or downturned notochord produces an increased depth of the caudal fin, a shape that is important in rapid acceleration (Webb and Smith 1980). In addition, the gnathostomes with their collagenous fin rays had a stiffened caudal web of considerable area, further enhancing acceleration. Burst swimming is important in predator avoidance, and provides significant economies in terms of locomotor energy when bursts of acceleration are alternated with glides. All fishes with a fin-strengthening upturned or downturned axial skeleton tip have a noncollapsible caudal fin that is effective for burst swimming.

Earliest Jawed Fishes

The earliest possible evidence of gnathostomes dates back to the Middle Ordovician, and they are known with certainty from the Early Silurian (see Chapter 6). However, it is not until the Devonian that they are well known as entire body fossils, by which time they can be divided into four distinctive clades. One of these clades, the placoderms, was isolated from the other three (chondrichthyans, acanthodians, and osteichthyans) despite sharing many derived gnathostome characters. The inferred jaw muscles of placoderms are different from those of the other three groups, placoderms have nothing comparable to the teeth of the other gnathostomes, and the skeletal anatomy of the paired fins of placoderms lacks homologies with those of other gnathostomes. The placoderms seem to have left no descendants in the modern fauna. A second clade, the Chondrichthyes, which is clearly related to all

other gnathostomes, evolved distinctive reductions and specializations of dermal armor, internal calcification, jaw and fin mobility, and reproduction. These chondrichthyans have successfully survived to the present.

The final two clades of fishes, the acanthodians and Osteichthyes (together = teleostomes), may be closely related and form the root of all subsequent vertebrate evolution (Chapter 8). Before studying the teleostomes, the majority of fish species past and present, we turn to the placoderms and chondrichthyans to examine the variety of early gnathostomes.

Placoderms: The Armored Fishes

Among the earliest gnathostomes in the fossil record is a confusingly diverse assemblage of generally heavily armored fishes, the placoderms (Figure 7–3). R. L. Carroll (1987) has pointed out that the placoderms are without modern analogues, and their massive external armor makes interpretation of their ways of life particularly difficult. Placoderms must have been primarily benthic fishes; their bodies were generally dorsoventrally depressed with flattened ventral surfaces. Although placoderms share an impressive list of derived characters with other gnathostomes, several elements of their morphology appear to isolate placoderms from all other jaw-bearing vertebrates. The most profound of these characters is the position of the jaw musculature. In all other gnathostomes the jaw muscles lie external to the jaw's skeletal elements. In those placoderms where it can be determined, it appears that the main mass of the jaw musculature is *medial* to the upper jaw cartilages, the palatoquadrates. If this is true for placoderms in general, then jaws may have evolved more than once among ancestral fishes, and the immediate common ancestor of placoderms and all other gnathostomes may not have had a functional jaw. Placoderms also lack teeth that correspond to those of any other gnathostome. They have a hyoid arch that is not clearly involved in the same suspensory function as in other gnathostomes and is distinctively different in arrangement and number of elements from that of other vertebrates.

As the name placoderm (*placo* = plate, *derm* = skin) implies, the earliest placoderms, the arthrodires, were covered with a thick, often ornamented bony shield over the anterior one-half to one-third of their bodies (Figure 7–3a). By their extinction in the Early Carboniferous, some placoderms had muscular,

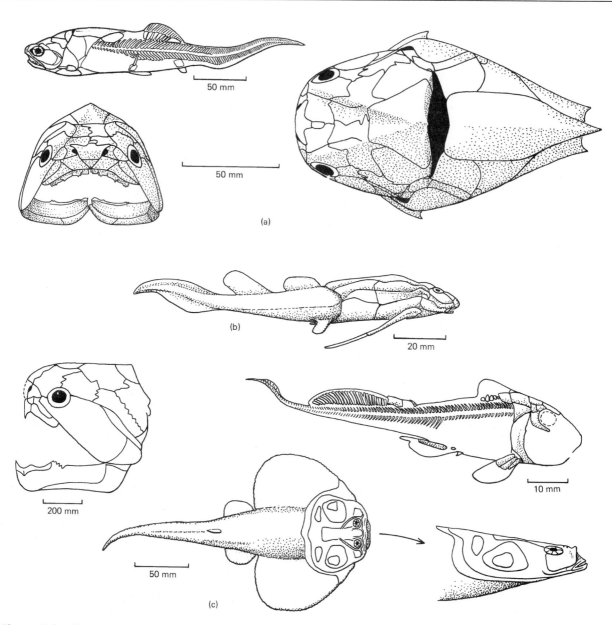

Figure 7–3 Placoderms. (a) Lateral, frontal, and dorsal views of an arthrodire, *Coccosteus*, Middle Devonian; (b) the peculiar placoderm *Bothriolepis*, with a jointed exoskeleton that supported pectoral appendages; (c) three widely varying types of placoderms: (left) the giant predator *Dunkleosteus*, Late Devonian; (right) the chimeralike *Rhamphodopsis* (compare with Figure 7–14a and b); (below) the raylike *Gemuendina*. (Modified after J. A. Moy–Thomas and R. S. Miles, 1971, *Paleozoic Fishes*, Saunders College Publishing, Philadelphia, PA.)

mobile pectoral fin structures that must have contributed to an active existence. Other placoderms, the antiarchs, developed pectoral appendages into stiff props by encasing all soft tissue in joined, bony tubes reminiscent of arthropod appendages (Figure 7–3b).

The head shield of early placoderms, which was formed by numerous large plates, was separated from the mosaic of small dermal bones that shielded the trunk by a narrow gap. A mobile connection between the anterior vertebrae and the skull allowed the head to be lifted. This craniovertebral joint permitted the mouth to be opened wider than it would by lowering only the mandible, or to be opened when the lower jaw was pressed against the seafloor as a placoderm quietly awaited the approach of its prey. During their evolution, predatory arthrodire placoderms developed a curious specialization that further increased the gape. The space between the head and the thoracic shields widened and a pair of joints evolved, one above each pectoral fin on a line that passed through the older cranioverteberal joint of the axial skeleton. This arrangement provided great flexibility between the shields and allowed an enormous head-up gape. In addition, it probably increased respiratory efficiency and improved steering control. Arthrodires, the name given to this order of placoderms, pays tribute to this strange specialization (*arthros* = a joint, plus *dira* = the neck).

Placoderms were mostly creatures of the Devonian. During that period placoderms radiated into a large number of lineages and types. Ancestral placoderms were primarily marine but a great many lineages became adapted to freshwater and estuarine habitats. They nevertheless maintained their robust armor, indicating their metabolic ability to control calcium phosphate in phosphate-poor environments. *Dunkleosteus* was a voracious, 10-meter-long, predatory arthrodire. *Bothriolepis*, an antiarch, supported itself on stiltlike pectoral fins. Another group of placoderms had the palatoquadrate firmly attached to the cranium and complex, solid tooth plates for crushing shellfish. In some placoderms, sexually dimorphic pelvic appendages suggest that internal fertilization occurred, probably coupled with complex courtship. Other groups show a tendency for exaggerated dorsoventral flattening, eyes on top of the head, and subterminal mouths, all indicating benthic specialization. *Gemuendina* bears a striking resemblance to modern skates, although it was completely armored with a mosaic of small plates and could not have used its broad pectoral fins in the skate's undulating manner of locomotion.

Placoderms lacked teeth. Slightly modified dermal bones lined the jaw cartilages of placoderms and, though they had long knifelike cutting edges and strong sharp points for slicing and piercing prey, they were subject to wear and breakage without replacement. The upper jaws of placoderms were often immovably bound to the cranium or tightly articulated to the rest of the head shield. This prevented their participation in any sucking action, a very important feeding process, as shown by its success in the jawless fishes and again in the vast majority of extant jawed fishes. The consensus among paleoichthyologists is that placoderms became extinct by the end of the Devonian without giving rise to any surviving forms.

■ Chondrichthyes: The Cartilagenous Fishes

The sharks and their relatives first appear in the fossil record in the Late Silurian (but see Young 1997 for possible Middle Ordovician remains). Since then, morphological refinements in some of their systems have evolved to levels surpassed by few other extant vertebrates; yet they retain many ancestral elements in their basic anatomy, and sharks have long been used to exemplify an ancestral vertebrate body form. Even at the molecular level these vertebrates appear to retain many ancestral character states (Martin et al. 1992) mixed with unexpectedly advanced systems, such as an immune system distinct but comparable with that of mammals (Litman 1996). Identified by a cartilaginous skeleton, extant forms can be divided into two groups: those with a single gill opening on each side of the head and those with multiple gill openings on each side. The Holocephali are so named because the upper jaw is fused to the cranium and the undivided appearance of the head that results from having a single gill opening. Their common names of ratfish and chimera come from their bizarre form: a long flexible tail, a fishlike body, and a head with big eyes and buckteeth that resembles a caricature of a rabbit. The Elasmobranchii, meaning plate-gilled, include the sharks, most often cylindrical forms with five to seven gill openings on each side of the head. They are also known as the Pleurotremata or Selachii. Two distinct clades of extant sharks are recognized: the classically sharky Galea (galeomorphs) and the Squalea, which include the sharklike squalomorphs, the less sharklike Squatiniformes (angel sharks) and Pristiophoriformes (the sawsharks), and the largest living clade of elasmobranchs, the dorsoventrally flattened sawfishes, guitarfishes, skates and rays, variously called the Hypotremata, Batoidea, or Rajiformes (Stiassny et al. 1996; for other arrangements see Greenwood et al. 1973, Nelson 1994, Bond 1996, Moyle and Cech 1996).

Evolutionary Specializations of Chondrichthyes

In spite of a rather good fossil record, the phylogeny of cartilaginous fishes remains unclear. Early Chondrichthyes, like extant species, were diverse in habits and habitats; in fact, in the Late Devonian sharks had invaded fresh waters to a greater extent than they do today. Their initial radiation from a common ancestor emphasized changes in teeth, jaws, and fins. Apparently, the feeding and locomotor apparatus evolved at different rates within different lineages. In some lineages, derived dentition was coincidental with ancestral fin structures, whereas the opposite combination is seen in others. As a result, fossil chondrichthyes display confusing mosaics of ancestral and derived characters.

Through time different lineages of Chondrichthyes tended to accumulate similar but not identical modifications in their feeding and locomotor structures, presumably because of similar selective pressures. This pattern of similar adaptations in related lineages is an example of parallel evolution: When similar selective forces act on similar body forms and developmental mechanisms, certain modifications appear independently and often repeatedly in the course of time.

Adaptations found in several lineages are known as general or broad adaptations. Examples are paired appendages, jaws, and use of muscular pump filter feeding. Broad adaptations have penetrating effects on the organisms' integration of behavior, physiology, and morphology. Broad adaptations define an organizational level in a horizontal (not phylogenetic) classification. Species showing characters of a particular organizational level belong to the same grade. A grade may contain different phylogenetic lineages. Each phylogenetic lineage is called a clade. For sharklike forms we can define three grades in their evolution, but at present it seems that only one of the clades was involved in the more recent evolutionary history of elasmobranchs (Figure 7–4) (Stiassny et al. 1996, Greenwood et al. 1973, Carroll 1987).

■ The Earliest Chondrichthyan Radiation

The stem chondrichthyans are identified by the form of the teeth common to the majority of the species—basically three-cusped with little root development (Figure 7–5). Although there is evidence of bone around their bases, the teeth are primarily dentine structures capped with an enameloid coat. The central cusp is the largest in *Cladoselache*, the best known genus, and smallest in *Xenacanthus*, a more specialized form.

Cladoselache was sharklike in appearance (Maisey 1996), about 2 meters long when fully grown, with large fins and mouth and five separate external gill openings. The mouth opened terminally and the chondrocranium had several large areas for the tight ligamentous attachment of the palatoquadrate. The jaw also obtained some support from the second visceral arch, the hyoid arch. The name **amphistylic** (*amphi* = both, *styl* = pillar or support) is applied to this mode of multiple sites of upper jaw suspension. The gape was large, the jaws extending well behind the rest of the skull. The three-pronged teeth were probably especially efficient for feeding on fishes or cephalopods that could be swallowed whole or severed by the knife-edge cusps.

Wear of teeth, which renders them less functional, is a problem faced by all vertebrates. The earliest sharks (and also some acanthodians and possibly early sarcopterygian bony fishes) solved this problem in a unique way. If teeth are derived from scales then a series of them would have wrapped over the edge of the mouth as the skin folded into the oral cavity even in jawless fishes. In ancient sharks each tooth on the functional edge of the jaw is but one member of a tooth whorl, attached to a ligamentous band that coursed down the inside of the jaw cartilage deep below the fleshy lining of the mouth (Figure 7–6). Aligned in each whorl in a file directly behind the functional tooth are a series of developing teeth. In extant sharks essentially the same dental apparatus is present. Tooth replacement is rapid: Young modern sharks under ideal conditions replace each lower jaw tooth every 8.2 days and each upper jaw tooth every 7.8 days. If *Cladoselache* replaced its teeth, as seems likely, then a significant advantage in feeding mechanics is indicated for Chondrichthyes compared with their placoderm contemporaries.

The body of *Cladoselache* was supported only by a notochord, but cartilaginous neural arches gave added protection to the spinal cord. The fins of *Cladoselache* consisted of two dorsal fins, paired pectoral and pelvic fins, and a well-developed forked tail. The first and sometimes the second dorsal fins were preceded by stout spines, triangular in cross section and thought by some to have been covered by soft tissue during the life of the shark. The dorsal fins were broad triangles with an internal structure consisting of a triangular basal cartilage and a parallel series of long radial cartilages that extended to the margin of the fin. The pectoral fins were larger but similar in construction.

Among the early radiations of sharks, almost every type seems to have had a different sort of internal pectoral fin arrangement (Figure 7–5), but all possessed basal elements that anchored the pectoral fins in place. From their structure the pectoral fins appear to have been hydrofoils with little capacity for altering their angle of contact with the water. The pelvic fins were smaller, but otherwise shaped like the pectorals. Some species in genera other than *Cladoselache* show evidence of pelvic fins with claspers: male copulatory organs. No anal fin is known; it is also lacking in many extant sharks.

The caudal fin of *Cladoselache* is distinctive (Figure 7–5). Externally symmetrical, its internal structure was asymmetrical and contained subchordal elements resembling the hemal arches that protect the caudal blood vessels in extant sharks. Long, unsegmented radial cartilages extended into the hypochordal (lower) lobe of the fin. At the base of the caudal fin were paired lateral keels that are identifying characteristics of extant rapid pelagic (open-water) swimmers.

The integument included only a few scales, but these resembled the teeth. Cusps of dentine were covered with an enamellike substance and contained a cellular core or pulp cavity. Unlike a tooth, each scale had several pulp cavities to match its several cusps. These scales were limited to the fins, the circumference of the eye, and within the mouth behind the teeth. Their structural similarities leave little doubt that the teeth of early sharks and other vertebrates in general are derived from specialized elements of the integument.

We can piece together the lives of many of the early chondrichthyes from their morphology and fossil localities. Probably pelagic predators, most early sharks, and *Cladoselache* in particular, swam after their prey in a sinuous manner, engulfing prey whole or slashing it with daggerlike teeth. The lack of body denticles and calcification suggests a tendency to reduce weight and thereby increase buoyancy.

Reproduction of some forms involved internal fertilization as evidenced by pelvic claspers, implying that a behavioral system existed to ensure successful mating. A potential reproductive change made possible by internal fertilization, as evidenced by claspers, is a reproductive strategy of producing young that are retained within the protection of the body of the mother for some period after fertilization. Because the size and resources of the female are finite, such retention would result in a relatively small number of young. Thus, as much as 350 million years ago, the elasmobranchs and possibly all chondrichthyans had evolved a reproductive life

history with profound biological and evolutionary constraints on their population biology.

Descriptions of two species of small (15-centimeter) sharklike forms from the Early Carboniferous of Montana may indicate just how complex reproductive behavior was in early chondrichthyes. A male can be identified by pelvic claspers, a sharp rostrum, and an enormous forwardly curved middorsal spine firmly embedded just behind the head (Figure 7–5c). Richard Lund considered that the great degree of sexual dimorphism and the discovery of many more males than females of at least one of these species suggested that males displayed during courtship in a regular male display site (a lek). He also suggested that one of the specimens discovered might be a pair in a precopulatory courtship position (Figure 7–5c) with the blunt-snouted female grasping the male's nuchal spine in her jaws.

An early group of chondrichthyan fishes had a suite of morphological characteristics seen also among other fusiform, fast-swimming marine sharks. These characters included large pectoral fins and stiff, symmetrical, deeply forked tails. These sharklike forms, the edestoids, were morphologically distinct from the main lines of chondrichthyan evolution, especially because of their peculiar dentition (Figure 7–6b). Most of the tooth whorls of edestoids were greatly reduced, but the symphysial (central) tooth row of the mandible was tremendously enlarged and each tooth interlocked with adjacent teeth at its base. Apparently, several members of this tooth whorl were functional at the same time. Blunt for crushing in some forms and compressed to create a series of knife-edge blades in others, the mandibular tooth row bit against small, flat teeth associated with a poorly developed palatoquadrate. Most edestoids replaced their teeth rapidly, the oldest worn teeth being shed from the tip of the mandible. In contrast, *Helicoprion* retained all its teeth in a specialized chamber into which the lifelong production of dentition spiraled (Figure 7–6b). Perhaps teeth no longer efficient in size or shape provided a solid foundation for the functional teeth.

One of the score or so of genera produced in this early radiation of chondrichthyan evolution is *Xenacanthus*, which had a braincase, jaws, and jaw suspension very similar to those of *Cladoselache*. But there the resemblance ends. The xenacanths were freshwater bottom dwellers. The idea that they were bottom dwellers derives from the similarity of their

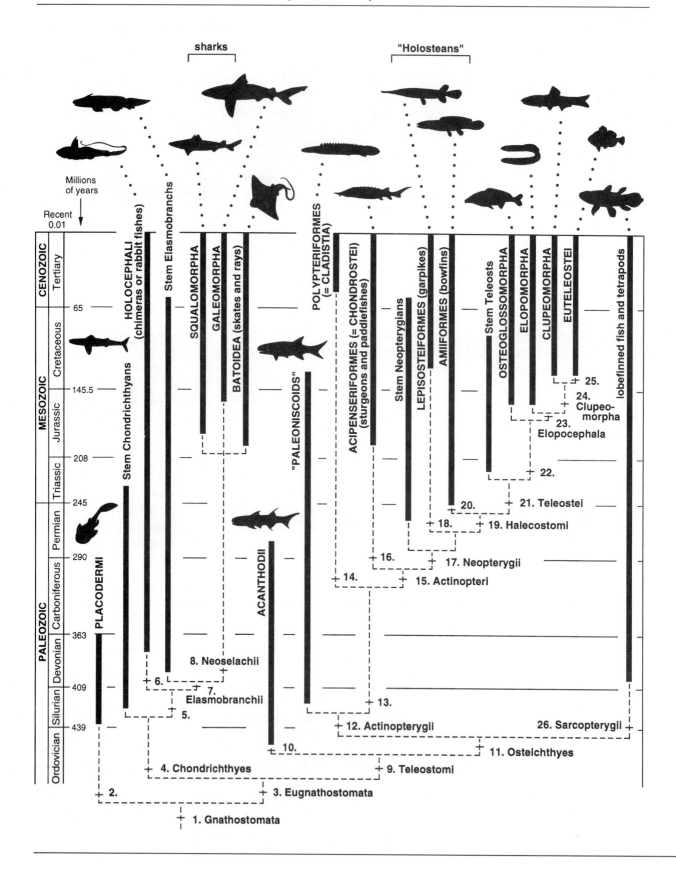

1. Gnathostomata: jaws formed of bilateral palatoquadrate (upper) and mandibular (lower) cartilages of the mandibular visceral arch at some stage of development, modified hyoid gill arch, major branchial elements internal to gill membranes, branchial arches contain four elements on each side plus one unpaired ventral median element, three semicircular canals, internal supporting girdles associated with pectoral and pelvic fins, plus many features of the soft anatomy (see Table 6–2). 2. Placodermi: Tentatively placed as the sister group of all other gnathostomes, but see Gardiner (1984) for a different view. Provisionally united by the following derived characters: a specialized joint in the neck vertebrae, a unique arrangement of dermal skeletal plates of the head and shoulder girdle, a distinctive articulation of the upper jaw, a unique pattern of lateral line canals on the head. 3. Chondrichthyes plus Teleostomi (Eugnathostoma): Epihyal element of second visceral arch modified as the hyomandibula, which is a supporting element for the jaw, true teeth rooted to the jaw (Osteichthyes) or in a tooth whorl. 4. Chondrichthyes: Unique perichondral and endochondral mineralization as prismatic hydroxyapatite tesserae, placoid scales, unique teeth and tooth replacement mechanisms, distinctive characters of the basal and radial elements of the fins, inner ear labyrinth opens externally via the endolymphatic duct, distinctive features of the endocrine system. 5. Elasmobranchii plus Holocephali: Claspers on male pelvic fins and at least four additional fin-support characters. 6. Holocephali: Hyostylic jaw suspension, gill arches beneath the braincase, dibasal pectoral fin, dorsal fin articulates with anterior elements of the axial skeleton. 7. Elasmobranchii: tribasal pectoral, shoulder joint narrowed, basibranchial separated by gap from basihyal. 8. Neoselachii: pectoral fin with three basal elements, the anteriormost of which is supported by the shoulder girdle, plus characteristics of the nervous system, cranium, and ill arches. 9. Teleostomi: hemibranchial elements of gills not attached to interbranchial septum, bony opercular covers, branchiostegal rays. 10. Acanthodii: fin spines on anal and paired fins as well as on dorsal fins, paired intermediate fin spines between pectoral and pelvic fins. 11. Osteichthyes: a unique pattern of dermal head bones, including dermal marginal mouth bones with rooted teeth, a unique pattern of ossification of the dermal bones of the shoulder girdle, presence of lepidotrichia (fin rays), differentiation of the muscles of the branchial region, presence of a lung or swim bladder derived from the gut, medial insertion of the mandibular muscle on the lower jaw. 12. Actinopterygii: basal elements of pectoral fin enlarged, median fin rays attached to skeletal elements that do not extend into fin, single dorsal fin, scales with unique arrangement, shape, interlocking mechanism, and histology (outer layer of ganoine). 13. Cladistia plus Actinopteri (plus fossils such as *Moythomasia* and *Mimia*): A specialized dentine (acrodin) forms a cap on the teeth, details of posterior braincase structure, specific basal elements of the pelvic fin are fused, and numerous features of the soft anatomy of extant forms that cannot be verified for fossils. 14. Polypteriformes (Cladistia): unique dorsal fin spines, facial bone fusion and pectoral fin skeleton and musculature. 15. Actinopteri: derived characters of the dermal elements of the skull and pectoral girdle and fins, a spiracular canal formed by a diverticulum of the spiracle penetrating the postorbital process of the skull, other details of skull structure, three cartilages or ossifications in the hyoid below the interhyal, swim bladder connects dorsally to the foregut, fins edged by specialized scales (fulcra). 16. Acipensiformes (Chondrostei): fusion of premaxillae, maxillae, and dermopalatines, unique anterior palatoquadrate sym-

physis. 17. Neopterygii: rays of dorsal and anal fins reduced to equal the number of endoskeletal supports, upper lobe of caudal fin containing axial skeleton reduced in size to produce a nearly symmetrical caudal fin, upper pharyngeal teeth consolidated into tooth-bearing plates, characters of pectoral girdle and skull bones. 18. Lepisosteiformes (Ginglymodi): vertebrae with convex anterior faces and concave posterior faces (opisthocoelus), toothed infraorbital bones contribute to elongate jaws. See character state "19." 19. Halecostomi: modifications of the cheek, jaw articulation, and opercular bones including a mobile maxilla. The relationships of the Lepisosteiformes, Amiiformes, their fossil relatives and the Teleostei are subject to many differing opinions at present with no clear resolution based on unique shared derived characters. More conservative phylogenies than presented here would represent them as an unresolved tricotomy. Others would unite the lepisosteiformes and the amiiformes as the "Holostei." 20. Amiidae (Recent Amiiformes): jaw articulation formed by both the quadrate and the symplectic bones. 21. Teleostei: elongate posterior neural arches (uroneurals), which contribute to the stiffening of the upper lobe of the internally asymmetrical caudal fin (the caudal is externally symmetrical = homocercal at least primitively in teleosts), unpaired ventral pharyngeal toothplates on basibranchial elements, premaxillae mobile, urohyal formed as an unpaired ossification of the tendon of the sternohyoideus muscle, details of skull foramina, jaw muscles, and axial and pectoral skeleton. 22. Recent Teleosts: presence of an endoskeletal basihyal, four pharyngobranchials and three hypobranchials, median toothplates overlying basibranchials and basihyals. 23. Elopocephala: two uroneural bones extend anteriorly to the second ural (tail) vertebral centrum, abdominal and anterior caudal epipleural intermuscular bones present. 24. Clupeocephala: pharyngeal toothplates fused with endoskeletal gill arch elements, neural arch of first caudal centrum reduced or absent, distinctive patterns of ossification and articulation of the jaw joint. 25. Euteleostei: this numerically dominant group of vertebrates is poorly characterized with no known unique shared derived character present in all or perhaps even in most forms. Nevertheless, the following have been used as a basis for establishing monophyly: presence of an adipose fin posteriorly on the mid-dorsal line, presence of nuptial tubercles on the head and body, paired anterior membranous outgrowths of the first uroneural bones of the caudal fin. (These characters are usually lost in the most derived euteleosts.) The nature of these characters leads to a lack of consensus on the interrelationships of the basal clupeocephalids, although the group's monophyly is still generally accepted. 26. Sarcopterygii: Fleshy pectoral and pelvic fins have a single basal skeletal element, muscular lobes at the bases of those fins, enamel (versus enameloid) on surfaces of teeth, cosmine (unique type of dentine) in body scales, unique characters of jaws, articulation of jaw supports, gill arches, and shoulder girdles. Details of the phylogenetic relationships within the Sarcopterygii are shown in Figure 10–2. (Based on G. V. Lauder and K. F. Liem, 1983, *Bulletin of the Museum of Comparative Zoology* 150:95–197; B. G. Gardiner, 1984, *Bulletin of the British Museum [Natural History] Geology* 37:173–427; J. G. Maisey, 1986, *Cladistics* 2:201–256; R. L. Carroll, 1988, *Vertebrate Paleontology and Evolution*, W. H. Freeman and Co., New York, NY; B. G. Gardiner and B. Schaeffer, 1989, *Zoological Journal of the Linnean Society* 97:135–187; P. E. Olsen and A. R. McCune, 1991, *Journal of Vertebrate Paleontology* 11:269–292; J. S. Nelson, 1994, *Fishes of the World*, Wiley, New York, NY, and P. Janvier, 1996, *Early Vertebrates*, Clarendon Press, Oxford.)

Figure 7–4 Phylogenetic relationships of jawed fishes. This diagram depicts the probable interrelationships among the major groups of basal gnathostomes. Extinct lineages are marked by a dagger (†). Dotted lines show interrelationships only; they do not indicate times of divergence nor the unrecorded presence of taxa in the fossil record. The numbers indicate derived characters that distinguish the lineages. Only the best-corroborated relationships are shown. The circle indicates that the relationships of the lineages at that node cannot yet be defined.

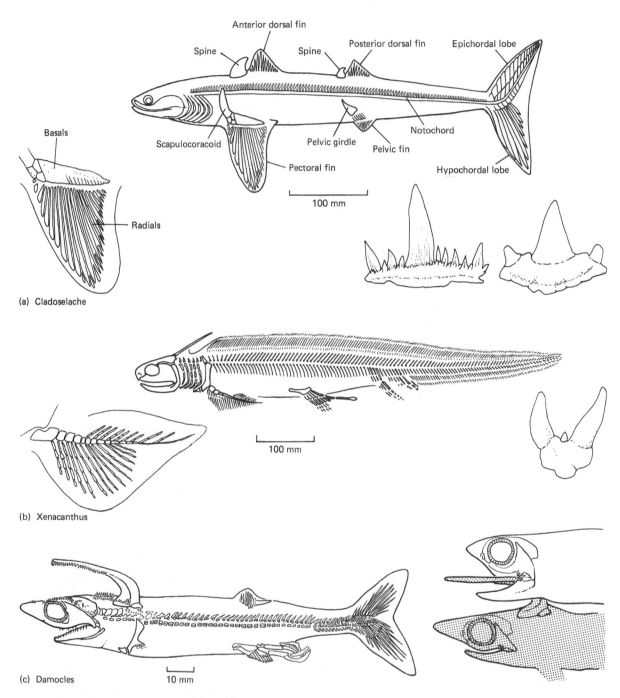

Figure 7–5 Early chondrichthyans. (a) *Cladoselache* with details of the pectoral structure and teeth of the "*Cladodus*" type; (b) *Xenacanthus*, a freshwater elasmobranch with details of its archipterygial pectoral fin structure and peculiar teeth; (c) left, male *Damocles serratus*, a 15-centimeter shark from the Late Carboniferous showing sexually dimorphic nuchal spine and pelvic claspers; right, male (below) and female (above) as fossilized, possibly in courtship position. (Modified after J. A. Moy–Thomas and R. S. Miles, 1971, *Paleozoic Fishes*, Saunders College Publishing, Philadelphia, PA; and R. Lund, 1985, *Journal of Vertebrate Paleontology* 5:1–19, and 1986, *Journal of Vertebrate Paleontology* 6:12–19.)

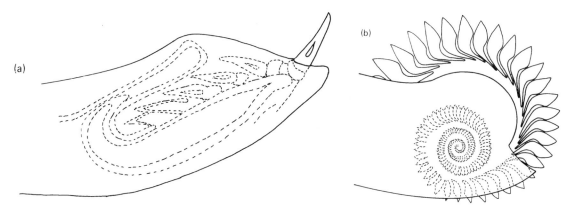

Figure 7–6 Tooth replacement by chondrichthyans. (a) Diagrammatic cross section of the jaw of an extant shark showing a single functional tooth backed by a band of replacement teeth in various stages of development; (b) lateral view of the symphysial (middle of the lower jaw) tooth whorl of the edestoid cladodont *Helicoprion*, showing the chamber into which the lifelong production of teeth spiraled.

fins to those of extant Australian lungfishes (which are bottom dwellers) and their heavily calcified cartilaginous skeleton that would have decreased their buoyancy. The xenacanths appeared in the Devonian and survived until the Triassic, when they died out without leaving direct descendants. Nevertheless, details of their gill, median, and paired fin skeletons indicate that they are at the base of the elasmobranch clade of Chondrichthyes (Janvier 1996).

The Early Mesozoic Elasmobranch Radiation

Further chondrichthyan evolution involved reorganization in feeding and locomotor systems. Species exhibiting these modifications appear in the Carboniferous and this radiation of stem elasmobranchs flourished until the Late Cretaceous. To identify these new adaptations, let us examine a late and well-known genus of the Triassic and Cretaceous, *Hybodus*. From it we have complete skeletons 2 meters in length that look very much like a modern shark except that the mouth is terminal, not underslung beneath a sensory rostrum (Figure 7–7a).

The heterodont dentition (that is, different shaped teeth along the jaw) of hybodont sharks seems pivotal to their success. The anterior teeth were sharp cusped and appear to have been used for piercing, holding, and slashing softer foods. The posterior teeth were stout, blunt versions of the anterior teeth. Instead of becoming functional one at a time, they appeared above the fleshy lining of the mouth in batteries consisting of several teeth from

each individual tooth whorl. An extant form with a similar dentition (Figure 7–7b) indicates how the mouth of a *Hybodus*-like shark might have looked: The extant horn sharks of the genus *Heterodontus*, which have *Hybodus*-like dentition, feed on small fishes, crabs, shrimp, sea urchins, clams, mussels, and oysters. The sharp teeth near the symphysis seize and dispatch soft-bodied food, and shelled foods are crushed by pavementlike posterior teeth.

Also characteristic of the hybodonts were their fins. The pectoral girdle remained divided into separate right and left halves, but the articulation between girdle and the fin consisted of three narrowed platelike basal cartilages instead of the long, often fused series seen in earlier sharks. This tribasal arrangement was also found in the pelvic fins, and both pairs of fins were supported on a narrow stalk composed of the three basals. Mobility of the distal portion of the paired fins was also increased. The cartilaginous radials did not extend to the fin margin and were segmented along their shortened length.

Proteinaceous, flexible fin rays called ceratotrichia extended from the outer radials to the margin of the fin. Intrinsic fin muscles arched the fin from anterior to posterior and along its long axis. This mobility allowed the paired fins to be used hydrodynamically in ways that seem impossible with the fin construction characteristic of *Cladoselache*. By assuming different shapes, the pectoral fins could produce lift anteriorly, aid in turning, or function as simple hydrofoils. Along with changes in the paired fins, the caudal fin assumed new func-

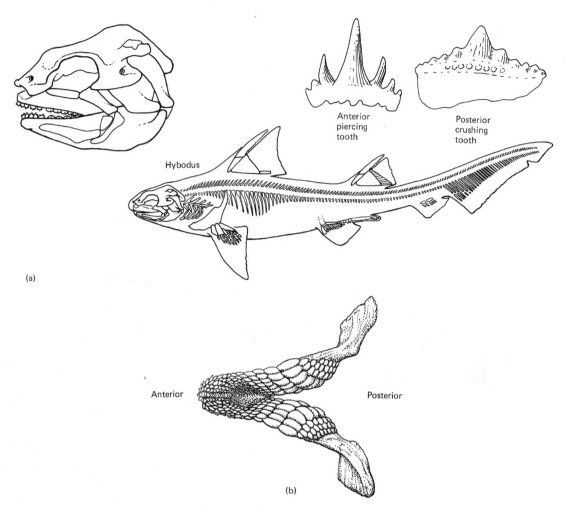

Figure 7–7 *Hybodus* and *Heterodontus*. (a) The fossil elasmobranch *Hybodus*. Detail of head skeleton and teeth. (Modified after J. A. Moy–Thomas and R. S. Miles, 1971, *Paleozoic Fishes*, Saunders College Publishing, Philadelphia, PA.) (b) Upper jaw of the extant hornshark, *Heterodontus*, with a dentition similar to that of many elasmobranchs in the second radiation during the late Paleozoic and early Mesozoic.

tions and an anal fin appeared. Caudal fin shape was altered by reduction of the hypochordal lobe, division of its radials, and addition of flexible ceratotrichia. This tail fin arrangement is generally known as **heterocercal** (*hetero* = different, *kerkos* = tail), although **epicercal** is a more precise name for a tail shape known from as far back as some Paleozoic jawless fishes (Chapter 6). The distinction of the elasmobranch heterocercal tail is in its flexibility (because of the more numerous radial skeletal elements) and intrinsic musculature for control. Undulated from side to side, the fin twisted as a result of water pressure so that the flexible lower lobe trailed behind the stiff upper one. This distribution of force produced forward thrust that, combined with the variable planing surfaces produced by flexible pectorals, could counter the shark's tendency to sink or could lift it from a benthic resting position. All gnathostomes from the early fossil record had similar, if stiffer, heterocercal caudal fins. The evolutionary success of the heterocercal fin compared with a straight or ventrally bent fin axis may relate to this generation of vertical forces, however slight they might have been (Webb and Smith 1980). Whatever mechanism the earlier sharks used to remain in the water column, it is likely that the dynamic design of the fins in this second radiation of sharks allowed them more behavioral flexibility.

Other morphological changes in the sharks of the second major radiation include the appearance of a complete set of hemal arches that protected the arteries and veins running ventral to the notochord, well-developed ribs, and narrow, more pointed dorsal fin spines closely associated with the leading edge of the dorsal fins. These spines were deeply inserted in the muscle mass, exposed above the skin, ornamented with ridges and grooves, and studded with numerous barbs on the posterior surface, indicating defensive functions. Claspers are common to all species, leaving little doubt about the development of courtship and internal fertilization. In addition, male *Hybodus* had one or two pairs of hooked spines above the eye that may have been used as claspers during copulation.

Hybodus and its relatives resembled their presumed *Cladoselache*-like ancestors in having terminal mouths, an amphistylic jaw suspension, unconstricted notochords, and multicusped teeth, but a direct line cannot be drawn between the two in time or in morphology. Some forms considered related to *Hybodus* had *Cladoselache*-like dentition combined with tribasal pectoral fins; others developed a very tetrapodlike support for highly mobile pectoral fins. Their caudal fin was reduced, and they probably moved around on the seafloor using their limblike pectoral fins. Another form, known only from a 5-centimeter juvenile, had a paddle-shaped rostrum one-third its body length. Other types were 2.5-meter giants with blunt snouts and enormous jaws. Despite their variety and the fact that they flourished during the Mesozoic, this second radiation of elasmobranchs became increasingly rare and disappeared from Earth at or shortly after at the close of that era.

The Extant Radiation: Sharks and Rays

As early as the Triassic, and perhaps even in the Late Carboniferous, fossilized indications of the extant radiation of elasmobranchs appear. By the Jurassic, sharks of modern appearance had evolved, and a surprising number of Jurassic and Cretaceous genera are still extant (Shirai in Stiassny et al. 1996). Paleontologists are not in agreement about the origin of extant sharks. They may have evolved from *Hybodus*-like sharks, but a few details of the morphology of *Hybodus*-like sharks seem to preclude them from the lineage of extant sharks. Perhaps the evolution of the extant sharks, skates, and rays (the

Neoselachii) was from a *Cladoselache*-like lineage that acquired characteristics in parallel with *Hybodus* and its relatives, or there may be a yet-unknown common ancestor for hybodonts and neoselachians. The most obvious difference between most members of the earlier radiations and extant sharks is the almost ubiquitous rostrum or snout that overhangs the ventrally positioned mouth in most extant forms. The technical characters distinguishing the clades of extant sharks and rays are more subtle.

Extant elasmobranchs have an enlarged hyomandibular cartilage (= hyomandibula), which braces the posterior portion of the palatoquadrate and attaches firmly but movably to the otic region of the cranium (Figure 7–8). A second connection to the chondrocranium is via paired palatoquadrate projections to either side of the braincase just behind the eyes and attached to it by elastic ligaments. Jaw suspension of this type is known as hyostylic. Hyostyly permits multiple jaw positions, each appropriate to different feeding opportunities (Moss 1984).

The right and left halves of the pectoral girdle are fused together ventrally into a single U-shaped scapulocoracoid cartilage. Muscles run from the ventral coracoid portion to the symphysis of the lower jaw and function in opening the mouth. The advantages of the jaws of extant elasmobranchs are displayed when the upper jaw is protruded. Muscles swing the hyomandibula laterally and anteriorly to increase the distance between the right and left jaw articulations and thereby increase the volume of the orobranchial chamber. This expansion, which sucks water and food forcefully into the mouth, was not possible with an amphistylic jaw suspension because the palatoquadrate was tightly attached to the chondrocranium.

With hyomandibular extension, the palatoquadrate is protruded to the limits of the elastic ligaments on its orbital processes. This protrusion allows delicate plucking of benthic foodstuffs. Protrusion also drops the mouth away from the head to allow an extant shark to bite an organism much larger than itself despite its large, sensitive rostrum. The dentition of the palatoquadrate is specialized; the teeth are stouter than those in the mandible and often recurved and strongly serrated. When feeding on large prey a shark opens its mouth, sinks its lower and upper teeth deeply into the prey, and protrudes its upper jaw ever more deeply into the slash initiated by the teeth. As the jaws reach their maximum initial penetration, the shark throws its

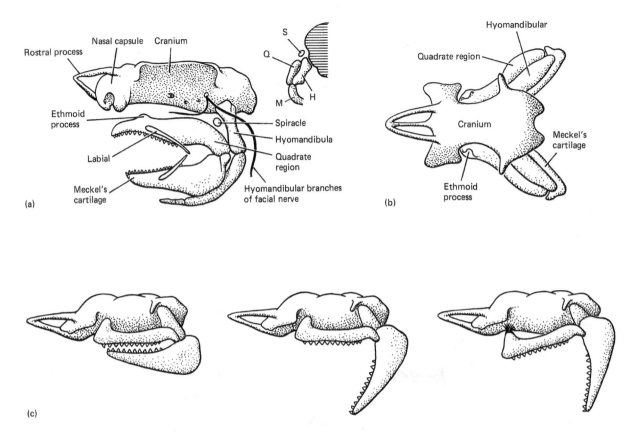

Figure 7–8   Anatomical relationships of the jaws and chondrocranium of extant hyostylic sharks. The drawings are based on *Scyllium* and *Carcharhinus*. (a) Lateral and cross-sectional views of the head skeleton of *Scyllium* with the jaws closed. (Modified after E. S. Goodrich, 1930, *Studies on the Structure and Development of Vertebrates*, Macmillan, London, UK.) (b) Dorsal view of *Carcharhinus*. (c) During jaw opening and upper jaw protrusion the hyomandibula rotates from a position parallel to the long axis of the cranium to a position nearly perpendicular to that axis. S, spiracle; Q, quadrate region of the palatoquadrate; H, hyomandibula; M, mandible. ([b, c] Modified after S. A. Moss 1984.)

body into exaggerated lateral undulations, which results in a violent side-to-side shaking of the head. The head movements bring the serrated upper teeth into action as saws to sever a large piece of flesh from the victim.

Mobility within the head skeleton, known as cranial kinesis, allows consumption of large food items. Cranial kinesis permits inclusion of large items in the diet of vertebrates, such as elasmobranchs, without excluding smaller, more diverse foodstuffs. Throughout their evolutionary history the Chondrichthyes have been consummate carnivores. In the third adaptive radiation of the elasmobranchs, locomotor, trophic, sensory, and behavioral characteristics evolved together in the mid-Mesozoic to produce forms still dominating the top levels of marine food webs. This position

has gone hand-in-hand with the evolution of gigantism, one advantage of which is avoiding predation. The 360 species of sharks (Figure 7–9) and 456 species of skates and rays (Figure 7–13) known today are large organisms, even for vertebrates. A typical shark is about two meters long, and a typical ray is half that length. Nevertheless, a few interesting miniature forms only 25 centimeters long have evolved and inhabit mostly deeper seas off the continental shelves.

In spite of their enormous range in size, all extant elasmobranchs have common skeletal characteristics that earlier shark radiations lacked. The continuous notochord was replaced in the extant radiation by cartilaginous centra that calcify in several distinctive ways. Although centra occur in many other gnathostomes, those of extant sharks

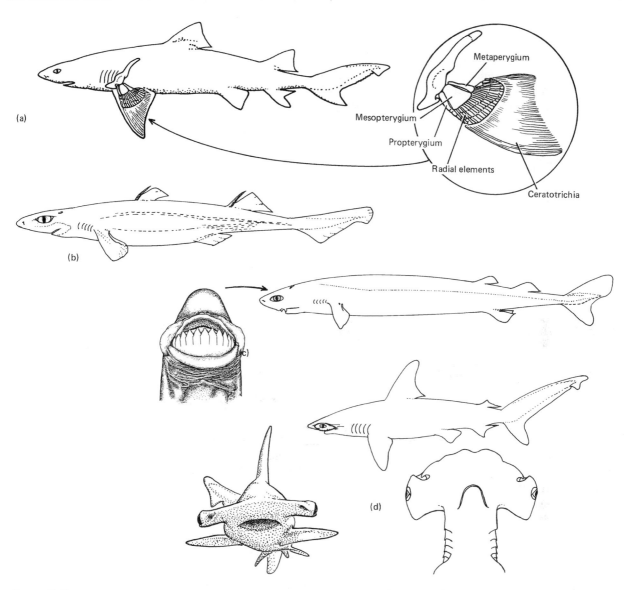

Figure 7–9 Some examples of extant sharks. (a) *Negaprion brevirostris*, the lemon shark, is widely used in elasmobranch research. It inhabits warm waters of the Atlantic frequented by bathers and divers and can attain a size sufficient to threaten humans. The internal anatomy of the pectoral girdle and fin are shown superimposed in their correct relative positions. (b) *Etmopterus vierens*, the green dogfish, is a miniature shark only 25 centimeters in length, yet it feeds on much larger prey items. (c) *Isistius brasiliensis*, the cookie-cutter shark, is another miniature species whose curious mouth (left) is able to take chunks from fish and cetaceans much larger than itself. (d) Hammerhead shark (*Sphyrna*) in lateral, ventral, and frontal views.

are so distinctive in morphology that they are considered to have evolved independently. Between centra, spherical remnants of the notochord fit into depressions on the opposing faces of adjacent vertebrae. Thus, the axial skeleton is a laterally flexible structure with rigid central elements swiveling on ball-bearing joints of calcified cartilage and notochordal remnants. In addition to the neural and hemal arches, extra elements not found in the axial skeleton of other vertebrates (the intercalary plates) protect the spinal cord above and the major arteries and veins below the centra.

Shark scales also changed. Although scales of the same general type are known from earlier chondrichthyes, they are often in clusters of fused into larger plates. The shagreen of modern elasmobranchs is a unique armor, flexible yet very protective. The scales of extant sharks are single cusped and have a single pulp cavity. Scales in more ancestral sharks may have begun development similarly but often fused to form larger scales later in life. Extant sharks add more individual scales to their skin as they grow, and new scales may be larger in proportion to the increase in size of the shark. The size, shape, and arrangement of these placoid scales reduce turbulence in the flow of water adjacent to the body surface and increase the efficiency of swimming. It seems that this simplification of denticles may relate to increased locomotor efficiency.

A characteristic that differentiates chondrichthyans from other extant jawed fishes is the absence of a gas-filled bladder. Elasmobranchs (and holocephalians) use their liver to counteract the weight of their placoid scales, teeth, and calcified cartilages. The average tissue densities of sharks with their livers removed is 1.062 to 1.089 grams per milliliter. Because seawater has a density of about 1.030 grams per milliliter, one might conclude that a shark that is not swimming would sink. The liver of a shark, however, is well known for its high oil content, which gives shark liver tissue a density of about 0.95 grams per milliliter. The liver may contribute as much as 25 percent of the body mass. By adjusting the oil content and size of their livers through growth and reabsorption, sharks can adjust their buoyancy as well as store energy. A 4-meter tiger shark (*Galeocerdo cuvieri*) weighing 460 kilograms on land may weigh as little as 3.5 kilograms in the sea. Not surprisingly, benthic sharks, such as nurse sharks, have livers with fewer and smaller oil vacuoles in their cells.

Long before it was realized that sharks may weigh very little in their natural habitat because of liver buoyancy, a very different mechanism was credited with preventing sharks from sinking. The peculiar hydrodynamics of a laterally oscillated heterocercal tail were hypothesized to produce an upward lift as well as a forward thrust. Anterior surfaces such as the pectoral fins and perhaps the snout, if properly oriented, will produce lift as the shark moves through the water. Thus, although gravity pulls a shark downward, two areas of lift—one anterior and one posterior—could act on a swimming shark, permitting it to remain in the water column and not sink. Two objections may be raised to this model. First, because of the low density of its large liver a motionless pelagic shark is nearly neutrally buoyant. Any lift, either anterior or posterior, during forward locomotion would therefore cause a shark to rise in the water column—something we know does not necessarily occur. Second, the amount of lift resulting from the heterocercal tail and the pectoral fins is proportional to the forward velocity; the gravitational force is constant. Hence a shark would be neutrally buoyant and able to remain at the same level in the water column only over a narrow range of swimming speeds. If the shark swam too slowly, it would sink; if it swam too rapidly, it would rise. Only a dynamic ability to alter the lift characteristics of the shark's body can resolve this paradox.

K. S. Thomson analyzed the swimming of several extant shark species from films made of captive specimen (see Moss 1984). Because dynamic adjustments of the muscles attached to the ceratotrichia of the hypochordal lobe could independently change the lobe's angle of attack, Thomson hypothesized that the heterocercal tail could deliver thrust over a wide range of angles, not simply forward and up as the classical model supposed. Thomson thinks that the highly controllable heterocercal tail of extant sharks, which appears in a great diversity of shapes and relative sizes, allows them to develop extremely powerful dives and climbs in the water over a wide range of speeds, permitting sharks to make oblique attacks and shear off flesh from large prey. But Thomson never offered any experimental proof of his assertions.

A single but detailed experimental test of the differing hypotheses of heterocercal tail function during swimming has been performed G. V. Lauder and his collaborators (Ferry and Lauder 1996). The study was conducted with one species of shark using only small (35-cm) individuals. Surprisingly perhaps, the tail components (the only ones studied) conformed to the classical model: The tail produced lift in an upward and forward vector. Clearly, Thomson's analysis of motion pictures was insufficient. By examining only the posterior margins of heterocercal tails in motion, the complex forces brought into play in the more anterior segments of these seemingly simple and clearly primitive tails have been overlooked. Exactly how a shark swimming at different speeds maintains a level in the water column is still unclear. A clue comes from identical analysis in Lauder's lab on the swimming in a primitive ray-finned fish with a heterocercal tail, a sturgeon. In contrast to the one species of shark measured, the species of sturgeon studied demonstrated no significant vertical thrust from its tail movements and thus did not conform to the classical model (Schmidt and Lauder 1995). Much more comparative and detailed study will be needed before we understand the function of heterocercal tails.

Although not unique, the sensory systems of extant sharks, skates, and rays are certainly refined and diverse (Hodgson and Mathewson 1978, Sweet et al. 1983). Sharks may detect prey via mechanoreceptors of their lateralis system, an interconnected series of superficial tubes, pores, and patches of sensory cells distributed over the head and along the sides that respond to vibrations transmitted through the water. The basic units of mechanoreceptors are the **neuromast organs**, a cluster of sensory and supporting cells that are found on the surface and within the lateral-line canals. The anatomically related **ampullae of Lorenzini**, mucus-filled tubes with sensory cells and afferent neurons at their base, are exquisitely sensitive to electrical potentials and can even detect prey from their weak electrical fields (Box 7–1).

Chemoreception is another important sense. In fact, sharks have been described as swimming noses, so acute is their sense of smell. Experiments have shown that some sharks respond to chemicals in concentrations as low as 1 part in 10 billion! Hammerhead sharks of the genus *Sphyrna* (Figure 7–9) may have enhanced the directionality of their olfactory apparatus by placing the nostrils far apart on the odd lateral expansions of their heads.

Finally, vision is important to the feeding behavior of sharks. Especially well developed are mechanisms for vision at low light intensities at which humans would find vision impossible. This sensitivity is due to a rod-rich retina and cells with numerous platelike crystals of guanine that are located just behind the retina in the choroid layer. Collectively called the tapetum lucidum, the cells containing the crystals act like microscopic mirrors to reflect light back through the retina and increase the chance that light will be absorbed. This mechanism, although of great benefit at night or in the depths, has obvious disadvantages in the bright sea surface of midday. To regulate the amount of bright light, cells containing the dark pigment melanin expand over the reflective surface to occlude the tapetum lucidum and absorb all light not stimulating the retina on first penetration. With so many sophisticated sensory systems, it is not surprising that the brains of many species of sharks are proportionately heavier than the brains of other fishes and approach the brain-to-body mass ratios of some tetrapods.

Anecdotal and circumstantial evidence suggests that sharks regularly use their various sensory modalities in an ordered sequence in locating, identifying, and attacking prey. Olfaction is often the first of the senses to alert a shark of potential prey, especially when the prey is wounded or otherwise releasing body fluids. A shark employs its sensitive sense of smell to swim up-current through an increasing odor gradient. Because of its exquisite sensitivity, a shark can use smell as a long-distance sense. Not as useful over great distances, but much more directional over a wide range of environmental conditions is another distance sense—a vibration sensitivity called mechanoreception. The lateralis system and the sensory areas of the inner ear are related forms of mechanoreceptors highly efficient in detecting vibrations such as those produced by a struggling fish. Mechanoreception is effective in drawing sharks from considerable distances to a sound source. This has been demonstrated in macabre sea-rescue operations in which sharks were apparently attracted by rescue helicopter rotor vibrations that fall into the same frequency range as those of a struggling fish. Under more controlled conditions, hydrophones can be used to attract sharks by broadcasting vibrations with frequencies like those produced by a struggling fish.

Whether by olfaction or vibration detection, once a shark is close to the stimulus source, vision takes over as the primary prey detection modality. If the prey is easily recognized visually, a shark may proceed directly to an attack. Unfamiliar prey is treated differently, as studies aimed at developing shark deterrents have discovered. A circling shark may suddenly turn and rush toward unknown prey. Instead of opening its jaws to attack, however, the shark bumps or slashes the surface of the object with its rostrum. Opinions differ as to whether this is an attempt to determine texture through mechanoreception, to make a quick electrosensory appraisal, or to use the rough placoid scales to abrade the surface releasing fresh olfactory cues. Following further circling and apparent evaluation of all sensory cues from the potential prey, the shark may either wan-

BOX 7–1   Electroreception by Elasmobranchs

The ability to detect electric fields is found in many fishes, especially elasmobranchs. On the heads of sharks, and on the heads and pectoral fins of rays, are structures known as the ampullae of Lorenzini. The ampullae are sensitive electroreceptors (Figure 7–10). The canal that connects the receptor to the surface pore is filled with an electrically conductive gel, and the wall of the canal is nonconductive. Because the canal runs for some distance beneath the epidermis, the sensory cell can detect a difference in electrical potential between the tissue in which it lies (which reflects the adjacent epidermis and environment) and the distant pore opening. Thus, it can detect electrical fields, which are changes in electrical potential in space. The ancestral electroreceptor cell is a modification of the hair cells of the lateral line (Figures 8–10 and 8–15). Electroreceptors of elasmobranchs respond to minute changes in the electrical field surrounding an animal. They act like voltmeters, measuring a difference in electric potentials at discrete locations across the body surface. Voltage sensitivities are remarkable: Ampullary organs have thresholds lower than 0.01 microvolt per centimeter, a level of detection achieved only by the best voltmeters.

Elasmobranchs use their electric sensitivity to detect prey and possibly for navigation. All muscle activity generates electric potential: Motor nerve cells produce extremely brief changes in electrical potential, and muscular contraction generates changes of longer duration. In addition, a steady potential issues from an aquatic organism as a result of the chemical imbalance between the organism and its surroundings.

A. J. Kalmijn (1974) demonstrated that neither visual nor olfactory cues were necessary, and electrical activity in the absence of any other stimuli was sufficient to elicit an oriented feeding response (Figure 7–11). Subsequently,

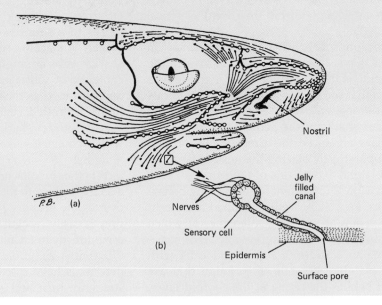

Figure 7–10 Ampullae of Lorenzini. (a) Distribution of the ampullae on the head of a spiny dogfish, *Squalus acanthius*. Open circles represent the surface pores and the black dots are the positions of the sensory cells. (b) A single ampullary organ.

Nostril

Jelly filled canal

P.B.   (a)

Nerves

Sensory cell

(b)

Epidermis

Surface pore

der off or attack. In the latter case the rostrum is raised, the jaws protruded, and in the last moments before contact many sharks draw an opaque eyelid across each eye to protect it. At this point it appears that sharks shift entirely to electroreception to track prey during the final stage of attack. This hypothesis was developed while studying the attacks by large sharks on bait suspended from boats and observed from submerged protective cages. After the occlusion of its eyes by the nictitating membrane, an attacking shark was frequently observed to veer from the bait and bite some inanimate, generally metallic object in the close vicinity (including the observer's cage, much to the dismay of the

Figure 7–11 Kalmijn's experiments illustrating the electrolocation capacity of elasmobranchs. (Modified from A. J. Kalmijn 1974, *Handbook of Sensory Physiology*, volume 3, part 3, edited by A. Fessard, Springer, New York, NY.)

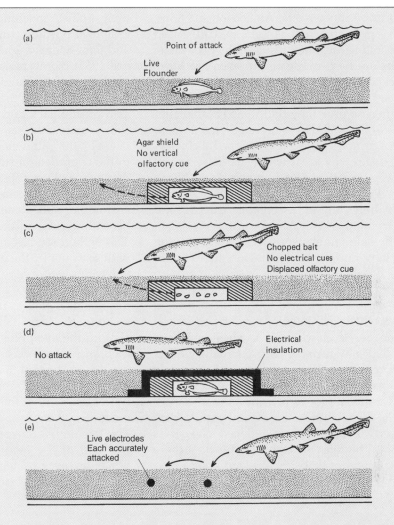

Kalmijn (1982) demonstrated electroreception by free-ranging sharks in the wild.

Electroreception might be used for navigation as well. The electromagnetic field at the Earth's surface produces tiny voltage gradients, and a shark swimming could encounter gradients as large as 0.4 microvolt per centimeter. In addition, ocean currents generate electric gradients as large as 0.5 microvolt per centimeter as they carry ions through the Earth's magnetic field. The use of these potentials for navigation has not been demonstrated. However, A. P. Klimley (1993) argued persuasively for hammerhead shark migration on and off of feeding grounds using electrodetection of geomagnetic gradients.

divers). Apparently, olfaction and vibration senses are of little use at very close range, leaving only electroreception to guide the attacking shark. The unnatural environment of the bait stations included stronger influences on local electric fields than the bait, and the sharks attacked these artificial sources of electrical activity.

Rare observations of sharks feeding under natural conditions indicate that these fishes are versatile and effective predators. The great white shark (*Carcharodon carcharias*) kills its mammalian prey by exsanguination—bleeding them to death (Klimley 1994, Klimley and Ainley 1996). They hold a seal tightly in their jaws until it is no longer bleeding, then bite down removing an enormous chunk of flesh. The carcass floats to the surface and the shark returns to it for another bite. Attacks on sea lions, which have powerful front flippers probably used effectively in defense, often result in the prey being released before they are dead. But even sea lions, once attacked are repeatedly recaptured until they too are dead of blood loss. White sharks also prematurely release prey they find unacceptable after initial mouthing. Klimley suggested that lack of blubber is a primary rejection criterion. This behavior may explain why great white sharks seize and then release sea otters and humans along North America's West coast. A white shark may feed rather leisurely on an acceptable carcass and defend it from other white sharks with typical fish-like side-by-side tail slaps, as well as tail lobbing and breaching into the air—behaviors more familiar among dolphins and whales.

Much of the success of the extant grade of elasmobranchs may be attributed to their sophisticated breeding mechanisms. Internal fertilization is universal. The pelvic claspers have a solid skeletal structure that may increase their copulatory effectiveness. During copulation (Figure 7–12a) a single clasper is bent at 90 degrees to the long axis of the body, and a dorsal groove present on each clasper comes to lie directly under the cloacal papilla from which sperm exit. The single flexed clasper is inserted into the female's cloaca and locked there by an assortment of barbs, hooks, and spines near the clasper's tip. Male sharks of small species secure themselves *in copulo* by wrapping around the female's body. Large sharks swim side by side, their bodies touching or enter copulation in a sedentary position with their heads on the substrate and their bodies angled upward (Tricas and LeFeuvre 1985). Some male sharks and skates bite the female's flanks or hold on to one of her pectoral fins with their jaws. In these species females may have skin on the back and flanks twice as thick as the skin of a male the same size. Whatever the position taken by the pair, when the single clasper is crossed to the contralateral side and securely inserted into the female cloaca, sperm from the genital tract are ejaculated into the clasper groove. Simultaneously, a muscular subcutaneous sac extending anteriorly beneath the skin of the male's pelvic fins contracts. This siphon sac has a secretory lining and is filled with seawater by the pumping activity of the male's pelvic fins before copulation. Seminal fluid from the siphon sac washes sperm down the groove into the female's cloaca, from which point the sperm swim up the female's reproductive tract.

With the evolution of internal fertilization elasmobranchs evolved a reproductive strategy favoring the production of a small number of offspring, retained, protected, and nourished for varying periods of time within the female's body. This requires a significant investment of her energy resources. The female has specialized structures at the anterior end of the oviducts, the nidimental glands, which secrete a proteinaceous shell around the fertilized egg. Most elasmobranch eggs are large (the

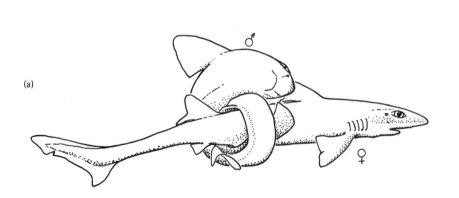
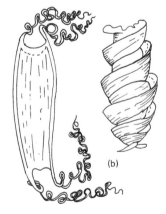

Figure 7–12 Reproduction by sharks. (a) Copulation in the European spotted catshark *Scyliorhinus*. Only a few other species of sharks and rays have been observed *in copulo*, but all assume postures so that one of the male's claspers can be inserted into the female's cloaca. (b) The egg cases of two oviparous sharks, *Scyliorhinus* (left) and *Heterodontus* (right). (Not to same scale.)

size of a chicken yolk or larger) and contain a very substantial store of nutritious yolk. Oviparous (*ovum* = egg, *pario* = to bring forth) elasmobranchs have large eggs enclosed in cases with openings for seawater exchange and protuberances which become tangled or wedged into protected sites of the substrate (Figure 7–12b). The zygote obtains nutrition exclusively from the yolk during the 6- to 10-month developmental period. Inorganic molecules including dissolved oxygen are taken from a flow of water through the shell openings induced by movements of the embryo. On hatching, the young are generally miniature replicas of the adults and seem to live much as they do when mature.

A significant step in the evolution of elasmobranch reproduction was prolonged retention of the fertilized eggs in the reproductive tract. Many species retain the developing young within the oviducts until they hatch and are able to lead an independent life, a pattern called **ovoviviparity**. Reduction in the nidimental gland's shell production and increased vascularization of the oviducts of the female and yolk sacs of the embryo are the only notable differences between oviparous and ovoviviparous forms. All nutrition comes from the yolk, and only inorganic ions and dissolved gases are exchanged between the maternal circulation and that of the developing young. This mode of reproduction is called **lecithotrophy** (*lecith* = egg, *troph* = nourishment). The eggs often hatch within the oviducts, and the young may spend as long in their mother after hatching as they did within the shell. As many as 100, but more often about a dozen, young are born at a time.

A natural step from the ovoviviparous condition is full viviparity or **matrotrophy** (*matro* = mother, *troph* = nourishment), the situation in which the nutritional supply is not limited to the yolk. Elasmobranchs have independently evolved matrotrophy several times. Some elasmobranchs develop long spaghettilike extensions of the oviduct walls that penetrate the mouth and gill openings of the internally hatched young and secrete a milky nutritive substance. Other species simply continue to ovulate, and the young that hatch in the oviducts feed on these eggs. The most common and most complex form of viviparity among sharks is the yolk sac placenta, whereby each embryo obtains nourishment from the maternal uterine bloodstream via the highly vascular yolk sac of the embryo. This mode of reproduction is called **placentotrophic viviparity** (*placenta* = a placenta).

No matter which of the various routes of nourishment have brought young elasmobranchs to their free-living size, once the eggs are laid or the young born there is no evidence of further parental investment in them through care, protection, or feeding. In fact, elasmobranchs have long been considered solitary and asocial, but this view is changing. Accumulating field observations, often from aerial surveys (Kenney et al. 1985) or by scuba divers in remote areas, indicate that elasmobranchs of many species may aggregate in great numbers periodically, perhaps annually. More than 60 giant basking sharks were observed milling together and occasionally circling in head-to-tail formations in an area off Cape Cod in summer, and an additional 40 individuals were nearby. Over 200 hammerhead sharks have been seen near the surface off the eastern shore of Virginia in successive summers. Divers on seamounts that reach to within 30 meters of the surface in the Gulf of California have observed enormous aggregations of hammerheads schooling in an organized manner around the seamount tip. Some observations include behavior thought to be related to courtship (Moss 1984). More than 1000 individuals of the blue shark (*Prionace glauca*) have been observed near the surface over canyons on the edge of the continental shelf off Ocean City, Maryland. Fishermen are all too familiar with the large schools of spiny dogfishes (genus *Squalus*) that seasonally move through shelf regions, ruining fishing by destroying gear, consuming bottom fishes and invertebrates, and displacing commercially valuable species. These dogfish schools are usually made up of individuals that are all the same size and the same sex. The distribution of schools is also peculiar: Female schools may be inshore and males offshore or male schools may all be north of some point and the females south.

A similar sort of geographic sex segregation by hammerhead shark schools has been suggested to be the result of differential feeding preferences in habitats with different biological productivities (Klimley 1987). Females feeding on richer grounds grow faster, thus being larger at sexual maturity than males and better able to support embryonic young successfully. Such arguments do not explain why males should choose to live in less productive habitats, thus growing more slowly. Our understanding of these phenomena is slim, but it is clear that not all elasmobranchs are solitary all the time.

Whatever the social behavior or the details of postcopulatory nutrition provided the embryo, sharks produce relatively few young during an individual female's lifetime. Although the young of sharks are relatively large compared with those of other fishes, they are subject to predation, especially from other sharks. Numerous species depend on protected nursery grounds—usually shallow inshore waters, which are the areas most subject to human disturbance and alteration. In addition, adult sharks are increasingly falling prey to humans. A rapid expansion in recreational and commercial shark fishing worldwide has threatened numerous species of these long-lived, slowly reproducing top predators. Internal fertilization and the life history characteristics that accompany it evolved in sharks fully 350 million years ago and have been a successful strategy throughout the world's oceans ever since. Now the alterations of habitat and heavy predation by humans threaten many species. The first U.S. shark fisheries management plan was established in 1993. Unfortunately, it applied only to national economic zone waters of the Eastern seaboard and the Gulf of Mexico. The success or failure of such efforts to sustain populations of elasmobranchs will not be clear for many years.

For the most part we have been examining the characteristics of pleurotremate elasmobranchs—the sharks with gill openings (*trem*) on the sides (*pleur*) of the head. These forms number about 360 extant species. Although similar in overall appearance, the pleurotremate sharks actually come from two lineages. The more ancestral in their general anatomy (especially the smaller size of their brain) are the 80 species of squaloid sharks and their numerous relatives, all grouped together as the Squalea. Squaloids include the spiny and green dogfish, the cookie-cutter shark, and the basking and megamouth sharks. These species usually live in cold, deep water. The other 280 or so species of sharks are almost all members of the galeoid or Galea lineage that includes the hornshark, the nurse and carpet sharks, the whale shark, the mackerel sharks (including the great white shark), the carcharhinid sharks, and the hammerhead sharks. Galeoid sharks are the dominant carnivores of shallow, warm, species-rich regions of the oceans.

Surprising to many is the fact that the hypotremate elasmobranchs—the skates and rays—are more diverse than are the sharks. Approximately 456 extant species of skates and rays are currently recognized (Figure 7–13). These fishes have a long history of phylogenetic isolation from the clades of extant sharks but appear to be derived from the squaloids and form the bulk of the species in the Squalea. The suite of specializations characteristic of skates and rays relates to their early assumption of a benthic, durophagous (*duro* = hard, *phagus* = to eat) habit. The teeth are almost universally hard, flat crowned plates that form a pavementlike dentition. The mouth is often highly and rapidly protrusible to provide powerful suction used to dislodge shelled invertebrates from the substrate.

Skates and rays are derivatives of the extant shark radiation adapted for benthic habitats. A handful of specialized shark species belonging to squatinoid lineage of the Squalea are bottom-living specialists which illustrate what an intermediate stage in the squaloid to skate and ray transition may have been like. In the skates and rays, radial cartilages extend to the tips of their pectoral fins, which are greatly enlarged. The anteriormost basal elements fuse with the chondrocranium in front of the eye and with one another in front of the rest of the head. Skates and rays swim by undulating these massively enlarged pectoral fins. The flexibility of the fins is complemented by a reduction in the number of placoid scales. The placoid scales so characteristic of the integument of a shark are absent from large areas of the bodies and pectoral fins of skates and rays. The few remaining denticles are often greatly enlarged to form sharp, stout bucklers along the dorsal midline. Many skates and rays rest on the seafloor and cover themselves with a thin layer of sand. They spend hours partially buried and nearly invisible except for the dorsally prominent eyes and spiracles through which they survey their surroundings or take in oxygenated respiratory water. More derived forms, such as stingrays (family Dasyatidae), have a very few greatly elongated and venomous modified placoid scales at the base of the tail. The most highly specialized rays (of the family Mobulidae) are derived from these entirely naked types but spend little of their time resting on the bottom. Using powerfully extended pectoral fins, these devilfishes or manta rays (up to 6 meters in width) swim through the open sea with flapping motions of the pectoral fins.

Skates and rays are primarily benthic invertebrate feeders (occasionally managing to capture small fishes), but the largest rays, like the largest sharks, are plankton strainers. The dentition of many benthic rays is sexually dimorphic. Different dentitions coupled with the generally larger size

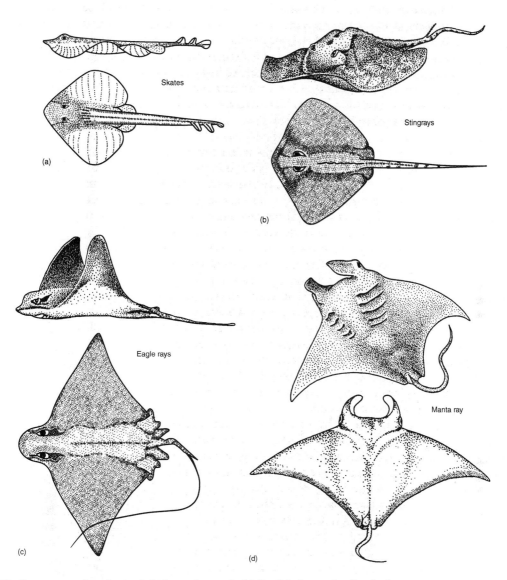

Figure 7–13 Some examples of extant skates and rays. (a, b) Benthic forms; (c, d) pelagic forms. (a) *Raja*, a typical skate, has an elongate but thick tail stalk containing electrogenic tissue and supporting two dorsal fins and a terminal caudal fin. Skates lay eggs enclosed in horny shells popularly called "mermaid's purses." (b) *Dasyatis*, a typical ray, has a whiplike tail stalk with fins represented by one or more enlarged, serrated, and venomous dorsal barbs. Rays bear living young; batoids display a reproductive diversity matching that of their shark kin. Pelagic batoids are closely related to the rays. (c) *Aetobatus* is representative of the eagle rays, wide-ranging shelled invertebrate predators. As befits their durophagus habit, they have batteries of broad, flat, crushing tooth plates. (d) *Manta* is representative of its family of gigantic sized fishes (up to 6 meters from wing tip to wing tip), which feed exclusively on zooplankton (Box 7–1). Extensions of the pectoral fins anterior to the eyes (the "horns" of these "devil rays") help funnel water into the mouth during filter feeding. (Modified in part from J. S. Nelson 1994; and P. B. Moyle, 1993, *Fish: An Enthusiasts Guide*, University of California Press, Berkeley, CA.)

of females might reduce competition for food resources between the sexes, but no difference in stomach contents has been found. Since the teeth of a male are used to hold or stimulate a female before and during copulation, sexual, not trophic selection may be at work. The stingray *Dasyatis sabina*, like numerous other skates and rays, was thought to have dimorphic dentition as a sexually invariant character. It has recently been demonstrated that the continually replacing teeth of males are only different from those of females during the breeding season (Kajiura and Tricas 1996). Sharp-cusped teeth benefit males' reproductive success but during most of the year blunt teeth better serve feeding functions.

Skates (family Rajidae) have specialized tissues in their long tails that are capable of emitting a weak electric discharge. Each species appears to have a unique pattern of discharge, and the discharges may identify conspecifics in the gloom of the seafloor. The electric rays and torpedo rays (family Torpedinidae) have modified gill muscles that produce electrical discharges of up to 200 volts used to stun prey.

■ A Second Radiation of Chondrichthyans: Holocephali

Most extant chondrichthyans are contained in the Elasmobranchii, but a small but fascinating portion are grouped as ratfishes or chimeras (Holocephali, Figure 7–14a). The approximately 30 extant forms of chimeras (none much over a meter in length) have a soft anatomy more similar to sharks and rays than to any other extant fishes (Didier 1995). They have long been grouped with elasmobranchs as Chondrichthyes because of these shared specializations but they have a bizarre suite of unique features. Generally found in water of deeper than 80 meters and thus not well known in the wild, the Holocephali move into shallow water to deposit their 10-centimeter horny shelled eggs from which hatch miniature chimeras. Several holocephalians have elaborate rostral extensions of unknown function (Figure 7–14a). From what is known, most species appear to feed on shrimp, gastropod mollusks, and sea urchins. Their locomotion is produced by lateral undulations of the body that throw the long tail into sinusoidal waves and by fluttering movements of the large, mobile pectorals. The solidly fused nip-ping and crushing tooth plates grow throughout life, adjusting their height to the wear they suffer. Of special interest are the armaments—a poison gland associated with the stout dorsal spine in some species, and macelike cephalic claspers of males.

There has long been little agreement about holocephalian ancestry. Two distinct fossil groups have been proposed as ancestors—ptyctodonts and iniopterygians. A group of peculiar placoderms, the ptyctodontids, is known from the mid-Devonian. Rarely exceeding 20 centimeters in length, they showed a reduction in the extent and number of head and thoracic shield plates. A short palato-quadrate bound to the cranium carried a single pair of large upper tooth plates that were opposed by a smaller mandibular pair. The gills were covered by a single operculum. Postcranial characters, such as fin spines, large paired appendages, claspers, and caudal development, are strongly reminiscent of extant holocephalans (Figures 7–3c and 7–14a). The first undoubted modern forms are of Jurassic age, and fossils proposed as earlier members of the chimaera lineage do not seem to link the ptyctodont placoderms to the extant forms. Ptyctodonts are more like extant holocephalians than they are like the truly ancestral holocephalians, which are in most cases rather sharklike (Janvier 1996).

Since the 1950s Rainer Zangerl and co-workers have described a group of bizarre and obviously specialized forms (Figure 7–14c). These Iniopterygia (*inion* = back of the neck, *pteron* = wings) have characteristics that convinced Zangerl they were evidence for a link between the earliest sharks and holocephalans. As in extant holocephalians, the palatoquadrate is fused to the cranium (autostylic suspension), but the teeth, unlike those of extant chimeras, are in replacement families like those of elasmobranchs. The earliest close relative of the modern holocephalans is now thought to be of Late Carboniferous age (Janvier 1996), too old to be descendent from the contemporaneous iniopterygians. Current thinking is that both iniopterygians and holocephalians arose from ancestral sharks following a somewhat parallel line of evolution. Now that a phylogenetic connection between holocephalans and ancestral-grade elasmobranchs seems clearly established, the ptyctodont placoderms and chimeras represent one of the most outstanding examples of convergent evolution in groups from different geologic eras.

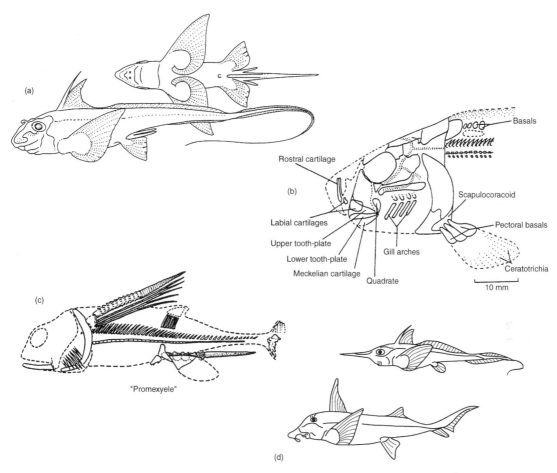

Figure 7–14 Chimeras. (a) Common chimera *Hydrolagus colliei*, an extant holocephalan, in lateral and ventral views (left) and (d) representatives of two other groups: plownose chimera (lower right) and longnose chimera (upper right). (Modified in part after H. B. Bigelow and W. C. Schroeder, 1953, *Fishes of the Western North Atlantic*, part 2, Sears Foundation for Marine Research, Yale University, New Haven, CT.) (b) *Ctenurella*, a Late Devonian ptyctodont placoderm claimed in the past to be related to chimeras; see also Figure 7–3c. (Modified after J. A. Moy–Thomas and R. S. Miles, 1971, *Paleozoic Fishes*, Saunders College Publishing, Philadelphia, PA.) (c) *Phomeryele*, a Carboniferous iniopterygian shark proposed by other paleontologists as a relative to the extant ratfishes. (Modified after P. H. Greenwood et al. 1973.)

■ Summary

A major evolutionary innovation of the vertebrates was the appearance in the Silurian of fishes with jaws and paired appendages that had internal musculature and skeletal supports. The first of these jawed fishes, the acanthodians (Chapter 8), were soon joined by the diverse but phylogenetically isolated placoderms. Remains of these first gnathostomes yield few clues to the origins of jaws and paired appendages. However, patterns of embryonic development indicate that jaws and their supports evolved from anterior skeletal elements related to the visceral arches The extant fauna includes descendants of these early jawed fishes: the Chondrichthyes, which include sharks, skates, rays, and chimeras. The evolution of chondrichthyans shows periods of relatively rapid changes in feeding and locomotor mechanisms followed by radiations and subsequent further morphological changes and reradiations, culminating in extant elasmobranchs and holocephalians.

From the array of adaptations present in extant chondrichthyans, it is not surprising that they have survived relatively unchanged since the Mesozoic. Perhaps the surprising fact is that they are not more diverse or found in a wider variety of habitats. To understand their limitations we must examine their competition—the bony fishes (Chapter 8).

■ References

Bond, C. E. 1996. *Biology of Fishes*, 2d edition. Saunders College Publishing, Philadelphia, PA.

Carroll, R. L. 1987. *Vertebrate Paleontology and Evolution*. Freeman, New York, NY.

Didier, D. A. 1995. Phylogenetic systematics of extant chimaeroid fishes (Holocephali, Chimaeroidei). *American Museum Novitates*, No. 3119.

Ferry, L. A. , and G. V. Lauder. 1996. Heterocercal tail function in leopard sharks: A three-dimensional kinematic analysis of two models. *Journal of Experimental Biology* 199:2253–2268.

Greenwood, P. H., R. S. Miles, and C. Patterson (editors). 1973. *Interrelationships of Fishes*. Academic, New York, NY.

Hodgson, E. S., and R. F. Mathewson (editors). 1978. *Sensory Biology of Sharks, Skates, and Rays*. Technical Information Division, Naval Research Laboratory, Washington, DC.

Janvier, P. 1996. *Early Vertebrates*. Clarendon Press, Oxford, UK.

Kajiura S. M. , and T. C. Tricas. 1996. Seasonal dynamics of dental sexual dimorphism in the Atlantic stingray *Dasyatis sabina*. *Journal of Experimental Biology* 199:2297–2306.

Kalmijn, A. J. 1974. The detection of electric fields from inanimate and animate sources other than electric organs. Pages 147–200 in *Handbook of Sensory Physiology*, volume 3, part 3, edited by A. Fessard. Springer, New York, NY.

Kalmijn, A. J. 1982. Electric and magnetic field detection in elasmobranch fishes. *Science* 218:916–918.

Kenney, R. D., R. E. Owen, and H. E. Winn. 1985. Shark distributions off the Northeast United States from marine mammal surveys. *Copeia* 1985:220–223.

Klimley, A. P. 1987. The determinants of sexual segregation in the scalloped hammerhead shark, *Sphyrna lewini*. *Environmental Biology of Fishes* 18:27–40.

Klimley, A. P. 1993. Highly directional swimming by scalloped hammerhead sharks, *Sphyrna lewini*, and subsurface irradiance, temperature, bathymetry, and geomagnetic field. *Marine Biology* 117:1–22.

Klimley, A. P. 1994. The predatory behavior of the white shark. *American Scientist* 82:122–133.

Klimley, A. P., and D. G. Ainley. 1996. *Great White Sharks: the biology of* Caraharodon carcharias. Academic, San Diego, CA.

Litman, G. W. 1996. The origins of vertebrate immunity. *Scientific American* 275(5):67–71.

Maisey, J. G. 1996. *Discovering Fossil Fishes*. Henry Holt, New York, NY.

Martin, A. P., G. J. P. Naylor, and S. R. Palumbi. 1992. Rates of mitochondrial DNA evolution in sharks are slow compared with mammals. *Nature* 357:153–155.

Moss, S. A. 1984. *Sharks: An Introduction for the Amateur Naturalist*. Prentice Hall, Englewood Cliffs, NJ.

Moyle, P. B., and J. J. Cech, Jr. 1996. *Fishes: An Introduction to Ichthyology*. Prentice Hall, Upper Saddle River, NJ.

Nelson, J. S. 1994. *Fishes of the World*, 3d edition. Wiley, New York, NY.

Romer, A. S. 1962. *The Vertebrate Body*, 3d edition. Saunders College Publishing, Philadelphia, PA.

Schmidt, E. M., and G. V. Lauder. 1995. Kinematics of locomotion in sturgeon: do heterocercal tails function similarly? *American Zoologist* 35(5):62A, Abstract No. 250.

Stiassny, M. L., L. R. Parenti, and G. D. Johnson (editors). 1996. *Interrelationships of Fishes*. Academic, San Diego, CA.

Sweet, W. J. A. J., R. Nieuwenhuys, and B. L. Roberts. 1983. *The Central Nervous System of Cartilaginous Fishes*. Springer, New York, NY.

Tricas, T. C., and E. M. LeFeuvre. 1985. Mating in the reef white-tip shark *Triaenodon obesus*. *Marine Biology* 84:233–237.

Webb, P. W., and R. Smith. 1980. Function of the caudal fin in early fishes. *Copeia* 1980:559–562.

Young, G. C. 1997. Ordovician microvertebrate remains from the Amadeus Basin, Central Australia. *Journal of Vertebrate Paleontology* 17:1–25.

CHAPTER
8

Dominating Life in Water: Teleostomes and the Major Radiation of Fishes

B y the end of the Silurian the agnathous fishes (Chapter 6) had diversified and the cartilaginous gnathostomes (Chapter 7) were in the midst of their first radiation. The stage was set for the appearance of the largest extant group of vertebrates, the bony fishes. The first fossils of bony fishes (Osteichthyes) occur in the Late Silurian. Osteichthyans are well represented from the Early Devonian and their radiation was in full bloom by the middle of the Devonian with two major groups diverging: the ray-finned fishes (Actinopterygii) and lobe-finned fishes (Sarcopterygii). Specialization of feeding mechanisms is one of the key features of the evolution of these major groups of vertebrates. An increasing flexibility among the bones of the skull and jaws allowed the ray-finned fishes in particular to exploit a wide range of prey types and predatory modes. Specializations of locomotion, habitat, behavior, and life histories have accompanied the specializations of feeding mechanisms, and the body forms, behaviors, mechanical functions, and physiology of bony fishes are intimately related to the characteristics of the aquatic habitat and to the properties of water as an environment for life.

■ Living in Water

Seventy-three percent of the surface of the Earth is covered by fresh or salt water. Most of this water is held in the great ocean basins, which are populated everywhere by vertebrates, especially by the bony fishes. The freshwater lakes and rivers of the planet hold a negligible percentage of all the water on earth—about 0.01 percent. This is much less than that tied up in the atmosphere, ice, and groundwater, but it is exceedingly rich biologically. Rivers and lakes are complex habitats with short histories on a geological time scale. Nevertheless, Earth's lakes and rivers have individual life spans long enough for evolutionary processes to occur within their iso-

lated shores. Nearly 40 percent of all bony fishes, the largest taxon of vertebrates, live in fresh waters.

Although each major clade of fishes solved environmental challenges in somewhat different ways, an examination of the specializations of the bony fishes for life in water illustrates one of their keys to evolutionary success—versatility. High rates of energy use, which are required to sustain the high activity levels characteristic of many fishes, depend on efficient gas exchange across the gills. Most fishes swim with undulatory contractions of the body muscles. Guidance is usually visual, but other senses include the inner ear and lateral line (for detection of low-frequency pressure waves) and electroreception. In this chapter we describe several basic specializations that have allowed fishes to become active and successful aquatic vertebrates. Many of the structures and functions of fishes set the stage for the possibility of life on land.

Obtaining Oxygen in Water: Gills

Most aquatic vertebrates possess gills, evaginations from the body surface where respiratory gases are exchanged. Fish gills are enclosed in pharyngeal pockets (Figure 8–1). The flow of water is usually unidirectional—in through the mouth and out beneath the gill covers (operculae). Buccal flaps just inside the mouth and flaps at the margins of the operculae act as valves to prevent back flow. The respiratory surfaces of the gills are delicate projections from the lateral side of each gill arch (Figure 8–1b). Two columns of gill filaments extend from

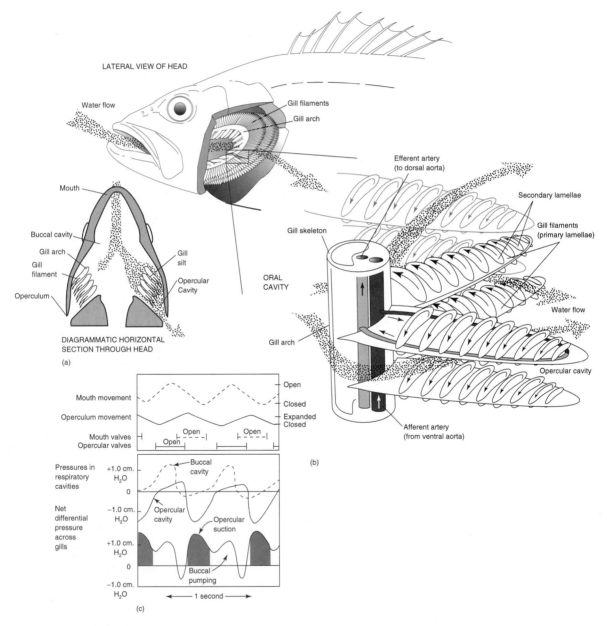

Figure 8–1   Anatomy and functional morphology of teleost gills. (a) Position of gills in head and general flow of water; (b) water flow (shaded arrows) and blood flow (solid arrows) patterns through the gills; (c) water pressure changes across the gills during various phases of ventilation. (Modified after G. M. Hughes, 1963, *Comparative Physiology of Vertebrate Respiration,* Harvard University Press, Cambridge, MA.)

each gill arch. The tips of the filaments from adjacent arches meet when the filaments are extended. As water leaves the buccal cavity it must pass over the filaments. Gas exchange takes place across numerous microscopic projections from the filaments, the secondary lamellae (Laurent and Dunel 1980).

The pumping action of the mouth and opercular cavities creates a positive pressure across the gills so that the respiratory current is only slightly interrupted during each pumping cycle (Figure 8–1c). The riverine filter-feeding paddlefishes (Bemis et al. in Birstein et al. 1997) and numerous pelagic fishes, such as mackerel, certain sharks, tunas, and swordfishes, have reduced or even lost the ability to pump water across the gills. A respiratory current is created by swimming with the mouth slightly opened, a method known as **ram ventilation**, and the fishes must perpetually swim. A great many other fishes switch to ram ventilation when they are swimming and rely on buccal pumping when they are at rest.

The vascular arrangement in the teleost gill maximizes oxygen exchange. Each gill filament has two arteries—an afferent vessel running from the gill arch to filament tip and an efferent vessel returning blood to the arch (Farrell 1980). Each secondary lamella is a blood space connecting the afferent and efferent vessels (Figure 8–2a). The direction of blood flow through the lamellae is opposite to the direction of flow of water across the gill. This structural arrangement, known as a countercurrent exchanger, assures that as much oxygen as possible diffuses into the blood (Figure 8–2b). Pelagic fishes such as tunas, which sustain activity over extended periods of time, have skeletal tissue reinforcement of gill filaments, large gill-exchange areas, and a high oxygen-carrying capacity per milliliter of blood compared with sluggish benthic fishes, such as toadfishes and flatfishes (Table 8.1).

Terrestrial vertebrates seldom encounter low oxygen concentrations, for air contains 20.9 percent oxygen by volume. In aquatic habitats the amount of oxygen dissolved in water is much less than that present in a similar volume of air (a liter of air contains 209 milliliters of oxygen, whereas a liter of fresh water may typically contain only 10 milliliters of oxygen). Increasing temperature reduces the solubility of oxygen in water. High temperatures and

Figure 8–2 Countercurrent exchange in the gills of actinopterygian fishes. (a) The direction of water flow across the gill opposes the flow of blood through the secondary lamellae. Blood cells are separated from oxygen-rich water by the thin walls of the gill epithelium and the capillary wall (cross section of secondary lamella). (b) This results in a higher oxygen-loading tension in the blood and lower oxygen tension in the water leaving the gills. (c) If water and blood flowed in the same direction over and within the secondary lamellae, an overall lower oxygen tension would occur in the blood leaving the gills. (d) Relative oxygen content of blood in secondary lamellae and the water passing over them. (Modified after G. M. Hughes, 1963, *Comparative Physiology of Vertebrate Respiration,* Harvard University Press, Cambridge, MA; M. Hildebrand, 1988, *Analysis of Vertebrate Structure,* 3d edition, Wiley, New York, NY; and P. B. Moyle, 1993, *Fish: An Enthusiast's Guide,* University of California Press, Berkeley, CA.)

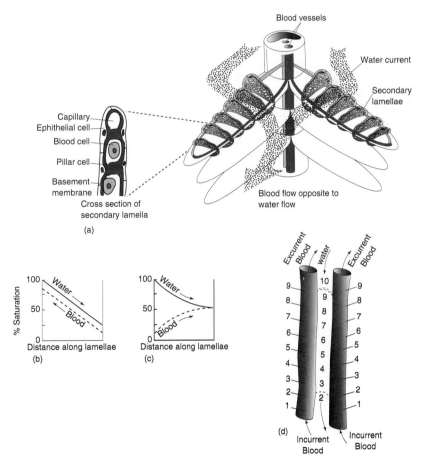

			No. Secondary		
		Oxygen	Gill Lamellae	Gill Area	Oxygen Capacity
		Consumption	mm⁻¹ of Primary	(mm²/g	(mL O₂/100 mL
Activity Level	Species of Fish	(mL O₂/g h⁻¹)	Gill Lamella	body mass)	blood)
High	Mackerel* (Scomber)	0.73	31	1160	14.8
Intermediate	Porgy (Stenotomus)	0.17	26	506	7.3
Sluggish	Toadfish† (Opsanus)	0.11	11	197	6.2

TABLE 8.1 The relation among general level of activity, rate of oxygen consumption, respiratory structures, and blood characteristics in fishes of three activity levels

*Modified carangiform swimmers; swim continuously.
†Benthic fish.

the metabolism of microorganisms can produce anoxic (without oxygen) conditions.

Although the vast majority of fishes depend on gills to extract dissolved oxygen from water and to vent carbon dioxide, many fishes that live in low oxygen conditions cannot obtain enough oxygen via gills and have accessory respiratory structures that enable them to breathe air. In the Amazon basin where seasonal or even diurnal oxygen levels may vary dramatically, at least nine families of fishes have air-breathing representatives (Val and Alemeida-Val 1995, Graham 1997). The morphological adaptations for air breathing in these Amazon fishes vary from enlarged lips, diverticulated and vascularized oral linings, all manner of lunglike vascularized swim bladders, to seasonally nondigestive but highly vascularized stomachs or even intestines. The electric eel, in addition to gills, has an extensive series of highly vascularized papillae in the pharyngeal region. The eels rise to the surface to gulp air, which diffuses across the papillae into the blood. Other fishes swallow air and extract oxygen through vascularized regions of the gut. The anabantid fishes of tropical Asia (e.g., the bettas and gouramies you see in pet stores) have vascularized chambers in the rear of the head, called labyrinths, which act in a similar manner. Many fishes are facultative air breathers; that is, oxygen uptake switches from gills to accessory organs when oxygen in the surrounding water becomes low. Others, like the electric eel and the anabantids, are obligatory air breathers. The gills alone cannot meet the respiratory needs of the fish even if the surrounding water is saturated with oxygen. These fishes drown if they cannot reach the surface to breathe air.

South American and African lungfish are obligate air breathers. Lungs are derived evaginations of the gut, and similar structures and responses can be found in the most primitive living ray-finned fishes, the polypterids. Air breathing is an ancestral characteristic of all osteichthyans, perhaps extending back to the Early Devonian acanthodians. The Early Devonian freshwater fishes probably encountered stresses like those faced by tropical freshwater fishes today, and the role of the air bladder in supplying oxygenated blood to the heart was discussed in Chapter 3. Early lungs may also have served as floats to produce a more nearly neutral density, as does the homologous swim bladder of teleosts.

Locomotion in Water

Fish swimming results from anterior to posterior sequential contractions of the muscle segments along one side of the body and simultaneous relaxation of those of the opposite side. Thus, a portion of the body momentarily bends and the bend is propagated posteriorly, and a fish oscillates from side to side as it swims. These lateral undulations are most visible in elongate fishes, such as lampreys and eels (Figure 8–3). Most of the power for swimming comes from muscles in the posterior region of the fish (Rome et al. 1993).

In 1926, Charles Breder classified the undulatory motions of fishes into three types: anguilliform—typical of highly flexible fishes capable of bending

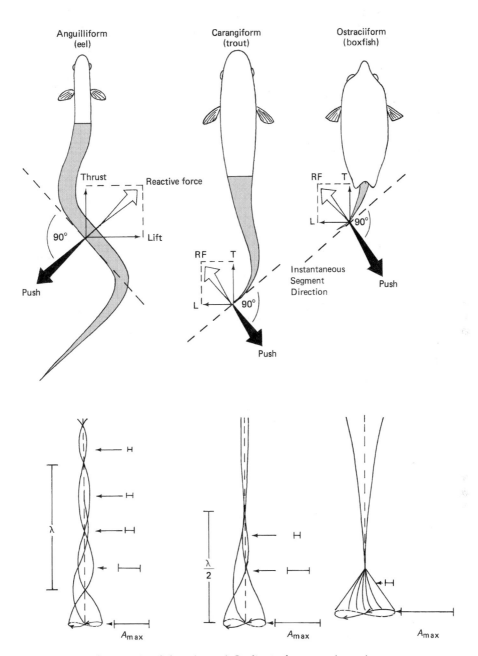

Figure 8–3 Basic movements of swimming fishes. (upper) Outlines of some major swimming types showing regions of body that undulate (shaded). Note that the lift component of the reactive force producea by one undulation's push on the water is canceled by that of the next, oppositely directed undulation. The thrust from each undulation is in the same direction and thus is additive; (lower) diagranunatic waveforms created by undulatlons of points along the body and tail. A_{max} represents the maximum lateral displacement of any point. Note that A_{max} increases posteriorly; λ is the wavelength of the undulatory wave. Ostraciiform swimming, as initially defined by C. M. Breder, refers to a limited number of very specialized fishes, like box fishes and trunk fishes. A variety of fishes swim by propulsion from various fins rather than the body (see Figure 8–6).

into more than half a sinusoidal wavelength; carangiform—undulations limited mostly to the caudal region, the body bending into less than half a wavelength; and ostraciiform—the body is inflexible, undulation is limited to the caudal fin (Figures 8–3 and 8–6). These basic categories, named for groups of fishes that exemplify the different forms of locomotion, have been extensively subdivided and redefined since 1926 (Lindsey 1978, Webb 1984, Webb and Blake 1985) but are still useful for understanding locomotion in water and are central to the most modern studies of fish locomotion (Lauder and Long 1996).

Overcoming Gravity: The Generation of Vertical Lift
Many specializations of body form, surface structure, fins, and muscle arrangement increase the efficiency of the different modes of swimming. A swimming fish must overcome the effect of gravity by producing lift and the drag of water by producing thrust (Figure 8–4).

Because the average tissue density of fishes exceeds that of water, they sink unless their total density is reduced by a flotation device or vertical lift is created by swimming. Sharks and some specialized pelagic bony fishes, such as the scombroids (tunas, mackerels, and swordfishes) are negatively buoyant (i.e., weigh more than an equal volume of water). These fishes must swim constantly to overcome gravity. In some cases lift is accomplished by extending large, winglike pectoral fins at a positive angle of attack to the water. Many bony fishes, however, are neutrally buoyant (i.e., have the same density as water) and maintain position without body undulations. Only the pectoral fins backpaddle to counter a forward thrust produced by water ejected from the gills. Neutral buoyancy results from an internal float—a gas-filled swim bladder lying below the spinal column (Figure 8–5a). Fishes that are capable of hovering in the water usually have well-developed swim bladders.

The swim bladder is located dorsal to the peritoneal cavity and ventral to the vertebral column. It is a gas-filled sac that arises as an evagination from the embryonic gut. The bladder occupies about 5 percent of the body volume of marine teleosts, and 7 percent of the volume of freshwater teleosts. The difference in volume corresponds to the difference in density of salt water and fresh water. The swim bladder wall, which is composed of interwoven collagen fibers, is virtually impermeable to gas diffusion. A teleost with a well-developed swim bladder neither rises nor sinks, and needs to expend little energy to maintain its vertical position in the water column.

As a fish swims vertically up or down through the water column, its body is subjected to changing pressures from the weight of the overlying water column. Increased pressure at depth tends to compress the swim bladder, whereas decreased pressure toward the surface allows the bladder to expand. In either case neutral buoyancy is lost. A

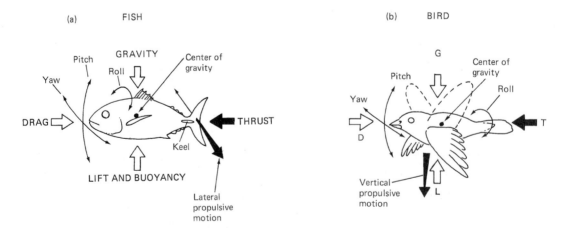

Figure 8–4 Comparison of forces associated with locomotion for a swimming and a flying vertebrate. (a) Motion of the caudal fin produces a lateral movement far from the center of gravity. The reactive force of the water to this movement causes the head to yaw in the same direction as the tail. (b) In a bird the major propulsive stroke of the wings is downward. Since both the propulsive stroke and the reactive force (lift) act near the center of gravity, the bird does not pitch.

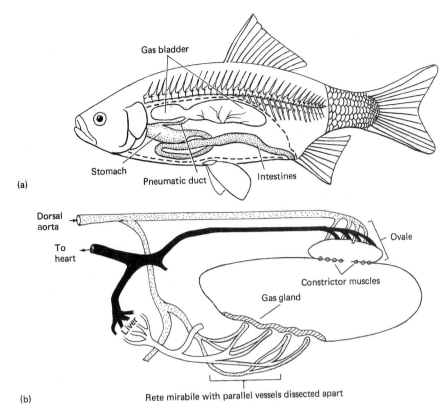

Figure 8–5 Swim bladder of actinopterygians. (a) The swim bladder is dorsal in the coelomic cavity just beneath the veitebral column; (b) vascular connections of a physoclistous swim bladder.

mechanism is needed to maintain constant volume if the bladder is to act as a neutral buoyancy float. This is accomplished by moving gas into the bladder when a fish swims downward, and removing gas when it swims tip. Plesiomorphic teleosts, such as bony tongues, eels, herrings, anchovies, salmons, and the minnows, and their kin, retain a connection, the pneumatic duct, between gut and swim bladder (Figure 8–5). These fishes, referred to as physostomes (*phys* = bladder, *stom* = mouth), can gulp air at the surface to fill the bladder, and can burp gas out to reduce the volume of the swim bladder. (Many physostomes also use the bladder as a lung. The pneumatic duct serves the same purpose as the windpipe or trachea of terrestrial vertebrates.)

The pneumatic duct is absent in adult teleosts from more derived clades, a condition termed physoclistic (*clist* = closed). Physoclists regulate the volume of the swim bladder by secreting gas into the bladder. Both physostomes and physoclists have a gas gland, which is located in the anterior ventral floor of the swim bladder (Figure 8–5b). Underlying the gas gland is a highly vascular rete mirabile. This structure moves gas (especially oxygen) from blood to gas bladder, and is remarkably effective. Gas secretion occurs in many deep-sea fishes despite the enormous gas pressure within the bladder that is the result of bladder inflation against the surrounding water pressure.

The gas gland releases lactic acid, which acidifies the blood in the rete mirabile. Acidification causes hemoglobin to release oxygen into solution (the Bohr effect). Because of the anatomical relations of the rete mirabile, which folds back upon itself in a countercurrent multiplier arrangement (Figure 8–5b), oxygen released from the hemoglobin accumulates and is retained within the rete mirabile until its pressure exceeds the oxygen pressure within the swim bladder. When this occurs, oxygen diffuses into the bladder, increasing its volume. The maximum multiplication of gas pressure that can be achieved is proportional to the length of the capillaries of the rete mirabile, and deep-sea fishes thus have very long rete.

To compensate for gas expansion during ascent, physoclists open a muscular valve, called the ovale, located dorsally in the posterior region of the bladder adjacent to a capillary bed. The high internal pressure of gases in the bladder (especially oxygen) causes them to diffuse into the blood of this capillary bed when the ovale sphincter is opened.

Many deep-sea fishes have oily deposits of low density in the gas bladder, or have reduced or lost the gas bladder entirely and have lipids distributed in rich deposits throughout the body. These lipids provide static lift, as do the oils in shark livers. Because a smaller volume of the bladder contains gas, the amount of secretion required for a given vertical descent is less. Nevertheless, a long rete mirabile is needed to secrete oxygen at high pressures, and the gas gland in deep-sea fishes is very large. Mesopelagic fishes, such as lanternfishes, which migrate large vertical distances depend more on lipids such as wax esters than on gas for buoyancy. Their close relatives that do not undertake such extensive vertical movements depend more on swim bladders for buoyancy. (For additional details, see Bone and Marshall [1982].)

Overcoming Drag: The Generation of Thrust   In general, fishes swim forward by pushing backward on the water. For every *active* force there is an opposite *reactive* force (Newton's third law of motion). Undulations produce an active force directed backward, and also a lateral force. The overall reactive force is directed forward and at an angle to the side.

Anguilliform and carangiform swimmers increase speed by increasing the frequency of their body undulations. Increasing the frequency of body undulations applies more power (force per unit time) to the water. Different fishes achieve very different maximum speeds—some (e.g., eels) are slow and others (e.g., tunas) are very fast.

An eel's long body limits speed because it induces drag from the friction of water on the elongate surface of the fish. Fishes that swim rapidly are proportionately shorter and less flexible. Force from the contraction of anterior muscle segments is transferred through ligaments to the caudal peduncle and the tail. Morphological specializations of this swimming mode reach their zenith in fishes like tunas, where the caudal peduncle is slender and the tail greatly expanded vertically (Magnuson 1978).

Other fishes seldom flex the body to swim, but undulate the median fins (referred to as amiiform, gymnotiform, or balistiform swimming). Usually, several complete waves are observed along the fin (Figure 8–6), and very fine adjustment in the direction of motion can be produced. Many fishes (for example, ratfishes, surf perches, and many coral reef fishes, such as surgeonfishes, wrasses, and parrot fishes) generally do not oscillate the body or median fins, but row the pectoral fins to produce movement (labriform swimming).

Improving Thrust: Minimizing Drag   A swimming fish experiences drag of two forms: viscous drag from friction between the fish's body and the water, and inertial drag from pressure differences created by the fish's displacement of water. Viscous drag is relatively constant over a range of speeds, but inertial drag is low at slow speeds and increases rapidly with increasing speed. Viscous drag is affected by surface smoothness, whereas inertial drag is influenced by body shape. Streamlined (teardrop) shapes produce minimum inertial drag when their maximum width is about one-fourth of their length and is placed about one-third of the length from the leading tip (Figure 8–7). The shape of many rapidly swimming vertebrates closely approximates these dimensions. A thin body has high viscous drag because it has a large surface area relative to its muscle mass, and a thick body induces high inertial drag because it displaces a large volume of water as it moves forward. Usually, fast-swimming fishes have small scales or are scaleless, with smooth body contours lowering viscous drag. (Of course, many slow-swimming fishes also are scaleless, which shows that universal generalizations are difficult to make.) Mucus also contributes to the reduction of viscous drag.

Swimming movements in which only the caudal peduncle and caudal fin undulate are usually called modified carangiform motion. Scombroids and many pelagic sharks have a caudal peduncle that is narrow dorsoventrally but is relatively wide from side to side. The peduncle of carangids is often studded laterally with bony plates called scutes. These structures present a knife-edge profile to the water as the peduncle undulates from side to side and contribute to the reduction of drag on the laterally sweeping peduncle. The importance of these seemingly minor morphological changes is underscored by the tail stalk of whales and porpoises, which is also narrow and has a double knife-edge profile. But the tail stalk of cetaceans is narrow laterally, whereas the caudal peduncle of scombroid fishes is narrow vertically. The difference reflects the plane of undulation—dorsoventrally for cetaceans and laterally for fishes. These strikingly similar specializa-

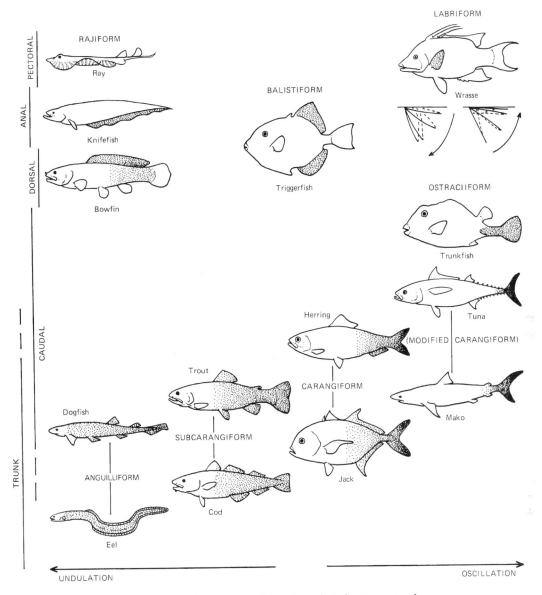

Figure 8–6 Location of swimming movements in various fishes. Stipple indicates areas of body undulated or moved in swimming. The names, such as carangiform, are used to describe the major types of locomotion found in fishes and are not a phylogenetic identification of all fishes using a given mode. (Modified after C. C. Lindsey 1978.)

tions of modified carangiform swimmers—whether shark, scombroid, or cetacean—produce convergently evolved efficient conversion of muscle contractions into forward motion.

The tail creates turbulent vortices of swirling water in a fish's wake, which may be a source of inertial drag, or the vortices may be modified to produce beneficial thrust (Stix 1994, Triantafyllou and Triantafyllou 1995). The total drag created by the caudal fin depends on its shape. When the

aspect ratio of the fin (dorsal-to-ventral length divided by the anterior-to-posterior width) is large, the amount of thrust produced relative to drag is high. The stiff sickle-shaped fin of scombroids (mackerels, tunas) and of certain sharks (mako, great white) results in a high aspect ratio and efficient forward motion. Even the cross section of the forks of these caudal fins assumes a streamlined teardrop shape, which further reduces drag. Many forms with these specializations swim continu-

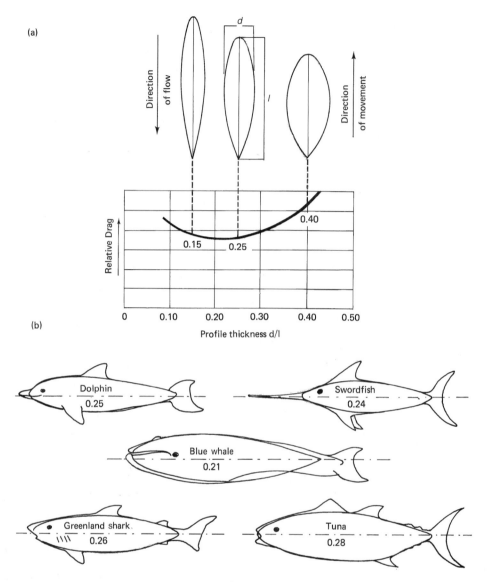

Figure 8–7 Effect of body shape on drag. (a) Streamlined profiles with width (*d*) equal to approximately one-fourth of length (*l*) minimize drag. The examples are for solid, smooth test objects with thickest section about two-fifths of the distance from the tip. (b) Width-to-length ratios (*d/l*) for several swimming vertebrates. Like the test objects these vertebrates tend to be circular in cross section. Note that the ratio is near 0.25 and that the general body shape approximates a fusiform shape. (Modified after H. Hertel, 1966, *Structure, Form, Movement*. Krausskopf, Mainz, Germany.)

ously. But high-aspect-ratio fins do not present enough area to the water to power a quick start from a resting position.

The caudal fins of trout, minnows, and perches are not stiff and seldom have high aspect ratios. These subcarangiform swimmers change caudal fin area and regional stiffness to modify propulsive thrust and to produce vertical movements of the posterior part of the body. The latter action is achieved when the fish is at rest by propagating an undulatory wave up or down the flexible caudal fin (Figure 8–6). In these subcarangiforms propulsion often proceeds in bursts, usually from a standstill with rapid acceleration initiated by special neural systems, the Mauthner cells. The caudal peduncle of these fishes, unlike that of modified carangiform swimmers, is laterally compressed and deep. Under these circumstances the peduncle contributes a substantial part of the total force of propulsion.

Our understanding of these varied adaptations is the result of extensive study of vertebrate swimming (especially that of bony fishes) over the past several decades. Nevertheless, it is still not well understood how the extraordinary propulsion efficiencies, accelerations, and maneuverability of fishes are achieved. Fluid mechanics engineers and naval architects remain unable to design vehicles that perform nearly as well (Triantafyllou and Triantafyllou 1995). New visualization and recording methods and computer-assisted data analysis are beginning to bring much new information to light (Lauder and Long 1996).

■ Water and the Sensory World of Fishes

Water possesses properties that strongly influence the behaviors of fishes and other aquatic vertebrates. Light is absorbed by water molecules and scattered by suspended particles. Objects become invisible at a distance of a few hundred meters even in the very clearest water, whereas distance vision is virtually unlimited in clean air.

Fishes generally possess well-developed eyes. A major difference between aerial and aquatic vision relates to focusing light rays on the retina to produce a sharp image. Air, by definition, has an index of refraction of 1.00. The cornea in the eye of both terrestrial and aquatic vertebrates has an index of refraction of about 1.37, which is only slightly greater than the index of refraction of water (1.33). Light rays are bent as they pass through a boundary between media with different refractive indices. The amount of bending is proportional to the difference in indices of refraction. Because the index of refraction of the cornea is substantially different from that of air, light rays are bent as they pass from air into the cornea, and the cornea is an important part of the focusing system of the eyes of terrestrial vertebrates. This relationship does not hold true in water because the refractive index of the cornea is too close to that of water to have much effect in focusing light. Terrestrial vertebrates rely on the lens, which often is flattened and pliable, for detailed focus. Fishes possess a less pliable spherical lens with high refractive power. The entire lens is moved toward or away from the retina to focus images. A similar spherical lens has

evolved in aquatic mammals, such as cetaceans. Otherwise, a fish's eye is similar to the eye of a terrestrial vertebrate.

Fishes have taste bud organs in the mouth and around the head and anterior fins. In addition, receptors of general chemical sense detect substances that are only slightly soluble in water, and olfactory organs on the snout detect soluble substances. Sharks and salmon are capable of detecting odoriferous compounds at less than 1 part per billion. Homeward migrating salmon are directed to their stream of origin from astonishing distances by a chemical signature from the home stream permanently imprinted when they were juveniles. Plugging the nasal olfactory organs destroys their ability to home (Cromie 1982).

Mechanical receptors provide the basis for detection of displacement—touch, sound, pressure, and motion. Like all vertebrates, fishes possess an internal ear (the labyrinth organ, not to be confused with the organ of the same name that assists in respiration in some fishes), including the semicircular canals, which inform the animal of changes in speed and direction of motion. They also have gravity detectors at the base of the semicircular canals that allow them to distinguish up from down. Most vertebrates also have an auditory region of the inner ear sensitive to sound pressure waves (Tavolga et al. 1981). These diverse functions of the labyrinth depend on basically similar types of sense cells, the hair cells (Figure 8–8). In fishes and aquatic amphibians clusters of hair cells and associated support cells form neuromast organs that are dispersed over the surface of the head and body. In jawed fishes neuromast organs are often located in a series of canals on the head, and one or more canals pass along the sides of the body onto the tail. This unique surface receptor system of fishes and aquatic amphibians is referred to as the lateral-line system.

Detection of Water Displacement: The Lateral Line

Neuromasts of the lateral-line system are distributed in two configurations—within tubular canals or exposed in epidermal depressions. Many kinds of fishes have both. Hair cells have a kinocilium placed asymmetrically in a cluster of microvilli. Hair cells are arranged in pairs with the kinocilia positioned on opposite sides of adjacent cells. A neuromast contains many such hair cell pairs. Each neuromast

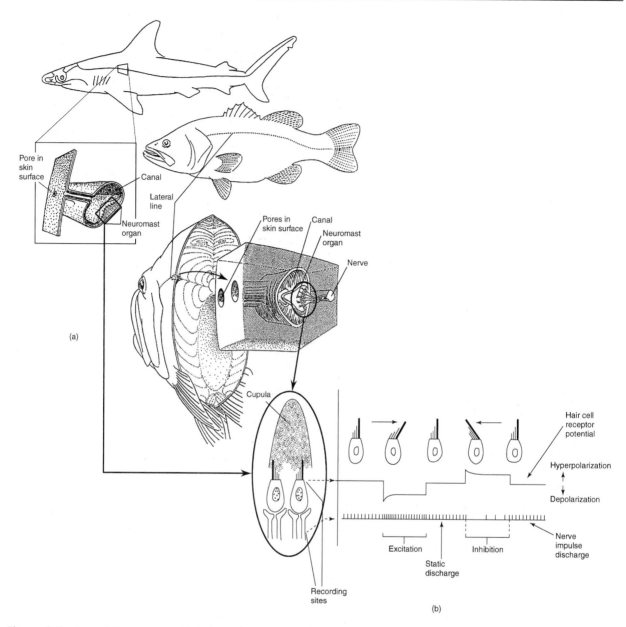

Figure 8–8 Lateral line systems. (a) Semidiagrammatic representations of the two configurations of lateral line organs in fishes. (b) Hair cell deformations and their effect on hair cell transmembrane potential (receptor potential) and afferent nerve cell discharge rates. Kinocilium indicated in bold. (Modified after A. Flock, 1967, in *Lateral Line Detectors,* edited by P. Cahn, Indiana University Press, Bloomington, IN; and R. F. Hueter and P. W. Gilbert in S. H. Gruber, editor, 1991, *Underwater Naturalist,* Special Double Issue, 19[4] and 20[1]: 48–55.)

is innervated by two afferent nerves: One transmits impulses from hair cells with kinocilia in one orientation, and the other carries impulses from cells with kinocilia positions reversed by 180 degrees.

All kinocilia and microvilli are embedded in a gelatinous structure, the cupula. Displacement of the cupula causes the kinocilia to bend. The resul-

tant deformation either excites or inhibits the neuromast's nerve discharge. Each hair cell pair, therefore, encodes unambiguously the direction of cupula displacement. The excitatory output of each pair has a maximum sensitivity to displacement along the line joining the kinocilia and falling off in other directions. The net effect of cupula displacement is to increase the firing rate in one afferent nerve and to decrease it in the other nerve. These changes in lateral-line nerve-firing rates thus inform a fish of the direction of water currents on different surfaces of its body.

Water currents of only 0.025 millimeter per second are detected by the exposed neuromasts of the aquatic frog, *Xenopus laevis*, with maximum response to currents of two or three millimeters per second. Similar responses occur in fishes. The lateral-line organs also respond to low-frequency sound, but controversy exists as to whether sound is a natural lateral-line stimulus. Sound induces traveling pressure waves in the water and also causes local water displacement as the pressure wave passes. It has been difficult to be sure whether neuromast output results from the accompanying water motions on the body surface or the sound's compression wave.

Several surface-feeding fishes and *Xenopus* provide vivid examples of how the lateral-line organs act under natural conditions. These species find insects on the water surface by detecting surface waves created by the prey's movements. In a series of clever experiments, E. Schwartz (see Fessard 1974) demonstrated that each neuromast group on the head of the killifish, *Aplocheilus lineatus*, provides information about surface waves coming from a different direction (Figure 8–9). All groups, however, show stimulus field overlaps. Bilateral interactions between neuromast groups are indicated by the fact that extirpation of an organ from one side of the head disturbs the directional response to stimuli arriving from several directions.

The large numbers of neuromasts on the heads of some fishes might be important for sensing vortex trails in the wake of adjacent fishes in a school. Many of the fishes that form extremely dense schools lack lateral-line organs along the flanks (herrings, atherinids, mullets, and so on) and retain only the cephalic canal organs. Their well-developed cephalic canal organs concentrate sensitivity to water motion in the head region, where it is needed to sense the degree of turbulence into which the fish is swimming, and the reduction of flank lateral-line elements would reduce the constant noise from turbulence beside the fish. Over periods of time the reduction in drag through avoidance of turbulence could achieve a considerable metabolic saving economy, as well as an even spacing between school members (Lindsey 1978).

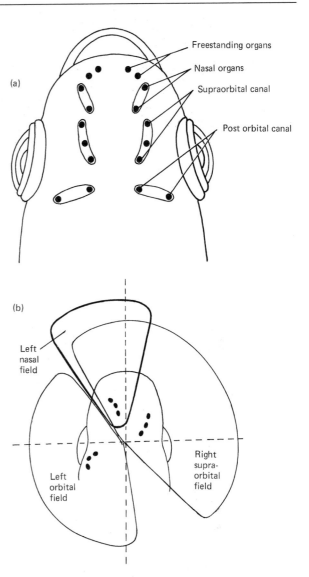

Figure 8–9   Distribution of the lateral line canal organs. (a) On the dorsal surface of the head of the killifish *Fundulus notatus,* and (b) the perceptual fields of the head canal organs in another killifish, *Aplocheilus lineatus.* The wedge-shaped areas indicate the relative directional sensitivity for each group of canal organs. Note that fields overlap on opposite sides as well as on the same side of the body. (Modified after E. Schwartz, 1974, in *Handbook of Sensory Physiology,* volume 3, part 3, edited by A. Fessard, Springer, New York, NY.)

Electric Discharge and Electroreception

The torpedo ray in the Mediterranean, the electric catfish in the Nile, and the electric eel of South America can discharge enough electricity to stun other animals. The source of the electric current is

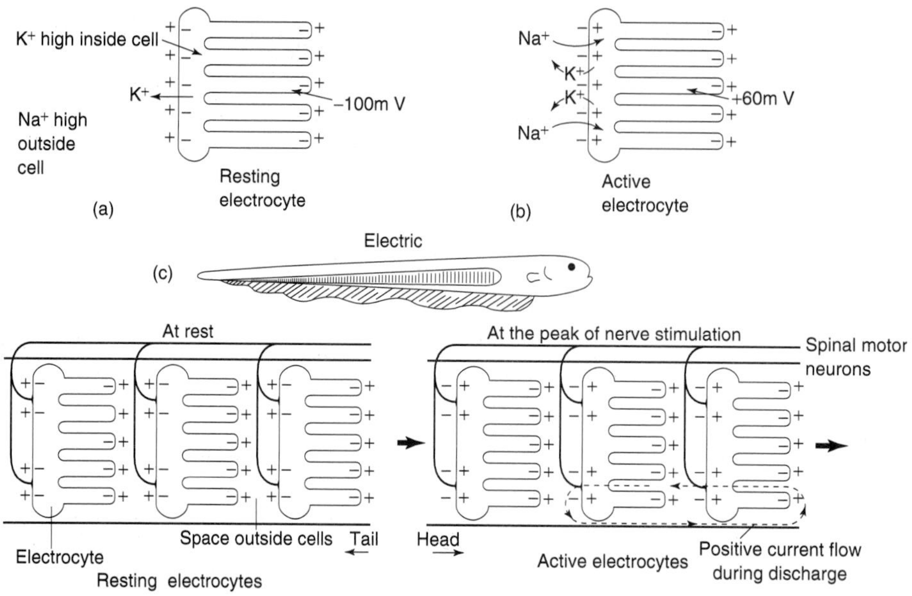

Figure 8–10 Use of transmembrane potentials of modified muscle cells by electric fishes to produce a discharge. K^+ (potassium ion) is maintained at a high and Na^+ (sodium ion) at a low internal concentration by the action of a Na^+/K^+ cell membrane pump. At rest, permeability of the membrane to K^+ exceeds the Na^+ membrane permeability. As a result, K^+ diffuses outward faster than Na^+ diffuses inward (arrow) and sets up the 100 millivolt resting potential. (a) At rest; (b) stimulated, sodium diffuses into the cell and potassium diffuses out; (c) differential movement of ions across the rough and smooth surfaces of electrocyte cells produces a directional current flow. By arranging electrocytes in series, some electric fishes can generate very high voltages. Electric eels, for example, have 6000 electrocytes in series and produce potentials in excess of 600 volts. (Modified in part from J. Bastian, 1994, *Physics Today* 47[2]:30–37.)

modified muscle tissue. The cells of such modified muscles, called electrocytes, have lost the capacity to contract but are specialized for generating an ion current flow (Figure 8–10). When at rest the membranes of muscle cells or neurons are electrically charged, with the intracellular fluids about 100 millivolts negative relative to the extracellular fluids, primarily due to sodium ion exclusion (Figure 8–10a). A stimulus increases the permeability of the membrane to sodium ions, and a large, rapid local influx of sodium ions occurs (Figure 8–10b). This influx inverts the membrane potential and excites adjacent membranes to depolarize. As a result, the disturbance propagates over the cell surface. In an electrocyte, which is a modified noncontracting muscle cell, one cell surface is rough and the opposite surface smooth (Figure 8–10c). Innervation is associated with the smooth surface, and only the smooth surface depolarizes. The resulting sodium ion flux across the smooth surface into the cell and a potas-

sium ion leakage across the rough surface and out of the cell yield a net positive current in one direction.

Because electrocytes are arranged in stacks or in series, like the batteries in a flashlight, the discharge potentials across each cell of the stack sum to produce high voltages. Synchrony of discharge is required, and this is produced by simultaneity of nerve impulses arriving at each electrocyte. The African electric catfish and the South American electric eel generate potentials in excess of 300 and 600 volts, respectively.

Most electric fish are found in tropical fresh waters of Africa and South America. Few marine forms can generate specialized electric discharges— only the torpedo ray *(Torpedo)*, the ray genus *Narcine*, some skates among elasmobranchs, and the stargazers (family Uranoscopidae) among the teleosts produce specialized discharges.

Unusual anatomical structures of electrocytes are present in several species of fishes that do not pro-

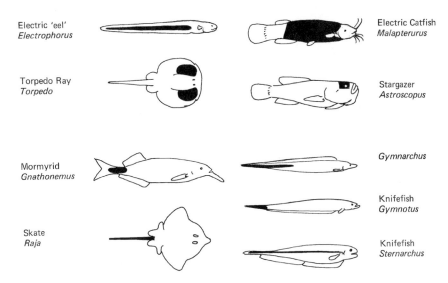

Figure 8–11 Electric fishes. Morphology and position of electric organs and convergent aspects of body form are shown. Four strongly electric fishes are shown above and five weakly electric fishes below. Shaded areas indicate position of electrogenic organs. (Modified after M. V. L. Bennett 1971a, *Fish Physiology*, Volume 5, Academic, New York, NY.)

duce electric shocks (Figure 8–11). Because of their anatomical similarities to the electrocytes of strongly electric fishes, these organs were presumed to generate electric potentials, but not until the 1950s was their weak electric nature in certain teleosts demonstrated (Bennett 1971a, Bass 1986). In these fishes, the discharge voltages are too small to be of direct defensive or offensive value. Instead, weakly electric teleost fishes use their discharges for electrolocation and social communications (Bastian 1994). When a fish discharges its electric organ an electric field is established in its immediate vicinity (Figure 8–12). Because of the high energy costs of maintaining a continuous discharge, electric fishes produce a discontinuous, pulsating discharge and field. Some species produce a lifelong constant-frequency discharge, while others emit a variable-frequency discharge. Most weakly electric teleost fishes pulse at rates between 50 and 300 cycles per second, but the stenarchid knifefishes of South America reach 1700 cycles per second, which is the most rapid continuous firing rate known for any vertebrate muscle or nerve.

The electric field from even weak discharges may extend outward for a considerable distance in fresh water because electric conductivity is low. This electric field will be distorted by the presence of both conductive and resistant objects. Rocks are highly resistive but other fishes, invertebrates, and

plants are conductive. Distortions of the field cause a change in the distribution of electric potential across the fish's body surface. An electric fish detects the presence, position, and movement of objects by sensing where on its body maximum distortion of its electric field occurs.

The skin of weakly electric teleosts contains special sensory receptors: ampullary organs and tuberous organs (Fessard 1974). These organs detect tonic (steady) and phase (rapidly changing) discharges, respectively. Electroreceptors of teleosts are modified lateral-line neuromast receptors. Like lateral-line receptors, they have double innervation—an afferent channel sending impulses to the brain and an efferent channel that causes inhibition of the receptors (Bennett 1971b). Theodore Bullock and his collaborators have shown that during each electric organ discharge an inhibitory command is sent to the electroreceptors and the fish is rendered insensitive to its own discharge. Between pulses, electroreceptors sense distortion in the electric field or the presence of a foreign electric field. The electric organs and receptors of weakly electric fishes provide a sixth sense. African and South American electric fishes are mostly nocturnal and usually inhabit turbid waters where vision is limited to short distances even in daylight.

Electric organ discharges vary with habits and habitat. Species that form groups or that live in shal-

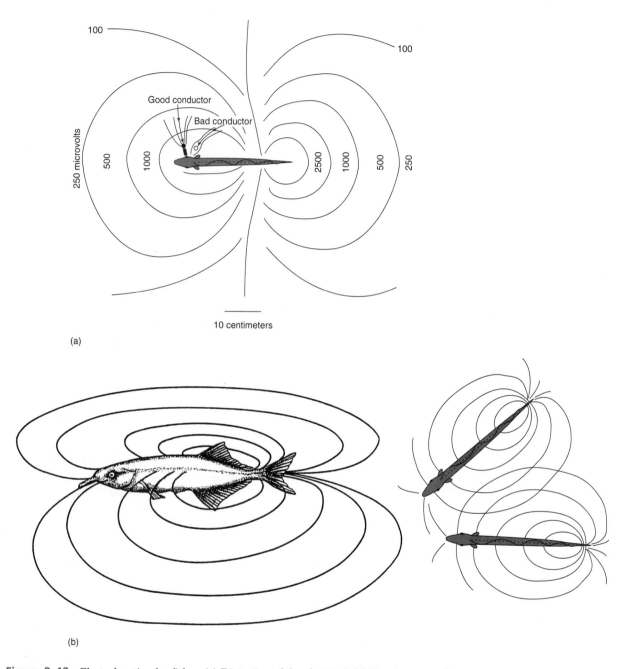

Figure 8–12   Electrolocation by fishes. (a) Distortion of the electric field (lines) surrounding a weakly electric fish by conductive and nonconductive objects. (Reference electrode 150 cm lateral to fish.) Conductive objects concentrate the field on the skin of the fish where the increase in electrical potential is detected by the electroreceptors. Nonconductive objects spread the field and diffuse potential differences along the body surface. (b) The electric field surrounding a weakly electric fish can be modulated by variations in the electric organ discharge for communication (left). When two electric fish come sufficiently close to one another significant interference can occur, requiring changes in the electric organ discharge (right).

low, narrow streams generally have discharges with high frequency and short duration. These characteristics reduce the chances of interference from the discharges of neighbors. Territorial species, in contrast, have long electric organ discharges. Electric organ discharges vary from species to species. In fact, some species of electric fishes were first identified by their electric organ discharges. During the breeding season electric organ discharges distinguish immature individuals, ripe females, and sexually active males of some species.

Electrogenesis and electroreception are not restricted to a single group of aquatic vertebrates (Figure 8–13). Precisely localized activity occurs in the brain of the lamprey in response to electric fields (Bodznick and Northcutt 1981), and it seems likely that the earliest vertebrates also possessed electroreceptive capacity. All fishlike vertebrates of lineages evolved before the earliest neopterygians (represented by living gars and *Amia*) have electroreceptor cells. These cells have a prominent

kinocilium, fire when the environment around the kinocilium is negative relative to the cell, and project to the medial region of the posterior third of the brain. The neopterygians lost electrosensitivity, and teleosts demonstrate at least two separate new evolutions of electroreceptors, which are distinct from those of other vertebrates: They *lack* a kinocilium and fire when the environment is *positive* relative to the cell, and project to the *lateral* aspect of the rhombencephalon. At least one mammal, the duck-billed platypus, also uses electroreception to detect prey (Scheich et al. 1986)

■ The Appearance of Teleostomes

The Devonian is known as the Age of Fishes because all major lineages of fishes, extant and extinct, coexisted in the fresh and marine waters of the planet during its 48–million-year duration. Most groups of gnathostomous fishes either made

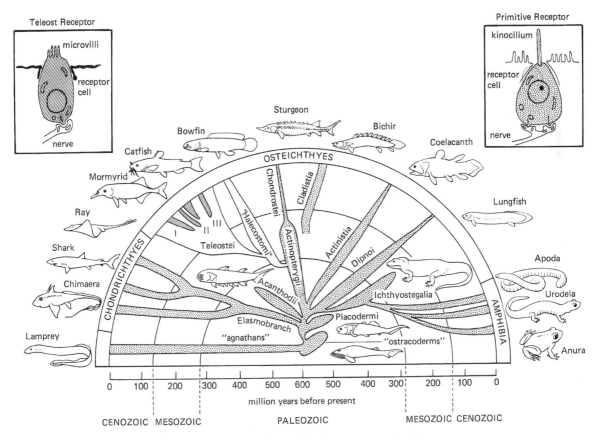

Figure 8–13 Phylogenetic distribution of electrosensitivity. Stippling and crosshatching identify two classes of electroreceptors as indicated in the upper right and left panels. (Produced with the assistance of Carl Hopkins.)

their first appearance or significantly diversified during this period, including the most species-rich and morphologically diverse lineage of vertebrates, the Teleostomi (Figure 7–4), encompassing acanthodians and bony fishes.

Acanthodians

The earliest jawed fishes in the fossil record are called acanthodians because of the stout spines (*acanthi*) anterior to their well-developed dorsal, anal, and often numerous paired fins (Denison 1979). The first fossil remains of acanthodians are isolated spines from the Early Silurian and possible fragmentary remains from the Late Ordovician. Later in the Silurian nearshore marine deposits contain more fin spines, scales, and teeth. Each of these elements is distinct from any comparable structures in other vertebrates. If they alone were available for study, the acanthodians would be considered as isolated from other vertebrate clades as are the placoderms. Such is not the case, however. When more complete specimens were discovered (Early Devonian through the Early Permian) they had the unmistakable spines, scales, and teeth of the Silurian fossils coupled with a mosaic of dermal, axial, and appendicular characters very like those of the majority of other gnathostomes. Many of these characters seem to be ancestral for gnathostomes, as we might expect from such early forms Nevertheless, these characters have been used to suggest relationships between acanthodians and (1) placoderms (on the basis of shared characters in the number of ossification centers in the jaws, gill arches, and shoulder girdles); (2) chondrichthyans (special border scales along the lateral line, details of the cranial and gill skeleton); and (3) osteichthyans (operculum, gill soft tissue and skeleton, branchiostegal rays, otoliths, and numerous other functional and morphological characters, especially of the cranium and jaw). In spite of considerable study, we must still wonder if these early gnathostomes had a cranium, jaw suspension, and dentition typical of other gnathostomes.

Most workers now accept acanthodians as the sister group of the Osteichthyes (Lauder and Liem 1983, Janvier 1996). The Teleostomi (acanthodians + osteichthyans) are diagnosed by a unique mechanism of opening the mouth by lowering the mandible through movements of a hyoid apparatus transmitted to the lower jaw by ligaments, the presence of an ossified dermal operculum, a closely associated new element in the hyoid arch, the interhyal bone, and branchiostegal rays. All these elements become important in the later evolution of osteichthyan feeding mechanisms.

Acanthodians (Figure 8–14) were usually not more than 20 centimeters in length, although some 2-meter species are known. These marine and freshwater fishes were often clad in small, square-crowned scales, each of which grew in size as the animal grew. The head was large and blunt and housed large eyes. The mouth was large, and many species had jaws studded with teeth.

Unlike the teeth of all other gnathostomes, however, acanthodian teeth lack enamel and are not known to have been regularly replaced. Some acanthodians had a few enlarged scales that formed gill covers. In others, the head scales were lost completely except along the cephalic sensory canals. The brain was encased in a well-developed cartilaginous box, which also housed three semicircular canals. There are remains of neural and hemal arches, but no vertebral centra. The well-developed heterocercal tail, the fusiform body, and the arrangement of the fins indicate that acanthodians were good swimmers and probably were not bottom dwellers.

This basic body form lasted throughout acanthodian history, but several variations are evident. Some forms had robust spines in the position of the pectoral and pelvic fins. Between these were other pairs of spines of variable size. These spines were not embedded deeply in the body. Often the pectoral spines were associated with ventral dermal plates in a supportive girdle (Figure 8–14b). Other species lacked this dermal skeleton, and the spines were set more deeply in the body. The respiratory apparatus changed during the evolution of the acanthodian lineage and teeth were lost in more than one lineage. Jaw articulation and gill changes accompanying tooth loss indicate that toothless acanthodians were able to open their mouths and orobranchial chambers very widely. These species had long gill rakers, and probably were plankton feeders that swam with their enormous mouths open, straining small organisms from the water.

Such feeding specializations would have placed acanthodians at a key position in the aquatic and marine food webs of the late Paleozoic, transferring energy from tiny zooplankton into their own tissue and providing prey for larger fishes. Acanthodians may have been very abundant in Devonian seas, but during the Early Permian the last forms disap-

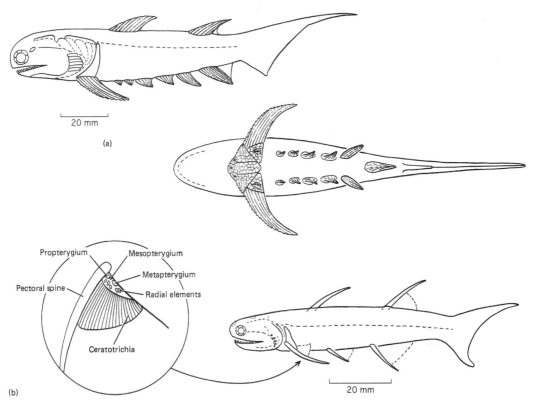

Figure 8–14   Reconstructions of acanthodians. (a) Ancestral type: *Climatius,* Early Devonian, with multiple superficially attached spines (lateral view above, ventral view below); (b) more derived type: *Ischnacanthus,* Early Devonian, with fewer, more deeply embedded spines. (Inset) Detail of pectoral fin and spine of *Acanthodes,* Early Carboniferous.

peared, leaving the waters of the world to the Chondrichthyes and the most species-rich clade of vertebrates yet evolved—the bony fishes.

■ The Earliest Osteichthyes and the Major Groups of Bony Fishes

Fragmentary remains of bony fishes are known from the Late Silurian. It is not until the Devonian that more complete remains are found. These animals resemble acanthodians in details of cranial structure. The similarities suggest a common teleostome ancestor for acanthodians and osteichthyans in the Early Silurian.

Remains of the bony fishes representing a radiation of forms already in full bloom appear in the Early to Middle Devonian. Two major and distinctive osteichthyan (*osteo* = bone, *ichthys* = fish) types possessed locomotor and feeding characters that made them dominant fishes during the Devonian. Some evolved specializations that led to land ver-

tebrates. Most lineages, however, retained fishlike characteristics and from among them rose the derived modern bony fishes, the teleosts, which are the largest group of living vertebrates (Table 8.2).

Fossils of the two basic types of osteichthyans are abundant from the Middle Devonian onward. The Sarcopterygii (*sarcos* = fleshy, *pterygium* = fin; Figure 8–15a–d) and the Actinopterygii (*actinos* = stout ray; Figure 8–15e, f) are sister taxa. Synapomorphies of the Osteichthyes include patterns of lateral-line canals, similar opercular and pectoral girdle dermal bone elements, and fin webs supported by bony dermal rays. A fissure allowed movement between the anterior and posterior halves of the neurocranium in many forms. The presence of bone is not a unifying osteichthyan characteristic because agnathans, placoderms, and acanthodians also possess true bone, and the absence of bone in chondrichthyans is derived. What is unique to the group is endochondral bone (bone that replaces cartilage ontogenetically) and they have the more primitive dermal and perichondral bone-forming mechanisms

TABLE 8.2	Classification and geographic distribution of Osteichthyes, the bony fishes*

Osteichtyes (bony fishes), about 24,000 living species described
  Sarcopterygii (fleshy-finned fishes), 7 living species
          Dipnoi (lungfishes), 6 living species; Southern Hemisphere, fresh water
          "Ripidistia"[†]
          Actinistia [Coelacanthiformes] (coelacanths), 1 living species; Indian Ocean islands, deep
              water marine
    Actinopterygii (ray-finned fishes), 20,850 living species
          "Paleoniscoids"[†]
          Polypteriformes [Cladistia] (bichirs), 11 living species; African, fresh water
          Acipenseriformes (sturgeons and paddlefishes), 25 living species; Northern Hemisphere,
              coastal and fresh water
      Neopterygii[‡], 20,814 living species (numbers of living species are conservative minima)
          Lepisosteiformes [Ginglymodi] (gars), 7 living species; North and Central America, fresh
              and brackish water
          Amiiformes (bowfins), 1 living species; North America, fresh water
    Teleostei
        Osteoglossomorpha (bony tongues), 206 living species; worldwide tropical fresh water
        Elopomorpha (tarpons and eels), 633 living species; worldwide, mostly marine
        Clupeomorpha (herrings and anchovies), 331 living species; worldwide, especially marine
        Euteleostei, 19,636 living species
          Ostariophysi (catfish and minnows), 6050 living species; worldwide, fresh water
          "Protacanthopterygii" (trouts and relatives), 320 living species; temperate Northern and
              Southern Hemisphere, fresh water
          Scopelomorpha = "Myctophiformes" (lanternfishes and relatives), 677 living species;
              worldwide, mesopelagic (middle depth), marine
          Paracanthopterygii (cods and anglerfishes), 1160 living species; Northern Hemisphere,
              primarily marine
          Acanthopterygii (spiny-rayed fishes), 10,349 living species, including the
              Atherinomorpha (silversides), 1080 living species; worldwide, surface-dwelling, fresh
              water and marine; and Perciformes (perches), 7800 living species; worldwide,
              primarily marine

*Taxa in quotation marks are known to be artificial, but interrelationships are unresolved.

[†]Extinct.

[‡]The subdivision of the Neopterygii varies greatly from author as does the number of living species claimed for the larger taxa.

as well. The name Osteichthyes was coined before the occurrence of bone in other primitive vertebrates was recognized. Likewise, the various names long in use for the extant actinopterygian subgroups imply an increase in the ossification of the skeleton as an evolutionary trend (for example, chondrosteans (cartilaginous bony fishes—sturgeons and paddlefishes) are the sister group of a radiation often called the holosteans (entirely bony fishes—gar and *Amia*), which culminated in teleosteans (final bony fishes). The fossil record indicates that a regular sequence of increasing ossification did not occur. To the contrary, a tendency to reduce ossification, especially in the skull and scales, is apparent when the full array

of early Osteichthyes is compared with their derived descendants.

Relationships among early osteichthyans are not presently describable by a single widely acceptable phylogeny (Bemis et al. 1987). Although relationships among the ray-finned fishes are generally agreed on because they are supported by several shared derived characters, the phylogenetic relationships of the Sarcopterygii are more controversial. This controversy is important because from within the Sarcopterygii arose the tetrapods and with them terrestrial vertebrate life. Primitive Sarcopterygii have similar body shapes and sizes (20 to 70 centimeters), two dorsal fins, an epichordal

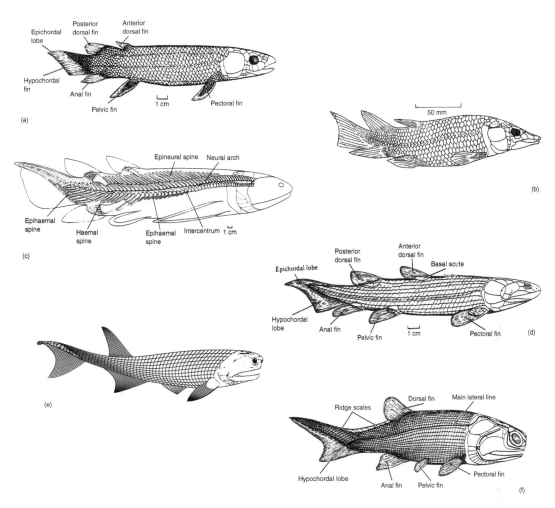

Figure 8–15 Primitive osteichthyans. (a, b) Dipnoans; (c, d) other Sarcopterygil;
(e, f) actinopterygians. (a) Relatively unspecialized dipnoan *Dipterus,* Middle Devonian;
(b) long-snouted dipnoan *Griphognathus,* Late Devonian; (c) laterally compressed porolepi-
form *Holoptychius,* Late Devonian to Early Carboniferous; (d) cylindrical osteolepiform *Oste-
olepis,* Middle Devonian; (e) fine-scaled actinopterygian *Cheirolepis,* Middle to Late Devonian;
(f) typical early actinopterygian *Moythomasia,* Late Devonian. (Modified from J. A. Moy-
Tomas and R. S. Miles, 1971, *Paleozoic Fishes,* Saunders College Publishing, Philadelphia, PA.)

lobe on the heterocercal caudal fin, and paired fins
that were fleshy, scaled, and had a bony central
axis. The paired fins' rays extend in a feather or
compound leaflike manner in contrast to the fanlike form of the fin rays in actinopterygian paired
fins.

The jaw muscles of sarcopterygians were massive by comparison with those of actinopterygians,
and the size of these muscles influenced the details
of cranium, hyoid, and dermal skull characters that
set sarcopterygians apart from the actinopterygians. Finally, the early sarcopterygians were
coated with a peculiar layer of dentinelike material,

cosmine (Bemis and Northcutt 1992), that spread
right across the sutures between dermal bones and
shows indications of being periodically reabsorbed.

The Dipnoi have unique derived features that
clearly indicate that the lineage is monophyletic.
The other Sarcopterygii have been variously combined as a single taxon, the **Crossopterygii**, now
considered by most workers not to be monophyletic, or as two equally ancient sister groups,
rhipidistians (entirely extinct forms) and **actinistians** (for the sole surviving form *Latimeria,* the living coelacanth and its undisputed fossil relatives).
Even this set of subdivisions has been brought into

question by the revision of the rhipidistians into two or more separate clades, some more closely related to lungfish and others to tetrapods.. We shall take a further look at fossil sarcopterygians when we examine the origin of their sister taxon, the tetrapods.

The Evolution of the Actinopterygii

Basal actinopterygians include a variety of diverse taxa, formerly placed in a group of extinct fishes, the "paleoniscids," which is no longer considered to be monophyletic. Although fragments of Late Silurian Actinopterygii exist, complete fossil skeletons are not found earlier than the Middle to Late Devonian. Early actinopterygians were small fishes (usually 5 to 25 centimeters long, although some were over a meter in length) with a single dorsal fin, a strongly heterocercal forked caudal fin with little fin web. Paired fins with long bases were common, but several taxa had lobate pectoral fins (Figure 8–15e, f). The interlocking scales, although thick like those of sarcopterygians, were otherwise distinct in structure and in growth pattern. In sarcopterygians the hard outer coating of the scales was cosmine (which is derived from dentine) and in actinopterygians it was ganoine (derived from enamel). Parallel arrays of closely packed radial bones supported the bases of the fins. The number of bony rays supporting the fin membrane was greater than the number of supporting radials and these rays were clearly derived from elongated scales aligned end to end. Two morphological aspects of the early ray-finned fishes deserve special attention: specializations for locomotion and for feeding. Unfortunately, the extant cladistians (polypterids) and chondrosteans are so specialized in these respects that they shed little light on the biology of early actinopterygians.

These primitive actinopterygians were diverse and successful in freshwater and marine habitats from 380 to 280 million years ago. There is no evidence that the fishes grouped together as "paleoniscoids" were a monophyletic group, with characters distinguishing them from later, more derived fishes. The different types share numerous characters but these are all primitive relative to later members of the Actinopterygii and thus of no use in defining a distinct taxon. Near the end of the Paleozoic, the ray-finned fishes showed signs of change. The upper and lower lobes of the caudal fin were often nearly symmetrical, and all fin membranes were supported by fewer bony rays, for example, in the dorsal and anal fins about one bony ray for each internal supporting radial. This morphological reorganization may have increased the flexibility of the fins.

The dermal armor of late Paleozoic ray-finned fishes was also reduced. The changes in fins and armor may have been complementary—more mobile fins mean more versatile locomotion, and increased ability to avoid predators may have permitted a reduction in heavy armor. This reduction of weight could have further stimulated the evolution of increased locomotor ability that was probably enhanced by perfection of the swim bladder as a delicately controlled hydrostatic device.

The lower jaw of early actinopterygians was supported by the hyomandibula, and in most forms was snapped closed in a scissorslike action by the adductor mandibulae muscles, which resulted in the piercing of prey by small conical teeth. This muscle originated in a narrow enclosed cavity between the maxilla and the palatoquadrate and inserted on the lower jaw near its articulation with the quadrate (Schaeffer and Rosen 1961). As a result, the bite was swift but the force created was low. The close-knit dermal bones of the cheeks permitted little expansion of the orobranchial chamber beyond that required for respiration. Some early actinopterygians had a more specialized jaw apparatus; for example, *Chirodus* had crushing tooth plates and a modified jaw to support them.

Better locomotion enhances predatory capacity. The food-gathering apparatus of several clades underwent radical changes to produce, in the Late Permian, a new clade of actinopterygians—the neopterygians. For over a century the most primitive neopterygians (represented by the extant gars and bowfin) have been called holosteans, but the characters they share may simply be ancestral for neopterygians as a whole, and the bowfin appears to be more closely related to teleosts than to gars. A new jaw mechanism was characterized by a short maxilla and a freeing of the posterior end of the maxilla from the other bones of the cheek. Because the cheek no longer was solid, the nearly vertically oriented hyomandibtila could swing out *laterally*, thus increasing the volume of the orobranchial chamber in a rapid motion to produce a powerful suction useful in capturing prey. The power of the sharply toothed jaw could be increased because the adductor muscle was not limited in size by a solid bony cheek. No longer enclosed, the jaw muscle mass expanded dorsally through the space opened by the freeing of the maxilla. In addition, an extra lever arm, a coronoid process, developed on different jaw bones in different lineages always at the site of insertion of the adductor muscle on the lower jaw. In most modern fishes any coronoid process is on the dentary and angular bones (Gardiner et al. in Stiassny et al. 1996). Its exact position notwithstanding, a coronoid process adds torque and thus power to the closure of the mandible of many of the more forceful biters.

In the more derived neopterygians the bones of the gill cover (operculum) were connected to the mandible so that expansion of the orobranchial chamber aided in opening the mouth. The anterior, articulated end of the maxilla developed a ball-and-socket joint with the neurocranium. Because of its ligamentous connection to the mandible, the free posterior end of the maxilla was rotated forward as the mouth opened. This directed the maxilla's mar-

ginal teeth forward, aiding in grasping prey. The folds of skin covering the maxilla changed the shape of the gape from a semicircle to a circular opening. The result was enhanced directionality of suction and elimination of a possible side-door escape route for small prey. These changes probably increased the suction produced during opening of the mouth.

Thus, neopterygians had considerable trophic and locomotor advantages. The neopterygians first appeared in the Late Permian (Figure 8–16) and became the dominant fishes of the Mesozoic. During the Late Triassic, basal neopterygians gave rise to fishes with further feeding and locomotor specializations. These fishes constitute the largest vertebrate radiation, the Teleostei. Although teleosts probably evolved in the sea, they soon radiated into fresh water. By the Late Cretaceous, teleosts seem to have replaced most of the more primitive neopterygians, and most of the more than 400 families of modern teleosts had evolved. Their first specializations involved changes in the fins.

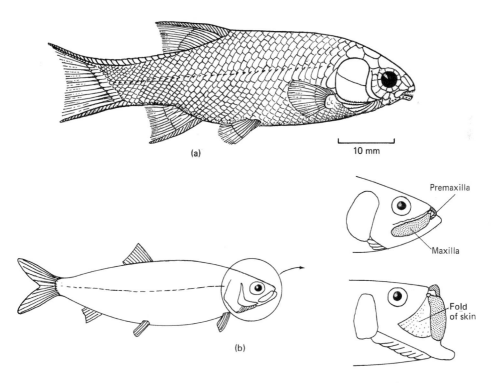

Figure 8–16   Early teleosts. (a) *Acentrophorus* of the Permian illustrates an early member of the late Paleozoic neopterygian radiation (b) *Leptolepis* an Early Jurassic teleost with enlarged mobile maxillae, which form a nearly circular mouth when the jaws are fully opened. Membranes of skin close the gaps behind the protruded bony elements. Modern herrings have a similar jaw structure.

The caudal fin of adult actinopterygians is supported by a few enlarged and modified hemal spines called hypural bones that articulate with the tip of the abruptly upturned vertebral column. In general, the number of hypural bones decreases during the transition from the earliest actinopterygians to more derived teleosts. Modified posterior neural arches—the uroneurals—add additional support to the dorsal side of the tail. These uroneurals are a derived character of teleosts (Lauder and Liem 1983). Thus supported, the caudal fin of teleosts is symmetrical and flexible. This type of caudal structure is known as homocercal. In conjunction with a gas bladder, a homocercal tail has always been thought to allow a teleost to swim horizontally without using its paired fins as control surfaces, and drag is reduced by folding the fins close to the body. Relieved of a lift function, the paired fins of teleosts became more flexible, mobile, and diverse in shape, size, and position. Teleost fins, especially the paired fins, have become specialized for activities from food getting to courtship and from sound production to walking and flying. The logical basis for the hypothesis that the symmetrical tail produces a symmetrical forward force has recently been questioned. While this may be true in burst and sprint swimming, it appears that active intrinsic muscle action during steady speed swimming renders the homocercal tail asymmetrical in function (Lauder 1994). The advantage of such asymmetry of function is not yet clear but may relate to enhanced maneuverability of a body experiencing torque.

As we saw among earlier groups, improvements in locomotion were accompanied by reduction of armor. Modern teleosts are thin scaled by Paleozoic and Mesozoic standards, or lack scales entirely. The few heavily armored exceptions generally show a secondary reduction in locomotor abilities.

Teleosts, like most fishes that preceded them, also evolved improvements in their feeding apparatus. Trophic specializations in the earliest teleosts involved only a slight loosening of the premaxillae, so that they moved during jaw opening to accentuate the round mouth shape. One early clade of teleosts showed an enlargement of the free-swinging posterior end of the maxilla to form a nearly circular mouth when the jaws were fully opened. Later in the radiation of the teleosts distinctive changes in the jaw apparatus permitted a wide vari-

ety of feeding modes based on the speed of opening of the jaws and the powerful suction produced by the highly integrated jaw, gill arch, and cranium.

Most of the main themes in actinopterygian evolution involve changes in the jaws from a simple prey-grabbing device to a highly sophisticated suction device. Suction is important in prey capture. A rapid approach by a predator toward prey pushes a wave of water in front of the predator. This diverts water around and away from the mouth. Potential prey thus can be deflected around the predator's body and away from the grasp of its jaws. If flow leading directly into the mouth could be created, prey would be drawn into the mouth. This is exactly what is done by neopterygians and some marine mammals. By rapidly increasing the volume of their orobranchial chamber, neopterygians create suction, which draws a stream of water into the mouth.

In addition to speed and forceful suction, many teleosts have evolved a great deal of mobility in the skeletal elements that rim the mouth opening. This mobility allows the grasping margins of the jaws to be extended forward from the head, often at remarkable speed. The functional result is called the protrusible jaw and has evolved three or four times in different euteleost clades.

Although jaw protrusibility is generally associated with perciform fishes (Figure 8–17), it occurs in the related atherinid and paracanthopterygian fishes and in the unrelated cypriniform ostariophysans as well. Jaw morphology differs significantly among fishes with protrusible jaws, which clearly indicates that some of these protrusibilities have evolved independently.

All protrusion mechanisms involve complex ligamentous attachments that allow the ascending processes of the premaxilla to slide forward on the top of the cranium without dislocation. In addition, since no muscles are in position to pull the premaxillae forward, they must be pushed by leverage from behind. Two sources provide the necessary leverage. First, the premaxillae may be protruded by opening the lower jaw through ligamentous ties to the posterior tip of the premaxillae. Second, leverage can be provided by complex movements of the maxillae, which become isolated from the rim of the mouth by long, often toothed, posterior projections of the premaxillae.

The independent movement of the protrusible upper jaw also permits closure of the mouth

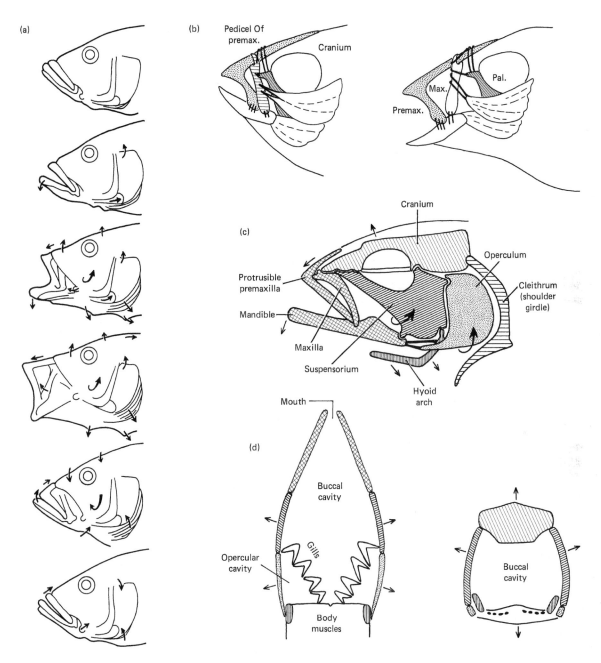

Figure 8–17 Jaw protrusion in suction feeding. (a) Top to bottom: The sequence of jaw movements in an African cichlid fish, *Serranochromis*. (Modified from K F. Liem in A G. Kluge et al., 1977, *Chordate Structure and Function*, 2d edition, Macmillan, New York, NY.) (b) Muscle, ligament, and bone movements during premaxillary protrusion; (c) skeletal movements and ligament actions during jaw protrusion. (After G. V. Lauder 1980.) (d) Frontal section (left) and cross section (right) of buccal expansion during suction feeding.

through maximum extension of the premaxillae while the orobranchial cavity is still expanded. Thus, engulfed prey are entrapped before the orobranchial cavity volume has been reduced through evacuation of water from the gill openings.

With so many groups converging on the same complex function, the adaptive significance of protrusibility would seem to be great. Surprisingly, there is no single hypothesis of advantage that has much experimental support (Lauder and Liem 1981). Protrusion may have enhanced the hydrodynamic efficiency of the circular mouth opening of primitive teleosts, but this hypothesis seems insufficient to explain the complex anatomical changes necessary for protrusibility. Protrusion may aid in gripping prey, or the mouth's mobile jaws may be fitted to the substrate during feeding while the body remains in the horizontal position required for rapid escape from one's own predators. Protrusion also allows the mouth to close without reducing the volume of an expanded orobranchial cavity. This prevents prey from being flushed out of the mouth as the orobranchial cavity contracts at the end of an ingestion cycle. In many fishes with protrusible jaws, prey are clearly sucked into the mouth, but which part of the suction is produced by the protrusion itself depends greatly on the relative timing of the action of all parts of the system No consistent pattern of steps in the feeding sequence indicates that protrusion is a significant contributor to suction efficiency. Another set of advantages of protrusible jaws may lie in the functional independence of the upper jaws relative to other parts of the feeding apparatus. Some fishes, such as the silversides and killifishes, can greatly protrude, moderately protrude, or not protrude the upper jaw while opening the mouth and creating suction. These modulations direct the mouth opening and major axis of suction either ventrally, straight ahead, or dorsally, allowing the fish to feed from substrate, water column, or surface with equal ease. Perhaps the most broadly applicable hypothesis for the strong selection for jaw protrusion is that shooting out the jaws in front of the head allows a predator to approach the prey with a portion of its feeding apparatus more rapidly than can fishes that lack protrusion. Protrusion can add significant velocity to the final moment of a predator's approach. The shooting out of protrusible jaws has been measured to increase the approach velocity of the predator by 39 to 89 percent in the crucial last instant.

Powerful mobile pharyngeal jaws also evolved several times. Ancestrally, ray-finned fishes have numerous dermal tooth plates in the pharynx. These plates are aligned with (but not fused to) both dorsal and ventral skeletal elements of the gill arches. A general trend of fusion of these tooth plates to one another and to a few gill arch elements above and below the esophagus can be traced in the Neopterygii. Ancestrally, these consolidated pharyngeal jaws are not very mobile and are used primarily to hold and manipulate prey in preparation for swallowing it whole. In the ostariophysan minnows and their relatives, the suckers, the primary jaws are toothless but protrusible and the pharyngeal jaws are greatly enlarged and can chew against a horny pad on the base of the skull. These feeding and digestive specializations allow extraction of nutrients from thick-walled plant cells and the minnows and suckers represent one of the largest radiations of herbivores among vertebrates.

In the Neoteleostei the muscles associated with the branchial skeletal elements supporting the pharyngeal jaws have undergone radical evolution, resulting in a variety of powerful movements of the pharyngeal jaw tooth plates. Not only are the movements of these second jaws completely unrelated to the movements and functions of the primary jaws, but the upper and lower tooth plates of the pharyngeal jaws move quite independently of each other. With so many separate systems to work with, it is little wonder that some of the most extensive adaptive radiations among teleosts have been in fishes endowed with protrusible primary jaws and specialized mobile pharyngeal jaws.

■ Extant Actinopterygii: Ray-Finned Fishes

With an estimated 24,000 extant species so far described (Nelson 1994) and with new species being discovered regularly, the extant actinopterygians present a fascinating, even bewildering, diversity of forms of vertebrate life. Because of their numbers we are forced to examine them in a disproportionately brief survey compared with other vertebrate taxa, focusing on the primary characteristics of selected groups and their evolution.

The study of the phylogenetic relationships of actinopterygians entered its current active state in 1966 with a major revised scheme of teleostean phylogeny proposing several new relationships. The following three decades have seen a phenomenal growth in our understanding of the interrelationships of ray-finned fishes (Rosen 1982). Nevertheless, some of the relationships are uncertain and, should be considered hypotheses (Lauder and Liem 1983, Nelson 1994, Stiassny et al. 1996).

Why are there so many actinopterygians? For one thing their habitats cover seventy-three percent of the planet. But why then are the chondrichthyians and the sarcopterygian fishes relatively species poor? Recent studies (McCune 1996, McCune 1997, McCune and Lovejoy 1998) indicate that both fossil and living actinopterygians may have rates of speciation that are higher than those estimated for birds or even some insects. Fish species flocks evolving in the isolation of lakes appear to take the least time for speciation of all the highly derived organisms surveyed (vertebrates and insects). Perhaps this is because under such circumstances actinopterygians are particularly prone to sympatric speciation.

Polypteriformes and Acipenseriformes

Although "Paleoniscoids" were replaced during the early Mesozoic by neopterygians, a few specialized forms of primitive ray-finned fishes have survived. The most primitive surviving lineage of actinopterygian fishes is the Polypteriformes. They are similar to paleoniscoids in many ways. However, polypteriforms have enough specializations to obscure their relationships to other fishes. Sometimes called the Cladistia, the Polypteriformes include 10 species of elongate, heavily armored fishes—the African bichirs and reedfishes (Figure 8–18). They are modest-size (less than a meter), slow-moving fishes with modified heterocercal tails. Polypteriforms differ from other extant basal actinopterygians in having well-ossified skeletons. In addition to a full complement of dermal and endochondral bones, polypteriforms are covered by thick, interlocking, multilayered scales. These ganoid scales are covered with a coat of ganoine, an enamellike tissue characteristic of primitive actinopterygians. Larval bichirs (*Polypterus*) have external gills, possibly an ancestral

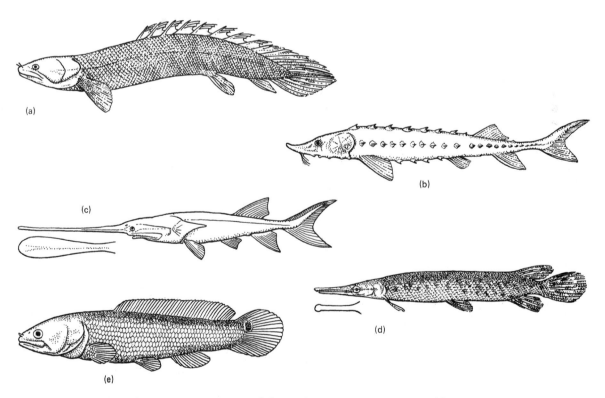

(a)

(b)

(c)

(d)

(e)

Figure 8–18 Extant nonteleostean actinopterygian fishes and primitive neopterygians. Not to scale. Actinopterygians (a) *Polypterus*, a bichir, (b) *Acipenser*, a sturgeon, and (c) *Polyodon spathula*, one of two extant species of paddlefishes. Primitive neopterygians (d) *Lepisosteus*, a gar, and (e) *Amia calva*, the bowfin.

condition for Osteichthyes. *Erpetoichthys,* the reed-fish, is eellike although armored with a full complement of ganoid scales. All polypteriforms are predatory, and their jaw mechanics provide our best model of the original actinopterygian condition. Their peculiar flaglike dorsal finlets and the fleshy bases of their pectoral fins are among their unique specializations, but so little is known about their natural history that the significance of these features cannot yet be appreciated.

Acipenseriformes includes two living and two fossil families of specialized actinopterygians (Bemis et al in Birstein et al. 1997). The 24 species of sturgeons, family Acipenseridae, are large (1- to 6-meter), active, benthic fishes. They lack endochondral bone and have lost much of the dermal skeleton of more primitive actinopterygians. Sturgeons have a strongly heterocercal tail armored with a specialized series of scales extending from the dorsal margin of the caudal peduncle along the upper edge of the caudal fin. This armored caudal cut-water (the caudal fulcral scales) is an ancestral character of the earliest Paleozoic actinopterygians. Most sturgeons have five rows of enlarged armorlike scales along the body. The protrusible jaws of sturgeons make them effective suction feeders. The mode of jaw protrusion is unique and independently derived and these plus their adaptations for benthic life are the basis for considering them specialized. Sturgeons are found only in the Northern Hemisphere and are either anadromous (ascending into fresh water to breed) or entirely freshwater in habit. Commercially important both for their rich flesh and as a source of the best caviar, they have been severely depleted by intensive fisheries in much of their range. Dams and river pollution have also taken their toll on anadromous sturgeon (Birstein et al. 1997).

The two surviving species of paddlefishes, Polyodontidae, are closely related to the sturgeons but have a still greater reduction of dermal ossification. Their most outstanding feature is a greatly elongate and flattened rostrum, which extends nearly one-third of their 2-meter length. The rostrum is richly innervated with ampullary organs that are believed to detect minute electric fields. Contrary to the common notion that the paddle is used to stir food from muddy river bottoms, the American paddlefish is a planktivore that feeds by actively swimming with its prodigious mouth agape, straining crustaceans and small fishes from the water using modified gill rakers as strainers (Burggren and Bemis 1992). The two species of paddlefishes have a disjunct zoogeographic distribution similar to that of alligators: One is found in the Yangtze River valley of China where it feeds on fishes, and the planktivorous species is in the Mississippi River valley of the United States. Fossil paddlefishes are known from western North America (Grande and Bemis 1991).

Primitive Neopterygians

The two extant genera of primitive neopterygians, formerly grouped together as holosteans, are currently limited to North America and represent widely divergent types. The seven species of gars, generally all considered to be in the genus *Lepisosteus,* are medium- to large-size (1- to 4-meter) predators of warm temperate fresh and brackish (estuarine) waters. The elongate body, jaws and teeth are specialized features, but their interlocking multilayered scales are similar to those of many Paleozoic and Mesozoic actinopterygians. These peculiar scales and the thick dermis associated with them play a significant role not only in protection but in swimming, aerial respiration, etc. (Long et al. 1996). It would be surprising if the same were not true of their ancient and much more diverse kin. Gars feed on other fishes taken unaware when the seemingly lethargic and excellently camouflaged gar dashes alongside them and, with a sideways flip of the body, grasps prey with its needlelike teeth.

Sympatric with gars is the single species of bowfin, *Amia calva.* The head skeleton is not specialized by long prey-holding jaws like that of gar, but points toward the condition in more derived fishes in its modifications as a suction device (Lauder 1980a,b,c). *Amia,* which are 0.5 to 1 meter long, prey on almost any organism smaller than themselves. Scales of the bowfin are comparatively thin and made up of a single layer of bone as in teleost fishes; however, the asymmetric caudal fin is very similar to the heterocercal caudal fin of more primitive fishes. The nature of the interrelationships of gars, *Amia,* and the teleosts have long been controversial (Grande and Bemis 1997).

Teleosteans

Most extant fishes are teleosts. They share many characters of caudal and cranial structure and are grouped into four clades of varying size and diversity.

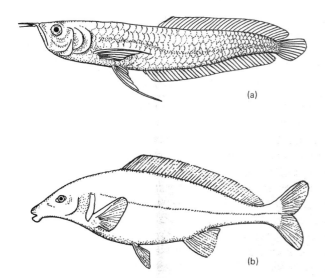

Figure 8–19   Extant osteoglossomorphs. (a) *Osteoglossum,* the arawana from South America; (b) *Mormyrus,* an elephant-nose from Africa. Not to scale.

The **Osteoglossomorpha**, which appeared in Late Jurassic seas, are now restricted to about 217 species in tropical fresh waters. *Osteoglossum* (Figure 8–19) is a 1-meter-long predator from the Amazon, familiar to tropical fish enthusiasts. *Arapaima* is an even larger Amazonian predator (perhaps the largest strictly freshwater fish, before intense fishing reduced the populations they were known to reach a length of at least 3 meters and perhaps 4.5 meters), and *Mormyrus* is representative of the small African bottom feeders that use weak electric discharges to communicate with conspecifics. As dissimilar as they may seem, the osteoglossomorph fishes are united by unique osteological characters of the mouth and feeding mechanics.

The **Elopomorpha** (Figure 8–20) had appeared by the Late Jurassic. A specialized leptocephalous larva is a unique character of elopomorphs. These larvae spend a long time adrift usually at the ocean surface, and are widely dispersed by currents. Elopomorphs include about 35 species of tarpons (Megalopidae), ladyfish (Elopidae), and bonefish (Albulidae) and 764 species of eels (Anguilliformes and Saccopharyngiformes).

Most elopomorphs are eellike and marine, but some species are tolerant of fresh waters. The common American eel, *Anguilla rostrata,* has one of the most unusual life histories of any fish (Norman and Greenwood 1975). After growing to sexual maturity (which takes as long as 10 to 12 years) in rivers,

lakes, and even ponds, the **catadromous** (downstream migrating) eels enter the sea. The North Atlantic eels migrate to the Sargasso Sea. Here they are thought to spawn and die, presumably at great depth. The eggs and newly hatched leptocephalous larvae float to the surface and drift in the currents. Larval life continues until the larvae reach continental margins, where they transform into miniature eels and ascend rivers to feed and mature.

Most of the more than 350 species of Clupeomorpha are specialized for feeding on minute plankton gathered by a specialized mouth and gill-straining apparatus. They are silvery, mostly marine schooling fishes of great commercial importance. Common examples are herrings, shad, sardines, and anchovies (Figure 8–20). Several clupeomorphs are anadromous; the springtime migrations of American shad (*Alosa sapidissima*) from the North Atlantic into rivers in eastern North America involve millions of individuals, but they, too, have been greatly depleted by dams and pollution of aquatic environments (Warren and Burr 1994).

The vast majority of extant teleosts belong to the fourth clade, the **Euteleostei**, which evolved before the Late Cretaceous. With so many thousands of species it is impossible to give more than scant information about them here. For more about these fishes refer to Bond 1996, Moyle and Cech 1996, Nelson 1994 and the beautifully illustrated Paxton and Eschmeyer 1994. The basal euteleostian stock is represented today by the specialized ostariophysans and the generalized salmoniforms, but how these two monophyletic groups relate to each other and to the more derived (and monophyletic) neoteleostei is a matter of much dispute (Stiassny et al. 1996).

The Ostariophysi, the predominant fishes of the world's fresh waters, seem to be at the very base of the euteleostean radiation but have a distinctive derived character. Their name refers to small bones (*ostar* = a little bone) that connect the swim bladder (*physa* = a bladder) with the inner ear (Figure 8–21). Using the swim bladder as an amplifier and the chain of bones as conductors, this **Weberian apparatus** greatly enhances hearing sensitivity of these fishes. The ostariophysans are more sensitive to sounds and have a broader frequency range of detection than other fishes (Popper and Coombs 1980). Although all Ostariophysi have a Weberian apparatus, in other respects they are a diverse taxon of 6500 species and include the characins of

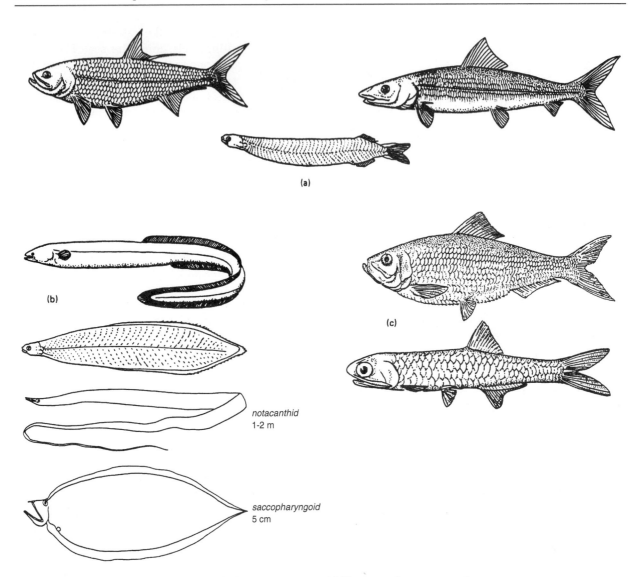

Figure 8–20 Extant teleosts of isolated phylogenetic position. (a) Elopomorpha represented by a tarpon (left) and a bonefish (right) and a typical fork-tailed leptocephalous larva (below); (b) anguilliform elopormorphs represented by the common eel, *Anguilla rostrata* (above), its leptocephalous larva (immediately below), and two other very different eel leptocephali; (c) clupeomorpha represented by a herring (above) and an anchovy (below). Not to scale.

South America and Africa, the carps and minnows (all continents except South America, Antarctica, and Australia), and the catfishes (all continents except Antarctica and they inhabit many shallow marine areas as well).

About 80 percent of the fish species in fresh water are ostariophysans. As a group they display diverse traits. For example, many ostariophysans have protrusible jaws and are adept at obtaining food in a variety of ways. In addition, pharyngeal teeth act as second jaws. Many forms have fin spines or special armor for protection, and the skin typically contains glands that produce substances used in olfactory communication. Although they have diverse reproductive habits, most lay sticky eggs or otherwise guard the eggs, preventing their loss downstream.

The other basal group of euteleostians, the esocid and salmonid fishes (Figure 8–22a) include important commercial and game fishes. These fishes have often been lumped into a taxon, the "Protacanthopterygii," but the basis for this classification was often no more than shared ancestral

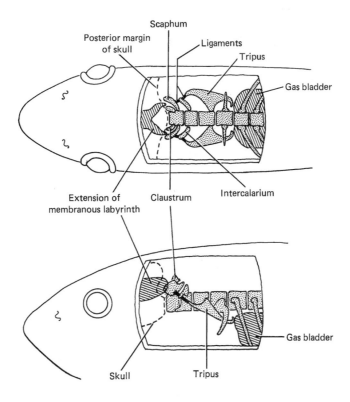

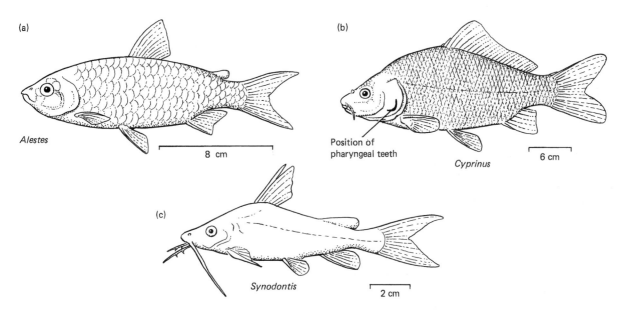

Figure 8–21   The Weberian Apparatus of ostariophysans. Ostariophysan fishes have a sound-detection system, the Weberian apparatus, which is a modification of the swim bladder and the first few vertebrae and their processes. Sound (pressure) waves impinging on the fish cause the air bladder to vibrate. The tripus is in contact with the air bladder; as the bladder vibrates the tripus pivots on its articulation with the vertebra. This motion is transmitted by ligaments to the intercalarium and scaphum. Movement of the scaphum compresses an extension of the membranous labyrinth (inner ear) against the claustrum, stimulating the auditory region of the brain. Typical ostariophysans include (a) characins, (b) minnows, and (c) catfishes.

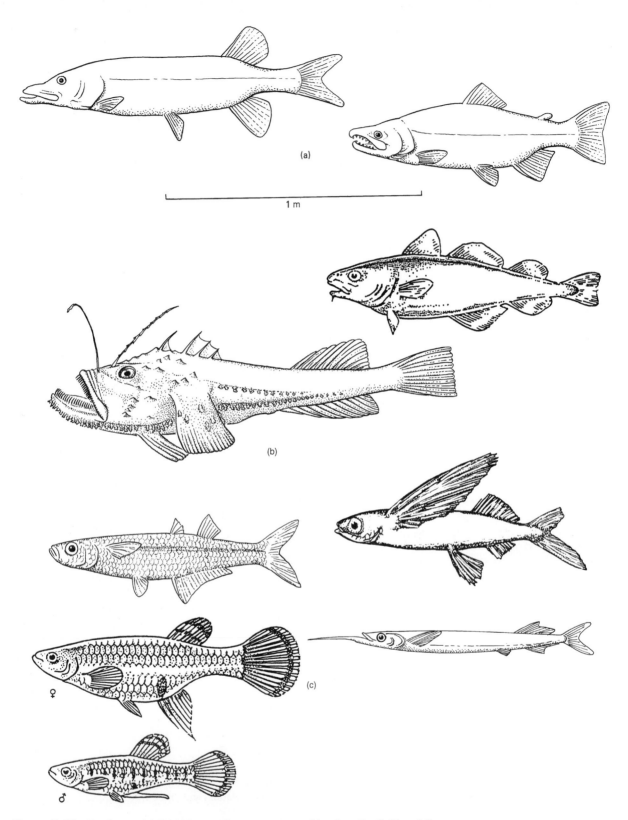

Figure 8–22 Euteleosts. (a) Primitive euteleosts represented by the pike (left) and the salmon (right); (b) Paracanthopterygians represented by the cod (right) and the goosefish angler (left). (c) Atherinomorph fishes represented by (clockwise from upper left) an Atlantic silverside (*Menidia*), a flying fish, a halfbeak, and live bearing killifish, the male of which has a modified anal fin used in internal fertilization. Not to scale.

euteleostean characters that are not valid for determining phylogenetic relationships. A new usage of the term includes only salmonids and some deepwater relatives and may be monophyletic (Stiassny et al. 1996). The salmonids include the anadromous salmon which usually spend their adult lives at sea, as well as the closely related trouts which live in fresh waters. Among the most primitive extant euteleosteans at the base of the radiation of all other more derived teleosts may be the esocids. These Northern Hemisphere temperate freshwater fishes include game species such as pickerel, pikes, and muskellunges and their relatives. The Southern Hemisphere galaxiids are also primitive euteleosts and live in habitats similar to those occupied by salmonids.

Mobile jaws and protective, lightweight spines in the median fins have evolved in several groups of teleosts. About 1200 species of fishes, including cods and anglerfishes, are grouped as the Paracanthopterygii, although their similarities may represent convergence (Figure 8–22b) However, the Acanthopterygii, or true spiny-rayed fishes, whose 13,500 species dominate the open ocean surface and shallow marine waters of the world, appear to be monophyletic. Among the acanthopterygians, the atherinomorphs have protrusible jaws and specializations of form and behavior that suit them to shallow marine and freshwater habitats. This group includes the silversides, grunions, flying fishes, halfbeaks, as well as the egg-laying and live-bearing cyprinodonts (Figure 8–22c). Killifish are examples of egg-laying cyprinodonts, and the live bearers include the guppies, mollies, and swordtails commonly maintained in home aquaria.

The majority of species of acanthopterygians and the largest order of fishes is the Perciformes, with over 9300 extant species (Nelson 1994). A few of the well-known members are snooks, sea basses, sunfishes, perches, darters, dolphins (mahi mahi), snappers, grunts, porgies, drums, cichlids, barracudas, tunas, billfish, and a majority of the fishes found on coral reefs.

■ Actinopterygian Reproduction and Conservation

Reproductive modes of actinopterygians show a greater diversity than is known in any other vertebrate taxon. Despite this diversity, the vast majority of ray-finned fishes are oviparous (producing eggs that develop outside the body of the mother). Within oviparous teleosts, marine and freshwater species show contrasting specializations.

Marine Teleosts

Most marine teleosts release large numbers of small, buoyant, transparent eggs into the water. These eggs are fertilized externally and left to develop and hatch while drifting in the open sea. The larvae are also small, and usually have little yolk reserve. They begin feeding on microplankton soon after hatching. Marine larvae are generally very different in appearance from their parents, and many larvae have been described for which the adult forms are unknown. Such larvae are often specialized for life in the oceanic plankton, feeding and growing while adrift at sea for weeks or months, depending on the species. The larvae eventually settle into the juvenile or adult habitats appropriate for their species. It is not yet generally understood whether arrival at the appropriate adult habitat (deep-sea floor, coral reef, or river mouth) is an active or passive process on the part of larvae. However, the arrival coincides with metamorphosis from larval to juvenile morphology in a matter of hours to days. Although juveniles are usually identifiable to species, relatively few premetamorphosis larvae have successfully been reared in captivity to resolve unknown larval relationships.

This strategy of producing planktonic eggs and larvae exposed to a prolonged and risky pelagic existence appears to be wasteful of gametes. Nevertheless, complex life cycles of this sort are the principal mode of reproduction of marine fishes. Several hypotheses have been proposed to explain this paradox (Thresher 1984). One view involves the selective advantages gained by reduction of some types of predation on their zygotes that fishes may achieve by spawning pelagically. Predators that would capture the zygotes may be abundant in the parental habitat but relatively absent from the pelagic realm. Pelagic spawning fishes often migrate to areas of strong currents to spawn, or spawn in synchrony with maximum monthly or annual tidal currents, thus assuring rapid offshore dispersal of their zygotes. A second hypothesis explaining the advantages of pelagic spawning involves the high biological productivity of the sunlit surface of the pelagic environment. Microplankton of the appropriate size for food of pelagic larvae (bacteria, algae, protozoans, rotifers, and minute crustaceans) are abundant where sufficient nutrients reach sunlit waters. If energy is limiting to the adult population, a successful strategy might be to produce eggs with a minimum of energy reserve (yolk) that hatch into specialized larvae able to use this pelagic productivity. A final hypothesis involves species-level selection. Floating, current-borne eggs and larvae increase the chances of young arriving at all possible patches of appropriate adult habitat. A widely dispersed species is not vulnerable to local environmental changes that could extinguish a species with a restricted geographic distribution. Perhaps the predominance of pelagic spawning species in the marine environment reflects the results of millions of years of extinctions of species with less dispersal-promoting habits.

Some marine species and the majority of freshwater species lay adhesive eggs on rocks or plants or in gravel or sand, where they may guard the spawn. Nests vary from depressions in sand or gravel to elaborate constructions of woven plant material held together by parental secretions. Species of marine fishes that construct nests are smaller than species that are pelagic spawners, perhaps because small species are better able to find secure nest sites than are large species. Parental guarding of eggs may be unwittingly assisted by other organisms near, on, or in which the eggs are laid. Among these are stinging anemones, mussels, crabs, sponges and tunicates. Perhaps the ultimate in protection of eggs is portage by one of the parents. Species are known that carry eggs on fins, under lips, in the mouth or gill cavities, or on specialized protuberances, skin patches, or even in pouches.

In spite of this diversity of reproductive habits among marine teleosts, the fact remains that the vast majority of species produce eggs that are shed into the environment with little further parental investment. These eggs tend to be small relative to the size of the adult fish, and they are produced in prodigious numbers. As a consequence of this reproductive characteristic of most marine and some freshwater teleosts, the number of individuals breeding in any given year (breeding stock size) bears no clear relationship to the number of individuals in the next generation (recruited stock year class strength). Thus, a breeding season rich with spawning adults may produce few or no offspring that survive to breed in subsequent seasons if environmental factors prevent the survival of eggs, larvae, or juveniles. Conversely, a few breeding

adults could, under exceptionally favorable circumstances, produce a very large number of offspring that survive to maturity. This is possible because of the large number of eggs a single female is capable of producing. The characteristic low predictability of future stock size based on current stock size has been a major stumbling block to effective fisheries management. Because so much of a population's future size depends on the environment experienced by eggs and larvae—conditions not usually obvious to fishermen or scientists—it is difficult to demonstrate the effects of overfishing in its early stages or the direct results of conservation efforts.

These inherent problems in fisheries management have resulted in destruction of commercial fish populations and entire marine foodwebs by overfishing (Pauly et al. 1998). Many of the world's richest fisheries are on the verge of collapse. The Georges Bank, which lies east of Cape Cod, is an example of what overfishing can do. For years, conservation organizations called for a reduction in catches of cod, yellowtail flounder, and haddock. They were not heeded, and populations of those fishes crashed dramatically in the 1990s. By October 1994, the situation was so bad that an industry group, the New England Fishery Management Council, directed its staff to devise measures that would reduce the catch of those species essentially to zero. Many of those bottom-dwelling fishes are caught unintentionally by vessels fishing for other species. Thus thousands of fishermen are affected by draconian measures such as complete moratoria on fishing. Some of them will shift their boats to other heavily fished areas, such as the mid-Atlantic coast and the Gulf of Mexico and the depletion process will repeat itself.

Freshwater Teleosts

In contrast to their marine counterparts, freshwater teleosts generally produce and care for a small number of large, nonplanktonic eggs that hatch into miniature but adultlike body forms and behaviors. This reproductive strategy in fresh water has been related to the flowing and ephemeral characteristics of upland waters, which could easily flush a larval fish from its preferred habitat. Large yolk-rich demersal eggs may be ancestral for actinopterygians, and parental care may have evolved frequently throughout the evolution of ray-finned fishes. Producing pelagic eggs and larvae may be a derived characteristic of euteleosts. To understand more precisely the myriad variations on these two basic themes of actinopterygian reproduction, it will be necessary to know more about the early life history of fishes in the wild (Box 8–1).

Like their economically important marine kin, freshwater actinopterygians are threatened by human activities. However, the nearly 40 percent of fish species that live in the world's fresh waters are *all* threatened, regardless of their economic value.

BOX 8–1 What a Fish's Ears Tell About Its Life

Following minute fish eggs or translucent larvae in the open sea or turbid rivers seems an insurmountable problem. However, there is an indirect method of tracing the details of the life history of an individual fish (Campana and Neilson 1985). A characteristic of Teleostomi is the presence of up to three compact mineralized structures suspended in the interior of each inner ear (Schultze 1990). These structures are especially well developed in the majority of teleosts, where these otoliths are often curiously shaped, fitting into the spaces of the membranous labyrinth very exactly and growing in proportion to the growth of the fish. They are important in orientation and locomotion, and they are formed in most teleosts during late incubation.

Otoliths grow in concentric layers much like the layers of an onion (Figure 8–23). Each of these layers reflects a day's growth. The relative width, density, and interruptions of the layers show the environmental conditions the individual encountered daily from hatching, including variations in temperature and food capture. Minute quantities of substances characteristic of the environment in which the fish has spent each day may also be incorporated in the bands, further enhancing the loglike nature of the otolith. A day-by-day record of the individual is written in its otoliths. It is even possible to imprint a permanent code in the otoliths by subjecting young fish to a series of temperature increases and decreases (Brothers 1990). Fishery managers are using this method to mark juvenile fishes before they are released. Years later, when the fishes are recaptured as adults, the code embedded in the otoliths shows which brood they belong to. While still fraught with problems of interpretation, the study of otolith microstructure is significantly advancing our understanding of reproduction and early life history of fishes (Thresher 1988, Kingsmill 1993).

Figure 8–23 Scanning electron micrograph of an otolith from a juvenile French grunt, *Haemulon flavolineatum*. The central area represents the focus of the otolith from which growth proceeds. The alternating dark and light rings are daily growth increments. Note that the width of the growth increments varies, signifying day-to-day variation in the rate of growth. (Photograph courtesy of Edward Brothers.)

This universal threat is the result of global alteration and pollution of lakes, rivers, and streams (Warren and Burr 1994). Draining, damming, canalization, and diversion of rivers create habitats that no longer sustain indigenous fishes. In addition to the loss and physical degradation of fish habitat, much of the world—especially the Western nations and urbanized regions elsewhere—has fresh waters polluted by silt and toxic chemicals of human origin (Allan and Flecker 1993).

The United States has had, in recent years, over 2,400 instances *annually* of beaches and flowing waterways closed to human use because of pollution. These sites are too dangerous to human health for people to play in them, and those conditions are often lethal to organisms trying to live in them! Of the nearly 800 species of native freshwater fishes in the United States, almost 20 percent are considered imperiled. As much as 85 percent of the fish fauna of some states is endangered, threatened, or of special concern.

■ Deep Sea Fishes

Of all regions on Earth, the deep sea is the least studied. Two major life zones exist in the sea: the **pelagic**, where organisms live a free-floating or swimming existence, and the benthic, where organisms associate with the bottom (Figure 8–24). Solar light is totally extinguished at a depth of 1000 meters in the clearest oceans and at much shallower depths in the less clear coastal seas. As a result, about 75 percent of the ocean is perpetually dark, illuminated only by the flashes and glow of bioluminescent organisms. A distinctive and bizarre array of deep-sea fishes with representatives from five orders has evolved in those zones.

The abundance, size, and species diversity of fishes decrease as you descend into the ocean depths. These trends are not surprising, for all animals ultimately depend on plant photosynthesis, which is limited to the epipelagic regions. Below the epipelagic, animals must depend on descent of food from above—a rain of detritus from the surface into the deep sea. The decrease of fishes with depth is inevitable, for the amount of food available must diminish if it is consumed during descent. Sampling confirms this decrease in food: Surface plankton can reach biomass levels of 500 milligrams wet mass per cubic meter; at a depth of 1000 meters, where aphotic conditions commence,

plankton decrease to 25 milligrams per cubic meter; at depths of 3000 to 4000 meters, to 5 milligrams per cubic meter; and at 10,000 meters, to 0.5 milligram per cubic meter.

Fish diversity parallels this decrease: About 800 species of deep-sea fishes are estimated to occupy the mesopelagic zones and only 150 species the bathypelagic regions. Deep seas that lie under areas of high surface productivity contain more and larger fish species than do regions that underlie less productive surface waters. High productivity occurs in areas of upwelling, where currents recycle nutrients previously removed by the sinking of detritus. In these places deep-sea fishes tend to be most diverse and abundant.

In tropical waters, photosynthesis continues throughout the year. Away from the tropics it is more cyclic, following seasonal changes in light, temperature, and sometimes currents. Diversity and abundance of deep-sea fishes decrease away from the tropics. Over 300 species of meso- and bathypelagic fishes occur in the vicinity of tropical Bermuda. In the entire Antarctic region, only 50 species have been described. The high productivity of Antarctic waters is restricted to a few months of each year. Apparently, the sinking of detritus through the rest of the year is insufficient to nourish a diverse assemblage of deep-sea fishes.

We emphasize that availability of food (energy) is the most formidable environmental problem that deep-sea fishes encounter and, indeed, many of their specific characteristics may have been selected by food scarcity. Another variable factor is hydrostatic pressure, whereas low temperature and the absence of light are constants.

Mesopelagic Fishes

With increased depth each species is further removed from a primary source of food. In general, mesopelagic fishes and invertebrates, which inhabit depths from 100 to 1000 meters, migrate vertically. At dusk they ascend toward the surface, only to descend again near dawn apparently following light-intensity levels (Figure 8–25). Several benefits and costs probably result from this behavior. By rising at dusk, mesopelagic fishes enter a region of higher productivity where food is more concentrated. However, they also increase their exposure to predators. Furthermore, ascending mesopelagic fishes are exposed to temperature increases that can exceed 10°C. The energy costs of maintenance at

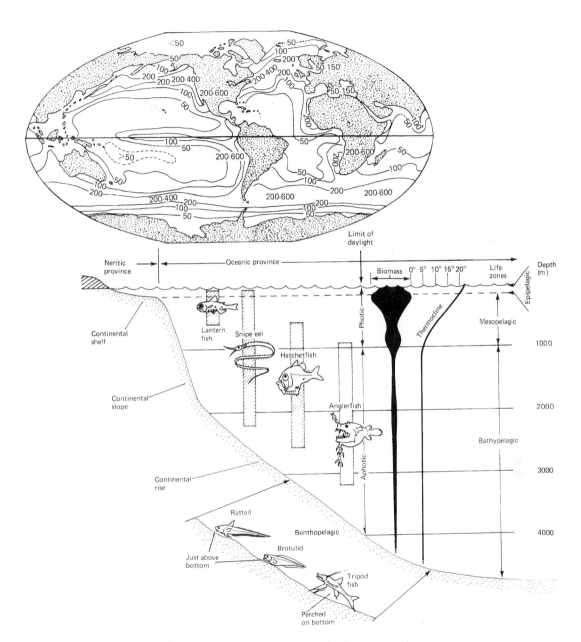

Figure 8–24 Life zones of the ocean depths. (a) Annual productivity at the ocean surface. Numbers are grams of carbon produced per square meter per year. Rich assemblages of deep-sea fishes occur where highly productive waters overlie deep waters. (b) Schematic cross section of the life zones within the deep sea. Various pertinent physical and biotic parameters are superimposed on the arbitrary life zones, as are the vertical ranges of several characteristic fish species, some of which migrate on a daily basis. ([a] Modified from H. Friedrich, 1973, *Marine Biology* University, of Washington Press, Seattle, WA; [b] modified from N. B. Marshall, 1971, *Explorations of the Life of Fishes,* Harvard University Press, Cambridge, MA.)

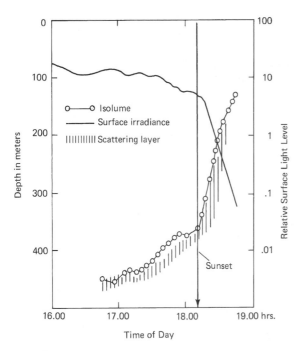

Figure 8–25 Upward migration of mesopelagic fishes as indicated by changes in depth of deep scattering layer. Sonar signals readily reflect off the swim bladders of mesopelagic fishes, and aggregations of them produce an acoustic scattering layer. At sunset the intensity of light at the surface decreases (right axis) as does the light penetrating the sea. Plotting the depth of a single light intensity (isolume, read depth on left axis) against time illustrates the progressively shallower depth at which a given light intensity occurs during dusk. The light intensity chosen for this example falls between that of starlight and full moonlight, and it corresponds closely with the upper boundary of the deep scattering layer, which rises rapidly with the upward migration of mesopelagic fishes. (Modified from E. M. Kampa and B. P. Boden, 1957, *Deep-Sea Research* 4:73–92.)

these higher temperatures can double, or even triple. In contrast, daytime descent into cooler waters lowers metabolism, which conserves energy and reduces the chance of predation because fewer predators exist at increased depth.

Bathypelagic Fishes

It is less certain that bathypelagic fishes undertake daily vertical migrations. There is little metabolic economy from vertical migration within this aphotic zone because temperatures are uniform (about 5°C). Furthermore, the cost and time of migration over the several thousand meters from the bathypelagic region to the surface would probably outweigh the energy gained from invading the rich surface waters. Instead of migrating, bathypelagic fishes are specialized to live a less active life than those of their meso- and epipelagic counterparts.

Pelagic deep-sea fishes display a series of structures related to their particular life-styles. For example, eye size and function correlate with depth. Mesopelagic fishes have large eyes, pelagic fishes have smaller eyes, and benthic fishes vary in eye size. The retina contains a high concentration of visual pigment, the photosensitive chemical that absorbs light in the process of vision. The visual pigments of deep-sea fishes are most efficient in absorbing blue light, which is the wavelength of light that is most readily transmitted through clear water. Many deep-sea fishes and invertebrates are emblazoned with startling bioluminescent designs formed by photophore organs that emit blue light. (See color insert.)

Deep-sea fishes have less dense bone and less skeletal muscle than do fishes from shallower depths (Figure 8–26). Surface fishes have strong ossified skeletons and large red muscles especially adapted for continuous cruising. Mesopelagic fishes, which swim mostly during vertical migration, have a more delicate skeleton and less axial red muscle. In bathypelagic fishes, the axial skeleton and the mass of muscles are greatly reduced and locomotion is limited.

The jaws and teeth of deep-sea fishes are often enormous in proportion to the rest of the body. If a fish rarely encounters potential prey, it is probably important to have a mouth large enough to engulf nearly anything it does meet and a gut that can extend to accommodate a meal (Figure 8–27). Increasing the chances of encountering prey is also important to survival in the deep sea. Rather than searching for prey through the blackness of the depths, the **ceratioid** anglerfishes dangle a bioluminescent bait in front of them. The bioluminescent lure is believed to mimic the movements of zooplankton and to lure fishes and larger crustaceans to the mouth. Prey is sucked in with a sudden opening of the mouth, snared in the teeth, and then swallowed. The jaws of many anglerfishes expand and the stomach stretches to accommodate prey larger than the predator. Thus deep-sea fishes, like most teleosts, show major specializations in locomotor and feeding structures. Unlike surface teleosts, however, the scarcity of food has selected for structures

Figure 8–26 Reduction of bone in deep-sea fishes. X-rays show the reduced bone density of mesopelagic and bathypelagic fishes compared to a surface dweller. Top: The surface-dwelling jackfish (Carangidae). Middle: A mesopelagic, vertically migrating lanternfish (Myctophidae). Bottom: A mesopelagic, deep-living bristlemouth (Gonostomatidae). (Source: F. Harvey Pough.)

that minimize the costs of foraging and maximize the capture of prey.

Most features of the biology of deep-sea fishes are directly related to the scarcity of food, but in some cases the relationship is indirect. For example, most species are small (the average length is less than 5 centimeters) and individuals of a species are not abundant. In so vast a habitat the number of anglerfishes (ceratioids) when most concentrated does not exceed 150,000 individuals per cubic mile. This estimate represents all ceratioid species. The density of females in the most common species is typically less than one female per cubic mile. Imagine trying to find another human under similar circumstances! Yet to reproduce, each fish must locate a mate and recognize it as its own species.

Distinctive bioluminescent patterns characterize the males and females of many bathypelagic fishes (see Figure 8–28 and the color insert). Tiny, light-producing organs called photophores are arranged on their bodies in species- and even sex-specific patterns. The light is produced by symbiotic species of *Photobacterium* and previously unknown groups of bacteria related to *Vibrio* (Haygood and Distel 1993). Some photophores probably act as signals to conspecifics in the darkness of the deep sea, where mates may be difficult to find. Others, such as those in the modified fin ray lures of anglerfishes, probably attract prey. Female anglerfishes possess a bioluminescent lure that is species-specific in appearance. Although it is used to lure prey, the bait is probably also used to attract males. Visual detection of other individuals much beyond 40 or 50 meters is not possible, however, because light does not travel far in water and other senses must be used. Scent trails are used by many deep-sea fishes. The females secrete a pheromone, and males usually have enlarged olfactory organs. Sensing the pheromone during searching movements, males swim upstream to an intimate encounter.

The life history of ceratioid anglerfishes dramatizes how selection adapts a vertebrate to its habitat. The adults typically spend their lives in aphotic regions below 1000 meters. Fertilized eggs, however, rise to the surface, where they hatch into larvae. The larvae remain mostly in the upper 30 meters where they grow, and later descend to the aphotic region. Descent is accompanied by metamorphic changes that differentiate females and males. During metamorphosis, young females descend to great depths, where they feed and grow slowly, reaching maturity after several years. Many species resemble a large mouth accompanied by a stomach, a description that certainly fits their appearance.

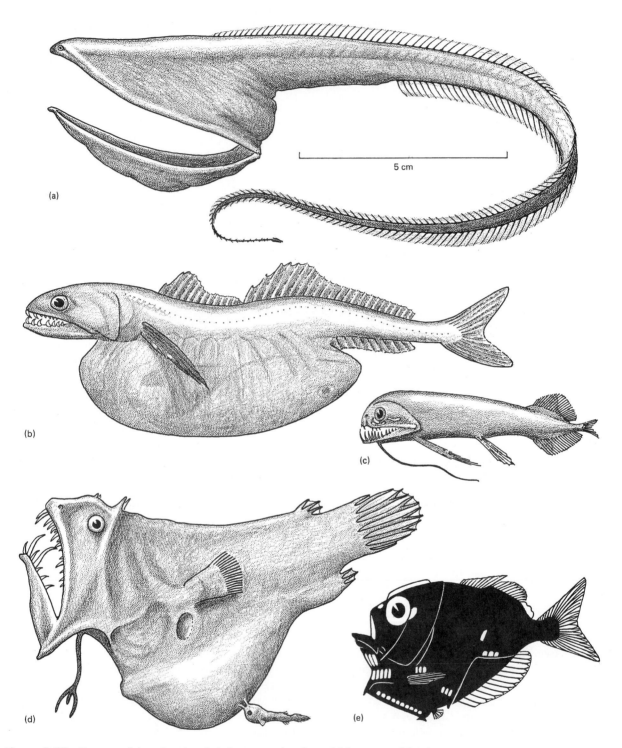

Figure 8–27   Deep-sea fishes showing their large mouths, distendable guts, and luminescent organs. (a) Pelican eel, *Eurypharynx pelecanoides;* (b) deep-sea perch, *Chiasmodus niger,* its belly distended by a fish bigger than itself; (c) stomiatoid, *Aristostomias grimaldii;* (d) female angler-fish, *Liophryne argyresca,* with a parasitic male attached to her belly; (e) hatchet fish, *Sternoptyx diaphana.* The light areas are luminous photophores.

Female anglerfishes feed throughout their lives, whereas males feed only during the larval stage. Metamorphic changes in males prepare them for a different future, for their function is reproduction, literally by lifelong matrimony. The body may elongate and axial red muscles develop. The males cease eating, and the enlarged liver apparently provides energy for an extended period of swimming. The olfactory organs of males enlarge at metamorphosis and the eyes continue to grow. These changes suggest that adolescent males spend a brief, but active, free-swimming period concentrated on finding a female. The search must be precarious, for males must search vast, dark regions for a single female while running a gauntlet of other deep-sea predators. In the young adults there is an unbalanced sex ratio; often more than 30 males exist for every female. Apparently, at least 29 of those males cannot expect to locate a virgin female.

Having found a female, a male does not want to lose her, and he ensures a permanent union by attaching himself as a parasite to the female. When a male finds a female, he bites into her flesh and attaches himself firmly. Preparation for this encounter begins during metamorphosis when the male's teeth degenerate and strong toothlike bones develop at the tips of the jaws. A male remains attached to the female for life, and in this parasitic state he grows and his testes mature. Monogamy prevails in this pairing, for females invariably have but one attached male. As humans we consider this life-style bizarre, and, indeed, it is unknown among other vertebrates. But it has been successful—some 200 ceratioid species exist. The lesson these unique fishes provide is that vertebrate life is a plastic venture capable of adapting to extreme conditions. In the ceratioids, two features stand out: efficient energy use and reproduction. Actually, adaptations in all vertebrates relate to these two goals, but they are not often painted in such bold relief.

■ Extant Sarcopterygii: Lobe-Finned Fishes

Although they were abundant in the Devonian, the number of primarily aquatic sarcopterygians dwindled in the late Paleozoic and Mesozoic. (All terrestrial vertebrates are technically sarcopterygians, so the total number of extant sarcopterygians is enormous.) The early evolution of sarcopterygians resulted in a significant radiation in fresh and marine waters. Today only four nontetrapod genera remain: the dipnoans or lungfishes (*Protopterus* in Africa, *Lepidosiren* in South America, *Neoceratodus* in Australia; Figure 8–28), and the actinistian *Latimeria* (the coelacanth) in waters 260 to 300 meters deep near the Comoro Archipelago off East Africa (Figure 8–29). We will discuss fossil sarcopterygians in more detail with their sister group, the tetrapods, in Chapter 10.

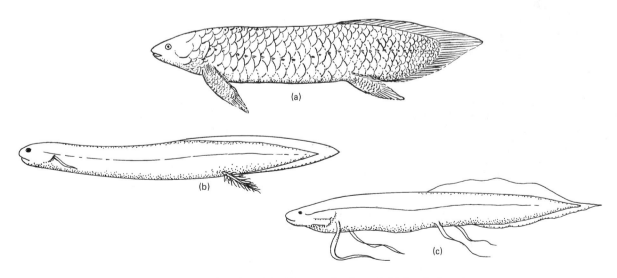

Figure 8–28 Extant dipnoans. (a) Australian lungfish, *Neoceratodus forsteri*; (b) South American lungfish, *Lepidosiren paradoxa*, male; note the specialized pelvic fins of the male. These vascularized extensions develop during the breeding season and are probably used to supply oxygen from the male's blood to the young in the nest cavity; (c) African lungfish, *Protopterus*.

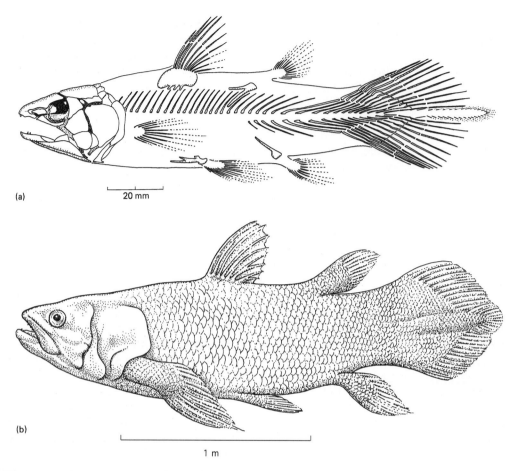

Figure 8–29 Representative Actinistia (coelacanths). (a) *Rhabdoderma*, a Carboniferous actinistian; (b) *Latimeria chalumnae*, the extant coelacanth.

Dipnoans

The Dipnoi are distinguishable by the lack of articulated tooth-bearing premaxillary and maxillary bones and the fusion of the palatoquadrate to the undivided cranium. The teeth are scattered over the palate and fused into tooth ridges along the lateral palatal margins. Powerful adductor muscles of the lower jaw spread upward over the neurocranium. Throughout their evolution, this durophagous (feeding on hard foods) crushing apparatus has persisted. The earliest dipnoans were marine. During the Devonian, lungfishes evolved a body form quite distinct from the other Osteichthyes. The median fins fused around the posterior third of the body; the caudal fin, originally heterocercal, became symmetrical; and the mosaic of small dermal bones of the earliest dipnoan skulls (often covered by a continuous sheet of cosmine, an enameloid substance) evolved a pattern of fewer large elements without the cosmine cover. The majority of this transforma-

tion can be explained as a result of paedomorphosis (Bemis in Bemis et al. 1987). Extant dipnoans are probably not very different from their Late Devonian ancestors (Thomson 1969).

The monotypic Australian lungfish, *Neoceratodus forsteri,* is morphologically most similar to Paleozoic and Mesozoic Dipnoi. Like all other extant dipnoans, *Neoceratodus* is restricted to fresh waters; naturally occurring populations are limited to southeastern Queensland. The Australian lungfish may attain a length of 1.5 meters and a reported weight of 45 kilograms. It swims by body undulations or slowly walks across the bottom of a pond on its pectoral and pelvic appendages. Chemical senses seem important to lungfishes, and their mouths contain numerous taste buds. The nasal passages are located near the upper lip, with the incurrent openings on the rostrum just outside the mouth and the excurrent openings within the oral cavity. Thus, gill ventilation draws water across the nasal epithelium. *Neoceratodus* respires almost exclusively via its gills and uses its single lung only when stressed. Little is known of its behavior. Although lungfishes go through a complex courtship, which perhaps includes male territoriality and are very selective about the vegetation upon which they lay their adhesive eggs, no parental care has been observed after spawning. The jelly-coated eggs, 3 millimeters in diameter, hatch in 3 to 4 weeks, but the young have proved elusive and nothing is known of their juvenile life. Surprisingly little is known about the single South American lungfish, *Lepidosiren paradoxa,* but the closely related African lungfishes, *Protopterus,* with four recognized species, are better known. These two genera are distinguished by different numbers of weakly developed gills. Because their gills are very small, these lungfishes drown if they are prevented from using their paired lungs. Nevertheless, the gills are important in eliminating carbon dioxide. These thin-scaled, heavy-bodied, elongate fishes, 1 or 2 meters long, have unique filamentous and highly mobile paired appendages. For a time after their discovery 150 years ago lungfishes were considered to be specialized urodele amphibians (salamanders), which they do superficially resemble. Although the skeletons of these lungfishes are mostly cartilaginous, their tooth plates are heavily mineralized and fossilize readily.

One habit of some species of African dipnoans, estivation, considerably increases the chance of fossilization. Similar in some ways to hibernation, estivation is induced by drying of the habitat rather than by cold. African lungfishes frequent areas that flood during the wet season and bake during the dry season—habitats not available to actinopterygians except by immigration during floods. The lungfishes enjoy the flood periods, feeding heavily and growing rapidly. When the flood waters recede, the lungfish digs a vertical burrow in the mud that ends in an enlarged chamber and varies in length in proportion to the size of the animal, the deepest being less than a meter. As drying proceeds, the lungfish becomes more lethargic and breathes air from the burrow opening. Eventually, even the water of the burrow dries up, and the lungfish enters the final stages of estivation. In the deep chamber, the lungfish remains folded into a U-shape with its tail over its eyes. Heavy mucus secretions the fish has produced since entering the burrow condense and dry to form a protective envelope around its body. Only an opening at its mouth remains to permit breathing.

Although the rate of energy consumption during estivation is very low, metabolism continues, using muscle proteins as an energy source. Lungfishes normally spend less than 6 months in estivation, but they have been revived after 4 years of enforced estivation. When the rains return, the withered and shrunken lungfish becomes active and feeds voraciously. In less than a month it regains its previous size.

Estivation is an ancient trait of dipnoans. Fossil burrows containing lungfish tooth plates have been found in Carboniferous and Permian deposits of North America and Europe. Without the unwitting assistance of the lungfishes, which initiated fossilization by burying themselves, such fossils might not exist.

Actinistians

Actinistians are unknown before the Middle Devonian. Their hallmarks are fleshy lobed fins except for an unlobed first dorsal fin and a unique symmetrical three-lobed tail with a central fleshy lobe that ends in a fringe of rays (Figure 8–29). Actinistians also differ from all other sarcopterygians in the head bones (they lack, among other elements, a maxilla), in details of the fin structure, and in the presence of a curious rostral organ. Following rapid evolution during the Devonian, the actinistians show a history of stability. Late Devonian actinistians differ from the more recent Cretaceous fossils mostly in the degree of skull ossification. Some early actinistians lived in shallow fresh waters, but the fossil remains of these and other osteichthyans during the Mesozoic are largely marine. The osteichthyans radiated into a variety of niches, but the actinistians retained their peculiar form. Fossil actinistians are not known after the Cretaceous, and until 60 years ago they were thought to be extinct.

In 1938, an African fisherman bent over an unfamiliar catch from the Indian Ocean and nearly lost his hand to its ferocious snap. Imagine the astonishment of the scientific community when J. L. B. Smith of Rhodes University announced that the catch was an actinistian. This large fish was so similar to Mesozoic fossil coelacanths that its systematic position was unquestionable. Smith named this living fossil *Latimeria chalumnae* in honor of his former student Courtenay Latimer, who saw the strange catch, recognized it as unusual and brought the specimen to his attention (Smith 1956).

Despite public appeals, no further specimens of *Latimeria* were captured until 1952. Since then more than 150 specimens ranging in size from 75 centimeters to slightly over 2 meters and weighing from 13 to 80 kilograms have been caught, all in the Comoro Archipelago between Madagascar and Mozambique. Coelacanths are hooked near the bottom, usually in 260 to 300 meters of water about 1.5 kilometers offshore. Strong and aggressive, *Latimeria* is steely blue-gray with irregular white spots and reflective golden eyes. The reflection comes from a tapetum lucidum that enhances visual ability in dim light. A large cavity in the midline of the snout communicates with the exterior by three pairs of rostral tubes enclosed by canals in the wall of the chondrocranium. These tubes are filled with gelatinous material and open to the surface through a series of six pores. The rostral organ is almost certainly an electroreceptor (Bemis and Hetherington 1982). *Latimeria* is a predator—stomachs have contained fishes and cephalopods.

A fascinating glimpse of the life of the coelacanth was reported by Hans Fricke and his colleagues who used a small submarine to observe the fishes (Fricke et al. 1987; Fricke 1988). They saw six coelacanths at depths between 117 and 198 meters off a short stretch of the shoreline of one of the Comoro Islands. Coelacanths were seen only in the middle of the night and only on or near the bottom. Unlike extant lungfishes, the coelacanths did not use their paired fins as props or to walk across the bottom. However, when they swam the pectoral and pelvic appendages were moved in the same sequence as tetrapods move their limbs.

The discovery of *Latimeria* has confirmed earlier reconstructions based on coelacanth fossils (Thomson 1986, Musick et al. 1991). A case in point is the mode of coelacanth reproduction. In 1927, D. M. S. Watson described two small skeletons from inside the body cavity of *Undina*, a Jurassic coelacanth, and suggested that coelacanths gave birth to their young. Because copulatory structures have never been found on any coelacanth fossil, some dismissed Watson's specimen as a case of cannibalism. Female *Latimeria* containing up to 19 spherical eggs, each 9 centimeters in diameter, have now been captured. R. W. Griffith and K. S. Thomson surmised that Watson was correct because of the small number of eggs and their lack of a shell or other coating to provide osmotic protection if released into the sea. While C. L. Smith and others at the American Museum of Natural History were dissecting a 1.6-meter specimen they discovered five young, each 30 centimeters long and at an advanced stage of embryonic development, in the single oviduct. Internal fertilization must occur, but how copulation is achieved is unknown, since males show no specialized copulatory organs. In spite of some excellent fossils and numerous specimen of the extant coelacanths, there has never been stable agreement about the relationships of the Actinistia with other gnathostomes. Workers have disagreed about the position of the coelacanths more than that of most other vertebrate taxa. In part this is due to the surprising combinations of morphology and physiology shown by *Latimeria*, which has many derived characters, some of which are most similar to Chondrichthyes, others to the Dipnoi, some to Actinopterygii, and also a curious collection of unique features (McCosker and Lagios 1979). Currently it is generally agreed that coelacanths are the sister group of the lineage that produced the lungfishes and the tetrapods (Stiassny et al. 1996).

■ Summary

Because of its physical properties, water is a demanding medium for vertebrate life. Nevertheless, the greatest number of vertebrate species, the vast majority of them Osteichthyes, are found exclusively in the planet's oceans, lakes, and rivers. Highly efficient respiratory systems, the gills facilitate rapid oxygen uptake to sustain the activity of fishes. Their locomotion is generally accomplished with undulations produced by contraction of the body muscles. Sensory guidance for activity is often visual, but other sensory systems also are highly refined. Fishes detect low-frequency pressure waves via the lateral line system or navigate and communicate through electroreception.

At their first appearance in the fossil record, osteichthyans, the largest vertebrate taxon, are separable into distinct lineages. The Sarcopterygii (fleshy-finned fishes: lungfishes, actinistians, and other lobe-finned fishes) and the Actinopterygii (ray-finned fishes) show indications of common ancestry. Extant sarcopterygian fishes offer exciting glimpses of adaptations evolved in Paleozoic environments. Actinopterygian fishes were distinct as early as the Silurian. Actinopterygians inhabit the 73 percent of the Earth's surface that is covered by water and are the most numerous and species rich lineages of vertebrates. Several levels of development in food-gathering and locomotory structures characterize actinopterygian evolution. The radiations of these levels are represented today by relict groups: cladistians bichirs and reedfishes), chondrosteans (sturgeons and paddlefishes), and the primitive neopterygians (gars and *Amia*). The most derived level—teleosteans—may number close to 24,000 extant species with two groups, ostariophysans in fresh water and acanthopterygians in seawater, constituting a large proportion of these species.

■ References

Allan, J. D., and A. S. Flecker. 1993. Biodiversity conservation in running water. *Bioscience* 43:32–43.

Bass, A. H. 1986. Electric organs revisited: evolution of vertebrate communication and orientation organs. Pages 13–70 In *Electroreception*, edited by T. H. Bullock and W. Heiligenberg. Wiley, New York, NY.

Bastian, J. 1994. Electrosensory organisms. *Physics Today* 47(2):30–37.

Bemis, W. E., W. W. Burggren, and N. E. Kemp (editors). 1987. *The Biology and Evolution of Lungfishes*. Liss, New York, NY.

Bemis, W. E., and T. E. Hetherington. 1982. The rostral organ of *Latimeria chalumnae*. Morphological evidence of an electroreceptive function. *Copeia* 1982:467–471.

Bemis, W. E., and R. G. Northcutt. 1992. Skin and blood vessels of the snout of the Australian lungfish, *Neoceratodus forsteri*, and their significance for interpreting the cosmine of Devonian lungfishes. *Acta Zoologica* (Stockholm) 73(2):115–139.

Bennett, M. V. L. 1971a. Electric organs. Pages 347–491 in *Fish Physiology*, volume 5. *Sensory Systems and Electric Organs*, edited by W. S. Hoar and D. J. Randall. Academic, New York, NY.

Bennett, M. V. L. 1971b. Electroreception. Pages 493–574 in *Fish Physiology*, volume 5. *Sensory Systems and Electric Organs*, edited by W. S Hoar and D. J. Randall. Academic, New York, NY.

Birstein, V. J., J. R. Waldman, and W. E. Bemis (editors). 1997. Sturgeon biodiversity and conservation. *Environmental Biology of Fishes* 48 (1–4):9–435.

Bodznick, D., and R. G. Northcutt. 1981. Electroreception in lampreys: evidence that the earliest vertebrates were electroreceptive. *Science* 212:465–467.

Bond, C. E. 1996. *Biology of Fishes*, 2d edition. Saunders College Publishing, Fort Worth, TX.

Bone, Q., and N. B. Marshall. 1982. *Biology of Fishes*. Blackie & Son, Glasgow, UK.

Brothers, E. B. 1990. Otolith marking. *American Fisheries Society Symposium* 7:183–202.

Burggren, W., and W. E. Bemis. 1992. Metabolism and ram gill ventilation in juvenile paddlefish, *Polyodon spathula* (Chondrostei: Polyodontidae). *Physiological Zoology* 65:515–539.

Campana, S. E., and J. D. Neilson. 1985. Microstructure of fish otoliths. *Canadian Journal of Fisheries and Aquatic Science* 42:1014–1032.

Cromie, W. J. 1982. Born to navigate. *Mosaic* 13(4):17–23.

Denison, R. H. 1979. *Acanthodii*. In *Handbook of Paleoichthyology*, volume 5. Gustav Fischer, Stuttgart, Germany.

Farrell, A. P. 1980. Vascular pathways in the gill of ling cod, *Ophiodon elongatus*. *Canadian Journal of Zoology* 58:796–806.

Fessard, A. (editor). 1974. Electroreceptors and other specialized receptors in lower vertebrates. Pages 59–124 in *Handbook of Sensory Physiology*, volume 3, part 3. Springer, New York, NY.

Fricke, H. 1988. Coelacanths, the fish that time forgot. *National Geographic* 173:824–838.

Fricke, H., O. Reinicke, H. Hofer, and W. Nachtigall. 1987. Locomotion of the coelacanth *Latimeria chalumnae* in its natural environment. *Nature* 324:331–333.

Graham, J. B. 1997. *Air-Breathing Fishes*. Academic, San Diego, CA.

Grande L., and W. E. Bemis. 1991. Osteology and phylogenetic relationships of fossil and Recent paddlefishes (Polyodontidae) with comments on the interrelationships of Acipenseriformes. *Journal of Vertebrate Paleontology* Special Memoir No. 1, 11(1):supplement 1–121.

Grande L., and W. E. Bemis. 1997. A comprehensive phylogenetic study of amiid fishes (Amiidae) based on comparative skeletal anatomy. *Journal of Vertebrate Paleontology* Memoir No. 4, 17.

Haygood, M. C., and D. L Distel. 1993. Bioluminescent symbionts of flashlight fishes and deep-sea anglerfishes form unique lineages related to the genus *Vibrio*. *Nature* 363:154–156.

Janvier, P. 1996. *Early Vertebrates*. Clarendon Press, Oxford, UK.

Kingsmill, S. 1993. Ear stones speak volumes to fish researchers. *Science* 260:1233–1234.

Lauder, G. V. 1980a. Evolution of the feeding mechanism in primitive actinopterygian fishes: a functional anatomical analysis of *Polypterus, Lepisosteus* and *Amia*. *Journal of Morphology* 163:283–317.

Lauder, G. V. 1980b. On the evolution of the jaw adductor musculature in primitive gnathostome fishes. *Breviora* 460:1–10.

Lauder, G. V. 1980c. Hydrodynamics of prey capture by teleost fishes. *Biofluid Mechanics* 2:161–181.

Lauder, G. V. 1994. Caudal fin locomotion by teleost fishes: function of the homocercal tail. *American Zoologist* 34(5): 13A abst. No. 66.

Lauder, G. V., and K. F. Liem. 1981. Prey capture by *Luciocephalus pulcher*: implications for models of jaw protrusion in teleost fishes. *Environmental Biology of Fishes* 6:257–268.

Lauder, G. V., and K. F. Liem. 1983. The evolution and inter-relationships of the actinopterygian fishes. *Bulletin of the Museum of Comparative Zoology* 150:95–197.

Lauder, G. V., and J. H. Long (editors). 1996. Aquatic locomotion: New approaches to invertebrate and vertebrate biomechanics. *American Zoologist* 36:535–709.

Laurent, P., and S. Dunel. 1980. Morphology of gill epithelia in fish. *American Journal of Physiology* 238:147–149 (R).

Lindsey, C. C. 1978. Form, function, and locomotory habits in fish. Pages 1–100 in *Fish Physiology,* volume 7, *Locomotion,* edited by W. S. Hoar and D. J. Randall. Academic, New York, NY.

Long, J. H., Jr., M. E. Hale, M. J. McHenry, and M. W. Westneat. 1996. Functions of fish skin: flexural stiffness and steady swimming of longnose gar *Lepisosteus osseus. Journal of Experimental Biology* 199:2139–2151.

Magnuson, J. J. 1978. Locomotion by scombroid fishes: hydromechanics, morphology, and behavior. Pages 239–313 in *Fish Physiology,* volume 7, *Locomotion,* edited by W. S. Hoar and D. J. Randall. Academic, New York, NY.

McCosker, J. E., and M. D. Lagios (editors). 1979. The biology and physiology of the living coelacanth. *California Academy of Sciences Occasional Papers* 134:1–175.

McCune, A. R. 1996. Biogeographic and stratigraphic evidence for rapid speciation in semionotid fishes. *Paleobiology* 22(1):34–48.

McCune, A. R. 1997. How fast is speciation: molecular, geologic and phylogenetic evidence from adaptive radiations of fishes. In *Molecular Evolution and Adaptive Radiation,* edited by T. Givnish and K. Sytsma. Cambridge University Press, Cambridge, Mass.

McCune, A. R., and N. R. Lovejoy. 1998. The relative rate of sympatric and allopatric speciation in fishes: tests using DNA sequence divergence between sister species and among clades. In *Endless Forms: Species and Speciation.* Edited by D. Howard and S. Berlocher, Oxford Press, Oxford, UK.

Moyle, P. B., and J. J. Cech, Jr. 1996. *Fishes: An Introduction to Ichthyology.* Prentice Hall, Upper Saddle River, NJ.

Musick, J. A., M. N. Bruton, and E. K. Balon (editors). 1991. The biology of *Latimeria chalumnae* and evolution of coelacanths. *Environmental Biology of Fishes* 32(1-4):9–435.

Nelson, J. S. 1994. *Fishes of the World,* 3d edition. Wiley, New York, NY.

Norman, J. R., and P. H. Greenwood. 1975. *A History of Fishes,* 3d edition. Ernest Benn, London, UK.

Pauly, D., V. Christensen, J. Dalsgaard, R. Froese, and F. Torres, Jr. 1998. Fishing down marine food webs. *Science* 279:860–863.

Paxton, J. R., and W. N. Eschmeyer (editors). 1994. *Encyclopedia of Fishes.* Academic, San Diego, CA.

Popper, A. N., and S. Coombs. 1980. Auditory mechanisms in teleost fishes. *American Scientist* 68:429–440.

Rome, L. C., D. Swank, and D. Corda. 1993. How fish power swim. *Science* 261:340–343.

Rosen, D. E. 1982. Teleostean interrelationships, morphological function and evolutionary inference. *American Zoologist* 22:261–273.

Schaeffer, B., and D. E. Rosen. 1961. Major adaptive levels in the evolution of the actinopterygian feeding mechanism. *American Zoologist* 1:187–204.

Scheich, H., G. Langner, C. Tidemann, R. B. Coles, and A. Guppy. 1986. Electroreception and electrolocation in platypus. *Nature* 319:401–402.

Schultze, H. P. 1990. A new acanthodian from the Pennsylvanian of Utah, U.S.A., and the distribution of otoliths in gnathostomes. *Journal of Vertebrate Paleontology* 10:49–58.

Smith, J. L. B. 1956. *Old Four Legs.* Longman, London, UK.

Stiassny, M. L., L. R. Parenti, and G. D. Johnson. 1996. *Interrelationships of Fishes.* Academic, San Diego, CA.

Stix, G. 1994. Robotuna. *Scientific American* 270(1):142.

Tavolga, W. N., A. N. Popper, and R. R. Fay (editors). 1981. *Hearing and Sound Communication in Fishes.* Springer, New York, NY.

Thomson, K. S. 1969. The biology of the lobe-finned fishes. *Biological Review* 44:91–154.

Thomson, K. S. 1986. Marginalia: a fishy story. *American Scientist* 74(2)169–171.

Thresher, R. E. 1984. *Reproduction in Reef Fishes.* T. F. H. Publications, Neptune City, NJ.

Thresher, R. E. 1988. Otolith microstructure and the demography of coral reef fishes. *Trends in Ecology and Evolution* 3:78–80.

Triantafyllou, M. S., and G. S. Triantafyllou. 1995. An efficient swimming machine. *Scientific American* 274(3):64–70.

Val, A. L. , and V. M. Almeida-Val. 1995. *Fishes of the Amazon and their environment: physiological and biochemical aspects.* Springer Verlag, New York.

Warren, M. L., Jr., and B. M. Burr. 1994. Status of fresh water fishes of the United States: overview of an imperiled fauna. *Fisheries* 19:6–18.

Webb, P. W. 1984. Form and function in fish swimming. *Scientific American* 251:72–82.

Webb, P. W., and R. W. Blake. 1985. Swimming. Pages 110–128 in *Functional Vertebrate Morphology,* edited by M. Hildebrand, D. M. Bramble, K. F. Liem, and D. B. Wake. Belknap, Cambridge, MA.

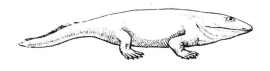

CHAPTER
9

Geography and Ecology from the Mid-Devonian to the Late Permian

Terrestrial environments in the mid-Devonian supported a substantial diversity of plants, some of which were as much as 2 meters tall. Plant life probably was confined to moist areas such as the edges of streams and lakes and low-lying swamps. The presence of plants creates local microclimates—shaded areas that are cool and humid, producing favorable conditions for the plants themselves and also for terrestrial animals. Terrestrial invertebrates diversified in the late Paleozoic, with flying insects appearing in the Carboniferous. The first terrestrial vertebrates appeared in the Late Devonian. Carboniferous vertebrate communities primarily represented near water habitats. Permian communities show a predominance of amniotes, and represent both near water and upland habitats. The first herbivorous vertebrates appeared in the Permian.

■ Late Paleozoic Continental Geography

From the Devonian through the Permian, the continents were drifting together (Scotese and McKerrow 1990). The continental blocks that correspond to parts of modern North America, Greenland, and western Europe had come into proximity along the equator (Figure 9–1). With the later addition of Siberia, these blocks formed a northern supercontinent known as **Laurasia**.

Most of Gondwana was in the far south, overlying the South Pole, but its northern edge was separated from the southern part of Laurasia only by a narrow extension of the **Tethys Sea.** The arm of the Tethys Sea between Laurasia and Gondwana did not close completely until the Late Carboniferous, when Africa moved northward to contact the east coast of North America (Figure 9–2). During the Carboniferous, the process of coalescence continued, and by the Permian most of the continental surface was united in a single continent, **Pangaea** (sometimes spelled Pangea). At its maximum extent, the land area of Pangaea covered 36 percent of the Earth's surface, compared with 31 percent for the present arrangement of continents (Veevers 1994). This supercontinent persisted for 160 million years, from the mid-Carboniferous to the mid-Jurassic, and profoundly influenced the evolution of terrestrial plants and animals.

■ Late Paleozoic Terrestrial Ecosystems

The terrestrial environment of the mid-Devonian had substantially more species of plants and animals than any previous period, but it differed in many respects from the modern ecosystems we are used to. In the first place, of course, there were no terrestrial vertebrates—the earliest of those appear in the Late Devonian. Furthermore, plant life was

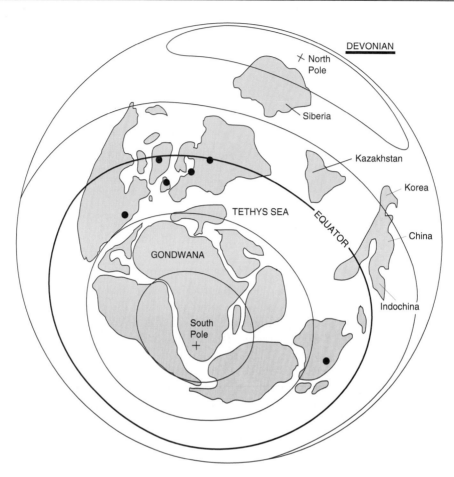

Figure 9–1 Location of continental blocks in the Late Devonian. The black dots indicate fossil localities where Devonian tetrapods have been found. Laurentia, Greenland, and Baltica lie on the equator. An arm of the Tethys Sea extends westward between Gondwana and the northern continents.

limited to wet places—the margins of streams, rivers, and lakes and low-lying areas. In these areas plants grew in patches, each patch dominated by a single species, rather than in communities with a mixture of species as we see now. Still more unusual to our eyes would be the absence of insects that fed on living plants (DiMichele and Hook 1992). Terrestrial animal communities in the mid-Devonian apparently were based on detritivores such as millipedes, springtails, and mites (Shear et al. 1989b). Those animals in turn were preyed on by scorpions, pseudoscorpions, and spiders (Shear and Kukalová–Peck 1990). The earliest evidence of silk production by a spider is from the mid-Devonian (Shear et al. 1989a).

Terrestrial ecosystems became increasingly complex during the remainder of the Paleozoic. Plants diversified and increased in size, invertebrates with new specializations appeared (including flying insects and insects that fed on living plants), and terrestrial vertebrates appeared and diversified. The Late Devonian saw the spread of forests of the progymnosperm (primitive seed plant) *Archaeopteris*, large trees with trunks up to a meter in diameter and reaching heights of at least 10 meters. Most species of *Archaeopteris* put out horizontal branches that bore leaves, and stands of these trees would have created a shaded forest floor in low-lying areas. Giant horsetails (*Calamites*), relatives of the living horsetails you can find growing in moist areas today, reached heights of several meters. There were also many species of giant clubmosses (lycophytes, a few of which survive today as small ground plants). Both male and female lycophytes produced large cones,

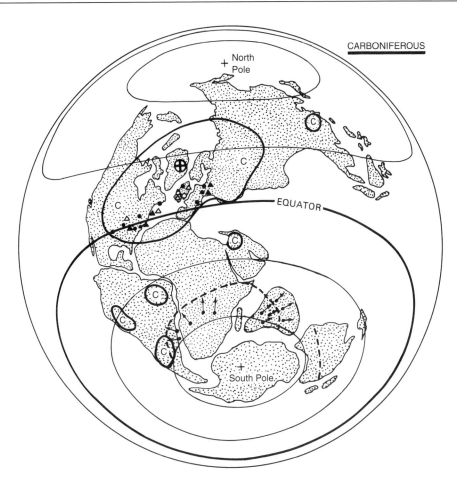

Figure 9–2   Location of continental blocks in the Carboniferous. This map illustrates an early stage of Pangaea. The location and extent of continental glaciation in the Late Carboniferous is shown by the dashed lines and arrows radiating out from the South Pole. The extent of coal forests is marked by the heavy lines enclosing the "C"s. The small circles and triangles mark the locations of Carboniferous tetrapods. Circles are "labyrinthodonts" and triangles are "lepospondyls." Filled symbols represent Early Carboniferous localities and open symbols represent Late Carboniferous ones. The circle enclosing a cross marks the major Late Devonian tetrapod locality.

and spent most of their lives as an unbranched trunk looking rather like telephone poles. Other areas were apparently covered by bushlike plants, vines, and low-growing ground cover.

The diversity and habitat specificity of Late Devonian floras continued to expand in the Carboniferous. Most of the major taxonomic groups of plants evolved during this time, although the flowering seed plants (**angiosperms**) that dominate the world today were as yet unknown. Seed ferns (the extinct pteridosperms) and ferns (which survive today) lived in well-drained areas, and swamps were dominated by lycophytes, with horsetails, ferns, and seed ferns also present. During the Early

Carboniferous the vegetation became structurally modern in aspect. Plants covered a variety of lowland habitats. There were forests consisting of trees of varying heights, giving stratification to the canopy, with vinelike plants hanging from the branches. The terrestrial vegetation would have looked superficially like it does today, although the actual types of plants present were completely different (DiMichele and Hook 1992).

The taxonomic composition of the plant communities changed somewhat in the Late Carboniferous and Permian. Seed plants such as conifers became an important component of the flora, and by the end of the Paleozoic they were the major group of plants.

In the Late Carboniferous the more primitive spore-bearing plants that had been present earlier declined in numbers, and ferns moved their dominance from more upland habitats to more lowland ones. In the Permian the newer, seed plant-dominated flora spread worldwide, possibly corresponding with a greater diversity of drier, more upland types of plant communities (DiMichele and Hook 1992).

Terrestrial invertebrates burgeoned during the Carboniferous. Millipedes, arachnids, and insects were common. Flying insects are known from the late Early Carboniferous. Detritivores continued to be an important part of the food web, but insect herbivory appears to have been well established by the end of the Carboniferous. Fossil leaves have ragged holes, seeds and wood are penetrated by tunnels, and pollen is found in the guts and feces of fossilized insects. Dragonflies (one species with a wingspan of 63 centimeters) flew through the air, and predatory invertebrates such as scorpions and arachnids prowled the forest floor. The extinct arthropleurids were terrestrial predators, with body lengths that reached nearly 2 meters. Late Paleozoic arthropod communities were rather different from those of today. Predatory forms were larger, but species diversity was lower. Although spiders were abundant, most appear to have been burrow-building forms rather than web builders. New arthropod types appearing in the Permian include hemipterans (bugs), beetles, and forms resembling blood-sucking mosquitoes (but not closely related to true mosquitoes) (DiMichele and Hook 1992).

Terrestrial vertebrates appeared in the Late Devonian and diversified during the Carboniferous. The first **amniotes** (tetrapods laying shelled eggs) were mid-Carboniferous in age, and by the Late Carboniferous amniotes had split into the two major lineages, one leading to the mammals, and the other to modern reptiles and birds. The Carboniferous was dominated by a diversity of semi-aquatic primitive tetrapods, but by the Permian the more terrestrially-adapted amniotes were common, and many fossil vertebrate communities appear to represent more upland habitats.

By the Early Permian several vertebrate lineages had given rise to small insectivorous predators, rather like modern salamanders and lizards. Larger vertebrates (up to 1.5 meters long) were probably predators of these small species, and still larger predators topped the food web. An important development in the Permian was the appearance of herbivorous vertebrates. For the first time vertebrates were able to exploit the primary production of terrestrial plants directly, and the food web was no longer based solely on invertebrates. By the end of the Permian, the structure and function of terrestrial ecosystems were essentially modern, although the kinds of plants and animals in those ecosystems were almost entirely different from the ones we know today (DiMichele and Hook 1992).

■ Late Paleozoic Climates

In Chapter 5 we suggested that the climate of equatorial latitudes in the early Paleozoic was fairly equable, apart from the period of glaciation in the Late Ordovician, and this pattern appears to have continued through the mid-Devonian. However, further glacial episodes characterized the late Paleozoic. Some glaciation was evident in the Late Devonian, with major glaciation over Gondwana from the mid-Carboniferous until the mid-Permian. The waxing and waning of the glaciers created oscillations in sea level, which created the cyclic coal deposits of eastern North America, western Europe, and other parts of the Earth. The climate over Pangaea was fairly uniform in the Early Carboniferous, but in the Late Carboniferous and Early Permian it was highly differentiated, as the result of this glaciation, with significant regional differences in the flora (Hallam 1994). Most vertebrates are known from equatorial regions during this time.

■ Late Paleozoic Extinctions

Major extinctions occurred at the end of the Paleozoic in both terrestrial and marine environments. These were the most severe extinctions of the Phanerozoic, affecting approximately 57 percent of marine invertebrate families and 95 percent of all marine species, including 12 families of fishes (Erwin 1993). Theories for the cause of this extinction abound, including loss of coastal shelf with the final coalescence of continents to form Pangaea, volcanic eruptions (Renne et al. 1995), and toxic levels of dissolved carbon dioxide (Knoll et al. 1996). There were also significant casualties on land: Twenty-seven families of tetrapods (49 percent) became extinct, with especially heavy losses among the mammallike reptiles (Benton 1989).

There was also a significant extinction among vertebrates at the end of the Early Permian, which was not paralleled in the marine invertebrate record.

Many types of archaic fishes that survived the Late Devonian extinctions, such as acanthodians and osteolepiform sarcopterygians, became extinct at this time (Janvier 1996). On land, 15 families of tetrapods became extinct, including many nonamniote tetrapods (many lepospondyl and labyrinthodont families) and pelycosaurs (mammallike reptiles) (Benton 1989). These extinctions may have been related to climatic changes associated with the end of the Permo-Carboniferous period of glaciation.

■ References

Benton, M. J. 1989. Patterns of evolution and extinction in vertebrates. Pages 218–241 in *Evolution and the Fossil Record*, edited by K. C. Allen and D. E. G. Briggs. Belhaven Press, London, UK.

DiMichele, W. A., and R. W. Hook (rapporteurs). 1992. Paleozoic terrestrial ecosystems. Pages 205–325 in *Terrestrial Ecosystems Through Time*, edited by A. K. Behrensmeyer, J. D. Damuth, W. A. DiMichele, R. Potts, H. Dieter–Sues, and S. L. Wing. University of Chicago Press, Chicago, IL.

Erwin, D. H. 1993. *The Great Paleozoic Crisis*. Columbia University Press, New York, NY.

Hallam, A. 1994. *An Outline of Phanerozoic Biogeography*. Oxford University Press, Oxford, UK.

Janvier, P. 1996. *Early Vertebrates*. Oxford Monographs on Geology and Geophysics—33. Clarendon Press, Oxford, UK.

Knoll, A., R. K. Bambach, D. E. Canfield, and J. P. Grotzinger. 1996. Comparative Earth history and Late Permian mass extinction. *Science* 273:452–457.

Renne, P. R., Z. Zhang, M. A. Richards, M. T. Black, and A. R. Basu. 1995. Synchrony and relations between Permian-Triassic boundary crises and Siberian flood volcanism. *Science* 269:1413–1416.

Scotese, C. R., and W. S. McKerrow. 1990. Revised world maps and introduction. Pages 1–21 in *Paleozoic Palaeogeography and Biogeography*, edited by W. S. McKerrow and C. R. Scotese. Geological Society Memoir No. 12.

Shear, W. A., and J. Kukalová–Peck. 1990. The ecology of Paleozoic terrestrial arthropods: the fossil evidence. *Canadian Journal of Zoology* 68:1807–1834.

Shear, W. A., J. M. Palmer, J. A. Coddington, and P. M. Bonamo. 1989a. A Devonian spinneret: early evidence of spiders and silk use. *Science* 246:479–481.

Shear, W. A., W. Schwaller, and P. Bonamo. 1989b. Record of Palaeozoic pseudoscorpions. *Nature* 341:527–529.

Veevers, J. J. 1994. Pangaea: evolution of a supercontinent and its consequences for Earth's paleoclimate and sedimentary environments. Pages 13–23 in *Pangea: Paleoclimate, Tectonics, and Sedimentation during Accretion, Zenith, and Breakup of a Supercontinent*, edited by G. D. Klein. Geological Society of America Special Paper 288.

PART 3

Terrestrial Ectotherms: Amphibians, Turtles, Crocodilians, and Squamates

The spread of plants and then invertebrates across the land provided a new habitat for vertebrates. The evolutionary transition from water to land is complex because water and air have such different properties: Aquatic animals are supported by water, whereas terrestrial animals need skeletons and limbs for support. Aquatic animals extract oxygen from a unidirectional flow of water across the gills, whereas terrestrial animals breathe air that they must pump in and out of saclike lungs. Aquatic animals face problems of water and ion balance as the result of osmolal flow, whereas terrestrial animals lose water by evaporation. Even sensory systems like eyes and ears work differently in water and air. The transition from aquatic to terrestrial habitats must have been facilitated by characteristics of fishes that were functional both in water and in air, although the functions may not have been exactly the same in the two fluids.

Once in terrestrial habitats, vertebrates radiated into some of the most remarkable animals that have ever lived. The dinosaurs are the best known of these, but many smaller groups contained forms that were just as bizarre, although not as large as many of the dinosaurs. One contribution of phylogenetic systematics has been the emphasis it has placed on the close evolutionary relationship of birds, crocodilians, and dinosaurs. This perspective indicates that the complex behaviors we consider normal for birds are ancestral characters of their lineage. Living crocodilians display parental care that is quite like that of birds (allowing for the differences in the size and body form of birds and crocodilians), and evidence is accumulating that at least some dinosaurs also showed extensive parental care and probably other behaviors we now associate with birds.

The distinction between ectotherms (animals that obtain the heat needed to raise their body temperatures from outside the body) and endotherms (animals that use metabolic heat production for thermoregulation) has important functional considerations that cut across phylogenetic lineages. In some respects crocodilians are more like turtles and squamates (lizards, snakes, and related forms) than like the birds that are their closest living relatives. The relationship between an ectothermal organism and its physical environment (solar radiation, air temperature, wind speed, and humidity) is often an important factor in its ecology and behavior. One consequence of relying on outside sources of energy to raise body temperature is efficient use of metabolic energy, and ectotherms transform a high proportion of the food they eat into their own body tissue. This characteristic gives them a unique position in the flow of energy through terrestrial ecosystems.

In this part of the book we describe the radiation of vertebrates into terrestrial habitats in the Paleozoic and Mesozoic and various theories to account for the extinction of dinosaurs and for mass extinctions generally, and we consider the advantages and disadvantages of being an ectotherm in the modern world.

CHAPTER
10

Origin and Radiation
of Tetrapods in the Late Paleozoic

By the Middle Devonian the stage was set for the appearance of terrestrial vertebrates, and the first vertebrate to venture onto the land was a sarcopterygian. The sarcopterygians, introduced with the other bony fishes in Chapter 8, did not participate in the evolutionary success of the ray-finned fishes. Indeed, the only surviving aquatic sarcopterygians are the lungfishes and the coelacanth. However, all the terrestrial vertebrates are sarcopterygians.

The far-reaching structural changes required for life on land were barely complete when some lineages of tetrapods became secondarily aquatic, returning to freshwater habitats. However, other lineages became increasingly specialized for terrestrial life. Once again, a radiation of vertebrates was associated with progressive changes in the jaws that allowed new ways of feeding and simultaneous changes in the limbs that appear to have increased the agility of predators. These structural changes were widespread, but only one of the terrestrial lineages of Paleozoic tetrapods made the next major transition in vertebrate history with the appearance of the embryonic membranes that define the amniote vertebrates. Amniote diversification shows an initial early split between the synapsids, the lineage that includes mammals, and the sauropsids, the lineage that includes reptiles and birds.

■ Tetrapod Origins

Our understanding of the origin of terrestrial vertebrates (**tetrapods**) is advancing rapidly. New fossil material in Latvia, Scotland, Australia, and North America has supplemented information from additional specimens of *Acanthostega* and *Ichthyostega* found in the same deposits in East Greenland that first produced *Ichthyostega* in 1932. Analysis of the new specimens has focused on derived characters, and this perspective has emphasized the sequence in which the characteristics of tetrapods were acquired. The gap between fishes and tetrapods has

narrowed; a newly defined group of sarcopterygian fishes has some otherwise strictly tetrapod characteristics, and the earliest tetrapods now appear to have been much more fishlike than we had previously realized. That information provides a basis for hypotheses about the ecology of animals at the transition between aquatic and terrestrial life.

The origin of tetrapods from **sarcopterygian** (lobe-finned) fishes between the Middle and Late Devonian can be inferred from features of the skull, teeth, and limbs. Cladistic analyses of the relationships of the sarcopterygians to tetrapods point to one of the sarcopterygian lineages as the most likely sister group of the tetrapods. This conclusion confirms and strengthens the classical view of tetrapod relationships that was based largely on ancestral characters shared by sarcopterygians and tetrapods.

The next stage in the history of tetrapods was their radiation into different lineages and different ecological types, during the late Paleozoic and Mesozoic. By the Late Devonian and Early Carboniferous, tetrapods had split into two lineages that are distinguished in part by the way the roof of the skull is fastened to the posterior portion of the braincase. One of these lineages is the **batrachomorphs**, which includes the temnospondyls which were the largest and longest-lasting group of primitive, extinct nonamniote tetrapods. Some lineages of temnospondyls extended into the Cretaceous, and at least some of the living amphibians may be derived from temnospondyls.

The second early lineage of tetrapods, the **reptilomorphs**, contains a diverse array of animals. The diadectomorphs, large terrestrial reptilomorphs, appear to be the most likely candidates for the sister group of the Amniota. The immediate ancestors of the major amniote groups appeared in the Late Carboniferous. They were small, agile animals that show modifications of the skeleton and jaws, which suggests that they fed on terrestrial invertebrates. The diversity of nonamniote tetrapods waned during the Late Permian and Triassic. Simultaneously, amniote tetrapods radiated into many of the terrestrial life zones that had been occupied by nonamniotes and developed feeding and locomotor specializations that had not previously been seen among tetrapods.

Fish–Tetrapod Relationships

Sarcopterygian fishes were originally considered to comprise the dipnoans (lungfishes) and the crossopterygians. We now consider the term "crossopterygian" to be invalid, as it groups together coelacanths and other nondipnoan sarcopterygians on primitive characters (mainly the absence of derived dipnoan characters). Another term that has fallen into disrepute is "rhipidistians." This grouping is a paraphyletic one, comprising some groups that are more closely related to lungfishes (porolepiforms and rhizodontiforms), and others that are more closely related to tetrapods (osteolepiforms).

Two groups of sarcopterygians have been considered alternatives as the closest relatives of tetrapods. The discovery of lungfishes seemed to provide an ideal model of a prototetrapod—what more could one ask than an air-breathing fish? However, lungfishes are very specialized animals, and Devonian lungfishes were scarcely less specialized than the living species. In contrast, a group of Devonian sarcopterygians, the osteolepiform fishes, were closer in many respects to what one would expect of a prototetrapod. The **Osteolepiformes** were cylindrical-bodied, large-headed fishes with thick scales, a single external nostril on each side, and variable caudal structures. Many osteolepiforms had paired, crescentic vertebral centra similar to the vertebrae found in the earliest tetrapods. Although all osteolepiforms were basically free-swimming predators of shallow waters, some may have been specialized for life at the water's edge.

Most evolutionary biologists favored osteolepiforms as the sister group of tetrapods, but in 1981 Donn Rosen and his colleagues revived the argument favoring lungfishes (Rosen et al. 1981). Although this hypothesis was vigorously criticized (Jarvik 1981, Holmes 1985, and Carroll 1987), it showed that the evidence in favor of osteolepiforms was not entirely convincing in a cladistic analysis. As a result, recent studies have reexamined the question of the origin of tetrapods with cladistic methods, and it appears that neither the lungfishes nor the coelacanths is the sister group of tetrapods. The most likely sister group to tetrapods is a newly defined lineage of Late Devonian sarcopterygians, a family of osteolepiforms called the Panderichthyidae (Vorobyeva and Schultze 1991, Ahlberg 1995).

The panderichthyids resemble other osteolepiforms in most respects, but have lost their dorsal fins, and have much reduced their tail (Ahlberg and Milner 1994). Only two genera are known, *Panderichthys* and *Elpistostege*. Their bodies and heads were flattened, their snouts were long, and their eyes were on the top of the head (Figure 10–1). In addition, panderichthyids and tetrapods have distinct frontal bones and their ribs project ventrally from the vertebral column, whereas in other osteolepiforms the frontal bone is medial, and they have dorsally projecting ribs. These shared derived characters suggest that panderichthyids should be placed as the sister group of tetrapods, with other osteolepiforms as the sister group of panderichthyids plus tetrapods (Figure 10–2).

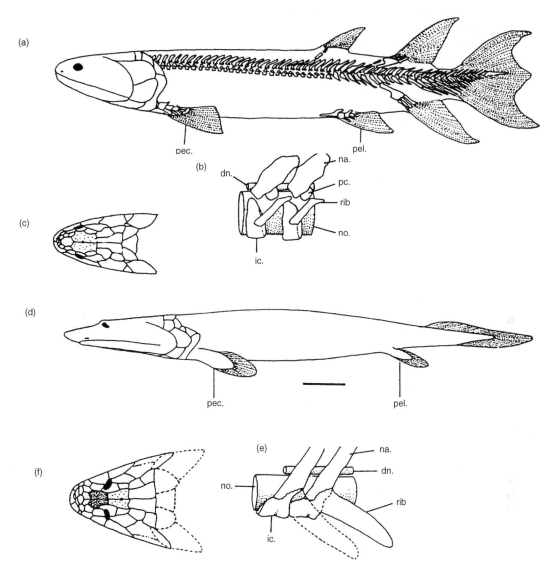

Figure 10–1 A Devonian osteolepiform and panderichthyid: (a) The osteolepiform
Eusthenopteron has a cylindrical body, and four unpaired fins (two dorsal fins, a caudal fin,
and an anal fin) in addition to the paired pectoral and pelvic appendages. This was a large
fish—the scale bar is 10 centimeters long. (b) A portion of the vertebral column showing the
position of the notochord and dorsal nerve cord. The intercentra are ventral to the notochord
and the pleurocentra are dorsal. The neural arches do not articulate with one another, and the
short ribs probably extended dorsally. (c) The skull roof of *Eusthenopteron*. The parietals are
shaded; note that the area anterior to the parietals is occupied by a single, median element.
(d) The panderichthyid *Panderichthys rhombolepis* has a dorsoventrally flattened body with a
long, broad snout, and eyes on top of the head. Note the absence of dorsal and anal fins.
(Compare these features to *Ichthyostega*, Figure 10–6.) (e) A section of the vertebral column.
There are no ossified pleurocentra, which are present in early tetrapods, although cartilaginous pleurocentra might have been present. The ribs are larger than those of osteolepiforms,
and project laterally and ventrally. (f) The skull roof of *Panderichthys*. Panderichthyids and
tetrapods both have a single pair of large frontal bones (dark shading) immediately anterior to
the parietals. dn, dorsal nerve cord; i, intercentrum; na, neural arch; no, notochord; pc, pleurocentrum; pec, pectoral appendage; pel, pelvic appendage. (From Ahlberg and Milner 1994.)

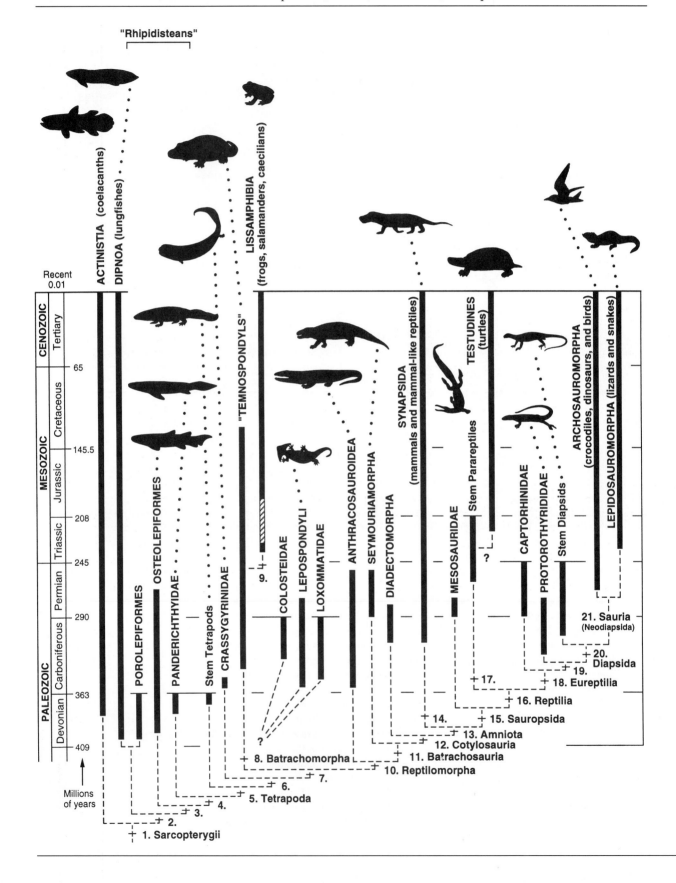

■ Early Tetrapods

The new fossils, especially specimens of *Acanthostega* from East Greenland, have shed light on the characteristics of early tetrapods, suggesting that they were more aquatic than we thought. In addition, one of the most widespread features of tetrapods, the pentadactyl (five-fingered) limb, turns out not to be an ancestral character.

The evidence for an aquatic way of life for early tetrapods comes partly from the presence of a groove on the ventral surface of the ceratobranchials (Coates and Clack 1991). The ceratobranchials are part of the branchial apparatus, which supports the

1. Sarcopterygii: fleshy pectoral and pelvic fins with a single basal element, muscular lobes at the base of those fins, true enamel on teeth, plus features of jaws and limb girdles. **2.** Heart with partial ventricular septum and separated pulmonary and systemic circulations. **3.** True choana (internal nostril), labyrinthine folding of tooth enamel, and details of limb skeleton. **4.** Flattened head with elongate snout, orbits on top of skull, body flattened, absence of dorsal and anal fins, enlarged ribs. **5.** Tetrapoda: limbs with carpals, tarsals, and digits, vertebrae with zygapophyses, iliac blade of pelvis attached to vertebral column, loss of contact between dermal skull and pectoral girdle. ("Stem Tetrapoda" is a paraphyletic assemblage of Late Devonian genera, including [in order of more primitive to more derived] *Acanthostega, Ichthyostega,* and *Tulerpeton,* plus others known from fragmentary material.) **6.** Absence of anocleithrum, five or fewer digits. **7.** Occipital condyles present, notochord excluded from braincase in adult. **8.** Batrachomorpha: skull roof attached to braincase via the exoccipitals, loss of skull kinesis, only four fingers in hand. **9.** Lissamphibia: pedicellate teeth, teeth bicuspid or multicuspid. (Lissamphibia includes the Salientia [frogs], the Caudata [salamanders], and the Apoda [caecilians].) **10.** Reptilomorpha: several skull characters, plus vertebrae with the pleurocentrum as the predominant element. **11.** Batracosauria: intercentrum reduced in size, enlarged maxillary caninelike tooth. **12.** Cotylosauria: sacrum with more than one vertebra, robust claws on feet, more derived atlas-axis complex, plus other skull characters. **13.** Amniota: loss of labyrinthodont teeth, hemispherical and well-ossified occipital condyle, frontal bone contacts orbit in skull, transverse pterygoid flange present (reflects differentiation of pterygoideus muscle), three ossifications in scapulocoracoid (shoulder girdle), distinct astragalus in ankle. **14.** Synapsida: presence of lower temporal fenestra. **15.** Sauropsida: single centrale in ankle, maxilla separated from quadratojugal, single coronoid bone in jaw.

16. Reptilia: suborbital foramen in palate, tabular small or absent, large post-temporal fenestra. **17.** Parareptilia: loss of caniniform maxillary teeth, posterior emargination of skull, quadratojugal expanded dorsally, expanded iliac blade. ("Stem Parareptiles" includes the Late Permian Millerettidae and Pareiasauridae, and the Late Permian and Triassic Procolophonidae. Opinions vary as to whether Testudines [turtles] are derived from pareiasaurs or from procolophonids, or even if they might be included with the diapsids [see Chapter 12].) **18.** Eureptilia: supratemporal small, parietal and squamosal broadly in contact, tabular not in contact with opisthotic, horizontal ventral margin of postorbital portion of skull, ontogenetic fusion of atlas pleurocentrum and axis intercentrum. **19.** Postorbital region of skull short, anterior pleurocentra keeled ventrally, limbs long and slender, hands and feet long and slender, metapodials overlap proximally. **20.** Diapsida: upper and lower temporal fenestrae present, exoccipitals not in contact on occipital condyle, ridge-and-groove tibia–astralagal joint. ("Stem diapsids" is a paraphyletic assemblage of Late Carboniferous and Permian diapsids including [in order of more primitive to more derived] Araeoscelidia, Coelurosauravidae, and Younginiformes.) **21.** Sauria (Neodiapsida): dorsal origin of temporal musculature, quadrate exposed laterally, tabular bone lost, unossified dorsal process of stapes, loss of caniniform region in maxillary tooth row, sacral ribs oriented laterally, ontogenetic fusion of caudal ribs, modified ilium, short and stout fifth metatarsal, small proximal carpals and tarsals. (Modified from J. A. Gauthier, A. G. Kluge, and T. Rowe, 1988, pages 103–155 in *The Phylogeny and Classification of the Tetrapods,* volume 1: *Amphibians, Reptiles, Birds,* edited by M. J. Benton, Clarendon Press, Oxford, UK; R. L. Carroll, 1988, *Vertebrate Paleontology and Evolution,* Freeman, New York, NY; M. J. Benton, 1997, *Vertebrate Paleontology,* 2d edition, Harper Collins Academic, London, UK; Ahlberg and Milner 1994; Gauthier 1994; and Reisz 1997.)

Figure 10–2 Phylogenetic relationships of sarcopterygians and tetrapods. This diagram shows the probable relationships among some of the sarcopterygian fishes and early tetrapods. Dotted lines show interrelationships only, and are not indicative of the times of divergence of or the unrecorded presence of taxa in the fossil record. Crosshatched bars indicate ranges of time when the taxon is known to be present, but is unrecorded in the fossil record. Numbers indicate derived characters that distinguish the lineages.

gills of fishes. Elements of the branchial apparatus are retained in all tetrapods, including birds and mammals, so it is not merely the presence of ceratobranchials in *Acanthostega* that is important—it is the groove on their ventral surface. In derived fishes that groove accommodates the afferent branchial aortic arches, which carry blood to the gills. The presence of a similar groove on the ceratobranchials of *Acanthostega* strongly suggests that these tetrapods also had gills. In addition, the cleithrum (shoulder girdle) of *Acanthostega* has a flange, the postbranchial lamina, on its anterior margin. In fishes, this ridge supports the posterior wall of the opercular chamber. The picture of *Acanthostega* that emerges from these features is an animal with fishlike internal gills and an open opercular chamber; that is, an animal with aquatic respiration, like a fish.

A second unexpected feature of *Acanthostega* is found in its feet—it had eight toes on its front feet (Coates and Clack 1990). Furthermore, *Acanthostega* was not alone in its polydactyly (having more than five toes). *Ichthyostega* had seven toes on its hind foot (Figure 10–3), and *Tulerpeton,* a Devonian tetrapod from Russia, had six toes. In fact, not one of the Devonian tetrapods yet known had five toes. These discoveries confound long-standing explanations of the supposed homologies of bones in the fins of sarcopterygian fins with those in tetrapod limbs, but they correspond beautifully with predictions based on a study of the embryology of limb development (Box 10–1).

These new discoveries leave us with a paradoxical situation: Animals with well-developed limbs and other structural features that suggest they were capable of locomotion on land appear to have retained gills that would function only in water. How does a land animal evolve in water?

Evolution of Tetrapod Characters in an Aquatic Habitat

Tantalizingly incomplete as the skeletal evidence is, it is massive compared to the information we have about the ecology of panderichthyids and early tetrapods. It is not possible even to be certain if the evolution of tetrapods occurred in purely freshwater habitats (Panchen 1977, Thomson 1980). Greenland and Australia, the two land masses from which Devonian tetrapods are known, are believed to have been separated by marine environments in the Devonian. Furthermore, *Tulerpeton* was found in a deposit that formed in a large, shallow marine basin, which was a considerable distance from the nearest known land mass. Tetrapods may have evolved in brackish or saline lagoons, or even in marine habitats (Thomson 1993).

What sorts of lives did the panderichthyids lead? What was their habitat like? What were their major competitors and predators? What were the earliest tetrapods able to do that panderichthyids could not? This is the sort of information we need to assess the selective forces that shaped the evolution of tetrapods.

How Does a Land Animal Evolve in Water?

Certain inferences can be drawn from the fossil material available. We start from the basis that any animal must function in its habitat. If it does not, it does not leave descendants and its phylogenetic lineage becomes extinct. Evolutionary change occurs because the naturally occurring variation in organisms is subject to selection. Looking backward, we may see an evolutionary trend if progressive changes conferred an advantage on the individuals possessing them; but it is merely a fortunate coincidence if some features turn out to be advantageous for a different way of life. Tetrapod characteristics did not evolve because they would someday be useful to animals that would live on land; they evolved because they were advantageous for animals that were still living in water.

Panderichthyids were large fish, as much as a meter long, with heavy bodies, long snouts, and large teeth. They probably either stalked their prey or lay in ambush and made a sudden rush. One can picture a panderichthyid prowling through the dense growth of plants on the bottom of a Devonian pond or estuary. The flexible lobe fins would support it as it waited motionless for prey. A group of living fishes, the frogfishes, provides a model for the usefulness of a tetrapodlike limb in water (Edwards 1989). The pectoral fins of frogfishes are modified into structures that look remarkably like the limbs of tetrapods (Figure 10–5), and are used to walk over the substrate. An analysis of frogfish locomotion revealed that they employ two gaits that are used by tetrapods—a walk and a (slow!) gallop.

Although there is no direct fossil evidence of lungs in Devonian sarcopterygians, we believe they were present, because every related group (basal actinopterygians, dipnoans, actinistians, and tetrapods) is known to have lungs or the remnants

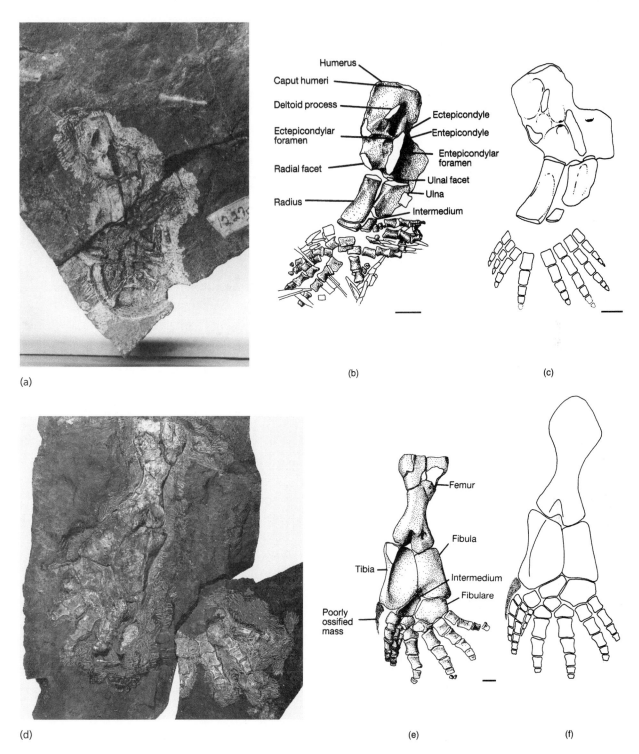

Figure 10–3 The polydactyl feet of *Acanthostega* (top row) and *Ichthyostega* (bottom row):
(a) Fossilized forelimb of *Acanthostega*; (b) drawing of the fossil with the bones identified;
(c) restoration of the forelimb of *Acanthostega*; (d) fossilized hindlimb of *Ichthyostega* with its
counterpart half; (e) drawing of the fossil with the bones identified; (f) restoration of the forelimb of *Ichthyostega*. The scale bars are 1 centimeter long. (Photographs [a, d] From M. I.
Coates and J. A. Clack 1990, Nature 347:66-69. Courtesy of M. I. Coates and J. A. Clack.)

BOX 10–1 **Early Feet**

How a tetrapod limb could evolve from the fin of a sarcopterygian fish has been hotly debated for more than a century. Until recently, the various theories were based on equating specific bones in the limbs of tetrapods with their presumed counterparts in the limbs of sarcopterygian fishes. Thus, Gegenbaur in the nineteenth century suggested that extension and additional segmentation of the radials seen in the limb of *Eusthenopteron* could produce a limb with digits like those seen in tetrapods (Figure 10–4a, b). The same speculation about equivalent structures has been applied to the fin skeletons of lungfishes (Figure 10–4c, d).

A new perspective on the evolution of tetra-pod limbs has been supplied by studies of the embryonic development of the limbs of derived vertebrates (Shubin and Alberch 1986). Recent work detailing the involvement of *Hox* genes in tetrapod limb formation is reviewed in Shubin et al. (1997). All tetrapod limbs have a common pattern of development, and the same sequence of events applies to the forelimbs and the hindlimbs. In the developing forelimb, the humerus branches to form the radius (anteriorly) and the ulna (posteriorly). The developmental axis runs through the ulna. Subsequent development on the anterior side of the limb occurs (1) by segmentation of the radius, which produces the radiale (shown in Figure 10–4e) and sometimes two additional segments, and (2)

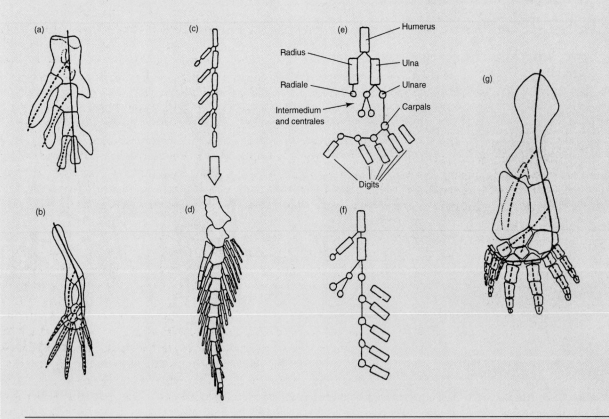

by both branching and segmentation of the ulna. A preaxial branch of the ulna produces the proximal bones in the wrist—the intermedium and centrales. The carpals (distal wrist bones) and metacarpals (bones of the palm), and digits (fingers) result from postaxial branching. The postaxial digits are a new feature of tetrapods—nothing like them is known in any fish.

For pentadactyl tetrapods, the formation of digits starts with digit 4 and concludes with digit 1 (which is the thumb of humans). Digit 5 (our little finger) forms at different times in different lineages, and one of the attractive features of this developmental process is the ease with which more or fewer than five digits can develop. If the process of segmentation and branching continues, a polydactylous foot is produced with the extra digits forming beyond the thumb. If the developmental process is shortened, fewer than five digits are produced, and the thumb is the first digit to be lost.

Changes in the timing of development do not have to produce an all-or-none addition or loss of a digit; a reduction in size is common. Dogs, for example, have four well-developed digits (numbers 2 through 5), plus a vestigial digit (number 1) called a dewclaw. Many dogs are born without external dewclaws (a carpal may be present internally), and some breeds of dogs are required by their breed standards to have double dewclaws. This pattern of increase or reduction in the number of digits results from a change in the timing of development during evolution. Reduction in the number of digits in evolutionary lineages of birds and mammals is frequently associated with specialization for high-speed running—ostriches and some artiodactyls (e.g., antelope) have two digits, and some perissodactyls (horses) have a single digit. The embryonic process by which toes are formed explains why variation in the number of digits is so widespread.

Figure 10–4 Three hypotheses of the origin of tetrapod limbs. In every case the head of the animal is to the left. Thus, the preaxial direction (i.e., anterior to the axis of the limb) is to the left. (a) The pectoral fin skeleton of *Eusthenopteron*. The limb has a longitudinal axis (solid line) and preaxial radials. (b) Gegenbaur's nineteenth-century hypothesis of the origin of the vertebrate forefoot and fingers from preaxial radials. (c, d) The pectoral fin skeleton of the Australian lungfish *Neoceradotus*. (c) The fin axis and the preaxial radials that appear early in embryonic development by branching from the axis. The radials of *Eusthenopteron* may have developed in the same way. (d) The postaxial radials seen in the adult fin of *Neoceradotus* develop by condensation of tissue, not by branching. (e, f) A diagram of the forelimb skeleton of a mouse during early development. (e) The proximal (= nearest to the shoulder) parts of the limb skeleton consist of an axis with preaxial branches (radials) as seen in *Eusthenopteron* and *Neoceradotus* [compare the upper part of (e) with (a) and (c)]. The digits, however, are formed as postaxial branches. This pattern is unknown in fishes. (f) The embryonic limb skeleton of a mouse straightened for comparison with *Eusthenopteron* (a) and *Neoceradotus* (c). (g) The hindlimb of *Ichthyostega* showing the inferred position of the axis (solid line) and radials. Note that the tibia and fibula and the first two rows of tarsal bones in the foot are formed by preaxial radials, whereas the third row of tarsals, the metatarsals, and the digits originate as postaxial branches. (From Ahlberg and Milner 1994, *Nature* 348:507–514.)

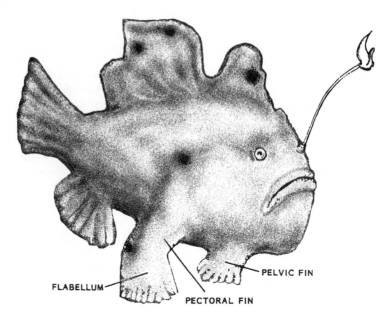

Figure 10–5 The frogfish *Antennarius pictus* in its typical posture, with its pectoral and pelvic fins planted firmly on the substrate. Only the right pectoral and pelvic fins can be seen in this view. The small pelvic fins are in an anterior position, but are not fused. When the animal walks, the left and right pelvic fins make contact with the substrate independently, allowing the gait of the fish to be compared with the gaits of tetrapods. (From J. L. Edwards 1989, *American Zoologist* 29:235–254. Courtesy of J. L. Edwards.)

FLABELLUM

PELVIC FIN

PECTORAL FIN

of lungs. Panderichthyids presumably could breathe atmospheric oxygen by swimming to the surface and gulping air, or by propping themselves on their pectoral fins in shallow water to lift their heads to the surface.

What Were the Advantages of Terrestrial Activity?

This question has fascinated biologists for a century or more, and there is no shortage of theories (Romer 1958, Szarski 1962, Schaeffer 1965, and Bray 1985). These ideas can often be combined. The classic theory proposed is that the Devonian was a time of seasonal droughts. Shallow ponds that formed during the monsoon period often evaporated during the dry season, stranding their inhabitants in rapidly shrinking bodies of stagnant water. Fishes trapped in such situations are doomed unless the next rainy season begins before the pond is completely dry. We know that the living African and South American lungfishes cope with this situation by estivating in the mud of their dry pond until the rains return, but perhaps certain Devonian sarcopterygians had limbs that allowed them to crawl from a drying pond and move overland to larger ponds that still held water. Could millions of years of selection of the fishes best able to escape death by finding their way to permanent water produce a lineage showing increasing ability on land?

This theory has been criticized on several grounds. After all, a fish that succeeds in moving from a drying pond to one that still holds water has enabled itself to go on leading the life of a fish. That seems a backward way to evolve a terrestrial animal. Various alternative theories have been proposed that stress positive selective values associated with increasing terrestrial activity. One emphasizes the contrast between terrestrial and aquatic habitats in the Devonian. The water was swarming with a variety of fishes that had radiated to fill a multiplicity of ecological niches. Active, powerful predators and competitors abounded. In contrast, the land was free of vertebrates. Any sarcopterygian that could occupy terrestrial situations had a predator- and competitor-free environment at its disposal. The exploitation of this habitat can be seen as proceeding by gradual steps.

The reinterpretation of early tetrapods as basically aquatic animals suggests that we should base speculations about selection for terrestrial activity on *Acanthostega* and *Ichthyostega,* rather than on panderichthyids. Juvenile *Ichthyostega* and *Acanthostega* might have congregated in shallow water, as do juveniles of living fishes and amphibians, to escape the attention of larger predatory fishes that are restricted to deeper water. At the edge of a lake or estuary many of the morphological and physiological characteristics of terrestrial vertebrates would have been useful to a still-aquatic tetrapod. Warm water holds little oxygen, and shallow pond edges are likely to be especially warm during the day. Thus, lungs are important to a vertebrate in that habitat, whether it be fish or tetrapod. Similarly, legs would have borne the weight of the animal in the absence of water deep enough to float. In shallow water an air-breathing, upstanding tetrapod could have lifted its head above the water, and the change in the shape of the lens of the eye associated with the differences in the refractive indices of water and air could have started to occur. These behavioral and morphological features can be found among a number of living fishes, such as the mudskippers, climbing perches, and walking catfishes, which make extensive excursions out of the water, even climbing trees and capturing food on land.

Starting from aquatic tetrapods that snapped up terrestrial invertebrates that fell into the water, one can envision a gradual progression of increasingly agile forms capable of exploiting the terrestrial habitat for food as well as for shelter from aquatic predators. Terrestrial agility might have developed to the stage at which juvenile tetrapods moved overland from the pond of their origin to other ponds. Many vertebrates include a dispersal stage in their life history, usually in the juvenile period. In this stage individuals spread from the place of their origin to colonize suitable habitats, sometimes long distances from their starting point. This type of behavior is so widespread among living vertebrates that we may guess that it occurred in the early tetrapods as well.

Perhaps the main selection for terrestrial life occurred in the juvenile stages of tetrapods' lives. The adults were large animals, and it is hard to imagine an adult *Ichthyostega* being sufficiently agile to capture a terrestrial invertebrate such as a scorpion scuttling about in its own terrestrial habitat. It is much easier to visualize a 15-centimeter-long juvenile following the scorpion under a log and grabbing it. A small body size would have greatly simplified the difficulties of support, locomotion, and respiration in the transition from an aquatic to a terrestrial habitat.

Figure 10–20, which also covers the transition from primitive tetrapod to amniote covered later in this chapter, summarizes some of the morphological and physiological features that would have been transformed in the transition between fish and tetrapod.

Devonian Tetrapods: *Acanthostega,* *Ichthyostega, Tulerpeton*, and *Hynerpeton*

Specimens collected mostly in the past decade have greatly increased our knowledge of tetrapods in the Late Devonian. It is clear that substantial diversity had evolved among tetrapods by this time. They ranged from about 0.5 to 1.2 meters in length and, as we have noted, these animals have more than five digits: *Acanthostega* has eight toes on both front and rear feet (Figure 10–6a), *Ichthyostega* has seven digits on its rear foot (its front foot is unknown), and *Tulerpeton* has six digits on its front and rear feet.

Ichthyostega is the best known of the Devonian tetrapods, and an examination of its skeleton illustrates basic structural features associated with terrestrial life (Figure 10–6b). Most of the structures distinguishing aquatic from terrestrial animals are a consequence of the differences between water and air. Vertebrates never had to cope with being heavy until they emerged from the water. Water buoys an animal up, but air gives little support. Resistance to gravity is of minor importance in the skeleton of a fish—the demands of locomotion are paramount. In contrast, resistance to the downward pull of gravity is a major factor shaping the skeleton of a terrestrial vertebrate.

When a terrestrial vertebrate stands, its body hangs from the vertebral column, which, like the arch of a suspension bridge, supports the weight of the trunk and transmits it to the ground through two sets of vertical supports, the girdles and legs. The vertebral column must resist collapsing, and the girdles and legs must be sturdy and firmly connected with the vertebral column. Without all of these features, a terrestrial vertebrate cannot stand. In osteolepiforms such as *Eusthenopteron* (Figure 10–7a), each segment of the body contained two sets of bones that together formed the vertebral centrum. The anterior elements (intercentra) were wedge shaped in lateral view and crescentic when viewed from the end. They lay beneath the notochord and extended upward around it. The posterior elements were a pair of small bones (pleurocentra) that lay on the dorsal surface of the notochord. The neural arches of adjacent vertebrae did not articulate with one another. The structure of the vertebrae of *Ichthyostega* (Figure 10–7b) was similar to that of the osteolepiforms, but articulations between the neural arches transmitted forces from one vertebra to the next, providing some of the support needed by a terrestrial animal. These articulations were still more extensive in later forms such as the Permian temnospondyl *Eryops* (Figure 10–7c).

The broad, overlapping ribs of *Ichthyostega* probably added rigidity to its trunk. Coates and Clack

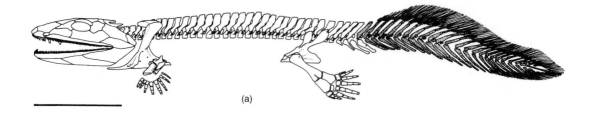

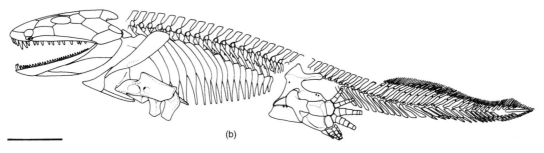

Figure 10–6 Skeletal reconstructions of Devonian tetrapods from East Greenland: (a) *Acanthostega:* provisional restoration omitting ribs and gastralia. Stippled regions of the tail are hypothetical, but the length of the fin rays in the tail is based on fossil material; (b) new restoration of *Ichthyostega;* the forefoot is unknown. Scale bars = 10 cm. (From Coates and Clack 1995.)

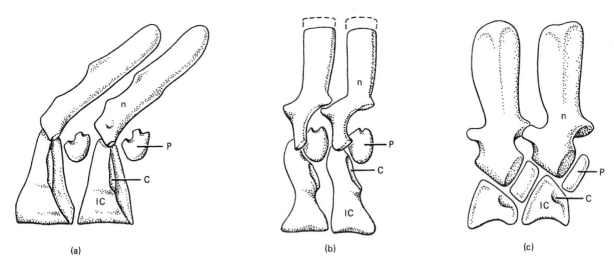

Figure 10–7 Vertebral structure of sarcopterygians and tetrapods (anterior is to the left): (a) The osteolepiform *Eusthenopteron*—the neural arches do not interlock; (b) the early tetrapod *Ichthyostega*—zygapophyses form articulations between adjacent neural arches; (c) the terrestrial temnospondyl *Eryops*—zygapophyses are more fully developed. n, neural arch; pre, prezygapophysis; po, postzygaphphysis; p, pleurocentrum; ic, intercentrum; c, articulation for head of rib. (From A. S. Romer, 1966, *Vertebrate Paleontology,* 3d edition, University of Chicago Press, Chicago, IL.)

(1995) pointed out that the ribcage of *Ichthyostega* is remarkably similar to that of an extant arboreal mammal, the two-toed anteater *Cyclopes didactylus*. The anteater can extend itself horizontally from a tree limb by contracting its intercostal muscles to lock the overlapping ribs together while it anchors itself to the branch with its hindlimbs and tail.

The posttemporal and supracleithral bones, which in fishes attach the cleithrum and clavicle to the skull, had disappeared completely from the pectoral girdle of *Ichthyostega*. A large interclavicle in the ventral midline braced the ventral part of the pectoral girdle, and the scapulocoracoid provided a strong dorsal attachment for the muscles that bound the pectoral girdle to the trunk. The forelimb of *Ichthyostega* was a strong prop, which was permanently bent at the elbow. In the pelvic region, the two bony ventral plates of fishes were greatly enlarged compared to their condition in osteolepiforms and formed a skidlike structure, and were attached to the vertebral column via a sacral rib.

Acanthostega, Tulerpeton, and *Hynerpeton* are not as well known as *Ichthyostega,* but they differ enough to show that by the end of the Devonian, some 7 million years after their appearance, tetrapods had diversified into several niches. *Tulerpeton* was more lightly built than *Ichthyostega,* and had proportionally longer limbs, suggesting that it might have led a more active life. *Acanthostega* was probably less terrestrial than *Ichthyostega.* Its forelimb is less robust than that of *Ichthyostega* and more finlike than its hindlimb. The articulating surfaces of the vertebrae are small, the neural arches are weakly ossified, the ribs are short and straight, not broad and overlapping like the ribs of *Ichthyostega,* and the fin rays on the tail are longer than those of *Ichthyostega.* *Acanthostega* appears to have retained gills. *Hynerpeton* had lost the postbranchial lamina on the cleithrum, suggesting that it did not have an internal gill chamber like that of *Acanthostega* (Daeschler et al. 1994).

The combination of fishlike and terrestrial characters seen in Devonian tetrapods is puzzling. Coates and Clack (1995) called attention to similarities between *Ichthyostega* and extant pinnipeds, such as the elephant seal (*Mirounga leonina*). The fore legs of pinnipeds are props for the body on land, and the pelvic limbs are used as paddles and rudders in the water. The proportions of humerus and femur of the elephant seal are very similar to those of *Ichthyostega,* and the permanently bent forelimb of *Ichthyostega* forms a prop like the fore-

limb of a seal. Figure 10–6b shows a restoration of *Ichthyostega* that reflects these seallike features.

The mosaic of ancestral and derived features of Devonian tetrapods suggests that the origin of tetrapods and the origin of terrestrial life were two separate events. But the loss of the internal gills in all these tetrapods more derived than *Acanthostega* suggests that their ancestry must lie in a more terrestrial form (Janis and Farmer in press). No living amphibious fish loses the gills entirely, as it relies on them for the excretion of carbon dioxide and nitrogenous wastes when back in the water.

■ The Radiation and Diversity of Nonamniote Paleozoic Tetrapods

For over 200 million years, from the Late Devonian to the Early Cretaceous, nonamniote tetrapods radiated into an unimaginable variety of terrestrial and aquatic forms. It is no wonder that the fossil record is confusing. Parallel and convergent evolution were widespread, and it is hard to separate phylogenetic relationship from convergent evolution. Large gaps in the fossil record, especially the lack of early representatives of many groups, still obscure relationships.

Crassigyrinus is a case in point. "Enigmatic" appears frequently in discussions of this Early Carboniferous tetrapod from Scotland. It was a large animal (1.3 meters long), with tiny legs, and a massive skull with prominent teeth and fangs (Figure 10–8). Despite its relatively late appearance (in the Carboniferous), *Crassigyrinus* retained some ancestral characters, including limited ossification of the vertebral centra, the absence of an occipital condyle, and the presence of some skull bones that were reduced or absent in *Ichthyostega.* Clearly, *Crassigyrinus* was aquatic, but which way was it going? That is, was it a late survivor of a lineage that, like the Devonian tetrapods, had probably never become fully terrestrial? Or was it one of the earliest of the terrestrial vertebrates to return to the water and lose many of the characters associated with life on land? It is not yet possible to choose between those hypotheses (Ahlberg and Milner 1994, Coates and Clack 1995).

General Patterns of Radiation

Nonamniote tetrapods are often called amphibians, but that term is now reserved for the extant (living)

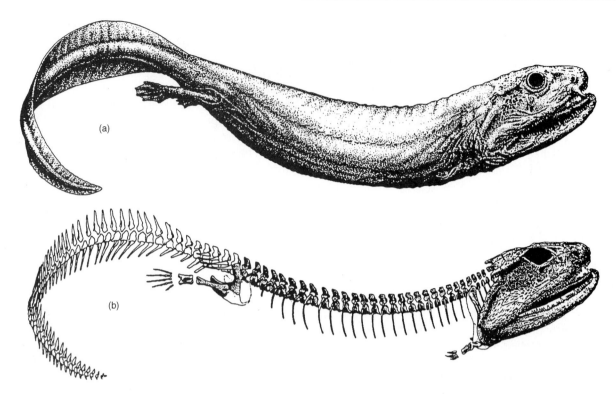

Figure 10–8 *Crassigyrinus* had a skull as big as that of a leopard, armed with lateral teeth that had sharp anterior and posterior keels and large fangs in the palate. (From A. L. Panchen and T. R. Smithson, 1990, *Transactions of the Royal Society of Edinburgh: Earth Sciences* 81:31–44.)

nonamniote tetrapods, the lissamphibians (frogs, salamanders, and caecilians). It is misleading to think of the primitive Paleozoic tetrapods as being amphibians for a number of reasons. First, many of them were much larger than any living amphibians, and would have been more crocodilelike in appearance and habits. Second, they would have lacked the specializations of modern amphibians: For example, many forms had dermal scales, making it unlikely that they used their skin for respiration, as do the modern forms. Finally, and most important, many of them were actually more closely related to amniotes than to modern amphibians (Figure 10–2).

Table 10.1 lists the different types of Paleozoic tetrapods, and Figure 10–2 illustrates one current consensus of their interrelationships. The groups listed in Table 10.1 are all well-established groups; the problem comes in trying to understand how these different groups are related to one another and to the modern groups of tetrapods, the lissamphibians and the amniotes. A major problem lies in the fact that we are missing a critical piece of the geological record of tetrapod history: Although fossils are known from the Late Devonian, the subsequent record is a complete blank for 20 to 30 million years, with no further fossils known until the later part of the Early Carboniferous. The record for the rest of the Early Carboniferous is also pretty sparse. Thus, during the time when the major groups of tetrapods were diversifying, the fossil record can provide us with little or no information, which potentially biases our understanding of how the groups known from the later Carboniferous are related to one another (Carroll 1995, 1997). The interrelationship of early tetrapods shown in Figure 10–2 broadly agrees with the 1994 review by Ahlberg and Milner (see also Benton 1997), but since that time a plethora of new phylogenies has been suggested, most offering diametrically different opinions (see some discussion later). The discovery of more Early Carboniferous tetrapod fossils is crucially needed to help confirm or refute the various competing hypotheses. For the purposes of this volume, we will treat the phylogeny in Figure 10–2 as a possible hypothesis of interrelationships, adopted for the time being, at least.

These Paleozoic tetrapods were originally divided into groups called "**labyrinthodonts**" and "**lep-**

TABLE 10.1	Major groups of paleozoic nonamniotic tetrapods

"Labyrinthodonts"

Batracomorphs

Temnospondyli: The most diverse, longest-lived group, ranging from the mid-Carboniferous to the Early Cretaceous. Possessed large heads with akinetic skulls. Paleozoic forms (e.g., *Eryops*, *Cacops*) were terrestrial or semiaquatic; Mesozoic forms (e.g., *Cyclotosaurus*, *Archegosauarus*, *Gerrothorax*) were all secondarily fully aquatic (Figures 10–9c, 10–14, 10–15).

Colosteidae: Aquatic Carboniferous forms, possibly secondarily so, with elongate, flattened bodies, small limbs, and lateral line grooves (e.g., *Greererpeton*, *Pholidogaster*, *Colosteus*).

Loxommatidae: Mid and Late Carboniferous forms with crocodilelike skulls and distinctive keyhole-shaped orbits.

Reptilomorphs

Anthracosauroidea: The other diverse, long-lived group, although to a lesser extent than the temnospondyls. Known from the Early Carboniferous to the Late Permian. Anthracosaurs had deeper skulls than temnospondyls with prominent tabular horns, and retained cranial kinesis. Some forms (e.g., *Gephyrostega*) were terrestrial. Others, grouped together as embolomeres, were secondarily aquatic (e.g., *Pholiderpeton*, *Archeria*). (Figure 10–11.)

Seymouriamorpha: Known from the Permian only. Early Permian forms known from North America (e.g., *Seymouria*, Figure 10–16b) were large and fully terrestrial. Later Permian forms known from Europe and China (discosaurids and kotlassiids) were secondarily fully aquatic.

Diadectomorpha: Known from the Late Carboniferous and the Early Permian. Large, fully terrestrial forms, now considered to be the sister group of amniotes. Diadectidae (e.g., *Diadectes*, Figure 10–16a) had laterally expanded cheek teeth suggestive of a herbivorous diet. Limnoscelidae and Tseajaiidae had sharper, pointed teeth and were probably carnivorous.

"Lepospondyls"

Microsauria: Distinguished by a single bone in the temporal series termed the tabular. Many (e.g., the tuditanomorphs) were terrestrial and rather lizardlike with deep skulls and elongate bodies (*microsaur* = small reptile) (Figure 10–12). Some forms (microbrachomorphs) had evidence of external gill supports and lateral line grooves and were probably aquatic. Known from the Late Carboniferous and the Early Permian of North America and Europe.

Aïstopoda: Limbless forms, lacking limb girdles, with elongate bodies (up to 200 trunk vertebrae) and rather snakelike skulls that may have allowed for the swallowing of large prey items (Figure 10–13a). They may have been aquatic or have lived in leaf litter. Known from the mid- to Late Carboniferous of North America and Europe.

Adelogyrinidae: Limbless, long-trunked forms, but retaining the dermal shoulder girdle. Known from the Early Carboniferous of Europe.

Lysorophia: Elongate forms with greatly reduced limbs. Known from the Late Carboniferous and the Early Permian of North America.

Nectridia: Also rather elongate, but with a long tail rather than a long trunk. Distinguished by having fan-shaped neural and haemal arches in the vertebral column. Limbs small and poorly ossified, indicative of an aquatic mode of life (Figure 10–13b). Some nectridians (keraterpetontids) had broad flattened skulls with enlarged tabular bones (Figure 10–13d). These tabular horns were up to five times the width of the anterior part of the skull, and skin imprints show that they were covered by a flap of skin extending back to the shoulder. They may have served as a hydrofoil to help in underwater locomotion, or to support highly vascularized skin to help in underwater respiration. Known from the Late Carboniferous and the Early Permian of North America, Europe, and North Africa

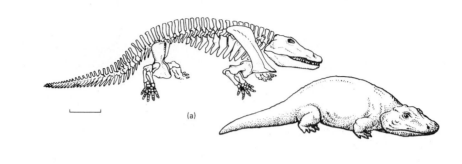

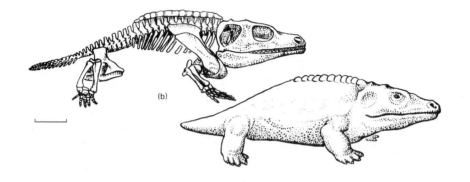

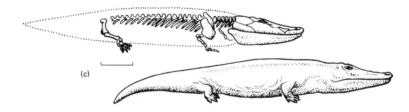

Figure 10–9 Temnospondyls radiated in both terrestrial and aquatic habitats. *Eryops*, an eryopid (a), and *Cacops* (b) a dissorophid, both from the Permian, were relatively terrestrial. *Eryops* was about 1.6 meters long, and its head comprised one fifth of its total length. *Cacops* was only about 40 centimeters long, but its head was nearly one-third the total length of its body. *Cyclotosaurus* (c) a capitosaur from the Late Triassic, was an aquatic form. The scale marks represent 10 centimeters. ([a] From E. A. Colbert, 1969, *Evolution of the Vertebrates*, Wiley, New York, NY; [b] from B. J. Stahl, 1974, *Vertebrate History: Problems in Evolution*, McGraw-Hill, New York, NY; [c] from C. L. Fenton and M. A. Fenton, 1958, *The Fossil Book*, Doubleday, New York, NY.)

ospondyls" (see Table 10.1). Labyrinthodonts were mainly larger forms (large lizard- to crocodile-size) (Figure 10–9) with a multipartite vertebral centrum (Figure 10–7) and teeth with complexly infolded enamel (labyrinthodont teeth). Lepospondyls were small forms (small lizard- or salamander-size) with a single, spool-shaped vertebral centrum and without the labyrinthine form of enamel. The characters supporting these divisions most likely relate to body size, and probably do not reflect phylogenetic relationships. The larger labyrinthodonts probably required the bipartite centrum for twisting movements of the spinal column on land, as the heavy head would tend to rotate around the trunk axis during locomotion. The labyrinthodont teeth probably reflect the ability for inertial feeding only. That is, feeding with only a simple snap of the jaws, without fine control of jaw movements. Thus the teeth might need to be strong to resist the forces generated during feeding. The smaller absolute size of lepospondyls would reduce the forces experienced in locomotion and feeding, and thus reduce the need for specializations of the teeth and a more mobile vertebral column. Despite the paraphyletic nature of these tetrapod groupings, the names retain a certain descriptive usefulness.

Current consensus perceives two main clades of labyrinthodonts: the Batrachomorpha (with the temnospondyls as the predominant group, see Figures 10–9 and 10–10) and the Reptilomorpha (with the anthracosaurs as the predominant group, see Figure 10–11). Batracomorphs were in general more aquatic, characterized by flat, immobile skulls and the reduction of the number of fingers in the hand to four. The modern amphibians (**Lissamphibia**), or at least frogs, may have their origin within this group. Reptilomorphs were in general more terrestrial, characterized by more domed skulls retaining some kinetic ability, and the retention of a five-fingered hand. Amniotes may have their origins within the Reptilomorphs, as the name suggests.

The affinities of the lepospondyls (Figures 10–12 and 10–13) are more open to question. Figure 10–2 shows them as a monophyletic group within the Batrachomorpha, mainly for convenience of illus-

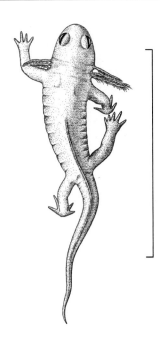

Figure 10–10 The paedomorphic temnospondyl *Branchiosaurus* was about the size of a salamander. The scale mark represents 5 centimeters.

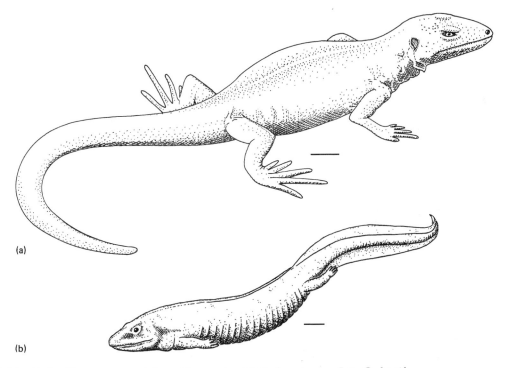

(a)

(b)

Figure 10–11 Carboniferous nonamniote reptilomorphs. (a) *Gephyrostegus*, a Late Carboniferous anthracosauroid, was terrestrial. It was about a meter long, with sturdy legs supporting a deep body. (b) *Pholiderpeton*, an embolomere of the same period, was aquatic. Its legs were small and its body was cylindrical. The scale marks represent 10 centimeters. ([a] From R. L. Carroll, 1972, *Handbuch der Palaeoherpetologie,* part 5B, pages 1–19 Gustav Fischer, Stuttgart, Germany; [b] from A. R. Milner, 1980, *The Terrestrial Environment and the Origin of Land Vertebrates,* edited by A. L. Panchen, Academic, London, UK.)

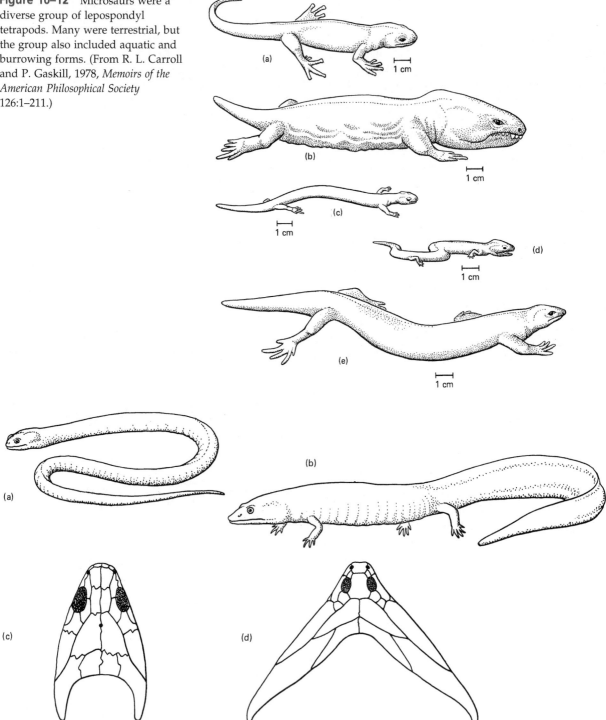

Figure 10–12 Microsaurs were a diverse group of lepospondyl tetrapods. Many were terrestrial, but the group also included aquatic and burrowing forms. (From R. L. Carroll and P. Gaskill, 1978, *Memoirs of the American Philosophical Society* 126:1–211.)

(a) 1 cm

(b) 1 cm

(c) 1 cm

(d) 1 cm

(e) 1 cm

(a)

(b)

(c)

(d)

Figure 10–13 Other lepospondyls. (a) The legless aïstopod *Ophiderpeton* was about 75 centimeters long. (b) The aquatic nectrideans were more varied than the aïstopods. One type, illustrated by *Sauropleura,* had an elongated body and small legs, a laterally flattened tail, and a sharply pointed snout. The tabular bones of "horned nectrideans," (c) *Keraterpeton* and (d) *Diploceraspis,* were greatly elongated. ([a] and [b] From A. R. Milner and [c] from A. C. Milner, both in *The Terrestrial Environment and the Origin of Land Vertebrates,* edited by A. L. Panchen, 1980, Academic, London, UK; [d] from J. R. Beerbower, 1963, *Bulletin of the Museum of Comparative Zoology* 130:31–108.)

tration, but the different lepospondyl groups were probably not closely related. Other recent phylogenetic schemes portray them as a paraphyletic or even polyphyletic assemblage within the Batrachomorpha, as the sister group to modern amphibians (Laurin and Reisz 1997), or with some or all of them closely related to amniotes (Panchen 1991, Carroll 1995). Likewise the origins of the Lissamphibia are somewhat questionable. Although current consensus has them derived from within the temnospondyls (from a group of terrestrial, mainly small-size forms, the dissorophids) (see Trueb and Cloutier 1991), other researchers would prefer to derive only frogs from this group, and claim that the origin of other modern amphibians lies within various lepospondyl groups (Carroll 1987). This scheme would make Lissamphibia polyphyletic. Another recent opinion would make lissamphibians (plus lepospondyls) the sister group to amniotes (Laurin and Reisz 1997). The study of the interrelationships of nonamniote tetrapods is an ongoing one of much debate and dissension.

Nonamniote tetrapods reached their peak of generic diversity in the Late Carboniferous and Early Permian, when they consisted of fully aquatic, semiaquatic, and terrestrial forms. Most lineages were extinct by the mid-Permian. The only groups to survive into the Mesozoic were the ancestors of the modern groups of amphibians, and the fully aquatic temnospondyls. Temnospondyls were extinct in most of the world by the end of the Triassic but persisted into the Early Cretaceous in Australia. Although all living lissamphibian groups had their origins in the Mesozoic, the generic diversity of nonamniote tetrapods did not reattain Permian levels until the mid Tertiary (Fracasso 1994).

Ecological and Adaptive Trends

One of the most striking aspects of the early tetrapods is the number and diversity of forms that returned to a fully aquatic mode of life. Forms that were apparently fully aquatic as adults include colosteids, nectridians, microbrachid microsaurs, embolomerous anthracosauroids, and numerous groups within the temnospondyls. The temnospondyls were the only group of nonamniote tetrapods (aside from the lissamphibians) to survive the Paleozoic, and all of the Mesozoic forms were large, flattened fully aquatic predators. Among living amphibians, many salamanders and some frogs are fully aquatic as adults (see Chapter 11).

The diversity of aquatic temnospondyls includes the capitosaurs and metoposaurs of the Triassic, with skulls nearly a meter long. *Cyclotosaurus* from the Late Triassic was an aquatic form with small legs and a dorsoventrally flattened body (Figure 10–9c). These impressive temnospondyls may have represented the top of the aquatic food chain, feeding on their smaller relatives as well as any terrestrial animals incautious enough to enter the water in their vicinity. The Plagiosauridae and the Brachyopidae were bizarre, flat-headed, short-snouted temnospondyls. *Gerrothorax*, a Late Triassic plagiosaurid, was about 1 meter long (Figure 10–14). The body was very flat and armored dorsally and ventrally. The dorsal position of the eyes suggests that *Gerrothorax* lay in ambush on the bottom of the pond until a fish or another temnospondyl swam close enough to be seized with a sudden rush and gulp. The broad head and wide mouth would enable *Gerrothorax* to suck in a rush of water including potential prey items. The broad, short skull and retention of external gills in at least some forms suggest that the brachyopids and plagiosaurids evolved by paedomorphosis from the larvae of temnospondyl ancestors. Because brachyopids and plagiosaurids were separated in both distance and

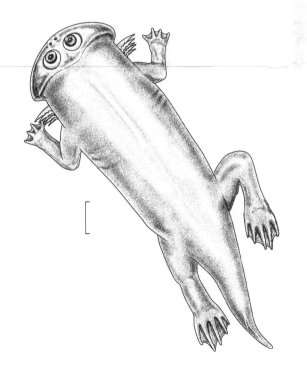

Figure 10–14 *Gerrothorax*, a plagiosaur. The scale mark represents 10 centimeters.

Figure 10–15 Specialized long-snouted, fish-eating temnospondyls like *Archegosaurus* (a) appeared in the Early Permian. The trematosaurs like *Aphaneramma* (b) were still more specialized marine forms of the Triassic.

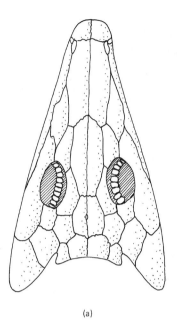

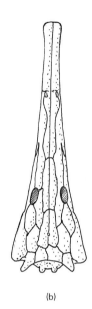

(a)

(b)

time, it is likely that they represent at least two separate derivations.

The trematosaurids were among the most remarkable temnospondyls. As early as the Permian some temnospondyls reversed the trend toward a broad, flat skull and evolved the elongate snout characteristic of specialized fish eaters (Figure 10–15). Forms such as *Archegosaurus* may later have given rise to even more specialized fish eaters including *Aphaneramma,* or the later forms may represent a convergent evolutionary lineage. The trematosaurids are found in Early Triassic marine beds. Salt water is an unusual habitat for nonamniote tetrapods. The scaly covering that trematosaurs might have retained from sarcopterygian ancestors could have helped to protect them from the osmotic stress of either fresh or salt water, or they may have retained high levels of urea to raise their internal osmotic pressure, like some modern estuarine frogs. How could the larvae have coped with these conditions? Were trematosaurs viviparous like a few living amphibians, or could their larvae tolerate at least moderate salinity as do tadpoles of a few frogs and toads? Furthermore, if trematosaurs were able to invade the sea, why didn't other temnospondyls?

In contrast to the temnospondyls, the reptilomorph tetrapods appear to have been predominantly terrestrial as adults, and many have been mistaken for early reptiles (especially animals like *Diadectes* and *Seymouria,* Figure 10–16). Terrestriality also evolved convergently among other early

tetrapods, predominately in the microsaurs (Figure 10–12) and the dissorophid temnospondyls (Figure 10–9b).

A final trend in nonamniote tetrapods is for the evolution of forms with elongated bodies and limbs that are either greatly reduced or lost entirely. Several groups of lepospondyls independently acquired this body form (see Table 10.1). It is probably associated with an aquatic or burrowing mode of life, as in the living limbless caecilian amphibians.

■ Amniotes

Amniotes are more derived tetrapods than those groups we have discussed, and comprise the majority of tetrapods alive today (mammals, birds, and reptiles). Their name refers to the **amniotic egg,** which is one of the most obvious features distinguishing amniotes from amphibians today. Amniotes appeared somewhat later in the fossil record than nonamniote tetrapods; the earliest known sister-taxon of amniotes is the Early Carboniferous *Westlothiana* (Figure 10–17), appearing some 30 million years after the first known tetrapods of the Late Devonian.

Carboniferous and Permian Tetrapods

Several groups of vertebrates, both nonamniotes and amniotes, evolved specializations for terrestrial

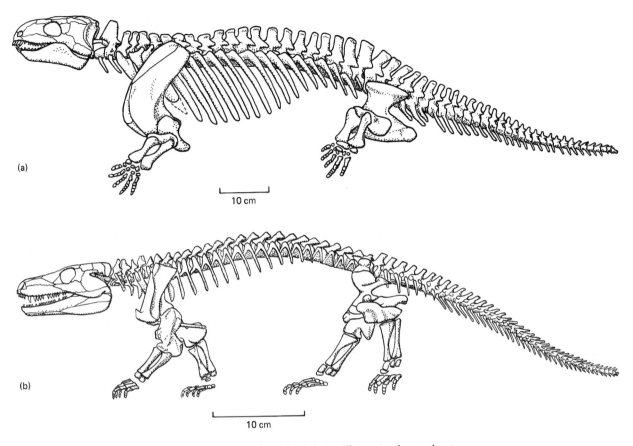

Figure 10–16 Permian nonamniote reptilomorphs: (a) *Diadectes*. This animal was about 2 meters long. Note the short sturdy vertebral column and the well-ossified limbs and limb girdles, indicative of terrestriality. (b) *Seymouria*. This animal was about 1 meter long. (From R. L. Carroll, 1969, in *Biology of the Reptilia,* volume 1, edited by C. Gans, A. d'A. Bellairs, and T. S. Parsons, Academic, London, UK.)

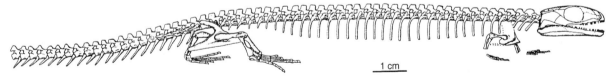

Figure 10–17 *Westlothiana lizziae,* from the Early Carboniferous of Scotland, is considered to be earliest known sister taxon to amniotes. (From T. R. Smithson, R. L. Carroll, A. L. Panchen, and S. M. Andrews, 1994, *Transactions of the Royal Society of Edinburgh: Earth Sciences* 84:383–412.)

life in the Carboniferous (Figure 10–2). Most, if not all, terrestrial vertebrates at this time were carnivorous (including eating fish and invertebrates). No adult amphibian among living forms is herbivorous, and there is little evidence in the fossil record to suggest that Paleozoic nonamniote tetrapods were herbivores. *Diadectes* is the only likely exception to this generalization.

Amniotes began to radiate in the Carboniferous and Early Permian into many of the life zones occupied by nonamniote tetrapods. A key event in their radiation may have been the great diversification of insects in the Late Carboniferous, probably in response to the increasing quantity and diversity of terrestrial vegetation (see Chapter 9). Carnivorous vertebrates could not respond directly to the

Figure 10–18 Diversity of Paleozoic amniotes: Early amniotes varied in size from a few centimeters long to a couple of meters, and their ecological roles were equally diverse. (a) *Hylonomus*, a protorothyridid (lizard-size), represents the typical lizardlike body form of many early amniotes. (b) *Haptodus*, a synapsid (dog-size). (c) *Mesosaurus*, a mesosaur (cat-size). (d) *Captorhinus*, a captorhinid (lizard-size). (e) *Petrolacosaurus kansensis*, a stem diapsid (araeoscelidian) (lizard-size). (f) *Procolophon*, a procolophonid (dog-size). (g) *Pareiasaurus*, a pareiasaur (cow-size).

energy supply offered by terrestrial plants, but they could and apparently did respond to the opportunities presented by the radiation of insects. Probably for the first time in evolutionary history there was an adequate food supply to support a diverse fauna of fully terrestrial vertebrate predators.

The morphological and ecological diversity of the amniotes that had developed by the late Paleozoic (see Figure 10–18) testifies to the success of this clade. As the terrestrial amniotes diversified, the terrestrial nonamniotes became less varied. Terrestrial nonamniote tetrapods were at their peak in the Permian; the groups that survived through the Triassic were mostly the flattened, fully aquatic forms. From the start of the Mesozoic onward, terrestrial habitats were dominated by a series of radiations of amniote tetrapods.

Derived Features of Amniotes

Traditionally, amniotes have been distinguished by the possession of an amniotic egg and a waterproof skin (i.e., a thicker skin than in amphibians with a keratinized epidermis). The amniotic egg (Figure 10–19) is characteristic of turtles, lepidosaurs (lizards and their relatives), crocodilians, birds, monotremes (egg-laying mammals), and, in modified form, of therian mammals (the membranes that form the placenta are homologous to certain membranes in the egg; see Chapter 21). It is assumed to have been the

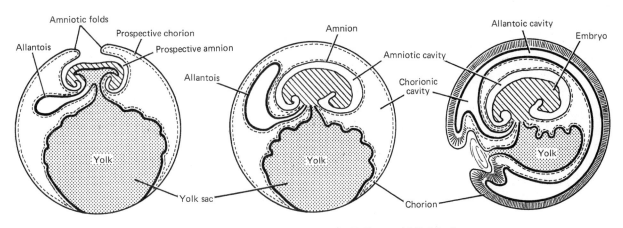

Figure 10–19   The distinctive features of the amniotic egg. (From T. W. Torrey, 1962, *Morphogenesis of the Vertebrates*, Wiley, New York, NY.)

reproductive mode of Mesozoic diapsids, and dinosaur eggs are relatively common as fossils. But there are many other ways in which amniotes represent a more derived kind of tetrapod than both living amphibians and Paleozoic nonamniote tetrapods, affecting many systems of anatomy and physiology (Figure 10–20).

Frolich (1997) suggested that the notion of waterproof skin by the addition of keratin may be erroneous. Skin permeability actually varies widely among living amphibians and amniotes, and the presence of lipids in the skin is probably the most important determining factor. Although amniotes have a greater variety of skin elaborations than amphibians, such as scales, hair, and feathers, the lack of such structures in living amphibians may be related to their use of the skin in respiration. The nature of amniote skin may be more related to protection and support. A more important derived amniote feature, in terms of independence from the water, might be costal (rib) ventilation of the lungs, with the ability to get rid of all carbon dioxide waste via the lungs, rather than relying on diffusion across a moist skin.

The amniotic egg is sometimes referred to as the land egg, but this is a misnomer. Many species of living amphibians and even some fishes have nonamniotic eggs that develop quite successfully on land, and terrestrial invertebrates also lay nonamniotic eggs. Both amniotic and nonamniotic eggs must have relatively moist conditions to avoid desiccation. The term cleidoic egg (*cleido* = closed or locked) is often used as a synonym for the amniotic egg, but this is not entirely correct. Technically, this term should be reserved for the rigid-shelled calcareous egg of birds that, unlike the eggs of most other amniotes, does not allow water uptake through the shell (Packard and Packard 1980).

An amniotic egg is a remarkable example of biological engineering (Figure 10–19). The shell, which may be leathery and flexible (as in lizards), or calcified and rigid (as in birds), provides mechanical protection while being porous enough to allow movement of respiratory gases and water vapor. The albumin (egg white) gives further protection against mechanical damage and provides a reservoir of water and protein. The large yolk is the energy supply for the developing embryo. At the beginning of embryonic development, the embryo is represented by a few cells resting on top of the yolk. As development proceeds these multiply, and endodermal and mesodermal tissue surround the yolk and encloses it in a **yolk sac** that is part of the developing gut. Blood vessels differentiate rapidly in the mesodermal tissue surrounding the yolk sac and transport food and gases to the embryo. By the end of development, only a small amount of yolk remains, and this is absorbed before or shortly after hatching.

In these respects the amniotic egg does not differ greatly from the nonamniotic eggs of amphibians and fishes: all vertebrates have a yolk sac extraembryonic membrane. The significant differences lie in three additional extraembryonic membranes—the **chorion, amnion,** and **allantois.** The chorion and amnion develop from outgrowths of the body wall at the edges of the developing platelike embryo. These two pouches spread outward and around the embryo until they meet. At their junction, the membranes merge and leave an outer membrane, the chorion, which surrounds the embryo and yolk sac,

Figure 10–20 Morphological and physiological differences among fishes, primitive tetrapods, and amniotes: (a) An osteolepiform fish (e.g., *Eusthenopteron*); (b) a primitive, non-amniote tetrapod (e.g., *Eryops*); (c) an early amniote tetrapod (e.g., *Hylonomus*). The numbers refer to the numbers on the figure.

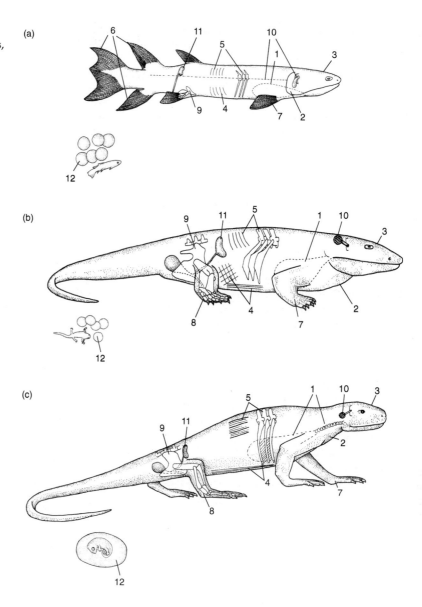

1. Lungs are probably primitively present in all three animals (a primitive feature of bony fishes). The fish and the primitive tetrapod use simple, saclike lungs primarily for oxygen uptake only (carbon dioxide can be lost through the gills in the fish, or perhaps through moist skin in the primitive tetrapod, especially in water). The amniote has larger, more complexly infolded lungs, and the lungs are joined to the pharynx via a trachea, strengthened with cartilaginous rings. With a more keratinized skin, almost all carbon dioxide must now be lost via the lungs. **2.** The fish retains gills and a bony operculum for its ventilation; it thus lacks a neck (the opercular bones link the head to the shoulder girdle). In the primitive tetrapod the gills are lost (in terrestrial adults) and the shoulder girdle is no longer connected to the head. Specialized neck vertebrae (the atlas–axis complex) are now developed to allow movement of the head on the vertebral column. In the amniote the neck may be lengthened. **3.** The head of the fish has a short snout; movements of the jaws allow for suction of water for both gill ventilation and feeding. The primitive tetrapod has a large, flat, wide head with a long snout; pumping movements of the gular region (floor of the mouth) help ventilate the lungs (buccal pumping). A muscular tongue is present in all tetrapods, helping with obtaining food and with food transport through the mouth to the gullet. The amniote no longer uses its head for buccal pumping (see point 5); its head is smaller, narrower, and more domed. **4.** The ventral axial muscles (hypaxials) of the fish are fairly undifferentiated and used solely for locomotion. In the primitive tetrapod the hypaxials are more differentiated, including an inner transverse abdominus (used for exhaling the air from the lungs) and a ventral rectus abdominus, helping to support the weight of the viscera on land. In amniotes there is further differentiation of the hypaxials into the intercostal muscles that move the ribs (see point 5). **5.** The ribs of the fish lack a solid centrum and interconnections; their main role is for the attachment of axial muscles for locomotion. The ribs are small and insignificant. The vertebrae are enlarged in the primitive tetrapod, with a definitive centrum (bipartite in some forms), and the vertebrae are connected via zygapophyses. The ribs are enlarged, and may overlap one another. The axial skeleton (vertebral column plus ribs) is now important in supporting the body weight on land, and in maintaining the animal's posture. The ribs of amniotes are lighter, and connect ventrally to a sternum; they are now used for inhaling air into the lung (costal ventilation). Some of the postural role of the ribs is now assumed by the differentiation of the dorsal axial muscles (the epaxials), which in fishes and primitive tetrapods are used for locomotion alone. **6.** The fish has median fins (dorsal, caudal, and anal) in addition to the paired fins (pectoral and pelvic). These fins are lost in tetrapods (although Devonian tetrapods may retain a small caudal [tail] fin). **7.** The fish has bones in its fins (as in all lobe-finned fishes), but no equivalent to hands or feet, and limited mobility within the joints of the fin; fin rays are present. All tetrapods have jointed limbs (with a forwardly pointing knee and a backwardly pointing elbow), and hands and feet with digits, and wrist/ankle joints; fin rays are lost. The limb bones and joints of the amniote are more lightly constructed, possibly reflecting the evolution of proprioreceptive feedback from the muscles. **8.** The feet of primitive tetrapods are used mainly as holdfasts, to provide frictional contact with the ground, with movement generated by the body axial musculature. The feet of amniotes are used more as levers to propel the animal, and the ankle forms a distinct hinge joint (mesotarsal joint). (Some nonamniotes, e.g., frogs, parallel amniotes in this condition.) **9.** The pelvic girdle of fish merely serves to anchor the pelvic fins in the body wall; there is no connection with the vertebral column. In tetrapods the pelvic girdle is tripartite (consisting of the ilium, pubis, and ischium); the ilia on each side connect the pelvic limbs to the vertebral column, forming an attachment at the sacrum via a modified rib. Primitive tetrapods have only one sacral vertebra and rib; primitive amniotes have two or three. **10.** Sensation in fish is via a lateral-line system; the hyomandibula bone acts to help move the operculum. The lateral line cannot function on land, and so is lost in terrestrial adult primitive tetrapods, and in all amniotes. Amniotes hear sound waves via a tympanum (eardrum) that connects to the inner ear via the stapes (= the hyomandibula, which loses its original function with the loss of the operculum, see point 2) in a middle ear cavity (note that this set-up was not present in the earliest tetrapods, and evolved convergently in various tetrapod lineages). **11.** The kidney of fishes acts to regulate water balance and for the excretion of divalent ions (the bean-shaped mammallike kidney in these pictures is for diagrammatic purposes only); excretion of nitrogen and monovalent ions are primarily carried out via the gills. There is no urinary bladder. In the terrestrial adults of primitive tetrapods the kidney takes over the functions of nitrogen excretion and monovalent ion excretion (some ion regulation may be done by the skin). A urinary bladder is present for storage of urine on land, and water may be reclaimed from the bladder. In amniotes there is a new duct linking the kidney and the cloaca, the ureter, separate from the gamete-bearing ducts. The bladder acts primarily to store urine; most water reclamation (all in mammals) is carried out via the kidney. **12.** Both fishes and primitive tetrapods lay unshelled eggs with a yolk sac extraembryonic membrane in the water (some primitive tetrapods may lay them on land in moist environments), and the young go through a gilled larval stage (either in the water or within the egg). Amniotes lay a shelled egg with additional extraembryonic membranes (the amniotic egg); the gilled larval stage is bypassed. A copulatory organ (penis) is usually present for internal fertilization. Amniote eggs can be laid in dry environments, but cannot be laid in the water. All three types of animals may be viviparous.

and an inner membrane, the amnion, which surrounds the embryo itself. The allantoic membrane develops as an outgrowth of the hindgut posterior to the yolk sac and lies within the chorion. The allantois appears to have evolved as a storage place for nitrogenous wastes produced by the metabolism of the embryo, and the urinary bladder of the adult grows out from its base. It also serves a respiratory organ as it is vascularized and so can transport oxygen from the surface of the egg back to the embryo (and transport carbon dioxide in the opposite direction). The allantois is left behind in the egg when the embryo emerges, and the nitrogenous wastes stored in it do not have to be reprocessed.

How and why might the amniotic egg have evolved? It is possible for nonamniotic eggs to be laid on land, but only at very small sizes. Larger-size eggs (more than 10 millimeters in diameter) may be too large for effective diffusion of oxygen across their surface for the needs of the developing embryo, and they may also collapse under their own weight. Presence of the additional extraembryonic membranes would enable larger eggs to be supported (as would a shell) and to provide exchange of respiratory gases. Robert Carroll (1970) developed an evolutionary scenario in which the ancestors of amniotes would have to have been small animals. The precursor to the amniote egg would have to be an nonamniote egg laid on land (otherwise there would be no evolutionary pressure to improve the situation); but as egg size and adult size are correlated, only animals of small adult size (6 to 7 centimeters in length) would be able to lay eggs small enough to survive. The evolution of the amniotic egg might have been most important in allowing an increase in the size of the adults that could lay eggs on the land.

Carroll's ideas have been criticized (e.g., Reisz 1997) on the grounds that more recent phylogenies of early tetrapods show that the sister groups to the amniotes were actually fairly large animals, such as seymouriamorphs and diadectomorphs (Figure 10–16). But our fossil record of Paleozoic tetrapods is still very sparse (Carroll 1997): A large-sized sister group does not preclude an as-yet unknown small common ancestor for both groups, or for amniotes alone. Additionally the oldest known sister-taxon to amniotes, *Westlothiana* (Figure 10–19), was quite small. A completely alternative view of the evolution of the amniotic egg was that the membranes evolved in the context of viviparity (reviewed in Stewart 1997).

How could we tell if a given fossil animal laid an amniotic egg or not? We call modern amniotes by that name because they lay eggs that contain extraembryonic membranes. We infer that some extinct tetrapods may have been amniotes because of their bony morphology, but clearly we cannot determine for certain whether or not they possessed extraembryonic membranes. How might we infer the reproductive mode of fossil animals called amniotes?

The capacity to lay an amniotic egg is not preserved in features of the skeleton, but we can make a fair estimate of its point of origin by use of the tetrapod phylogeny (Figure 10-2). As shown in Figure 10–2, the synapsids (mammals and extinct relatives) branched off from the other reptiles very early on, and all the other fossil animals that we consider to be amniotes are actually more closely related to living reptiles and birds. As mammals have (or had) the same type of egg as other living amniotes, then all animals higher than node number thirteen in the cladogram must have inherited this type of egg from the common ancestor of mammals and other amniotes.

A more difficult question is whether any of the fossil tetrapods lower down in the phylogeny might have laid an amniotic egg. We know that this was not true of seymouriamorphs, because larval forms are known that have external gills and lateral lines, showing that they still had aquatic larvae (Špinar 1952). That leaves the diadectomorphs as the only possible candidates. Diadectomorphs such as *Diadectes* have morphological features indicative of herbivory, as previously mentioned. It has been suggested that terrestrial reproduction would be essential for a herbivorous tetrapod. Herbivorous young must ingest the symbiotic microorganisms needed to aid in digesting herbage immediately after hatching, and these must be obtained from terrestrial microbial decomposers (Hotton et al. 1997). Thus, it might be inferred (although we cannot be certain) that diadectomorphs had a fully terrestrial form of reproduction and hence possessed the amniotic egg (Lee and Spencer 1997). The term cotylosaur has been used for the group including diadectomorphs with amniotes.

Patterns of Amniote Temporal Fenestration

Amniotes have been traditionally subdivided by the features of the skull, specifically by the number of holes in their head, or **temporal fenestration** (*fenes-*

tra = window). The major configurations (giving the name to different amniote lineages) are: **anapsid** (without arches, *apsid* = arch), seen in primitive amniotes and in turtles; **synapsid** (single arch), seen in mammals and their ancestors; and **diapsid** (double arch), seen in other reptiles and in birds. The arch term in the name refers to the temporal bars (also known as temporal arcades) that lie below and between the holes. Figure 10–21 illustrates the different patterns in the different groups. Note that the phylogenetic pattern of the acquisition of these holes suggests that the condition arose independently in the synapsid and diapsid lineages, as sauropsids more primitive than diapsids lack holes entirely.

Even though the skull of living mammals is highly modified from the primitive synapsid condition, you can still feel these skull features in yourselves. If you put your hands on either side of your eyes, you can feel your cheek bone (the zygomatic arch)—that is the temporal bar that lies below your synapsid skull opening. Then, if you clench your jaw, you can feel the muscles bulging above the arch; they are passing through the temporal opening, running from their origin from the top of the skull to the insertion on your lower jaw (see Figure 10–21j).

What is the function of these holes? As you saw in the above experiment, the holes allow room for muscles to bulge. Amniotes have, in the main, larger and more differentiated jaw muscles than nonamniotes, and this notion of room for bulging was originally the preferred evolutionary explanation. However Frazzetta (1968) pointed out that the *initial* evolutionary reason for developing these holes must have been something different. Only a large hole will allow enough room for a bulging muscle, so what could be the evolutionary advantage of an initial, small hole? And why does no nonamniote ever develop temporal fenestration?

Frazetta saw the key in light of changes in the complexity and orientation of the jaw muscles. In fishes and nonamniote tetrapods the jaw muscles are a simple little-differentiated mass, and the feeding movements consist of a simple inertial snap. The more domed skull of amniotes now allows muscles to originate directly from the underside of the skull roof and to run vertically down to the jaw. This new orientation of one portion of the jaw adductor complex allows the animal to apply static pressure between the teeth when the jaws are closed. The other portion of the original adductor complex is now the pterygoideus muscle, originating from the pterygoid flange on the palate, a new feature in amniotes (Figure 10–22).

The skull of nonamniotes is too flat and shallow to allow this orientation of muscles (possibly related to their need to use their head for a buccal-pumping mode of lung ventilation). A muscle in this position in a nonamniote's skull would simply be too short to allow the jaw to open very far, as muscles can be stretched only one third of their resting length (see Chapter 3). Increased differentiation of the adductor muscle mass in amniotes would allow for greater sophistication in jaw movements, and thus permit a greater diversity of feeding types. But muscles with this new 90-degree orientation to the bone of attachment would result in considerable stress on the periosteal covering of the bone. A way of compensating for this would be to leave portions of the skull partially unossified (the temporal fenestrae always form at the junction of three or four skull bones), and to have the muscle originate from the connective tissue covering the fenestra (Figure 10–23). In this way a small hole would still reflect an important structural change to reduce stresses on the skull. Later evolutionary developments would then include the enlargement of this hole, with the muscles running through the hole to attach to the outside of the skull roof, as they do in ourselves and other extant amniotes (Figure 10–21j).

This evolutionary scenario explains how a small, initial temporal fenestra might still have an important function, but it does not explain why the pattern is different in synapsids and diapsids, nor why some primitive, early amniotes do not have any fenestration. Although turtles have skulls that are technically anapsid, they have a posterior emargination of the skull (Figure 10–21b) that also allows expansion of the jaw muscles, and is analogous to a fenestra. Frogs and salamanders also have emarginated skulls. Early synapsids and diapsids were rather different kinds of animals; synapsids were more carnivorous and diapsids more insectivorous (Figure 10–18). Perhaps differences in muscle actions, relating to different feeding styles, encouraged temporal fenestration to take a different form in the two groups. An emphasis on static pressure in synapsids (as seen in modern mammals during feeding) might have allowed seizing and crushing larger, slower prey, while an emphasis on intertial snapping in early diapsids (as seen in modern diapsids during feeding) might have been beneficial for capturing small, agile prey.

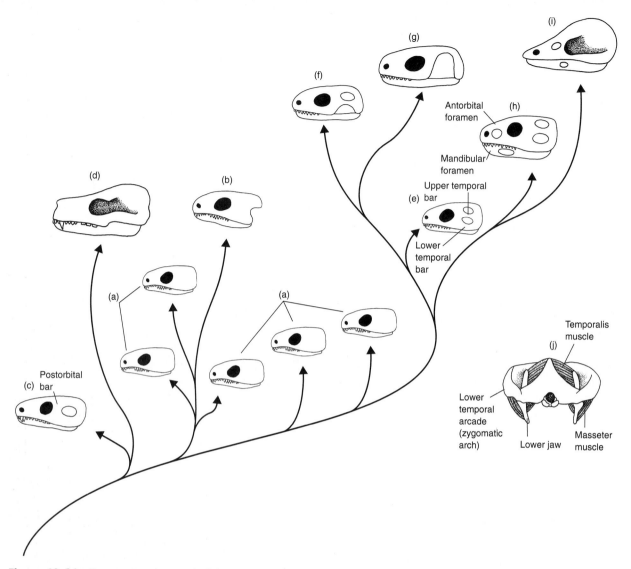

Figure 10–21 Patterns in amniote skull fenestration: (a) Primitive anapsid condition, as seen in the common ancestor of all amniotes, and in basal members of the parareptiles and eureptiles; (b) modified anapsid condition with emargination of the posterior portion of the skull, as seen in turtles; (c) primitive synapsid condition, with lower temporal fenestra only; (d) derived mammalian synapsid condition, where the orbit has become merged with the temporal opening, and dermal bone has grown down from the skull roof to surround the braincase; (e) primitive diapsid condition, as seen today in the reptile *Sphenodon*; both upper and lower temporal fenestrae are present; (f) lizardlike condition, typical of all squamates, where lower temporal bar has been lost; (g) snake condition, upper temporal bar has been lost in addition to the lower bar; (h) primitive archosaur diapsid condition, as seen in thecodonts and most dinosaurs; an antorbital foramen and a mandibular foramen have been added to the basic diapsid pattern (note that the antorbital foramen is secondarily reduced or lost in crocodiles); (i) derived avian archosaur condition; convergently with the condition in mammals, the orbit has become merged with the temporal openings and the braincase is enclosed in dermal bone; (j) posterior view through the skull of a synapsid (a cynodont mammallike reptile) showing how the temporal fenestra allows for muscles to insert onto the outside of the skull roof. The temporalis and masseter muscles are divisions of the original amniote adductor muscle complex, see Chapter 19. Note that there is no separate "euryapsid" or "parapsid" condition shown here. This condition, with the supposed existence of an upper temporal fenestra only, was thought to characterize marine reptiles. It is now realized that the so-called euryapsid condition is merely a modified diapsid one.

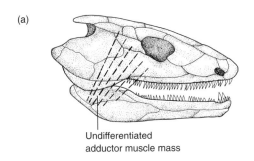

(a)

Undifferentiated
adductor muscle mass

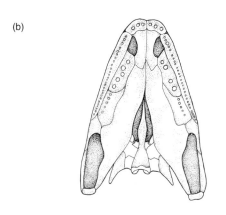

(b)

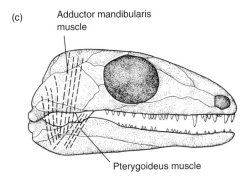

(c)

Adductor mandibularis
muscle

Pterygoideus muscle

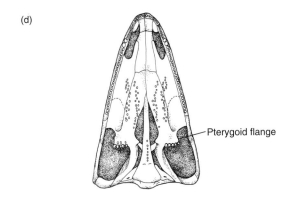

(d)

Pterygoid flange

Differences Between Major Amniote Groups

It can be seen from the phylogeny in Figure 10–2 that the major splits in the diversification of amniote lineages happened very early, soon after the origin of the amniotes themselves. The initial split was into synapsids (mammals and their extinct relatives) and sauropsids (reptiles and birds). A second major split, in the sauropsid lineage, was into the parareptiles (probably including turtles) and the eureptiles (including other reptiles and birds) (Reisz 1997) (see Table 10.2). Although there is some debate about the monophyletic nature of the parareptiles, this grouping emphasizes the fact that the late Paleozoic radiation included many lineages that have little or no relationship to the living groups of reptiles (apart from turtles). Although all amniotes share the basic derived features listed in Figure 10–20, nevertheless different amniote lineages have long and independent evolutionary histories, and have some profound differences from one another.

First, it is very important to remember how different the mammal lineage is from the other amniotes. Although we loosely talk about mammals coming from reptiles they branched off from the other amniotes very early on. Mammals lack some of the derived features that we usually attribute to reptiles in general, and actually retain some features usually considered more typical of amphibians (Hotton 1991). Most notably, they retain a glandular skin. This provides mammals with their ability to sweat and to produce milk, and may also be related to their possession of hair rather than scales. The keratin that makes mammalian hair is more like amphibian keratin than is reptilian keratin, and hair is always found in association with sebaceous (oil-producing) glands. Second, mammals are unable to excrete uric acid, the more derived product of nitro-

Figure 10–22   Differences in jaw muscles between nonamniote and amniote tetrapods. (a) Diagrammatic typical nonamniote tetrapod skull (anthracosauroid) in lateral view, showing the flat skull and the lack of differentiation of the jaw adductor muscles; (b) nonamniotic tetrapod skull in palatal view; (c) diagrammataic typical amniote skull (captorhinid) in lateral view, showing the more domed skull and the differentiation of the jaw adductor muscles into the adductor mandibularis and the pterygoideus; (d) amniote skull in palatal view, showing the pterygoid flanges for the origin of the pterygoideus muscles.

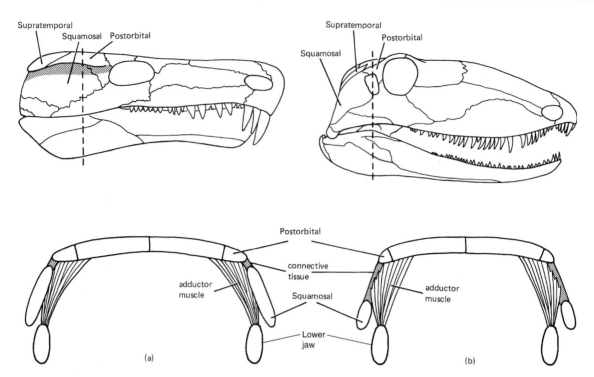

Figure 10–23 Hypothetical origin of the temporal fenestra in amniotes. Skulls are shown in lateral view (upper portion of figure) and in a cross-sectional view though the skull (lower portion of figure) at the place indicated by the dotted line in the lateral view. (a) *Limnoscelis*, a diadectomorphid (anapsid), showing a line of weakness between the cheek area and skull roof, an incipient condition for the development of a true fenestra; (b) *Ophiacodon*, a synapsid, showing how a small fenestra can allow for the origination of the jaw adductor muscles to come from connective tissue covering a small fenestra. (Modified from Kemp 1982.)

gen excretion characterizing living reptiles and birds (Chapter 4). Although mammals can concentrate their urine in the kidney, they cannot conserve water as efficiently through their waste production as do sauropsids. An implication of this may be that mammals never had the oviparous strategy of living sauropsids, where a switch from the production of urea to the production of uric acid in development is an essential component of water conservation for the embryo (Packard 1966). Synapsids may have always been somewhat ovoviviparous (egg-retaining) in their reproductive habits, as are living monotremes.

Sauropsids have a number of other features that distinguish them from mammals, apart from those of their skull anatomy listed in Figure 10–21. In particular, they all have good color vision, and the morphology of their eyes suggests that they all came from an essentially diurnal ancestry. In contrast, mammals (except for higher primates) and most other vertebrates are fundamentally nocturnal animals. Sauropsids also all have a new type of

harder keratin, forming the scales (or feathers), called beta keratin (Gauthier 1994). The split between parareptiles and eureptiles also reveals some fundamental differences. All living eureptiles, at least, have hindlimbs longer than the forelimbs, granting the capacity to run swiftly and even bipedally. Anatomical evidence also indicates that the middle ear and ear drum evolved separately in these different sauropsid lineages. In early amniotes the stapes forms a stout skull brace, and is transformed into a lighter auditory ossicle independently in different groups. All major groups of living sauropsids (turtles, lepidosaurs, and crocodiles plus birds) may have acquired a fully enclosed middle ear independently (Bolt and Lombard 1992, Clack 1997). (Chapter 19 discusses the evolution of the middle ear in synapsids as a further example of independent evolution within amniotes.)

It might seem strange that a middle ear system, using the stapes as an auditory ossicle, could evolve convergently so many times. But it must be remembered that the stapes, as in its original fish

TABLE 10.2	Major groups of Paleozoic amniotes

Synapsida

Synapsids, or "mammallike reptiles" are covered in Chapter 19. Early synapsids (Figure 10–18b) were of similar body size to early eureptiles, protorothyrids (Figure 10–18a), but their larger heads and teeth suggest a more specialized carnivorous habit.

Sauropsida

Mesosaurs: The first secondarily aquatic amniotes (Figure 10–18c). Known from freshwater deposits in the Early Permian of South Africa and South America, they provide one of the classic pieces of evidence for continental drift, as these continents were united in Gondwana at this time. Swimming adaptations include large, probably webbed, hind feet, a laterally flattened tail, and heavily ossified ribs that may have acted as ballast in diving. The long jaws and slender teeth may have been used to strain small crustaceans from the surrounding water.

Parareptilia

Millerettids: Rather like the eureptile protorothyrids. Known from the Late Permian of South Africa.
Procolophonids: Medium size, with peglike teeth that were laterally expanded in later members of the group, apparently specialized for crushing or grinding, suggestive of herbivory. Known from the Late Permian to Late Triassic worldwide except Australia (Figure 10–18f).
Pareiasaurs. Large size, approaching 3 meters in length (Figure 10–18g). Known from the Late Permian of Europe, Asia, and Africa. Their teeth were laterally compressed and leaf-shaped, like the teeth of herbivorous lizards. Pareiasaurs were evidently the dominant terrestrial herbivores of the later Permian.

Eureptilia

Protorothyrids: Small, relatively short-legged, rather lizardlike forms, probably insectivorous in habits (Figure 10–18a). Known from the mid-Carboniferous to Early Permian, North America and Europe.
Captorhinids: Tetrapods with more robust skulls and flatter teeth than protorothyrids and early diapsids, and may have had more of an omnivorous diet that required crushing (Figure 10–18d). Known from the Early and mid-Permian of North America and Europe, and the Late Permian of East Africa.
Areaoscelidans (stem diapsids): Early diapsids were shorter bodied and longer legged than protorothyrids, but probably also were insectivorous (Figure 10–18e). Araeoscelidians were known from the Late Carboniferous and Early Permian of North America and Europe.

function as the hyomandibula bone, abuts the otic capsule at one end and the cheek at the other (Chapter 3). Once freed from its original roles of jaw and opercular suspension it will transmit airborne sound vibrations to the inner ear, whether by design or not. The stapes of early tetrapods did not have a specific auditory function. It was a short, stout bone bracing the dermal skull roof against the braincase, but in more derived tetrapods it became lightened to form an auditory ossicle.

Eureptiles also have a fairly early split, certainly by the mid-Permian, into lepidosaur and archosaur lineages. We often think of lizards as typical amniotes, as their general body form is probably rather like those of the most primitive known forms (see Figures 10–18 and 10–20). But there are various ways in which lizards, like other living lepidosaurs, are highly specialized (Gauthier 1994). The forked tongue (seen in certain lizards and snakes) is one classically derived feature (all those old movies that portray dinosaurs with forked tongues are completely incorrect). Lizards and snakes (squamates) also have paired bifurcate penes (the hemipenes) that lie in the tail base. Lepidosaurs also shed their skin in its entirety, rather than in small fragments. We all know that snakes shed their skins, but we rarely consider the fact that we do as well. In fact, the great majority of house dust is made up of shed pieces of human skin! Archosaurs also have some unique specializations, including the presence of a muscular gizzard, a chamber situated in the gut behind the stomach that helps in food processing. They also have a more upright stance and a more stiffened torso than lepidosaurs, and larger and more complexly subdivided lungs (Gauthier 1994).

Posture and Locomotion in Derived Amniotes

One of the new roles of the axial muscles in tetrapods is that of ventilation on land (Chapter 3). However, in tetrapods such as lizards that still move via axial movements there arises a conflict between the use of the axial muscles for locomotion and for ventilation (Carrier 1987). In primitive tetrapods the trunk muscles are used for both respiration and locomotion, and thus they are unable to run and breathe at the same time. This is an acceptable situation for animals with a fairly low metabolic rate, such as present-day ectothermic amniotes, which are not highly active, and rely primarily on anaerobic metabolism for short bursts of activity. But for a more active animal, especially an endotherm, this arrangement of the muscles would be highly problematical, as it would limit the capacity for sustained, aerobic activity. (Chapters 4, 16, and 22 discuss the issue of ecothermy versus endothermy in vertebrates.) This locomotory conflict is discussed in more detail in Chapter 19 in connection with mammalian evolution, but basically the same problem was faced by all more active amniotes, especially more derived archosaurs such as dinosaurs and birds.

The conflict arising from the dual use of the trunk muscles is solved in part by the adoption of an upright posture, with the limbs held more directly underneath the body, and with the trunk held more rigidly in locomotion. With this posture, the limbs (rather than the trunk) provide the predominant propulsive force. This new posture was associated solely with a quadrupedal stance in the mammalian (synapsid) lineage of amniotes, but in the archosaurs was adopted in association with a tendency toward bipedality (with obligate bipedality being a feature of early dinosaurs). Running on two legs rather than on four also isolates the trunk from the effects of locomotor bending; this may be why some lizards will run bipedally in certain circumstances. Crocodiles are archosaurs that are sprawling-stanced quadrupeds today, but this is probably in association with their aquatic mode of life. Fossil record evidence suggests that they were derived from ancestors with an upright stance, and some early crocodiles appear to have been bipedal (Parrish 1987).

■ Summary

The origin of tetrapods from panderichthyid lobe-finned fishes in the Devonian is inferred from similarities in the bones of the skull and braincase, vertebral structure, and limb skeleton. Paleozoic tetrapods comprise about a dozen distinct lineages of uncertain relationships. One current view divides them into major two clades, batrachomorphs and reptilomorphs. The batrachomorphs (mainly the temnospondyls) were predominantly aquatic, and a few were as large as crocodiles. Temnospondyls radiated extensively in the Late Carboniferous and Permian, and several lineages extended through the Triassic into the Early Cretaceous. Modern amphibians—the salamanders, frogs, and caecilians—may be derived from the temnospondyl lineage. The reptilomorphs were never as diverse as the temnospondyls. They included terrestrial and aquatic forms that radiated during the Carboniferous, and became extinct in the Permian. Amniotes may be derived from the reptilomorphs.

The amniotic egg, with its distinctive extraembryonic membranes, is a shared derived character that distinguishes the amniotes (turtles, squamates, crocodilians, birds, and mammals) from the nonamniotes (fishes and amphibians). The earliest amniotes were small animals, and their appearance coincided with a major radiation of terrestrial insects in the Carboniferous. Progressive modifications of the postcranial skeleton of early amniotes appear to show increased agility, and simultaneous changes in the jaws may be related to predation on insects. By the end of the Carboniferous, amniotes had begun to radiate into most of the terrestrial life zones that had been occupied by nonamniotes, and only the relatively aquatic groups of nonamniote tetrapods maintained much diversity through the Triassic.

The major groups of amniotes can be distinguished by different patterns of temporal fenestration, holes in the dermal skull roof that reflect increasing complexity of jaw musculature. The major division of amniotes is into synapsids (mammals and their relatives) and sauropsids (reptiles and birds). Synapsids retain a number of primitive features, such as a glandular skin. The sauropsids can be subdivided into the parareptiles (probably including the turtles), and the eureptiles. The basic division within eureptiles is lepidosaurs (including lizards and snakes) and archosaurs (including crocodiles, birds and dinosaurs).

A number of derived amniote features probably evolved convergently in the different groups.

An enclosed middle ear was evolved independently within synapsids, turtles, lepidosaurs, and archosaurs (and also in temnospondyls and frogs). The conflict between breathing and running was solved independently in synapsids and archosaurs with the adoption of an upright posture, but only archosaurs combined this with a predominately bipedal stance.

■ References

Ahlberg, P. E. 1995. *Elginerpeton panchei* and the earliest tetrapod clade. *Nature* 373:420–425.

Ahlberg, P. E., and A. R. Milner. 1994. The origin and early diversification of tetrapods. *Nature* 368:507–514.

Benton, M. J. 1997. *Vertebrate Palaeontology*, 2d edition. Chapman & Hall, London, UK.

Bolt, J. R., and R. E. Lombard. 1992. Nature and quality of the fossil evidence for otic evolution in early tetrapods. Pages 377–403 in *The Evolutionary Biology of Hearing*, edited by D. B. Webster, R. R. Fay, and A. N. Popper. Springer-Verlag, New York.

Bray, A. A. 1985. The evolution of terrestrial vertebrates: environmental and physiological considerations. *Philosophical Transactions of the Royal Society of London* B309:289–322.

Carrier, D. R. 1987. The evolution of locomotor stamina in tetrapods: circumventing a mechanical constraint. *Paleobiology* 12:326–341.

Carroll, R. L. 1970. Quantitative aspects of the amphibian-reptilian transition. *Forma et Functio* 3:165–178.

Carroll, R. L. 1987. *Vertebrate Paleontology and Evolution*. Freeman, New York, NY.

Carroll, R. L. 1995. Problems of the phylogenetic analysis of Paleozoic tetrapods. *Bulletin de Musée national Histoire naturelle, Paris, 4ᵉ series* 17:389–445.

Carroll, R. L. 1997. *Patterns and Processes of Vertebrate Evolution*. Cambridge University Press, Cambridge, UK.

Clack, J. A. 1997. The evolution of tetrapod ears and the fossil record. *Brain, Behavior and Evolution* 50:198–212.

Coates, M. I., and J. A. Clack. 1990. Polydactyly in the earliest known tetrapod limbs. *Nature* 347:66–69.

Coates, M. I., and J. A. Clack. 1991. Fish-like gills and breathing in the earliest known tetrapod. *Nature* 352:234–235.

Coates, M. I., and J. A. Clack. 1995. Romer's gap: tetrapod origins and terrestriality. *Bulletin de Musée national Histoire naturelle, Paris, 4ᵉ series* 17:373–388.

Daeschler, E. B., N. H. Shubin, K. S. Thomson, and W. W. Amaral. 1994. A Devonian tetrapod from North America. *Science* 265:639–642.

Edwards, J. L. 1989. Two perspectives on the evolution of the tetrapod limb. *American Zoologist* 29:235–254.

Fracasso, M. A. 1994. Amphibia: disparity and diversification of early tetrapods. Pages 108–128 in *Major Features of Vertebrate Evolution*, edited by D. R. Prothero and R. M. Schoch. Short Courses in Paleontology number 7. Paleontological Society and University of Tennessee Press, Knoxville, TN.

Frazzetta, T. H. 1968. Adaptive problems and possibilities in the temporal fenestration of tetrapod skulls. *Journal of Morphology* 125:145–158.

Frolich, L. M. 1997. The role of the skin in the origin of amniotes: permeability barrier, protective covering and mechanical support. Pages 327–352 in *Amniote Origins: Completing the Transition to the Land*, edited by S. S. Sumida and K. L. M. Martin. Academic, San Diego, CA.

Gauthier, J. A. 1994. The diversification of the amniotes. Pages 129–159 in *Major Features of Vertebrate Evolution*, edited by D. R. Prothero and R. M. Schoch. Short Courses in Paleontology number 7. Paleontological Society and University of Tennessee Press, Knoxville, TN.

Holmes, E. B. 1985. Are lungfishes the sister group of tetrapods? *Biological Journal of the Linnean Society* 25:379–397.

Hotton, N., III. 1991. The nature and diversity of synapsids: prologue to the origin of mammals. Pages 598–634 in Origin of the Higher Groups of Tetrapods: Controversy and Consensus, edited by H.-P. Schultz and L. Trueb. Cornell University Press, Ithaca, NY.

Hotton, N., III, E. C. Olson and R. Beerbower. 1997. Amniote origins and the discovery of herbivory. Pages 207–264 in *Amniote Origins: Completing the Transition to the Land*, edited by S. S. Sumida and K. L. M. Martin. Academic, San Diego, CA.

Janis, C. M., and C. Farmer. (In press). Proposed habits of early tetrapods. Gills, kidneys, and the water-land transition. *Zoological Journal of the Linnean Society*.

Jarvik, E. 1981. (Review of) Lungfishes, tetrapods, paleontology, and plesiomorphy. *Systematic Zoology* 30:378–384.

Laurin, M., and R. R. Reisz. 1997. A new perspective on tetrapod phylogeny. Pages 9–59 in *Amniote Origins: Completing the Transition to the Land*, edited by S. S. Sumida and K. L. M. Martin. Academic, San Diego, CA.

Lee, M. S. Y., and P. Spencer. 1997. Crown-clades, key characters and taxonomic stability: when is an amniote not an amniote? Pages 61–84 in *Amniote Origins: Completing the Transition to the Land*, edited by S. S. Sumida and K. L. M. Martin. Academic, San Diego, CA.

Packard, G. C. 1966. The influence on ambient temperature and aridity on modes of reproduction and excretion of amniote vertebrates. *American Naturalist* 100:667–682.

Packard, G. C., and M. J. Packard. 1980. Evolution of the cleidoic egg among reptilian antecedents of birds. *American Zoologist* 20:351–362.

Panchen, A. L. 1977. Geographical and ecological distribution of the earliest vertebrates. Pages 723–738 in *Major Patterns in Vertebrate Evolution*, edited by M. K. Hecht, P. C. Goody, and B. M. Hecht. NATO Advanced Study Series. Plenum, New York, NY.

Panchen, A. L. 1991. The early tetrapods: classification and the shapes of cladograms. Pages 110–144 in *Origin of the Higher Groups of Tetrapods: Controversy and Consensus,* edited by H.-P. Schultz and L. Trueb. Cornell University Press, Ithaca, NY.

Parrish, J. M. 1987. The origin of crocodilian locomotion. *Paleobiology* 13:396–414.

Reisz, R. R. 1997. The origin and early evolutionary history of amniotes. *Trends in Ecology and Evolution* 12:218–222.

Romer, A. S. 1958. Tetrapod limbs and early tetrapod life. *Evolution* 12:365–369.

Rosen, D. E., P. L. Forey, B. G. Gardiner, and C. Patterson. 1981. Lungfishes, tetrapods, paleontology, and plesiomorphy. *Bulletin of the American Museum of Natural History* 167:159–276.

Schaeffer, B. 1965. The rhipidistian–amphibian transition. *American Zoologist* 5:267–276.

Shubin, N. H., and P. Alberch. 1986. A morphogenetic approach to the origin and basic organization of the tetrapod limb. *Evolutionary Biology* 20:319–387.

Shubin, N. H., C. Tabin, and S. Carroll. 1997. Fossils, genes and the evolution of animal limbs. *Nature* 388:639–648.

Špinar, Z. V. 1952. Revision of some Moravian Discosauriscidae. *Rozpravy ustredeniho Ustavu Geologickeho* 15:1–160.

Stewart, J. R. 1997. Morphology and evolution of the egg in oviparous amniotes. Pages 291–326 in *Amniote Origins: Completing the Transition to the Land,* edited by S. S. Sumida and K. L. M. Martin. Academic, San Diego, CA.

Szarski, H. 1962. The origin of the amphibia. *Quarterly Review of Biology* 37:189–241.

Thomson, K. S. 1980. The ecology of Devonian lobe-finned fishes. Pages 187–222 in *The Terrestrial Environment and the Origin of Land Vertebrates,* edited by A. L. Panchen. Academic, London, UK.

Thomson, K. S. 1993. The origin of the tetrapods. *American Journal of Science* 293A:33–62.

Trueb, L., and R. Cloutier. 1991. A phylogenetic investigation of the inter- and intra-relationships of the Lissamphibia (Amphibia: Temnospondyli). Pages 223–313 in *Origins of the Higher Groups of Tetrapods: Controversy and Consensus,* edited by H.-P. Schultze and L. Trueb. Cornell University Press, Ithaca, NY.

Vorobyeva, E., and H.-P. Schultze. 1991. Description and systematics of panderichthyid fishes with comments on their relationship to tetrapods. Pages 68–109 in *Origins of the Higher Groups of Tetrapods: Controversy and Consensus,* edited by H.-P. Schultze and L. Trueb. Cornell University Press, Ithaca, NY.

CHAPTER
11

Salamanders, Anurans, and Caecilians

The three lineages of extant amphibians (salamanders, frogs, and caecilians) have very different body forms, but they are identified as a monophyletic evolutionary lineage by several shared derived characters. Some of these characters—especially the moist, permeable skin—have channeled the evolution of the three extant lineages in similar directions. Frogs are the most successful amphibians, and it is tempting to think that the variety of locomotor modes permitted by their specialized morphology may be related to their success: Frogs can jump, walk, climb, and swim. In contrast to frogs, salamanders retain the ancestral tetrapod locomotor pattern of lateral undulations combined with limb movements. The greatest diversity among salamanders is found in the Plethodontidae, many species of which project the tongue to capture prey on its sticky tip.

The range of reproductive specializations of amphibians is nearly as great as that of fishes, a remarkable fact when one remembers that there are more than five times as many species of fishes as amphibians. The ancestral reproductive mode of amphibians probably consisted of laying large numbers of eggs that hatched into aquatic larvae, and many amphibians still reproduce this way. An aquatic larva gives a terrestrial species access to resources that would not otherwise be available to it. Modifications of the ancestral reproductive mode include bypassing the larval stage, viviparity, and parental care of eggs and young, including females that feed their tadpoles.

The permeable skin of amphibians is central to many aspects of their lives. The skin is a major site of respiratory gas exchange, and must be kept moist. Evaporation of water from the skin limits the activity of most amphibians to relatively moist microenviroments. The skin contains glands that produce substances used in courtship and other glands that produce toxic substances that deter predators. Many amphibians advertise their toxicity with bright warning colors, and some nontoxic species deceive predators by mimicking the warning colors of toxic forms.

■ Amphibians

The extant amphibians, or Lissamphibia (*liss* = smooth), are tetrapods with moist, scaleless skins. The group includes three distinct lineages: anurans (frogs), urodeles (salamanders), and gymnophionans (caecilians). Most amphibians have four well-developed limbs, although a few salamanders and all caecilians are limbless. Frogs lack tails (hence the name anura, which means without a tail),

297

whereas most salamanders have long tails. The tails of caecilians are short, as are those of other groups of elongate, burrowing animals.

At first glance, the three lineages of amphibians appear to be very different kinds of animals: Frogs have long hindlimbs and short, stiff bodies that don't bend when they walk, salamanders have forelimbs and hindlimbs of equal size and move with lateral undulations, and caecilians are limbless and employ serpentine locomotion. These obvious differences are all related to locomotor specializations, however, and closer examination shows that amphibians have many derived characters in common, indicating that they form a monophyletic evolutionary lineage (Table 11.1). We will see that many of these shared characters play important roles in the functional biology of amphibians. Perhaps the most important derived character of extant amphibians is a moist, permeable skin. The name applied to the lineage, Lissamphibia, refers to the texture of the skin (*liss* = smooth). Many of the Paleozoic temnospondyls, the group from which lissamphians are derived, had scales and the

absence of scales is a derived character shared by extant amphibians and their probable sister group, the branchiosaur temnospondyls (see Chapter 10).

All living adult amphibians are carnivorous, and relatively little morphological specialization is associated with different dietary habits within each group. Amphibians eat almost anything they are able to catch and swallow. The tongue of aquatic forms is broad, flat, and relatively immobile, but some terrestrial amphibians can protrude the tongue from the mouth to capture prey. The size of the head is an important determinant of the maximum size of prey that can be taken, and sympatric species of salamanders frequently have markedly different head sizes, suggesting that this is a feature that reduces competition. Frogs in the tropical American genus *Ceratophrys*, which feed largely on other frogs, have such large heads that they are practically walking mouths.

The anuran body form probably evolved from a more salamanderlike starting point. Both jumping and swimming have been suggested as the mode of locomotion that made the change advantageous.

TABLE 11.1	Shared derived characters of amphibians

1. *Structure of the skin and the importance of cutaneous gas exchange.* All amphibians have mucous glands that keep the skin moist. A substantial part of an amphibian's exchange of oxygen and carbon dioxide with the environment takes place through the skin. All amphibians also have poison (granular) glands in the skin.

2. *Papilla amphibiorum.* All amphibians have a special sensory area, the papilla amphibiorum, in the wall of the sacculus of the inner ear. The papilla amphibiorum is sensitive to frequencies below 1000 hertz (cycles per second), and a second sensory area, the papilla basilaris, detects sound frequencies above 1000 hertz.

3. *Operculum–plectrum complex.* Most amphibians have two bones that are involved in transmitting sounds to the inner ear. The columella (plectrum) is derived from the hyoid arch and is present in salamanders and caecilians and in most frogs. The operculum develops in association with the fenestra ovalis of the inner ear. The columella and operculum are fused in anurans and caecilians and in some salamanders.

4. *Green rods.* Salamanders and frogs have a distinct type of retinal cell, the green rod. Caecilians apparently lack green rods, but the eyes of caecilians are extremely reduced and these cells may have been lost.

5. *Pedicellate teeth.* Nearly all modern amphibians have teeth in which the crown and base (pedicel) are composed of dentine and are separated by a narrow zone of uncalcified dentine or fibrous connective tissue. A few amphibians lack pedicellate teeth, including salamanders of the genus *Siren* and frogs of the genera *Phyllobates* and *Ceratophrys*; the boundary between the crown and base is obscured in some other genera. Pedicellate teeth also occur in some actinopterygian fishes, which are not thought to be related to amphibians.

6. *Structure of the levator bulbi muscle.* This muscle is a thin sheet in the floor of the orbit that is innervated by the fifth cranial nerve. It causes the eyes to bulge outward, thereby enlarging the buccal cavity. This muscle is present in salamanders and anurans and in modified form in caecilians.

Salamanders and caecilians swim as fishes do by passing a sine wave down the body. Anurans have inflexible bodies and swim with simultaneous thrusts of the hind legs. Some paleontologists have proposed that the anuran body form evolved because of the advantages of that mode of swimming. An alternative hypothesis traces the anuran body form to the advantage gained by an animal that could rest near the edge of a body of water and escape aquatic or terrestrial predators with a rapid leap followed by locomotion on either land or water.

The oldest fossils that may represent modern amphibians are isolated vertebrae of Permian age that appear to include both salamander and anuran types. The oldest frog, *Prosalirus*, is from the Early Jurassic of North America. Salamanders and caecilians also are known from the Jurassic. Clearly, the modern orders of amphibians have had separate evolutionary histories for a long time. The continued presence of such common characteristics as a permeable skin after at least 250 million years of independent evolution suggests that the shared characteristics are critical in shaping the evolutionary success of modern amphibians. In other characters, such as reproduction, locomotion, and defense, they show tremendous diversity.

Salamanders (Urodela)

The salamanders have the most generalized body form and locomotion of the living amphibians. Salamanders are elongate, and all but a very few species of completely aquatic salamanders have four functional limbs (Figure 11–1). Their walking gait is probably similar to that employed by the earliest tetrapods. It combines the lateral bending characteristic of fish locomotion with leg movements. The 10 families, containing approximately 415 species, are almost entirely limited to the Northern Hemisphere; their southernmost occurrence is in northern South America (Table 11.2). North and Central America have the greatest diversity of salamanders—more species of salamanders are found in Tennessee than in all of Europe and Asia combined. Paedomorphosis is widespread among salamanders, and several families of aquatic salamanders are constituted solely of such paedomorphic forms. These forms can be recognized by the retention of larval characteristics, including larval tooth and bone patterns, the absence of eyelids, retention of a functional lateral-line system, and (in some cases) retention of external gills.

The largest living salamanders are the Japanese and Chinese giant salamanders (*Andrias*), which reach lengths of 1 meter or more. The related North American hellbenders (*Cryptobranchus*) grow to 60 centimeters. All are members of the Cryptobranchidae and are paedomorphic and permanently aquatic. As their name indicates (*crypto* = hidden, *branchus* = gill), they do not retain external gills, although they do have other larval characteristics. Another group of large aquatic salamanders, the mudpuppies (*Necturus*, Proteidae), consists of paedomorphic species that retain external gills. Mudpuppies occur in lakes and streams in eastern North America.

Several lineages of salamanders have adapted to life in caves. The constant temperature and moisture of caves makes them good salamander habitats, and food is supplied by cave-dwelling invertebrates. The brook salamanders (*Eurycea*, Plethodontidae) include species that form a continuum from those with fully metamorphosed adults inhabiting the twilight zone near cave mouths to fully paedomorphic forms in the depths of caves or sinkholes. The Texas blind salamander, *Typhlomolge*, is a highly specialized cave dweller—blind, white, with external gills, extremely long legs, and a flattened snout used to probe underneath pebbles for food. The unrelated European olm (*Proteus*, Proteidae) is another cave salamander that has converged on the same body form.

Terrestrial salamanders like the North American mole salamanders (*Ambystoma*) and the European salamanders (*Salamandra*) have aquatic larvae that lose their gills at metamorphosis. The most fully terrestrial salamanders, the lungless plethodontids, include species in which the young hatch from eggs as miniatures of the adult and there is no aquatic larval stage.

Feeding Specializations of Plethodontid Salamanders Lungs seem an unlikely organ for a terrestrial vertebrate to abandon, but among salamanders the evolutionary loss of lungs has been a successful tactic. The Plethodontidae is characterized by the absence of lungs and contains more species and has a wider geographic distribution than any other lineage of salamanders. Furthermore, many plethodontids have evolved specializations of the hyobranchial apparatus that allow them to protrude the tongue a considerable distance from the mouth to capture prey. This ability has not evolved in salamanders with lungs, probably because the hyobranchial

Figure 11–1 Diversity of salamanders. The body forms of salamanders reflect differences in life histories and habitats. Aquatic salamanders: (a) mudpuppy (*Necturus*); (b) siren (*Siren*); (c) hellbender (*Cryptobranchus*); (d) congo eel (*Amphiuma*). Specialized cave dwellers: (e) Texas blind salamander (*Typhlomolge*); (f) olm (*Proteus*). Terrestrial salamanders: (g) tiger salamander (*Ambystoma*) and its aquatic larval form; (h) fire salamander (*Salamandra*); (i) slimy salamander (*Plethodon*).

apparatus in these forms is an essential part of the respiratory system.

Salamanders lack ribs, so they cannot use expansion and contraction of the rib cage to move air in and out of the lungs. Instead, they employ a buccal pump that forces air from the mouth into the lungs. A sturdy hyobranchial apparatus in the floor of the mouth and throat is an essential part of this pumping system, whereas tongue protrusion requires that parts of the hyobranchial apparatus be elongated and lightened. The modification of the hyobranchial apparatus that allows tongue protrusion is not compatible with buccal pump respiration. Reliance on the skin instead of the lungs for gas exchange may

TABLE
11.2 Families of salamanders

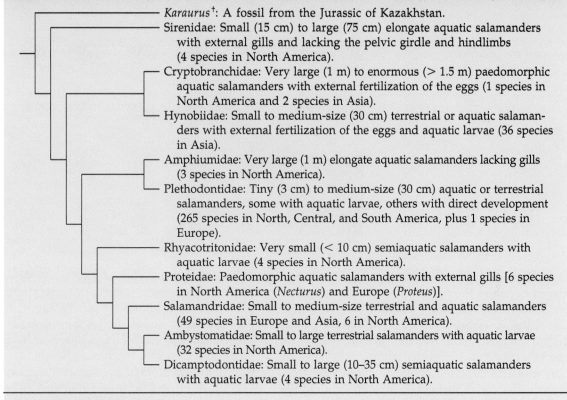

Karaurus†: A fossil from the Jurassic of Kazakhstan.

Sirenidae: Small (15 cm) to large (75 cm) elongate aquatic salamanders with external gills and lacking the pelvic girdle and hindlimbs (4 species in North America).

Cryptobranchidae: Very large (1 m) to enormous (> 1.5 m) paedomorphic aquatic salamanders with external fertilization of the eggs (1 species in North America and 2 species in Asia).

Hynobiidae: Small to medium-size (30 cm) terrestrial or aquatic salamanders with external fertilization of the eggs and aquatic larvae (36 species in Asia).

Amphiumidae: Very large (1 m) elongate aquatic salamanders lacking gills (3 species in North America).

Plethodontidae: Tiny (3 cm) to medium-size (30 cm) aquatic or terrestrial salamanders, some with aquatic larvae, others with direct development (265 species in North, Central, and South America, plus 1 species in Europe).

Rhyacotritonidae: Very small (< 10 cm) semiaquatic salamanders with aquatic larvae (4 species in North America).

Proteidae: Paedomorphic aquatic salamanders with external gills [6 species in North America (*Necturus*) and Europe (*Proteus*)].

Salamandridae: Small to medium-size terrestrial and aquatic salamanders (49 species in Europe and Asia, 6 in North America).

Ambystomatidae: Small to large terrestrial salamanders with aquatic larvae (32 species in North America).

Dicamptodontidae: Small to large (10–35 cm) semiaquatic salamanders with aquatic larvae (4 species in North America).

The symbol † indicates a fossil.

Phylogenetic relationships and numbers of species are based on Pough, F. H., R. M. Andrews, J. E. Cadle, M. L. Crump, A. H. Savitzky, and K. D. Wells. 1998. *Herpetology*. Prentice Hall, Upper Saddle River, NJ.

---

have been a necessary first step in the evolution of tongue protrusion by plethodontids.

The modifications of the respiratory system and hyobranchial apparatus that allow tongue protrusion appear to be linked with a number of other characteristics of the biology of plethodontids (Roth and Wake 1985, Wake and Marks 1993). These associations can be seen most clearly in the bolitoglossine plethodontids, which have the most specialized tongue-projection mechanisms (Figure 11–2). Bolitoglossine plethodontids (*bolis* = dart, *glossa* = tongue) can project the tongue a distance equivalent to their head plus trunk length and can pick off moving prey. This ability requires fine visual discrimination of distance and direction, and the eyes of bolitoglossines are placed more frontally on the head than the eyes of less specialized plethodontids. Furthermore, the eyes of bolitoglossines have a large number of nerves that travel to the ipsilateral (= same side) visual centers of the brain as well as

the strong contralateral (= opposite side) visual projection that is typical of salamanders. As a result of this neuroanatomy, bolitoglossines have a complete dual projection of the binocular visual fields to both hemispheres of the brain and can make very exact and rapid estimation of the distance of a prey object from the salamander.

Tongue projection is reflected in many different aspects of the life-history characteristics of plethodontid salamanders, including their reproductive modes. Aquatic larval salamanders employ suction feeding, opening the mouth and expanding the throat to create a current of water that carries the prey item with it. The hyobranchial apparatus is an essential part of this feeding mechanism, and the first ceratobranchial becomes well developed during the larval period. In contrast, enlargement of the second ceratobranchial is associated with the tongue-projection mechanism of adult plethodontids. Furthermore, larval salamanders have laterally

Figure 11–2   Prey capture by a bolitoglossine salamander, *Hydromantes*. (Courtesy of Professor Gerhard Roth, University of Bremen.)

placed eyes and the optic nerves project mostly to the contralateral side of the brain. Thus, the morphological specializations that make aquatic plethodontid larvae successful are different from the specializations of adults that allow tongue projection, and this situation creates a conflict between the selective forces that act on juveniles and adults.

The bolitoglossines do not have aquatic larvae, and the morphological specializations of adult bolitoglossines appear during embryonic development. In contrast, hemidactyline plethodontids do have aquatic larvae that use suction feeding. As adults, hemidactylines have considerable ability to project the tongues, but they retain the large first ceratobranchial that appears in the larvae. This is a mechanically less efficient arrangement than the large second ceratobranchial of bolitoglossines, and the ability of hemidactylines to project their tongues is correspondingly less than that of bolitoglossines. Thus, the development of a specialized feeding mechanism by plethodontid salamanders has gone hand-in-hand with such diverse aspects of their biology as respiratory physiology and life history, and demonstrates that organisms evolve as whole functioning units, not as collections of independent characters.

Social Behavior of Plethodontid Salamanders   Plethodontid salamanders can be recognized externally by the nasolabial groove that extends ventrally from each external naris to the lip of the upper jaw (Figure 11–3). These grooves are an important part

of the chemosensory system of plethodontids. As a plethodontid salamander moves about, it repeatedly presses its snout against the substrate. Fluid is drawn into the grooves and moves upward to the external nares, into the nasal chambers, and over the chemoreceptors of the vomeronasal organ.

Studies of plethodontid salamanders have contributed greatly to our understanding of the roles of competition and predation in shaping the structure of ecological communities. Much of the recent work in this area has focused on experimental manipulations of animals in the field or laboratory. Because plethodontid salamanders have small home ranges and often remain in a restricted area for their entire lives, they are excellent species to use for these studies.

Males of many plethodontid salamanders defend all-purpose territories that are used for feeding and reproduction. Studies of these salamanders have

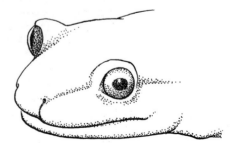

Figure 11–3   Nasolabial grooves of a plethodontid salamander.

revealed patterns of social behavior and foraging that seem remarkably complex for animals with skulls the size of a match head and brains little larger than the head of a pin. Robert Jaeger and his colleagues have studied the territorial behavior of the red-backed salamander, *Plethodon cinereus*, a common species in woodlands of eastern North America. Male red-backed salamanders readily establish territories in cages in the laboratory. A resident male salamander marks the substrate of its cage with pheromones (chemical substances that are released by an individual and stimulate responses by other individuals of the species). A salamander can distinguish between substrates it has marked and those marked by another male salamander or by a female salamander. Male salamanders can also distinguish between the familiar scent of a neighboring male salamander and the scent of a male they have not previously encountered, and they react differently to those scents.

In laboratory experiments, red-backed salamanders select their prey in a way that maximizes their energy intake: When equal numbers of large and small fruit flies are released in the cages, the salamanders first capture the large flies. This is the most profitable foraging behavior for the salamanders because it provides the maximum energy intake per capture. In a series of experiments, Jaeger and his colleagues showed that territorial behavior and fighting can interfere with the ability of salamanders to select the most profitable prey (Jaeger et al. 1983). These experiments used surrogate salamanders that were made of a roll of moist filter paper the same length and diameter as a salamander. The surrogates were placed in the cages of resident salamanders to produce three experimental conditions: a control surrogate, a familiar surrogate, and an unfamiliar surrogate. In the control experiment, male red-backed salamanders were exposed to a surrogate that was only moistened filter paper; it did not carry any salamander pheromone. For both of the other groups the surrogate was rolled across the substrate of the cage of a different male salamander to absorb the scent of that salamander before it was placed in the cage of a resident male.

The experiments lasted 7 days; the first 6 days were conditioning periods and the test itself occurred on the seventh day. For the first 6 days, the resident salamanders in both of the experimental groups were given surrogates bearing the scent of another male salamander. The residents thus had the opportunity to become familiar with the scent

of that male. On the seventh day, however, the familiar and unfamiliar surrogate groups were treated differently. The familiar surrogate group once again received a surrogate salamander bearing the scent of the same individual it had been exposed to for the previous 6 days, whereas the resident salamanders in the unfamiliar surrogate group received a surrogate bearing the scent of a different salamander, one to which they had never been exposed before. After a 5-minute pause, a mixture of large and small fruit flies was placed in each cage, and the behavior of the resident salamander was recorded.

The salamanders in the familiar surrogate group showed little response to the now-familiar scent of the other male salamander. They fed as usual, capturing large fruit flies. In contrast, the salamanders that were exposed to the scent of an unfamiliar surrogate began to give threatening and submissive displays, and their rate of prey capture decreased as a result of the time they spent displaying. In addition, salamanders exposed to unfamiliar surrogates did not concentrate on catching large fruit flies, so the average energy intake per capture also declined. The combined effects of the reduced time spent feeding and the failure to concentrate on the most profitable prey items caused an overall 50-percent decrease in the rate of energy intake for the salamanders exposed to the scent of an unfamiliar male.

The ability of male salamanders to recognize the scent of another male after a week of habituation in the laboratory cages suggests that they would show the same behavior in the woods. That is, a male salamander could learn to recognize and ignore the scent of a male in the adjacent territory, while still being able to recognize and attack a strange intruder. Learning not to respond to the presence of a neighbor may allow a salamander to forage more effectively, and it may also help to avoid injuries that can occur during territorial encounters. Resident male red-backed salamanders challenge strange intruders, and the encounters involve aggressive and submissive displays and biting (Figure 11–4). Most bites are directed at the snout of an opponent, and may damage the nasolabial grooves. Salamanders with damaged nasolabial grooves apparently have difficulty perceiving olfactory stimuli. Twelve salamanders that had been bitten on the snout were able to capture an average of only 5.8 fruit flies in a 2-hour period compared with an average of 18.6 flies for 12 salamanders that

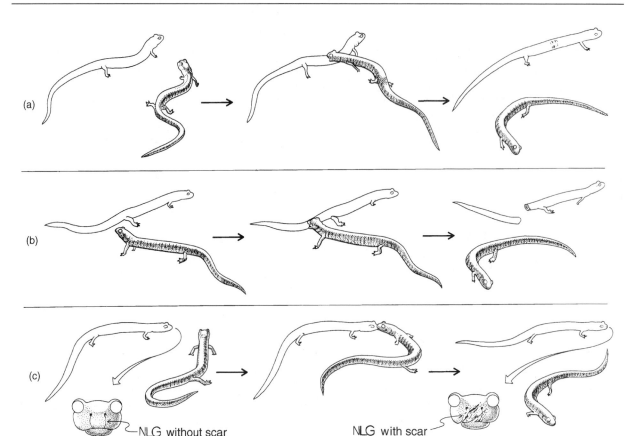

NLG without scar   NLG with scar

Figure 11–4 Aggressive behaviors of the red-backed salamander, *Plethodon cinereus*. The resident salamander is dark and the intruder is light in these drawings. (a) Resident bites the intruder on the body. Injuries in this region are unlikely to do permanent damage. (b) Bitten on the tail by the resident, the intruder autotomizes (breaks off) its tail to escape. Salamanders store fat in their tails, and this injury may delay reproduction for a year while the tail is regenerated. (c) Resident bites intruder on the snout, injuring the nasolabial grooves. The nasolabial grooves are used for olfaction, and these injuries can reduce a salamander's success in finding prey. (From R. Jaeger, 1981, *The American Naturalist* 117:968. Courtesy of Robert Jaeger. © 1981 The University of Chicago Press. All rights reserved.)

had not been bitten. In a sample of 144 red-backed salamanders from the Shenandoah National Forest, 11.8 percent had been bitten on the nasolabial grooves, and these animals weighed less than the unbitten animals, presumably because their foraging success had been reduced (Jaeger 1981).

The possibility of serious damage to an important sensory system during territorial defense provides an additional advantage for a red-backed salamander in being able to distinguish neighbors (which are always there and are not worth attacking) from intruders (which represent a threat and should be attacked). The phenomenon of being able to recognize territorial neighbors has been called dear enemy recognition, and may be generally advantageous because it minimizes the time and energy that territorial individuals expend on territorial defense and also minimizes the risk of injury during territorial encounters. Similar dear enemy recognition has been described among territorial birds that show more aggressive behavior on hearing the songs of strangers than they do when hearing the songs of neighbors.

Anurans

In contrast to the limited number of species of salamanders and their restricted geographic distribution, the anurans (*an* = without, *uro* = tail) include 27 families, nearly 3750 species, and occur on all the continents except Antarctica (Table 11.3). Specialization of the body for jumping is the most conspicu-

TABLE 11.3	Families of anurans

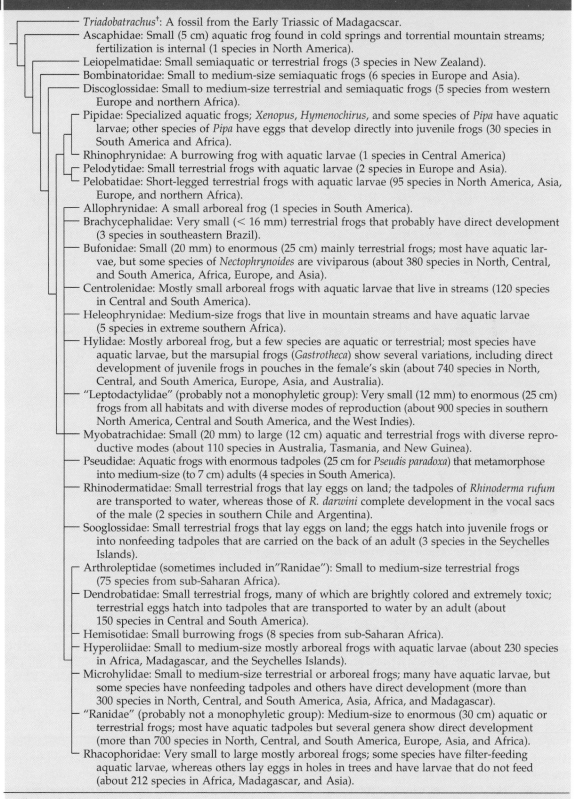

Triadobatrachus[†]: A fossil from the Early Triassic of Madagcscar.

Ascaphidae: Small (5 cm) aquatic frog found in cold springs and torrential mountain streams; fertilization is internal (1 species in North America).

Leiopelmatidae: Small semiaquatic or terrestrial frogs (3 species in New Zealand).

Bombinatoridae: Small to medium-size semiaquatic frogs (6 species in Europe and Asia).

Discoglossidae: Small to medium-size terrestrial and semiaquatic frogs (5 species from western Europe and northern Africa).

Pipidae: Specialized aquatic frogs; *Xenopus, Hymenochirus,* and some species of *Pipa* have aquatic larvae; other species of *Pipa* have eggs that develop directly into juvenile frogs (30 species in South America and Africa).

Rhinophrynidae: A burrowing frog with aquatic larvae (1 species in Central America)

Pelodytidae: Small terrestrial frogs with aquatic larvae (2 species in Europe and Asia).

Pelobatidae: Short-legged terrestrial frogs with aquatic larvae (95 species in North America, Asia, Europe, and northern Africa).

Allophrynidae: A small arboreal frog (1 species in South America).

Brachycephalidae: Very small (< 16 mm) terrestrial frogs that probably have direct development (3 species in southeastern Brazil).

Bufonidae: Small (20 mm) to enormous (25 cm) mainly terrestrial frogs; most have aquatic larvae, but some species of *Nectophrynoides* are viviparous (about 380 species in North, Central, and South America, Africa, Europe, and Asia).

Centrolenidae: Mostly small arboreal frogs with aquatic larvae that live in streams (120 species in Central and South America).

Heleophrynidae: Medium-size frogs that live in mountain streams and have aquatic larvae (5 species in extreme southern Africa).

Hylidae: Mostly arboreal frog, but a few species are aquatic or terrestrial; most species have aquatic larvae, but the marsupial frogs (*Gastrotheca*) show several variations, including direct development of juvenile frogs in pouches in the female's skin (about 740 species in North, Central, and South America, Europe, Asia, and Australia).

"Leptodactylidae" (probably not a monophyletic group): Very small (12 mm) to enormous (25 cm) frogs from all habitats and with diverse modes of reproduction (about 900 species in southern North America, Central and South America, and the West Indies).

Myobatrachidae: Small (20 mm) to large (12 cm) aquatic and terrestrial frogs with diverse reproductive modes (about 110 species in Australia, Tasmania, and New Guinea).

Pseudidae: Aquatic frogs with enormous tadpoles (25 cm for *Pseudis paradoxa*) that metamorphose into medium-size (to 7 cm) adults (4 species in South America).

Rhinodermatidae: Small terrestrial frogs that lay eggs on land; the tadpoles of *Rhinoderma rufum* are transported to water, whereas those of *R. darwini* complete development in the vocal sacs of the male (2 species in southern Chile and Argentina).

Sooglossidae: Small terrestrial frogs that lay eggs on land; the eggs hatch into juvenile frogs or into nonfeeding tadpoles that are carried on the back of an adult (3 species in the Seychelles Islands).

Arthroleptidae (sometimes included in"Ranidae"): Small to medium-size terrestrial frogs (75 species from sub-Saharan Africa).

Dendrobatidae: Small terrestrial frogs, many of which are brightly colored and extremely toxic; terrestrial eggs hatch into tadpoles that are transported to water by an adult (about 150 species in Central and South America).

Hemisotidae: Small burrowing frogs (8 species from sub-Saharan Africa).

Hyperoliidae: Small to medium-size mostly arboreal frogs with aquatic larvae (about 230 species in Africa, Madagascar, and the Seychelles Islands).

Microhylidae: Small to medium-size terrestrial or arboreal frogs; many have aquatic larvae, but some species have nonfeeding tadpoles and others have direct development (more than 300 species in North, Central, and South America, Asia, Africa, and Madagascar).

"Ranidae" (probably not a monophyletic group): Medium-size to enormous (30 cm) aquatic or terrestrial frogs; most have aquatic tadpoles but several genera show direct development (more than 700 species in North, Central, and South America, Europe, Asia, and Africa).

Rhacophoridae: Very small to large mostly arboreal frogs; some species have filter-feeding aquatic larvae, whereas others lay eggs in holes in trees and have larvae that do not feed (about 212 species in Africa, Madagascar, and Asia).

The symbol † indicates a fossil.

Phylogenetic relationships and numbers of species are based on Pough, F. H., R. M. Andrews, J. E. Cadle, M. L. Crump, A. H. Savitzky, and K. D. Wells. 1998. *Herpetology.* Prentice Hall, Upper Saddle River, NJ.

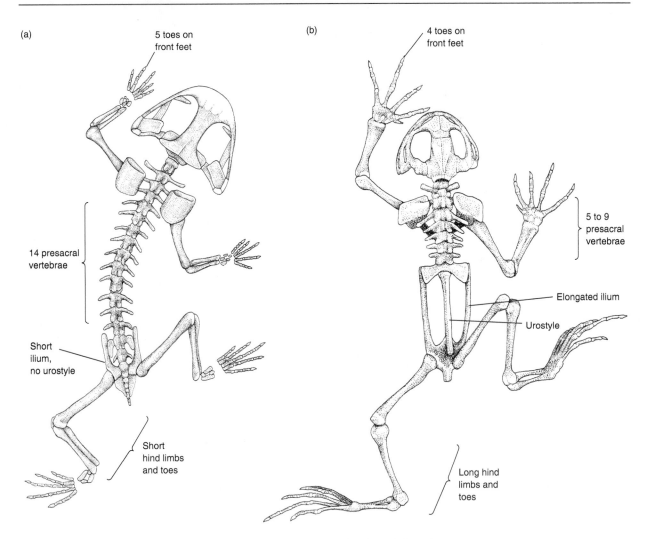

(a)

5 toes on front feet

14 presacral vertebrae

Short ilium, no urostyle

Short hind limbs and toes

(b)

4 toes on front feet

5 to 9 presacral vertebrae

Elongated ilium

Urostyle

Long hind limbs and toes

Figure 11–5 *Triadobatrachus* and a modern anuran. The Triassic fossil *Triadobatrachus* is considered the sister group of anurans. Derived characters of anurans visible in this comparison include shortening of the body, elongation of the ilia, and fusion of the posterior vertebrae to form a urostyle.

ous skeletal feature of anurans. The hindlimbs and muscles form a lever system that can catapult an anuran into the air (Figure 11–5), and numerous morphological specializations are associated with this type of locomotion; the hind legs are elongate and the tibia and fibula are fused. A powerful pelvis strongly fastened to the vertebral column is clearly necessary, as is stiffening of the vertebral column. The ilium is elongate and reaches far anteriorly, and the posterior vertebrae are fused into a solid rod, the **urostyle.** The pelvis and urostyle render the posterior half of the trunk rigid. The vertebral column is short, with only five to nine presacral vertebrae, and these are strongly braced by zygapophyses that

restrict lateral bending. The strong forelimbs and flexible pectoral girdle absorb the impact of landing. The eyes are large and are placed well forward on the head, giving binocular vision.

The hindlimbs generate the power to propel the frog into the air, and this high level of power production results from structural and biochemical features of the limb muscles (Lutz and Rome 1994). The internal architecture of the semimembranosus muscle and its origin on the ischium and insertion below the knee allow it to operate at the length that produces maximum force during the entire period of contraction. In addition, the muscle shortens faster and generates more power than muscles

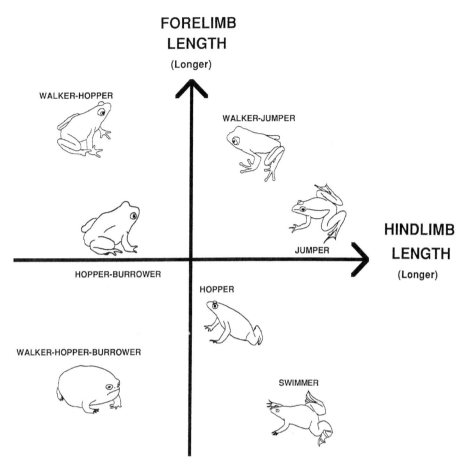

Figure 11–6   The relation of body form and locomotor mode among anurans. (From F. H. Pough, 1992, Behavioral energetics, pages 395–436 in *Environmental Physiology of the Amphibia*, edited by M. E. Feder and W. W. Burggren, The University of Chicago Press, Chicago, IL. © 1992 The University of Chicago Press. All rights reserved.)

from most other animals. Furthermore, the intracellular physiological processes of muscle contraction continue at the maximum level throughout contraction, rather than declining as is the case in muscles of most vertebrates.

Specializations of the locomotor system can be used to distinguish many different kinds of anurans (Figure 11–6). The difficulty is finding names for them—the diversity of anurans exceeds the number of common names that can be used to distinguish various ecological specialties (Figure 11–7). Animals called frogs usually have long legs and move by jumping. Many species of ranids have this body form, and very similar jumping frogs are found in other lineages as well. Semiaquatic forms are moderately streamlined and have webbed feet. Stout-bodied terrestrial anurans that make short hops instead of long leaps are often called toads. They

usually have blunt heads, heavy bodies, relatively short legs, and little webbing between the toes. This body form is represented by members of the Bufonidae, and very similar body forms are found in other families, including the spadefoot toads of western North America and the horned frogs of South America. Spadefoot toads take their name from a keratinized structure on the hind foot that they use for digging backward into the soil with rapid movements of their hind legs. The horned frogs have extremely large heads and mouths. They feed on small vertebrates, including birds and mammals, but particularly on other frogs. The tadpoles of horned frogs also are carnivorous and feed on other tadpoles. Many frogs that burrow headfirst have pointed heads, stout bodies, and short legs.

Arboreal frogs usually have large heads and eyes, and often slim waists and long legs. Arboreal frogs in

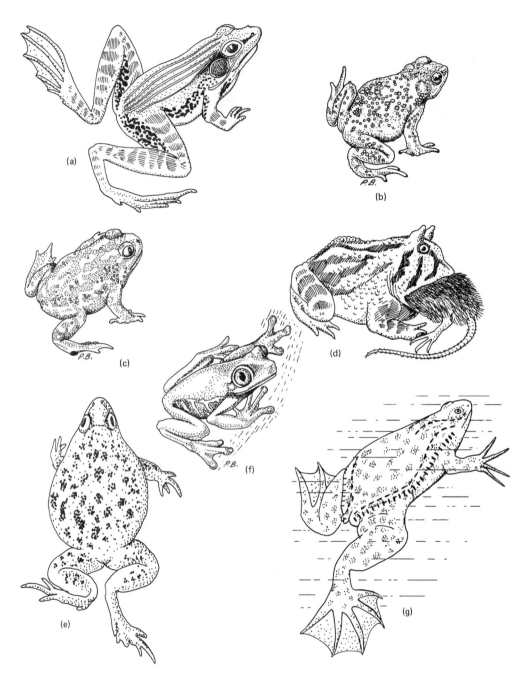

Figure 11–7 Anuran body forms reflect specializations for different habitats and different methods of locomotion. Semiaquatic form: (a) African ridged frog (*Ptychadena*, Ranidae). Terrestrial anurans: (b) true toad (*Bufo*, Bufonidae); (c) spadefoot toad (*Scaphiopus*, Pelobatidae); (d) horned frog (*Ceratophrys*, Leptodactylidae). Burrowing species (e), African shovel-nosed frog (*Hemisus*, Hemisotidae). Arboreal frog: (f) Central American leaf frog (*Agalychnis*, Hylidae). Specialized aquatic frog: (g) African clawed frog (*Xenopus*, Pipidae).

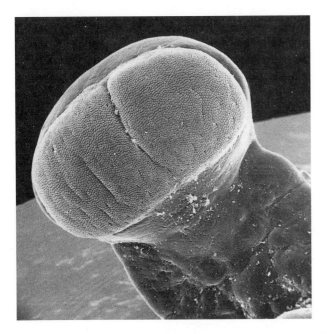 

Figure 11–8   Toe disks of a hylid frog. (a) A single toe pad; (b) detail of the polygonal plates. (Photographs courtesy of Sharon B. Emerson, University of Utah.)

many different families move by quadrupedal walking and climbing as much as by leaping. Many arboreal species of hylids and rhacophorids have enlarged toe disks and are called tree frogs. The surfaces of the toe pads consist of an epidermal layer with peglike projections separated by spaces or canals (Figure 11–8). Mucous glands distributed over the disks secrete a viscous solution of long-chain, high-molecular-weight polymers in water. Arboreal species of frogs use a mechanism known as wet adhesion to stick to smooth surfaces. (This is the same mechanism by which a wet scrap of paper sticks to glass.) The watery mucus secreted by the glands on the toe disks forms a layer of fluid between the disk and the surface and establishes a meniscus at the interface between air and fluid at the edges of the toes. As long as no air bubble enters the fluid layer, a combination of surface tension (capillarity) and viscosity holds the toe pad and surface together.

Frogs can adhere to vertical surfaces and even to the undersides of leaves. Cuban tree frogs (*Osteopilus septentrionalis*, Hylidae) can cling to a sheet of smooth plastic as it is rotated past the vertical; the frogs do not begin to slip until the rotation reaches an average of 151 degrees—that is, 61 degrees past vertical (Hanna and Barnes 1991). Adhesion and detachment of the pads alternate as a frog walks across a leaf. When a frog moves forward its pads are peeled loose, starting at the rear, as the toes are lifted. The two most specialized families of tree frogs, the Hylidae and Rhacophroidae, have a cartilage (the intercalary cartilage) that lies between the last two bones in the toes. The intercalary cartilage may promote adhesion by increasing the angle through which the toe can move before peeling begins.

Tree frogs are not able to rest facing downward because in that orientation the weight of the frog causes the toe pads to peel off the surface. Frogs invariably orient their bodies facing upward or across a slope, and they rotate their feet if necessary to keep the toes pointed upward. When a frog must descend a vertical surface, it moves backward. This orientation keeps the toes facing upward. During backward locomotion toes are peeled loose from the tip backward by a pair of tendons that insert on the dorsal surface of the terminal bone of the toe.

Toe disks have evolved independently in several lineages of frogs, and show substantial convergence in structure. Expanded toe disks are not limited exclusively to arboreal frogs; many terrestrial species that move across fallen leaves on the forest floor also have toe disks.

Several aspects of the natural history of anurans appear to be related to their different modes of locomotion. In particular, short-legged species that move by hopping are frequently wide-ranging predators that cover large areas as they search for food. This behavior makes them conspicuous to predators, and their short legs prevent them from fleeing rapidly enough to escape. Many of these anurans have potent defensive chemicals that are released from glands in the skin when they are attacked. Species of frogs that move by jumping, in contrast to those that hop, are usually sedentary predators that wait in ambush for prey that passes their hiding places. These species are usually cryptically colored, and they often lack chemical defenses. If they are discovered by a predator, they rely on a series of rapid leaps to get away. Anurans that forage widely encounter different kinds of prey from those that wait in one spot, and differences in dietary habits may be associated with differences in locomotor mode. Aquatic anurans use suction to engulf food in water, but most species of semiaquatic and terrestrial anurans have sticky tongues that can be flipped out to trap prey and carry it back to the mouth (Figure 11–9).

Caecilians

The third group of living amphibians is the least known and does not even have an English common name (Figure 11–10). These are the caecilians (Gymnophiona), legless burrowing or aquatic amphibians that occur in tropical habitats around the world (Table 11.4). The eyes of caecilians are covered by skin or even by bone. Some species lack eyes entirely, but the retinae of other species have the layered organization that is typical of vertebrates and appear to be able to detect. Conspicuous dermal folds (annuli) encircle the bodies of caecilians. The primary annuli overlie vertebrae and myotomal septa and reflect body segmentation. Many species of caecilians have dermal scales in pockets in the annuli; scales are not known in the other groups of living amphibians. A second unique feature of caecilians is a pair of protrusible tentacles, one on each side of the snout between the eye and nostril. Some structures that are associated with the eyes of other vertebrates have become associated with the tentacles of caecilians. One of the eye muscles, the retractor bulbi, has become the retractor muscle for the tentacle; the levator bulbi moves the tentacle sheath; and the Harderian gland lubricates the channel of the tentacle. It is likely that the tentacle is a sensory organ that allows chemical

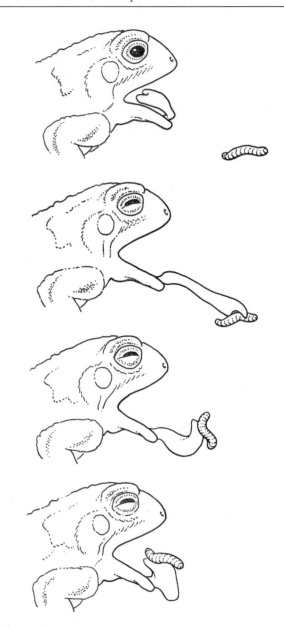

Figure 11–9   Prey capture by a toad.

substances to be transported from the animal's surroundings to the vomeronasal organ on the roof of the mouth. The eye of caecilians in the African family Scolecomorphidae is attached to the side of the tentacle near its base. When the tentacle is protruded, the eye is carried along with it and moves out the tentacular aperature beyond the roofing bones of the skull (O'Reilly et al. 1996.).

The earliest caecilian known is *Eocaecilia*, an Early Jurassic fossil from the Kayenta formation of western North America. It has a combination of

Figure 11–10   Caecilians. (a) Adult, showing body form; (b) a female coiled around her eggs. Embryos of terrestrial (c) and aquatic (d) species. ([b] Modified from H. Gadow, 1909, *Amphibia and Reptiles*, Macmillan, London, UK; [c] and [d] modified from E. H. Taylor, 1968, *The Caecilians of the World*, University of Kansas Press, Lawrence, KS.)

ancestral and derived characters, and is the sister taxon of extant caecilians (Table 11.4). *Eocaecilia* has a fossa for a chemosensory tentacle, which is a unique derived character of apodans, but it also has four legs, whereas all living apodans are legless (Jenkins and Walsh 1993).

Caecilians feed on small or elongate prey—termites, earthworms, and larval and adult insects—and the tentacle may allow them to detect the presence of prey when they are underground. Females of some species of caecilians brood their eggs, whereas other species give birth to living young. The embryos of terrestrial species have long, filamentous gills, and the embryos of aquatic species have saclike gills.

■ Diversity of Life Histories of Amphibians

Of all the characteristics of amphibians, none is more remarkable than the variety they display in modes of reproduction and parental care. It is astonishing that the range of reproductive modes among the 4600 species of amphibians far exceeds that of any other group of vertebrates except for fishes, which outnumber amphibian species by five to one. Most species of amphibians lay eggs. The eggs may be deposited in water or on land and they may hatch into aquatic larvae or into miniatures of the terrestrial adults. The adults of some species of frogs carry eggs attached to the surface

TABLE 11.4	Families of caecilians

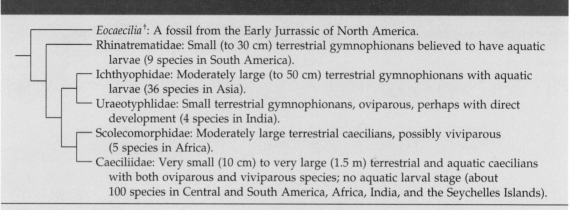

Eocaecilia[†]: A fossil from the Early Jurrassic of North America.

Rhinatrematidae: Small (to 30 cm) terrestrial gymnophionans believed to have aquatic larvae (9 species in South America).

Ichthyophidae: Moderately large (to 50 cm) terrestrial gymnophionans with aquatic larvae (36 species in Asia).

Uraeotyphlidae: Small terrestrial gymnophionans, oviparous, perhaps with direct development (4 species in India).

Scolecomorphidae: Moderately large terrestrial caecilians, possibly viviparous (5 species in Africa).

Caeciliidae: Very small (10 cm) to very large (1.5 m) terrestrial and aquatic caecilians with both oviparous and viviparous species; no aquatic larval stage (about 100 species in Central and South America, Africa, India, and the Seychelles Islands).

The symbol † indicates a fossil.

Phylogenetic relationships and numbers of species are based on Pough, F. H., R. M. Andrews, J. E. Cadle, M. L. Crump, A. H. Savitzky, and K. D. Wells. 1998. *Herpetology*. Prentice Hall, Upper Saddle River, NJ.

of their bodies. Others carry their eggs in pockets in the skin of the back or flanks, in the vocal sacs, or even in the stomach. In still other species the females retain the eggs in the oviducts and give birth to metamorphosed young. Many amphibians have no parental care of their eggs or young, but in many other species a parent remains with the eggs and sometimes with the hatchlings, transports tadpoles from the nest to water, and in a few species an adult even feeds the tadpoles.

Caecilians

The reproductive adaptations of caecilians are as specialized as their body form and ecology. Internal fertilization is accomplished by a male intromittent organ that is protruded from the cloaca. Some species of caecilians lay eggs, and the female may coil around the eggs, remaining with them until they hatch (Figure 11–10). Viviparity is widespread, however, and about 75 percent of the species are viviparous (Wake 1993). At birth young caecilians are 30 to 60 percent of their mother's body length. A female *Typhlonectes* 500 millimeters long may give birth to nine babies, each 200 millimeters long. The initial growth of the fetuses is supported by yolk contained in the egg at the time of fertilization, but this yolk is exhausted long before embryonic development is complete. *Typhlonectes* fetuses have absorbed all of the yolk in the eggs by the time they are 30 millimeters long. Thus, the energy they need to grow to 200 millimeters (a 6.6-fold increase in length) must be supplied by the mother. The energetic demands of

producing nine babies, each one increasing its length 6.6 times and reaching 40 percent of the mother's length at birth, must be considerable.

The fetuses obtain this energy by scraping material from the walls of the oviducts with specialized embryonic teeth. The epithelium of the oviduct proliferates and forms thick beds surrounded by ramifications of connective tissue and capillaries. As the fetuses exhaust their yolk supply, these beds begin to secrete a thick, white, creamy substance that has been called uterine milk. When their yolk supply has been exhausted, the fetuses emerge from their egg membranes, uncurl, and align themselves lengthwise in the oviducts. The fetuses apparently bite the walls of the oviduct, stimulating secretion and stripping some epithelial cells and muscle fibers that they swallow with the uterine milk. Small fetuses are regularly spaced along the oviducts. Large fetuses have their heads spaced at intervals, although the body of one fetus may overlap the head of the next. This spacing probably gives all the fetuses access to the secretory areas on the walls of the oviducts.

Gas exchange appears to be achieved by close contact between the fetal gills and the walls of the oviducts. All the terrestrial species of caecilians have fetuses with a pair of triple-branched filamentous gills. In preserved specimens the fetuses frequently have one gill extending forward beyond the head and the other stretched along the body. In the aquatic genus *Typhlonectes*, the gills are saclike but are usually positioned in the same way. Both the gills and the walls of the oviducts are highly vascularized, and it seems likely that exchange of gases, and possibly of small molecules such as metabolic substrates and waste products, takes place across the adjacent gill and oviduct. The gills are absorbed before birth, and cutaneous gas exchange may be important for fetuses late in development.

Details of fetal dentition differ among species of caecilians, suggesting that this specialized form of fetal nourishment may have evolved independently in different phylogenetic lines. Analogous methods of supplying energy to fetuses are known in some elasmobranch fishes.

Salamanders

Most groups of salamanders use internal fertilization, but the Cryptobranchoidea (Cryptobranchidae and Hynobiidae) and probably the Sirenidae retain external fertilization. Internal fertilization in salamanders is accomplished not by an intromittent organ but by the transfer of a packet of sperm (the **spermatophore**) from the male to the female (Figure 11–11). The form of the spermatophore differs in various species of salamanders, but all consist of a sperm cap on a gelatinous base. The base is a cast of the interior of the male's cloaca, and in some species it reproduces the ridges and furrows in accurate detail. Males of the Asian salamandrid *Euproctus* deposit a spermatophore on the body of a female and then, holding her with their tail or jaws, use their feet to insert the spermatophore into her cloaca. Females of the hynobiid salamander *Ranodon sibiricus* deposit egg sacs on top of a spermatophore. In derived species of salamanders the male deposits a spermatophore on the substrate and the female picks off the cap with her cloaca.

The sperm are released as the cap dissolves, and fertilization occurs in the oviducts.

Courtship   Courtship patterns are important for species recognition, and they show great interspecific variation. Males of some species have elaborate secondary sexual characters that are used during courtship (reviewed by Halliday 1990). Pheromones (chemicals used for communication) are released primarily by males and play a large role in the courtship of salamanders; they probably contribute to species recognition, and may stimulate endocrine activity that increases the receptivity of females.

Pheromone delivery by most salamanders that breed on land involves physical contact between a male and female during which the male applies secretions of specialized courtship glands (hedonic glands) to the nostrils or body of the female. Several modes of pheromone delivery have been described. Males of many plethodontids (e.g., *Plethodon jordani*) have a large gland beneath the chin (the mental gland), and secretions of the gland are applied to the nostrils of the female with a slapping motion (Figure 11–12a). The anterior teeth of males of many species of *Desmognathus* and *Eurycea* (both members of the Plethodontidae) hypertrophy during the breeding season. A male of these species spreads secretion from his mental gland on the female's skin, and then abrades the skin with his teeth, inoculating the female with the pheromone (Figure 11–12b). Males of two small species of *Desmognathus* use specialized mandibular teeth to bite and stimulate the female. Male salamandrids (Salamandridae) rub the female's snout with hedonic glands on their cheeks (the red-spotted newt, *Notophthalmus viridescens*), chin (the rough-skinned newt, *Taricha granulosa*

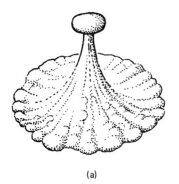

(a)

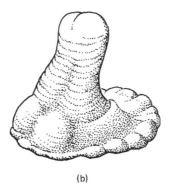

(b)

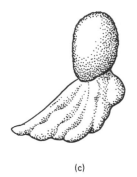

(c)

Figure 11–11   Spermatophores. (a) Red-spotted newt, *Notophthalmus viridescens*; (b) dusky salamander, *Desmognathus fuscus*; (c) two-lined salamander, *Eurycea bislineata*. (Modified from G. K. Noble, 1931, *The Biology of the Amphibia*, McGraw-Hill, New York, NY.)

Figure 11–12 Transfer of pheromones by male salamanders. (a) The rough-skinned, *Taricha granulosa*; (b) Jordan's salamander, *Plethodon jordani*; (c) the two-lined salamander, *Eurycea bislineata*; (d) the smooth newt, *Triturus vulgaris*. (Redrawn from T. R. Halliday, 1990, *Advances in the Study of Behavior* 19:139. © 1990 Academic Press, Inc.)

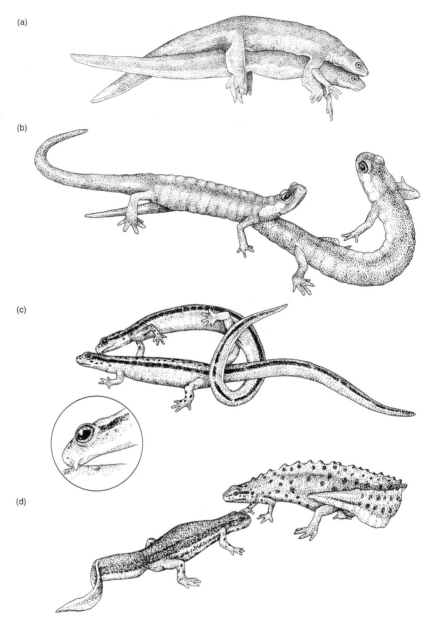

[Figure 11–12c]), or cloaca (the Spanish newt, *Pleurodeles waltl*). Newts in the genera *Triturus* and *Cynops* transfer pheromones without physical contact between the male and female. The males of these species perform elaborate courtship displays in which the male vibrates its tail to create a stream of water that wafts pheromones, secreted by a gland in his cloaca, toward the female (Figure 11–12d).

Three groups of *Triturus*, probably representing evolutionary lineages, are tentatively recognized within the genus, and the evolution of courtship probably reflects this phylogenetic relationship (Arntzen and Sparreboom 1989, Halliday 1990, Hal-

liday and Arano 1991). Two trends are apparent: an increase in diversity of the sexual displays performed by the male, and an increase in the importance of positive feedback from the female. The behaviors seen in *Triturus alpestris* may represent the ancestral condition. This species shows little sexual dimorphism (Figure 11–13c), and the male's display consists only of fanning (a display in which the tail is folded back against the flank nearest the female and the tail tip is vibrated rapidly). The male's behavior is nearly independent of response by the female—a male *T. alpestris* may perform his entire courtship sequence and deposit a sper-

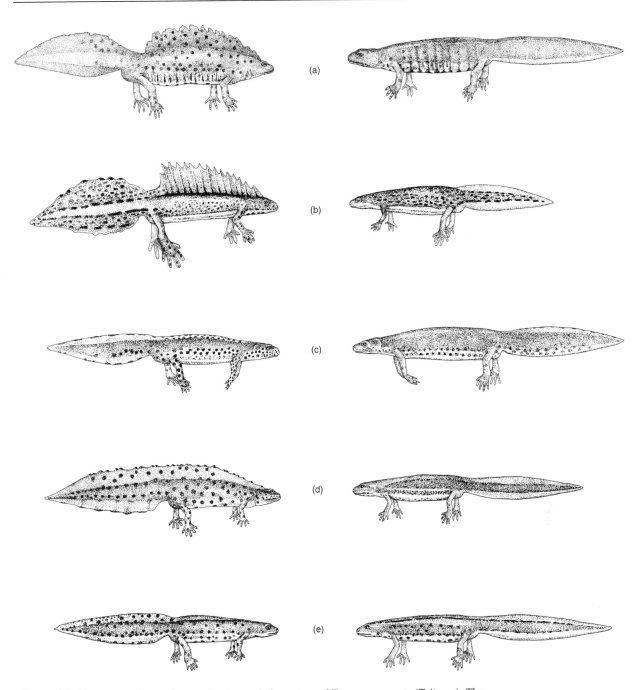

Figure 11–13   Dimorphism of secondary sexual characters of European newts (*Triturus*). The male is on the left, the female is on the right. (a) The great crested newt, *T. cristatus*; (b) the banded newt, *T. vittatus*; (c) the alpine newt, *T. alpestris*; (d) the smooth newt, *T. vulgaris*; (e) Bosca's newt, *T. boscai*. The scale bar represents 5 centimeters. (Redrawn from T. R. Halliday and B. Arano, 1991, *Trends in Ecology and Evolution* 6:114. © 1991 Elsevier Science Publishers Ltd.)

matophore without active response by the female he is courting.

A group of large newts, including *Triturus cristatus* and *T. vittatus* (Figure 11–13a, b) show derived morphological and behavioral characters. They are

highly sexually dimorphic, and males defend display sites. Their displays are relatively static, and lack the rapid fanning movements of the tail that characterize other groups of *Triturus*. A male of these species does not deposit a spermatophore unless the female he is courting touches his tail with her snout.

A group of small-bodied species includes *Triturus vulgaris* and *T. boscai* (Figure 11–13d, e). These newts show less sexual dimorphism than the large species, and have a more diverse array of behaviors, which include a nearly static lateral display, whipping the tail violently against the female's body, fanning with the tail tip, and other displays with names like wiggle and flamenco that occur in some of the species in the group. Response by the female is an essential component of courtship for these species—a male will not move on from the static display that begins courtship to the next phase unless the female approaches him repeatedly, and he will not deposit a spermatophore until the female touches his tail.

These trends to greater sexual dimorphism, more diverse displays, and more active involvement of the female in courtship may reflect sexual selection by females within the derived groups. Halliday (1990) has suggested that in the ancestral condition there was a single male display, and females mated with the males that performed it most vigorously. That kind of selection by females would produce a population of males, all of which displayed vigorously, and males that added new components to their courtship might be more attractive to females than their rivals.

Eggs and Larvae   In most cases, salamanders that breed in water lay their eggs in water. The eggs may be laid singly, or in a mass of transparent gelatinous material. The eggs hatch into gilled aquatic larvae that, except in paedomorphic forms, transform into terrestrial adults. Some families, including the lungless salamanders (Plethodontidae), have a number of species that have dispensed in part or entirely with an aquatic larval stage. The dusky salamander, *Desmognathus fuscus*, lays its eggs beneath a rock or log near water, and the female remains with them until after they have hatched. The larvae have small gills at hatching, and may either take up an aquatic existence or move directly to terrestrial life. The redbacked salamander, *Plethodon cinereus*, lays its eggs in a hollow space in a rotten log or beneath a rock. The embryos have gills, but these are reabsorbed before hatching and the hatchlings are miniatures of the adults.

Viviparity   Only four species of salamanders give birth to young. The European salamander (*Sala-*

mandra salamandra) produces 20 or more small larvae, each about one-twentieth the length of an adult. The embryos probably get all the energy needed for growth and development from egg yolk. The larvae are released in water and have an aquatic stage that lasts about 3 months. The closely related alpine salamander (*S. atra*) gives birth to one or two fully developed young, each about one-third the adult body length. The embryos of this species are nourished by oviductal secretions, as is the case for caecilians.

Paedomorphosis   Paedomorphosis is the rule in families like the Cryptobranchidae and Proteidae and characterizes most cave dwellers. It also appears as a variant in the life history of species of salamanders that usually metamorphose, and can be a short-term response to conditions in aquatic or terrestrial habitats. The life histories of two species of salamanders from eastern North America provide examples of the flexibility of paedomorphosis.

The small-mouthed salamander, *Ambystoma talpoideum*, is the only species of mole salamander in eastern North America that displays paedomorphosis, although a number of species of *Ambystoma* in the western United States and in Mexico are paedomorphic. Small-mouthed salamanders breed in the autumn and winter, and during the following summer some larvae metamorphose to become terrestrial juveniles. These animals become sexually mature by autumn and return to the ponds to breed when they are about a year old. Ponds in South Carolina also contain paedomorphic larvae that remain in the ponds through the summer and mature and breed in the winter. Some of these paedomorphs metamorphose after breeding, whereas others do not metamorphose and remain in the ponds as permanently paedomorphic adults.

Anurans

Anurans are the most familiar amphibians, largely because of the vocalizations associated with their reproductive behavior. It is not even necessary to get outside a city to hear them. In springtime a weed-choked drainage ditch beside a highway or a trash-filled marsh at the edge of a shopping center parking lot is likely to attract a few toads or tree frogs that have not yet succumbed to human usurpation of their habitat.

The mating systems of anurans can be divided roughly into *explosive breeding*, in which the breeding season is very short, sometimes only a few days, and *prolonged breeding*, with breeding seasons that may extend for several months. Explosive breeders include many species of toads and other anurans that breed in temporary aquatic habitats such as vernal ponds or pools created in the desert. Because these bodies of water do not last very long, breeding congregations of anurans usually form as soon as the site is available. Males and females arrive at the breeding sites nearly simultaneously and often in very large numbers. Because the entire population breeds in a short time, the number of males and females present is approximately equal. Time is the main constraint on how many females a male is able to court, and mating success is usually approximately the same for all the males in a chorus.

In species with prolonged breeding seasons, the males usually arrive at the breeding sites first. Males of some species, such as green frogs (*Rana clamitans*), establish territories in which they spend several months, defending the spot against the approach of other males. The males of other species move between daytime retreats and nocturnal calling sites on a daily basis. Females come to the breeding site just to breed, and leave when they have finished. Just a few females arrive every day, and the number of males at the breeding site is greater than the number of females every night. Mating success may be very skewed, with many of the males not mating at all, and a few males mating several times. Males of anuran species with prolonged breeding seasons compete to attract females, usually by vocalizing. The characteristics of a male frog's vocalization (pitch, length, or repetition rate) might provide information that a female frog could use to evaluate his quality as a potential mate. This is an active area of study in anuran behavior.

Vocalizations   Anuran calls are diverse; they vary from species to species, and most species have two or three different sorts of calls used in different situations. The most familiar calls are the ones usually referred to as mating calls, although a less specific term such as **advertisement calls** is preferable. These calls range from the high-pitched *peep* of a spring peeper to the nasal *waaah* of a spadefoot toad or the bass *jug-o-rum* of a bullfrog. The characteristics of a call identify the species and sex of the calling individual. Many species of anurans are territorial, and males of at least one species, the

North American bullfrog (*Rana catesbeiana*) recognize one another individually by voice.

An advertisement call is a conservative evolutionary character, and among related taxa there is often considerable similarity in advertisement calls. Superimposed on the basic similarity are the effects of morphological factors, such as body size, as well as ecological factors that stem from characteristics of the habitat. Most toads (*Bufo*) have a trilled advertisement call that consists of a train of repeated pulses (a trill), but the pitch of the call varies with the body size. The oak toad (*B. quercicus*), which has a body length of only 2 or 3 centimeters, has a dominant frequency of 5200 hertz. The larger southwestern toad (*B. microscaphus*), which is 8 centimeters long, has a lower dominant frequency, 1500 hertz, and the giant toad (*B. marinus*), with a body length of nearly 20 centimeters, has the lowest pitch of all, 600 hertz.

Female frogs are responsive to the advertisement calls of males of their species for a brief period when their eggs are ready to be laid. The hormones associated with ovulation are throught to sensitize specific cells in the auditory pathway that are responsive to the species-specific characteristics of the male's call. Mixed choruses of anurans are common in the mating season; a dozen species may breed simultaneously in one pond. A female's response to her own species' mating call is a mechanism for species recognition in that situation.

Costs and Benefits of Vocalization   The vocalizations of male frogs are costly in two senses. The actual energy that goes into call production can be very large, and the variations in calling pattern that accompany social interactions among male frogs in a breeding chorus can increase the cost per call (see Box 11–1). Another cost of vocalization for a male frog is the risk of predation. A critical function of vocalization is to permit a female frog to locate a male, but female frogs are not the only animals that can use vocalizations as a cue to find male frogs—predators of frogs also find that calling males are easy to locate. The túngara frog (*Physalaemus pustulosus*) is a small terrestrial leptodactylid that occurs in Central America (Figure 11–14). Stanley Rand and Michael Ryan have studied the costs and benefits of vocalization for this species (Ryan 1985).

Túngara frogs breed in small pools, and breeding assemblies range from a single male to choruses of several hundred males. The advertisement call of

Male túngara frog, *Physalaemus pustulosus*, vocalizing. Air is forced from the lungs (a) into the vocal sacs (b). (Photographs courtesy of Theodore L. Taigen, University of Connecticut.)

a male túngara frog is a strange noise, a whine that sounds as if it would be more at home in an arcade of video games than in the tropical night. The whine starts at a frequency of 900 hertz and sweeps downward to 400 hertz in about 400 milliseconds (Figure 11–15). The whine may be produced by itself, or it may be followed by one or several *chucks* with a dominant frequency of 250 hertz. When a male túngara frog is calling alone in a pond it usually gives only the whine portion of the call, but as additional males join a chorus, more and more of the frogs produce calls that include chucks. By playing recordings of the whine calls to male frogs in breeding ponds, Rand was able to make them shift to giving calls that included chucks. That observation suggested that it was the presence of other calling males that stimulated frogs to make their calls more complex by adding chucks to the end of the whine.

What advantage would a male frog in a chorus gain from using a whine–chuck call instead of a whine? Rand suggested that the complex call might be more attractive to female frogs than the simple call. He tested that hypothesis by placing female túngara frogs in a test arena with a speaker at each side. One speaker broadcast a whine call and the second speaker broadcast a whine–chuck. Rand released female frogs individually in the center of the arena and noted which speaker they moved toward. As he had predicted, most of the female frogs (14 of the 15 he tested) chose the speaker broadcasting the whine–chuck call.

If female frogs are attracted to whine–chuck calls in preference to whine calls, why do male frogs give whine–chuck calls only when other males are present? Why not always give the most attractive call possible? One possibility is that whine–chuck calls require more energy than whines, and males save energy by using whine–chucks only when competition with other males makes the energy expenditure necessary. However, measurements of the energy expenditure of calling male túngara frogs showed that energy cost was not related to the number of chucks. Another possibility is that male frogs giving whine–chuck calls are more vulnerable to predators than frogs giving only whine calls. Túngara frogs in breeding choruses are preyed upon by frog-eating bats, *Trachops cirrhosus*, and the bats locate the frogs by homing on their vocalizations.

In a series of playback experiments Ryan and Merlin Tuttle placed pairs of speakers in the forest and broadcast vocalizations of túngara frogs. One speaker played a recording of a whine and the other a recording of a whine–chuck. The bats responded as if the speakers were frogs: They flew toward the speakers and even landed on them. In five experiments at different sites, the bats approached speakers broadcasting whine–chuck calls twice as frequently as those playing simple whines (168 approaches versus 81). Thus, female frogs are not alone in finding whine–chuck calls more attractive than simple whines—an important predator of frogs also responds more strongly to the complex calls. Predation can be a serious risk for male túngara frogs. Ryan and his colleagues measured the rates of predation in choruses of different sizes. The major predators were frog-eating bats, a species of opossum (*Philander opossum*), and a larger species of frog (*Leptodactylus pentadactylus*); the bats were the

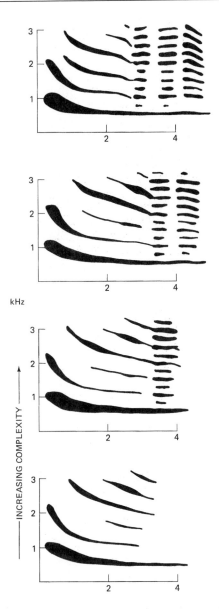

Figure 11–15 Sonograms of the advertisement call of *Physalaemus pustulosus*. The calls increase in complexity from bottom (a whine only) to top (a whine followed by three chucks). A sonogram is a graphic representation of a sound: Time is shown on the horizontal axis and frequency on the vertical axis. (Modified from Ryan 1985.)

from a simple whine to a whine–chuck call, it increases its chances of attracting a female, but it simultaneously increases its risk of attracting a predator. In small choruses the competition from other males for females is relatively small and the risk of predation is relatively large. Under those conditions it is apparently advantageous for a male túngara frog to give simple whines. However, as chorus size increases, competition with other males also increases while the risk of predation falls. In that situation the advantage of giving a complex call apparently outweighs the risks.

Modes of Reproduction   Fertilization is external in most anurans; the male uses his fore legs to clasp the female in the pectoral region (**axillary amplexus**) or pelvic region (**inguinal amplexus**). Amplexus may be maintained for several hours or even days before the female lays eggs. Males of the tailed frog of the Pacific northwest (*Ascaphus truei*) have an extension of the cloaca (the "tail" that gives them their name) that is used to introduce sperm into the cloaca of the female. Internal fertilization has been demonstrated for the Puerto Rican coquí (*Eleutherodactylus coquí*) and may be widespread among frogs that lay eggs on land (Townsend et al. 1981). Fertilization must also be internal for the few species of anurans that give birth to living young.

Anurans show even greater diversity in their modes of reproduction than salamanders. Similar reproductive habits have clearly evolved independently in different groups. Large eggs produce large offspring that probably have a better chance of surviving than smaller ones, but large eggs also require more time to hatch and are exposed to predators for a longer period. Thus, the evolution of large eggs and hatchlings has often been accompanied by the simultaneous evolution of behaviors that protect the eggs, and sometimes the tadpoles as well, from predation. A study of Amazon rainforest frogs revealed a positive relationship between the intensity of predation on frogs eggs in a pond and the proportion of frog species in the area that laid eggs in terrestrial situations (Magnusson and Hero 1991). Many arboreal frogs (represented in Figure 11–18a by *Centrolenella*) lay their eggs in the leaves of trees overhanging water. The eggs undergo their embryonic development out of the reach of aquatic egg predators, and when the tadpoles hatch they drop into the water and take up an aquatic existence. Other frogs, such as *Physalaemus pustulosus* (Figure 11–18b), achieve the same result by constructing

most important predators of the túngara frogs. Large choruses of frogs did not attract more bats than small choruses, and consequently the risk of predation for an individual frog was less in a large chorus than in a small one. Predation was an astonishing 19 percent of the frogs per night in the smallest chorus and a substantial 1.5 percent per night even in the largest chorus. When a male frog shifts

BOX 11–1 **The Energy Cost of Vocalization by Frogs**

The vocalizations of frogs, like most acoustic signals of tetrapods, are produced when air from the lungs is forced over the vocal cords, causing them to vibrate. Contraction of trunk muscles provides the pressure in the lungs that propels the air across the vocal cords, and these contractions require metabolic energy. Measurement of the actual energy expenditure by frogs during calling is technically difficult because a frog must be placed in an airtight metabolism chamber to measure the amount of oxygen it consumes, and that procedure can frighten the frog and prevent it from calling. Ted Taigen and Kent Wells (1985) at the University of Connecticut overcame that difficulty in studies of the gray tree frog, *Hyla versicolor*, by taking the metabolism chambers to the breeding ponds. Calling male frogs were placed in the chambers early in the evening and then left undisturbed. With the stimulus of the chorus around them, frogs would call in the chambers. Their vocalizations were recorded with microphones attached to each chamber, and the amount of oxygen they used during calling was determined from the decline in the concentration of oxygen in the chamber over time (Figure 11–16).

The rates at which individual frogs consumed oxygen were directly proportional to their rates of vocalization (Figure 11–17). At the lowest calling rate, 150 calls per hour, oxygen consumption was barely above resting levels. However, at the highest calling rates, 1500 calls per hour, the frogs were consuming oxygen even more rapidly than they did during high levels of locomotor activity. Examination of the trunk muscles of the male frogs, which hypertrophy enormously during the breeding season, revealed biochemical specializations that appear to permit this high level of oxygen consumption during vocalization (Marsh and Taigen 1987).

The advertisement call of the gray tree frog is a trill that lasts from 0.3 to 0.6 second. During their studies, Wells and Taigen found that gray tree frogs gave short calls when they were in small choruses, and lengthened their calls when many other males were calling near them (Wells and Taigen 1986). It has subsequently been shown that long calls are more attractive to female frogs than short calls (Klump and Gerhardt 1987), but the long calls require more energy. A 0.6-second call requires about twice as much energy as a 0.3-second call, and the

Figure 11–16 Measuring oxygen consumption of a calling frog. Gray tree frog (*Hyla versicolor*) in a metabolism chamber beside a breeding pond. A microphone in the chamber records the frog's calls, and a thermocouple measures the temperature inside the chamber. Gas samples are drawn from the tube for measurements of oxygen consumption. (Photograph courtesy of Theodore L. Taigen, University of Connecticut.)

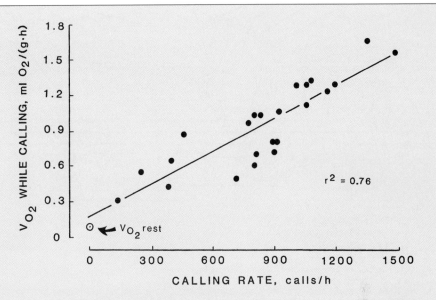

Figure 11–17 Energetic cost of calling. Rates of oxygen consumption of frogs calling inside metabolism chambers (on the vertical axis) as a function of the rate of calling (on the horizontal axis). The energy expended by a calling frog increases linearly with the number of times it calls per hour. (From Taigen and Wells 1985, *Journal of Comparative Physiology* B155:163–170.)

rate of oxygen consumption during calling increases as the length of the calls increases. That relationship suggests that, all else being equal, a male gray tree frog that increased its call duration to be more attractive to female frogs would pay a price for its attractiveness with a higher rate of energy expenditure.

Indirect evidence suggests that the energy cost of calling might limit the time a male gray tree frog could spend in a breeding chorus. The tree frogs call for only 2 to 4 hours each night, and stores of glycogen (the metabolic substrate used by calling frogs) decreased by 50 percent in that time. Wells and Taigen were able to simulate the effects of different chorus sizes by playing tape recordings of vocalizations to frogs. The frogs matched their own calls to the recorded calls they heard—short responses to short calls, medium to medium calls, and long responses to long calls. As the length of their calls increased, the frogs reduced the rate at which they called. The reduction in rate of calling approximately balanced the increased length of each call, so the overall calling effort (the number of seconds of vocalization per hour) was nearly independent of call duration.

Thus, it appears that male gray tree frogs compensate for the higher energy cost of long calls by giving fewer of them. However, that compromise may not entirely eliminate the problem of high energy costs for frogs giving long calls. Even though the calling effort was approximately the same, males giving long calls at slow rates spent fewer hours per night calling than did frogs that produced short calls at higher rates.

The high energy cost of calling offers an explanation for the pattern of short and long calls produced by male gray tree frogs. The length of time that an isolated male can call may be the most important determinant of his success in attracting a female, and the trade-off, between rate of calling and call duration suggests that male frogs are performing at or near their physiological limits. Giving short calls and calling for several hours every night may be the best strategy if a male has that option avilable. In a large chorus, however, competition with other males is intense and giving a longer and more attractive call may be important, even if the male can call for only a short time.

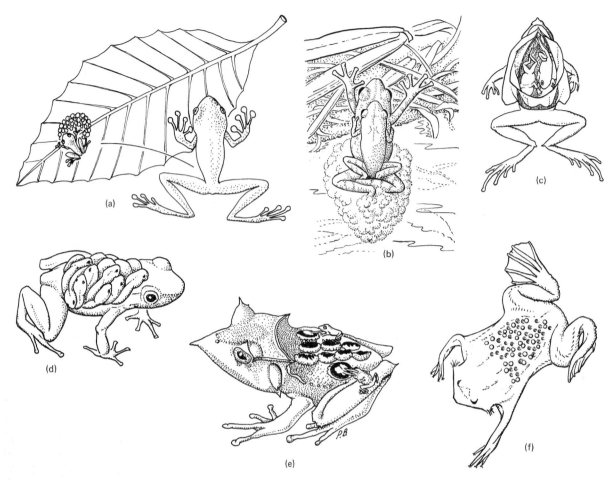

Figure 11–18   Reproductive modes of anurans. (a) Eggs laid over water, *Centrolenella*; (b) eggs in a nest of foam, *Physalaemus*; (c) eggs carried by the adult, *Rhinoderma*; (d) tadpoles carried by the adult, *Colostethus*. Eggs carried on the back of an adult: (e) *Hemiphractus*; (f) *Pipa*. ([c] From G. K. Noble, 1931, *The Biology of the Amphibia*, McGraw-Hill, New York, NY; [e] from W. E. Duellman, 1970, *The Hylid Frogs of Middle America*, Monograph of the Museum of Natural History, 1, The University of Kansas, Lawrence, KS; [f] from M. Lamotte and J. Lescure, 1977, *La Terre et la Vie* 31:225–311.)

foam nests that float on the water surface. The female emits a copious mucus secretion during amplexus that the pair of frogs beat into a foam with their hind legs. The eggs are laid in the foam mass, and when the tadpoles hatch they drop through the foam into the water.

Although these methods reduce egg mortality, the tadpoles are subjected to predation and competition. Some anurans avoid both problems by finding or constructing breeding sites free from competition and predation. Some frogs, for example, lay their eggs in the water that accumulates in bromeliads—epiphytic tropical plants that grow in trees and are morphologically specialized to collect rainwater. A large bromeliad may hold several liters of water, and the frogs pass through egg and larval stages in that protected microhabitat. Many tropical frogs lay eggs on land near water. The eggs or tadpoles may be released from the nest sites when pond levels rise after a rainstorm. Other frogs construct pools in the mud banks beside streams. These volcano-shaped structures are filled with water by rain or seepage and provide a favorable environment for the eggs and tadpoles. Some frogs have eliminated the tadpole stage entirely. These frogs lay large eggs on land that develop directly into little frogs. This pattern is characteristic of about 20 percent of all anuran species.

Parental Care   Adults of many species of frogs guard the eggs specifically. In some cases it is the male that protects the eggs, in others it is the female, and in most cases it is not clearly known which sex is involved because external sex identification is difficult for many anurans. Some of the frogs that lay their eggs over water remain with them. Some species sit beside the eggs, others rest on top of them. Many of the terrestrial frogs that lay direct-developing eggs remain with the eggs and will attack an animal that approaches the nest. Removing the guarding frog frequently results in the eggs desiccating and dying before hatching or being eaten by predators (Taigen et al. 1984, Townsend et al. 1984). Male African bullfrogs (*Pyxicephalus adspersus*) guard their eggs, and then continue to guard the tadpoles after they hatch. The male frog moves with the school of tadpoles, and will even dig a channel to allow the tadpoles to swim from one pool in a marsh to an adjacent one. Tadpoles of several species of the tropical American frog genus *Leptodactylus* follow their mother around the pond. *Leptodactylus* are large and aggressive frogs that are able to deter many potential predators.

Some of the dart-poison frogs of the American tropics deposit their eggs on the ground, and one of the parents remains with the eggs until they hatch into tadpoles. The tadpoles adhere to the adult and are transported to water (Figure 11–18d). Females of the Panamanian frog *Colostethus inguinalis* carry their tadpoles for more than a week and the tadpoles increase in size during this period. The largest tadpoles being carried by females had small amounts of plant material in their stomachs, suggesting that they had begun to feed while they were still being transported by their mother (Wells 1980). Females of another Central American dart-poison frog, *Dendrobates pumilio*, release their tadpoles in small pools of water, and then return at intervals to the pools to deposit unfertilized eggs that the tadpoles eat (Brust 1993).

Other anurans, instead of remaining with the eggs, carry the eggs with them. The male of the European midwife toad (*Alytes obstetricians*) gathers the egg strings about his hind legs as the female lays them. He carries them with him until they are ready to hatch, at which time he releases the tadpoles into water. The male of the terrestrial Darwin's frog (*Rhinoderma darwinii*) of Chile snaps up the eggs the female lays and carries them in his vocal pouches, which extend back to the pelvic region (Figure 11–18c). The embryos pass through metamorphosis in the vocal sacks and emerge as fully developed froglets. Males are not alone in caring for eggs. The females of a group of tree frogs carry the eggs on their back, in an open oval depression, a closed pouch, or individual pockets (Figure 11–18e). The eggs develop into miniature frogs before they leave their mother's back (Del Pino 1989). A similar specialization is seen in the completely aquatic Surinam toad, *Pipa pipa*. In the breeding season the skin of the female's back thickens and softens. In egg laying the male and female in amplexus swim in vertical loops in the water. On the upward part of the loop the female is above the male and releases a few eggs, which fall onto his ventral surface. He fertilizes them and, on the downward loop, presses them against the female's back. They sink into the soft skin and a cover forms over each egg, enclosing it in a small capsule (Figure 11–18f). The eggs develop through metamorphosis in the capsules.

Tadpoles of the two species of the Australian frog genus *Rheobatrachus* are carried in the stomach of the female frog. The female swallows eggs or newly hatched larvae and retains them in her stomach through metamorphosis. This behavior was first described in *Rheobatrachus silus* and is accompanied by extensive morphological and physiological modifications of the stomach. These changes include distension of the proximal portion of the stomach, separation of individual muscle cells from the surrounding connective tissue, and inhibition of hydrochloric acid secretion, perhaps by prostaglandin released by the tadpoles (Tyler 1983). In January 1984, a second species of gastric brooding frog, *R. vitellinus*, was discovered in Queensland. Strangely, this species lacks the extensive structural changes in the stomach that characterize the gastric brooding of *R. silus* (Leong et al. 1986). The striking differences between the two species suggest the surprising possibility that this bizarre reproductive mode might have evolved independently. Both species of *Rheobatrachus* disappeared within a few years of their discovery, and there is no obvious explanation for the apparent extinction of these fascinating frogs. The repeated pattern of amphibian population declines, even for species from habitats that appear undisturbed, suggests that some of these declines may be produced by global-level effects of human activities.

Viviparity   Only six species of anurans are viviparous (Wake 1993). The five species in the African bufonid genus *Nectophrynoides* show a spectrum of reproductive modes. One species deposits eggs that are fertilized externally and hatch into aquatic tadpoles, two species produce young that are nourished by yolk, and the two remaining species have embryos that feed on secretions from the walls of the oviduct. The golden coquí (*Eleutherodactylus jasperi*, a Puerto Rican leptodactylid) also gives birth to fully formed young, but in this case the energy and nutrients come from the yolk of the egg. (The golden coquí is yet another species of amphibian that has vanished and is presumed to be extinct.)

The Ecology of Tadpoles   Although many species of frogs have evolved reproductive modes that bypass an aquatic larval stage, a life history that includes a tadpole has certain advantages. A tadpole is a completely different animal from an adult anuran, both morphologically and ecologically.

Tadpoles are as diverse in their morphological and ecological specializations as adult frogs and occupy nearly as great a range of habitats (Figure 11–19). Tadpoles that live in still water usually have ovoid bodies and tails with fins that are as large as the muscular part of the tail, whereas tadpoles that live in fast-flowing water have more streamlined bodies and smaller tail fins. Semiterrestrial tadpoles wiggle through mud and leaves and climb on damp rock faces; they are often dorsoventrally flattened and have little or no tail fin, and many tadpoles that live in bromeliads have a similar body form. Direct-developing tadpoles have large yolk supplies, and reduced mouth parts and tail fins. The mouth parts of tadpoles also show variation that is related to diet (Figure 11–20). Filter-feeding tadpoles that hover in midwater lack keratinized mouth parts, whereas species that graze from surfaces have small beaks that are often surrounded by rows of denticles. Predatory tadpoles have larger beaks that can bite pieces from other tadpoles. Funnel-mouthed, surface-feeding tadpoles have greatly expanded mouth parts that skim material from the surface of the water.

Tadpoles of most species of anurans are filter-feeding herbivores, whereas all adult anurans are carnivores that catch prey individually. Because of

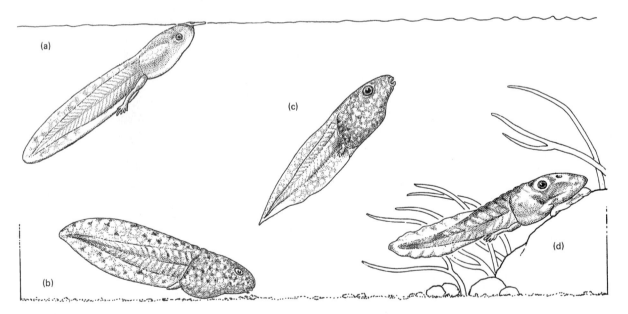

Figure 11–19   Body forms of tadpoles. (a) *Megophrys minor*, a pelobatid. The mouth parts unfold into a platter over which water and particles of food on the surface are drawn into the mouth. (b) *Rana aurora*, a ranid. A generalized feeder that nibbles and scrapes food from surfaces. (c) *Agalychnis callidryas*, a hylid. A midwater suspension feeder shows the large fins and protruding eyes that are typical of midwater tadpoles. It maintains its position in the water column with rapid undulations of the terminal part of its tail. (d) An unidentified species of *Nyctimystes*, a hylid. A stream-dwelling tadpole that adheres to rocks in swiftly moving water with a suckerlike mouth while scraping algae and bacteria from the rocks. The low fins and powerful tail are characteristic of tadpoles living in swift water.

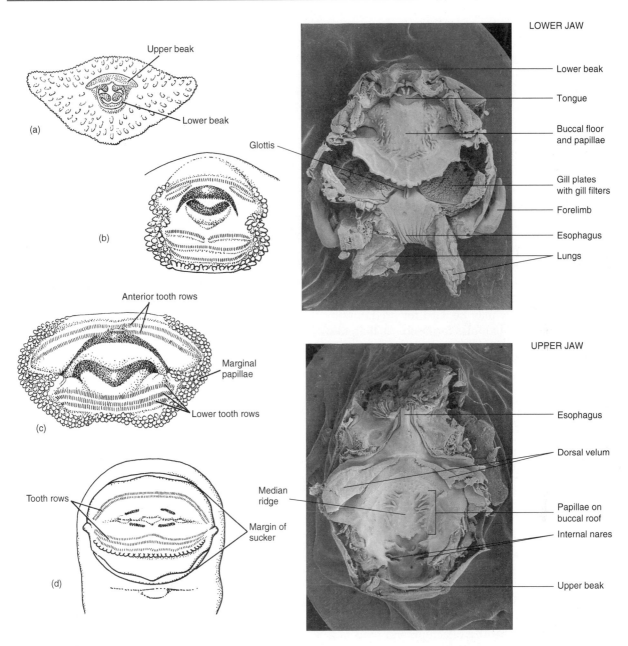

Figure 11–20   Mouths of tadpoles. (a) *Megophrys minor*; (b) *Rana aurora*; (c) *Agalychnis callidryas*; (d) *Nyctimystes* sp.; (e) scanning electron micrograph of the inside of the mouth and buccal region of a tadpole (*Alsodes monticola*, a leptodactylid). ([e] courtesy of Richard J. Wassersug.)

these differences, tadpoles can exploit resources that are not available to adult anurans. This advantage may be a factor that has led many species of frogs to retain the ancestral pattern of life history in which an aquatic larva matures into a terrestrial adult. Many aquatic habitats experience annual flushes of primary production when nutrients washed into a pool by rain or melting snow stimulate the rapid growth of algae. The energy and nutrients in this algal bloom are transient resources that are available for a brief time to organisms that are able to exploit them.

Tadpoles are excellent eating machines. All tadpoles are filter feeders, and feeding and ventilation of the gills are related activities. The stream of water that moves through the mouth and nares to ventilate the gills carries with it particles of food. As the stream of water passes through the branchial basket, small food particles are trapped in mucus secreted by epithelial cells. The mucus, carrying particles of food with it, is moved from the gill filters to the ciliary grooves on the margins of the roof of the pharynx and then transported posteriorly to the esophagus.

Although all tadpoles filter food particles from a stream of water that passes across the gills, the method by which the food particles are put into suspension differs among species. Some tadpoles filter floating plankton from the water. Tadpoles of this type are represented in several families of anurans, especially the Pipidae and Hylidae, and usually hover in the water column. Midwater-feeding tadpoles are out in the open, where they are vulnerable to predators and they show various characteristics that may reduce the risk of predation. Tadpoles of the African clawed frog, for example, are nearly transparent and they may be hard for predators to see. Some midwater tadpoles form schools that, like schools of fishes, may confuse a predator by presenting it with so many potential prey that it has difficulty concentrating its attack on one individual.

Many tadpoles are bottom feeders and scrape bacteria and algae off the surfaces of rocks or the leaves of plants. The rasping action of keratinized mouth parts frees the material and allows it to be whirled into suspension in the water stream entering the mouth of a tadpole, and then filtered out by the branchial apparatus. Some bottom-feeding tadpoles like toads and spadefoot toads form dense aggregations that create currents that lift particles of food into suspension in the water. These aggregations may be groups of siblings. Toad (*Bufo americanus*) and cascade frog tadpoles (*Rana cascadae*) are able to distinguish siblings from nonsiblings and they associate preferentially with siblings (Blaustein and O'Hara 1981, Waldman 1982). Recognition is probably accomplished by olfaction, and toad tadpoles can distinguish full siblings (both parents the same) from maternal half-siblings (only the mother the same), and they can distinguish maternal half-siblings from paternal half-siblings. Prior experience and diet also play a role in kin recognition by tadpoles, and kin recognition might be an artifact of habitat selection (Pfennig 1990b, Gamboa et al. 1991).

Some tadpoles are carnivorous and feed on other tadpoles. The large Central American form *Leptodactylus pentadactylus* that preys on smaller species of anurans such as the túngara frog has a carnivorous tadpole that preys on eggs and tadpoles of other species of anurans. Predatory tadpoles have large mouths with a sharp keratinized beak. Predatory individuals appear among the tadpoles of some species of anurans that are normally herbivorous. Some species of spadefoot toads in western North America are famous for this phenomenon. Spadefoot tadpoles are normally herbivorous, but when tadpoles of the southern spadefoot toad, *Scaphiopus multiplicatus*, eat the freshwater shrimp that occur in some breeding ponds they are transformed into the carnivorous morph (Pfennig 1990a). These carnivorous tadpoles have large heads and jaws and a powerful beak. In addition to eating shrimp, they prey on other tadpoles.

In an Amazonian rainforest, tadpoles are by far the most important predators of frog eggs. In fact, egg predation decreases as the density of fish increases, apparently because the fish eat tadpoles that would otherwise eat frog eggs (Magnusson and Hero 1991). Carnivorous tadpoles are also found among some species of frogs that deposit their eggs or larvae in bromeliads. These relatively small reservoirs of water may have little food for tadpoles. It seems possible that the first tadpole to be placed in a bromeliad pool may feed largely on other frog eggs—either unfertilized eggs deliberately deposited by the mother of the tadpole, as is the case for the dart-poison frog *Dendrobates pumilio*, or fertilized eggs subsequently deposited by unsuspecting female frogs.

The feeding mechanisms that make tadpoles such effective collectors of food particles suspended in the water allow them to grow rapidly, but that growth contains the seeds of its own termination. As tadpoles grow bigger they become less effective at gathering food because of the changing relationship between the size of food-gathering surfaces and the size of their bodies. The branchial surfaces that trap food particles are two dimensional. Consequently, the food-collecting apparatus of a tadpole increases in size approximately as the square of the linear dimensions of the tadpole. However, the food the tadpole collects must nourish its entire body, and the volume of the body increases in proportion to the cube of the linear dimensions of the tadpole. The result of that relationship is a decreasing effectiveness of food collection as a tadpole grows; the body it must nourish increases in size faster than its food-collecting apparatus.

The morphological specializations of tadpoles are entirely different from those of adult frogs, and the transition from tadpole to frog involves a very complete metamorphosis in which tadpole structures are broken down and their chemical constituents are rebuilt into the structures of adult frogs.

■ Amphibian Metamorphosis

The importance of thyroid hormones for amphibian metamorphosis was discovered quite by accident in the early twentieth century by the German biologist Friedrich Gudersnatch. He was able to induce rapid precocious metamorphosis in tadpoles by feeding them extracts of beef thyroid glands. Some of the details of the interaction of neurosecretions and endocrine gland hormones have been worked out, but no fully integrated explanation of the mechanisms of hormonal control of amphibian metamorphosis is yet possible (Hayes 1997).

The most dramatic example of metamorphosis is found among anurans, where almost every tadpole structure is altered. Anuran larval development is generally divided into three periods: (1) During premetamorphosis tadpoles increase in size with little change in form; (2) in prometamorphosis the hind legs appear and growth of the body continues at a slower rate; and (3) during metamorphic climax the fore legs emerge and the tail regresses. These changes are stimulated by the actions of thyroxine, and production and release of thyroxine is controlled by a product of the pituitary gland, thyroid stimulating hormone (TSH).

The action of thyroxine on larval tissues is both specific and local. In other words, it has a different effect in different tissues, and that effect is produced by the presence of thyroxine in the tissue; it does not depend on induction by neighboring tissues. The particular effect of thyroxine in a given tissue is genetically determined, and virtually every tissue of the body is involved (Table 11.5). In the liver, for example, thyroxine stimulates the enzymes responsible for the synthesis of urea (the urea cycle enzymes) and starts the synthesis of serum albumin. In the eye it induces the formation of rhodopsin. When thyroxine is administered to the striated muscles of a tadpole's developing leg, it stimulates growth; but when administered to the striated muscles of the tail, it stimulates the breakdown of tissue. When a larval salamander's tail is treated with thyroxine, only the tail fin disappears; but thyroxine causes the complete absorption of the tail of a frog tadpole.

TABLE 11.5	Metamorphosis. Some of the morphological and physiological changes induced by thyroid hormones during amphibian metamorphosis

Body form and structure

Formation of dermal glands
Restructuring of mouth and head
Intestinal regression and reorganization
Calcification of skeleton

Appendages

Degeneration of skin and muscle of tail
Growth of skin and muscle of limbs

Nervous system and sense organs

Increase in rhodopsin in retina
Growth of extrinsic eye muscles
Formation of nictitating membrane
  of the eye
Growth of cerebellum
Growth of preoptic nucleus of the
  hypothalamus

Respiratory system

Degeneration of the gill arches and gills
Degeneration of the operculum that
  covers the gills
Development of lungs
Shift from larval to adult hemoglobin

Organs

Pronephric resorption in the kidney
Induction of urea-cycle enzymes in the
  liver
Reduction and restructuring of the
  pancreas

Source: Based on B. A. White and C. S. Nicoll, 1981, in *Metamorphosis, a Problem in Developmental Biology,* edited by L. I. Gilbert and E. Freeden, Plenum, New York, NY.

Metamorphosis of salamanders is relatively undramatic compared with the process in anurans. Extensive changes occur at the molecular and tissue level in salamanders, but the loss of gills and absorption of the tail fin are the obvious external changes. In contrast, the metamorphosis of a tadpole to a frog involves readily visible changes in almost every part of the body. The tail is absorbed and recycled into the production of adult structures. The small tadpole mouth that accommodated algae broadens into the huge mouth of an adult frog. The long tadpole gut, characteristic of herbivorous vertebrates, changes to the short gut of a carnivorous animal. Respiration is shifted from gills to lungs, and partly metamorphosed froglets can be seen swimming to the surface to gulp air.

Metamorphic climax begins with the appearance of the forelimbs and ends with the disappearance of the tail. This is the most rapid part of metamorphosis, occupying only a few days after a larval period that lasts for weeks or months. One reason for the rapidity of metamorphic climax may lie in the vulnerability of larvae to predators during this period. A larva with legs and a tail is neither a good tadpole nor a good frog: The legs inhibit swimming and the tail interferes with jumping. As a result, predators are more successful at catching anurans during metamorphic climax than they are in prometamorphosis or following the completion of metamorphosis. Metamorphosing chorus frogs (*Pseudacris triseriata*) were most vulnerable to garter snakes when they had developed legs and still retained a tail. Both tadpoles (with a tail and no legs) and metamorphosed frogs (with legs and no tail) were more successful than the metamorphos-

ing individuals at escaping from snakes (Figure 11–21). Life-history theory predicts that selection will act to shorten the periods in the lifetime of a species when it is most vulnerable to predation, and the speed of metamorphic climax may be a manifestation of that phenomenon.

■ Exchange of Water and Gases

Amphibians have a glandular skin that lacks external scales and is highly permeable to gases and water. Both the permeability and glandularity of the skin have been of major importance in shaping the ecology and evolution of amphibians. Mucous glands are distributed over the entire body surface and secrete mucopolysaccharide compounds. The primary function of the mucus is to keep the skin moist and permeable. For an amphibian, a dry skin means reduction in permeability. That, in turn, reduces oxygen uptake and the ability of the animal to use evaporative cooling to maintain its body temperature within equable limits. Experimentally produced interference with mucus gland secretion can lead to lethal overheating of frogs undergoing normal basking activity.

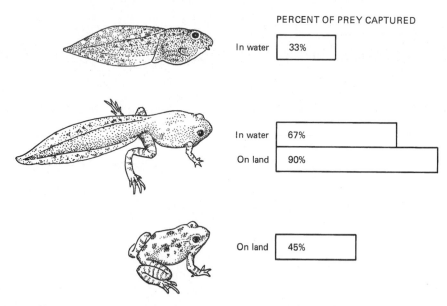

PERCENT OF PREY CAPTURED

In water   33%

In water   67%
On land   90%

On land   45%

Figure 11–21 Predation on tadpoles and frogs. Metamorphosing chorus frogs (*Pseudacris triseriata*) were more vulnerable to garter snakes than were tadpoles or fully transformed frogs. In water, the snakes captured 33 percent of the tadpoles offered compared with 67 percent of the transforming frogs. On land the snakes captured 45 percent of the fully transformed frogs that were offered and 90 percent of the transforming ones. (Data from R. J. Wassersug and D. G. Sperry, 1977, *Ecology* 58:830–839.)

Both water and gases pass readily through amphibian skin. In biological systems, permeability to water is inseparable from permeability to gases, and amphibians depend on cutaneous respiration for a significant part of their gas exchange. Although the skin permits passive movement of water and gases, it controls the movement of other compounds. Sodium is actively transported from the outer surface to the inner, and urea is retained by the skin. These characteristics are important in the regulation of osmolal concentration and in facilitating uptake of water by terrestrial species.

Cutaneous Respiration

All amphibians rely on the skin surface for gas exchange, especially for the release of carbon dioxide. The balance between cutaneous and pulmonary uptake of oxygen varies among species, and within

a species it depends on body temperature and how active the animal is. Amphibians show increasing reliance on the lungs for oxygen uptake as temperature and activity increase (Boutilier et al. 1992, Shoemaker et al. 1992).

The heart of amphibians reflects the use of two respiratory surfaces in the patterns of blood flow within the heart and the distribution of oxygenated and deoxygenated blood to different parts of the body. The anuran heart is best understood, and is the basis for the following description (Figure 11–22). The atrium of the heart is divided into right and left chambers, either anatomically by an interatrial septum or functionally by flow patterns. Blood from the systemic veins flows into the right side of the heart and blood from the lungs flows into the left side. The ventricle shows a variable subdivision that correlates with the physiological importance of pulmonary respiration to the species.

(a)

(b)

(c)

Figure 11–22 Male Puerto Rican coquí. (a) During vocalization nearly all the body surface is exposed to evaporation. (b) In the alert posture in which frogs wait to catch prey most of the body surface is exposed. (c) In the water-conserving posture adopted on dry nights half the body surface is protected from exposure. (Photographs by F. Harvey Pough.)

In frogs the ventricle is undivided, but the position within the ventricle of a particular parcel of blood before ventricular contraction appears to determine its fate on leaving the contracting ventricle. The short conus arteriosus contains a spiral valve of tissue that differentially guides the blood from the left and right sides of the ventricle to the aortic arches. The anatomical relationships within the heart are such that oxygen-rich blood returning to the heart from the pulmonary veins enters the left atrium, which injects it on the left side of the common ventricle. The spongy muscular lumen of the ventricle minimizes the mixing of right- and left-side blood. Contraction of the ventricle tends to eject blood in laminar streams that spiral out of the pumping chamber carrying the left-side blood into the ventral portion of the spirally divided conus. This half of the conus is the one from which the carotid (head-supplying) and systemic aortic arches arise.

Thus, when the lungs are actively ventilated, oxygen-rich blood returning from them to the heart is selectively distributed to the tissues of the head and body. Oxygen-poor venous blood entering the right atrium is directed into the dorsal half of the spiral-valved conus. It goes to the pulmocutaneous arch, destined for oxygenation in the lungs. However, when the skin is the primary site of gaseous exchange, as it is when a frog is underwater, the highest oxygen content is in the systemic veins that drain the skin. The lungs may actually be net users of oxygen, and because of vascular constriction little blood passes through the pulmonary circuit. Because the ventricle is undivided and the majority of the blood is arriving from the systemic circuit, the ventral section of the conus receives blood from an overflow of the right side of the ventricle. The scant left atrial supply to the ventricle also flows through the ventral conus. Thus, the most oxygenated blood coming from the heart flows to the tissues of the head and body during this shift in primary respiratory surface, a phenomenon possible only because of the undivided ventricle. Thus, variability of the cardiovascular output in amphibians is an essential part of their ability to use alternative respiratory surfaces effectively.

Permeability to Water

The internal osmolal pressure of amphibians is approximately two-thirds that characteristic of most other vertebrates. The primary reason for the dilute body fluids of amphibians is low sodium content— approximately 100 milliequivalents compared with 150 milliequivalents in other vertebrates. Amphibians can tolerate a doubling of the normal sodium concentration, whereas an increase from 150 milliequivalents to 170 milliequivalents is the maximum humans can tolerate.

Amphibians are most abundant in moist habitats, especially temperate and tropical forests, but a surprisingly large number of species live in dry regions. Anurans have been by far the most successful amphibian invaders of arid habitats. All but the harshest deserts have substantial anuran populations, and in different parts of the world, different families have converged on similar specializations. Avoiding the harsh conditions of the ground surface is the most common mechanism by which amphibians have managed to invade deserts and other arid habitats. Anurans and salamanders in deserts may spend 9 or 10 months of the year in moist retreat sites, sometimes more than a meter underground, emerging only during the rainy season and compressing feeding, growth, and reproduction into just a few months (Chapter 16).

Many species of arboreal frogs have skins that are less permeable to water than the skin of terrestrial frogs, and a remarkable specialization is seen in a few tree frogs. The African rhacophorid *Chiromantis xerampelina* and the South American hylid *Phyllomedusa sauvagei* lose water through the skin at a rate only one-tenth that of most frogs. *Phyllomedusa* has been shown to achieve this low rate of evaporative water loss by using its legs to spread the lipid-containing secretions of dermal glands over its body surface in a complex sequence of wiping movements, but the basis for the impermeability of *Chiromantis* is not yet understood. These two frogs are unusual also because they excrete nitrogenous wastes as salts of uric acid rather than as urea (see Chapter 4). This uricotelism provides still more water conservation.

Behavioral Control of Evaporative Water Loss

For animals with skins as permeable as those of most amphibians, the main difference between rain forests and deserts may be how frequently they encounter a water shortage. The Puerto Rican coquí lives in wet tropical forests; nonetheless, it has elaborate behaviors that reduce evaporative water loss during its periods of activity (Pough et al. 1983). Male coquís emerge from their daytime retreat sites at dusk and move 1 or 2 meters to calling sites on leaves in the understory vegetation. They remain at their calling sites until shortly before dawn, when they return to their daytime retreats. The activities of the frogs vary from night to night, depending on whether it rained during the afternoon. On nights after a rainstorm, when the forest is wet, the coquís begin to vocalize soon after dusk and continue until about midnight, when they fall silent for several hours. They resume calling briefly just before dawn. When they are calling, coquís extend their legs and raise themselves off the surface of the leaf (Figure 11–23). In this position they lose water by evaporation from the entire body surface.

On dry nights the behavior of the frogs is quite different. The males move from their retreat sites to their calling stations, but they call only sporadically. Most of the time they rest in a water-conserving posture in which the body and chin are flattened against the leaf surface and the limbs are pressed against the body. A frog in this posture exposes only half its body surface to the air, thereby reducing its rate of evaporative water loss. The effectiveness of the postural adjustments is illustrated by the water losses of frogs in the forest at El Verde,

Puerto Rico, on dry nights. Frogs in one test group were placed individually in small wire mesh cages that were placed on leaf surfaces. A second group was composed of unrestrained frogs sitting on leaves. The caged frogs spent most of the night climbing around the cages trying to get out. This activity, like vocalization, exposed the entire body surface to the air, and the caged frogs had an evaporative water loss that averaged 27.5 percent of their initial body mass. In contrast, the unrestrained frogs adopted water-conserving postures and lost an average of only 8 percent of their initial body mass by evaporation.

Experiments showed that the jumping ability of coquís was not affected by an evaporative loss of as much as 10 percent of the initial body mass, but a loss of 20 percent or more substantially decreased the distance frogs could jump (Beuchat et al. 1984). Thus, coquís use behavior to limit their evaporative water losses on dry nights to levels that do not affect their ability to escape from predators or to capture prey. Without those behaviors, however, they would probably lose enough water by evaporation to affect their survival.

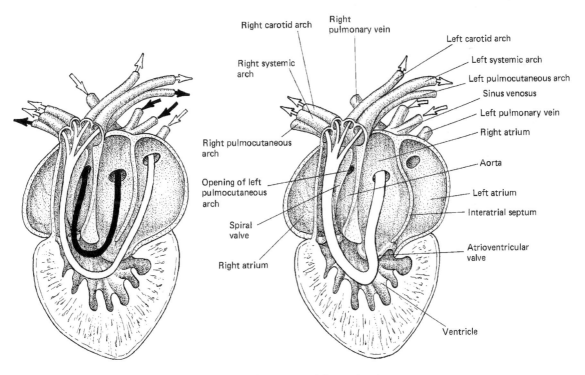

Figure 11–23   Blood flow in the amphibian heart. Left, pattern of flow when lungs are being ventilated; right, flow when only cutaneous respiration is taking place. Dark arrows, blood with low oxygen content; light arrows, most highly oxygenated blood.

Uptake and Storage of Water

The mechanisms that amphibians use for obtaining water in terrestrial environments have received less attention than those for retaining it. Amphibians do not drink water. Because of the permeability of their skins, species that live in aquatic habitats face a continuous osmolal influx of water that they must balance by producing urine. The impressive adaptations of terrestrial amphibians are ones that facilitate rehydration from limited sources of water. One such specialization is the **pelvic patch.** This is an area of highly vascularized skin in the pelvic region that is responsible for a very large portion of an anuran's cutaneous water absorption. Toads that are dehydrated and completely immersed in water rehydrate only slightly faster than those placed in water just deep enough to wet the pelvic area. In arid regions, water may be available only as a thin layer of moisture on a rock, or as wet soil. The pelvic patch allows an anuran to absorb this water.

The urinary bladder plays an important role in the water relations of terrestrial amphibians, especially anurans. Amphibian kidneys produce urine that is hyposmolal to the blood, so the urine in the bladder is dilute. Amphibians can reabsorb water from urine to replace water they lose by evaporation, and terrestrial amphibians have larger bladders than aquatic species. Storage capacities of 20 to 30 percent of the body mass of the animal are common for terrestrial anurans, and some species have still larger bladders: The Australian desert frogs *Notaden nicholsi* and *Neobatrachus wilsmorei* can store urine equivalent to about 50 percent of their body mass, and a bladder volume of 78.9 percent of body mass has been reported for the Australian frog *Helioporus eyrei*.

Behavior is as important in facilitating water uptake as it is in reducing water loss. Leopard frogs, *Rana pipiens*, spend the summer activity season in grassy meadows where they have no access to ponds. The frogs spend the day in retreats they create by pushing vegetation aside to expose moist soil. In the retreats, the frogs rest with the pelvic patch in contact with the ground, and tests have shown that the frogs are able to absorb water from the soil. On nights when dew forms, many frogs move from their retreats and spend some hours in the early morning sitting on dew-covered grass before returning to their retreats. Leopard frogs show a daily pattern of water gain and loss during a period of several days when no rain falls: In the morning the frogs are sleek and glistening with moisture, and they have urine in their bladders. That observation indicates that in the morning the frogs have enough water to form urine. By evening the frogs have dry skins, and little urine in the bladder, suggesting that as they lost water by evaporation during the day they had reabsorbed water from the urine to maintain the water content of their tissues.

By the following morning the frogs have absorbed more water from dew and are sleek and well hydrated again. Net gains and losses of water are shown by daily fluctuations in body masses of the frogs; In the mornings they are as much as 4 or 5 percent heavier than their overall average mass, and in the evenings they are lighter than the average by a similar amount (Dole 1965, 1967). Thus, these terrestrial frogs are able to balance their water budgets by absorbing water from moist soil and from dew to replace the water they lose by evaporation and in urine. As a result, they are independent of sources of water like ponds or streams and are able to colonize meadows and woods far from any permanent sources of water.

■ Poison Glands and Other Defense Mechanisms

The mucus that covers the skin of an amphibian has a variety of properties. In at least some species it has antibacterial activity, and a potent antibiotic that may have medical applications has been isolated from the skin of the African clawed frog. It is mucus that makes some amphibians slippery and hard for a predator to hold. Other species have mucus that is extremely adhesive. Many salamanders, for example, have a concentration of mucous glands on the dorsal surface of the tail. When one of these salamanders is attacked by a predator, it bends its tail forward and buffets its attacker. The sticky mucus causes debris to adhere to the predator's snout or beak, and with luck the attacker soon concentrates on cleaning itself, losing interest in the salamander. When the California slender salamander is seized by a garter snake, the salamander curls its tail around the snake's head and neck. This behavior makes the salamander hard for the snake to swallow, and also spreads sticky secretions on the snake's body. A small snake can find its body glued into a coil from which it is unable to escape.

Figure 11–24 Amphibian skin. Cross section of skin from the base of the tail of a red-backed salamander, *Plethodon cinereus.* Three types of glands can be seen. (Modified from G. K. Noble, 1931, *The Biology of the Amphibia,* McGraw-Hill, New York, NY.)

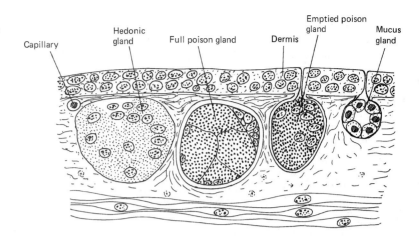

Although secretions of the mucous glands of some species of amphibians are irritating or toxic to predators, an amphibian's primary chemical defense system is located in the poison glands (Figure 11–24). These glands are concentrated on the dorsal surfaces of the animal, and defense postures of both anurans and salamanders present the glandular areas to potential predators.

A great diversity of pharmacologically active substances has been found in the skins of amphibians. Some of them are extremely toxic and others are less toxic but capable of producing unpleasant sensations when a predator bites an amphibian. Biogenic amines such as serotonin and histamine, peptides such as bradykinin, and hemolytic proteins have been found in frogs and salamanders belonging to many families. Many of these substances, such as bufotoxin, physalaemin, and leptodactyline, are named for the animals in which they were discovered. Epibatidine, a toxic compound isolated from the skin of the Central American frog *Epipedobates tricolor,* is a potent painkiller. Unlike opioids such as morphine, epibatidine works by blocking a receptor for the neurotransmitter acetylcholine. An artificial form of epibatidine has been synthesized (Bannon et al. 1998). Known as ABT-594, this compound lacks the toxic side effects of natural epibatidine and also lacks the addictive effect of opioids. It is currently undergoing safety trials in preparation for clinical tests of its effectiveness for relief of chronic pain in humans (Strauss 1998).

Cutaneous alkaloids are abundant and diverse among the dart-poison frogs, the family Dendrobatidae, of the New World tropics. More than 200 new alkaloids have been described from dendrobatids, mostly species in the genera *Dendrobates,* *Minyobates, Epidobates,* and *Phyllobates.* Most of these frogs are brightly colored and move about on the ground surface in daylight, making no attempt at concealment.

The name dart-poison frogs refers to the use by South American Indians of the toxins of some of these frogs to poison the tips of the blowgun darts used for hunting. The use of frogs in this manner appears to be limited to three species of *Phyllobates* that occur in western Colombia, although plant poisons like curare are used to poison blowgun darts in other parts of South America (Myers et al. 1978). A unique alkaloid, batrachotoxin, occurs in the genus *Phyllobates.* Batrachotoxin is a potent neurotoxin that prevents the closing of sodium channels in nerve and muscle cells, leading to irreversible depolarization and producing cardiac arrhythmias, fibrillation, and cardiac failure.

The bright yellow *Phyllobates terribilis* is the largest and most toxic species in the genus. The Emberá Choco Indians of Colombia use *Phyllobates terribilis* as a source of poison for their blowgun darts. The dart points are rubbed several times across the back of a frog, and set aside to dry. The Indians handle the frogs carefully, holding them with leaves—a wise precaution because batrachotoxin is exceedingly poisonous. A single frog may contain up to 1900 micrograms of batrachotoxin, and less than 200 micrograms is probably a lethal dose for a human if it enters the body through a cut. Batrachotoxin is also toxic when it is eaten. In fact, the investigators inadvertently caused the death of a dog and a chicken in the Indian village in which they were living when the animals got into garbage that included plastic bags in which the frogs had been carried. Cooking destroys the poison and makes prey killed by darts anointed with the skin secretions of *Phyllobates terribilis* safe to eat.

Skin secretions from another frog are used in the hunting magic of several Amazonian tribes. *Phyllomedusa bicolor*, a large, green hylid frog, secretes a variety of peptides, including a hitherto unknown compound that has been named adenoregulin (Daly et al. 1992). Mucus scraped from a frog's skin is dried and stored for later use. When it is mixed with saliva and rubbed into areas of freshly burned skin, it induces a feeling of illness, followed by listlessness, and finally a profound euphoria. Adenoregulin, the constituent of the mucus that is responsible for these effects, apparently enhances binding of adenosine and its analogs to A_1 receptors of the brain. These receptors are distributed throughout the brain, and a way to modify their function could contribute to treatments for a variety of central nervous system disorders, including depression, seizures, and loss of cognitive function in conditions such as Alzheimer's disease. Adenoregulin may be yet another example of a medically important compound from the rapidly dwindling tropical forests.

Many amphibians advertise their distasteful properties with conspicuous **aposematic** (warning) colors and behaviors. A predator that makes the mistake of seizing one is likely to spit it out because it is distasteful. The toxins in the skin may also induce vomiting that reinforces the unpleasant experience for the predator. Subsequently, the predator will remember its unpleasant experience and avoid the distinctly marked animal that produced it. Some toxic amphibians combine a cryptic dorsal color with an aposematic ventral pattern. Normally, the cryptic color conceals them from predators, but if they are attacked they adopt a posture that displays the brightly colored ventral surface (Figure 11–25).

Some salamanders have a morphological specialization that enhances the defensive effects of their chemical secretions. The European salamander *Pleurodeles waltl* and two genera of Asian salamanders (*Echinotriton* and *Tylotriton*) have ribs that pierce the body wall when a predator seizes the salamander. You can imagine the shock for a predator that bites a salamander and finds its tongue and palate impaled by a dozen or more bony spikes! Even worse, the ribs penetrate poison glands as they emerge through the body wall and each rib carries a drop of poison into the wound.

Many anurans make long leaps to escape a predator, and others feign death. Some cryptically colored frogs extend their legs stiffly when they play dead. In this posture they look so much like the leaf litter on the ground that they may be hard for a visually oriented predator such as a bird to

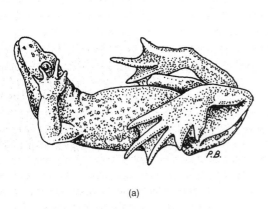

(a)

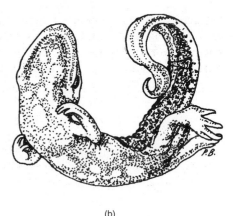

(b)

Figure 11–25   Aposematic displays by amphibians. Warningly colored species of amphibians have displays that present bright colors that predators can learn to associate with the animals' toxic properties. (a) The European fire-bellied toad has a cryptically colored dorsal surface and a brightly colored underside that is displayed in the *unken* reflex when the animal is attacked. (b) The Hong Kong newt has a brownish dorsal surface and a mottled red and black venter that is revealed by its aposematic display. ([a] Modified from H. Gadow, 1909, *Amphibia and Reptiles*, Macmillan and Company Ltd. London, UK; [b] from a photograph by E. D. Brodie, Jr.)

see. Very large frogs attack potential predators. They increase their apparent size by inflating the lungs, and hop toward the predator, often croaking loudly. That can be an unnerving experience, and some of the carnivorous species such as the horned frogs of South America (*Ceratophrys*), which have recurved teeth on the maxillae and toothlike serrations on the mandibles, can inflict a painful bite.

Red efts are classic examples of aposematic animals (see the color insert). They are bright orange and are active during the day, making no effort to conceal themselves. Efts contain tetrodotoxin, which is a potent neurotoxin. Touching an eft to your lips produces an immediate unpleasant numbness and tingling sensation, and the behavior of animals that normally prey on salamanders indicates that it affects them the same way. As a result, an eft that is attacked by a predator is likely to be rejected before it is injured. After one or two such experiences, a predator will no longer attack efts. Support for the belief that this protection may operate in nature is provided by the observation that 4 of 11 wild-caught bluejays (*Cyanocitta cristata*) refused to attack the first red eft they were offered in a laboratory feeding trial (Tilley et al. 1982). That behavior suggests that those four birds had learned to avoid red efts before they were captured. The remaining seven birds attacked at least one eft, but dropped it immediately. After one or two experiences of this sort, the birds made retching movements at the sight of an eft and refused to attack.

Of course, aposematic colors and patterns work to deter predation only if a predator can see the aposematic signal. Nocturnal animals may have difficulty being conspicuous if they rely on visual signals. One species of dendrobatid frog apparently deters predators with a foul odor (Myers et al. 1991). The aptly named *Aromobates nocturnus* from the cloud forests of the Venezuelan Andes is the only nocturnal dendrobatid. It is an inconspicuous frog, about 5 centimeters long with a dark olive color. The frogs emit a foul, skunklike odor when they are handled.

■ Mimicry

The existence of unpalatable animals that deter predators with aposematic colors and behaviors offers the opportunity for other species that lack noxious qualities to take advantage of predators that have learned by experience to avoid the aposematic species. In this phenomenon, known as **mimicry**, the mimic (a species that lacks noxious properties) resembles a noxious model and that resemblance causes a third species, the dupe, to mistake the mimic for the model. Some of the best known cases of mimicry among vertebrates involve salamanders (Pough 1988). One that has been investigated involves two color morphs of the common red-backed salamander, *Plethodon cinereus*.

Red-backed salamanders normally have dark pigment on the sides of the body, but in some regions an erythristic (*erythr* = red) color morph is found that lacks the dark pigmentation and has red-orange on the sides as well as on the back. These erythristic morphs resemble red efts, and could be mimics of efts. Red-backed salamanders are palatable to many predators, and mimicry of the noxious red efts might confer some degree of protection on individuals of the erythristic morph. That hypothesis was tested in a series of experiments (Brodie and Brodie 1980). Salamanders were put in leaf-filled trays from which they could not escape, and the trays were placed in a forest where birds were foraging. The birds learned to search through the leaves in the trays to find the salamanders. This is a very lifelike situation for a test of mimicry because some species of birds are important predators of salamanders. For example, red-backed salamanders and dusky salamanders (*Desmognathus ochrophaeus*) made up 25 percent of the prey items fed to their young by hermit thrushes in western New York.

Three species of salamanders were used in the experiments, and the number of each species was adjusted to represent a hypothetical community of salamanders containing 40 percent dusky salamanders, 30 percent red efts, 24 percent striped red-backed salamanders, and 6 percent erythristic red-backed salamanders. The dusky salamanders are palatable to birds and are light brown; they do not resemble either efts or red-backed salamanders and they served as a control in the experiment. The striped red-backed salamanders represent a second control: The hypothesis of mimicry of red efts by erythristic salamanders leads to the prediction that the striped salamanders, which do not look like efts, will be eaten by birds, whereas the erythristic salamanders, which are as palatable as the striped ones but which do look like the noxious efts, will not be eaten.

A predetermined number of each kind of salamander was put in the trays and birds were allowed to forage for 2 hours. At the end of that

TABLE 11.6 Differential survival of salamanders exposed to foraging birds

Experimental Design

Hypothesis: The erythristic morph of *Plethodon cinereus* is a mimic of the red eft.

Predictions: 1. Birds will not eat red efts because the efts are noxious.
2. Birds will readily eat dusky salamanders, which are palatable and not mimetic.
3. Birds will eat the striped *Plethodon*, which are also palatable and not mimetic.
4. Birds will mistake the erythristic *Plethodon* for efts and will not eat them.

Results

Percentage of Salamanders Gone from Trays

		Plethodon	
Red Efts	Dusky Salamanders	Striped	Erythristic
1.0	52.6	60.1	43.9

Interpretation

The predictions of the hypothesis were supported:
1. Birds did not eat the noxious red efts (prediction 1).
2. Birds did eat the palatable, nonmimetic dusky salamanders (prediction 2).
3. Birds ate the striped morph of *Plethodon* (prediction 3).
4. Birds ate significantly fewer of the mimetic morph of *Plethodon* than of the striped morph (prediction 4).

Source: Based on Brodie and Brodie 1980.

time the salamanders that remained were counted. As expected, only 1 percent of the efts had been taken by birds, whereas 44 to 60 percent of the palatable salamanders had disappeared (Table 11.6). As predicted, the birds ate fewer of the erythristic form of the red-backed salamanders than they ate of the striped form.

These results show that the erythristic morph of the red-backed salamander does obtain some protection from avian predators as a result of its resemblance to the red eft. In this case the resemblance is visual, but mimicry can exist in any sensory mode to which a dupe is sensitive. Olfactory mimicry by amphibians might be effective against predators such as shrews and snakes, which rely on scent to find and identify prey. This possibility has scarcely been considered, but careful investigations may yield fascinating new examples.

■ Why Are Amphibians Vanishing?

The global decline of amphibian populations described in Chapter 1 is alarming, especially because we may have no idea *why* a species has disappeared from places in which it was formerly abundant. In some cases local events appear to provide an explanation. Habitat changes produced by logging are usually destructive to amphibians, for example, because frogs and salamanders depend on cool, moist microhabitats on the forest floor. When the forest canopy is removed, sunlight reaches the ground and conditions become too hot and dry for amphibians. Mining and extraction of oil also cause damage that can extend over large areas. The rock removed from mines often releases acid or toxic chemicals, cyanide used to extract gold from ore poisons surface water, and oil wells spread toxic hydrocarbons—the list of abuses is nearly endless.

Some local causes of amphibian mortality are not only obvious, they are positively undignified. Federal land in the western United States is leased for grazing, and cattle drink from the ponds that are breeding sites for anurans. As the ponds shrink during the summer, they leave a band of mud that cattle cross when they come to drink. The deep hoof prints the cattle make can be death traps for newly metamorphosed frogs and toads that tumble in and cannot climb out. Even worse, a few juvenile anurans that have the bad luck to pass behind a cow at exactly the wrong moment are trapped and suffocated beneath a pile of fresh manure!

But the truly disturbing questions involve species such as the Costa Rica golden toad (*Bufo periglenes*) and other high-altitude frogs that live in habitats where there is no sign of local environmental damage (Pounds and Crump 1994). The global scope of the problem suggests that we should look for global explanations (Blaustein and Wake 1995). Two factors that have probably contributed to some of these declines are acid precipitation and increased ultraviolet radiation.

Precipitation (rain, snow, and fog) over large parts of the world, especially the Northern Hemisphere, is at least a hundredfold more acidic than it would be if the water were in equilibrium with carbon dioxide in the air. The extra acidity is produced by nitric and sulfuric acids that form when water vapor combines with oxides of nitrogen and sulfur released by combustion of fossil fuels. Water in the breeding ponds of many amphibians in the Northern Hemisphere has become more acidic in the past 50 years, and this acidity has both direct and indirect effects on amphibian eggs and larvae (Dunson and Wyman 1992). Embryos of many species of frogs and salamanders are killed or damaged at pH 5 or less (Figure 11–26). Larvae that hatch may be smaller than normal, and sometimes have strange lumps or kinks in their bodies. Spotted salamander larvae grow slowly in acid water because their prey-capture efforts are clumsy and they eat less than do larvae at higher pH (Preest 1993).

Another global phenomenon is an increase in the amount of ultraviolet radiation reaching the Earth's surface as a result of destruction of ozone in the stratosphere by chemical pollutants. The effects are most dramatic at the poles, and are spreading into lower latitudes in both hemispheres. Ultraviolet light, especially the 280- to 320-nanometer UV-B band, kills amphibian eggs and embryos (Blaustein et al. 1994). Only 50 to 60 percent of the eggs of the Cascade frog (*Rana cascadae*) and the western toad (*Bufo boreas*) in ponds in the Cascade Mountains of Oregon survived when they were exposed to incident sunlight, but when a filter that blocked UV-B was placed over the eggs, survival climbed to 70 to 85 percent. Eggs of the Pacific tree frog (*Hyla regilla*) were not affected by unfiltered sunlight. The enzyme photolyase repairs UV-induced damage to DNA, and the different sensitivity of the three

species of anurans to UV-B corresponded to differences in the activity of photolyase in their eggs.

Sensitivity of amphibian eggs to UV-B may be contributing to the decline of some species. Because ozone depletion is a global phenomenon, this mechanism might account for the species that are declining in habitats that show no evidence of local environmental degradation. High-altitude species, which represent some of the most puzzling examples of declines, may be especially vulnerable to thinning of the ozone layer because the intensity of ultraviolet radiation normally increases with altitude. However, neither ozone depletion nor acid precipitation is yet severe at tropical latitudes, and other mechanisms—still unknown—must be responsible for the disappearance of golden toads and other tropical frogs.

Biologists from many countries met in England in 1989 at the First World Congress of Herpetology. In a week of formal presentations of scientific studies and in casual conversations at meals and in hallways the participants discovered that an alarmingly large proportion of them knew of populations of amphibians that had once been abundant and now were rare, or even entirely gone. Events that had appeared to be isolated instances turned out to be part of a global pattern. As a result of that discovery, David Wake, of the University of California at Berkeley, persuaded the National Academy of Sciences to convene a meeting of biologists concerned about vanishing amphibians. Biologists from all over the world met at the West Coast center of the Academy in February 1990. All reported that populations of amphibians in their countries were disappearing, and often there was no apparent reason. Following that meeting, an international effort to identify the causes of amphibian declines was initiated by the Declining Amphibian Populations Task Force of the Species Survival Commission of the World Conservation Union (IUCN). This work is being conducted almost entirely by the voluntary efforts of concerned scientists. Regional working groups of the task force are composed of scientists who monitor the status of amphibian populations in their areas. Issue-based working groups are responsible for assembling lists of chemical contaminants and climatic factors that are likely to affect amphibian populations and for coordinating the efforts of individual scientists.

Standard methods of surveying populations and marking individual animals are critical for an effort of this sort, which reaches across national bound-

DEVELOPMENT OF SPOTTED SALAMANDER EGGS

NORMAL

ABNORMAL

A. Cells divide evenly.

a. When exposed to highly acid conditions, cells divide unevenly.

B. Yolk plug retracts.

b. Yolk plug fails to retract fully and results in "c."

C. Embryo's development includes growth of its posterior portion.

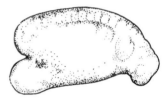

c. Posterior portion of embryo is deformed. Deformities in "a" through "c" are always lethal to an embryo.

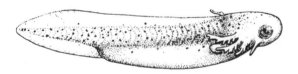

D. The gills and forelimbs develop as the embryo reaches a later stage.

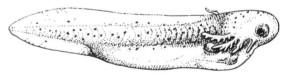

d. Less acid conditions produce damage at a later stage of development, including a swelling of the chest near the heart.

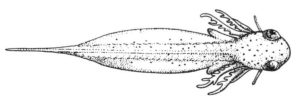

E. Gills become more lobed as the embryo nears hatching.

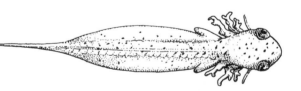

e. Less acidity also produces stunted gills. Deformities in "d" through "e" are frequently lethal to the embryo.

Figure 11–26 Effects of acidity on embryos of the spotted salamander, *Ambystoma maculatum.* Normal embryonic development is shown on the left and abnormalities observed in acid conditions on the right. Highly acidic conditions (pH values below about 5) kill embryos at early stages of development, whereas less acid conditions (between pH 5 and 6) produce abnormalities later in development. Above pH 6 embryos of spotted salamanders develop normally. (From F. H. Pough, 1978, *NAHO* 11[1]:6–9. Courtesy of NAHO. Published by the New York State Museum.)

aries and relies on the efforts of many investigators over periods of years. *Measuring and Monitoring Biological Diversity: Standard Methods for Amphibians* (Heyer et al. 1993) was compiled to provide a framework for studies of vanishing amphibian populations. *Tracking the Vanishing Frogs* (Phillips 1994) traces the discovery of the phenomenon of amphibian population declines, and examines the evidence for various possible causes. "FROGLOG", the newsletter of the Task Force, is published at the Department of Biology of The Open University (Walton Hall, Milton Keynes, MK7 6AA, United Kingdom), and is partly funded by Frog's Leap Winery in St. Helena, California.

Probably most population declines represent the combined effects of several factors. Physical conditions, such as acidity or ultraviolet radiation, may interact with biological factors. Amphibians that are stressed by acidity or ultraviolet radiation may be susceptible to diseases or parasites that they would ordinarily be able to resist. Interacting mechanisms of that sort are hard to identify, and harder still to ameliorate. The prospect for many species of amphibians appears bleak.

■ Summary

Locomotor adaptations distinguish the lineages of amphibians. Salamanders (Urodela) usually have short, sturdy legs that are used with lateral undulation of the body in walking. Aquatic salamanders use lateral undulations of the body and tail to swim, and some specialized aquatic species are elongate and have very small legs. Frogs and toads (Anura) are characterized by specializations of the pelvis and hindlimbs that permit both legs to be used simultaneously to deliver a powerful thrust used both for jumping and for swimming. Many anurans walk quadrupedally when they move slowly and some are agile climbers. The caecilians (Gymnophiona) are legless tropical amphibians; some are burrowers and others are aquatic.

The diversity of reproductive modes of amphibians exceeds that of any other group of vertebrates except the fishes. Fertilization is internal in derived salamanders, but most frogs rely on external fertilization. All caecilians have internal fertilization. Many species of amphibians have aquatic larvae. Tadpoles, the aquatic larvae of anurans, are specialized for life in still or flowing water, and some species of frogs deposit their tadpoles in very specific sites, such as the pools of water that accumulate in the leaf axils of bromeliads or other plants. The specializations of tadpoles are entirely different from the specializations of frogs, and metamorphosis causes changes in all parts of the body. Direct development that omits the larval stage is also widespread among anurans and is often combined with parental care of the eggs. Viviparity occurs in all three orders.

In many respects the biology of amphibians is determined by properties of their skin. Hedonic glands are key elements in reproductive behaviors, poison glands protect the animals against predators, and mucous glands keep the skin moist, facilitating gas exchange. Above all, the permeability of the skin to water limits most amphibians to microhabitats in which they can control water gain and loss. That sounds like a severe restriction, but in the proper microhabitat amphibians can utilize the permeability of their skin to achieve a remarkable degree of independence of standing water. Thus, the picture that is sometimes presented of amphibians as animals barely hanging on as a sort of evolutionary oversight is misleading. Only a detailed examination of all facets of their biology can produce an accurate picture of amphibians as organisms.

An examination of that sort reinforces the view that the skin is a dominant structural characteristic of amphibians. This is true not only in terms of the limitations and opportunities presented by the skin's permeability to water and gases, but also as a result of the intertwined functions of the skin glands in defensive and reproductive behaviors. The structure and function of the skin may be primary characteristics that have shaped the evolution and ecology of amphibians, and may also be responsible for some aspects of their susceptibility to pollution. All over the world populations of amphibians are disappearing at an alarming rate, and some of these extinctions may be caused by regional or global effects of human activities that are likely to affect other organisms as well.

■ References

Arntzen, J. W., and M. Sparreboom. 1989. A phylogeny for Old World newts, genus *Triturus*: biochemical and behavioural data. *Journal of Zoology* (London) 219:645–664.

Bannon, A. W., M. W. Decker, M. W. Holladay, P. Curzon, D. Donnelly-Roberts, P. S. Puttfarken, R. S. Bitner, A. Diaz, A. H. Dickenson, R. D. Porsolt, M. Williams, and S. P. Aneric. 1998. Broad-spectrum, non-opioid analgesic activity by selective modulation of neuronal nicotinic acetylcholine receptors. *Science* 279:77–81.

Beuchat, C. A., F. H. Pough, and M. M. Stewart. 1984. Response to simultaneous dehydration and thermal stress in three species of Puerto Rican frogs. *Journal of Comparative Physiology* B154:579–585.

Blaustein, A. R., and R. K. O'Hara. 1981. Genetic control of sibling recognition? *Nature* 290:246–248.

Blaustein, A. R., P. D. Hoffman, D. G. Hokit, J. M. Kiesecker, S. C. Walls, and J. B. Hays. 1994. UV repair and resistance to solar UV-B in amphibian eggs: a link to population declines. *Proceedings of the National Academy of Sciences, USA* 91:179–1795.

Blaustein, A. R. and D. B. Wake. 1995. The puzzle of declining amphibian populations. *Scientific American* 272(4):56–61.

Boutilier, R. G., D. F. Stiffler, and D. P. Toews. 1992. Exchange of respiratory gases, ions, and water in amphibious and aquatic amphibians. Pages 81–124 in *Environmental Physiology of the Amphibia*, edited by M. E, Feder and W. W. Burggren. The University of Chicago Press, Chicago, IL.

Brodie, E. D., Jr., and E. D. Brodie III. 1980. Differential avoidance of mimetic salamanders by free-ranging birds. *Science* 208:181–182.

Brust, D. G. 1993. Maternal brood care by *Dendrobates pumilio*: a frog that feeds its young. *Journal of Herpetology* 27:96–98.

Daly, J. W., J. Caceres, R. W. Moni, F. Gusovsky, M. Moos, Jr., K. B. Seamon, K. Milton, and C. W. Myers. 1992. Frog secretions and hunting magic in the upper Amazon: identification of a peptide that interacts with an adenosine receptor. *Proceedings of the National Academy of Sciences, USA* 89:10960–10963.

Del Pino, E. M. 1989. Modifications of oogenesis and development in marsupial frogs. *Development* 107:169–187.

Dole, J. W. 1965. Summer movements of adult leopard frogs, *Rana pipiens* Schreber, in northern Michigan. *Ecology* 46:236–255.

Dole, J. W. 1967. The role of substrate moisture and dew in the water economy of leopard frogs, *Rana pipiens. Copeia* 1967:141–149.

Dunson, W. A., and R. L. Wyman (editors). 1992. Amphibian declines and habitat acidification. *Journal of Herpetology* 26:349–442.

Gamboa, G. J., K. A. Berven, R. A. Schemidt, T. G. Fishwild, and K. M. Jankens. 1991. Kin recognition by larval wood frogs (*Rana sylvatica*): effects of diet and prior exposure to conspecifics. *Oecologia* 86:319–324.

Halliday, T. R. 1990. The evolution of courtship behavior in newts and salamanders. *Advances in the Study of Behavior* 19:137–169.

Halliday, T. R., and B. Arano. 1991. Resolving the phylogeny of European newts. *Trends in Ecology and Evolution* 6:113–121.

Hanna, G., and W. J. P. Barnes. 1991. Adhesion and detachment of the toe pads of tree frogs. *Journal of Experimental Biology* 155:103–125.

Hayes, T. B. (editor). 1997. Amphibian metamorphosis: an integrative approach. *American Zoologist* 37:121–207.

Heyer, W. R., M. A. Donnelly, R. W. McDiarmid, L.-A. C. Hayek, and M. S. Foster (editors). 1993. *Measuring and Monitoring Biological Diversity: Standard Methods for Amphibians*. Smithsonian Institution Press, Washington, DC.

Jaeger, R. G. 1981. Dear enemy recognition and the costs of aggression between salamanders. *American Naturalist* 117:962–974.

Jaeger, R. G., K. C. B. Nishikawa, and D. E. Barnard. 1983. Foraging tactics of a terrestrial salamander: costs of territorial defense. *Animal Behaviour* 31:191–198.

Jenkins, F. A., Jr., and D. M. Walsh. 1993. An early Jurassic caecilian with limbs. *Nature* 365:246–250.

Klump, G. M., and H. C. Gerhardt. 1987. Use of non-arbitrary acoustic criteria in mate choice by female gray tree frogs. *Nature* 326:286–288.

Leong, A. S.-Y., M. J. Tyler, and D. J. C. Shearman. 1986. Gastric brooding: a new form in a recently discovered Australian frog of the genus *Rheobatrachus. Australian Journal of Zoology* 34:205–209.

Lutz, G. J., and L. C. Rome. 1994. Built for jumping: the design of the frog muscular system: *Science* 263:370–372.

Magnusson, W. E., and J.-M. Hero. 1991. Predation and evolution of complex ovoposition behaviour in Amazon rainforest frogs. *Oecologia* 86:310–318.

Marsh, R. L., and T. L. Taigen. 1987. Properties enhancing aerobic capacity of calling muscles in gray tree frogs, *Hyla versicolor. American Journal of Physiology* 252:R786–R793.

Myers, C. W., J. W. Daly, and B. Malkin. 1978. A dangerously toxic new frog (*Phyllobates*) used by Embera Indians of western Colombia, with discussion of blowgun fabrication and dart poisoning. *Bulletin of the American Museum of Natural History* 161:307–366.

Myers, C. W., A. Paolillio O., and J. W. Daly. 1991. Discovery of a defensively malodorous and noctural frog in the family Dendorbatidae: phylogenetic significance of a new genus and species from the Venezuelan Andes. *American Museum Novitates Number* 3002:1–33.

O'Reilly, J. C., R. A. Nussbaum, and D. Boone. 1996. Vertebrate with protrusible eyes. *Nature* 382:33.

Pfennig, D. W. 1990a. The adaptive significance of an environmentally-cued developmental switch in an anuran tadpole. *Oecologia* 85:101–107.

Pfennig, D. W. 1990b. "Kin recognition" among spadefoot toad tadpoles: a side-effect of habitat selection? *Evolution* 44:785–798.

Phillips, K. 1994. *Tracking the Vanishing Frogs*. St. Martin's Press, New York, NY.

Pough, F. H. 1988. Mimicry of vertebrates: are the rules different? *American Naturalist* 131 (Suppl.):S67–S102.

Pough, F. H., T. L. Taigen, M. M. Stewart, and P. F. Brussard. 1983. Behavioral modification of evaporative water loss by a Puerto Rican frog. *Ecology* 64:244–252.

Pounds, J. A., and M. L. Crump. 1994. Amphibian declines and climate disturbance: the case of the golden toad and harlequin frog. *Conservation Biology* 8:72–85.

Preest, M. R. 1993. Mechanism of growth rate reduction in acid-exposed larval salamanders, *Ambystoma maculatum.* *Physiological Zoology* 66:686–707.

Roth, G., and D. B. Wake. 1985. Trends in the functional morphology and sensorimotor control of feeding behavior in salamanders: an example of the role of internal dynamics in evolution. *Acta Biotheoretica* 34:175–192.

Ryan, M. J. 1985. *The Túngara Frog: A Study in Sexual Selection and Communication.* University of Chicago Press, Chicago, IL.

Shoemaker, V. H., S. S. Hillman, S. D. Hillyard, D. C. Jackson, L. L. McClanahan, P. C. WIthers, and M. L Wygoda. 1992. Exchange of respiratory gases, ions, and water in terrestrial amphibians. Pages 81–124 in *Environmental Physiology of the Amphibia*, edited by M. E. Feder and W. W. Burggren. The University of Chicago Press, Chicago, IL.

Strauss, E. 1998. New nonopioid painkiller shows promise in animal tests. *Science* 279:32–33.

Taigen, T. L., F. H. Pough, and M. M. Stewart. 1984. Water balance of terrestrial anuran eggs (*Eleutherodactylus coquí*): importance of parental care. *Ecology* 65:248–255.

Taigen, T. L., and K. D. Wells. 1985. Energetics of vocalization by an anuran amphibian (*Hyla versicolor*). *Journal of Comparative Physiology* B155:163–170.

Tilley, S. G., B. L. Lundrigan, and L. P. Brower. 1982. Erythrism and mimicry in the salamander *Plethodon cinereus. Herpetologica* 38:409–417.

Townsend, D. S., M. M. Stewart, and F. H. Pough. 1984. Male parental care and its adaptive significance in a neotropical frog. *Animal Behaviour* 32:421–431.

Townsend, D. S., M. M. Stewart, F. H. Pough, and P. F. Brussard. 1981. Internal fertilization in an oviparous frog. *Science* 212:465–471.

Tyler, M. J. (editor). 1983. *The Gastric Brooding Frog.* Croom Helm, Beckenham, Kent, UK.

Wake, D. B., and S. B. Marks. 1993. Development and evolution of plethodontid salamanders: a review of prior studies and a prospectus for future research. *Herpetologica* 49:194–203.

Wake, M. H. 1993. Evolution of oviductal gestation in amphibians. *Journal of Experimental Zoology* 266:394–413.

Waldman, B. 1982. Sibling association among schooling toad tadpoles: field evidence and implications. *Animal Behaviour* 30:700–713.

Wells, K. D. 1980. Evidence for growth of tadpoles during parental transport in *Colostethus inguinalis. Journal of Herpetology* 14:428–430.

Wells, K. D., and T. L. Taigen. 1986. The effect of social interactions on calling energetics in the grey treefrog (*Hyla versicolor*). *Behavioral Ecology and Sociobiology* 19:9–18.

CHAPTER
12
Turtles

Turtles provide a contrast to amphibians in the relative lack of diversity in their life histories. All turtles lay eggs and none exhibits parental care of the hatchlings. Turtles show morphological specializations associated with terrestrial, freshwater, and marine habitats, and marine turtles make long-distance migrations that rival those of birds. Probably turtles and birds use many of the same navigation mechanisms to find their way. Most turtles are long-lived animals with relatively poor capacities for rapid population growth, and many, especially sea turtles and large tortoises, are endangered by human activities. Some efforts to conserve turtles have apparently been frustrated by a feature of the embryonic development of some species of turtles—the sex of an individual is determined by the temperature to which it is exposed in the nest. This experience emphasizes the critical importance of information about the basic biology of animals to successful conservation and management.

■ Everyone Recognizes a Turtle

Turtles found a successful approach to life in the Triassic and have scarcely changed since. The shell, which is the key to their success, has also limited the diversity of the group (Figure 12–1). For obvious reasons, flying or gliding turtles have never existed, and even arboreality is only slightly developed. Shell morphology reflects the ecology of turtle species: The most terrestrial forms, the tortoises of the family Testudinidae, have high domed shells and elephantlike feet (Figure 12–1a). Smaller species of tortoises may show adaptations for burrowing. The gopher tortoises of North America are an example—their fore legs are flattened into scoops and the dome of the shell is reduced. The Bolson tortoise of northern Mexico constructs burrows a meter or more deep and several meters long in the hard desert soil. These tortoises bask at the mouths of their burrows, and when a predator appears they throw themselves down the steep entrance tunnels of the burrows to escape, just as an aquatic turtle dives off a log. The pancake tortoise of Africa is a radical departure from the usual tortoise morphology (Figure 12–1b). The shell is flat and flexible because its ossification is much reduced. This turtle lives in rocky foothill regions and scrambles over the rocks with nearly as much agility as a lizard. When threatened by a predator, the pancake tortoise crawls into a rock crevice and uses its legs to wedge itself in place. The flexible shell presses against the overhanging rock and creates so much friction that it is almost impossible to pull the tortoise out.

Other terrestrial turtles have moderately domed **carapaces** (upper shells), like the box turtles of the family Emydidae (Figure 12–1c). This is one of sev-

Figure 12–1   Body forms of turtles: (a) Tortoise, *Testudo*; (b) pancake tortoise, *Malacochersus*; (c) terrestrial box turtle, *Terrapene*; (d) pond turtle, *Trachemys*; (e) soft-shelled turtle, *Aplone*; (f) mud turtle, *Kinosternon*; (g) alligator snapping turtle, *Macroclemys*; (h) African pond turtle, *Pelusios*; (i) Australian snake-necked turtle, *Chelodina*; (j) South American matamata, *Chelys*; (k) loggerhead sea turtle, *Caretta*; (l) leatherback sea turtle, *Dermochelys*.

eral kinds of turtles that have evolved flexible regions in the **plastron** (lower shell), which allow the front and rear lobes to be pulled upward to close the openings of the shell. Aquatic turtles have low carapaces that offer little resistance to movement through water. The Emydidae and Bataguridae contain a large number of pond turtles (Figure 12–1d), including the painted turtles and the red-eared turtles often seen in pet stores and anatomy and physiology laboratory courses.

The snapping turtles (family Chelydridae) and the mud and musk turtles (family Kinosternidae) prowl along the bottoms of ponds and slow rivers and are not particularly streamlined (Figure 12–1f, g). The mud turtle has a hinged plastron, but the musk and snapping turtles have very reduced plastrons. They rely on strong jaws for protection. A reduction in the size of the plastron makes these species more agile than most turtles, and musk turtles may climb several feet into trees, probably to bask. If a turtle falls on your head while you are canoeing, it is probably a musk turtle.

The soft-shelled turtles (family Trionychidae) are fast swimmers (Figure 12–1e). The ossification of the shell is greatly reduced, lightening the animal, and the feet are large with extensive webbing. Soft-shelled turtles lie in ambush partly buried in debris on the bottom of the pond. Their long necks allow them to reach considerable distances to seize the invertebrates and small fishes on which they feed.

Extant turtles can be placed in 13 families (Table 12.1). The two lineages of living turtles can be traced

through fossils to the Mesozoic (Gaffney et al. 1987, Gaffney and Kitching 1994). The **cryptodires** (*crypto* = hidden, *dire* = neck) retract the head into the shell by bending the neck in a vertical S-shape. The **pleurodires** (*pleuro* = side) retract the head by bending the neck horizontally. All the turtles discussed so far have been cryptodires, and these are the dominant group of turtles. Cryptodires are the only turtles now found in most of the Northern Hemisphere, and there are aquatic and terrestrial cryptodires in South America and terrestrial ones in Africa. Only Australia has no cryptodires. Pleu-

TABLE 12.1	Families of turtles

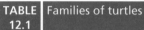

Chelydridae: Large (*Chelydra*, 50 cm) to very large (*Macroclemys*, 70 cm and 80 kg) freshwater turtles (2 species in North and Central America).

Platysternidae: A small (18 cm), agile turtle living in mountain streams (1 species from southeast China to Burma and Thailand).

Trionychidae: Small (25 cm) to very large (130 cm) freshwater turtles with flattened bodies and reduced ossification of the shell (about 25 species in North America, Africa, and Asia).

Carettochelyidae: A large (70 cm) freshwater turtle that lacks epidermal scutes on the shell and has paddlelike forelimbs (1 species in New Guinea and extreme northern Australia).

Dermatemydidae: A large (65 cm) freshwater turtle (1 species in Mexico and Central America).

Kinosternidae: Small (11 cm) to medium (40 cm) bottom-dwelling aquatic turtles (about 22 species from North American to South America).

Testudinidae: Small (10 cm) to very large (130 cm) terrestrial turtles, usually with domed shells. Many species have forelimbs specialized for digging (about 40 species, worldwide in temperate and tropical regions).

"Bataguridae": Small (12 cm) to large (75 cm) aquatic, semiaquatic, and terrestrial turtles (about 60 species, primarily Asian with 1 genus in Central America).

Emydidae: Small (12 cm) to large (60 cm) freshwater, semiaquatic, and terrestrial turtles (about 35 species mostly in North America, 1 genus in Central and South America, and 1 in Europe, Asia, and north Africa).

Cheloniidae: Large (70 cm) to very large (150 cm) sea turtles with bony shells covered with epidermal scutes and paddlelike forelimbs (7 species found worldwide in tropical and temperate oceans).

Dermochelyidae: The largest extant turtle (up to 240 cm), a marine turtle in which the shell is reduced to thousands of small bones embedded in a leathery skin (1 species, worldwide and extending north and south into cold seas).

Chelidae: Small (15 cm) to large (50 cm) aquatic turtles (about 40 species in South America, Australia, and New Guinea).

Pelomedusidae: Small (15 cm) to very large (90 cm) aquatic turtles. All extant pelomedusids inhabit freshwater, but some extinct species may have been marine (about 25 species in South America, Africa, Madagascar, and the Seychelles Islands).

The phylogenetic relationships and numbers of species are based on Pough, F. H., R. M. Andrews, J. E. Cadle, M. L. Crump, A. H. Savitzky, and K. D. Wells. 1998. *Herpetology*. Prentice Hall, Upper Saddle River, NJ. The family "Bataguridae" is probably not monophyletic.

rodires are now found only in the Southern Hemisphere, although they had worldwide distribution in the late Mesozoic and early Cenozoic. *Stupendemys*, a pleurodire from the Pliocene of Venezuela, had a carapace more than 2 meters long. All the living pleurodires are at least semiaquatic, but some fossil pleurodires had high, domed shells that suggest they may have been terrestrial. The most terrestrial of the living pleurodires are probably the African pond turtles (Figure 12–1h), which readily move overland from one pond to another.

The snake-necked pleurodiran turtles (family Chelidae) are found in South America, Australia, and New Guinea (Figure 12–1i). As their name implies, they have long, slender necks. In some species the length of the neck is considerably greater than that of the body. These forms feed on fishes that they catch with a sudden dart of the head. Other snake-necked turtles have much shorter necks. Some of these feed on mollusks and have enlarged palatal surfaces used to crush shells. The same specialization for feeding on mollusks is seen in certain cryptodiran turtles.

An unusual feeding method among turtles is found in a pleurodire, the matamata of South America (Figure 12–1j). Large matamatas reach shell lengths of 40 centimeters. They are bizarre-looking animals. The shell and head are broad and flattened, and numerous flaps of skin project from the sides of the head and the broad neck. To these are added trailing bits of adhering algae. The effect is exceedingly cryptic. It is hard to recognize a matamata as a turtle even in an aquarium, and it is practically invisible against the mud and debris of a river bottom. In addition to obscuring the shape of the turtle, the flaps of skin on the head are sensitive to minute vibrations in water caused by the passage of a fish. When it senses the presence of prey, the matamata abruptly opens its mouth and expands its throat. Water rushes in, carrying the prey with it, and the matamata closes its mouth, expels the water, and swallows the prey. The matamata lacks the horny beak that other turtles use for seizing prey or biting off pieces of plants.

Marine turtles are cryptodires. The families Cheloniidae and Dermochelyidae show more extensive specialization for aquatic life than any freshwater turtle. All have the forelimbs modified as flippers. Cheloniids retain epidermal scutes on the shell (Figure 12–1k). The largest of the sea turtles of the family Cheloniidae is the loggerhead, which once reached weights exceeding 400 kilograms. The largest marine turtle, the leatherback, reaches shell lengths of more than 2 meters and weights in excess of 600 kilograms (Figure 12–1l). The dermal ossification has been reduced to bony platelets embedded in connective tissue. This is a pelagic turtle that ranges far from land, and it has a wider geographic distribution than any other ectothermal amniote; leatherback turtles penetrate far into cool temperate seas, and have been recorded in the Atlantic from Newfoundland to Argentina and in the Pacific from Japan to Tasmania. In cold water leatherback turtles maintain body temperatures substantially above water temperature, using countercurrent heat exchangers to retain the heat released by muscular activity (Paladino et al. 1990). Leatherback turtles dive to depths of more than 1000 meters. One dive that drove the depth recorder off scale is estimated to have reached 1200 meters, which exceeds the deepest dive recorded for a sperm whale (1140 meters). Leatherback turtles feed largely on jellyfishes, whereas the smaller hawksbill sea turtles eat sponges that are defended by spicules of silica (glass) as well as a variety of chemicals (including alkaloids and terpenes) that are toxic to most vertebrates (Meylan 1988). Green turtles (*Chelonia mydas*) are the only herbivorous marine turtles.

■ Phylogenetic Relationships of Turtles

Nearly 200 of the approximately 250 species of turtles are cryptodires. Turtles show a combination of ancestral features and highly specialized characters that are not shared with any other group of vertebrates, and their phylogenetic affinities are not clearly known. The turtle lineage probably originated among the early amniotes of the Late Carboniferous. Like those animals, turtles have anapsid skulls, but the shells and postcranial skeletons of turtles are unique. Two of the groups of parareptiles that were discussed in Chapter 10, the procolophonids and the parieasaurs, have been proposed as the sister group for turtles (Reisz and Laurin 1991, Lee 1993). A radically different opinion places turtles among the diapsids (Rieppel and de Braga 1996). At the moment, the case for parieasaurs appears strongest, but a lively debate is in progress and the issue is far from resolved.

The earliest turtles are found in Late Triassic deposits in Germany, Thailand, and Argentina (Gaffney 1990, Rougier et al. 1995). These animals had nearly all the specialized characteristics of derived turtles, and shed no light on the phylogenetic affinities of the group. *Proganochelys*, from Triassic deposits in Germany, was nearly a meter long (larger than most living turtles) and had a high, arched shell. The marginal teeth had been lost and the maxilla, premaxilla, and dentary bones were probably covered with a horny beak as they are in derived turtles. The skull of *Proganochelys* retained the supratemporal and lacrimal bones and the lacrimal duct, and the palate had rows of denticles; all these structures have been lost by derived turtles. The plastron of *Proganochelys* also contained some bones that have been lost by derived turtles, and the vertebrae of the neck lack specializations that would have allowed the head to be retracted into the shell. *Palaeochersis* (Late Triassic of Argentina) and *Australochelys* (Early Jurassic of South Africa) are probably the sister group of later turtles, including Cryptodira + Pleurodira (Gaffney and Kitching 1994, Rougier et al. 1995).

Turtles with neck vertebrae specialized for retraction are not known before the Cretaceous, but differences in the skulls and shells allow the pleurodiran and cryptodiran lineages to be traced back to the Late Triassic (shells of pleurodires) and Late-Jurassic (skulls of cryptodires). The otic capsules of all turtles beyond the proganochelids are enlarged, and the jaw adductor muscles bend posteriorly over the otic capsule (Figure 12–2). The muscles pass over a pulleylike structure, the **trochlear process.** In cryptodires the trochlear process is formed by the anterior surface of the otic capsule itself, whereas in pleurodires it is formed by a lateral process of the pterygoid. Fusion of the pelvic girdle to the carapace and plastron distinguishes pleurodires from cryptodires, which have a suture attaching the shell to the girdle. The beginnings of these changes are seen in *Australochelys*.

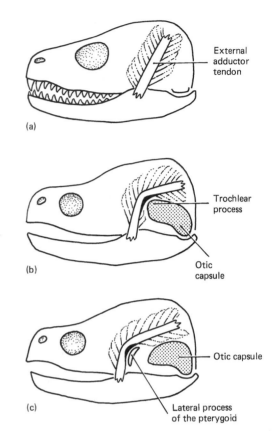

Figure 12–2   Position of the external adductor tendon. (a) In the ancestral (parareptilian) condition; (b) in cryptodiran turtles; and (c) in pleurodiran turtles. (From E. S. Gaffney, 1975, *Bulletin of the American Museum of Natural History* 15:387–436.)

propriately, because they are so specialized). In fact, much of the morphology and physiology of turtles is derived rather than ancestral, and turtles are ecologically quite different from the other ectothermal amniotes, the crocodilians (which are archosaurs) and the lepidosaurs (tuatara, lizards, snakes, and amphisbaenians).

■ Turtle Structure and Functions

Turtles are among the most bizarre vertebrates. Covered in bone, with the limbs inside the ribs, and with horny beaks instead of teeth—if turtles had become extinct at the end of the Mesozoic they would rival dinosaurs in their novelty. However, because they survived they are regarded as commonplace, and are used in comparative anatomy courses to represent ectothermal amniotes (inap-

Shell and Skeleton

The shell is the most distinctive feature of a turtle (Figure 12–3). The carapace is composed of dermal bone that typically grows from 59 separate centers of ossification. Eight plates along the dorsal midline form the neural series and are fused to the neural arches of the vertebrae. Lateral to the neural bones are eight paired costal bones, which are fused to the broadened ribs. The ribs of turtles are unique

Figure 12–3 Shell and vertebral column of a turtle: (a) Epidermal scutes of the carapace (left) and plastron (right); (b) dermal bones of the carapace (left) and plastron (right); (c) vertebral column of a turtle, seen from the inside of the carapace. Note that anteriorly the ribs articulate with two vertebral centra. (From R. Zangerl, 1969, in *Biology of the Reptilia*, volume 1, edited by C. Gans, A. d'A. Bellairs, and T. S. Parsons, Academic, London, UK.)

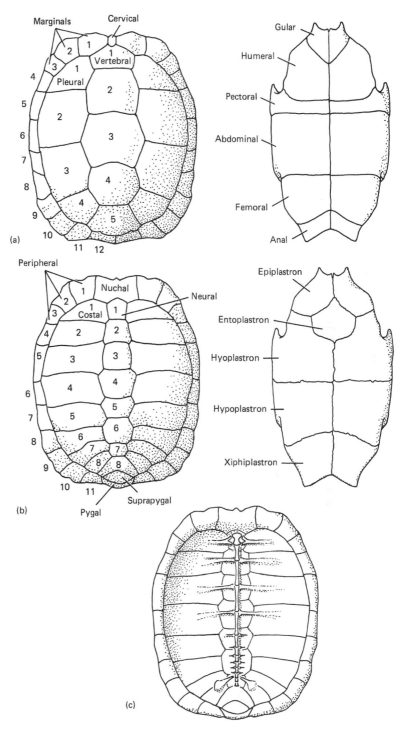

among tetrapods in being external to the girdles. Eleven pairs of peripheral bones, plus two unpaired bones in the dorsal midline, form the margin of the carapace. The plastron is formed largely from dermal ossifications, but the entoplastron is derived from the interclavicle, and the paired epiplastra anterior to it are derived from the clavicles. Processes from the hypoplastron fuse with the first and fifth pleurals, forming a rigid connection between the plastron and carapace.

The bones of the carapace are covered by horny scutes of epidermal origin that do not coincide in number or position with the underlying bones. The carapace has a row of five central scutes, bordered on each side by four lateral scutes. Eleven marginal scutes on each side turn under the edge of the carapace. The plastron is covered by a series of six paired scutes.

Flexible areas, called hinges, are present in the shells of many turtles. The most familiar examples are the North American and Asian box turtles (*Terrapene* and *Cuora*) in which a hinge between the hyoplastral and hypoplastral bones allows the anterior and posterior lobes of the plastron to be raised to close off the front and rear openings of the shell. Mud turtles (*Kinosternon*) have two hinges in the plastron; the anterior hinge runs between the epiplastra and the entoplastron (which is triangular in kinosternid turtles rather than diamond shaped), and the posterior hinge is between the hypoplastron and xiphiplastron. In the pleurodiran turtle *Pelusios* a hinge runs between the mesoplastron and the hypoplastron. Some species of tortoises have plastral hinges; in *Testudo* the hinge lies between the hyoplastron and xiphiplastra as it does in *Kinosternon*, but in another genus of tortoise, *Pyxis*, the hinge is anterior and involves a break across the entoplastron. The African forest tortoises (*Kinixys*) have a hinge on the posterior part of the carapace. The margins of the epidermal shields and the dermal bones of the carapace are aligned, and the hinge runs between the second and third pleural bones and the fourth and fifth costals. The presence of hinges is sexually dimorphic in some species of tortoises. The erratic phylogenetic occurrence of kinetic shells and differences among related species indicate that shell kinesis has evolved many times in turtles.

Asymmetry of the paired epidermal scutes is quite common among turtles, and modifications of the bony structure of the shell are seen in some families. Soft-shelled turtles lack peripheral ossifications and epidermal scutes. The distal ends of the broadened ribs are embedded in flexible connective tissue, and the carapace and plastron are covered with skin. The New Guinea river turtle (*Carretochelys*) is also covered by skin instead of scutes, but in this species the peripheral bones are present and the edge of the shell is stiff. The leatherback sea turtle (*Dermochelys*) has a carapace formed of cartilage with thousands of small polygonal bones embedded in it, and the plastral bones are reduced to a thin rim around the edge of the plastron. The neural and pleural ossifications of the pancake tortoise (*Mala-*

cochersus) are greatly reduced, but the epidermal plates are well developed.

Extant turtles have only 18 presacral vertebrae, 10 in the trunk and 8 in the neck. The centra of the trunk vertebrae are elongated and lie beneath the dermal bones in the dorsal midline of the shell. The centra are constricted in their centers and fused to each other. The neural arches in the anterior two-thirds of the trunk lie between the centra as a result of anterior displacement, and the spinal nerves exit near the middle of the preceding centrum. The ribs are also shifted anteriorly; they articulate with the anterior part of the neurocentral boundary, and in the anterior part of the trunk, where the shift is most pronounced, the ribs extend onto the preceding vertebra.

Cryptodires have two sacral vertebrae (the 19th and 20th vertebrae) with broadened ribs that meet the ilia of the pelvis. Pleurodires have the pelvic girdle firmly fused to the dermal carapace by the ilia dorsally and by the pubic and ischial bones ventrally, and the sacral region of the vertebral column is less distinct. The ribs on the 17th, 18th, 19th, and sometimes the 20th vertebrae are fused to the centra and end on the ilia or the ilium–carapacial junction.

The cervical vertebrae of cryptodires have articulations that permit the S-shaped bend used to retract the head into the shell. Specialized condyles (ginglymes) permit vertical rotation. This type of rotation, ginglymoidy, is peculiar to cryptodires, but the anatomical details vary within the group. In most families the hinge is formed by two successive ginglymoidal joints between the 6th and 7th and the 7th and 8th cervical vertebrae. The lateral bending of the necks of pleurodiran turtles is accomplished by ball-and-socket or cylindrical joints between adjacent cervical vertebrae.

The Heart

The circulatory systems of tetrapods can be viewed as consisting of two circuits: The systemic circuit carries oxygenated blood from the heart to the head, trunk, and appendages, whereas the pulmonary circuit carries deoxygenated blood from the heart to the lungs. The blood pressure in the systemic circuit is higher than the pressure in the pulmonary circuit, and the two circuits operate in series. That is, blood flows from the heart through the lungs, back to the heart, and then to the body. The morphology of the hearts of birds and mammals makes this sequential flow obligatory, but the hearts of turtles, squamates, and amphibians have the ability to shift blood between the pulmonary and systemic circuits.

This flexibility in the route of blood flow can be accomplished because the ventricular chambers in the hearts of turtles and squamates are in anatomical continuity instead of being divided by a septum like the ventricles of birds and mammals. The pattern of blood flow can best be explained by considering the morphology of the heart and how intracardiac pressure changes during a heartbeat. Figure 12–4 shows a schematic view of the heart of a turtle. The left and right atria are completely separate, and three subcompartments can be distinguished in the ventricle. A muscular ridge in the core of the heart divides the ventricle into two spaces, the **cavum pulmonale** and the **cavum venosum**. The muscular ridge is not fused to the wall of the ventricle, and thus the cavum pulmonale and the cavum venosum are only partly separated. A third subcompartment of the ventricle, the **cavum arteriosum**, is located dorsal to the cavum pulmonale and cavum venosum. The cavum arteriosum communicates with the cavum venosum through an intraventricular canal. The pulmonary artery opens from the cavum pulmonale, and the left and right aortic arches open from the cavum venosum.

The right atrium receives deoxygenated blood from the body via the sinus venosus and empties into the cavum venosum, and the left atrium receives oxygenated blood from the lungs and empties into the cavum arteriosum. The atria are separated from the ventricle by flaplike atrioventricular valves that open as the atria contract, and then close as the ventricle contracts, preventing blood from being forced back into the atria. The anatomical arrangement of the connections between the atria, their valves, and the three subcompartments of the ventricle are crucial, because it is those connections that allow pressure differentials to direct the flow of blood and to prevent mixing of oxygenated and deoxygenated blood.

When the atria contract the atrioventricular valves open, allowing blood to flow into the ventricle. Blood from the right atrium flows into the cavum venosum, and blood from the left atrium flows into the cavum arteriosum. At this stage in the heartbeat the large median flaps of the valve between the right atrium and the cavum venosum are pressed against the opening of the intraventric-

ular canal, sealing it off from the cavum venosum. As a result, the oxygenated blood from the left atrium is confined to the cavum arteriosum. Deoxygenated blood from the right atrium fills the cavum venosum and then continues over the muscular ridge into the cavum pulmonale.

When the ventricle contracts, blood pressure inside the heart increases. Ejection of blood from the heart into the pulmonary circuit precedes flow into the systemic circuit because resistance is lower in the pulmonary circuit. As deoxygenated blood flows out of the cavum pulmonale into the pulmonary artery, the displacement of blood from the cavum venosum across the muscular ridge into the cavum pulmonale continues. As the ventricle shortens during contraction, the muscular ridge comes into contact with the wall of the ventricle and closes off the passage for blood between the cavum venosum and cavum pulmonale.

Simultaneously, blood pressure inside the heart increases, and the flaps of the right atrioventricular valve are forced into the closed position, preventing back flow of blood from the cavum venosum into the atrium. When the valve closes, it no longer blocks the intraventricular canal. Oxygenated blood from the cavum pulmonale can now flow through the intraventricular canal and into the cavum venosum. At this stage in the heartbeat, the wall of the ventricle is pressed firmly against the muscular ridge, separating the oxygenated blood in the cavum venosum from the deoxygenated blood in the cavum pulmonale.

As pressure in the ventricle continues to rise, oxygenated blood in the cavum venosum is ejected into the aortic arches. This system effectively prevents mixing of oxygenated and deoxygenated blood in the heart, despite the absence of a permanent morphological separation of the two circuits.

Respiration

Primitive amniotes probably used movements of the rib cage to draw air into the lungs and to force it out, and lizards still employ that mechanism. The fusion of the ribs of turtles with their rigid shells makes that method of breathing impossible. Only the openings at the anterior and posterior ends of the shell contain flexible tissues. The lungs of a turtle, which are large, are attached to the carapace dorsally and laterally. Ventrally, the lungs are attached to a sheet of nonmuscular connective tissue that is itself attached to the viscera (Figure 12–5). The

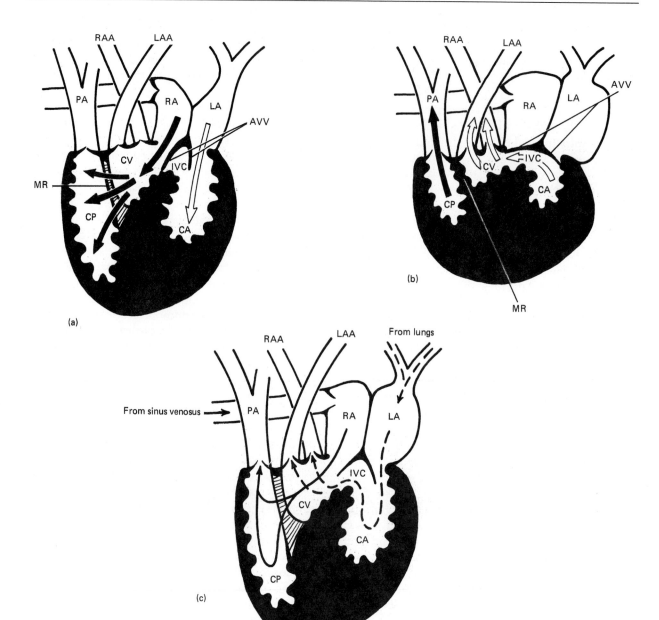

Figure 12–4   Blood flow in the heart of a turtle. (a) As the atria contract oxygenated blood (open arrows) from the left atrium (LA) enters the cavum arteriosum (CA) while deoxygenated blood (dark arrows) from the right atrium (RA) first enters the cavum venosum (CV) and then crosses the muscular ridge (MR) and enters the cavum pulmonale (CP). The atrioventricular valve (AVV) blocks the intraventricular canal (IVC) and prevents mixing of oxygenated and deoxygenated blood. (b) As the ventricle contracts the deoxygenated blood in the cavum pulmonale is expelled through the pulmonary arteries; the AVV closes, no longer obstructing the ICV; and the oxygenated blood in the cavum arteriosum is forced into the cavum venosum and expelled through the aortic arches. The adpression of the wall of the ventricle to the muscular ridge prevents mixing of deoxygenated and oxygenated blood. (c) Summary of the pattern of blood flow through the heart of a turtle. (Modified from N. Heisler et al., 1983, *Journal of Experimental Biology* 105:15–32.)

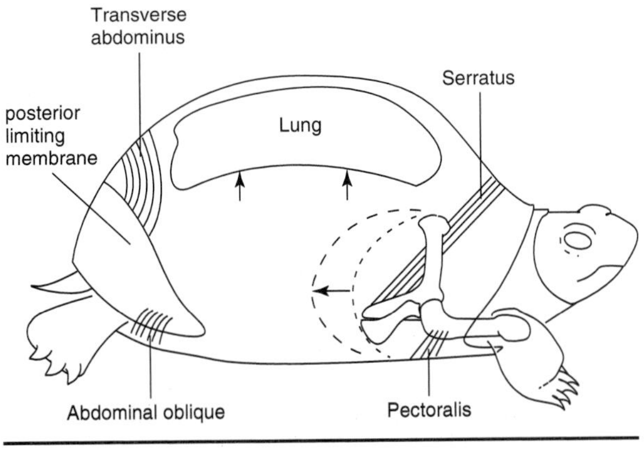

Figure 12–5 Schematic view of the lungs and respiratory movements of a tortoise. (Modified from C. Gans and G. M. Hughes, 1967, *Journal of Experimental Biology* 47:1–20.)

weight of the viscera keeps this diaphragmatic sheet stretched downward.

Turtles produce changes in pressure in the lungs by contraction of muscles that force the viscera upward, compressing the lungs and expelling air, followed by contraction of other muscles that increase the volume of the visceral cavity, allowing the viscera to settle downward. Because the viscera are attached to the diaphragmatic sheet, which in turn is attached to the lungs, the downward movement of the viscera expands the lungs, drawing in air. In tortoises both inhalation and exhalation require muscular activity. The viscera are forced upward against the lungs by the contraction of the transverse abdominus muscle posteriorly and the pectoralis muscle anteriorly. The transverse abdominus inserts on the cup-shaped connective tissue, the posterior limiting membrane, that closes off the posterior opening of the visceral cavity. Contraction of the transverse abdominus flattens the cup inward, thereby reducing the volume of the visceral cavity. The pectoralis draws the shoulder girdle back into the shell, further reducing the volume of the visceral cavity.

The inspiratory muscles are the abdominal oblique, which originates near the posterior margin of the plastron and inserts on the external side of the posterior limiting membrane, and the serratus, which originates near the anterior edge of the carapace and inserts on the pectoral girdle. Contraction of the abdominal oblique pulls the posterior limiting membrane outward, and contraction of the serratus rotates the pectoral girdle outward. Both of these movements increase the volume of the visceral cav-

ity, allowing the viscera to settle back downward and causing the lungs to expand. The in-and-out movements of the forelimbs and the soft tissue at the rear of the shell during breathing are conspicuous.

The basic problems of respiring within a rigid shell are the same for most turtles, but the mechanisms show some variation. For example, aquatic turtles can use the hydrostatic pressure of water to help move air in and out of the lungs. In addition, many aquatic turtles are able to absorb oxygen and release carbon dioxide to the water. The pharynx and cloaca appear to be the major sites of aquatic gas exchange. In 1860, in *Contributions to the Natural History of the U. S. A.*, Louis Agassiz pointed out that the pharynx of soft-shelled turtles contains fringe-like processes and suggested that these structures are used for underwater respiration. Subsequent study has shown that when soft-shelled turtles are confined under water they use movements of the hyoid apparatus to draw water in and out of the pharynx, and that pharyngeal respiration accounts for most of the oxygen absorbed from the water. The Australian turtle *Rheodytes leukops* uses cloacal respiration. Its cloacal orifice is as much as 30 millimeters in diameter, and the turtle holds it open. Large bursae (sacks) open from the wall of the cloaca, and the bursae have a well-vascularized lining with numerous projections (villi). The turtle pumps water in and out of the bursae at rates of 15 to 60 times per minute. Captive turtles rarely surface to breathe, and experiments have shown that the rate of oxygen uptake through the cloacal bursae is very high.

Patterns of Circulation and Respiration

The morphological complexity of the hearts of turtles and of squamates allows them to adjust blood flow through the pulmonary and systemic circuits to meet short-term changes in respiratory requirements. The key to these adjustments is changing pressures in the systemic and pulmonary circuits.

Recall that in the turtle heart deoxygenated blood from the right atrium normally flows from the cavum venosum across the muscular ridge and into the cavum pulmonale. The blood pressure inside the heart increases as the ventricle contracts, and blood is first ejected into the pulmonary artery because the resistance to flow in the pulmonary circuit is normally less than the resistance in the systemic circuit. However, the resistance to blood flow in the pulmonary circuit can be increased by muscles that narrow the diameter of blood vessels.

When this happens, the delicate balance of pressure in the heart that maintained the separation of oxygenated and deoxygenated blood is changed. When the resistance of the pulmonary circuit is essentially the same as that of the systemic circuit, blood flows out of the cavum pulmonale and cavum venosum at the same time and some deoxygenated blood bypasses the lungs and flows into the systemic circuit (Figure 12–6). This process is called a **right-to-left intracardiac shunt**. "Right-to-left" refers to the shift of deoxygenated blood from the pulmonary into the systemic circuit, and intracardiac means that it occurs in the heart rather than by flow between the major blood vessels. (Left-to-right shunts also occur, and may be important in supplying oxygen to the heart muscle [Farmer 1997]—see Chapter 3. More information can be found in Hicks et al. [1996].)

Why would it be useful to divert deoxygenated blood from the lungs into the systemic circulation?

The ability to make this shunt is not unique to turtles—it occurs also among squamate reptiles and in crocodilians. The heart morphology of squamates is very like that of turtles and the same mechanism of changing pressures in the pulmonary and systemic circuits is used to achieve an intracardiac shunt. Crocodilians have hearts in which the ventricle is permanently divided into right and left halves by a septum, and they employ a different mechanism to achieve a right-to-left shunt (Chapter 13).

The widespread occurrence of blood shunts among amniotic ectotherms suggests that the ability has important consequences for the animals, and one of these has already been discussed in Chapter 4: Lizards and crocodilians use a right-to-left shunt of blood for thermoregulation. By increasing systemic blood flow as they are warming, they increase the transport of heat from the limbs and body surface into the core of the body, thereby warming more rapidly.

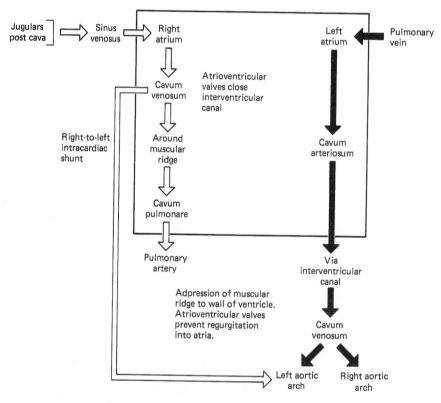

Figure 12–6   Diagram of the right-to-left shunt of blood in the heart of a turtle. Light arrows show deoxygenated blood and dark arrows show oxygenated blood. The box encloses the cycle of events during normal blood flow. (Compare with Figure 12–4.) When resistance in the pulmonary circuit increases, some deoxygenated blood from the cavum venosum flows into the left aortic arch instead of into the pulmonary arteries. (Modified from M. S. Gordon et al., 1982, *Animal Physiology: Principles and Adaptations*, 4th edition, Macmillan, New York, NY.)

The most general function for blood shunts may lie in the ability they provide to match patterns of lung ventilation and pulmonary gas flow (Wang et al. 1997). Squamates, crocodilians, and turtles normally breathe intermittently, and periods of lung ventilation alternate with periods of **apnea** (no breathing). A mathematical model indicates that a combination of right-to-left and left-to-right shunts could stabilize oxygen concentration in blood during alternating periods of apnea and breathing.

A third function of intracardiac shunts may be to reduce blood flow to the lungs during breath-holding to permit more effective use of the oxygen stored in the lungs. Diving is one situation in which reptiles hold their breath. Many reptiles are excellent divers, and even terrestrial and arboreal forms such as green iguanas may dive into water to escape predators, but that is not the only situation in which defensive behaviors interfere with breathing. Turtles are particularly prone to periods of breath-holding because their method of lung ventilation means they cannot breathe when they withdraw their heads and legs into their shells. A lizard such as a chuckwalla that inflates its lungs to wedge itself into a rock crevice cannot breathe, and right-to-left shunts probably occur during all these defensive behaviors.

Temperature Regulation by Turtles

Turtles are ectotherms, and like lizards and crocodilians, they can achieve a considerable degree of stability in body temperature by regulating their exchange of heat energy with the environment. Turtles basking on a log in a pond are a familiar sight in many parts of the world, and this basking probably has primarily a thermoregulatory function. The body temperatures of basking pond turtles are higher than water and air temperatures, and these higher temperatures may speed digestion, growth, and production of eggs. In addition, aerial basking may help aquatic turtles to rid themselves of algae and leeches. A few turtles are quite arboreal; these turtles have small plastrons that provide considerable freedom of movement for the limbs. The big-headed turtle (*Platysternon megacephalum*), a chelydrid from southeast Asia, lives in fast-flowing streams at high altitudes and is said to climb on rocks and trees to bask. In North America musk turtles (*Sternotherus*) bask on overhanging branches and drop into the water when they are disturbed.

Terrestrial turtles can thermoregulate by moving between sun and shade. Small tortoises warm and cool quite rapidly, and they appear to behave very much like other small ectotherms in selecting suitable microclimates for thermoregulation. Familiarity with a home range may facilitate this type of thermoregulation. A study conducted in Italy compared the thermoregulation of resident Hermann's tortoises (animals living in their own home ranges) with individuals that were brought to the study site and tested before they had learned their way around (Chelazzi and Calzolai 1986). The resident tortoises warmed faster and maintained more stable shell temperatures than did the strangers.

The large body size of many tortoises provides a considerable thermal inertia, and large species like the Galápagos and Aldabra tortoises heat and cool slowly. The giant tortoises of Aldabra Atoll (*Geochelone gigantea*) allow their body temperatures to rise to 32 to 33°C on sunny days and they cool to 28 to 30°C overnight. Aldabra tortoises weigh 60 kilograms or more, and even for these large animals, overheating can be a problem. The difficulty is particularly acute for some tortoises on Grande Terre (Swingland and Frazier 1979, Swingland and Lessells 1979). During the rainy season each year a portion of this population moves from the center of the island to the coast. The migrant turtles gain access to a seasonal flush of plant growth on the coast, and migrant females are able to lay more eggs than females that remain inland. However, shade is limited on the coast and the rainy season is the hottest time of the year. Tortoises must restrict their activity to the vicinity of patches of shade, which may be no more than a single tree in the midst of a grassy plain. During the morning tortoises forage on the plain, but as their temperatures rise they move back to the shade of the tree. Competition for shade appears to result in death from overheating of smaller tortoises, especially females.

Marine turtles are large enough to achieve a considerable degree of endothermy (Spotila and Standora 1985). A body temperature of 37°C was recorded by telemetry from a green turtle swimming in water that was 29°C. The leatherback turtle is the largest living turtle; adults may weigh more than 600 kilograms. It ranges far from warm equatorial regions, and in the summer can be found off the coasts of New England and Nova Scotia in water as cool as 8 to 15°C. Body temperatures of these turtles appear to be 18°C or more above water temperatures, and a countercurrent arrangement of blood vessels in the flippers may contribute to retaining heat produced by muscular activity.

■ Ecology and Behavior of Turtles

Turtles are long-lived animals. Even small species like the painted turtle (*Chrysemys picta*) do not mature until they are 7 or 8 years old, and they may live to be 14 or older. Larger species of turtles live longer. Estimates of centuries for the life spans of tortoises are exaggerated, but large tortoises and sea turtles may live as long as humans, and even box turtles may live over 50 years. These longevities make the life histories of turtles hard to study. Furthermore, a long lifetime is usually associated with a low replacement rate of individuals in the population, and species with those characteristics are at risk of extinction when hunting or habitat destruction reduces their numbers (Gibbons 1990). Conservation efforts for sea turtles and tortoises are especially important areas of concern.

Social Behavior and Courtship

Tactile, visual, and olfactory signals are employed by turtles during social interactions. Many pond turtles have distinctive stripes of color on their heads, necks, and on their forelimbs, hindlimbs, and tail. These patterns are used by herpetologists to distinguish the species, and they may be species-isolating mechanisms for the turtles as well. During the mating season male pond turtles swim in pursuit of other turtles, and the color and pattern on the posterior limbs may enable males to identify females of their own species. At a later stage of courtship, when the male turtle swims backward in front of the female and vibrates his claws against the sides of her head, both sexes can see the patterns on their partner's head, neck, and forelimbs (Figure 12–7).

Among terrestrial turtles, the behavior of tortoises is best known. Many tortoises vocalize during courtship; the sounds they produce have been described as grunts, moans, and bellows. The frequencies of the calls that have been measured range from 500 to 2500 hertz. Some tortoises have glands that become enlarged during the breeding season and appear to produce pheromones. The secretion of the subdentary gland found on the underside of the jaw of tortoises in the North American genus *Gopherus* appears to identify both the species and the sex of an individual. During courtship, males

and females of the Florida gopher tortoise rub their subdentary gland across one or both forelimbs, and then extend the limbs toward the other individual, which may sniff at them. Males also sniff the cloacal region of other tortoises, and male tortoises of some species trail females for days during the breeding season. Fecal pellets may be territorial markers; fresh fecal pellets from a dominant male tortoise have been reported to cause dispersal of conspecifics.

Tactile signals used by tortoises include biting, ramming, and hooking. These behaviors are used primarily by males, and they are employed against other males and also against females. Bites are usually directed at the head or limbs, whereas ramming and hooking are directed against the shell. The epiplastral region is used for ramming, and in some species the epiplastral bones of males are elongated and project forward beneath the neck. A tortoise about to ram another individual raises itself on its legs, rocks backward, and then plunges forward, hitting the shell of the other individual with a thump that can be heard from a distance of 100 meters in large species. During hooking the epiplastral projections are placed under the shell of an adversary, and the aggressor lifts the front end of its shell and walks forward. The combination of lifting and pushing hustles the adversary along and may even overturn it.

Movements of the head appear to act as social signals for tortoises, and elevating the head is a signal of dominance in some species. Herds of tortoises have social hierarchies that are determined largely by aggressive encounters. Ramming, biting, and hooking are employed in these encounters, and the larger individual is usually the winner, although experience may play some role. These social hierarchies are expressed in the priority of different individuals in access to food or forage areas, mates, and resting sites. Dominance relationships also appear to be involved in determining the sequence in which individual tortoises move from one place to another. The social structure of a herd of tortoises can be a nuisance for zookeepers trying to move the animals from an outdoor pen into an enclosure for the night, because the tortoises resist moving out of their proper rank sequence.

Nesting Behavior

All turtles are oviparous. Female turtles use their hindlimbs to excavate a nest in sand or soil, and

(a)

(b)

Figure 12–7   Social behavior of turtles. (a) Male painted turtle (*Chrysemys picta*) courting a female by vibrating the elongated claws of his forefeet against the sides of her head. (b) The head-raising dominance posture of a Galápagos tortoise, *Geochelone*. (This behavior can sometimes be elicited by crouching in front of a male tortoise and raising your arm.) (*Source:* [a] modified from J. A. Oliver, 1955, *The Natural History of North American Amphibians and Reptiles*, Van Nostrand, Princeton, NJ; [b] modified from S. F. Schafer and C. O. Krekorian, 1983, *Herpetologica* 39:448–456.)

deposit a clutch that ranges from 4 or 5 eggs for small species to more than 100 eggs for the largest sea turtles. Turtles in the families Cheloniidae, Dermochelyidae, and Chelydridae lay eggs with soft, flexible shells, as do most species in the families Bataguridae, Emydidae, and Pelomedusidae. The eggs of turtles in the families Carettochelyidae, Chelidae, Kinosternidae, Testudinidae, and Trionychidae have rigid shells. Embryonic development typically requires 40 to 60 days, and in general softshelled eggs develop more rapidly than hardshelled eggs.

Environmental Effects on Egg Development   Temperature, wetness, and the concentrations of oxygen and carbon dioxide can have profound effects on the embryonic development of turtles (Packard and Packard 1988). The temperature of a nest affects the rate of embryonic development, and excessively high or low temperatures can be lethal. The discovery that the sex of some reptiles is determined by the temperature they experienced during embryonic development has important implications for understanding patterns of life history and for conservation of these species. Temperature-dependent sex determination is widespread among turtles, apparently universal among crocodilians, and is known for tuatara and a few species of lizards. The effect of temperature on sex determination is correlated with sexual size dimorphism of adults—high incubation temperatures produce the larger sex, which is usually females for turtles (Ewert and Nelson 1991). The switch from one sex to the other occurs within a span of 3 or 4°C (Figure 12–8). Male

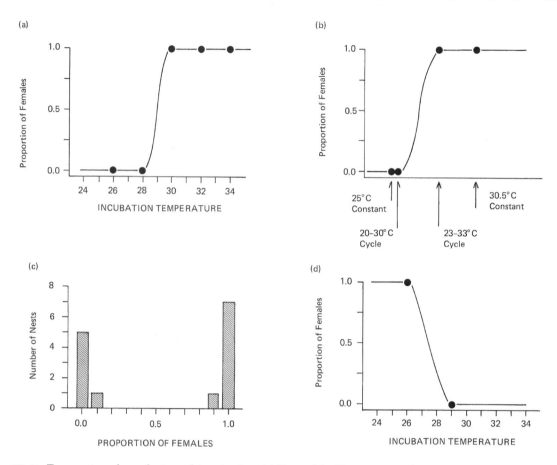

Figure 12–8 Temperature-dependent sex determination. (a) Eggs of the European pond turtle *Emys orbicularis* hatch into males when they are incubated at 26 or 28°C and into females at 30°C or above. (b) The North American map turtle *Graptemys ouachitensis* shows the same pattern. A temperature that cycles between 20 and 30°C produces males, whereas a temperature cycle of 23 to 33°C produces females. (c) Natural nests of map turtles produce predominantly males or females, depending on the nest temperature. (d) Eggs of the lizard *Agama agama* also show temperature-dependent sex determination, but the male- and female-determining temperatures are the opposite of those in turtles—for the lizard low temperatures produce females and high temperatures produce males. (Source: [a] and [d] modified from J. J. Bull, 1980, *Quarterly Review of Biology* 55:13–21; [b] and [c] modified from J. J. Bull and R. C. Vogt, 1979, *Science* 206:1186–1188.)

crocodilians, tuatara, and lizards are usually larger than females, and in these groups high temperatures during embryonic development produce males. Temperatures of natural nests are not completely stable, of course. There is some daily temperature variation superimposed on a seasonal cycle of changing environmental temperatures. The middle third of embryonic development is the critical period for sex determination; the sex of the embryos depends on the temperatures they experience during those few weeks. When eggs are exposed to a daily temperature cycle, the high point of the cycle is most critical for sex determination.

As a consequence of the narrowness of the thermal windows that are involved in sex determination and the variation that exists in environmental temperatures, both sexes are produced under field conditions, but not necessarily in the same nests. A nest site may be cooler in late summer when it is shaded by vegetation than it was early in the spring when it was exposed to the sun. Thus, eggs laid early in the season would produce females, whereas eggs deposited in the same place later in the year would produce males. Temperature can also differ between the top and the bottom of a nest. For example, temperatures averaged from 33 to 35°C in the top center of dry nests of American alligators in marshes, and males hatched from eggs in this area. At the bottom and sides of the same nests, average temperatures were from 30 to 32°C and eggs from those regions hatched into females.

Temperature-dependent sex determination has important implications for efforts to conserve endangered species. Nests of the American alligator in marshes are cooler than those built on levees; females hatch from marsh nests and males from nests built on levees. The sex ratio of hatchlings from 8000 eggs collected from natural nests was five males to one female, reflecting the relative abundance of levee and marsh nests. It is not clear whether this large imbalance of the sexes represents a normal condition for alligators, or if it reflects a recent change in the availability of nest sites as a result of construction of levees.

Some conservation efforts have been confounded by temperature-dependent sex determination in sea turtles. A number of programs have depended on collecting eggs from natural nests and incubating them under controlled conditions. Unfortunately, these unnaturally uniform conditions of incubation can result in producing hatchlings of only one sex (Mrosovsky and Yntema 1981).

The amount of moisture in the soil surrounding a turtle nest is another important variable during embryonic development of the eggs. The wetness of a nest interacts with temperature in sex determination and also influences the rate of embryonic development and the size and vigor of the hatchlings that are produced (Miller et al. 1987). Dry substrates induced the development of some female painted turtles at low temperatures (26.5 and 27.0°C) that would normally have produced only males. The wetness of the substrate did not affect the sex of turtles from eggs incubated at 30.5 and 32°C: All the hatchlings from these eggs were females, as would be expected on the basis of temperature-dependent sex determination alone.

Wet incubation conditions produce larger hatchlings than do dry conditions, apparently because water is needed for metabolism of the yolk. When water is limited, turtles hatch early and at smaller body sizes, and their guts contain a quantity of yolk that was not used during embryonic develop-ment. Hatchlings from nests under wetter conditions are larger and contain less unmetabolized yolk. The large hatchlings that emerge from moist nests are able to run and swim faster than hatchlings from drier nests, and as a result they may be more successful at escaping from predators and at catching food.

Hatching and the Behavior of Baby Turtles

Turtles are self-sufficient at hatching, but in some instances interactions among the young may be essential to allow them to escape the nest. Sea turtle nests are quite deep; the eggs may be buried 50 centimeters beneath the sand, and the hatchling turtles must struggle upward through the sand to the surface. After several weeks of incubation the eggs all hatch within a period of a few hours, and a hundred or so baby turtles find themselves in a small chamber at the bottom of the nest hole. Spontaneous activity by a few individuals sets the whole group into motion, crawling over and under one another. The turtles at the top of the pile loosen sand from the roof of the chamber as they scramble about, and the sand filters down through the mass of baby turtles to the bottom of the chamber.

Periods of a few minutes of frantic activity are interspersed by periods of rest, possibly because the turtles' exertions reduce the concentration of oxygen in the nest and they must wait for more oxygen to diffuse into the nest from the surrounding sand. Gradually, the entire group of turtles moves upward through the sand as a unit until it reaches the surface. As the baby turtles approach the surface, high sand temperatures probably inhibit further activity, and they wait a few centimeters below the surface until night when a decline in temperature triggers emergence. All the babies emerge from a nest in a very brief period, and all the babies in different nests that are ready to emerge on a given night leave their nests at almost the same time, probably because their behavior is cued by temperature. The result is the sudden appearance of hundreds or even thousands of baby turtles on the beach, each one crawling toward the ocean as fast as it can.

Simultaneous emergence is an important feature of the reproduction of sea turtles, because the babies suffer severe mortality crossing the few meters of beach and surf. Terrestrial predators—crabs, foxes, raccoons, and other predators—gather at the turtles' breeding beaches at hatching time and await their appearance. Some of the predators come from distant places to prey on the baby turtles. In the surf, sharks and bony fishes patrol the beach. Few, if any, baby turtles would get past that gauntlet if it were not for the simultaneous emergence that brings all the babies out at once and temporarily swamps the predators.

Turtles exhibit no parental care, and the long period of embryonic development renders their nests vulnerable to predators. Females of many species of turtles scrape the ground in a wide area around the nest when they have finished burying their eggs. This behavior may make it harder for predators to identify the exact location of the nest. Major breeding sites of sea turtles are often on islands that lack mammalian predators that could excavate the nests. Another important feature of a nesting beach is provision of suitable conditions for the hatchling turtles. Newly hatched sea turtles are small animals; they weigh 25 to 50 grams, which is less than 0.05 percent of the body mass of an adult sea turtle. The enormous disparity in body size of hatchling and adult turtles is probably accompanied by equally great differences in their ecological requirements and their swimming abilities. Many of the major sea turtle nesting areas are upstream from the feeding grounds, and that location may allow currents to carry the baby turtles from the breeding beaches to the feeding grounds.

We know even less about the biology of baby sea turtles than we do about the adults. Where the turtles go in the period following hatching has been a long-standing puzzle in the life cycle of sea turtles (Carr 1987). For example, green turtles hatch in the late summer at Tortuguero. The turtles disappear from sight as soon as they are at sea, and they are not seen again until they weigh 4 or 5 kilograms. Apparently, they spend the intervening period floating in ocean currents. Material drifting on the surface of the sea accumulates in areas where currents converge, forming drift lines of flotsam that include sargassum (a brown algae) and the vertebrate and invertebrate fauna associated with it. These drift lines are probably important resources for juvenile sea turtles.

Navigation and Migration

Pond turtles and terrestrial turtles usually lay their eggs in nests that they construct within their home ranges. The mechanisms of orientation that they use to find nesting areas are probably the same ones they use to find their way among foraging and resting areas. Familiarity with local landmarks is an effective method of navigation for these turtles, and they may also use the sun for orientation. Sea turtles have a more difficult time, partly because the open ocean lacks conspicuous landmarks, and also because feeding and nesting areas are often separated by hundreds or thousands of kilometers. Most sea turtles are carnivorous. The leatherback turtle feeds on jellyfishes, ridley and loggerhead turtles eat crabs and other benthic invertebrates, and the hawksbill turtle uses its beak to scrape encrusting organisms (sponges, tunicates, bryozoans, mollusks, and algae) from reefs. Juvenile green turtles are carnivorous, but the adults feed on vegetation, particularly turtle grass (*Thalassia testudinium*), which grows in shallow water on protected shorelines in the tropics. The areas that provide food for sea turtles often lack the characteristics needed for successful nesting, and many sea turtles move long distances between their feeding grounds and their breeding areas.

The ability of sea turtles to navigate over thousands of kilometers of ocean and find their way to nesting beaches that may be no more than tiny coves on a small island is astonishing. The migrations of sea turtles, especially the green turtle, have been studied for decades. Turtles captured at breeding sites in the Caribbean and Atlantic Oceans have been individually marked with metal tags since 1956, and tag returns from turtle catchers and fishing boats have allowed the major patterns of movements of the populations to be established (Figure 12–9). Similar studies by investigators in other parts of the world are beginning to shed light on movements of other species of turtles.

Four major nesting sites of green turtles have been identified in the Caribbean and South Atlantic: one at Tortuguero on the coast of Costa Rica, one on Aves Island in the eastern Caribbean, one on the coast of Surinam, and one on Ascension Island between South America and Africa. Male and female green turtles congregate at these nesting grounds during the nesting season. The male turtles remain offshore, where they court and mate with females, and the female turtles come ashore to lay eggs on the beaches. A typical female green turtle at Tortuguero produces three clutches of eggs about 12 days apart. About a third of the female turtles in the Tortuguero population nest in alternate years, and the remaining two-thirds of the turtles follow a

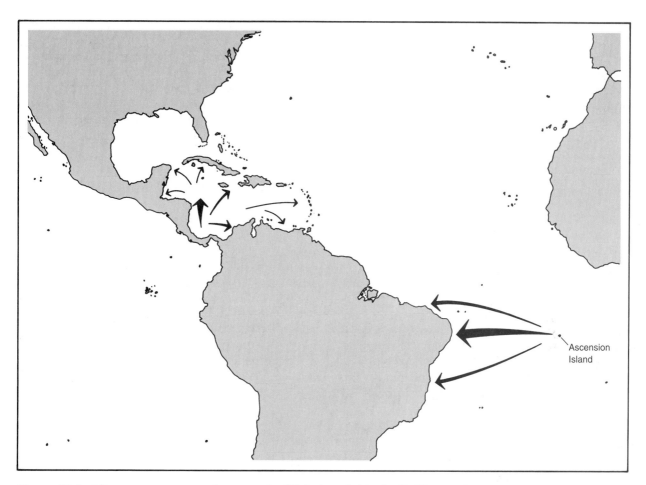

Figure 12–9 Migratory movements of green turtles (*Chelonia mydas*) in the Caribbean and South Atlantic. The population that nests on beaches in the Caribbean is drawn from feeding grounds in the Caribbean and Gulf of Mexico. The turtles that nest on Ascension Island feed along the coast of northern South America.

3-year breeding cycle. The coast at Tortuguero lacks the beds of turtle grass on which green turtles feed, and the turtles come to Tortuguero only for nesting. In the intervals between breeding periods, the turtles disperse around the Caribbean. The largest part of the Tortuguero population spreads northward along the coast of Central America. The Miskito Bank off the northern coast of Nicaragua appears to be the main feeding ground for the Tortuguero colony. A smaller number of turtles from Tortuguero swim south along the coast of Panama, Colombia, and Venezuela. Female green turtles return to their natal beaches to nest (Meylan et al. 1990), and the precision with which they home is astonishing. Female green turtles at Tortuguero return to the same kilometer of beach to deposit each of the three clutches of eggs they lay in a breeding season.

Probably the most striking example of the ability of sea turtles to home to their nesting beaches is provided by the green turtle colony that nests on Ascension Island, a small volcanic peak that emerges from the ocean 2200 kilometers east of the coast of Brazil. The island is less than 20 kilometers in diameter—a tiny target in the vastness of the South Atlantic. The Ascension Island population has its feeding grounds on the coast of Brazil. Migrating and homing birds use a variety of orientation mechanisms, including the ability to detect the magnetic field of the earth, to perceive polarized light, to use the sun and stars for orientation, and to hear very-low-frequency sounds. Sea turtles probably have a similarly wide repertoire of mechanisms for navigation.

A study of navigation by hatchling loggerhead turtles showed that they used at least three cues for orientation: light, wave direction, and magnetism

(Lohmann 1991). These stimuli play sequential roles in the turtles' behavior. When they emerge from their nests, the hatchlings crawl toward the brightest light they see. Normally the sky at night is lighter over the ocean than over land, and this behavior brings them to the water's edge. (Shopping centers, street lights, even porch lights on beachfront houses can confuse these and other species of sea turtles and lead them inland, where they are crushed on roads or die in the sun the next day.)

In the ocean, the loggerhead hatchlings swim into the waves. This response moves them away from shore and ultimately into the Gulf Stream. They drift with the current along the coast of the United States, and then eastward across the Atlantic. Off the coast of Portugal, the Gulf Stream divides into two branches. One turns north toward England, and the other swings south past the bulge of Africa and eventually back westward across the Atlantic. It's essential for the baby turtles to turn right at Portugal; if they fail to make that turn they are swept past England into the chilly North Atlantic, where they perish. If they do turn southward off the coast of Portugal, they are eventually carried back to the coast of tropical America—a round-trip that takes 5 to 7 years.

Magnetic orientation appears to tell the turtles when to turn right to catch the current that will carry them to the South Atlantic. We usually think of the Earth's magnetic field as providing two-dimensional information—north–south and east–west—but it's more complicated than that. The field loops out of the north and south magnetic poles of the Earth. At the Equator the field is essentially parallel to the Earth's surface (in other words, it forms an angle of 0 degrees), and at the poles it intersects the surface at an angle of 90 degrees. Thus, the three-dimensional orientation of the Earth's magnetic field provides directional information (which way is magnetic north?) and information about latitude (what is the angle at which the magnetic field intersects the Earth's surface?).

When loggerheads in a pool on land that had no waves were exposed to an artificial magnetic field at the 57-degree angle of intersection with the Earth's surface that is characteristic of Florida, they swam toward artificial east even when the magnetic field was changed 180 degrees so that the direction they thought was east was actually west. That is, they were able to use a compass sense to determine direction. But that wasn't all they could do. When the angle of intersection of the artificial magnetic field was increased to 60 degrees, as if they were further north than they really were, the turtles turned south. A 60-degree angle of intersection corresponds to the latitude where the Gulf Stream forks off the coast of Portugal, and where the turtles must turn south to reach the South Atlantic. Thus, it appears that loggerhead turtles can use magnetic sensitivity to recognize both direction and latitude.

Still more senses may be involved in navigation by sea turtles. An animal like a sea turtle that crosses thousands of miles of open ocean, and can raise its head only a few centimeters above the water's surface, probably uses every cue it can. Olfaction may assist some kinds of orientation, such as location of a specific beach when a turtle has reached the breeding grounds, and a sun compass could be used for short-term movements between the beach and offshore areas, as well as for long-distance navigation. Sea turtles are inherently difficult animals to study, but evidence for these mechanisms is accumulating.

■ Conservation of Turtles

Many species of turtles have slow rates of growth and require long periods to reach maturity. These are characteristics that predispose a species to the risk of extinction when changing conditions increase the mortality of adults or drastically reduce recruitment of juveniles into the population (Congdon et al. 1993, 1994). The plight of large tortoises and sea turtles is particularly severe, partly because these species are among the largest and slowest growing of turtles, and also because other aspects of their biology expose them to additional risk (Figure 12–10). The conservation of tortoises and sea turtles is a subject of active international concern and has led to the founding of a new journal, *Chelonian Conservation and Biology* (Swingland and Klemens 1989, Burke et al. 1993, Gibbons 1994).

The largest living tortoises are found on the Galápagos and Aldabra Islands. The relative isolation of these small and (for humans) inhospitable landmasses has probably been an important factor in the survival of the tortoises. Human colonization of the islands has brought with it domestic animals such as goats and donkeys that compete with the tortoises for the limited quantities of vegetation to be found in these arid habitats, and dogs, cats, and rats that prey on tortoise eggs and on baby tortoises.

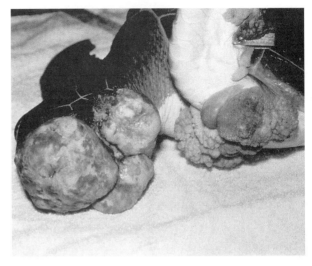

(b)

(a)

Figure 12–10 A green turtle with cutaneous papillomas. (a) These tumors, which are probably caused by a virus, have been found on most species of sea turtles and in most parts of the world (Herbst 1994). The tumors grow to more than 30 centimeters in diameter and can appear on any skin-covered surface. (b) They are especially common on the conjuctiva of the eyes, and may row over the cornea. Tumors were not recorded on green turtles in the Indian River Lagoon, Florida, until 1982, and by 1994 approximately 50 percent of the green turtles were affected. The first record of papilloma on green turtles in Kaneohe Bay, Hawaii, was in 1958, and since 1989 the incidence has ranged from 49 to 92 percent. The tumors can be lethal, and their increased frequency is an ominous development for species that were already endangered (Herbst 1994). (Photographs courtesy of Larry Herbst, University of Florida.)

The limited geographic range of a tortoise that occurs only on a single island makes it vulnerable to extinction. In 1985 and again in 1994 brush fires on the island of Isabela in the Galápagos Archipelago threatened the 20 surviving individuals of *Geochelone guntheri*, and emphasized the advantage of moving some or all of the turtles to the breeding station operated by the Charles Darwin Research Station on Santa Cruz Island. This station has a successful record of breeding and releasing another species of Galápagos tortoise, *Geochelone nigra hoodensis*, which is native to Espanola Island. In the early 1960s only 14 individuals of this form could be located. All were adults and apparently had not bred successfully for many years. All the tortoises were moved to the research station, and the first babies were produced in 1971. Since then, more than 400 tortoises have been raised, and half of them have been released on Española. This success story

shows that carefully controlled captive breeding and release programs can be an effective method of conservation for endangered species of turtles. These programs carry with them the risk of introducing diseases into wild populations, however, and have the potential to do substantial harm (Box 12–1).

Conservation of sea turtles provides special challenges. These species range over thousands of square kilometers of ocean, including international waters and also coastal areas that are under the jurisdictions of many different nations. For example, female leatherback turtles (*Dermochelys coriacea*) that had laid eggs on Playa Grande on the Pacific coast of Costa Rica were tracked by tethering radio transmitters to their shells. Signals from the transmitters were picked up by satellite when the turtles were on the surface, allowing the animals to be tracked across the open ocean (Morreale et al. 1996). From 1992 through 1995 a total of seven turtles were

BOX 12–1 Sick Turtles

The desert tortoise (*Gopherus agassizi*) is one of the largest terrestrial turtles in North America. Its geographic range includes the southwestern corner of Utah plus the southwestern third of Arizona and adjacent parts of Nevada and California, and extends southward into Mexico. (Some of the behavioral and physiological mechanisms that allow these tortoises to survive in a harsh desert environment are discussed in Chapter 16.)

Populations of desert tortoises have declined since the 1950s as human activity has intruded on the desert habitat. Between 1979 and 1989, most tortoise populations in the Mohave and Colorado Deserts decreased by 30 to 70 percent (Berry 1989). The situation has become even more grave with the appearance of upper respiratory tract disease (URTD), which attacks desert tortoises, often with fatal results. Infected turtles first have a runny nose, which becomes progressively worse until the turtles exude foam from their nostrils, wheeze when they breathe, cease feeding, become listless, and ultimately die (Figure 12–11). In 1988 tortoises in the Desert Tortoise Natural Area in Kern County, California, first showed symptoms of URTD (Jacobson et al. 1991). In 1989, 627 dead tortoises were found and 43 percent of the live tortoises on the Natural Area showed symptoms of URTD.

A large variety of bacteria were cultured from the nasal passages of the sick turtles, including *Mycoplasma*, which has subsequently been shown to be the cause of the disease (Jacobson et al. 1995). Desert tortoises are popular pets in the desert southwest, and a high proportion of pet turtles are infected by *Mycoplasma*. The infection may have been introduced to the Desert Tortoise Natural Area when pet tortoises were released, and its spread may have been accelerated by the poor physical condition of the wild tortoises that resulted from habitat degradation and a prolonged drought. *Mycoplasma* infections are notoriously difficult to cure. Captive tortoises can be treated with a combination of antibiotics, but there is no practical treatment for wild tortoises.

URTD has now been reported in a population of the gopher tortoise (*Gopherus polyphenus*) on Sanibel Island off the coast of Florida (Jacobson 1993). Again, captive tortoises appear to have introduced the infection into a wild population: Until 1978 tortoises used in tortoise races in Fort Myers were released on Sanibel Island, and infected tortoises from the races may have carried *Mycoplasma* with them.

These examples emphasize the risk of releasing animals that have been held in captivity into wild populations. Captive breeding programs must take extraordinary measures to ensure that the animals to be released are quarantined in a facility that is isolated from other animals. A breeding colony should be self-contained; once it is established, no outside animals should be introduced, and no equipment or containers should be moved in or out. Even the clothing of animal caretakers can carry pathogens, and a dressing room must be provided so they can wash and change their clothes when they enter or leave. These precautions are time consuming and expensive, but neglecting them can be disastrous.

Figure 12–11 A gopher tortoise with a runny nose. Nasal discharge and swollen eyes are signs that this tortoise is infected with the *Mycoplasma* that causes upper respiratory tract disease. (Photograph courtesy of Elliott R. Jacobson, University of Florida.)

tracked for periods of 29 to 87 days as they traveled over distances of 417 to 2780 kilometers. Remarkably, the turtles all followed the same path to the southwest, passing by the Galápagos Islands and continuing into the Pacific Ocean. With the vastness of the entire Pacific Ocean before them, the seven turtles remained in a corridor that was no more than 500 kilometers wide. In the process, they passed from the territorial limits of Costa Rica into international waters, then into Ecuadorian waters around the Galápagos Islands and back into international waters. Green turtles breeding in the Caribbean may pass through the territorial waters of a half dozen countries as they swim from their feeding grounds to the nesting beaches. These movements between national jurisdictions and international waters add enormously to the problem of establishing and enforcing provisions to protect the turtles.

Protection of sea turtles presents biological challenges as well as legal ones. The extreme faithfulness that turtles show for a particular breeding site limits the amount of genetic variation at each site. For example, an examination of loggerhead turtles (*Caretta caretta*) in the Mediterranean Sea showed substantial genetic separation between turtles nesting at adjacent sites on the coast of Turkey (Schroth et al. 1996). Some of these breeding sites are being destroyed by real estate development. Because the turtles nesting at each site are genetically distinct from those at other sites, the loss of a single breeding site results in the loss of a portion of the genetic variation of the species. Thus, preserving the genetic diversity of the species as a whole depends on preserving the breeding sites of all the subpopulations.

All seven species of sea turtles face threats, but the melancholy distinction of being the most endangered sea turtle goes to Kemp's ridley (*Lepidochelys kempi*, Figure 12–12). This species has only one major nesting site, a 14-mile stretch of beach on the coast near Rancho Nuevo in Tamauliapas, Mexico. Kemp's ridley nests by day, and once did so in enormous numbers. The influx of female turtles to the beach is called an *arribada* (Spanish for arrival), and a movie made in 1947 shows an *arribada* estimated to contain 47,000 turtles all nesting at once.

Figure 12–12　An adult female Kemp's ridley sea turtle. (Photograph courtesy of Donna Shaver.)

Although Kemp's ridley turtles had probably been an important source of food for inhabitants of the region since pre-Columbian times, the location of the nesting beach was unknown to the scientific community until 1966. By then the largest *arribadas* consisted of only 3000 to 5000 turtles, and their numbers have continued to decrease as adult females and eggs taken from the nesting beach have been used for food, and as adults and juveniles have drowned in fishing and shrimping nets in the Gulf of Mexico. By 1994, despite conservation efforts, the entire population probably contained fewer than 800 females (Shaver 1990).

From 1978 to 1988 the Mexican Instituto Nacional de Pesca worked with the U. S. Fish and Wildlife Service, the National Marine Fisheries Services, the National Park Service, and the Texas Parks and Wildlife Department to establish a second breeding population of Kemp's ridley at Padre Island National Seashore in Texas. Each year about 2000 eggs were collected in Mexico as they were laid, and

then shipped to Padre Island where they were incubated and hatched while additional eggs were incubated on the beach at Rancho Nuevo.

The goal of the project was to produce at least a 1:1 ratio of male and female hatchlings, and preferably a preponderance of females to establish a population of turtles that would return to Padre Island to breed. Several individuals, including National Parks Service employee Donna Shaver, cooperated in a study of the sex ratio of the hatchling turtles that had been produced between 1978 and 1984. Embryos that had failed to hatch had been preserved for later examination, and the sex of the dead turtles could be determined by histological examination of their gonads. The results were discouraging (Figure 12–13). In three of the five years for which adequate samples were available only one-third of the hatchlings were females, and the highest proportion of females ever achieved was only 50 percent (Shaver et al. 1988). Those ratios were far from the project's goal of at least a 1:1 sex

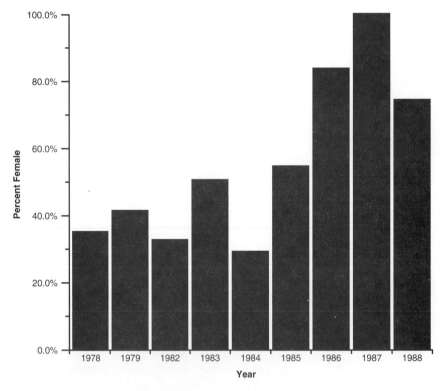

Figure 12–13 Temperature-dependent sex determination and sea turtle conservation. Proportion of female hatchlings produced in the egg house at Padre Island National Seashore from 1978 through 1988. Note the increase in the proportion of females from 1985 onward, after incubation temperatures were raised. (No reliable samples are available for 1980 and 1981.) (Based on data in Shaver et al. 1988 and Donna Shaver, personal communication.)

ratio, and the deviation was in the wrong direction—an excess of males was being produced.

The phenomenon of temperature-dependent sex determination in turtles had been described in the biological literature some 30 years earlier, but its implications for conservation of sea turtles had not been appreciated (Mrosovsky and Yntema 1981). The Padre Island project, like many other sea turtle conservation projects around the world, incubated the eggs in moist sand in styrofoam boxes that were kept in a covered egg house on the beach. Shaver found that the temperature inside the boxes was slightly too cool, and this was why most of the eggs developed into male turtles.

From 1985 onward, temperatures in the egg houses at Rancho Nuevo and Padre Island were raised about 3°C. This small increase in incubation temperature was sufficient to shift sex determination in favor of females, and from 1985 through the end of the project in 1988 the proportion of female hatchlings increased dramatically (Figure 12–13).

This example illustrates the importance of applying basic biological information about organisms to management and conservation programs, and shows how effective even one person can be in applying that information.

Attempts to save sea turtles are in progress all over the world, sponsored by a variety of government agencies, private organizations, and even dedicated individuals. The problems they face are massive, and the most effective methods to employ are still subject to disagreement (Pritchard 1980, Ehrenfeld 1981). For example, is controlled exploitation of sea turtles more feasible than an outright ban on the use of sea turtles and their products? Do turtle farming operations benefit conservation by producing captive-bred individuals, or do they indirectly harm natural populations by sustaining a demand for turtle products that would otherwise vanish?

These questions have their origins in the ways people in rich and poor nations respond to the often-conflicting demands of earning a living versus conserving natural resources. But beyond these is another series of questions that arise from our inadequate knowledge of the biology of sea turtles. For example, is it a wise management practice to dig up nests of turtle eggs from the nesting beaches and incubate them in a protected area? Predation on eggs in natural nests can be high, but sea turtles display temperature-dependent sex determination, and the widespread technique of incubating eggs in plastic foam boxes appears to produce predominantly male hatchlings. Is the practice of head-starting sea turtles beneficial? In this technique, baby turtles are kept in captivity for some weeks or months and allowed to grow before they are released at sea. This method avoids the very high losses of baby turtles to predators that occur when the newly hatched babies make their own way down the beach and into the sea. However, imprinting on the characteristics of the beach and the adjacent water might occur as the baby turtle makes its own way to sea. If that is the case, head-starting may prevent the imprinting that is essential for successful navigation by an adult turtle back to the nesting beach. If head-started turtles are not released carefully and in appropriate places a head-starting project may do no more than subsidize the predators at the site of release. We simply cannot evaluate the effects of these manipulations because we do not know enough about the biology of sea turtles.

These questions are a subset of a broader set of questions about the effectiveness of conservation methods as they have been applied to reptiles (Dodd and Siegel 1991, Burke 1991, Reinert 1991). The problems cited by these authors emphasize the central role of information about all aspects of the biology of organisms in successful conservation plans. This sort of information is not easy to obtain for any species of organism, and turtles are more difficult to study than most animals. For example, a total of 22,255 yearling Kemp's ridley turtles were tagged and released by the Galveston Laboratory of the National Marine Fisheries Service during the head-start experiment, which lasted from 1978 to 1993 (Caillouet et al. 1995). During that period 805 tagged turtles were recaptured, and estimates of annual survival range from 10 to 50 percent. Kemp's ridley turtles are believed to mature in 10 years, and a mathematical calculation shows that an annual survival of 45 percent would be needed to produce one surviving turtle at age 10 from the average of 1437 hatchlings that were released each year. It is not yet known whether enough Kemp's ridley turtles from the head-start project survived to maturity to affect the population, but the odds faced by an individual head-started turtle are daunting.

■ Summary

The earliest turtles known, fossils from the Triassic, have nearly all the features of derived turtles. The first Triassic forms were not able to withdraw their heads into the shell, but this ability appeared in the two major lineages of living turtles, which were established by the Late Triassic. The cryptodiran turtles retract the head with a vertical flexion of the neck vertebrae, whereas the pleurodires use a sideward bend.

Turtles are among the most morphologically specialized vertebrates. The shell is formed of dermal bone that is fused to the vertebral column and ribs. In most turtles the dermal shell is overlain by a horny layer of epidermal scutes. The limb girdles are inside the rib cage. Breathing presents special difficulties for an animal that is encased in a rigid shell: Exhalation is accomplished by muscles that squeeze the viscera against the lungs, and inhalation is accomplished by muscles that increase the volume of the visceral cavity, thereby allowing the lungs to expand. The heart of turtles (and of squamates as well) is able to shift blood between the pulmonary and systemic circuits in response to the changing requirements of gas exchange and thermoregulation.

The social behavior of turtles includes visual, tactile, and olfactory signals used in courtship. Dominance hierarchies shape the feeding, resting, and mating behaviors of some of the large species of tortoises. All species of turtles lay eggs, and none provides parental care. Coordinated activity by hatchling sea turtles may be necessary to enable them to dig themselves out of the nest, and simultaneous emergence of baby sea turtles from their nests helps them to evade predators as they rush down the beach into the ocean. Sea turtles migrate tens, hundreds, and even thousands of kilometers between their feeding areas and their nesting beaches, and use a large variety of cues for navigation.

The life history of many turtles makes them vulnerable to extinction. Slow rates of growth and long periods required to reach maturity are characteristic of turtles in general and of large species of turtles in particular. Tortoises and sea turtles are especially threatened, and conservation efforts are in progress in many countries. Recently discovered features of the basic biology of turtles have important implications for conservation efforts. For example, many species of turtles show temperature-dependent sex determination. That is, the sex of an individual turtle is determined by the temperature it experiences in the egg during embryonic development. Some conservation efforts undertaken before this phenomenon was appreciated resulted in the production and release of thousands of hatchling baby turtles, nearly all of which were probably males. Using information about basic aspects of the biology of turtles is a crucial part of efforts to sustain existing populations and to reestablish populations that have been lost.

■ References

Berry, K. 1989. *Gopherus agassizi*, desert tortoise. Pages 5–7 in The conservation biology of tortoises. *Occasional Papers of the IUCN Species Survival Commission*, No. 5, edited by I. R. Swingland and M W. Klemens. IUCN, Gland, Switzerland.

Burke, R. L. 1991. Relocations, repatriations, and translocations of amphibians and reptiles: taking a broader view. *Herpetologica* 47:350–357.

Burke, V. J., N. B. Frazer, and J. W. Gibbons. 1993. Conservation of turtles: the chelonian dilemma. Pages 35–38 in *Proceedings of the 13th Annual Symposium on Sea Turtle Biology and Conservation*. U.S. Department of Commerce, National Oceanic and Atmospheric Administration, Jekyll Island, GA.

Caillouet, C. W., Jr., C. T. Fontaine, S. A. Manzella-Tirpak, and D. J. Shaver. 1995. Survival of head-started Kemp's ridley sea turtles (*Lepidoshelys kempii*) released into the Gulf of Mexico or adjacent bays. *Chelonian Conservation and Biology* 1:285–292.

Carr, A. 1987. New perspectives on the pelagic stage of sea turtle development. *Conservation Biology* 1:103–121.

Chelazzi, G., and R. Calzolai. 1986. Thermal benefits from familiarity with the environment in a reptile. *Oecologia* 68:557–558.

Congdon, J. D., A. E. Dunham, and R. C. Van Loben Sels. 1993. Delayed sexual maturity and demographics of Blanding's turtles (*Emydoidea blandingii*): implications for conservation and management of long-lived organisms. *Conservation Biology* 7:826–833.

Congdon, J. D., A. E. Dunham, and R. C. Van Loben Sels. 1994. Demographics of common snapping turtles (*Chelydra serpentina*): implications for conservation and management of long-lived organisms. *American Zoologist* 34:397–408.

Dodd, C. K., Jr., and R. A. Siegel. 1991. Relocations repatriation, and translocation of amphibians and reptiles: Are they conservation strategies that work? *Herpetologica* 47:336–350.

Ehrenfeld, D. 1981. Options and limitations in the conservation of sea turtles. Pages 457–463 in *Biology and Conservation of Sea Turtles*, edited by K. A. Bjorndal. Smithsonian Institution Press, Washington, DC.

Ewert, M. A., and C. E. Nelson. 1991. Sex determination in turtles: diverse patterns and some possible adaptive values. *Copeia* 1991:50–69.

Farmer, C. 1997. Did the lungs and intracardiac shunt evolve to oxygenate the heart in vertebrates? *Paleobiology* 23:358–372.

Gaffney, E. S. 1990. The comparative osteology of the Triassic turtle *Proganochelys*. *Bulletin of the American Museum of Natural History* 194:1–263.

Gaffney, E. S., and J. W. Kitching. 1994. The most ancient African turtle. *Nature* 369:55–58.

Gaffney, E. S., J. H. Hutchison, F. A. Jenkins Jr., L. J. Meeker. 1987. Modern turtle origins: the oldest known cryptodire. *Science* 237:289–291.

Gibbons, J. W. (editor). 1990. *Life History and Ecology of the Slider Turtle*. Smithsonian Institution Press, Washington, D. C.

Gibbons, J. W. 1994. Reproductive patterns of reptiles and amphibians: considerations for captive breeding and conservation. Pages 119–123 in *Captive Management and Conservation of Amphibians and Reptiles*, edited by J. B. Murphy, K. Adler, and J. T. Collins. Contributions to Herpetology, volume 2. Society for the Study of Amphibians and Reptiles, Ithaca, NY.

Herbst, L. H. 1994. Fibropapillomatosis of marine turtles. *Annual Review of Fish Diseases* 4:389–425.

Hicks, J. W., A. Ishimatsu, S. Molloi, A. Erskin, and N. Heisler. 1996. The mechanism of cardiac shunting in reptiles: a new synthesis. *Journal of Experimental Biology* 199:1435–1446.

Jacobson, E. R. 1993. Implications of infectious diseases for captive propagation and introduction programs of threatened/endangered reptiles. *Journal of Zoo and Wildlife Medicine* 24:245–255.

Jacobson, E. R., M. B. Brown, I. M. Schumacher, B. R. Collins, R. K. Harris, and P. A. Klein. 1995. Mycoplasmosis and the desert tortoise (*Gopherus agassizii*) in Las Vegas Valley, Nevada. *Chelonian Conservation and Biology* 1:279–284.

Jacobson, E R., J. M. Gaskin, M. B. Brown, R. K. Harris, C. H. Gardiner, J. L. LaPointe, H. P. Adams, and C. Reggiardo. 1991. Chronic upper respiratory disease of free-ranging desert tortoises (*Xerobates agassizi*). *Journal of Wildlife Disease* 27:296–316.

Lee, M. S. Y. 1993. The origin of the turtle body plan: bridging a famous morphological gap. *Science* 261:1716–1720.

Lohmann, K. J. 1991. Magnetic orientation by hatchling loggerhead sea turtles. *Journal of Experimental Biology* 155:37–49.

Meylan, A. 1988. Spongivory in hawksbill turtles: a diet of glass. *Science* 239:393–395.

Meylan, A. B., B. W. Bowen, and J. C. Avise. 1990. A genetic test of the natal homing versus social facilitation model for green turtle migration. *Science* 248:724–727.

Miller, K., G. C. Packard, and M. J. Packard. 1987. Hydric conditions during incubation influence locomotor performance of hatchling snapping turtles. *Journal of Experimental Biology* 127:401–412.

Morreale, S. J., E. A. Standora, J. R. Spotila, and F. V. Paladino. 1996. Migration corridor for sea turtles. *Nature* 384:319–320.

Mrosovsky, N., and C. L. Yntema. 1981. Temperature dependence of sexual differentiation in sea turtles: implications for conservation practices. Pages 271–280 in *Biology and Conservation of Sea Turtles*, edited by K. A. Bjorndal. Smithsonian Institution Press, Washington, DC.

Packard, G. C., and M. J. Packard. 1988. Physiological ecology of reptile eggs. Pages 523–605 in *Biology of the Reptilia*, volume 16, edited by C. Gans and R. B. Huey. Alan Liss, Philadelphia, PA.

Paladino, F. V., M. P. O'Connor, and J. R. Spotila. 1990. Metabolism of leatherback turtles, gigantothermy, and thermoregulation of dinosaurs. *Nature* 344:858–860.

Pritchard, P. C. H. 1980. The conservation of sea turtles: practices and problems. *American Zoologist* 20:609–617.

Reinert, H. K. 1991. Translocations as a conservation strategy for amphibians and reptiles: some comments, concerns, and observations. *Herpetologica* 47:357–363.

Rieppel, O. and M. de Braga. 1996. Turtles as diapsid reptiles. *Nature* 384:453–455.

Reisz, R. R., and M. Laurin. 1991. *Owenetta* and the origin of turtles. *Nature* 349:324–326.

Rougier, G. W., M. S. de la Fuente, and A. B. Arcucci. 1995. Late Triassic turtles from South America. *Science* 268:855–858.

Schroth, W., B. Streit, and B. Schierwater. 1996. Evolutionary handicap for turtles. *Nature* 384:521–522.

Shaver, D. 1990. Kemp's ridley project at Padre Island enters a new phase. *Park Science* 10(1):12–13.

Shaver, D., D. W. Owens, A. H. Chaney, C. W. Caillouet, Jr., P. Burchfield, and R. Marquez M. 1988. Styrofoam box and beach temperatures in relation to incubation and sex ratios of Kemp's ridley sea turtles. Pages 103–108 in *Proceedings of the Eighth Annual Workshop on Sea Turtle Conservation and Biology*, Feb. 24–26, 1988, Fort Fisher, NC. NOAA Technical Memorandum NMFS-SEFC-214.

Spotila, J. R., and E. A. Standora. 1985. Environmental constraints on the thermal energetics of sea turtles. *Copeia* 1985:694–702.

Swingland, I. R., and J. G. Frazier. 1979. The conflict between feeding and overheating in the Aldabran giant tortoise. Pages 611–615 in *A Handbook on Biotelemetry and Radio Tracking*, edited by C. J. Amlaner Jr., and D. W. MacDonald. Pergamon, Oxford, UK.

Swingland, I. R., and M. W. Klemens (editors). 1989. The conservation biology of tortoises. *Occasional Papers of the IUCN Species Survival Commission*. No. 5. IUCN, Gland, Switzerland.

Swingland, I. R., and C. M. Lessells. 1979. The natural regulation of giant tortoise populations on Aldabra Atoll. Movement polymorphism, reproductive success and mortality. *Journal of Animal Ecology* 48:639–654.

Wang, T., E. H. Krosniunas, and J. W. Hicks. 1997. The role of cardiac shunts in the regulation of arterial blood gases. *American Zoologist* 37:12–22.

CHAPTER
13

Mesozoic Diapsids: Dinosaurs, Birds, Crocodilians, and Others

At the same time that turtles were evolving in the Triassic, the most diverse lineage of amniotic vertebrates, the Diapsida, was well into its radiation. The most spectacular diapsids were the dinosaurs, but the lineage also gave rise to a majority of the species of extant terrestrial vertebrates. Birds are diapsids, as are the squamates (lizards and snakes). A variety of other, lesser known forms fills the roster of diapsids, including crocodilians, ichthyosaurs, and pterosaurs, to name only a few.

The dinosaur fauna of the Mesozoic was unlike anything that has existed before or since. (As we noted in Chapter 1, birds are part of the dinosaur lineage and there is no cladistically correct term that refers only to dinosaurs minus birds. For convenience we will use dinosaurs in this sense.) Many dinosaurs were enormous, and it is difficult to recreate the details of the lives they led because we have no living models of truly large terrestrial vertebrates. Even elephants are only as large as a medium-size dinosaur.

A second group of diapsids, the lepidosauromorphs, radiated into a variety of animals in the Mesozoic and then had another radiation, which produced somewhat different animals that survive today. The extant lepidosauromorphs are such successful animals in their own right that they will be discussed in the next chapter; however, a discussion of the Mesozoic world would be incomplete without considering the secondarily aquatic marine forms (ichthyosaurs, plesiosaurs, placodonts, and the strange *Hupehsuchus*), and these were probably lepidosauromorphs.

The remarkable success of large diapsids in the Mesozoic ended at the close of that era with the extinction of the dinosaurs. That mass extinction has attracted more than its share of attention because dinosaurs have great popular appeal; but as mass extinctions go, it was modest. However, it does provide a good opportunity to consider in detail the merits of two types of explanations of mass extinctions, the gradualism versus the catastrophism schools of thought.

■ The Mesozoic Fauna

The Mesozoic era, frequently called the Age of Reptiles, extended for some 180 million years from the close of the Paleozoic 245 million years ago to the beginning of the Cenozoic only 65 million years ago. Through this vast period evolved a worldwide fauna that diversified and radiated into most of the adaptive zones occupied by all the terrestrial vertebrates living today and some that no longer exist (for example, the enormous herbivorous and carnivorous tetrapods called dinosaurs). Although the dinosaurs are the most familiar representatives of the Age of Reptiles, they are only one of many groups.

Inevitably such a huge number of animals is complicated and confusing, not only on first acquaintance, but even after study. Parallel and convergent evolution was widespread in Mesozoic tetrapods. Long-snouted fish eaters evolved repeatedly, as did heavily armored quadrupeds and highly specialized marine forms. A trend to bipedalism was general, and a secondary reversion to quadrupedal locomotion is seen in many forms. Knowledge of phylogenetic relationships is in a state of flux, and the scheme outlined in Figure 13–1 will undoubtedly need revision as additional material is analyzed. Current views of the ecology of dinosaurs are likewise undergoing a radical revision.

This chapter commences with a brief review of the phylogenetic relationships of Mesozoic tetrapods and some aspects of their functional morphology and major evolutionary trends. More detailed information on these topics and additional illustrations of members of the groups discussed can be found in the references cited at the end of the chapter. Following a consideration of some aspects of the ecology of dinosaurs, we consider their disappearance at the end of the Cretaceous.

■ Phylogenetic Relationships among Diapsids

Our understanding of the phylogenetic relationships of several groups of Mesozoic tetrapods has changed in the past decade. Many of these forms (thecodonts, crocodilians, pterosaurs, dinosaurs, squamates, and rhynchosaurs) had skulls with two temporal openings (a **diapsid** skull), and the Diapsida is considered a monophyletic lineage that includes most of the major groups of Mesozoic tetrapods (dinosaurs) as well as the living crocodilians, birds, tuatara (*Sphenodon*), and squamates (lizards, snakes, and amphisbaenians) (Figure 13–1).

The name diapsid means two arches and refers to the presence of an upper and a lower fenestra in the temporal region of the skull. More distinctive than the openings themselves is the morphology of the bones that form the arch separating them. The upper temporal arch is composed of a three-pronged postorbital bone and a three-pronged squamosal. The lower temporal arch is formed by the jugal and

quadratojugal bones. The lower arch has been lost repeatedly in the radiation of diapsids, and the upper arch is also missing in some forms. Living lizards and snakes clearly show the importance of those modifications of the skull in permitting increased skull flexion (kinesis) during feeding, and the same significance may attach to loss of the arches in some extinct forms. In addition to the two temporal fenestrae, derived diapsids have a suborbital fenestra on each side of the head anterior to the eye, and the presence of this fenestra modifies the relationships among the bones of the palate and the side of the skull.

The earliest diapsid known is *Petrolacosaurus*, from Late Carboniferous deposits in Kansas. It is a moderately small animal, 60 to 70 centimeters from snout to tail tip, with a long neck, large eyes, and long limbs (Figure 13–2). It gives the impression of having been an agile terrestrial animal that may have fed on large insects and other arthropods. The derived diapsids can be split into two groups, the **Archosauromorpha** and the **Lepidosauromorpha** (Figure 13–1). The archosauromorphs include crocodilians and birds, the extinct pterosaurs, dinosaurs, and several Late Permian and Triassic forms. The lepidosauromorphs include the tuatara (sphenodontidae) and squamates plus their extinct relatives. In addition, four groups of specialized marine tetrapods (the placodonts, plesiosaurs, ichthyosaurs, and *Hupehsuchus*) are tentatively considered to be lepidosauromorphs. The skulls of these animals have a dorsal temporal opening, but lack a lower temporal fenestra, and the postorbital and squamosal bones do not have the three-pronged shape characteristic of diapsids. However, these patterns are within the range of modifications of the basic diapsid skull that is seen among other members of the clade.

■ The Archosauromorpha

The Archosauromorpha includes the most familiar of the Mesozoic diapsids, the dinosaurs, as well as their close relatives, the crocodilians, phytosaurs, birds, and pterosaurs (Figure 13–1), and some less familiar forms. The archosauromorphs are distinguished by several characteristics of the skull and axial skeleton. The proterosuchians (probably not a monophyletic group) include the Triassic forms known as thecodontians in earlier classifications such as that of Romer (1966). *Proterosuchus* was a quadrupedal, lizard-shaped carnivore, 2 or 3

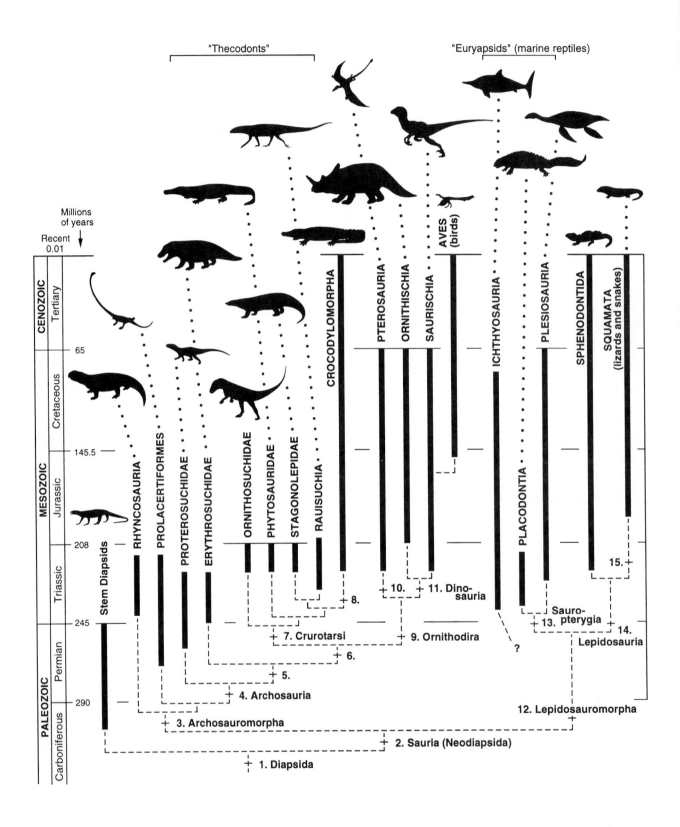

meters long, which is known from South Africa. Related forms are known from deposits in China, Bengal, Eurasia, Australia, and Antarctica. *Erythrosuchus*, another Triassic quadruped, was twice the size of *Proterosuchus* and massively built, whereas *Euparkeria* was a lightly built animal about 150 centimeters long. Its hindlimbs were half again as long as the forelimbs, suggesting that it was capable of bipedal locomotion (Figure 13–2).

Modifications of the diapsid skull have played an important role in the evolution of archosauromorphs. The bar formed by the jugal and quadratojugal bones, which closes the ventral side of the lower temporal opening in the diapsid skull was incomplete in the animals grouped as Prolacerti-

formes. In extant squamates this condition imparts mobility to the quadrate bone that increases the efficiency of the lower jaw. Grouped among the Prolacertiformes are several medium-size tetrapods such as *Prolacerta* and *Protorosaurus* with lizardlike body proportions that appear to have been agile, terrestrial predators.

Also included in the Prolacertiformes is the bizarre genus *Tanystropheus*. Several species of *Tanystropheus* are known, some of which were 6 meters in length. The body, limbs, and tail of *Tanystropheus* were of normal lizardlike proportions, but the neck, which contained 9 to 12 enormously elongate vertebrae, was as long as the body and tail combined. A small head, its jaws armed with coni-

---

1. Diapsida: Skull with upper and lower temporal fenestrae, upper temporal arch formed by triradiate postorbital and triradiate squamosal, suborbital fenestra, ossified sternum, complex ankle joint between tibia and astragalus, first metatarsal less than half the length of the fourth metatarsal. 2. Sauria (Neodiapsida): anterior process of squamosal narrow, squamosal mainly restricted to top of skull, tabular absent, stapes slender, cleithrum absent, fifth metatarsal hooked, trunk ribs mostly single-headed. 3. Archosauromorpha: Cervical ribs with two heads, various features of limbs including concave-convex articulation between astragalus and calcaneum. 4. Archosauria: Presence of an antorbital fenestra, orbit shaped like an inverted triangle, teeth laterally compressed with serrations. 5. Pubis and ilium elongated, fourth trochanter on femur. 6. Crown group Archosauria: Parietal foremen absent, no palatal teeth on pterygoid, palatine or vomer. 7. Crurotarsi: Ankle (tarsus) in which the astragalus forms a distinct peg that fits into a deep socket on the calcaneum, plus characters of the cervical ribs and the humerus. 8. Crocodylomorpha. Secondary palate formed at least from maxillae. 9. Ornithodira: Anterior cervical vertebrae longer than mid-dorsals, interclavicles absent, clavicles reduced or absent, tibia longer than femur, calcaneal tuber rudimentary or absent, metatarsals bunched together and 2-4 elongated. 10. Pterosauria. Hand with three short fingers and elongate fourth finger supporting wing membrane, pteroid bone in wrist, short trunk, short pelvis with prepubic bones. 11. Dinosauria: S-shaped swanlike neck, forelimb less than half the length of hindlimb, hand

digit 4 reduced, plus other characteristics of the palate, pectoral and pelvic girdles, hand, hindlimb, and foot. 12. Lepidosauromorpha: Postfrontal enters border of upper temporal fenestra, supratemporal absent, teeth absent on lateral pterygoid flanges, characteristics of the vertebrae, ribs, and sternal plates. 13. Sauropterygia: Elongation of postorbital region of skull, enlargement of upper temporal fenestra, elongate and robust mandibular symphysis, curved humerus, equal length of radius and ulna. 14. Lepidosauria: Determinant growth with epiphyses on the articulating surfaces of the long bones, postparietal and tabular absent, fused astragalus and calcaneum, and other characteristics of the skull, pelvis, and feet. 15. Squamata: Loss of lower temporal bar (including loss of quadratojugal), highly kinetic skull with reduction or loss of squamosal, nasals reduced, plus other characteristics of the palate and skull roof, vertebrae, ribs, pectoral girdle, and humerus. (Based on M. J. Benton, 1985, *Zoological Journal of the Linnaean Society* 84:97–164; J. Gauthier, 1986, pages 1–55 in *The Origin of Birds and the Evolution of Flight*, edited by K. Padian, *Memoirs of the California Academy of Sciences*, Number 8; H.-D. Sues, 1987, *Zoological Journal of the Linnaean Society* 90:109–131; M. J. Benton [editor], 1988, *The Phylogeny and Classification of the Tetrapods*, Special Volume No. 35B, The Systematics Association, Oxford University Press, Oxford, UK; R. L. Carroll, 1988, *Vertebrate Paleontology and Evolution*, Freeman, New York, NY; M. J. Benton [editor], 1993, *The Fossil Record 2*, Chapman & Hall, London, UK; and M. J. Benton, 1997, *Vertebrate Paleontology*, second edition, Chapman and Hall, London, UK.

Figure 13–1   Phylogenetic relationships of the Diapsida. This diagram shows the probable relationships among the major groups of diapsids. Dotted lines show interrelationships only; they do not indicate times of divergence nor the unrecorded presence of taxa in the fossil record. The numbers indicate derived characters that distinguish the lineages.

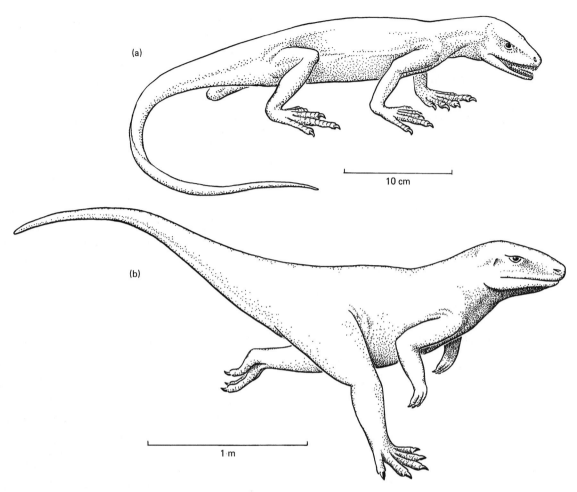

Figure 13–2   Early diapsids. (a) *Petrolacosaurus* from the Late Carboniferous had forelimbs and hindlimbs that were about the same length; (b) *Euparkeria*, an early archosaur, had hindlimbs that were much longer than its forelimbs and was probably bipedal. ([a] From R. R. Reisz, 1977, *Science* 196:1091–1093.)

cal teeth, perched on the end of this remarkable neck. The two parts of the body appear so different that when the first complete skeleton of this genus was discovered, it was found that bones from the front part of the animal had previously been described as belonging to a pterosaur and bones from the trunk had been identified as being from a dinosaur. Fossilized stomach contents have shown that *Tanystropheus* ate cephalopods (octopus and squid), but it is not clear how these strange animals captured their prey. The neck vertebrae did not have space for the attachment of strong muscles for bending, and thin ribs that extended backward from each vertebra would have stiffened the entire structure. Perhaps *Tanystropheus* cruised slowly in shallow water, probing in hollows in rocks or coral reefs in search of concealed prey.

Archosauria

The archosaurs are the animals most frequently associated with the great radiation of tetrapods in the Mesozoic. Dinosaurs and pterosaurs are distinctive components of many Mesozoic faunas, and other less familiar archosaurs were also abundant. The archosaurs are distinguished by the presence, in many forms, of an antorbital (in front of the eye) fenestra. The skull was deep, the orbit of the eye was shaped like an inverted triangle rather than being circular, and the teeth were laterally compressed (Figure 13–3). A trend toward bipedalism was widespread but not universal among archosaurs, and the ventral side of the shaft of the femur had a distinctive area with a rough surface, the fourth trochanter, which was the site of insertion of the powerful caudiofemoral muscle (Figure 13–3).

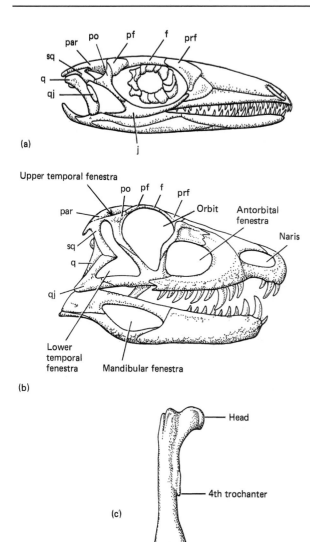

Figure 13–3 Morphological features of diapsids. (a) Skull of *Prolacerta* showing the incomplete lower temporal arch; (b) skull of *Ornithosuchus* showing the characteristic features of archosaurs: two temporal arches, a keyhole-shaped orbit, and an antorbital fenestra; (c) femur of *Thescelosaurus* showing the fourth trochanter. Key: f, frontal; par, parietal; pf, postfrontal; po, postorbital; prf, prefrontal; sq, squamosal; q, quadrate; qj, quadratojugal. ([a] and [b] From Romer 1966; [c] from A. S. Romer, 1956, *Osteology of the Reptiles*, University of Chicago Press, Chicago, IL.)

Crurotarsi   The archosaur stock gave rise to two lineages of aquatic fish eaters, the phytosaurs and crocodilians. The phytosaurs were the earlier radiation, and during the Late Triassic they were abundant and important elements of the shoreline fauna.

In contrast to crocodilians, in which the nostrils are at the tip of the snout and a secondary palate separates the nasal passages from the mouth, phytosaur nostrils were located on an elevation just anterior to the eyes. True crocodilians appeared in the Triassic and seem to have replaced phytosaurs by the end of that period. In most respects crocodilians conform closely to the skeletal structure of archosaurs, but the skull and pelvis are specialized. Crocodilians retained the nostrils at the tip of the snout and developed a secondary palate that carries the air passages posteriorly to the rear of the mouth. A flap of tissue arising from the base of the tongue can form a watertight seal between the mouth and throat. Thus, a crocodilian can breathe while only its nostrils are exposed without inhaling water. The increasing involvement of the premaxilla, the maxillae, and pterygoids in the secondary palate can be traced from Mesozoic crocodilians to modern forms.

Modern crocodilians are semiaquatic animals, but Triassic crocodilians were terrestrial. They were thin, slender animals about the size of a large cat, and give the impression of having been active hunters that probably preyed on smaller diapsids. Traces of this terrestrial origin persist in living crocodilians. They have well-developed limbs, and some species make extensive overland movements. Crocodilians can gallop, moving the limbs from their normal laterally extended posture to a nearly vertical position beneath the body.

The Cretaceous was the high point in crocodilian evolution. The extension of warm climates to land areas that are now in cool temperate climate zones favored both diversity and large size. *Deinosuchus* (terrible crocodile) from the Cretaceous of Texas had a skull that was nearly 2 meters long. If this crocodilian had the same body proportions as extant forms, it would have had a total length of 12 to 15 meters, and might well have preyed on dinosaurs.

Enormous crocodilians persisted long after dinosaurs disappeared. A skull of the Miocene crocodile *Purussaurus brasiliensis* found in the Amazon Basin in 1986 is 1.5 meters long. If the animal that bore that skull had the same proportions as an alligator, it would have had a total length of 11 to 12 meters and have stood 2.5 meters tall—that is, the height of the ceiling in most houses. An isolated lower jaw in the paleontology museum at the Universidade do Acre is 30 centimeters longer than the jaw of the complete skull, and may have come from an animal 13 to 14 meters long. These crocodilians would have been as large as *Tyrannosaurus rex*.

A heavy, laterally flattened tail propels the body of a crocodilian in water, and the legs are held against the sides of the body. In the Late Jurassic, a lineage of specialized marine crocodiles enjoyed brief success. These thallatosuchians had long skulls with pointed snouts. They lacked the dermal body armor typical of most crocodilians, and had developed a lobed tail very like that of the early ichthyosaurs, with the vertebral column turned downward into the lower lobe and the upper lobe supported by stiff tissue. The feet were paddlelike.

Only 21 species of crocodiles now survive. Most are found in the tropics or subtropics, but three species have ranges that extend into the temperate zone. In many respects crocodilians are the living archosaurs most like Mesozoic forms, and they have been used as models in attempts to analyze the ecology and behavior of dinosaurs.

Systematists divide living crocodilians into three families: The Alligatoridae includes the two species of living alligators and the caimans (Figure 13–4). With the exception of the Chinese alligator, the Alligatoridae is solely a New World group. The American alligator is found in the Gulf coast states, and several species of caimans range from Mexico to South America and through the Caribbean. Alligators and caimans are freshwater forms, whereas the Crocodylidae includes species such as the saltwater crocodile that inhabits estuaries, mangrove swamps, and the lower regions of large rivers. This species occurs widely in the Indo-Pacific region and penetrates the Indo-Australian archipelago to northern Australia. In the New World, the American crocodile is quite at home in the sea, and occurs in coastal regions from the southern tip of Florida through the Caribbean to northern South America.

The saltwater crocodile is probably the largest living species of crocodilian. Until recently, adults may have reached lengths of 7 meters. Crocodilians

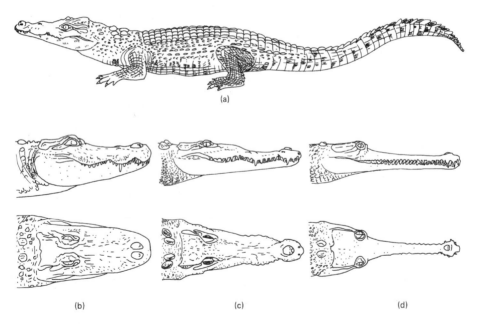

(a)

(b)   (c)   (d)

Figure 13–4 Crocodilians. Modern crocodilians differ little from one another or from Late Mesozoic forms. The greatest interspecific variation in living crocodilians is seen in the shape of the head. Alligators and caimans are broad-snouted forms with varied diets. Crocodiles include a range of snout widths. The widest crocodile snouts are almost as broad as those of most alligators and caimans, and these species of crocodilians have varied diets that include turtles, fishes, and terrestrial animals. Other crocodiles have very narrow snouts, and these species are primarily fish eaters. (a) Cuban crocodile; (b) Chinese alligator; (c) American crocodile; (d) gharial. (Modified from H. Wermuth and R. Mertens, 1961, *Schildkröten, Krocodile, Brückenechsen*, Gustav Fisher, Jena, East Germany.)

grow slowly once they reach maturity, and it takes a long time to attain large size. In the face of intensive hunting in the past two centuries, few crocodilians now attain the sizes they are genetically capable of reaching. Not all crocodilians are giants—several diminutive species live in small bodies of water. The dwarf caiman of South America and the dwarf crocodile of Africa are about a meter long as adults and live in swift-flowing streams.

The third family of crocodilians, the Gavialidae, contains only a single species—the gharial, which once lived in large rivers from northern India to Burma. This species has the narrowest snout of any crocodilian; the mandibular symphysis (the fusion between the mandibles at the anterior end of the lower jaw) extends back to the level of the 23rd or 24th tooth in the lower jaw. A very narrow snout of this sort is a specialization for feeding on fish that are caught with a sudden sideward jerk of the head. We have already called attention to the evolution of similar skull shapes in a variety of Mesozoic animals, including trematosaurs, phytosaurs, and the short-necked plesiosaurs.

Living crocodilians are ectotherms and small individuals bask in the sun to raise their body temperatures. A basking crocodilian can increase its rate of heating by using a right-to-left intracardiac blood shunt to increase blood flow in the peripheral circulation, just as lizards do. However, the structure of the crocodilian heart is different from that of the squamate and turtle heart, and the intracardiac blood shunt is achieved in a different way. Crocodilians, like birds and mammals, have a septum that separates the left and right sides of the ventricle. (It is the absence of that septum in the hearts of squamates and turtles that permits them to use pressure differentials to shift blood from the pulmonary [right] side of the ventricle across the muscular ridge to the systemic [left] side.)

In the crocodilian heart, the right aortic arch opens from the left ventricle and receives oxygenated blood (Figure 13–5). The left aortic arch and the pulmonary artery both open from the right ventricle. Deoxygenated blood enters the pulmonary artery, and you would expect that it would also flow into the left aortic arch, but studies of alligators have shown that the pattern of blood flow in the heart depends on what the alligator is doing (Jones and Shelton 1993). When an alligator is at rest, blood pressure is approximately the same in the right and left ventricles. In this situation, deoxy-

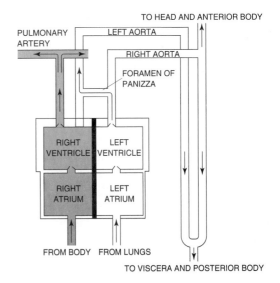

Figure 13–5 The relationship of the heart and major vessels of a crocodilian. The right aortic arch opens from the left ventricle and receives oxygenated blood, which flows to both the anterior and posterior parts of the body. The left aortic arch opens from the right ventricle. When pressure in the right ventricle equals or exceeds pressure in the left, the atrioventricular valve opens and deoxygenated blood flows into the left aorta, which carries blood only to the posterior part of the body. When pressure in the left ventricle exceeds pressure in the right ventricle, the right atrioventricular valve is held shut, and oxygenated blood flows via the foramen of Panizza into the left aortic arch. (From A. G. Kluge (editor), 1977, *Chordate Structure and Function*, Macmillan, New York, NY.)

genated blood does flow from the right ventricle into the left aortic arch, (this is a right-to-left intracardiac shunt, because right and left refer to the ventricles, not to the aortic arches) and then posteriorly to the viscera. Deoxygenated blood contains hydrogen ions that are produced when carbon dioxide combines with the bicarbonate buffering system of the blood. The hydrogen ions that enter the left aortic arch may be used for the secretion of hydrochloric acid in the stomach during digestion. Note that the right aortic arch supplies the blood to the head, so the brain receives only oxygenated blood.

A different pattern of blood flow occurs when the alligator is active and pressure in the left ventricle rises above that of the right ventricle. The left and right aortic arches are connected via the Foramen of Panizza. When pressure in the right aortic arch exceeds that in the left, blood flows through this passage from the right aortic arch into the left.

The increased pressure in the left aortic arch holds the ventricular valve closed, preventing entry of deoxygenated blood from the right ventricle, and both aortic arches receive oxygenated blood.

A third situation probably occurs when an alligator dives or is using the right-to-left shunt to increase blood flow to the limbs to accelerate heating. When blood vessels in the pulmonary circuit are constricted, pressure in the right ventricle rises and deoxygenated blood flows into the left aortic arch.

Pterosauria   The archosaurs gave rise to two independent radiations of fliers. The birds are one of these lineages, and their similarity to other archosaurs is so striking that if they had disappeared at the end of the Mesozoic, they would be considered no more than another group of highly specialized archosaurs. The other lineage of flying archosaurs were the pterosaurs of the Late Triassic to Cretaceous (Figure 13–6). They ranged from the sparrow-size *Pterodactylus* to *Quetzalcoatlus*, with a wingspan of 13 meters. The wing formation of pterosaurs was entirely different from that of birds. The fourth finger of pterosaurs was elongate and supported a membrane of skin anchored to the side of the body and perhaps to the hind leg. A small splint-like bone was attached to the front edge of the carpus and probably supported a membrane that ran forward to the neck. The early rhamphorhynchoid pterosaurs had a long tail with an expanded portion on the end that was presumably used for steering; the later pterodactyloids lacked a tail.

Flight is a demanding means of locomotion for a vertebrate, and it is not surprising that pterosaurs and birds show a high degree of convergent evolution. The long bones of pterosaurs were hollow, as they are in birds and many other archosaurs, reducing weight with little loss of strength. The sternum, to which the powerful flight muscles attach, was well developed in pterosaurs, although it lacked the keel seen in birds. The eyes were large, and casts of the brain cavities of pterosaurs show that the parts of the brain associated with vision were large and the olfactory areas small, as they are in birds. The cerebellum, which is concerned with balance and coordination of movement, was large in proportion to the other parts of the brain as it is in birds.

Some pterosaurs lost their teeth and evolved a birdlike beak. Others had sharp, conical teeth in blunt skulls reminiscent of those of bats. Some pterosaurs with elongate skulls and stout sharp teeth may have caught fish or small tetrapods. *Pterodaustro* had an enormously long snout lined with a comblike array of fine teeth that may have been used for sieving small aquatic organisms. *Dsungaripterus* had long jaws that met at the tips like a pair of forceps. The tips of the jaws were probably covered with a horny beak, and blunt teeth occupied the rear of the jaw. These animals may have plucked snails from rocks with their beaks and then crushed them with their broad teeth.

The flight capacities of pterosaurs have long been debated, and most hypotheses about their ecology have been based on the assumption that they were weak fliers. That assumption has led to suggestions of restrictions of activities and habitats of pterosaurs that seem unlikely for a group of animals that was clearly diverse and successful through much of the Mesozoic. An aerodynamic analysis suggests that the flying abilities of pterosaurs have been underestimated (Hazlehurst and Rayner 1992). This view suggests that small pterosaurs were slow, maneuverable fliers like bats. The large pterosaurs appear to have been specialized for soaring like frigate birds and some vultures.

Speculations about the flying abilities of pterosaurs depend on what assumption one makes about the shape of the wing. It extended outward to the tips of the fourth finger, but where was it attached to the body? Did it stop at the waist, or did it extend onto the hindlimbs as the wing does in bats? The structure of the wing may have varied among pterosaurs. A fossil of *Pterodactylus* shows the wing attached at least to the thigh (Padian and Rayner 1993), whereas an extremely well-preserved fossil of *Sordes pilosus* from Jurassic sediments in Kazakhstan shows that the hind legs were involved in the flight structures (Unwin and Bakhurina 1994). The wing of this species attached along the outside of the hindlimb to the ankle, and another flight membrane, the uropatagium, stretched between the hind legs and was controlled by the fifth toe. This degree of involvement of the hindlimbs with the wings would have limited their role in terrestrial locomotion (as is the case for bats), and *Sordes* may have been a clumsy walker on flat surfaces but a good climber on rocks and trees (Unwin 1987). Other pterosaurs, such as *Pterodactylus*, may have been capable of bipedal locomotion (Padian and Rayner 1993).

The new fossil of *Sordes* also corrects a mistaken interpretation of earlier material: Traces of thin

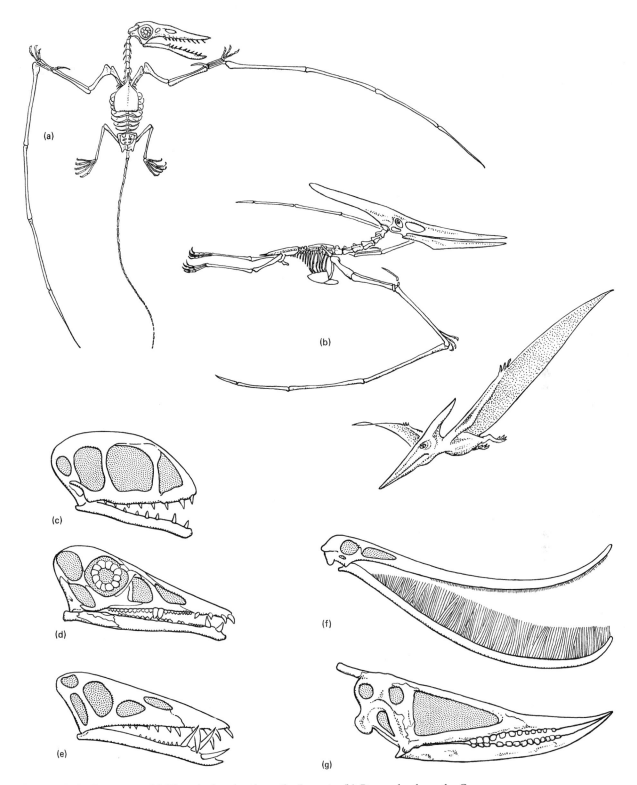

Figure 13–6 Pterosaurs. (a) *Rhamphorhynchus* from the Jurassic; (b) *Pteranodon* from the Cretaceous. The skulls of pterosaurs suggest dietary specializations. (c) *Anurognathus* may have been insectivorous; (d) *Eudimorphodon* may have eaten small vertebrates; (e) *Dorygnathus* may have been a fish eater; (f) *Pterodaustro* had a comblike array of teeth that may have been used to sieve plankton; (g) *Dsungaripterus* may have pulled mollusks from rocks with a horny beak and then crushed them with its molariform teeth. (Skulls modified from D. Norman, 1985, *The Illustrated Encyclopedia of Dinosaurs*, Salamander Books, London, UK.)

fibers had been interpreted as hair, and had led to the suggestion that *Sordes*, and perhaps all pterosaurs, were endotherms. The new fossil shows that these fibers were part of a system that stiffened the outer part of the wing (Unwin and Bakhurina 1994).

Dinosaurs   By far the most generally known of the archosaurs are the Saurischia and Ornithischia. These groups are linked in popular terminology as dinosaurs, but differ in the specializations they developed. Both groups appear to have been ancestrally bipedal and to have evolved some secondarily quadrupedal forms.

Many of the morphological trends that can be traced in archosaur evolution appear to be associated with increased locomotor efficiency. The two most important developments were the movement of the legs under the body and a widespread tendency toward bipedalism. Early archosauromorphs had a sprawling posture like that of many living amphibians and squamates. The humerus and femur were held out horizontally from the body, and the elbow and knee were bent at a right angle. Derived archosaurs had legs that were held vertically beneath the body.

Among early tetrapods, muscles originating on the pubis and inserting on the femur protract the leg (move it forward), muscles originating on the ischium abduct the femur (move it toward the midline of the body), and muscles originating on the tail retract the femur (move it posteriorly). The ancestral tetrapod pelvis, little changed from *Ichthyostega* through early archosauromorphs, was platelike (Figure 13–7a). The ilium articulated with one or two sacral vertebrae, and the pubis and ischium did not extend far anterior or posterior to the socket for articulation with the femur (acetabulum). The pubofemoral and ischiofemoral muscles extended ventrally from the pelvis to insert on the femur. (The downward force of their contraction was countered by iliofemoral muscles that ran from the ilium to the dorsal surface of the femur.) As long as the femur projected horizontally from the body, this system was effective. The pubofemoral and caudofemoral muscles were long enough to swing the femur through a large arc relative to the ground. As the legs were held more nearly under the body, the pubofemoral muscles became less effective. As the femur rotated closer to the pubis, the sites of muscle origin and insertion moved

closer together and the muscles themselves became shorter. A muscle's maximum contraction is about 30 percent of its resting length; thus the shorter muscles would have been unable to swing the femur through an arc large enough for effective locomotion had there not been changes in the pelvis associated with the evolution of bipedalism (Charig 1972).

The bipedal ornithischian and saurischian dinosaurs carried the legs completely under the body and show associated changes in pelvic structure. The two groups attained the same mechanically advantageous end in different ways (Figure 13–7). In quadrupedal saurischians, the pubis and ischium both became elongated and the pubis was rotated anteriorly, so that the pubofemoral muscles ran back from the pubis to the femur and were able to protract it . The pubis of early ornithischians did not project anteriorly. Instead, the ilium was elongated anteriorly, and it appears likely that the femoral protractors originated on the anterior part of the ilium, from which they ran posteriorly to the femur. This condition is seen in the pelvis of ornithischians such as *Scelidosaurus*, and appears to be maintained in the ankylosaurs, a group of derived quadrupedal ornithischians. Other ornithischians developed an anterior projection of the pubis that ran parallel to and projected beyond the anterior part of the ilium. This development occurred in both bipedal and quadrupedal lineages and provided a still more anterior origin for protractor muscles.

The trend toward bipedalism was important in terms of opening new adaptive zones to archosaurs. A fully quadrupedal animal uses its fore legs for walking, and any changes in limb morphology must be compatible with that function. As animals become increasingly bipedal, the importance of the fore legs for locomotion decreases and the scope of the specialized functions that can develop increases. Many of the smaller carnivorous dinosaurs that were fully bipedal used their fore legs to seize prey. Specialization of forelimbs as wings occurred twice among diapsids, once in the evolution of birds and once in pterosaurs.

Bipedal animals have hind legs that are considerably longer than their fore legs, and the degree of disproportion between hind legs and fore legs is assumed to reflect the extent of bipedalism in a given species. The quadrupedal archosaurs had longer hind legs than fore legs, and this condition is

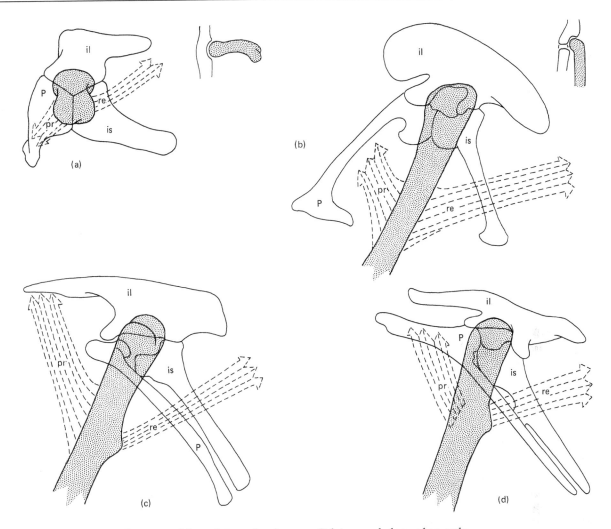

Figure 13–7 Functional aspects of the pelvises of archosaurs. Pelvic morphology of an early archosaur (a, *Euparkeria*), a saurischian dinosaur (b, *Ceratosaurus*), and two ornithischian dinosaurs (c, *Scelidosaurus*; d, *Thescelosaurus*). The presumed action of femoral protractor muscles (pr) and retractors (re) is shown by arrows. Insets show an anterior view of the articulation of the femur with the pelvis. p, pubis; il, ilium; is, ischium.

thought by most paleontologists to indicate that they were secondarily quadrupedal, having evolved from bipedal ancestors.

■ The Saurischian Dinosaurs and the Origin of Birds

Two groups of saurischian dinosaurs are distinguished, the **Theropoda** and the **Sauropodomorpha.** Theropods, which include the extant birds, are carnivorous bipeds, whereas the extinct sauropodomorphs included quadrupedal herbivores. Ten shared derived characters unite saurischi-

ans (Gauthier 1986); the most obvious is an elongate, mobile, S-shaped neck. This character distinguishes birds among living amniotes. Other birdlike characters of saurischians are found in modifications of the hand, skull, and postcranial skeleton.

Sauropodomorph Dinosaurs

The earliest sauropodomorph dinosaurs were the prosauropods, a group that was abundant and diverse in the Late Triassic and Early Jurassic (Galton 1990). Three types of prosauropods are known, differing in size and tooth structure. The anchisaurids ranged in size from *Anchisaurus* (2.5 meters) to

Figure 13–8 Sauropodomorph dinosaurs. (a) *Plateosaurus;* (b) *Camarasaurus;* (c) *Diplodocus.*

Plateosaurus (6 meters). The anchisaurids had long necks and small heads (Figure 13–8a), and the teeth of the best-known forms had large serrations. Modern herbivorous lizards (iguanas) have teeth with very much the same form, and anchisaurids were probably herbivorous. Supporting this view is the presence of **gastroliths** (*gast* = stomach, *lith* = stone) associated with some fossil prosauropods. These stones were probably swallowed by the dinosaurs and lodged in a muscular gizzard where they assisted in grinding plant material to a pulp that could be digested more readily; some birds use gastroliths in this manner. Prosauropods had cheeks that retained food in the mouth as it was processed by the teeth. The earliest prosauropods were small and bipedal. Later forms were larger, and their body proportions suggest that they could stand vertically

on their hind legs, but probably employed a quadrupedal posture most of the time.

Derived prosauropods, such as the melanorosaurids, were larger than the early prosauropods (*Riojasaurus* from the Late Triassic of Argentina was 11 meters long). No skulls of melanorosaurids have been found, so the structure of their teeth is unknown. The long, slender neck of *Riojasaurus* suggests that the head was small, like that of early prosauropods. The yunnanosaurids were smaller than the melanorosaurids and more lightly built, and they differed from the earlier prosauropods in having teeth shaped like flattened cylinders with a chisel-shaped tip. This is the tooth structure seen in the giant sauropod dinosaurs, and it is quite distinct from that of the laterally flattened, serrated teeth of early prosauropods, such as *Plateosaurus.*

The long necks of all the prosauropods suggest that they were able to browse on plant material at heights up to several meters above the ground. The ability to reach tall plants might have been a significant advantage during the shift from the low-growing *Dicroidium* flora to the taller bennettitaleans and conifers that occurred in the Late Triassic.

The derived sauropods of the Jurassic and Cretaceous were enormous quadrupedal herbivores. The sauropods were the largest terrestrial vertebrates that have ever existed, reaching lengths of 25 meters and weighing 20,000 to 50,000 kilograms. Three huge sauropods were discovered in Colorado (Jensen 1985). One of these, *Supersaurus*, may have been 40 meters long and have weighed more than 100,000 kilograms, the equivalent of 20 elephants. A new fossil from New Mexico, popularly known as *Seismosaurus*, may be even longer than *Supersaurus* (McIntosh 1989).

Two major types of giant sauropods can be distinguished, the diplodocoids and camarasauroids. The diplodocoids include *Apatosaurus* (formerly known as *Brontosaurus*) and *Diplodocus* (Figure 13–8b). These animals had long necks (15 cervical vertebrae) and long tails (up to 80 caudal vertebrae) that ended in a thin whiplash. Their front legs were relatively short, and the trunk slanted upward from the shoulders to the hips. Their skulls were elongate, teeth were limited to the front of the mouth, and the modest development of the bones of the lower jaw suggests that the jaw muscles were not particularly powerful.

Camarasauroids had necks with only 12 vertebrae, and their tails were shorter than those of diplodocoids (about 50 vertebrae), and lacked the whiplike extension that was characteristic of the diplodocoids (Figure 13–8c). The forelimbs of camarasauroids were relatively long, and the vertebral column was nearly horizontal. Brachiosaurids had still longer front legs, and the trunk sloped steeply downward from the shoulders to the hips. Camarasauroids and brachiosaurids had compact skulls with stout jaws and large chisel-shaped teeth. The teeth of *Camarasaurus* and *Brachiosaurus* show evidence of heavy wear, suggesting that they fed on abrasive material.

Both kinds of sauropods were enormously heavy, and their vertebrae show features that helped the spinal column to withstand the stresses to which it was subjected (Figure 13–9). The vertebrae themselves were massive, and the neural arches were well developed. Strong ligaments transmitted forces from one arch to adjacent ones to help equalize the stress. The head and tail were cantilevered from the body, supported by a heavy spinal ligament. The sides of the neural arches and centra had hollows in them, possibly occupied by air sacs in life, that reduced the mass of the bones with little reduction in strength. The feet of these forms were elephantlike, and fossilized tracks indicate that the hind legs bore about two-thirds of the body weight. Some trackways show no tail marks, suggesting that the tails were carried in the air, not dragged along the ground in the manner shown in almost all illustrations of these dinosaurs.

Another mechanical problem that the sauropods would have faced was the difficulty of pumping blood to a head that was sometimes as much as 20 meters above the ground and 6 or 7 meters above the level of the heart (Lillywhite 1991). Blood is mostly water, and water is heavy. When their heads were raised to browse on trees, the tallest sauropods would have required ventricular blood pressures exceeding 500 millimeters of mercury to overcome the hydrostatic pressure of a 7-meter column of blood between the heart and the brain. A column of blood extending to a head 20 meters above the ground could have produced blood pressures as great as 1000 millimeters of mercury in the vessels of the legs and feet of a large sauropod. Pressures that high would have tended to force water across the walls of the capillaries, causing the legs and feet to swell. Muscular constriction of small arteries in the limbs could have reduced pressure in the capillaries, and prevented this leakage of blood. Giraffes are the closest living parallel of the long-necked sauropod dinosaurs, and they encounter similar problems in pumping blood to the head and preventing the accumulation of water in the legs. Their hearts generate pressures approaching 300 millimeters of mercury to pump blood to the brain, and tight skin on the legs of giraffes prevents swelling.

Theropod Dinosaurs

The theropod dinosaurs include birds and all saurischian dinosaurs that are more closely related to birds than to sauropodomorph dinosaurs (Gauthier 1986). Theropod dinosaurs included three general types of animals: large predators that probably attacked large prey using their jaws as weapons (ceratosaurs, allosaurs, and tyranosaurs), fast-mov-

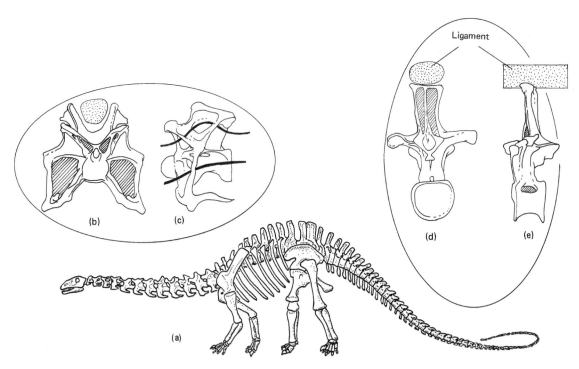

Figure 13–9   Structural features of sauropods. The skeletons of large diplodocid sauropods like *Apatosaurus* (a) combined lightness with strength. Vertebrae from the dorsal region (b, posterior view; c, lateral view) and neck (d, anterior view; e, lateral view) show the bony arches that acted like flying buttresses on a large building. (The black ribbons in [e] indicate the position of the arches.)

ing predators that seized small prey with their forelimbs (ornithomimids), and fast-moving predators that attacked prey larger than themselves with a hugh claw on the hind foot (dromeosaurs).

Large Theropods   The carnosaurs are the impressive predators that form the centerpieces of paleontological displays in many museums. Increasing body size these theropods through the Mesozoic paralleled a similar size increase in the herbivorous saurischians and ornithischians that were their prey. *Megalosaurus* of the Late Jurassic was 6 meters long, and more fully bipedal than earlier forms. The head was large in proportion to the body, and the long teeth were fearsome weapons. The Late Cretaceous tyrannosaurids such as *Tarbosaurus* and *Tyrannosaurus* were still longer, up to 15 meters in length, and stood some 6 meters high (Figure 13–10). The front legs of the most specialized of these giants seem absurdly small; they were too short even to reach the mouth and had only two small fingers on each hand. Instead of relying on the fore legs to capture prey as coelurosaurs

and ornithomimids probably did, large theropods appear to have concentrated their weapons in the skull. The size of the head increased relative to the body, and the neck shortened. The head was lightened by the elaboration of antorbital and mandibular fenestrae that reduced the skull to a series of bony arches providing maximum strength for a given weight.

The teeth of these large therapods were as much as 15 centimeters long, dagger-shaped with serrated edges and driven by powerful jaw muscles. Marks from the teeth of predatory dinosaurs are sometimes found on fossilized dinosaur bones, and these records of prehistoric predation provide a way to estimate the force of a dinosaur's bite. The pelvis of a horned dinosaur (*Triceratops*) found in Montana bears dozens of bite marks from a *Tyranosaurus rex*, some as deep as 11.5 mm. A fossilized *Tyranosaurus* tooth was used to make an indentation that deep in the pelvis of a cow (Erickson et al. 1996). The force required to make the marks on the *Triceratops* pelvis were estimated to range from 6,410 to 14,400 N. These values exceed the force that can be exerted by

Figure 13–10 Theropod dinosaurs. (a) *Coelophysis*, a Triassic ceratosaur; (b) *Ornithomimus*, a Cretaceous ornithomimid; (c) *Tyrannosaurus*, a large Cretaceous theropod; (d) *Deinonychus*, a Cretaceous deinonychosaur.

several extant predators (dog, wolf, lion, shark). Interestingly, an alligator is the only predator tested that can deliver a bite as powerful as that of the *Tyrannosaurus*, and the jaws and teeth of alligators have many of the same structural characters as the jaws and teeth of tyranosaurus.

Other experimental studies that used fossilized tyrannosaur teeth to bite meat showed that the serrations increased the cutting effect only slightly, but they trapped and retained meat fibers (Abler 1992). This debris would have supported the growth of bacteria, and a tyrannosaur bite would almost surely have become infected. Perhaps tyrannosaurs did not kill necessarily large prey such as sauropods in the initial attack, but relied on infection to weaken the victim and make it susceptible to a subsequent attack. Bacteria on the teeth and claws of

the largest extant lizards, Komodo dragons (*Varanus Komodoensis*) are thought to play exactly this role when the lizards prey on deer.

The spinosaurids, large (to 13 meters) theropods known from the Cretaceous of North America and Africa, are distinguished by having trunk vertebrae with neural spines that projected upward as much as 1.8 meters above the back. These spines are assumed to have supported a dorsal crest. A huge saillike structure of this sort might have had several functions. Dorsal crests composed of individual scales occur among lizards. They are sexually dimorphic—better developed in males than in females—and are used in social behavior. A function of this sort seems a plausible evolutionary origin for the sail of *Spinosaurus*, but was probably not its only function. The surface area of the sail of a

Spinosaurus or an *Acrocanthosaurus* was a substantial fraction of the total surface area of the animal, and the sail would have affected energy exchange between the animal and the environment.

Whatever the selective forces that led to the first appearance of the sail, thermoregulation was almost surely one of its ultimate functions, because it was too large not to have an effect on energy exchange. If a *Spinosaurus* oriented its body perpendicular to the rays of the sun, the sail would absorb heat that could be transported into the body by blood flow. Large lizards and crocodilians use this mechanism to speed warming in the morning, although they lack specialized heat exchange structures. The sail of a spinosaurid could also have been used to dissipate heat. If the animal faced into the sun, only the front edge of the sail would receive direct solar radiation, and the sides of the sail could transfer heat from the body by convection and radiation.

Small theropods   Many of the smaller theropods are found among the coelurosaurs, a mainly Cretaceous group which includes birds and all the theropods more closely related to birds than to allosaurs. Several characters of living birds are seen in coelurosaurs (Gauthier 1986). The most interesting of these from the perspective of the origin of birds include features usually thought to be associated with powered flight, especially a fused bony sternum and a furcula (wishbone) formed by fusion of the clavicles. The widespread occurrence of a furcula among nonflying relatives of birds shows that the original function of the furcula did not involve flight. Thus, the important role the furcula plays in flight by extant birds has evolved secondarily (Norell et al. 1997).

Small theropods were also found among the ceratosaurs, such as the Triassic form *Coelophysis* (Figure 13–10a), which was about 3 meters in total length. These were probably active, cursorial predators on small dinosaurs, lizards, and insects. *Ornithomimus* of the Late Cretaceous was ostrich-like in size, shape, and probably ecology as well. It had a small skull on a long neck, and its toothless jaws were covered with a horny bill. The fore legs were longer than those of *Coelophysis*, and only three digits were developed on the hands. The inner digit was opposable and the wrist was flexible, making the hand an effective organ for the capture of small prey. Like ostriches, *Ornithomimus* was probably omnivorous and fed on fruits, insects, small vertebrates, and eggs. Quite possibly it lived

in herds, as do ostriches, and its long legs suggest that it inhabited open regions rather than forests.

Apparently not all ornithomimds preyed on small animals. A fossil from the Gobi Desert, *Deinocheirus* (terrible hand), had fingers more than 60 centimeters long that appear to have been used for grasping and dismembering large prey. The proportions of the hands and arms are like those of coelurosaurs, and if this theropod had the same body proportions as other coelurosaurs, it may have been more than 7.5 meters tall, exceeding *Tyrannosaurus rex*, previously the tallest theropod known.

Dromeosaurs   *Deinonychus* was unearthed by an expedition from Yale University in Early Cretaceous sediments in Montana (Figure 13–10d). It is a small coelurosaurian theropod, a little over 2 meters long. Its distinctive features are the claw on the second toe of the hind foot and the tail. In other theropods the hind feet are clearly specialized for bipedal locomotion and are very similar to bird feet. In these forms the third toe is the largest, the second and fourth are smaller, and the fifth has sometimes disappeared entirely. The first toe is turned backward, as in birds, to provide support behind the axis of the leg. The second toe of dromeosaurs and especially the claw on that toe are enlarged (Figure 13–11). In its normal position the claw was apparently held off the ground and it could be bent upward even farther.

It seems likely that dromeosaurs used these claws in hunting, disemboweling prey with a kick. The structure of the tail was equally remarkable. The caudal vertebrae were surrounded by bony rods that were extensions of the prezygapophyses (dorsally) and hemal arches (ventrally) that ran forward about 10 vertebrae from their place of origin. Contraction of muscles at the base of the tail would be transmitted through these bony rods, drawing the vertebrae together and making the tail a rigid structure that could be used as a counterbalance or swung like a heavy stick. Possibly the tail was part of the armament of *Deinonychus*, used to knock prey to the ground where it could be kicked, and it may have served as a counterweight for balance as *Deinonychus* made sharp turns.

The discovery of *Deinonychus* stimulated a reexamination of fossils of several other genera of small theropod dinosaurs from the Cretaceous, including *Dromeosaurus* and *Velociraptor*. All these forms have an enlarged claw on the second toe of the hind foot, and they are now grouped with *Deinonychus* and

Figure 13–11   The foot of *Deinony-chus*, showing the enlarged claw. (Courtesy of Barbara Moore, Peabody Museum of Natural History, Yale University.)

birds in the Maniraptora. *Deinonychus*-like claws 35 centimeters long that were discovered in Early Cretaceous sediments in Utah in the autumn of 1991 probably came from a previously unknown theropod (nicknamed "Super-Slasher" by paleontologists) that was nearly as large as a *Tyrannosaurus rex* and had the speed, agility, and predatory behavior of *Deinonychus* (Figure 13–12).

Birds as Dinosaurs

The similarity of birds and dinosaurs has long been recognized. In the 1860s and 1870s Thomas Henry Huxley was an ardent advocate of that relationship, writing that birds are nothing more than "glorified reptiles." Huxley, in fact, was so impressed by their many similarities that he placed birds and reptiles together in his classification scheme as the Class Sauropsida. For most of the next century traditional systematics, with its emphasis on strict hierarchical categories, obscured that evolutionary relationship by placing reptiles and birds at the same level (Class Reptilia and Class Aves). Cladistic systematics emphasizes monophyltic evolutionary lineages, and birds are now viewed as the most derived theropod dinosaurs. The similarities of birds and theropods include the following derived characters:

Elongate, mobile S-shaped neck
Tridactyl foot with digitigrade posture
Intertarsal ankle joint
Hollow, pneumatic bones

Birds differ from other theropods mainly in features directly associated with flight and endothermy, both of which are dependent on feathers. Perhaps in no other major group of vertebrates has evolution been so determined by a single structural feature as in the case of birds with their highly modifiable and multifunctional feathers.

As we pointed out in Chapter 4, birds have nearly constant body temperatures of 40 to 41°C. These high temperatures depend on two characteristics: the high metabolic rates of birds and the excellent insulation provided by feathers. The paradox presented by the evolution of endothermy is that neither a high metabolic rate nor insulation

Figure 13–12 Two large deinonychosaurs ("super slashers") attacking a brachiosaurid. (From *The New York Times*, illustration by Michael Rothman. Copyright © 1992 by The New York Times Company. Reprinted by permission.)

is advantageous by itself; both are required for endothermal thermoregulation to be functional. Thus, the origin of feathers probably resulted initially from selection for some function other than endothermal thermoregulation. One possibility is that elongate scales initially facilitated ectothermal thermoregulation as explained in Chapter 4.

The second major difference between birds and the other living archosaurs (the crocodilians) is, of course, the ability of birds to fly. Is it possible that feathers evolved initially because they conferred an advantage in locomotion, and subsequently took on a thermoregulatory role? To answer this question we must examine hypotheses about the origin of flight. Three types of locomotion have been suggested as being important in the evolution of flight by birds: running along the ground, leaping into the air, and gliding from trees. Hypotheses about

the origin of flight can be divided into two categories: The from-the-ground-up hypothesis pictures flight as an outgrowth of selection for terrestrial locomotion (see Ostrom 1986), whereas the from-the-trees-down proposal suggests that birds were initially arboreal animals that first took to the air as gliders (see Rayner 1988). We will examine the evidence for both categories of hypotheses, but first we must consider the earliest bird, *Archaeopteryx.*

Archaeopteryx *and the Origin of Birds* At least three different groups of diapsids developed gliding or powered flight in the Mesozoic. The kuehneosaurids of the Late Triassic were the first tetrapods to become airborne. These were diapsids, up to a meter long, probably in the archosauromorph lineage. They are distinguished by extremely elongate ribs that probably supported a wing of skin like that seen in the living East Indian lizards of the genus *Draco*. *Draco* are arboreal lizards, and they use their wings to glide from tree to tree. A flight starts with a dive from an elevated perch. The lizard descends at an angle of about 45 degrees, then levels out and uses the kinetic energy developed during the dive to glide nearly horizontally. A brief upward glide immediately precedes landing on another perch. Glides as long as 60 meters have been recorded with a loss of altitude of less than 2 meters.

The ribs of *Draco* can be folded back against the body when they are not in use. The skin of the wings is brightly colored, and the wings are spread in social displays as well as for flight. Many lizards flatten the body laterally by spreading the ribs, making themselves look bigger during social interactions. The elongate ribs and wings of *Draco* and the kuehneosaurids might have had their origin in that widespread behavior.

True wings and powered flight (as distinct from airfoils used for gliding) evolved twice among diapsids—in the pterosaurs and independently in the birds. The oldest known birds are from the Late Jurassic and are even more dinosaurlike than extant birds. Knowledge of these birds is currently based on one fossilized impression of a feather and on seven fossilized skeletons, some with very distinct impressions of feathers (Figure 13–13). These fossil

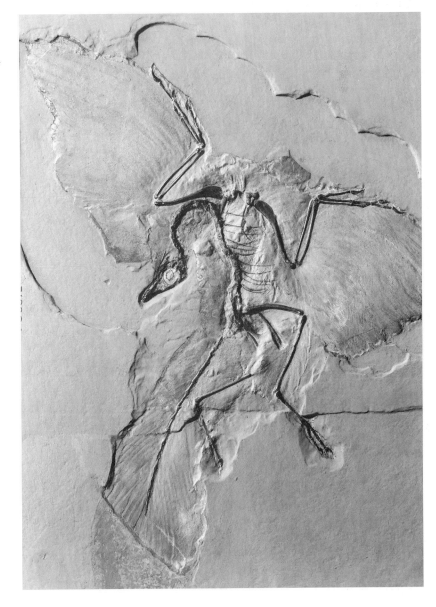

Figure 13–13 *Archaeopteryx lithographica*. (From the Sanford Bird Hall, American Museum of Natural History #325097. Courtesy Department Library Services.)

birds, which are about the size of a crow, have been given the name *Archaeopteryx* (ancient wing). Unquestionably, the most important features of these fossils are the feathers. Without the feather impressions, the fossils would be considered to be dinosaurs. In fact, that is exactly what happened to one *Archaeopteryx* fossil that was collected in Germany in 1951. It lacks obvious indications of feathers and was labeled as *Compsognathus* (a small theropod) until 1973, when it was recognized as the fifth known specimen of *Archaeopteryx.*

Feathers were well developed in *Archaeopteryx*, indicating that they had long been present in the lineage. In addition to a presumed covering of body feathers, the wing feathers were differentiated into an outer series of primaries on the hand bones and an inner series of secondaries along the outer arm. This arrangement of flight feathers is essentially the same as that seen in extant birds, and the flight feathers on the wings of *Archaeopteryx* have asymmetrical vanes like those of flying birds, suggesting that they had been shaped by aerodynamic forces associated with flapping flight (Feduccia and Tordoff 1979). In contrast, the feathers of flightless birds serve mostly as insulation and have symmetrical vanes on each side of the rachis. The long tail of *Archaeopteryx* is not known in any other bird. The rectrices (tail feathers) are arranged in 15 pairs along the sides of the 6th through 20th caudal vertebrae. Feathers are the definitive character of birds, and are believed to have evolved from scales. The evidence for this homology lies in the biochemical similarities of scales and feathers and the fact that feathers and scales develop from similar embryonic structures consisting of dermis and epidermis.

No intermediate fossils link *Archaeopteryx* with any of the groups from which it might have evolved, and the question of which theropods are the closest relatives of birds continues to be controversial. The generally accepted view places the closest relatives of birds among the dromeosaurs (Dingus and Rowe 1998). Support for this view, proposed in 1974 by John Ostrom of Yale University, rests on more than 20 features that *Archaeopteryx* shares with other Maniraptora (Figure 13–14). However, suggestions persist that birds were derived from archosaur lineages that separated from the saurischian stock earlier than the theropods (Feduccia and Wild 1993, Feduccia 1996 [for a contrasting view see Norell and Chiappe 1996 and Pedian and Chiappe 1998]).

The Origin of Flight　　Flapping flight has evolved in three separate groups of vertebrates: pterosaurs, birds, and bats. The wings of these different vertebrates represent examples of convergent evolution, and the actual structural details of the wing design are quite different in the three groups. Only birds employ a complicated series of overlapping epidermal derivatives (feathers) as the main wing surface.

What were the selective advantages for the evolution of wings and flight in the proavian ancestors of birds? Two competing hypotheses have existed for a century—the arboreal theory and the terrestrial theory (Figure 13–15). To examine these hypotheses, we need to give some further consideration to *Archaeopteryx*.

What kind of life did *Archaeopteryx* lead? It has often been considered an arboreal climber, jumper, and glider with limited powers of flapping flight that allowed it to extend the distance it could travel through the air between trees. Yalden (1985) and Feduccia (1993) interpreted the morphology of *Archaeopteryx* as indicating that it climbed in trees like a squirrel, and this view finds a parallel in current ideas about the biology of pterosaurs. In this scenario it scampered about bipedally on the branches of trees, aided by grasping toes, a reversed hallux, grasping claws on the leading edges of its wings, and a long tail that was used for balance. This conception finds a parallel among extant birds in the young hoatzin, which climbs about aided by functional clawed fingers on its wings.

The arboreal theory of the origin of avian flight has long dominated the field (Rayner 1988). According to this view, the proavian relatives of *Archaeopteryx* were tree climbers that jumped from branch to branch and from tree to tree much as some squirrels, lizards, and monkeys do. Under selective pressures favoring increased distance and accuracy of travel between trees, structures that provided some surface area for lift would be advantageous. A functional analogy can be made to gliding lizards such as *Draco*, although the morphological structures involved in the proavian model are the forelimbs, not the ribs. By this hypothesis, the evolution of flying forms passed from gliding stages through intermediate stages, such as *Archaeopteryx*, in which gliding was aided by weak flapping flight, to fully airborne flapping fliers. However, one problem that has not been satisfactorily explained by the arboreal theory is selection for bipedalism in an arboreal habitat (Gauthier and Padian 1985). Could

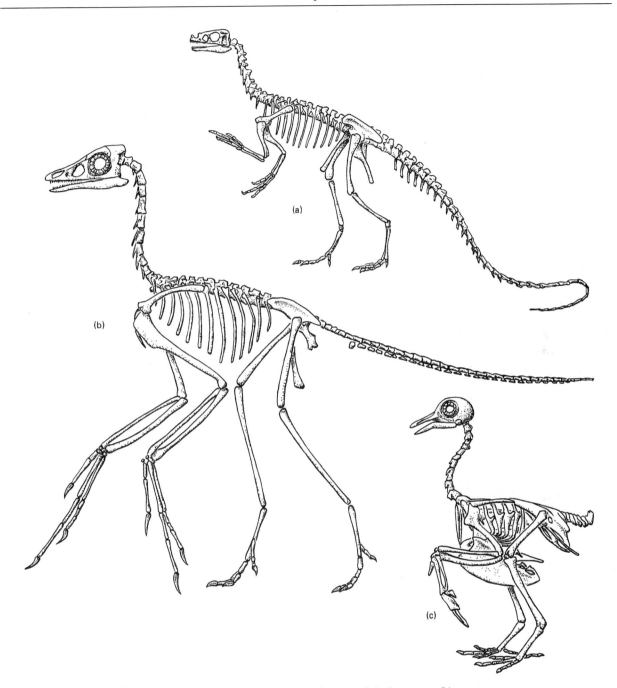

Figure 13–14 Structural similarities of dinosaurs and birds. Skeleton of *Archaeopteryx* (b) compared with that of *Ornitholestes*, a maniraptoran (a), and a modern bird (c). (Modified from D. Norman, 1985, *The Illustrated Encyclopedia of Dinosaurs*, Salamander Books, London, UK.)

a two-legged creature land upright on the branch of a tree without already possessing well-coordinated, aerodynamically controlled braking ability?

If, as seems reasonable from the fossil record of the coelurosaurs and the structure of *Archaeopteryx* itself, the lineage giving rise to birds consisted of bipedal, terrestrial forms, is it necessary to invoke arboreal selection pressures at all for the evolution of avian flight? The from-the-ground-up theory postulates that flapping flight evolved directly from ground-dwelling, bipedal runners (Ostrom 1974).

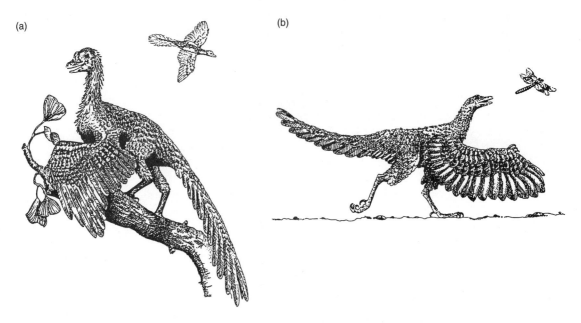

(a)

(b)

Figure 13–15 Two reconstructions of *Archaeopteryx*. (a) The from-the-trees-down hypothesis, showing *Archaeopteryx* as an arboreal climber and (rear) glider; (b) the from-the-ground-up hypothesis showing *Archaeopteryx* as a cursorial arboreal hunter. (From Rayner 1988.)

According to the first version of this hypothesis (the cursorial theory), proavians were fast, bipedal runners that used their wings as planes to increase lift and lighten the load for running. In a later development, the wings were flapped as the animal ran to provide additional forward propulsion, much as a chicken flaps across the barnyard to escape from a dog. Finally, the pectoral muscles and flight feathers became sufficiently developed for full-powered flight through the air.

The cursorial theory in its original form failed as an explanation because in physical and mechanical terms flapping is not an effective mechanism to increase running speed. Maximum traction on the ground is required to achieve acceleration, and this traction can be provided only by solid contact of the feet with a firm substrate. Planing with wings would have reduced traction, and the push from the small surfaces of the protowings probably would not have compensated the loss in speed from the hind legs, much less added to acceleration.

A recently identified specimen of *Archaeopteryx*, misidentified as a coelurosaur for over 100 years, revealed some previously unknown details of the hand and led John Ostrom to modify the cursorial theory. Some elements of the manus are extremely well preserved in this specimen and show the actual horny claws on digits 1 and 3. These claws look like the talons of a predatory bird.

The similarities in morphology between the hand, metacarpus, forearm, humerus, and pectoral apparatus of *Archaeopteryx* and those of several coelurosaurs may be evidence of a similarity in biological roles for both—a grasping function for predation. Although bearing feathers, the forelimb and shoulder of *Archaeopteryx* have not been structurally much modified from the skeletal condition of these small theropods, and they differ from all known birds in lacking several features that are critical for powered flight (fused carpometacarpus, restricted wrist and elbow joints, modified coracoids, and a platelike sternum with keel) (Jenkins 1993). In fact, the only skeletal feature suggesting flight is the well-developed furcula, which was present in coelurosaurs and is present in extant birds, although reduced or absent in flightless forms. Thus, the entire pectoral appendage (skeleton and muscles) of *Archaeopteryx* appears to have been as well adapted for predation as for flight. From these considerations, Ostrom postulated that the incipient wings of the proavians evolved first as snares to trap insects or other prey against the ground or to bat them down out of the air, making it easier for them to be grasped by the claws and teeth. The structures subsequently became further modified into flapping appendages capable of subduing larger prey and coincidentally aided in leaping attacks on that prey.

More recently, aerodynamic models have suggested that evolution of the avian wing could have assisted horizontal jumps after prey. By spreading or moving its forelimbs, the proavian cursor could control pitch, roll, and yaw during a jump and also maintain balance on landing (Caple et al. 1983).

Despite the details of anatomy detectable from the fossils, *Archaeopteryx* remains difficult to interpret in functional terms. The structural features of *Archaeopteryx* seem consistent with those of a basically ground-dwelling, running and jumping predator that was also capable of powered flight over short distances (Peterson 1985). A small cursorial predator of this sort fits well within the diversity of coelurosaurian dinosaurs, and emphasizes the remarkable similarities to birds that are seen in derived coelurosaurs.

A physiological perspective has enriched our interpretation of the biology of *Archaeopteryx* (Ruben 1991, 1993). Paleontologists have assumed that the energy requirements of takeoff and powered flight are too great for an ectotherm. These assumptions are not supported by our understanding of the metabolic capacities of modern lizards. During burst activity the locomotor muscles of terrestrial lizards produce at least twice as much power (measured as watts per kilogram of muscle) as do the locomotor muscles of birds and mammals. This power is derived largely from anaerobic metabolic pathways, as described in Chapter 4, and high levels of power output cannot be sustained indefinitely. Nonetheless, some modern lizards are capable of substantial periods of rapid locomotion—the Komodo monitor lizard is reported to sprint for a kilometer at a velocity of 30 kilometers per hour. Ruben calculated that a similar power output would have allowed an *Archaeopteryx* to fly at least 1.5 kilometers at a velocity of 40 kilometers per hour.

An animal that could take off from the ground and fly rapidly for several hundred meters would be able to escape predators or fly up into trees. Many living birds, including cursorial predators such as the North American roadrunner and the African secretary bird, use flight in exactly this way. The Central American chachalaca is somewhat more arboreal than roadrunners and secretary birds, and may be a still better model for the biology of *Archaeopteryx*.

■ The Ornithischian Dinosaurs

The difference in the structure of the pelvis of saurischian and ornithischian dinosaurs indicates an early separation of the two groups. However, ornithischians and saurischians show parallels in body form that probably reflect the mechanical problems of being very large terrestrial animals. Ornithischians were herbivorous and radiated into considerably more diverse morphological forms than did the herbivorous sauropod saurischians. All ornithischians had cheeks, and horny beaks rather than teeth at the front of the mouth. The larger ornithischians were not as bipedal as some large theropod saurischians, and the forelimbs were never greatly reduced.

Three groups of ornithischian dinosaurs can be distinguished (Figure 13–16).

Thyreophora: The armored dinosaurs. Quadrupedal forms including stegosaurs (forms with a double row of plates or spines on the back and tail) and ankylosaurs (heavily armored forms, some with clublike tails).

Ornithopoda: Bipedal forms, including the duck-billed dinosaurs.

Marginocephalia: The pachycephalosaurs (bipedal dinosaurs with enormously thick skulls) and ceratopsians (the quadrupedal horned dinosaurs).

Thyreophora: Stegosaurs and Ankylosaurs

The stegosaurs were a group of quadrupedal herbivorous ornithischians that were most abundant in the Jurassic, although some forms persisted to the end of the Cretaceous. *Stegosaurus*, a large form from the Jurassic of western North America, is the most familiar of these dinosaurs. It was up to 6 meters long, and its fore legs were much shorter than its hind legs (Figure 13–17). A double series of leaf-shaped plates were probably set alternately on the left and right sides of the vertebral column. Two pairs of spikes on the tail made it a formidable weapon. *Kentrosaurus*, an African species that was contemporaneous with *Stegosaurus*, was smaller (2.5 meters), and had a series of seven pairs of spikes that started near the middle of the trunk and extended down the tail. Anterior to these spikes

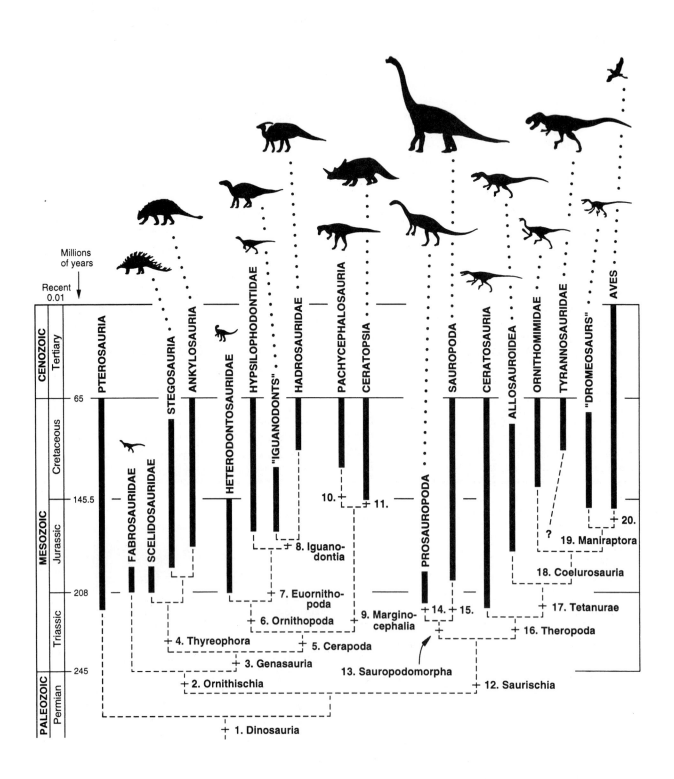

were about seven pairs of plates similar to those of *Stegosaurus*, but smaller.

The function of the plates of *Stegosaurus* has been a matter of contention for decades. Originally they were assumed to have provided protection from predators, and some reconstructions have shown the plates lying flat against the sides of the body as shields. A defensive function is not very convincing, however. Whether the plates were erect or flat, they left large areas on the sides of the body and the belly unprotected. Another idea is that the plates were used for heat exchange (Farlow et al. 1976). Examination shows that the plates were extensively vascularized and could have carried a large flow of blood to be warmed or cooled according to the needs of the animal (Buffrénil et al. 1986). *Kentrosaurus*, the African counterpart of *Stegosaurus*, had much smaller dorsal plates than *Stegosaurus* and the

---

1. Dinosauria: S-shaped swanlike neck, forelimb less than half the length of hindlimb, hand digit 4 reduced, plus other characteristics of the palate, pectoral and pelvic girdles, hand, hindlimb, and foot. **2.** Ornithischia: Cheek teeth with low subtriangular crowns, reduced antorbital opening, predentary bone, toothless and roughened tip of snout, jaw joint set below level of upper tooth row, at least five sacral vertebrae, ossified tendons above sacral region, pelvis with pubis directed backwards, small prepubic process on pubis. **3.** Genasauria: Muscular cheeks, reduction in size of mandibular foremen. **4.** Thyreophora: Characters of the orbit of the eye, rows of keeled scutes on the dorsal body surface. **5.** Cerapoda: Five or fewer premaxillary teeth, a diastema between premaxillary and maxillary teeth, characters of the pelvis. **6.** Ornithopoda: Premaxillary tooth row offset ventrally compared to maxillary tooth row, jaw joint set well below level of tooth rows by ventral extension of quadrate. **7.** Euornithopoda: Absence of prominent boss in cheek region; **8.** Iguanodontia: Premaxillary teeth absent, external naris enlarged, wrist bones fused, plus characters of the tooth surfaces and tooth enamel, lower jaw and skull. **9.** Marginocephalia: A shelf formed by the parietals and squamosals extends over the occiput, characters of the snout and pelvis. **10.** Pachycephalosauria: Thickened skull roof (frontals and parietals), other characters of the skull, dorsal vertebrae, forelimbs, and pelvis. **11.** Ceratopsia: Head triangular in dorsal view; tall, narrow anterior beak; jugals flare beyond the skull roof; deep, transversely arched palate, immobile mandibular symphysis. **12.** Saurischia: Construction of the snout including subnarial foramen, extension of the temporal musculature onto the frontal bones, elongation of the neck, modifications of the articulations between vertebrae, and modifications of the hand including a large thumb. **13.** Sauropodomorpha: Relatively small skull, anterior end of premaxilla deflected, teeth with serrated crowns, at least ten cervical vertebrae forming an elongated neck. **14.** Prosauropoda: Elongation of claw on digit one of hand. **15.** Sauropoda: Four or more sacral vertebrae, straight femur with lesser trochanter reduced or absent. **16.** Theropoda: Articulation in the middle of the lower jaw, construction of bones of the skull roof and palate, fenestra in the maxilla, characters of the vertebrae, neural arches, and transverse processes lacking posterior to a transition point in the middle of the tail, hand with elongated digits 1-3 armed with highly recurved claws, fibula and tibia closely adpressed, foot long and narrow with fifth metatarsal reduced to a splint, thin-walled (hollow) long bones. **17.** Tetanurae: Large fenestra posteriorly located in the maxilla, large fanglike teeth absent from dentally, maxillary tooth row ends anterior to orbit of eye, transition point in tail is farther anterior than in theropods, expanded distal portion of pubis, characters of the foot. **18.** Coelurosauria: Fenestra in roof of mouth, characters of cervical vertebrae and ribs, furcula (wishbone) formed by fused clavicles, fused bony sternal plates, elongate forelimb and hand, characters of the foot. **19.** Maniraptora: Prefrontal reduced or absent, characters of the vertebrae, transition point in tail vertebrae close to base of tail, characteristics of the feet and pelvis. **20.** Aves: Progressive loss of teeth on maxilla and dentary, well-developed bill, feathers, characteristics of skull, jaws, vertebrae, and axial and appendicular skeleton. (Based on J. Gauthier, 1986, pages 1–55 in *The Origin of Birds and the Evolution of Flight*, edited by K. Padian, Memoirs of the California Academy of Sciences, Number 8; P. C. Sereno, 1986, *National Geographic Research* 2:234–256; M. J. Benton (editor), 1988, *The Phylogeny and Classification of the Tetrapods*, Special Volume No. 35B, The Systematics Association, Oxford University Press, Oxford, UK; R. L. Carroll, 1988, *Vertebrate Paleontology and Evolution*, Freeman, New York, NY; M. J. Benton (editor), 1993, *The Fossil Record 2*, Chapman & Hall, London, UK; and M. J. Benton, 1997, *Vertebrate Paleontology*, second edition, Chapman and Hall, London, UK.)

Figure 13–16 Phylogenetic relationships of the Dinosauria. This diagram shows the probable relationships among the major groups of dinosaurs, including birds. Dotted lines show interelationships only; they do not indicate times of divergence nor the unrecorded presence of taxa in the fossil record. The numbers indicate derived characters that distinguish the lineages.

Figure 13–17 Quadrupedal ornithischians. (a) *Stegosaurus* and (b) *Kentrosaurus* were stegosaurians; (c) *Ankylosaurus*, an ankylosaurian; and (d) *Styracosaurus*, a ceratopsoid.

plates on *Kentrosaurus* extended only from the neck to the middle of the trunk. Posteriorly a double row of spikes extended down the tail. These spikes appear to have had a primarily defensive function rather than a thermoregulatory one. It is frustrating not to be able to compare the thermoregulatory behaviors of the two kinds of stegosaurs in a controlled experiment.

The short front legs of stegosaurs kept their heads close to the ground, and their heavy bodies do not give the impression that they were able to stand upright on their hind legs to feed on trees as ornithopods and perhaps sauropods did. Stegosaurs may have browsed on ferns, cycads, and other low-growing plants. The skull was surprisingly small for such a large animal, and had the familiar horny beak at the front of the jaws. The

teeth show none of the specializations seen in hadrosaurs or ceratopsians, and the coronoid process of the lower jaw is not well developed. Unlike hadrosaurs and ceratopsians, which appear to have been able to grind or cut plant material into small pieces that could be digested efficiently, stegosaurs may have eaten large quantities of food without much chewing and relied largely on the fermentative activity of symbiotic bacteria and protozoans to aid digestion. Stegosaurs may also have used gastroliths in a muscular gizzard to pulverize plant material.

The ankylosaurs are a group of heavily armored dinosaurs that are found in Jurassic and Cretaceous deposits in North America and Eurasia. Ankylosaurs were quadrupedal ornithischians that ranged from 2 to 6 meters in length. They had short legs and broad bodies, with **osteoderms** (bones embedded in the skin) that were fused together on the neck, back, hips, and tail to produce large shieldlike pieces. Bony plates also covered the skull and jaws, and even the eyelids of *Euoplocephalus* had bony armor. Ankylosaurs had short tails, and some species had a lump of bone at the end of the tail that could apparently be swung like a club. The posteriormost caudal vertebrae of these club-tailed forms have elongated neural and hemal arches that touch or overlap the arches on adjacent vertebrae and ossified tendons running down both sides of the vertebrae. Contraction of the muscles that inserted on these tendons probably pulled the posterior caudal vertebrae together to form a stiff handle for swinging the club head at the end of the tail. The tail of these animals resembles nothing so much as an enormous medieval mace. Other species had spines projecting from the back and sides of the body, and ankylosaurs must have been difficult animals for tyrannosaurids to attack. The brains of ankylosaurs appear to have had large olfactory stalks leading to complex nasal passages that probably had sheets of bone that supported an epithelium with chemosensory cells. If this interpretation is correct, ankylosaurs may have had a keen sense of smell.

Ornithopods

Ornithopods from the Early Jurassic, the heterodontosaurids and related groups, were mostly small (1 to 3 meters long) and bipedal. They had four toes on the hind feet and, unlike the bipedal saurischians, retained five toes on the forefeet. Their cheek teeth were specialized for grinding plant material. Some heterodontosaurids had sharp tusks that may have been better developed in males than in females. The Cretaceous hypsilophodontids had horny beaks with which they may have cropped plant material that was subsequently ground by the high-crowned cheek teeth that gave the family its name (high-ridged tooth).

The first dinosaur fossil to be recognized as such was an ornithopod, *Iguanodon*, found in Cretaceous sediments in England (Figure 13–18). Specimens have subsequently been found in Europe and Mongolia, and related forms have been discovered in Africa and Australia. *Iguanodon* reached lengths of 10 meters, although most specimens are smaller. Iguanodontids from the Early Cretaceous had large heads and elongated snouts that ended in broad,

toothless beaks. Their teeth, which were in the rear of the jaws, were laterally flattened and had serrated edges, very like the lateral teeth of living herbivorous lizards like *Iguana.*

The first digit on each forefoot of derived ornithopods was modified as a spine that projected upward. These spines show a striking resemblance to the spines on the forefeet of some frogs that are used as defensive weapons and during intraspecific encounters. *Ouranosaurus*, an ornithopod known from the early Middle Cretaceous of Africa, had a large sail that was supported by elongated neural spines on the vertebrae of the trunk and tail. Behavioral and thermoregulatory functions can be postulated for the sail of *Ouranosaurus* as they were for the similar structures of the spinosaurid carnosaurs.

Hadrosaurs   The derived ornithopods include several specialized forms of hadrosaurs (duck-billed dinosaurs). Hadrosaurs were the last group of ornithopods to evolve, appearing in the middle of the Cretaceous. As their name implies, some duck-billed dinosaurs had flat snouts with a ducklike bill (Figure 13–18d). These were large animals, some reaching lengths in excess of 10 meters and weights greater than 10,000 kilograms. The anterior part of the jaws was toothless, but a remarkable battery of teeth occupied the rear of the jaws. On each side of the upper and lower jaws were four tooth rows, each containing about 40 teeth packed closely side by side to form a massive tooth plate. Several sets of replacement teeth lay beneath those in use, so a hadrosaur had several thousand teeth in its mouth, of which several hundred were in use simultaneously. Fossilized stomach contents of hadrosaurs consist of pine needles and twigs, seed, and fruit of terrestrial plants.

The rise of the hadrosaurs was approximately coincident with a change in the terrestrial flora during the Middle Cretaceous. The bennettitaleans and seed ferns that had spread during the Triassic now were replaced by flowering plants (angiosperms). Simultaneous with the burgeoning of the angiosperms and hadrosaurian dinosaurs was a decline in the enormous sauropod dinosaurs such as *Diplodocus* and *Brachiosaurus.* Those lineages were most diverse in the Late Jurassic and Early Cretaceous, and only a few forms persisted after the middle of the Cretaceous.

Three kinds of hadrosaurs are distinguished: flat-headed, solid-crested, and hollow-crested (Figure 13–19). In the flat-headed forms (hadrosaurines) the

Figure 13–18 Bipedal ornithischians. (a) *Iguanodon*; (b) *Hadrosaurus*; (c) *Pachycephalosaurus*; (d) *Ouranosaurus*.

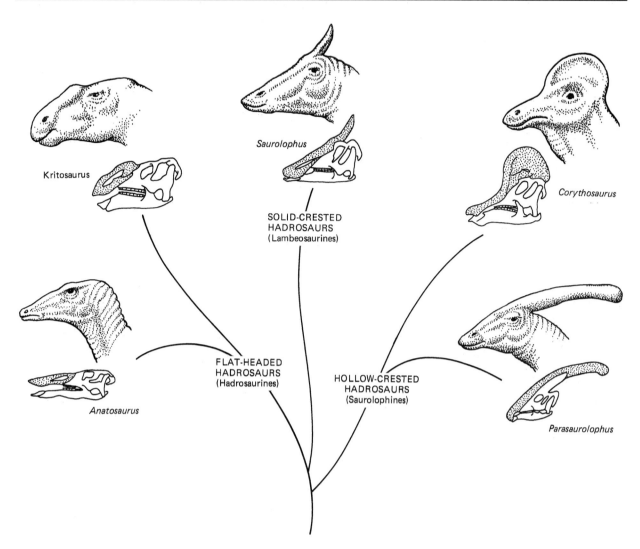

Figure 13–19 Hadrosaurs. The bizarre development of the nasal and maxillary bones of some hadrosaurs gave their heads a superficially antelopelike appearance. In the flat-headed and solid-crested forms the nasal passages ran directly from the external nares to the mouth. In the hollow-crested forms the premaxillary and nasal bones contributed to the formation of the crests, and the nasal passages were diverted up and back through the crests before they reached the internal nares.

nasal bones are not especially enlarged, although the nasal region may have been covered by folds of flesh. In the solid-crested forms (lambeosaurines) the nasal and frontal bones grew upward, meeting in a spike that projected over the skull roof. In the hollow-crested forms (saurolophines) a similar projection was formed by the premaxillary and nasal bones. In *Corythosaurus* those bones formed a helmetlike crest that covered the top of the skull, whereas in *Parasaurolophus* a long, curved structure extended over the shoulders. Although the crests of the lambeosaurines contained only bone, the nasal passages ran through the crests of the saurolophines.

Inspired air traveled a circuitous route from the external nares through the crest to the internal nares, which were located in the palate just anterior to the eyes.

Perhaps these bizarre structures were associated with species-specific visual displays and vocalizations (Hopson 1975). The crests might have supported a frill attached to the neck, which could have been utilized in behavioral displays analogous to the displays of many living lizards that have similar frills. Possibly in the noncrested forms the nasal regions were covered by extensive folds of fleshy tissue that could be inflated by closing the nasal valves. Analogous structures can be found in the inflatable proboscises of elephant seals and hooded seals. The inflated structures of seals are resonating chambers used to produce vocalizations. The size and shape of the nasal cavities of lambeosaurine hadrosaurs suggest that adults produced low-frequency sounds, but juveniles would have had higher-pitched vocalizations (Weishampel 1981).

Marginocephalia

Pachycephalosaurs The pachycephalosaurs are among the most bizarre ornithischians known (Figure 13–18c). The postcranial skeleton conforms to the bipedal pattern seen in ornithopods, but on the head an enormous bony dome thickens the skull roof. The bone is as much as 25 centimeters thick in a skull only 60 centimeters long. The angle of the occipital condyle indicates that the head was held so that the axis of the neck extended directly through the dome. The trunk vertebrae have articulations and ossified tendons that appear to have stiffened the vertebral column and resisted twisting. The pelvis was attached to at least six, and possibly to eight, vertebrae.

The thickened skull roof and the features of the postcranial skeleton have led some paleontologists to suggest that pachycephalosaurs used their heads like battering rams, perhaps for defense against carnivorous dinosaurs, or perhaps for intraspecific combat. An analogy has been drawn with goats and especially mountain sheep, in which males and females use head-to-head butting in social interactions. However, sheep and goats have horns that absorb some of the impact and they have protective air sacs at the front of the brain. Pachycephalosaurs had neither of these specializations, although stretchable ligaments in the neck may have helped to absorb the shock of impact. The Galapagos marine iguana may be a better model for the behavior of pachycephalosaurs. These lizards have blunt heads with spikes very like miniature versions of the heads of pachycephalosaurs. Male marine iguanas press their heads together, twisting and wrestling during territorial disputes. Perhaps pachycephalosaurs used their bony heads in the same way.

Ceratopsians The most diverse marginocephalians, the horned dinosaurs or ceratopsians, appeared in the Early Cretaceous. By this time the easy transit from one continent to another that had characterized much of the Mesozoic was coming to an end. Early ceratopsians are found in western North America and eastern Asia (which were connected across the Bering Sea), but they were apparently excluded from the rest of the world by the shallow epicontinental seas that covered the central parts of both North America and Eurasia in the late Mesozoic, and derived ceratopsians are known only from western North America.

The distinctive features of ceratopsians are found in the frill over the neck, which is formed by an enlargement of the parietal and squamosal bones, a parrotlike beak, and a battery of shearing teeth in each jaw. The earliest ceratopsians were the psittacosaurs from Asia. These were bipedal dinosaurs and they had no trace of a frill, but they did have a horny beak that covered a rostral bone at the front of the upper jaw. (The rostral bone is a distinctive feature of ceratopsian dinosaurs.) *Protoceratops*, one of the earliest of the quadrupedal ceratopsians, had developed a modest frill that extended backward over the neck and formed the origin for powerful jaw-closing muscles that extended anteriorly through slits at the rear of the skull and inserted on the coronoid process of the lower jaw. The teeth were arranged in batteries in each jaw somewhat like those of hadrosaurs, but with an important difference. The teeth of ceratopsians formed a series of knifelike edges rather than a solid surface like hadrosaur teeth. The feeding method of ceratopsians seems likely to have consisted of shearing vegetation into short lengths, rather than crushing it as hadrosaurs did.

Protoceratops had a simple frill, unadorned by spikes, and also lacked a nasal horn. Derived ceratopsians had both of these elaborations. Two groups can be distinguished: In the short-frilled ceratopsians (*Monoclonius*, *Styracosaurus*, and others) the frill extended backward over the neck, whereas in the long-frilled forms (*Chasmosaurus*, *Pentaceratops*, and others) the frill extended past the shoulders. Both short- and long-frilled ceratopsians had nasal and brow horns developed to varying degrees. The possible functions of the frills and horns of ceratopsians have attracted much speculation (Dodson 1993). Probably the initial stages in the evolution of the frill involved jaw mechanics and the importance of strong jaw muscles. Even in *Protoceratops*, however, males had larger frills than females, and that sexual dimorphism suggests that frills played a role in the social behavior of ceratopsians. Furthermore, the nasal and brow horns would have been formidable weapons for defense and for intraspecific combat. An analogy to the horns of antelope or the antlers of deer, which function in both defense and social behavior, seems appropriate for ceratopsians.

■ The Ecology and Behavior of Dinosaurs

Many of our ideas about the sorts of lives dinosaurs had persisted with little change from the nineteenth century. Although the amount of information available about such topics as biomechanics, paleoclimatology, and the ecology and behavior of living archosaurs has increased enormously in the past hundred years, it is only recently that paleontologists have returned to an examination of dinosaur fossils armed with this new perspective (Hopson and Radinsky 1980; Coombs 1990; Colbert 1993; Ruben et al. 1996, 1997).

Classic views of the lives of dinosaurs were extrapolated from a superficial view of the biology of large living diapsids, especially crocodilians and large lizards. These animals are usually seen in zoos, where they are well fed and isolated from the stimuli they experience in their normal habitats. Zoo animals present an exaggerated impression of the lethargy of large reptiles, and they are unsuitable as models for dinosaurs.

The Mesozoic world was quite different from the modern world, and the roles of Mesozoic archosaurs were correspondingly different from those of modern forms. Diapsids were the dominant terrestrial vertebrates of the Mesozoic, and they filled more adaptive zones than modern diapsids do in the mammal-dominated terrestrial ecosystems of the Cenozoic.

Recently some paleontologists have begun to compare the anatomy of dinosaurs with the anatomy of large mammals and birds, and to speculate about ecological and behavioral similarities on that basis. At the same time, studies of the behavior of crocodilians under field conditions have shown that they have much more complex behavior patterns than had been suspected from observations of captive animals. These lines of reasoning have led to the conclusion that dinosaurs were probably considerably more active than had been suspected, and that they probably had an intraspecific social organization at least as complex as that of crocodilians and birds. Peripheral infor-

mation about ecology and behavior of dinosaurs is provided by material such as fossilized stomach contents, fossilized footprints, and fossilized eggs, nests, and juveniles.

Crocodilians and Birds as Models for Dinosaurs

One of the strengths of the cladistic approach to classification is the emphasis it places on shared derived characteristics of related organisms. Usually these are morphological characters, and they are employed to draw inferences about phylogenetic relationships, but the process can be used in other ways. For example, if a phylogeny can be established by using morphological characters, other characteristics—ecological, behavioral, and physiological—can be superimposed on the phylogeny, and their evolution can be interpreted in a phylogenetic context.

A variety of morphological features common to crocodilians and birds places them both in the archosaur lineage, and this relationship can be combined with information about the social behavior of crocodilians and birds to draw inferences about the probable behavior of dinosaurs. The analysis of parental care is a good example of this approach. The extensive parental care provided to their young by many birds has long been known, partly because most birds are conspicuous animals that are relatively easy to study. Parental care by crocodilians is less well known, but it appears to be as extensive as that of most birds. All crocodilians probably protect their nests, and elaborate parental care has been described for some species (Pooley and Gans 1976, Ferguson 1985, Lang 1986).

Baby crocodilians begin to vocalize before they have fully emerged from the eggs, and these vocalizations are loud enough to be heard some distance away. The vocalizations of the babies stimulate one or both parents to excavate the nest, using their feet and jaws to pull away vegetation or soil (Figure 13–20). For example, the female American alligator bites chunks of vegetation out of her nest to release the young when they start to vocalize. Then she picks up the babies in her mouth and carries them, one or two at a time, to water where she releases them. This process is repeated until all of the hatchlings have been carried from the nest to the water. The parents of some species of crocodilians gently break the eggshells with their teeth to help the young escape. The sight of a crocodile, with jaws that could crush the leg of a cow, delicately rup-

(a)

(b)

Figure 13–20   Parental care by the mugger crocodile, *Crocodylus palustris*. The numbered tags allowed individual crocodiles to be recognized: (a) male parent picking a hatchling; (b,c) male parent carrying hatchlings to the water, 9 meters away, where the mother was waiting. (Photographs courtesy of Jeffrey W. Lang, University of North Dakota.)

(c)

turing the shell of an egg little larger than a hen's egg and releasing the hatchling unharmed is truly remarkable.

Young crocodilians stay near their mother for a considerable period—2 years for the American alligator—and may feed on small pieces of food the female drops in the process of eating. Like many birds, baby crocodilians are capable of catching their own food shortly after they hatch and are not dependent on their parents for nutrition.

Crocodilians, like birds, are vocal archosaurs (Lang 1989). Male crocodilians vocalize to announce their territorial status, and courtship is accompanied by vocalizations from males and females. Baby crocodilians begin to vocalize while they are still in the eggs, and frightened hatchlings emit a distress squeak that stimulates adult male and female crocodilians to come to their defense. When staff members at a crocodile farm in Papua New Guinea rescued a hatchling New Guinea crocodile that had

strayed from its pond, its distress call brought 20 adult crocodiles surging toward the hatchling (and the staff members!). The dominant male head-slapped the water repeatedly, and then charged into the chain link fence where the staff members were standing while the females swam about, gave deep guttural calls, and head-slapped the water.

The nesting behavior and parental care of crocodilians overlaps that of many birds. For example, the bush turkeys (megapods) of Australia bury their eggs in piles of soil and vegetation in craters they excavate in the ground and release their young at the end of incubation. The young of many birds, including bush turkeys, are well developed at hatching (precocial) and are able to find their own food. In these birds, as in crocodilians, the important function of parental care appears to be protection of the young from predators.

The most parsimonious explanation of the presence of well-developed parental care in crocodilians and birds is that it was present in the common ancestor of crocodilians and birds. In other words, parental care of young appears to be an ancestral character of the archosaur lineage, at least at the level of crocodilians. If that is the case, dinosaurs and pterosaurs would have inherited parental care as a part of their ancestral behavioral repertoire, and one would expect them to have exhibited behaviors seen in birds and crocodilians. Behavior is difficult to decipher from the fossil record, but evidence is accumulating to suggest that dinosaurs did, indeed, engage in parental care and other forms of complex social behaviors.

Ecology of Sauropods

The large sauropod dinosaurs, *Apatosaurus*, *Diplodocus*, and related forms, were the largest terrestrial animals that have ever lived. The largest of them may have reached body lengths exceeding 30 meters and weights of 100,000 kilograms. (For comparison, an elephant is about 5 meters long and weighs 5000 kilograms.) From the earliest discovery of their fossils, paleontologists doubted that such massive animals could have walked on land and felt they must have been limited to a semiaquatic life in swamps. Mechanical analysis of sauropod skeletons does not support that conclusion (Alexander 1989). The skeletons of the large sauropods clearly reveal selective forces favoring a combination of strength with light weight. The arches of the vertebrae acted like flying buttresses on a large building, while the V-shaped neural spines of diplodocoids held a massive and possibly elastic ligament that helped to support the head and tail. In cross section the trunk was deep, shaped like the body of a terrestrial animal such as an elephant rather than rounded like that of the aquatic hippopotamus. The tails of sauropods are not laterally flattened like tails used for swimming. Instead, they are round in cross section and, in diplodocoids, terminate in a long, thin whiplash. These structures look like counterweights and defensive weapons.

Fossil trackways of sauropods indicate that the legs were held under the body; the tracks of the left and right feet are only a single foot width apart. Analysis of the limb bones suggests that they were held straight in an elephantlike pose and moved fore and aft parallel to the midline of the body. This is what would be expected on mechanical grounds, because no other leg morphology is possible for a

very large animal. Bone is far less resistant to bending forces exerted across its long axis than it is to compressional forces exerted parallel to the axis. As an animal's body increases in size, mass grows as the cube of its linear dimensions, but the cross-sectional area of the bones increases as the square of their linear dimensions. The strength of bone is roughly proportional to its cross-sectional area. As a result, when the body size of an animal increases, the strength of the skeleton increases more slowly than the stress to which it is subjected. One evolutionary response to this relationship is disproportionate increase in the diameter of bones—an elephant skeleton is proportionally larger than a mouse skeleton. Another response is to transform bending forces to compression forces by bringing the legs more directly under the body. In a large animal, such as an elephant or a sauropod dinosaur, not only are the legs held under the body, but the knee joint tends to be locked as the animal walks. This morphology produces the ambling locomotion familiar in elephants, and it is likely that sauropods walked with an elephantlike gait, holding their heads and tails in the air.

Sauropod teeth are sometimes described as being small and weak. Certainly they were small in proportion to the size of the body, as was the entire skull. In absolute terms, however, they were neither small nor weak. They were larger than the teeth of browsing mammals, and there is no reason to believe that plant material was tougher in the Mesozoic than it is today. There were no flat (molariform) teeth to crush the ingested plant material. This function may have been served by gastroliths, stones that are deliberately eaten by an animal and retained in some part of the gut where they crush food, and the breakdown of plant material may have been aided by symbiotic microorganisms (Farlow 1987).

The fossilized stomach contents of a sauropod dinosaur, found in Jurassic sediments in Utah, includes pieces of twigs and small branches about 2.5 centimeters long and 1 centimeter in diameter. The fragmented and shredded character of the woody material indicates that even without molariform teeth the sauropod had some method of crushing its food. This discovery appears to confirm the view of sauropod ecology that was developed from study of the skeleton and analysis of plant fossils found in association with sauropod fossils: Sauropods probably occupied open country with an undergrowth of ferns and cycads and an upper story of conifers. They were preyed on by the large theropod carnivores and sought escape in flight or defended themselves by whipping their tails. Their long necks probably enabled them to graze from tree tops, perhaps standing on their hind legs by using the tail as a counterweight. It may be significant that Mesozoic conifers bore branches only near the tops of the trees, far out of reach of any but a very long-necked dinosaur.

Sauropods might have been an important force shaping the landscape and preventing ecological succession from transforming open countryside to dense forest. As such, their presence could have been important in creating and preserving suitable habitat for other species, such as the cursorial ornithomimids. Like many herbivorous lizards, the sauropods may have been omnivorous and opportunistic in their feeding, taking whatever was readily available, including carrion. The fossilized stomach contents mentioned previously contain traces of bone as well as a tooth from the contemporary carnivorous dinosaur *Allosaurus*.

Fossil trackways reveal a few details from which glimpses of dinosaur behavior can be reconstructed (Thulborn 1990). A famous trackway found in Texas, parts of which are now on display at the University of Texas at Austin and in the American Museum of Natural History in New York City, shows the footprints of a sauropod that was apparently being trailed by a large theropod that was a few steps behind and slightly to the left. The theropod tracks duplicate several small changes in direction by the sauropod, and the rhythm of the therapod's stride was adjusted to match the stride of the sauropod. Mammalian predators such as lions make similar adjustments to match the stride of their prey before they attack. A drag mark made by the sauropod's right rear foot and two consecutive marks of the theropod's right foot (i.e., a hop) may even mark the point of an attack (Thomas and Farlow 1997).

Some insight into possible herd behavior by sauropods may be revealed by a series of tracks found in Early Cretaceous sediments at Davenport Ranch in Texas. These reveal the passage of 23 brontosaurlike dinosaurs some 120 million years ago. A group of individuals moving in the same direction at the same time would be remarkable for most living diapsids, but the brontosaur tracks suggest that this is what happened. Furthermore, the tracks may show that the herd moved in a structured fashion with the young animals in the middle, surrounded by adults.

Predatory Behavior of Theropods

The carnivorous saurischian dinosaurs, like the herbivorous forms, present an impression of relatively small morphological diversity. The major evolutionary lineages have already been traced—the ostrichlike ornithomimids, the giant theropods, and the dromeosaurs that combined the speed of ornithomimids with the predatory habits of the theropods. The ornithomimids parallel flightless birds so closely in morphology that it seems reasonable to assume that they lived essentially the same life in the Cretaceous that ostriches, emus, and related forms live now. The appearance of increasingly cursorial forms that relied on running to escape predators may indicate that habitats became increasingly open during the Mesozoic.

There was probably a trend to increasingly specialized methods of prey capture among carnosaurs. This hypothesis is suggested by the reduction of the size of the forelimbs of carnosaurs, which presumably indicates an increased reliance on the teeth for both seizing and killing prey. The dromeosaurs probably relied instead on fleetness of foot to capture active prey. The discovery of five *Deinonychus* skeletons in close association with the skeleton of *Tenontosaurus*, an ornithischian three times their size, might indicate that *Deinonychus* hunted in packs (Figure 13–21). Deinonychosaurs probably used their clawed forefeet to seize prey and then slashed at it with the sicklelike claws on the hind feet. This tactic appears to be illustrated by a remarkable discovery in Mongolia of a dromeosaur called *Velociraptor*. It was preserved in combat with a *Protoceratops*, its hands grasping the head of its prey and its enormous claw embedded in the midsection of the *Protoceratops*.

Social Behavior of Ornithischians

The morphological diversity of the ornithischian dinosaurs suggests an equivalent diversity in behavior and ecology. Social interactions based on visual displays and vocalizations may have been well developed among hadrosaurs, and pachycephalosaurs may have engaged in shoving contests like those of ungulate mammals. Individual

Figure 13–21 Social behaviors of dinosaurs. (a) Deinonychosaurs may have hunted in packs to attack large prey such as ornithopods. (b) Ceratopsians (*Chasmosaurus*) may have formed a ring to confront predators. (c) Hadrosaurs (*Maiasaura*) may have nested in colonies. (Modified from D. Norman, 1985, *The Illustrated Encyclopedia of Dinosaurs*, Salamander Books, London, UK.)

interactions of these sorts may have been integrated into group behaviors. Fossilized eggs of dinosaurs provide information about nesting behaviors (Box 13–1). Evidence of parental care may be revealed by a nest of 15 baby hadrosaurs (*Maiasaura*) in the Late Cretaceous Two Medicine Formation in Montana

(Horner and Makela 1979). The babies were about a meter long, approximately twice the size of hatchlings found in the same area, indicating that the group had remained together after they hatched. Furthermore, the teeth of the baby hadrosaurs showed that they had been feeding; some teeth

BOX 13–1   **Dinosaur Eggs and Nests**

Fossils of dinosaur eggs have been found in late Cretaceous deposits in Mongolia, China, France, India, and the United States. Most of these fossils are fragments of eggshells, but intact eggs containing embryos have also been discovered, and the fossil of an adult dinosaur has been found apparently brooding a clutch of eggs (Figure 13–22).

Concentrations of nests and eggs ascribed to sauropods in Cretaceous deposits in southern France suggest that these animals had well-defined nesting grounds (Kerourio 1981). Eggs thought to be those of the large sauropod *Hypselosaurus priscus* are found in association with fossilized vegetation similar to that used by alligators to construct their nests. The orientation of the nests suggests that each female dinosaur probably deposited about 50 eggs. The eggs had an average volume of 1.9 liters, about 40 times the volume of a chicken egg. A total of 50 of these eggs would weigh about 100 kilograms, or 1 percent of the estimated body mass of the mother. Crocodilians and large turtles have egg outputs that vary from 1 to 10 percent of the adult body mass, so an estimate of 1 percent for *Hypselosaurus* seems reasonable. The eggs might have been deposited in small groups instead of all together, because 50 eggs in one clutch would have consumed oxygen faster than it could diffuse through the walls of the nest (Seymour 1979).

Two patterns of egg-laying can be distinguished (Mikhailov 1997). Sauropod dinosaurs laid eggs in nests dug into the soil, much like those of extant turtles. In contrast ornithischian and theropod dinosaurs laid eggs in an excavation that might have been filled with rotting vegetation that would have provided both heat and moisture for the eggs. (This method of egg incubation is used by many of the living crocodilians.) Nests of *Protoceratops* fall in this category—the 30 to 35 eggs in each nest are arranged in concentric circles with their blunt ends up. Eggs of *Orodromeus makelai*, a hypsilophodontid, are also oriented vertically with the blunt end up, but are arranged in a spiral within the circular nest.

The fossil of a theropod dinosaur that apparently died while attending a nest of eggs was discovered in the Gobi Desert in 1923, but its significance was not recognized until 70 years later (Norell et al. 1994). The eggs, which were about 12 centimeters long and 6 centimeters in diameter, were thought to have been deposited by the small ceratopsian *Protoceratops andrewsi* because adults of that species were by far the most abundant dinosaurs at the site. The theropod was assumed to have been robbing the nest, and was given the name *Oviraptor philoceratops*, which means "egg seizer, lover of ceratops." In 1993, paleontologists from the American Museum of Natural History, the Mongolian Academy of Sciences, and the Mongolian Museum of Natural History discovered a fossilized embryo in an egg identical to the supposed *Protoceratops* eggs. To their surprise, the embryo was an *Oviraptor* nearly ready to hatch. This discovery suggests that the adult *Oviraptor* found with a clutch of eggs in 1923 got a bum rap—it probably died while resting on its own nest.

were worn down to one-quarter of their original length. The object presumed to be a nest was a mound 3 meters in diameter and 1.5 meters high with a saucer-shaped depression in the center (Figure 13–21). Such a large structure would have made the babies conspicuous to predators, and it seems likely that a parent remained with the young. (*Maiasaura* can be translated as good mother reptile.) The morphology of the inner ears of lambeosaurs suggests that adults would have been able to hear the high-pitched vocalizations of juveniles, strengthening the inference of parental care (Weishampel 1981). The association between adults and young appears to have lasted for a considerable time. Fossils suggest that *Maiasauria* and the lambeosaur *Hypacrosaurus* grew to one-quarter of adult size before they left the nesting grounds, and a species of hypsilophodontid found at the same site grew to half its adult size (Horner 1994). Both vocal communication and prolonged association of parent dinosaurs and their young are plausible in the light of the behaviors known for crocodilians.

(a)

(b)   (c)

Figure 13–22 Dinosaur nests and eggs. (a) An adult oviraptor on a nest of eggs. This reconstruction is based on a fossil of an oviraptor found in the Gobi Desert. The adult was apparently brooding its eggs when it was buried by a giant sandstorm. (b) Fossilized nest of an oviraptorid dinosaur. (c) The fossilized skeleton of an embryo of an oviraptorid dinosaur (AMNHK17088). This is the first embryo of a carnivorous dinosaur ever found. ([a] Transparency # K17360, illustration by Mick Ellison/DVP, photo by Denis Finnin, courtesy of Dept. of Library Services, American Museum of Natural History. [b] Neg # 410765, Photo. Shackleford, courtesy of Dept. of Library Services, American Museum of Natural History.)

Additional fossils in the same formation suggest that the area contained nest sites of other species of hadrosaurs and of ceratopsians as well (Horner 1982, 1984). Eggshells and baby dinosaurs are abundant in the Two Medicine Formation but rare in adjacent sediments. A similar concentration of conspicuous nests, eggs, and juveniles of the small ceratopsian *Protoceratops* discovered in Mongolia suggests parental care in this species as well. The possibility of parental care and social behavior among sauropods is raised by the discovery of five baby prosauropod dinosaurs (*Mussaurus*) with the remains of two eggs in a nest in Late Triassic deposits in Argentina (Bonaparte and Vince 1979).

Protection of nests and juveniles from predators is a plausible reason for parental care (Kirkland 1994), and Katherine Troyer has suggested a second important reason for an association between juveniles and adults of herbivorous dinosaurs such as the hadrosaurs and ceratopsoids (Troyer 1984). Working with iguanas, which are herbivorous lizards, she showed that hatchlings must ingest the feces of adult iguanas (or of other hatchlings that have themselves ingested feces from adults) to inoculate their guts with the symbiotic microorganisms that permit them to digest plant material. The microorganisms responsible for the fermentation of plant material are anaerobic and soon die when feces are exposed to air. Thus, a close association between hatchlings and adults is necessary to achieve the transfer of the microorganisms. Herbivorous dinosaurs probably relied on fermentation of plant material just as most extant herbivorous vertebrates do, and some contact between juveniles and adults would have been necessary to inoculate hatchling dinosaurs with the symbiotic microorganisms.

■ Were Dinosaurs Endotherms?

The cladistic approach that was helpful for inferences about the social behavior of nonavian dinosaurs is less effective in deciding what thermoregulatory mechanisms they may have employed. Ectothermy is an ancestral characteristic in the archosaur lineage, and crocodilians are ectotherms. Clearly, the endothermy seen in birds is derived, but when did it appear? It could have been at any point between crocodilians and birds. That is, endothermy might be characteristic of pterosaurs + dinosaurs + birds, or of dinosaurs + birds, or it might be limited to birds. All the lineages between crocodilians and birds are extinct, so we cannot draw any direct evidence from them—paleophysiology is a speculative subject.

Much of the controversy about the temperature relations of dinosaurs stems from failure to distinguish between *homeothermy* and *endothermy*. Homeothermy means only that the body temperature of an organism is reasonably stable, whereas endothermy and ectothermy are mechanisms of temperature regulation. Either ectothermy or endothermy can produce homeothermy, as we saw in Chapter 4. Furthermore, ectothermy and endothermy are the ends of a spectrum, and many living animals occupy positions between those extremes.

The diversity of dinosaurs and the enormous size of many species complicate discussions of their thermoregulatory mechanisms. The great ecological and phylogenetic diversity of dinosaurs has largely been overlooked in the debate about their thermoregulatory mechanisms. Not all kinds of evidence apply to all species, and it is likely that there

were substantial differences in the biology of different lineages. Quite apart from any other consideration, the difference in body size of an ornithomimid and a sauropod would make them very different kinds of animals (Farlow 1990).

Furthermore, we have no terrestrial animals to compare to dinosaurs. Even elephants (which weigh about 5000 kilograms) are only as large as medium-size sauropods, and the largest living reptiles (leatherback sea turtles and saltwater crocodiles) weigh about 1000 kilograms. Thus, we have no models of dinosaurs to work with, and must extrapolate observations of living animals far beyond the size ranges for which we have measurements.

What can elephants and leatherback turtles tell us about the metabolism of dinosaurs? First, they tell us that when you compare animals of large body size, there is very little difference between the metabolic rates of endotherms and ectotherms: The metabolic rate of a 4000-kilogram elephant is 0.07 liters of oxygen per kilogram per hour, whereas the rate for a 400-kilogram leatherback turtle is 0.06 liters of oxygen per kilogram per hour. Thus, the metabolic distinction between endotherms and ectotherms disappears at large body sizes, and discussions of whether large dinosaurs were endotherms or ectotherms are meaningless.

Leatherback turtles employ a form of thermoregulation that has been called gigantothermy (Paladino et al. 1990). The large body mass of these animals has two important consequences for temperature regulation. First, it produces enormous thermal inertia, so body temperatures change slowly. Second, it allows the animals to change the effective thickness of their insulation by changing the distribution of blood flow to the surface of the body versus the core. When a leatherback is in cold water, it can retain the heat produced by muscular activity in its body by restricting blood flow to the surface of the body and employing countercurrent heat exchangers in its limbs. In warmer water, when it needs to dissipate metabolic heat to avoid overheating, it can increase blood flow to the surface and bypass the countercurrent system in its limbs. These mechanisms allow leatherback turtles to make migratory journeys of 10,000 kilometers between arctic oceans and the tropics.

Metabolic rates of leatherback turtles were used as a basis for computer simulations of body temperatures of dinosaurs (Spotila et al. 1991). Three metabolic rates were compared: (1) the standard resting metabolic rate of reptiles; (2) the measured

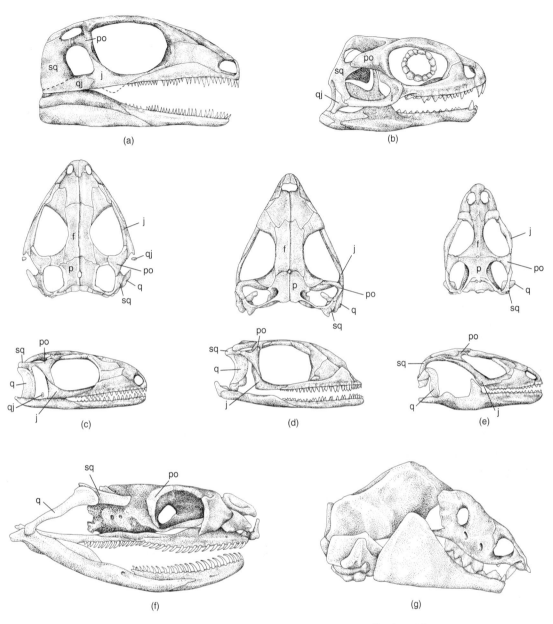

Figure 13–24 Modifications of the diapsid skull among lepidosauromorphs. Fully diapsid forms like the Permian *Petrolacosaurus* (a) retain two complete arches of bone that define the temporal fenestrae. This condition is seen in living tuatara, *Sphenodon* (b). Lizards have achieved a kinetic skull by developing a gap between the quadrate and quadratojugal and by simplifying the suture between the frontal and parietal bones, as shown by the modern collared lizard *Crotaphytus* (e). Probable transitional stages allowing increasing skull kinesis that occurred in a nonsquamate lineage are illustrated by *Paliguana* (c) and *Palaeagama* (d). In snakes (f) skull kinesis is further increased by loss of the upper temporal arch. Amphisbaenians (g), which use their heads for burrowing through soil, have specialized akinetic skulls. f, frontal; j, jugal; p, parietal; po, postorbital; q, quadrate; qj, quadratojugal; sq, squamosal. ([a] From R. R. Reisz, 1977, *Science* 196:1091–1093; [b,c] from Romer 1966; [f, g] from C. Gans, 1974, *Biomechanics: An Approach to Vertebrate Biology,* Lippincott, Philadelphia, PA.)

the skull produced the extreme flexibility of snake skulls. The role of skull kinesis in the ecology of snakes is discussed further in Chapter 15.

The third group of squamates has a completely different sort of skull specialization. The amphisbaenians are small, legless, burrowing animals. They use their heads as rams to construct tunnels in the soil, and the skull is heavy with rigid joints between the bones. Their specialized dentition allows them to bite small pieces out of large prey.

■ Other Terrestrial Vertebrates of the Late Mesozoic

There is a tendency to look on the Jurassic and Cretaceous as the Age of Dinosaurs and to forget that there was a very considerable nondinosaur terrestrial fauna as well as variations in the kinds of dinosaurs in different habitats (Lucas 1981). To a certain extent the dinosaurs do form a separate unit. The large theropods were probably the only animals capable of preying on adults of the large herbivores. Nonetheless, there must have been interactions between dinosaurs and nondinosaurs. As far as we know, all dinosaurs reproduced by laying eggs, and their eggs were a food source that could be exploited by small predators. The Nile monitor lizard today is a predator on eggs of crocodiles, and it is likely that Cretaceous monitor lizards had a taste for dinosaur eggs.

One of the distinctive features of dinosaurs is their large size. The smallest dinosaur skeletons known indicate a total adult length of about half a meter. Even that is large in comparison with living squamates; most lizards are smaller than 20 centimeters, and only crocodilians approach the bulk of even moderate-size dinosaurs. There were, of course, adaptive zones available for smaller vertebrates in the Jurassic and Cretaceous, and these were filled as they are now by squamates, turtles, amphibians, and mammals. Among these were the animals that might have stolen eggs from nests and served as food for juvenile dinosaurs.

Although dinosaurs are so impressive and distinctive that there is a tendency to think of them as inhabiting a world of their own, they were in reality a part of an ecosystem that included many vertebrates that would not appear strange to us today. As Benton (1985b) has pointed out, The assemblage of tetrapod families that includes all modern tetrapod groups—frogs, salamanders, lizards, snakes, turtles, crocodilians, birds, and mammals—arose in the Late Triassic, and increased in diversity through the Jurassic and Early Cretaceous. During the Cretaceous the diversity of these modern groups was approximately equal to that of dinosaurs and pterosaurs. In the latest Cretaceous the diversity of the modern groups rose dramatically and became twice that of the dinosaurs and pterosaurs, long before the terminal Cretaceous extinction event.

A striking feature of the Mesozoic world was the absence of large mammals, and the occupation of that adaptive zone by large archosaurs. Figure 13–25 shows the relative abundance of different groups of vertebrates at two Cretaceous fossil localities. The Lance locality appears to have been a wooded swampy habitat with large streams and some ponds. The Bug Creek locality was probably downstream from such a swamp, in the delta of a major waterway. In both localities dinosaurs are a minor component of the community in terms of species diversity, although one dinosaur is the equivalent of a great many smaller animals in terms of biomass. (Some paleontologists believe that the Bug Creek locality is of Paleocene rather than Cretaceous age [see Archibald (1989) for a review].) If this is true, the presence of dinosaurs and Cretaceous mammals at this site indicates either that these groups survived the Cretaceous–Tertiary extinction or that during the Paleocene fossils were eroded from older sediments and redeposited in the creek beds.)

■ Late Cretaceous Extinctions

After thriving and dominating the terrestrial habitat for 150 million years, dinosaurs disappeared near the end of the Cretaceous. The extinctions that occurred at the Cretaceous–Tertiary transition are an example of a recurrent biological phenomenon—mass extinction. In fact, the Cretaceous–Tertiary extinction was relatively small as mass extinctions go, but it is the most widely known because the disappearance of dinosaurs has captured the attention of both scientists and the public.

Biologists have struggled for years to explain the rapid change in faunal composition that occurred at the end of the Mesozoic, and there are nearly as many different hypotheses as there are authors. The catastrophism school of thought maintains that the

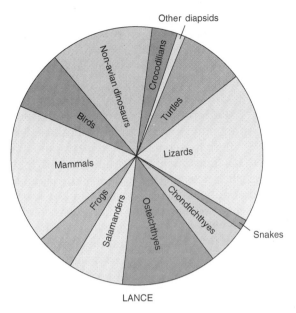

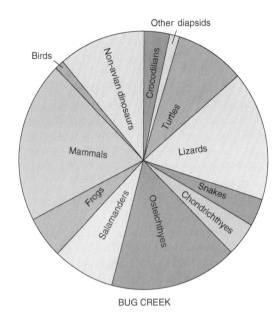

Figure 13–25 Relative abundance of genera at Late Cretaceous fossil sites. Although dinosaurs were the most spectacular terrestrial vertebrates during the Mesozoic, they were surrounded by a large assortment of animals that were not very different from living species. Mammals were well represented at both sites. (Calculated from data in R. Estes and P. Berberian, 1970, *Breviora*, No. 343.)

giant archosaurs were wiped out by some geological or cosmic disaster. The currently popular hypothesis in the catastrophism sweepstakes is the suggestion that the impact of a comet or an asteroid with Earth ignited worldwide firestorms or injected enough dust into the atmosphere to blot out the sun, thereby suppressing photosynthesis and leading to the extinctions of animals.

Other paleontologists have argued that the extinctions we associate with the transition from the Cretaceous to the Tertiary were gradual, not abrupt, and actually began millions of years before the end of the Cretaceous. Gradual extinctions could result from slow changes in climate or terrestrial habitats that might be consequences of continental drift and the accompanying changes in oceanic circulation.

Most paleontologists agree that an extraterrestrial impact did occur during the Late Cretaceous. A narrow band of rock containing a high concentration of iridium (known as an iridium anomaly) occurs in many parts of the world in sediments that were deposited in the Late Cretaceous. Iridium is normally a rare element in sedimentary rocks, but it occurs in high concentrations in the core of the Earth and in some volcanic deposits and it is found

in high concentrations in some extraterrestrial objects. Thus, a worldwide iridium anomaly suggests that some usual event—either a massive episode of volcanic activity or the impact of an extraterrestrial object—occurred in the very Late Cretaceous. Evidence suggesting that the event was an impact is provided by the presence of quartz crystals that show the effect of enormous force (known as shocked quartz) in Late Cretaceous. The enormous Chicxulub crater on the Yucatan coast of Mexico appears to be of the correct age (64.4 ± 0.5 million years) for this impact (Morgan et al. 1997).

There is much less agreement about the consequences of the impact than about its occurrence. The two hypotheses for the extinction of dinosaurs—an extraterrestrial event versus normal ecological processes—make very different predictions about the time course of extinction. The enormous ocean waves, firestorms, and darkness that could have been produced by an impact are short-term events with durations measured in days to years. In contrast, changes in climates and habitats would probably require thousands or hundreds of thousands of years to cause extinctions. With such different predictions from the two hypotheses, it should be possible to test them by looking at the fossil record to see whether extinctions were abrupt or gradual, but it's not possible to make that analysis.

The major difficulty if deciding if extinctions at the end of the Cretaceous were abrupt or gradual is the problem of resolution. Dating events at the end of the Cretaceous involves large uncertainties: 1 to 2 million years for correlations of marine and terrestrial deposits and 0.5 to 4 million years for dates based on rates of decay of radioactive elements (Benton 1990). Dates can help to determine the sequence of events but not their duration, so no direct test of the abruptness of the extinctions is possible.

Our inability to measure the duration of events applies to the fossil record of all kinds of life—marine invertebrates, terrestrial plants, and terrestrial vertebrates. A second difficulty is particularly acute for studies of dinosaurs. Only in western North America is there a fossil record of terrestrial vertebrates that extends from the Late Cretaceous across the Cretaceous–Tertiary boundary into the Paleocene (Archibald 1989, Dodson and Tatarinov 1990). Thus, we are basing inferences about worldwide changes on just one area.

Hypotheses based on long-term changes in climate have been proposed repeatedly. The Mesozoic was apparently characterized by stable temperatures with little variation from day to night, from summer to winter, and from north to south. Geological evidence suggests that climates became cooler and more variable as the flow of warm water into the Arctic Ocean was reduced at the end of the Cretaceous when the continents reached nearly their present locations. Casper, Wyoming, is an important dinosaur fossil locality, and a reconstruction of its Mesozoic temperature regime suggests that the long-term temperature extremes probably lay between 11 and 34°C, with a mean of 22°C. Clearly, the climate has changed since then: The present temperature extremes at Casper are −27 to +40°C, with a mean of 8°C.

In addition to these changes in climate, geological events at the end of the Cretaceous were changing the land surface and altering terrestrial habitats. A reduction in sea level of 150 to 200 meters drained the shallow inland seas that had filled the centers of the continents during the Late Cretaceous. Rivers cut their way down toward the new sea level, forming valleys instead of meandering across broad floodplains. Late Cretaceous dinosaurs appear to have been concentrated in river and floodplain habitats, and these changes would have reduced the habitat available to them (Schopf 1983). Furthermore, the floodplains were probably routes for north–south migration, and their interruption by valleys running east–west might have disrupted migratory patterns. The population sizes of large herbivorous dinosaurs and their theropod predators may have represented a delicate balance of predator–prey ratios and population densities (Farlow 1993). Perhaps changes in topography that restricted the movements of predators and their prey tilted the scales toward excessive predation or produced population densities that were too low to sustain normal social behavior and reproduction.

These hypotheses are based on what we know of the ecology of living animals and they address the biological characteristics of dinosaurs as best as we can infer them, but they cannot be tested because the fossil record does not provide enough information and does not allow us to resolve the time course of these changes in relation to changes in faunas.

The second problem presented by the Cretaceous–Tertiary extinctions is explaining why some evolutionary lineages became extinct and other persisted. Nonavian dinosaurs disappeared, but turtles and crocodilians survived, as did birds and mammals. Indeed, at least 22 separate evolutionary lineages of birds and 20 lineages of mammals appear to have survived the Cretaceous–Tertiary extinctions (Cooper and Penny 1997, Kumar and Hedges 1998). Nonavian dinosaurs were probably less diverse by the end of the Cretaceous than they once had been, but still they included many different kinds of animals—large and small, carnivorous and herbivorous, fast-moving and slow-moving. Modern crocodilians are probably similar in their ecology and physiology to some carnivorous dinosaurs, turtles have similarities to herbivorous dinosaurs, and Mesozoic birds and mammals were basically like extant forms. What conditions would exterminate dinosaurs and allow crocodilians, turtles, birds, and mammals to survive?

Paleontologists who advocate the impact hypothesis of Cretaceous extinctions are beginning to address this question, but so far only at a scale that is too coarse to be convincing in an ecological context. For example, a recent review of the Cretaceous extinctions classified aquatic organisms (a group that includes turtles and crocodilians) as detritus feeders and attributed their survival to this characteristic (Fastovsky and Weishampel 1996). As we have seen, however, even the 21 extant species of crocodilians and 400 species of turtles are too diverse to fit such a superficial characterization and the Cretaceous reptilian fauna was far more diverse.

The difficulty that proponents of the asteroid impact currently face in demonstrating a cause-and-effect relationship between the impact and the extinctions is a mismatch in the scale of the two events. An asteroid impact would have large-scale effects, whereas the Late Cretaceous extinctions appear to reflect fine-scale differences among lineages. Ascribing the late Mesozoic extinctions to an extraterrestrial impact is akin to trying to use a sledge hammer to swat a housefly while sparing the fruitfly beside it.

The difficulty in understanding the Cretaceous–Tertiary extinctions is paralleled by our difficulty in understanding many of the extinctions that are occurring now: Frogs and other amphibians are declining on a worldwide basis, but no one cause for these declines has been identified. It seems most likely that multiple factors and interactions of these factors are responsible for the current wave of extinctions, and that multiple factors were involved in the Late Cretaceous extinctions as well.

■ Summary

The major groups of tetrapods in the Mesozoic were members of the diapsid (two arches) lineage. This group is distinguished particularly by the presence of two fenestrae in the temporal region of the skull that are defined by arches of bone. The archosauromorph lineage of diapsids contains the most familiar of the Mesozoic tetrapods, the dinosaurs. Two major groups of dinosaurs are distinguished, the Saurischia and Ornithischia.

The saurischians included the sauropod dinosaurs—enormous herbivorous quadrupedal forms like *Apatosaurus* (formerly *Brontosaurus*), *Diplodocus*, and *Brachiosaurus*—and the theropods, which were bipedal carnivores. Large theropods (of which *Tyrannosaurus rex* is the most familiar example) probably preyed on large sauropods. Other theropods were smaller: ornithomimids were probably very like ostriches, and some had horny beaks and lacked teeth and dromeosaurs were fast-running predators. Ornithomimids probably seized small prey with hands that had three fingers armed with claws, whereas dromeosaurs probably were able to prey on dinosaurs larger than themselves. They may have hunted in packs and used the enormous claw on the second toe to slash their prey. Birds had evolved by the Jurassic: *Archaeopteryx*, the earliest bird known, is very like small coelurosaurs.

The ornithischian dinosaurs were herbivorous, and had horny beaks on the snout and batteries of specialized teeth in the rear of the jaw. The ornithopods (duck-billed dinosaurs) and pachycephalosaurs (thick-headed dinosaurs) were bipedal, and the stegosaurs (plated dinosaurs), ceratopsians (horned dinosaurs), and ankylosaurians (armored dinosaurs) were quadrupedal. Although the saurischians and ornithischians represent independent radiations and had different ecological specializations, they share many morphological features that appear to reflect the mechanical constraints of being very large terrestrial animals.

The lepidosauromorph lineage was less diverse in the Mesozoic than the archosauromorphs. Placodonts, plesiosaurs, and ichthyosaurs were marine mollusk eaters or fish eaters. The Younginiformes of the Late Permian were mostly lightly built terrestrial animals about 50 centimeters long. The champsosaurs are a problematic group of crocodilelike animals about 2 meters in length. The surviving lepidosauromorphs are all members of the lepidosaur lineage. The sphenodontids are stocky terrestrial forms, about 50 centimeters long. The tuatara (*Sphenodon punctatus* and *S. guentheri*) are the only extant sphenodontids, but the group was more diverse in the Mesozoic. Lizards, snakes, and amphisbaenians compose the squamate lineage. The basic diapsid skull form has been extensively modified among squamates, particularly in relation to feeding habits (lizards and snakes) and the use of the head for burrowing (amphisbaenians).

The phylogenetic relationship of crocodilians and birds allows us to draw inferences about some aspects of the biology of dinosaurs. Characters that are shared by crocodilians and birds are probably ancestral for dinosaurs. Social behavior and parental care are the norm for crocodilians and birds, and increasing evidence suggests that dinosaurs, too, had elaborate social behavior and that at least some species cared for the young.

The Mesozoic was marked by a series of faunal changes. The extinctions at the end of the Cretaceous were the most dramatic of these, partly because the dinosaur fauna of the time was so spectacular, but they are not unique. In the Middle Cretaceous the diversity of sauropod dinosaurs declined while the ornithischians burgeoned. This faunal change was contemporaneous with the decline of bennettitaleans and the appearance of flowering plants (angiosperms). In this context of shifting faunas and floras throughout the Mesozoic, explanations of the Late Cretaceous extinctions that depend on worldwide catastrophes are less persuasive than hypotheses based on the gradual changes in sea level, topography, and climate that are shown in the fossil record of the late Mesozoic.

■ References

Abler, W. L. 1992. The serrated teeth of tyrannosaurid dinosaurs and biting structures in other animals. *Paleobiology* 18:161–183.

Alexander, R. M. 1989. *Dynamics of Dinosaurs and Other Extinct Giants*. Columbia University Press, New York, NY.

Archibald, J. D. 1989. The demise of the dinosaurs and the rise of the mammals. Pages 48–57 in *The Age of Dinosaurs*, edited by K. Padian and D. J. Chure. The Paleontological Society, University of Tennessee Press, Knoxville, TN.

Benton, M. J. 1985a. Classification and phylogeny of diapsid reptiles. *Zoological Journal of the Linnaean Society (London)* 84:97–164.

Benton, M. J. 1985b. Mass extinctions among nonmarine tetrapods. *Nature* 316:811–814.

Benton, M. J. 1990. *Vertebrate Paleontology*. HarperCollins Academic, London, UK.

Bonaparte, J. F., and M. Vince. 1979. El hallazgo del primer nido de dinosaurios triasicos (Saurischia, Prosauropoda). Triásico superior de Patagonia, Argentina. *Ameghiana* 16:173–182.

Buffrénil, V. de, J. O. Farlow, and A. de Ricqles. 1986. Growth and function of *Stegosaurus* plates: evidence from bone histology. *Paleobiology* 12:450–458.

Caple, G., R. P. Balda, and W. R. Willis. 1983. The physics of leaping animals and the evolution of preflight. *American Naturalist* 121:455–476.

Carroll, R. L. 1977. The origin of lizards. Pages 359–396 in *Problems in Vertebrate Evolution*, edited by S. M. Andrews, R. S. Miles, and A. D. Wells. Academic, London, UK.

Carroll, R. L. 1987. *Vertebrate Paleontology and Evolution*. Freeman, New York, NY.

Charig, A. 1972. The evolution of the archosaur pelvis and hindlimb: an explanation in functional terms. In *Studies in Vertebrate Evolution*, edited by K. A. Joysey and T. S. Kemp. Winchester, Piscataway, NJ.

Colbert, E. H. 1993. Feeding strategies and metabolism in elephants and sauropod dinosaurs. *American Journal of Science* 293-A:1–19.

Coombs, W. P., Jr. 1990. Behavior patterns of dinosaurs. Pages 32–42 in *The Dinosauria*, edited by D. B. Weishampel, P. Dodson, and H. Osmólska. University of California Press, Berkeley, CA.

Cooper, A. and D. Penny. 1997. Mass survival of birds across the Cretaceous–Tertiary boundary: molecular evidence. *Science* 275:1109–1112.

Dingus, L., and T. Rowe. 1998. *The Mistaken Extinction: Dinosaur Evolution and the Origin of Birds*. Freeman, New York, NY.

Dodson, P. 1993. Comparative craniology of the Ceratopsia. *American Journal of Science* 293-A:200–234.

Dodson, P., and L. P. Tatarinov. 1990. Dinosaur extinction. Pages 55–62 in *The Dinosauria*, edited by D. B. Weishampel, P. Dodson, and H. Osmólska. University of California Press, Berkeley, CA.

Erickson, G. M., S. D. Van Kirk, J. Su, M. E. Levenson, W. E. Caler, and D. R. Carter. 1996. Bite-force estimation for *Tyrannosaurus rex* from tooth marks on bones. *Nature* 382:706–708.

Farlow, J. O. 1987. Speculations about the diet and digestive physiology of herbivorous dinosaurs. *Paleobiology* 13:60–72.

Farlow, J. O. 1990. Dinosaur energetics and thermal biology. Pages 43–55 in *The Dinosauria*, edited by D. B. Weishampel, P. Dodson, and H. Osmólska. University of California Press, Berkeley, CA.

Farlow, J. O. 1993. On the rareness of big, fierce animals: speculations about the body sizes, population densities, and geographic ranges of predatory mammals and large carnivorous dinosaurs. *American Journal of Science* 293-A:167–199.

Farlow, J. O., C. V. Thompson, and D. E. Rosner. 1976. Plates of the dinosaur *Stegosaurus*: forced convection heat loss fins? *Science* 192:1123–1125.

Fastovsky, D. E., and D. B. Weishampel. 1996. *The Evolution and Extinction of the Dinosaurs*. Cambridge University Press, Cambridge, UK.

Feduccia, A. 1993. Evidence from claw geometry indicating arboreal habits of *Archaeopteryx*. *Science* 259:790–793.

Feduccia, A. 1996. *The Origin and Evolution of Birds*. Yale University Press, New Haven, CT.

Feduccia, A., and H. B. Tordoff. 1979. Feathers of *Archaeopteryx*: asymmetric vanes indicate aerodynamic function. *Science* 203:1021–1022.

Feduccia, A., and R. Wild. 1993. Birdlike characters in the Triassic archosaur *Megalancosaurus*. *Naturwissenschaften* 80:564–566.

Ferguson, M. W. J. 1985. Reproductive biology and embryology of the crocodilians. Pages 329–491 in *Biology of the Reptilia*, volume 14, edited by C. Gans, F. Billett, and P. F. A. Maderson. Wiley, New York, NY.

Galton, P. M. 1990. Basal Sauropodamoprha—prosauropods. Pages 320–344 in *The Dinosauria*, edited by D. B. Weishampel, P. Dodson, and H. Osmólska. University of California Press, Berkeley, CA.

Gauthier, J. 1986. Saurischian monophyly and the origin of birds. Pages 1–55 in *The Origin of Birds and the Evolution of Flight*, edited by K. Padian. *Memoirs of the California Academy of Sciences*, No. 8.

Gauthier, J., and K. Padian. 1985. Phylogenetic, functional, and aerodynamic analyses of the origin of birds and their flight. Pages 185–197 in *The Beginning of Birds, Proceedings of the International* Archaeopteryx *Conference, Eichstätt 1984*, edited by M. K. Hecht, J. H. Ostrom, G. Viohl, and P. Wellnhofer. Jura Museum, Eichstätt, West Germany.

Hazlehurst, G. A., and J. M. V. Rayner. 1992. Flight characteristics of Triassic and Jurassic Pterosauria: an appraisal based in wing shape. *Paleobiology* 18:447–463.

Hopson, J. A. 1975. The evolution of cranial display structures in hadrosaurian dinosaurs. *Paleobiology* 1:21–43.

Hopson, J. A., and L. B. Radinsky. 1980. Vertebrate paleontology: new approaches and new insights. *Paleobiology* 6:250–270.

Horner, J. R. 1982. Evidence of colonial nesting and site fidelity among ornithischian dinosaurs. *Nature* 297:675–676.

Horner, J. R. 1984. The nesting behavior of dinosaurs. *Scientific American* 241(4):130–137.

Horner, J. R. 1994. Comparative taphonomy of some dinosaur and extant bird colonial nesting grounds. Pages 116–123 in *Dinosaur Eggs and Babies*, edited by K. Carpenter, K. F. Hirsch, and J. R. Horner. Cambridge University Press, Cambridge, UK.

Horner, J. R., and P. Makela. 1979. Nest of juveniles provides evidence of family structure among dinosaurs. *Nature* 282:296–298.

Jenkins, F. A., Jr. 1993. The evolution of the avian shoulder joint. *American Journal of Science* 293-A:253–267.

Jensen, J. A. 1985. Three new sauropod dinosaurs from the Upper Jurassic of Colorado. *Great Basin Naturalist* 45:697–709.

Jones, D. R., and G. Shelton. 1993. The physiology of the alligator heart: Left aortic flow patterns and right-to-left shunts. *Journal of Experimental Biology* 176:247–269.

Kerourio, P. 1981. Nouvelles observations sur le mode de nidification et de ponte achez les dinosauriens du Cretace terminal du Midi de la France. *Comptes Rendu Sommaire des Séances de la Societe geologique de France* No. 1, pp. 25–28.

Kirkland, J. I. 1994. Predation of dinosaur nests by terrestrial crocodilians. Pages 124–133 in *Dinosaur Eggs and Babies*, edited by K. Carpenter, K. F. Hirsch, and J. R. Horner. Cambridge University Press, Cambridge, UK.

Kumar, S. and S. B. Hedges. 1998. A molecular timescale for vertebrate evolution. *Nature* 392:917–920.

Lang, J. W. 1986. Male parental care in mugger crocodiles. *National Geographic Research* 2:519–525.

Lang, J. W. 1989. Social behavior. Pages 102–117 in *Crocodiles and Alligators*, edited by C. A. Ross. Facts on File, New York, NY.

Lillywhite, H. B. 1991. Sauropods and gravity. *Natural History* December 1991, p. 33.

Lucas, S. G. 1981. Dinosaur communities of the San Juan Basin: a case for lateral variations in the composition of Late Cretaceous dinosaur communities. Pages 337–393 in *Advances in San Juan Basin Paleontology*, edited by S. G. Lucas, J. K. Rigby, Jr., and B. S. Kues. University of New Mexico Press, Albuquerque, NM.

Massare, J. A. 1987. Tooth morphology and prey preference of Mesozoic marine reptiles. *Journal of Vertebrate Paleontology* 7:121–137.

Massare, J. A. 1988. Swimming capabilities of Mesozoic marine reptiles: implications for methods of predation. *Paleobiology* 14:187–205.

McIntosh, J. S. 1989. The sauropod dinosaurs: a brief survey. Pages 85–99 in *The Age of Dinosaurs*, Short Courses in Paleontology, No. 2, edited by K. Padian and D. J. Chure. The Paleontological Society, University of Tennessee Press, Knoxville, TN.

Mikhailov, K. E. 1997. Eggs, eggshells, and nests. Pages 205–209 in *Encyclopedia of Dinosaurs*, edited by P. J. Currie and K. Padian, Academic Press, San Diego, CA.

Morgan, J., M. Warner and the Chicxlub Working Group, J. Brittan, J. Buffler, A. Camargo, G. Christeson, P. Denton, A. Holdebrand, R. Hobbs, H. Macintyre, G. Mackenzie, P. Maguire, L. Marin, Y. Nakamura, M. Pilkongton, V. Sharpton, D. Snyder, G. Suarez, and A. Trejo. 1997. Size and morphology of the Chicxlub impact crater. *Nature* 390:472–476.

Motani, R., You H., and C. McGowan. 1996. Eel-like swimming in the earliest ichthyosaurs. *Nature* 382:347–348.

Norell, M. A., and L. M. Chiappe. 1996. Flight from reason. (Review of *The Origin and Evolution of Birds* by Alan Feduccia). *Nature* 384:230.

Norell, M. A., J. M. Clark, D. Demberclyin, B. Rinchen, L. M. Chiappe, A. R. Davidson, M. C. McKenna, P. Altangerel, and M. J. Novacek. 1994. A theropod dinosaur embryo and the affinities of the Flaming Cliffs dinosaur eggs. *Science* 266:779–782.

Norell, M. A., P. Makovicky, and J. M. Clark. 1997. A *Velociraptor* wishbone. *Nature* 389:447.

Ostrom, J. H. 1974. *Archaeopteryx* and the evolution of flight. *Quarterly Review of Biology* 49:27–47.

Ostrom, J. H. 1986. The cursorial origin of avian flight. Pages 73–81 in *The Origin of Birds and the Evolution of Flight*, edited by K. Padian. *Memoirs of the California Academy of Sciences*, No. 8.

Padian, K. and Luis M. Chiappe. 1998. The origin of birds and their flight. *Scientific American* 278(2):38–47.

Padian, K., and J. M. V. Rayner. 1993. The wings of pterosaurs. *American Journal of Science* 293-A:91–166.

Paladino, F. V., M. P. O'Connor, and J. R. Spotila. 1990. Metabolism of leatherback turtles, gigantothermy, and thermoregulation of dinosaurs. *Nature* 344:858–860.

Peterson, A. 1985. The locomotor adaptations of *Archaeopteryx*: glider or cursor? Pages 99–103 in *The Beginning of Birds, Proceedings of the International* Archaeopteryx *Conference, Eichstätt 1984*, edited by M. K. Hecht, J. H. Ostrom, G. Viohl, and P. Wellnhofer. Jura Museum, Eichstätt, West Germany.

Pooley, A. C., and C. Gans. 1976. The Nile crocodile. *Scientific American* 234:114–124.

Rayner, J. M. V. 1988. The evolution of vertebrate flight. *Biological Journal of the Linnean Society* 34:269–287.

Romer, A. S. 1966. *Vertebrate Paleontology*, 3d edition. University of Chicago Press, Chicago, IL.

Ruben, J. 1991. Reptilian physiology and the flight capacity of *Archaeopteryx*. *Evolution* 45:1–17.

Ruben, J. 1993. Powered flight in *Archaeopteryx*: response to Speakman. *Evolution* 47:935–938.

Ruben, J. A., W. J. Hillenius, N. R. Geist, A. Leitch, T. D. Jones, P. J. Currie, J. R. Horner, and G. Espe III. 1996. The metabolic status of some Late Cretaceous dinosaurs. *Science* 273:1204–1207.

Ruben, J. A., T. D. Jones, N. R. Geist, and W. J. Hillenius. 1997. Lung structure and ventilation in theropod dinosaurs and early birds. *Science* 278:1267–1270.

Schopf, T. J. M. 1983. Extinction of the dinosaurs: a 1982 understanding. Pages 415–422 in *Large Body Impacts and Terrestrial Evolution*, edited by L. T. Silver and P. Schultz. Geological Society of America Special Paper 190.

Seymour, R. S. 1979. Dinosaur eggs: gas conductance through the shell, water loss during incubation and clutch size. *Paleobiology* 5:1–11.

Smith, K. K. 1980. Mechanical significance of streptostyly in lizards. *Nature* 283:778–779.

Spotila, J. R., M. P. O'Connor, P. Dodson, and F. V. Paladino. 1991. Hot and cold running dinosaurs: body size, metabolism and migration. *Modern Geology* 16:203–227.

Storrs, G. W. 1993. Function and phylogeny in sauropterygian (Diapsida) evolution. *American Journal of Science* 293-A:63–90.

Thomas, D. A., and J. O. Farlow. 1997. Tracking a dinosaur attack. *Scientific American* 277(6):74–79.

Thulborn, T. 1990. *Dinosaur Tracks*. Chapman & Hall, London, UK.

Troyer, K. 1984. Microbes, herbivory and the evolution of social behavior. *Journal of Theoretical Biology* 106:157–169.

Unwin, D. M. 1987. Pterosaur locomotion: joggers or waddlers? *Nature* 327:13–14.

Unwin, D. M., and N. Bakhurina. 1994. *Sordes pilosus* and the nature of the pterosaur flight apparatus. *Nature* 371:62–64.

Weishampel, D. B. 1981. Acoustic analyses of potential vocalization in lambeosaurine dinosaurs (Reptilia: Ornithischia). *Paleobiology* 7:252–261.

Yalden, D. W. 1985. Forelimb function in *Archaeopteryx*. Pages 91–97 in *The Beginning of Birds, Proceedings of the International* Archaeopteryx *Conference, Eichstätt 1984*, edited by M. K. Hecht, J. H. Ostrom, G. Viohl, and P. Wellnhofer. Jura Museum, Eichstätt, West Germany.

CHAPTER
14

Geography and Ecology
of the Mesozoic

Pangaea reached its greatest development during the early Mesozoic—all of the Earth's land surface had coalesced into a single continent that stretched from the South Pole to the North Pole. Early Mesozoic faunas and floras showed some regional differentiation due to climate, but would have had no barriers to dispersal. With the breakup of Pangaea in the Jurassic and Cretaceous, floras and faunas became distinct in different parts of the world.

Many new types of insects appeared in the Mesozoic, including social insects like bees, ants, and termites. An important floral change was the appearance and rapid radiation of the angiosperms (flowering seed plants) in the Cretaceous. A major turnover occurred in terrestrial vertebrates at the end of the Triassic, with the more varied large animal fauna, including a diversity of mammallike reptiles, being replaced by dinosaurs. Jurassic dinosaurs added the new herbivorous ecology of high-level browsing to the ecosystem, and the Cretaceous saw the evolution of other types of herbivorous dinosaurs with complex cheek teeth. Other new vertebrates appearing in the Mesozoic include mammals, birds, and modern types of amphibians and reptiles.

■ Mesozoic Continental Geography

At the beginning of the Triassic, the entire land area of Earth was concentrated in the supercontinent Pangaea, which straddled the Equator. The maximum development of Pangaea occurred at approximately the Middle/Late Triassic boundary. The southern part of Pangaea, areas that now form Antarctica and Australia, was close to the South Pole, and the northern part of modern Eurasia was within the Arctic Circle (Figure 14–1). The fragmentation of Pangaea began in the Jurassic with the separation of Laurasia and Gondwana by a westward extension of the Tethys Sea (Figure 14–2) and continued through the remainder of the Mesozoic. By the Late Cretaceous, the continents were approach-

ing their current positions, although India was still close to Africa (Figure 14–3).

■ Mesozoic Terrestrial Ecosystems

The Mesozoic is marked by a series of large-scale changes in flora and fauna beginning with the Permian/Triassic event, which extended over a period of about 25 million years, and culminating in the Cretaceous/Tertiary transition. Terrestrial ecosystems had achieved an essentially modern food web by the end of the Permian. Plants grew in communities that contained mixtures of species, they were consumed by herbivorous insects and vertebrates, and carnivorous invertebrates and vertebrates

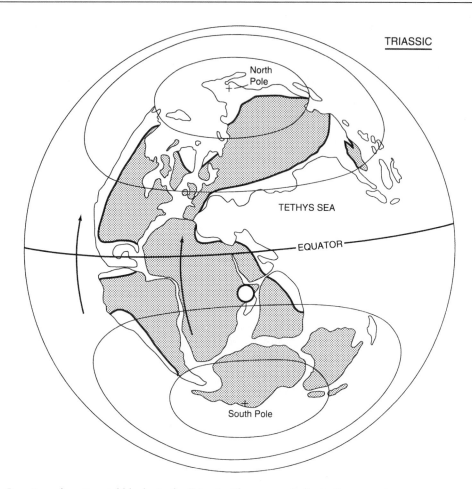

Figure 14–1 Location of continental blocks in the Triassic. The arrows indicate the general northward drift of Pangaea during the early Mesozoic. The continental land areas are shown by shading. Epicontinental seas (shown as unshaded areas within the confines of the outlines of the modern continents) were confined to the margins of continents.

preyed on the herbivores (DiMichele and Hook 1992). The kinds of plants and animals in Permian ecosystems were quite different from those in modern ecosystems, however. During the Mesozoic angiosperms (flowering plants) and mammals appeared and diversified, and ecosystems of the early Cenozoic have close modern analogues (Wing and Sues 1992).

Mesozoic vegetation included familiar modern groups of gymnosperms such as conifers (pines and other cone-bearing trees), ginkgophytes (relatives of the living ginkgo), as well as cycads. Despite the continuity of land from the extreme north of Pangaea to its southern tip, Triassic floras and faunas show regional characters that probably reflect differences in patterns of rainfall and seasonal temperature extremes in areas far from the sea. Triassic floras of Gondwana were dominated

by the seed fern *Dicroidium*, with conifers becoming the dominant form in the Jurassic. Conifers ranged from small bushes to tall forest trees, and many have structural characteristics that suggest they lived in relatively dry habitats. Cycads, too, appear to have lived in drier regions.

Angiosperms appear in the fossil record in the Early Cretaceous, although extrapolations of the time of origin of angiosperms based on analysis of DNA suggest that they might have originated as early as the Paleozoic (Martin et al. 1989). By the middle of the Cretaceous angiosperms were well established, especially in middle latitudes. Northern Laurasia and southern Gondwana continued to be dominated by conifers and ferns. A Late Cretaceous deposit in Wyoming that had been buried by volcanic ash allowed Wing and his colleagues to reconstruct the spatial relations of an upland plant

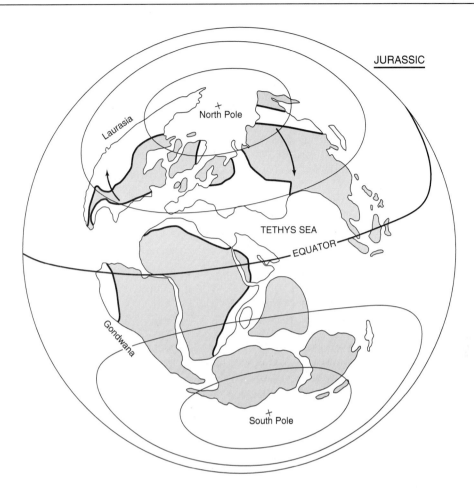

Figure 14–2   Location of continental blocks in the Jurassic. The northward drift of the continents continued, and Laurasia began to rotate as shown by the arrows, ripping North America from its contact with South America and diminishing the size of the Tethys Sea. The continental land areas are shown by shading. Epicontinental seas (shown as unshaded areas within the confines of the outlines of the modern continents) were more extensive than in the Triassic.

community as well as to determine the kinds of plants that had been present (Wing et al. 1993). Angiosperms accounted for 61 percent of the species of plants, but only 12 percent of the plant cover. In contrast, streamside sites of the same age were dominated by angiosperms. Thus, generalizations about the changing composition of vegetation during the Mesozoic may reflect local variation in the species present at the particular sites that have been studied. Clearly, ferns and gymnosperms remained significant elements of some floras through the entire Mesozoic. Angiosperms appear to have enjoyed their greatest success in disturbed habitats.

Insects lost a considerable amount of diversity at the end of the Permian, especially among plant-sucking forms, but new herbivorous forms appeared rapidly in the Mesozoic. Stick insects are first seen in the Triassic, thrips, leafhoppers, hymenopterans (wasps, termites, and bees), and many living groups of beetles appeared in the Jurassic, and butterflies, aphids, grasshoppers, and ants first appeared during the Cretaceous. Insects experienced little extinction at the end of the Mesozoic (Wing and Sues 1992).

The Permo-Triassic extinctions left a fairly impoverished terrestrial vertebrate fauna. Early Triassic faunas were dominated by the herbivorous dicynodont mammallike reptile *Lystrosaurus*, and also included cynodont mammallike reptiles and early archosaurs, diapsid reptiles that would eventually become dinosaur ancestors. Later in the Triassic the climate in the places where tetrapods are found shifted from warm and moist to hot and dry,

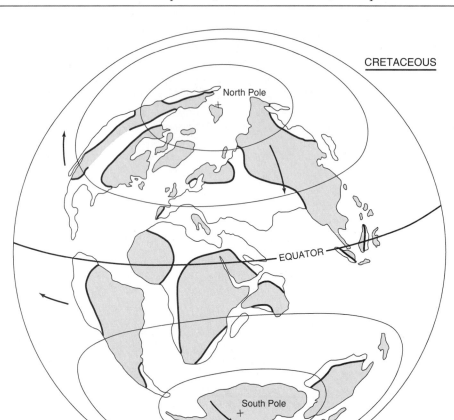

Figure 14–3 Location of continental blocks in the Cretaceous. The final breakup of Laurasia and Gondwana occurred in the Cretaceous. The northern continental blocks continued the rotation they began in the Jurassic, and were approaching their current positions by the end of the Cretaceous. The southern blocks moved apart (arrows). Note that India was still in the Southern Hemisphere and Australia, New Guinea, and New Zealand were well south of their current positions. The continental land areas are shown by shading. Extensive epicontinental seas (shown as unshaded areas within the confines of the outlines of the modern continents) covered large parts of North and South America, Eurasia, and Africa.

and the archosaurs increased in diversity and faunal predominance. Triassic faunas still contained a diversity of cynodonts, both herbivorous and carnivorous, dicynodonts, and rhyncosaurs (large herbivorous diapsid reptiles). But during the Late Triassic there was a shift in vegetational communities, especially in Gondwana where the floras dominated by seed ferns were replaced by ones dominated by conifers. This floral turnover was matched by a major faunal turnover; most of the Triassic tetrapods became extinct, replaced by a diversity of dinosaurs (Benton 1983). Mammals also made a first appearance at this time, as did a number of other modern groups such as sphenodontids

(lizard-related forms), turtles, crocodiles, and the ancestors of frogs.

The Late Triassic shift to a fauna dominated by dinosaurs also heralded an important shift in vertebrate herbivory. All earlier herbivorous tetrapods had been short-legged, short-necked forms, probably browsing on low-growing plants. The radiation of the prosauropod dinosaurs, with their longer legs and necks, greatly extended the range of vertebrate browsing behavior and may have had considerable effects on plant ecologies and life histories. The very large, true sauropods first appeared in the Middle Jurassic. These gargantuan herbivores would have been able to browse at heights of up to at least

10 meters, and they may have influenced patterns of vegetational growth and structure in a way similar to elephants today (Wing and Sues 1992). Other Jurassic dinosaurs included the low-browsing stegosaurs and the carnivorous allosaurids.

The Cretaceous saw the appearance of different types of herbivorous dinosaurs, the most important of these being the hadrosaurs and the ceratopsians, which were low-level feeders and had both developed complex shearing cheek teeth, probably for dealing with tough vegetation. With the breakup of Pangaea the tetrapod faunas started to show some distinct regional differences. The more derived tenanurine theropod dinosaurs became the dominant carnivores in Laurasia, whereas in South America the more primitive ceratosaurian theropods were dominant and tetanurans were rare. Sauropods appear to have continued as the dominant herbivores in South America and probably in Africa. In contrast, hadrosaurs and ceratopsians, which probably lived in migratory or nomadic herds that may have numbered in the thousands of individuals, dominated the faunas of Late Cretaceous in the Northern Hemisphere. The increase in the relative abundance of angiosperms in disturbed habitats is approximately coincident with the increase in abundance and diversity of hadrosaurs and ceratopsians in the Late Cretaceous of North America, and thus these dinosaurs may have facilitated angiosperm colonization of habitats (Wing and Sues 1992).

Other later Mesozoic faunal changes include the evolution of mammals with more complex (tribosphenic) molars in the Early Cretaceous, and later in the period the first appearance of mammals belonging to the three modern groups: monotremes, marsupials, and placentals. The earliest bird, *Archaeopteryx*, is known from the Late Jurassic, and there was a considerable radiation of birds during the Cretaceous. Lizards and the modern groups of amphibians first appeared in the Jurassic, and snakes and modern types of crocodiles are first known from the Cretaceous. The Mesozoic was also the time of a great radiation of marine reptiles, none of which survived the end of the Cretaceous, with the exception of turtles. The ecological roles played by Mesozoic marine tetrapods were reinvented in the Cenozoic marine by mammals such as whales and seals.

■ Mesozoic Climates

Mesozoic climates were equable worldwide, and there were no polar ice caps at any time during the

era. Large temnospondyls are found in Triassic deposits from Australia, Antarctica, Greenland, and Spitzbergen, and coal deposits in both the Northern and Southern Hemispheres point to moist climates. In contrast, low and middle latitudes were probably dry, either seasonally or year-round until the Late Cretaceous and early Cenozoic, when coal deposits in middle latitudes suggest that the climate had become wetter (Wilson et al. 1994, Manspeizer 1994). These dry lower latitudes had a type of vegetation different from the equatorial vegetation of today: there was no tropical rain forest during the Mesozoic (Ziegler et al. 1993). The Cretaceous plant record also suggests a highly equable world, with temperate forests extending into the polar regions, although some higher latitude cooling was apparent in the latest Cretaceous (Hallam 1994).

■ Mesozoic Extinctions

The extinctions at the end of the Cretaceous are famous as the ones that killed off the dinosaurs, even though the magnitude of the effect on the global fauna was nowhere near as large as the late Paleozoic (end Permian) extinctions. An astonishing number of ideas have been proposed for the reason that dinosaurs went extinct, ranging from the sublime (gonads zapped by an exploding supernova) to the ridiculous (constipation caused by angiosperms) (see Benton 1990). It must be remembered that dinosaurs were not the only animals that suffered extinctions at this time, and that any explanation for their demise must also account for that of a large variety of other vertebrates and invertebrates, both on land and in the sea, as well as for the survival of many other lineages. The possible role of an asteroid impact in the end Cretaceous extinctions was discussed in Chapter 13.

Thirty-six (40 percent) tetrapod families were extinct by the end of the Cretaceous, including not only all dinosaurs, but also all pterosaurs and marine reptiles, and there were lesser extinctions among other tetrapods such as mammals and birds. Another major extinction had occurred earlier, at the end of the Triassic. Only 18 families became extinct, but this was a time of major faunal turnover, as discussed above. Other, still smaller extinctions of tetrapods occurred in the Early Triassic and in the Late Jurassic (Benton 1989). All these terrestrial extinction events were paralleled in the marine realm (Raup and Sepkoski 1984, 1986).

■ References

Benton, M. J. 1983. Dinosaur success in the Triassic: a non-competitive evolutionary model. *Quarterly Review of Biology* 58:29–55.

Benton, M. J. 1989. Patterns of evolution and extinction in vertebrates. Pages 218–241 in *Evolution and the Fossil Record*, edited by K. C. Allen and D. E. G. Briggs. Belhaven Press, London, UK.

Benton, M. J. 1990. Scientific methodologies in collision: the history of the study of the extinction of the dinosaurs. *Evolutionary Biology* 24:371–400.

DiMichele, W. A., and R. W. Hook (rapporteurs). 1992. Paleozoic terrestrial ecosystems. Pages 205–325 in *Terrestrial Ecosystems Through Time*, edited by A. K. Behrensmeyer, J. D. Damuth, W. A. DiMichele, R. Potts, H. Dieter-Sues, and S. L. Wing. University of Chicago Press, Chicago, IL.

Hallam, A. 1994. *An Outline of Phanerozoic Biogeography*. Oxford University Press, Oxford, UK.

Manspeizer, W. 1994. The breakup of Pangea and its impact on climate: Consequences of Variscan–Alleghanide orogenic collapse. Pages 169–185 in *Pangea: Paleoclimate, Tectonics, and Sedimentation During Accretion, Zenith, and Breakup of a Supercontinent*, edited by G. D. Klein. Geological Society of America, Special Paper 288.

Martin, W., A. Gierl, and H. Saedler. 1989. Molecular evidence for pre-Cretaceous angiosperm origins. *Nature* 339:46–48.

Raup, D. M., and J. J. Sepkoski. 1984. Periodicities of extinctions in the geologic past. *Proceedings National Academy Sciences USA* 81:801–805.

Raup, D. M., and J. J. Sepkoski. 1986. Periodic extinction of families and genera. *Science* 231:833–836.

Wilson, K. M., D. Pollard, W. W. Hay, S. L. Thompson, and C. N. Wold. 1994. General circulation model simulations of Triassic climates: preliminary results. Pages 91–116 in *Pangea: Paleoclimate, Tectonics, and Sedimentation During Accretion, Zenith, and Breakup of a Supercontinent*, edited by G. D. Klein. Geological Society of America, Special Paper 288.

Wing, S. L., and H.-D. Sues (rapporteurs). 1992. Mesozoic and early Cenozoic terrestrial ecosystems. Pages 327–416 in *Terrestrial Ecosystems Through Time*, edited by A. K. Behrensmeyer, J. D. Damuth, W. A. DiMichele, R. Potts, H. Dieter–Sues, and S. L. Wing. University of Chicago Press, Chicago, IL.

Wing, S. L., L. J. Hickey, and C. C. Swisher. 1993. Implications of an exceptional fossil flora for Late Cretaceous vegetation. *Nature* 363:342–344.

Ziegler, A. M., J. M. Parrish, E. D. Gyllenhall, and D. B. Rowley. 1993. Early Mesozoic phytogeography and climate. *Philosophical Transactions of the Royal Society of London*, B341:297–305.

CHAPTER 15

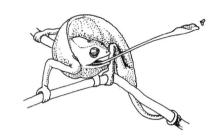

The Lepidosaurs: Tuatara, Lizards, and Snakes

Wenoted in our discussion of the fauna of the Mesozoic in Chapter 13 that many of the animals living then would not look strange in the modern world. Mammals, birds, and lepidosaurs (tuatara, lizards, and snakes) all originated and diversified in the Mesozoic, and their overshadowing by nonavian dinosaurs is as much a matter of our perception as of biological reality. Lizards and especially snakes are elements of the diapsid reptilian lineage that have had their greatest flowering in the Cenozoic, and the extant species of squamate diapsids outnumber the species of mammals.

Some aspects of the biology of squamates probably give us an impression of the ancestral way of life of amniotic tetrapods, although many of the structural characteristics of lizards and snakes are derived. One derived characteristic of lizards is determinate growth; that is, increase in body size stops when the growth centers of the long bones ossify. This mechanism sets an upper limit to the size of individuals of a species, and may be related to the specialization of most lizards as predators of insects. The predatory behavior of lizards ranges from sitting in one place and ambushing prey to seeking food by traversing a home range in an active, purposeful way. Broad aspects of the biology of lizards are correlated with these foraging modes, including morphology, exercise physiology, reproductive mode, defense against predators, and social behavior. The anatomical specializations of snakes are associated with their elongate body form and include modifications of the jaws and skull that allow them to subdue and swallow large prey.

■ The Lepidosaurs

Lepidosaurs are the largest group of nonavian reptiles, containing more than 3300 species of lizards and 2500 species of snakes in addition to the 2 species of tuatara (Table 15.1). Lepidosaurs are predominantly terrestrial tetrapods with some secondarily aquatic species, especially among snakes. The skin of lepidosaurs is scale covered and rela-

tively impermeable to water. The outer layer of the epidermis is shed at intervals. Tuatara and most lizards have four limbs, but reduction or complete loss of limbs is widespread among lizards and all snakes are limbless. Lepidosaurs have a transverse cloacal slit, rather than the longitudinal slit that characterizes other tetrapods.

Lepidosaurs are the sister lineage of archosaurs (crocodilians and birds). Within the Lepidosauria,

TABLE 15.1	Lineages of extant lepidosaurs

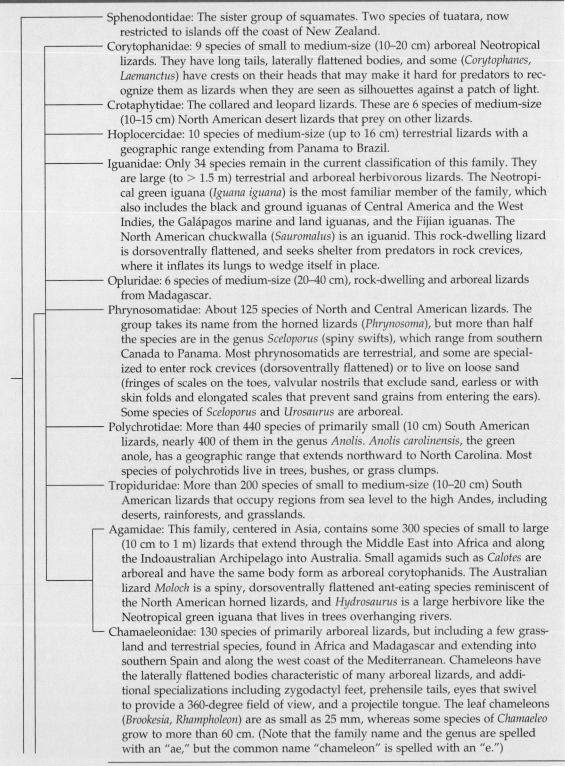

Sphenodontidae: The sister group of squamates. Two species of tuatara, now restricted to islands off the coast of New Zealand.

Corytophanidae: 9 species of small to medium-size (10–20 cm) arboreal Neotropical lizards. They have long tails, laterally flattened bodies, and some (*Corytophanes*, *Laemanctus*) have crests on their heads that may make it hard for predators to recognize them as lizards when they are seen as silhouettes against a patch of light.

Crotaphytidae: The collared and leopard lizards. These are 6 species of medium-size (10–15 cm) North American desert lizards that prey on other lizards.

Hoplocercidae: 10 species of medium-size (up to 16 cm) terrestrial lizards with a geographic range extending from Panama to Brazil.

Iguanidae: Only 34 species remain in the current classification of this family. They are large (to > 1.5 m) terrestrial and arboreal herbivorous lizards. The Neotropical green iguana (*Iguana iguana*) is the most familiar member of the family, which also includes the black and ground iguanas of Central America and the West Indies, the Galápagos marine and land iguanas, and the Fijian iguanas. The North American chuckwalla (*Sauromalus*) is an iguanid. This rock-dwelling lizard is dorsoventrally flattened, and seeks shelter from predators in rock crevices, where it inflates its lungs to wedge itself in place.

Opluridae: 6 species of medium-size (20–40 cm), rock-dwelling and arboreal lizards from Madagascar.

Phrynosomatidae: About 125 species of North and Central American lizards. The group takes its name from the horned lizards (*Phrynosoma*), but more than half the species are in the genus *Sceloporus* (spiny swifts), which range from southern Canada to Panama. Most phrynosomatids are terrestrial, and some are specialized to enter rock crevices (dorsoventrally flattened) or to live on loose sand (fringes of scales on the toes, valvular nostrils that exclude sand, earless or with skin folds and elongated scales that prevent sand grains from entering the ears). Some species of *Sceloporus* and *Urosaurus* are arboreal.

Polychrotidae: More than 440 species of primarily small (10 cm) South American lizards, nearly 400 of them in the genus *Anolis*. *Anolis carolinensis*, the green anole, has a geographic range that extends northward to North Carolina. Most species of polychrotids live in trees, bushes, or grass clumps.

Tropiduridae: More than 200 species of small to medium-size (10–20 cm) South American lizards that occupy regions from sea level to the high Andes, including deserts, rainforests, and grasslands.

Agamidae: This family, centered in Asia, contains some 300 species of small to large (10 cm to 1 m) lizards that extend through the Middle East into Africa and along the Indoaustralian Archipelago into Australia. Small agamids such as *Calotes* are arboreal and have the same body form as arboreal corytophanids. The Australian lizard *Moloch* is a spiny, dorsoventrally flattened ant-eating species reminiscent of the North American horned lizards, and *Hydrosaurus* is a large herbivore like the Neotropical green iguana that lives in trees overhanging rivers.

Chamaeleonidae: 130 species of primarily arboreal lizards, but including a few grassland and terrestrial species, found in Africa and Madagascar and extending into southern Spain and along the west coast of the Mediterranean. Chameleons have the laterally flattened bodies characteristic of many arboreal lizards, and additional specializations including zygodactyl feet, prehensile tails, eyes that swivel to provide a 360-degree field of view, and a projectile tongue. The leaf chameleons (*Brookesia*, *Rhampholeon*) are as small as 25 mm, whereas some species of *Chamaeleo* grow to more than 60 cm. (Note that the family name and the genus are spelled with an "ae," but the common name "chameleon" is spelled with an "e.")

Phylogenetic relationships and numbers of species are based on F. H. Pough, R. M. Andrews, J. E. Cadle, M. L. Crump, A. H. Savitzky, and K. D. Wells, 1998, *Herpetology*, Prentice Hall, Upper Saddle River, NJ.

TABLE 15.1 *(continued)* Lineages of extant lepidosaurs

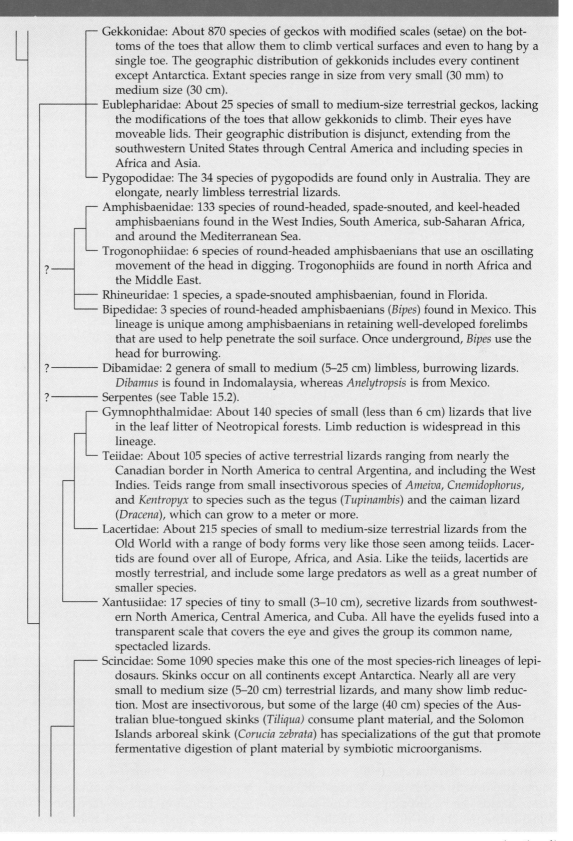

Gekkonidae: About 870 species of geckos with modified scales (setae) on the bottoms of the toes that allow them to climb vertical surfaces and even to hang by a single toe. The geographic distribution of gekkonids includes every continent except Antarctica. Extant species range in size from very small (30 mm) to medium size (30 cm).

Eublepharidae: About 25 species of small to medium-size terrestrial geckos, lacking the modifications of the toes that allow gekkonids to climb. Their eyes have moveable lids. Their geographic distribution is disjunct, extending from the southwestern United States through Central America and including species in Africa and Asia.

Pygopodidae: The 34 species of pygopodids are found only in Australia. They are elongate, nearly limbless terrestrial lizards.

Amphisbaenidae: 133 species of round-headed, spade-snouted, and keel-headed amphisbaenians found in the West Indies, South America, sub-Saharan Africa, and around the Mediterranean Sea.

Trogonophiidae: 6 species of round-headed amphisbaenians that use an oscillating movement of the head in digging. Trogonophiids are found in north Africa and the Middle East.

Rhineuridae: 1 species, a spade-snouted amphisbaenian, found in Florida.

Bipedidae: 3 species of round-headed amphisbaenians (*Bipes*) found in Mexico. This lineage is unique among amphisbaenians in retaining well-developed forelimbs that are used to help penetrate the soil surface. Once underground, *Bipes* use the head for burrowing.

Dibamidae: 2 genera of small to medium (5–25 cm) limbless, burrowing lizards. *Dibamus* is found in Indomalaysia, whereas *Anelytropsis* is from Mexico.

Serpentes (see Table 15.2).

Gymnophthalmidae: About 140 species of small (less than 6 cm) lizards that live in the leaf litter of Neotropical forests. Limb reduction is widespread in this lineage.

Teiidae: About 105 species of active terrestrial lizards ranging from nearly the Canadian border in North America to central Argentina, and including the West Indies. Teids range from small insectivorous species of *Ameiva*, *Cnemidophorus*, and *Kentropyx* to species such as the tegus (*Tupinambis*) and the caiman lizard (*Dracena*), which can grow to a meter or more.

Lacertidae: About 215 species of small to medium-size terrestrial lizards from the Old World with a range of body forms very like those seen among teiids. Lacertids are found over all of Europe, Africa, and Asia. Like the teiids, lacertids are mostly terrestrial, and include some large predators as well as a great number of smaller species.

Xantusiidae: 17 species of tiny to small (3–10 cm), secretive lizards from southwestern North America, Central America, and Cuba. All have the eyelids fused into a transparent scale that covers the eye and gives the group its common name, spectacled lizards.

Scincidae: Some 1090 species make this one of the most species-rich lineages of lepidosaurs. Skinks occur on all continents except Antarctica. Nearly all are very small to medium size (5–20 cm) terrestrial lizards, and many show limb reduction. Most are insectivorous, but some of the large (40 cm) species of the Australian blue-tongued skinks (*Tiliqua*) consume plant material, and the Solomon Islands arboreal skink (*Corucia zebrata*) has specializations of the gut that promote fermentative digestion of plant material by symbiotic microorganisms.

(continued)

TABLE 15.1	*(continued)* Lineages of extant lepidosaurs

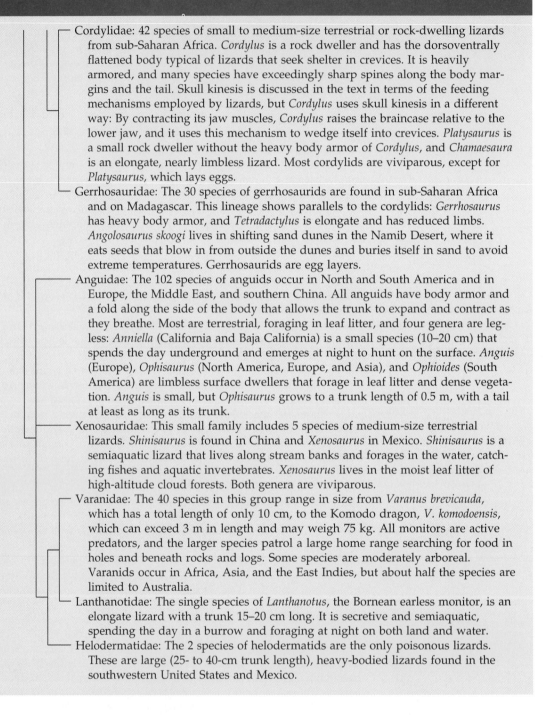

Cordylidae: 42 species of small to medium-size terrestrial or rock-dwelling lizards from sub-Saharan Africa. *Cordylus* is a rock dweller and has the dorsoventrally flattened body typical of lizards that seek shelter in crevices. It is heavily armored, and many species have exceedingly sharp spines along the body margins and the tail. Skull kinesis is discussed in the text in terms of the feeding mechanisms employed by lizards, but *Cordylus* uses skull kinesis in a different way: By contracting its jaw muscles, *Cordylus* raises the braincase relative to the lower jaw, and it uses this mechanism to wedge itself into crevices. *Platysaurus* is a small rock dweller without the heavy body armor of *Cordylus*, and *Chamaesaura* is an elongate, nearly limbless lizard. Most cordylids are viviparous, except for *Platysaurus*, which lays eggs.

Gerrhosauridae: The 30 species of gerrhosaurids are found in sub-Saharan Africa and on Madagascar. This lineage shows parallels to the cordylids: *Gerrhosaurus* has heavy body armor, and *Tetradactylus* is elongate and has reduced limbs. *Angolosaurus skoogi* lives in shifting sand dunes in the Namib Desert, where it eats seeds that blow in from outside the dunes and buries itself in sand to avoid extreme temperatures. Gerrhosaurids are egg layers.

Anguidae: The 102 species of anguids occur in North and South America and in Europe, the Middle East, and southern China. All anguids have body armor and a fold along the side of the body that allows the trunk to expand and contract as they breathe. Most are terrestrial, foraging in leaf litter, and four genera are legless: *Anniella* (California and Baja California) is a small species (10–20 cm) that spends the day underground and emerges at night to hunt on the surface. *Anguis* (Europe), *Ophisaurus* (North America, Europe, and Asia), and *Ophioides* (South America) are limbless surface dwellers that forage in leaf litter and dense vegetation. *Anguis* is small, but *Ophisaurus* grows to a trunk length of 0.5 m, with a tail at least as long as its trunk.

Xenosauridae: This small family includes 5 species of medium-size terrestrial lizards. *Shinisaurus* is found in China and *Xenosaurus* in Mexico. *Shinisaurus* is a semiaquatic lizard that lives along stream banks and forages in the water, catching fishes and aquatic invertebrates. *Xenosaurus* lives in the moist leaf litter of high-altitude cloud forests. Both genera are viviparous.

Varanidae: The 40 species in this group range in size from *Varanus brevicauda*, which has a total length of only 10 cm, to the Komodo dragon, *V. komodoensis*, which can exceed 3 m in length and may weigh 75 kg. All monitors are active predators, and the larger species patrol a large home range searching for food in holes and beneath rocks and logs. Some species are moderately arboreal. Varanids occur in Africa, Asia, and the East Indies, but about half the species are limited to Australia.

Lanthanotidae: The single species of *Lanthanotus*, the Bornean earless monitor, is an elongate lizard with a trunk 15–20 cm long. It is secretive and semiaquatic, spending the day in a burrow and foraging at night on both land and water.

Helodermatidae: The 2 species of helodermatids are the only poisonous lizards. These are large (25- to 40-cm trunk length), heavy-bodied lizards found in the southwestern United States and Mexico.

the Sphenodontidae (tuatara) is the sister group of Squamata (lizards and snakes). Within the squamates, lizards can be distinguished from snakes in colloquial terms but not phylogenetically, because snakes are derived from lizards. Thus "lizards" is a paraphyletic group (i.e., one that does not include all the descendants of a common ancestor). Nonetheless, lizards and snakes are distinct in many aspects of their ecology and behavior and a colloquial separation is useful in discussing them.

The Radiation of Sphenodontids and the Biology of Tuatara

The sphenodontids were a diverse group in the Mesozoic. Triassic forms were small, with body lengths of only 15 to 35 centimeters. Most Triassic sphenodontids had teeth that were fused to the top edges of the jaw bones (**acrodont**) like the teeth of extant tuatara (*Sphenodon*), but others had teeth attached to the inner sides of the jaw bones (**pleurodont**), like those of some lizards. The tooth structure of Triassic sphenodontids suggests that the lineage included both insectivores and herbivores. Some sphenodontids from the Jurassic and Cretaceous were small terrestrial forms, but others were marine animals as much as 1.5 meters long.

The two species of *Sphenodon,* known as tuatara, are the only extant sphenodontids. ("Tuatara" is a Maori word meaning "spines on the back," and no "s" is added to form the plural.) Tuatara formerly inhabited the North and South islands of New Zealand, but the advent of humans and their associates (cats, dogs, rats, sheep, and goats) exterminated tuatara on the mainland. Now populations are found on only about 30 small islands off the coast.

Tuatara have been fully protected in New Zealand since 1895, but only one species, *Sphenodon punctatus,* was recognized. In fact there is a second species of tuatara, *S. guentheri,* which was described in 1877. *Sphenodon guentheri* is much less common than *S. punctatus,* and the fact that there are two species of tuatara was overlooked when laws protecting tuatara were written. As a result, *S. guentheri* did not receive the special protection that it needed (Daugherty et al. 1990). The only surviving population of *S. guentheri* is a group of fewer than 300 adults living on 1.7 hectares of scrub on the top of North Brother Island, and these animals were regarded as not very important from a conservation perspective compared with the large populations of *S. punctatus* on some of the other islands. Probably it was only the presence of a lighthouse, which was staffed until 1990 by resident keepers who deterred illegal landings and poaching, that saved the tuatara. The East Island population of *S. guentheri* (the only other population of the species) became extinct during this century. This example illustrates the crucial role that taxonomy plays in conservation—a species must be recognized before it can be protected (May 1990).

Adult tuatara are about 60 centimeters long. They are nocturnal and in the cool, foggy nights that characterize their island habitats they cannot raise their body temperatures during activity by basking in the sun as lizards do. Body temperatures from 6 to 16°C have been reported for active tuatara, and these are low compared with most lizards. During the day, tuatara do bask in the sun and raise their body temperatures to 28°C or higher. Tuatara feed largely on invertebrates, with an occasional frog, lizard, or seabird for variety. The jaws and teeth of tuatara produce a shearing effect during chewing: The upper jaw contains two rows of teeth, one on the maxilla and the other on the palatine bones. The teeth of the lower jaw fit between the two rows of upper teeth, and the lower jaw closes with an initial vertical movement, followed by an anterior sliding movement. As the lower jaw slides, the food item is bent or sheared between the triangular cusps on the teeth of the upper and lower jaws.

Tuatara live in burrows that they may share with nesting seabirds. The burrows are spaced at intervals of 2 to 3 meters in dense colonies, and both male and female tuatara are territorial. They use vocalizations, behavioral displays, and color change in their social interactions (Gillingham et al. 1995).

The ecology of tuatara rests to a large extent on exploitation of the resources provided by colonies of seabirds. Tuatara feed on the birds, which are most vulnerable to predation at night. In addition, the quantities of guano produced by the birds, scraps of the food they bring to their nestlings, and the bodies of dead nestlings attract huge numbers of arthropods that are eaten by tuatara. These arthropods are largely nocturnal and must be hunted when they are active. Thus the crepuscular (= occurring at dusk and dawn) activity of tuatara and the low body temperatures that result from being active at those times of day are probably specializations that stem from the association of tuatara with colonies of nesting seabirds. This pattern of behavior and thermoregulation probably does not represent even the ancestral condition for sphenodontids, and there is no reason to interpret it as being ancestral for lepidosaurs or diapsids.

■ The Radiation of Squamates

Squamates are defined by a variety of derived characters (see Chapter 13), of which determinate growth may have the most general significance.

Growth occurs as cells proliferate in the cartilaginous epiphyseal plates at the ends of long bones. Growth continues while the epiphyseal plates are composed of cartilage, and stops completely when the epiphyses fuse to the shafts of the bones, obliterating the cartilaginous plates. Determinate growth of this sort is characteristic of squamates (and also of birds and mammals). Crocodilians and turtles continue to grow all through their lives, although the growth rates of adults are much slower than those of juveniles. The development of determinate growth in lepidosaurs may initially have been associated with the insectivorous diet that is believed to have been characteristic of early lepidosaurs. Lizard-size animals can prey on insects without requiring the sorts of morphological or ecological specializations that are necessary for large insect-eating vertebrates such as mammalian anteaters.

The fossil record of lizards is largely incomplete through the middle of the Mesozoic, but late Jurassic deposits in China and Europe include members of most of the lineages of extant lizards. The major groups of lizards had probably diverged by the end of the Jurassic.

The phylogenetic relationships of squamates are well understood in general, but disagreement surrounds some details. Two major lineages are recognized, the Iguania and the Scleroglossa. The Iguania includes the sister taxa Agamidae and Chamaeleonidae, plus eight lineages that used to be placed in the Iguanidae: Corytophanidae, Crotaphytidae, Hoplocercidae, Iguanidae, Opluridae, Phrynosomatidae, Polychrotidae, and Tropiduridae. Frost and Etheridge (1989) were unable to identify shared morphological characters uniting these clades, and therefore gave each of the eight lineages formal taxonomic status. More recently, Macey et al. (1997) found molecular characters that support a common origin of the lineages and proposed a return to the traditional nomenclature with a single clade, Iguanidae, including all eight groups. At this time the literature largely follows the arrangement proposed by Frost and Etheridge as shown in Table 15.1.

Within the Scleroglossa, the Gekkota, Scincomorpha, and Anguimorpha form successive clades. Note that the Amphisbaenia (specialized burrowing lizards) and Serpentes (snakes) are nested within the Scleroglossa. Both groups have morphological and ecological specializations that make it convenient to discuss them individually, but their evolutionary status as lineages within the scleroglossan squamates must be remembered.

Lizards

The approximately 3300 species of lizards range in size from diminutive geckos only 3 centimeters long to the Komodo monitor lizard, which is 3 meters long at maturity and weighs some 75 kilograms. A reconstruction of the skeleton of a fossil monitor lizard, *Megalania prisca,* from the Pleistocene of Australia, is 5.5 meters long, and in life the lizard might have weighed more than 1000 kilograms. About 80 percent of extant lizards weigh less than 20 grams as adults and are insectivorous. Spiny swifts and japalures (Figure 15–1a and b) are examples of these small, generalized insectivores. Other small lizards have specialized diets: The North American horned lizards and the Australian thorny devil (Figure 15–1e and f) feed on ants. Most geckos (Figure 15–1g) are nocturnal, and many species are closely associated with human habitations.

Lizards are adaptable animals that have occupied habitats ranging from swamp to desert and even above the timberline in some mountains. Many species are arboreal, and the most specialized of these are frequently laterally flattened and often have peculiar projections from the skull and back that help to obscure their outline. The Old World chameleons (Chamaeleonidae) are the most specialized arboreal lizards (Figure 15–1h). Their **zygo-dactylous** (*zygo* = joined, *dactyl* = digit) feet grasp branches firmly, and additional security is provided by a prehensile tail. The tongue and hyoid apparatus are specialized, and the tongue can be projected forward more than a body's length to capture insects that adhere to its sticky tip. This feeding mechanism requires good eyesight, especially the ability to gauge distances accurately so that the correct trajectory can be employed. The chameleon's eyes are elevated in small cones and are independently movable. When the lizard is at rest, the eyes swivel back and forth giving the lizard a view of its surroundings. When an insect is spotted, both eyes fix on it, and a cautious stalk brings the lizard within shooting range.

Most large lizards are herbivores. Many iguanas (family Iguanidae) are arboreal inhabitants of the tropics of Central and South America. Large terrestrial iguanas occur on islands in the West Indies and the Galápagos Islands, probably because the absence of predators has allowed them to spend a large part of their time on the ground. Smaller terrestrial herbivores like the black iguanas (Figure 15–1c) live on the mainland of Mexico and Central America, and still smaller relatives such as the chuckwallas and desert iguanas range as far north as the western United

States. Many species of lizards live on beaches, but few extant species actually enter the water. The marine iguana of the Galápagos Islands is an exception. The feeding habits of the marine iguana are unique. It feeds on seaweed, diving 10 meters or more to browse on algae growing below the tide mark.

An exception to the rule of herbivorous diets for large lizards is found in the monitor lizards (family Varanidae). Varanids are active predators that feed on a variety of vertebrate and invertebrate animals, including birds and mammals (Figure 15–1j). Few lizards are capable of capturing and subduing such prey, but varanids have morphological and physiological characteristics that make them effective predators of vertebrates. The Komodo monitor lizard is capable of killing adult water buffalo, but its normal prey is deer and feral goats (Auffenberg 1981). (Large monitor lizards were widely distributed on the islands between Australia and Indonesia during the Pleistocene and may have preyed on pygmy elephants that also lived on the islands [Diamond 1987].)

The hunting methods of the Komodo monitor are very similar to those employed by mammalian carnivores, showing that a simple brain is capable of complex behavior and learning. In the late morning a Komodo monitor waits in ambush beside the trails deer use to move from the hilltops—where they rest during the morning, to the valleys—where they sleep during the afternoon. The lizards are familiar with the trails the deer use and often wait where several deer trails converge. If no deer pass the lizard's ambush, it moves into the valleys, systematically stalking the thickets where deer are likely to be found. This purposeful hunting behavior, which demonstrates familiarity with the behavior of the prey and with local geography, is in strong contrast to the opportunistic seizure of prey that characterizes the behavior of many lizards, but it is very like the hunting behavior of some snakes (Greene 1997).

Limb reduction has evolved repeatedly among lizards, perhaps as many as 62 times (Greer 1991), and every continent has one or more families with legless, or nearly legless, species (Figure 15–1i). Leglessness in lizards is usually associated with life in dense grass or shrubbery in which a slim, elongate body can maneuver more easily than a short one with functional legs. Some legless lizards crawl into small openings among rocks and under logs, and a few are subterranean.

The amphisbaenians include about 150 species of extremely fossorial lizards (*fossor* = a digger),

which have specializations that are different from those of other squamates (Figure 15–2). The earliest amphisbaenian known is a fossil from the late Cretaceous (Wu et al. 1993). Most amphisbaenians are legless, but the three species in the Mexican genus *Bipes* have well-developed fore legs that they use to assist entry into the soil but not for burrowing underground. The skulls of amphisbaenians are used for tunneling, and they are rigidly constructed. The dental structure is also distinctive: Amphisbaenians possess a single median tooth in the upper jaw—a feature unique to this group of vertebrates. The median tooth is part of a specialized dental battery that makes amphisbaenians formidable predators, capable of subduing a wide variety of invertebrates and small vertebrates. The upper tooth fits into the space between two teeth in the lower jaw and forms a set of nippers that can bite out a piece of tissue from a prey item too large for the mouth to engulf as a whole.

The skin of amphisbaenians also is distinctive. The **annuli** (rings) that pass around the circumference of the body are readily apparent from external examination, and dissection shows that the integument is nearly free of connections to the trunk. Thus, it forms a tube within which the body of the amphisbaenian can slide forward or backward. The separation of the trunk and skin is employed during the concertina locomotion that all amphisbaenians use underground. Integumentary muscles run longitudinally from annulus to annulus. Their contraction causes the skin over the area of muscular contraction to telescope and to buckle outward, anchoring that part of the amphisbaenian against the walls of its tunnel. Next, contraction of muscles that pass anteriorly from the vertebrae and ribs to the skin slide the trunk forward within the tube of integument. Amphisbaenians can move backward along their tunnels with the same mechanism by contracting muscles that pass posteriorly from the ribs to the skin. (The name amphisbaenian is derived from the Greek roots [*amphi* = double, *baen* = walk] in reference to the ability of amphisbaenians to move forward and backward with equal facility.) A similar type of rectilinear (straight-line) locomotion is used by some heavy-bodied snakes, but the telescoping ability of the skin of snakes is generally restricted to the lateroventral portions of the body, whereas the skin is loose around the entire circumference of the body of amphisbaenians.

The burrowing habits of amphisbaenians make them difficult to study. Three major functional categories can be recognized: Some species have blunt

Figure 15–1 Parallel and convergent evolution of body forms among lizards. Small, generalized insectivores: (a) spiny swift, *Sceloporus*, Phrynosomatidae; (b) japalure, *Calotes*, Agamidae. Herbivores: (c) black iguana, *Ctenosaura*, Iguanidae; (d) mastigure, *Uromastyx*, Leiolepididae. Ant specialists: (e) horned lizard, *Phrynosoma*, Phrynosomatidae; (f) spiny devil, *Moloch*, Agamidae. Nocturnal lizards: (g) Tokay gecko, *Gekko*, Gekkonidae. Arboreal lizards: (h) African chameleon, *Chamaeleo*, Chamaeleonidae. Legless lizards: (i) North American glass lizard, *Ophisaurus*, Anguidae. Large predators: (j) monitor lizard, *Varanus* Varanidae.

heads; the rest have either vertically keeled or horizontally spade-shaped snouts. Blunt-snouted forms burrow by ramming their heads into the soil to compact it (Figure 15–2b). Sometimes an oscillatory rotation of the head with its heavily keratinized scales is used to shave material from the face of the tunnel. Shovel-snouted amphisbaenians ram the end of the tunnel, then lift the head to compact soil into the roof (Figure 15–2c). Wedge-snouted forms ram the snout into the end of the tunnel and then use the snout or the side of the neck to compress the material into the walls of the tunnel (Figure 15–2d, e, f). In parts of Africa representatives of the three types occur together and share the subsoil habitat. The unspecialized blunt-headed forms live near the surface where the soil is relatively easy to tunnel through, and the specialized forms live in deeper, more compact soil. The geographic range of the unspecialized forms is greater than that of the specialized ones, and in areas in which only a single species of amphisbaenian occurs it is a blunt-headed species.

The relationship between unspecialized and specialized burrowers is puzzling. One would expect that the specialized forms with their more elaborate methods of burrowing would replace the unspe-

(e)

(f)

(g)

(h)

(i)

(j)

cialized ones, but this has not happened. The explanation may lie in the conflicting selective forces on the snout. On one hand, it is important to have a snout that will burrow through soil, but on the other hand, it is also important to have a mouth capable of tackling a wide variety of prey. The specializations of the snout that make it an effective structure for burrowing appear to reduce its effectiveness for feeding. The blunt-headed amphisbaenians may be able to eat a wider variety of prey than the specialized forms can. Thus, in loose soil where it is easy to burrow, the blunt-headed forms may have an advantage. Only in soil too compact

for a blunt-headed form to penetrate might the specialized forms find the balance of selective forces shifted in their favor.

Snakes

The 2500 species of snakes range in size from diminutive burrowing species, which feed on termites and grow to only 10 centimeters, to the large constrictors, which approach 10 meters in length (Table 15.2). The Scolecophidia includes three families of small burrowing snakes with shiny scales and reduced eyes. Traces of the pelvic girdle remain in

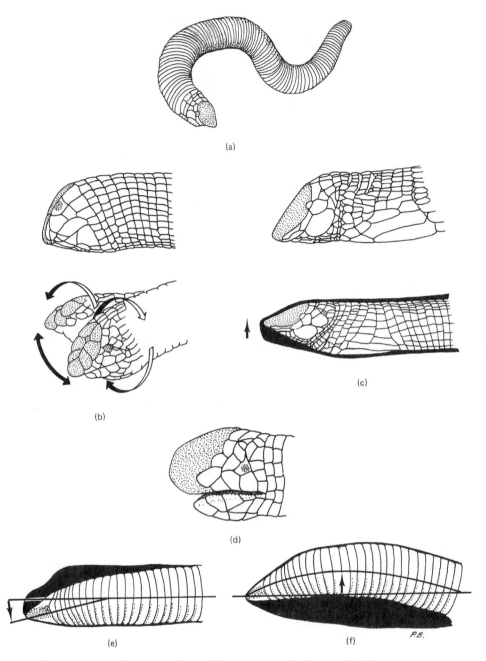

Figure 15–2   Amphisbaenians. (a) *Monopeltis*, from Africa; (b) blunt-snouted (*Agamodon*, from Africa); (c) shovel-snouted (*Rhineura* from Florida); (d) wedge-snouted (*Anops*, Brazil). ([b], [c], [e], and [f] modified from C. Gans, 1974, *Biomechanics*, Lippincott, Philadelphia, PA.)

most species, but the braincase is snakelike. Burrowing snakes in the families Aniliidae and Uropeltidae use their heads to dig through soil, and the bones of their skulls are solidly united. The sole xenopeltid, the sunbeam snake of southeastern Asia, is a ground-dwelling species that takes its common name from its highly iridescent scales. Boa constrictors (Boinae) are mostly New World snakes, whereas pythons (Pythoninae) are found in the Old World. The anaconda, a semiaquatic species of boa from South America, is considered the largest extant species of snake—it probably approaches a length of 10 meters—and the reticulated python of southeast Asia is nearly as large. Not all boas and pythons are large, however; some secretive and fossorial species are considerably less than 1 meter long as adults.

TABLE 15.2	Lineages of extant snakes

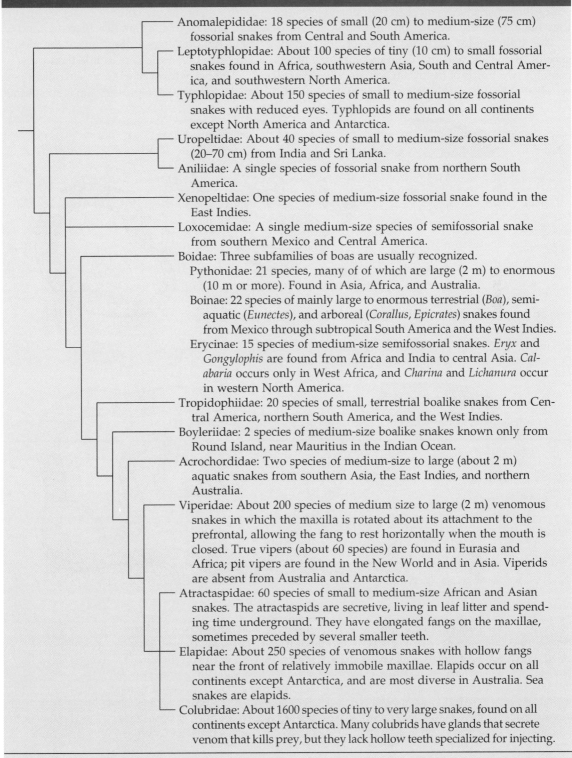

Anomalepididae: 18 species of small (20 cm) to medium-size (75 cm) fossorial snakes from Central and South America.

Leptotyphlopidae: About 100 species of tiny (10 cm) to small fossorial snakes found in Africa, southwestern Asia, South and Central America, and southwestern North America.

Typhlopidae: About 150 species of small to medium-size fossorial snakes with reduced eyes. Typhlopids are found on all continents except North America and Antarctica.

Uropeltidae: About 40 species of small to medium-size fossorial snakes (20–70 cm) from India and Sri Lanka.

Aniliidae: A single species of fossorial snake from northern South America.

Xenopeltidae: One species of medium-size fossorial snake found in the East Indies.

Loxocemidae: A single medium-size species of semifossorial snake from southern Mexico and Central America.

Boidae: Three subfamilies of boas are usually recognized.

Pythonidae: 21 species, many of of which are large (2 m) to enormous (10 m or more). Found in Asia, Africa, and Australia.

Boinae: 22 species of mainly large to enormous terrestrial (*Boa*), semi-aquatic (*Eunectes*), and arboreal (*Corallus*, *Epicrates*) snakes found from Mexico through subtropical South America and the West Indies.

Erycinae: 15 species of medium-size semifossorial snakes. *Eryx* and *Gongylophis* are found from Africa and India to central Asia. *Calabaria* occurs only in West Africa, and *Charina* and *Lichanura* occur in western North America.

Tropidophiidae: 20 species of small, terrestrial boalike snakes from Central America, northern South America, and the West Indies.

Boyleriidae: 2 species of medium-size boalike snakes known only from Round Island, near Mauritius in the Indian Ocean.

Acrochordidae: Two species of medium-size to large (about 2 m) aquatic snakes from southern Asia, the East Indies, and northern Australia.

Viperidae: About 200 species of medium size to large (2 m) venomous snakes in which the maxilla is rotated about its attachment to the prefrontal, allowing the fang to rest horizontally when the mouth is closed. True vipers (about 60 species) are found in Eurasia and Africa; pit vipers are found in the New World and in Asia. Viperids are absent from Australia and Antarctica.

Atractaspidae: 60 species of small to medium-size African and Asian snakes. The atractaspids are secretive, living in leaf litter and spending time underground. They have elongated fangs on the maxillae, sometimes preceded by several smaller teeth.

Elapidae: About 250 species of venomous snakes with hollow fangs near the front of relatively immobile maxillae. Elapids occur on all continents except Antarctica, and are most diverse in Australia. Sea snakes are elapids.

Colubridae: About 1600 species of tiny to very large snakes, found on all continents except Antarctica. Many colubrids have glands that secrete venom that kills prey, but they lack hollow teeth specialized for injecting.

Phylogenetic relationships and numbers of species are based on F. H. Pough, R. M. Andrews, J. E. Cadle, M. L. Crump, A. H. Savitzky, and K. D. Wells, 1998, *Herpetology*, Prentice Hall, Upper Saddle River, NJ.

The wart snakes in the family Acrochordidae are entirely aquatic; they lack the enlarged ventral scales that characterize most terrestrial snakes, and they have difficulty moving on land.

The Colubroidea includes most of the extant species of snakes, and the family Colubridae alone contains two-thirds of the extant species. The diversity of the group makes characterization difficult.

Colubroids have lost all traces of the pelvic girdle, they have only a single carotid artery, and the skull is very kinetic. Many colubroid snakes are venomous, and snakes in the families Elapidae and Viperidae have hollow fangs at the front of the mouth that inject extremely toxic venom into their prey.

The body form of even a generalized snake such as the kingsnake (Figure 15–3a) is so specialized that

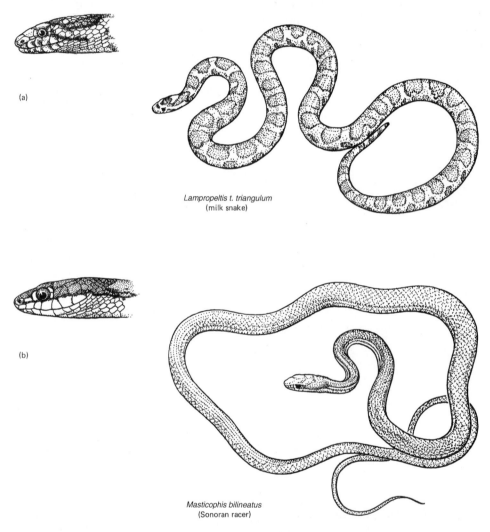

(a)

Lampropeltis t. triangulum
(milk snake)

(b)

Masticophis bilineatus
(Sonoran racer)

Figure 15–3 Body forms of snakes: (a) Constrictors such as the kingsnake (*Lampropeltis*) crawl slowly, poking their heads into holes and under logs. They are often nocturnal and probably rely on chemoreception to detect prey that is hidden from sight. (b) Active, visually oriented snakes like the whipsnakes (*Masticophis*) forage by moving rapidly across the ground with their heads raised. They are diurnal and have large eyes. Vision is probably an important sensory mode for these snakes. (c) Arboreal snakes such as *Leptophis* are often elongate; they probably rely mainly on vision to detect prey in their three-dimensional habitat. (d) Burrowing snakes like *Typhlops* have small rounded or pointed heads with little distinction between head and neck, short tails, and smooth, often shiny scales. Their eyes are greatly reduced in size. (e) Vipers, especially the African vipers like the puff adder (*Bitis arietans*), have large heads and stout bodies that accommodate large prey. (f) Sea snakes such as *Laticauda* have a tail that is flattened from side to side and valves that close the nostrils when they dive.

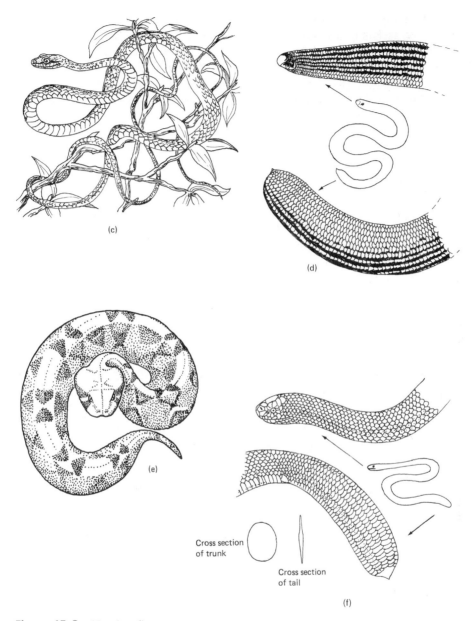

Figure 15–3 *(Continued)*

little further morphological specialization is associated with different habits or habitats. Kingsnakes are constrictors, and they crawl slowly, poking their heads under leaf litter and into holes that might shelter prey. Chemosensation is an important means of detecting prey for these snakes. Snakes have forked tongues, with widely separated tips that can move independently. When the tongue is projected, the tips are waved in the air or touched to the ground. Then the tongue is retracted, and chemical stimuli are transferred to the paired vomeronasal organs. (See Halpern 1992 for more details.) The forked shape of the tongue of snakes (which is seen also among the Amphisbaenia, Lacertiformes, and Varanoidea) may allow them to detect gradients of chemical stimuli and localize objects (Schwenk 1994).

Nonconstrictors such as the whipsnake (Figure 15–3b) move quickly and are visually oriented. They forage by crawling rapidly, frequently raising the head to look around. Many arboreal snakes are extremely elongated and frequently have large eyes (Figure 15–3c). Their length distributes their weight and allows them to crawl over even small twigs without breaking them. Burrowing snakes, at the opposite extreme of snake body form, are short and have blunt heads and very small eyes (Figure 15–3d). The head shape assists in penetrating soil, and a short body and tail create less friction in a burrow than would the same mass in an elongate body. Vipers, especially forms like the African puff adder (Figure 15–3e), are heavy bodied with broad heads.

The sea snakes (Figure 15–3f) are derived from terrestrial elapids. Sea snakes are characterized by extreme morphological specialization for aquatic life: The tail is laterally flattened into an oar, the large ventral scales are reduced or absent in most species, and the nostrils are located dorsally on the snout and have valves that exclude water. The lung extends back to the cloaca and apparently has a hydrostatic role in adjusting buoyancy during diving as well as a respiratory function. Oxygen uptake through the skin during diving has been demonstrated in sea snakes. *Laticauda* are less specialized than other sea snakes, and may represent a separate radiation into the marine habitat. They retain enlarged ventral scales and emerge onto land to bask and to lay eggs. The other sea snakes are so specialized for marine life that they are helpless on land, and these species are viviparous.

The locomotor specializations of snakes reflect differences in their morphology associated with dif-ferent predatory modes (discussed in the following section) and the properties of the substrates on which they move. In **lateral undulation** (Figure 15–4a) the body is thrown into a series of curves. The curves may be irregular, as shown in the illustration of a snake crawling across a board dotted with fixed pegs. Each curve presses backward; the pegs against which the snake is exerting force are shown in solid color. The lines numbered 1 to 7 are at 3-inch intervals, and the position of the snake at intervals of 1 second is shown.

Rectilinear locomotion (Figure 15–4b) is used primarily by heavy-bodied snakes. Alternate sections of the ventral integument are lifted clear of the ground and pulled forward by muscles that originate on the ribs and insert on the ventral scales. The intervening sections of the body rest on the ground and support the snake's body. Waves of contraction pass from anterior to posterior, and the snake moves in a straight line. Rectilinear locomotion is slow, but it is effective even when there are no surface irregularities strong enough to resist the sideward force exerted by serpentine locomotion. Because the snake moves slowly and in a straight line it is inconspicuous, and rectilinear locomotion is used by some snakes when stalking prey.

Figure 15–4   Locomotion of snakes. (a) Lateral undulation; (b) rectilinear; (c) concertina; (d) sidewinding.

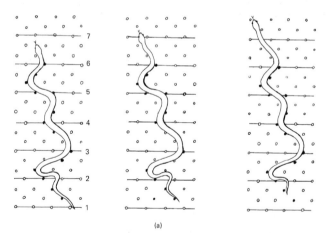

(a)

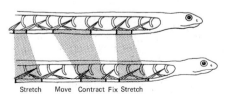

Stretch   Move Contract Fix Stretch

(b)

Figure 15–4   *(Continued)*

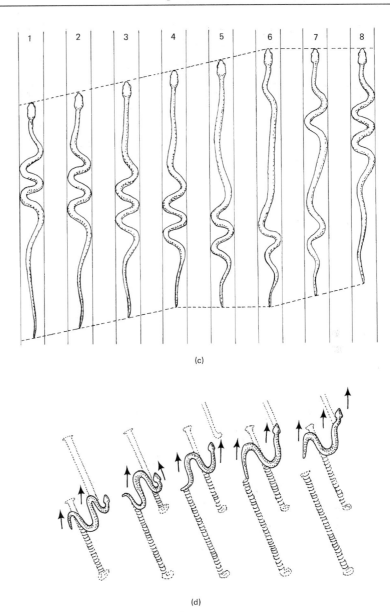

(c)

(d)

Concertina locomotion (Figure 15–4c) is used in narrow passages such as rodent burrows that do not provide space for the broad curves of serpentine locomotion. A snake anchors the posterior part of its body by pressing several loops against the walls of the burrow and extends the front part of its body. When the snake is fully extended it forms new loops anteriorly and anchors itself with these while it draws the rear end of its body forward.

Sidewinding locomotion (Figure 15–4d) is used primarily by snakes that live in deserts where wind-blown sand provides a substrate that slips away during serpentine locomotion. A sidewinding snake raises its body in loops, resting its weight on two or three points that are the only parts of the body in contact with the ground. The loops are swung forward through the air and placed on the ground, the points of contact moving smoothly along the body. Force is exerted downward; the lateral component of the force is so small that the snake does not slip sideward. This downward force is shown by imprint of the ventral scales in the tracks. Because the snake's body is extended nearly perpendicular to its line of travel, sidewinding is an effective means of locomotion only for small snakes that live in habitats with few plants or other obstacles.

Snake skeletons are delicate structures that do not fossilize readily. In most cases we have only vertebrae, and little information has been gained from the fossil record about the origin of snakes. The earliest fossils known are from Cretaceous deposits and seem to be related to boas. Colubrid snakes are first known from the Oligocene, and elapids and viperids appeared during the Miocene.

Functionally snakes are extremely specialized legless lizards. They may have reached this specialization from a fossorial stage. Differences in the eyes of lizards and snakes have been interpreted as evidence of that transition. In lizards the eye is focused by distorting the lens, thus changing its radius of curvature, whereas in snakes the lens is moved in relation to the retina to bring objects into focus. The morphology of the retina of snakes also differs from that of lizards. Snakes have no fovea centralis, their retinal cells lack colored oil droplets, and there is a unique ophidian double cone. These differences in the eyes may indicate that snake ancestors passed through a stage in which they were so specialized for burrowing that the eyes had nearly been lost. Among the most specialized burrowing snakes and lizards, the eyes are very reduced and probably capable of little more than distinguishing between light and darkness. According to this hypothesis, the eye reevolved when snakes reentered an aboveground niche, but the structural details of the original lizard eye were not exactly duplicated.

A fossorial stage is not the only plausible explanation for the origin of snakes, however. Both epigean (ground surface) and aquatic origins have been suggested. Legs are not particularly useful to a small predatory squamate in some habitats. Dense vegetation entangles the legs as an animal tries to draw them forward, and there is no space to use legs in small openings such as cracks in rocks. Possibly the initial radiation of snakes took advantage of these sorts of microhabitats. Extant lizards show an array of elongate forms with reduced legs, and Mesozoic lizards were probably at least equally diverse. Fossils of some elongate squamates with reduced limbs from Cretaceous marine deposits in Israel suggest that an aquatic stage is an alternative to the hypothesis of the evolution of snakes from fossorial lizards (Caldwell and Lee 1997). *Pachyrachis problematicus* was more than a meter long and had more than 100 presacral vertebrae. It had a lightly built skull with most of the derived features of snakes, including enclosure of the braincase by bone, and it retained a pelvic girdle and hindlimbs. If, as suggested by Caldwell and Lee, *Pachyrachis* is the sister group of snakes, the hypothesis of an aquatic origin of snakes deserves reevaluation.

The specializations with snakes compared with legless lizards appear to reflect two selective pressures—locomotion and predation. Elongation of the body is characteristic of snakes. The reduction in body diameter associated with elongation has been accompanied by some rearrangement of the internal anatomy of snakes. The left lung is reduced or entirely absent, the gallbladder is posterior to the liver, the right kidney is anterior to the left, and the gonads may show similar displacement.

Legless lizards face problems in swallowing prey. The primary difficulty is not the loss of limbs, because few lizards use the legs to seize or manipulate food. The difficulty stems from the elongation that is such a widespread characteristic of legless forms. As the body lengthens, the mass is redistributed into a tube with a smaller diameter. As the mouth gets smaller, the maximum diameter of the prey that can be swallowed also decreases, and an elongate animal is faced with the difficulty of feeding a large body through a small mouth. Most legless lizards are limited to eating relatively small prey, whereas snakes have morphological specializations that permit them to engulf prey considerably larger than the body diameter (see the following section). This difference may be one element in the great evolutionary success of snakes in contrast to the limited success of legless lizards and amphisbaenians.

■ Ecology and Behavior of Squamates

The past quarter century has seen an enormous increase in the number and quality of field studies of the ecology and behavior of snakes and lizards. As a result, our understanding of how these ectothermal amniotes function has been greatly broadened. Studies of lizards have been particularly fruitful, in large measure because many species of lizards are conspicuous and active during the day. Studies of these diurnal species dominate the literature—much less is known about species with cryptic habits. The discussions that follow rely on studies of particular species, and it is important to remember that no one species or family is representative of lizards or snakes as a group.

Foraging and Feeding

The methods that snakes and lizards use to find, capture, subdue, and swallow prey are diverse and are important in determining the interactions among species in a community. Astonishing specializations have evolved: blunt-headed snakes with long lower jaws that can reach into a shell to winkle out a snail, nearly toothless snakes that swallow bird eggs intact and then slice them open with sharp ventral processes (hypapophyses) on the neck vertebrae, and chameleons that project their tongues to capture insects or small vertebrates on the sticky tips are only a sample of the diversity of feeding specializations of squamates.

Studies of the ecology of snakes have emphasized the morphological specializations associated with different dietary habits (for examples, see Pough 1983), whereas similar studies of lizards have focused on correlations among physiological and behavioral characteristics (summarized by Huey and Bennett 1986).

Feeding Specializations of Snakes   The entire skull of a snake is much more flexible than the skull of a lizard. The snake skull contains eight links, with joints between them that permit rotation (Figure 15–5). This number of links gives a staggering degree of complexity to the movements of the

ophidian skull, and to make things more complicated, the linkage is paired—each side of the head acts independently. Furthermore, the pterygoquadrate ligament and quadratosupratemporal ties are flexible. When they are under tension they are rigid, but when they are relaxed they permit sideward movement as well as rotation. All of this results in a considerable degree of three-dimensional movement in a snake's skull.

The mandibles of lizards are joined at the front of the mouth in a bony symphysis, but in snakes the mandibles are attached only by muscles and skin so they can spread sideward and move forward or back independently. Loosely connected mandibles and flexible skin in the chin and throat allow the jaw tips to spread so that the widest part of the prey passes ventral to the articulation of the jaw with the skull.

Swallowing movements take place slowly enough to be observed easily (Figure 15–6). A snake usually swallows prey head first, perhaps because that approach presses the limbs against the body, out of the snake's way. Small prey may be swallowed tail first or even sideward. The mandibular and ptery-

Figure 15–5   Skull of a snake. (a) Lateral and (b) ventral views. A snake skull contains eight movable links: (1) braincase; (2) supratemporal; (3) prefrontal; (4) palatine; (5) pterygoid; (6) pterygoquadrate ligament; (7) quadrate; (8) quadratosupratemporal tie. ang, angular; art, articular; boc, basioccipital; bsp, basisphenoid; col, columella; den, dentary; ectpg, ectopterygoid; fro, frontal; max, maxilla; nas, nasal; pal, palatine; par, parietal; pmax, premaxilla; po, postorbital; prf, prefrontal; ptg, pterygoid; q, quadrate; spl, spenial; sur, surangular; sut, supratemporal; vom, vomer. (From C. Gans, 1961, *American Zoologist* 1:217–227.)

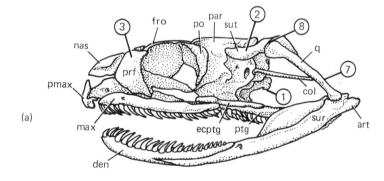

(a)

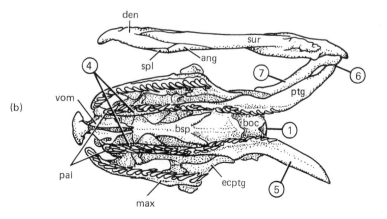

(b)

Figure 15–6 Jaw movements during feeding. Snakes use a combination of head movements and protraction and retraction of the jaws to swallow prey. (a) Prey grasped by left and right jaws at the beginning of the swallowing process. (b) The upper and lower jaws on the right side have been protracted, disengaging the teeth from the prey. (c) The head is rotated counterclockwise, moving the right upper and lower jaws over the prey. The recurved teeth slide over the prey like the runners of a sled. (d) The upper and lower jaw on the right side are retracted, embedding the teeth in the prey and drawing it into the mouth. Notice that the entire head of the prey has been engulfed by this movement. Next the left upper and lower jaws will be advanced over the prey by clockwise rotation of the head. The swallowing process continues with alternating left and right movements until the entire body of the prey has passed through the snake's jaws. (Modified from T. H. Frazetta, 1966, *Journal of Morphology* 118:217–296.)

goid teeth of one side of the head are anchored in the prey and the head is rotated to advance the opposite jaw as the mandible is protracted and grips the prey ventrally. As this process is repeated the snake draws the prey item into its mouth. Once the prey has reached the esophagus, it is forced toward the stomach by contraction of the snake's neck muscles. Usually the neck is bent sharply to push the prey along.

Most species of snakes seize prey and swallow it as it struggles. The risk of damage to the snake during this process is a real one, and various features of snake anatomy seem to give some protection from struggling prey. The frontal and parietal bones of a snake's skull extend downward, entirely enclosing the brain and shielding it from the protesting kicks of prey being swallowed. Possibly the kinds of prey that can be attacked by snakes without a specialized feeding mechanism are lim-

ited by the snake's ability to swallow the prey without being injured in the process.

Constriction and venom are predatory specializations that permit a snake to tackle large prey with little risk of injury to itself. Constriction is characteristic of the boas and pythons as well as a number of colubrid snakes. Despite travelers' tales of animals crushed to jelly by a python's coils, the process of constriction involves very little pressure. A constrictor seizes prey with its jaws and throws one or more coils of its body about the prey. The loops of the snake's body press against adjacent loops, and friction prevents the prey from forcing the loops open. Each time the prey exhales, the snake takes up the slack by tightening the loops slightly. Two hypotheses have been proposed to explain the cause of death from constriction. The traditional view holds that prey suffocates because it cannot expand its thorax to inhale. Another possibility is that the increased internal pressure interferes with, and eventually stops, the heart (Hardy 1994).

Snakes that constrict their prey must be able to throw the body into several loops of small diameter to wrap around the prey. Constrictors achieve these small loops by having short vertebrae and short trunk muscles that span only a few vertebrae from the point of origin to the point of insertion. Contraction of these muscles produces sharp bends in the trunk that allow constrictors to press tightly against their prey. However, the trunk muscles of snakes are also used for locomotion, and the short muscles of constrictors produce several small-radius curves along the length of the snake's body. That morphology limits the speed with which constrictors can move, because rapid locomotion by snakes is accomplished by throwing the body into two or three broad loops. This is the pattern seen in fast-moving species such as whipsnakes, racers, and mambas. The muscles that produce these broad loops are long, spanning many vertebrae, and the vertebrae also are longer than those of constrictors.

In North America fast-moving snakes (colubroids) first appear in the fossil record during the Miocene, a time when grasslands were expanding. Constrictors, largely erycines, predominated in the snake fauna of the early Miocene, but by the end of that epoch the snake fauna was composed primarily of colubroids. Alan Savitzky (1980) has suggested that fast-moving colubroid snakes had an advantage over slow-moving boids in the more open habitats that developed during the Miocene, and that the radiation of colubroids involved a complex interaction between locomotion and feeding. Rodents were probably the most abundant prey available to snakes, and rodents are dangerous animals for a snake to swallow while they are able to bite and scratch. Constriction provided a relatively safe way for boids to kill rodents, but the long vertebrae and long trunk muscles that allowed colubroids to move rapidly through the open habitats of the Miocene would have prevented them from using constriction to kill their prey.

Savitzky suggested that colubroids initially used venom to immobilize prey. Duvernoy's gland, found in the upper jaw of many extant colubrid snakes, is homologous to the venom glands of viperids and elapids and produces a toxic secretion that immobilizes prey. (Some extant colubrids have venom that is dangerously toxic, even to animals as large as humans.) Thus, the evolution of venom

that could kill prey may have been a key feature that allowed Miocene colubroid snakes to dispense with constriction and become morphologically specialized for rapid locomotion in open habitats. The presence of Duvernoy's gland appears to be an ancestral character for colubroid snakes, as this hypothesis predicts. Some colubrids, including the ratsnakes (*Elaphe*), gophersnakes (*Pituophis*), and kingsnakes (*Lampropeltis*), have lost the venom-producing capacity of the Duvernoy's gland, and these are the groups in which constriction has been secondarily developed as a method of killing prey.

In this context, the front-fanged venomous snakes (Elapidae and Viperidae) are not a new development, but instead represent alternative specializations of an ancestral venom delivery system. Given the ancestral nature of venom for colubroid snakes, one would expect that different specializations for venom delivery would be represented in the extant snake fauna, as indeed they are. A variety of snakes have enlarged teeth (fangs) on the maxillae. Three categories of venomous snakes are recognized (Figure 15–7): opisthoglyphous, proteroglyphous, and solenoglyphous. This classification is descriptive, and represents convergent evolution by different phylogenetic lineages.

Opisthoglyphous (*ophistho* = behind, *glyph* = hollowed) snakes have one or more enlarged teeth near the rear of the maxilla with smaller teeth in front. In some forms the fangs are solid; in others there is a groove on the surface of the fang that may help to conduct saliva into the wound. Several African and Asian opisthoglyphs can deliver a dangerous or even lethal bite to large animals, including humans, but their primary prey is lizards or birds, which are often held in the mouth until they stop struggling and are then swallowed.

Proteroglyphous snakes (*proto* = first) include the cobras, mambas, coral snakes, and sea snakes in the Elapidae. The hollow fangs of the proteroglyphous snakes are located at the front of the maxilla, and there are often several small, solid teeth behind the fangs. The fangs are permanently erect and relatively short.

Solenoglyphous (*solen* = pipe) snakes include the pitvipers of the New World and the true vipers of the Old World. In these snakes the hollow fangs are the only teeth on the maxillae, which rotate so that the fangs are folded against the roof of the mouth when the jaws are closed. This folding mechanism permits solenoglyphous snakes to have long fangs that inject venom deep into the tissues

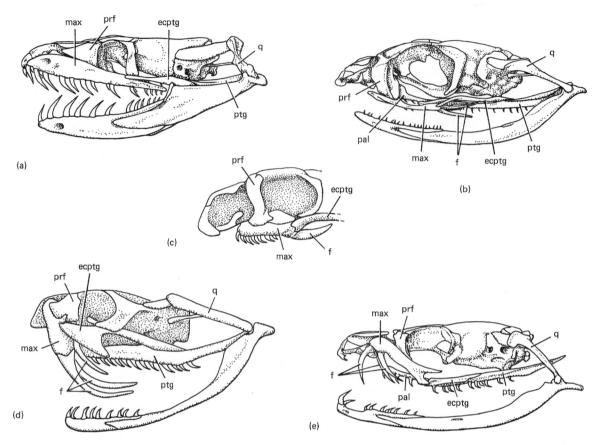

Figure 15–7 Dentition of snakes. (a) Aglyphous (without fangs), African python, *Python sebae*; (b, c) opisthoglyphous (fangs in the rear of the maxilla), African boomslang, *Dispholidus typus*, and Central American false viper, *Xenodon rhabdocephalus*; (d) solenoglyphous (fangs on a rotating maxilla), African puff adder, *Bitis arietans*; (e) proteroglyphous (permanently erect fangs at the front of the maxilla), African green mamba, *Dendroaspis jamesoni*. The fangs of solenoglyphs (d) are erected by an anterior movement of the pterygoid that is transmitted through the ectopterygoid and palatine to the maxilla, causing it to rotate about its articulation with the prefrontal, thereby erecting the fang. Some opisthoglyphs, especially *Xenodon* (c), have the same mechanism of fang erection. ecptg, ectopterygoid; fro, frontal; max, maxilla; pal, palatine; par, parietal; pmax, premaxilla; prf, prefrontal; ptg, pterygoid; q, quadrate; sut, supratemporal.

of the prey. The venom, a complex mixture of enzymes and other substances (Table 15.3), first kills the prey and then speeds its digestion after it has been swallowed.

Snakes that can inject a disabling dose of venom into their prey have evolved a very safe prey-catching method. A constrictor is in contact with its prey while it is dying and runs some risk of injury from the prey's struggles. A solenoglyphous snake needs only to inject venom and allow the prey to run off to die. Later the snake can follow the scent trail of the prey to find its corpse. This is the prey-capture pattern of most vipers, and experiments have shown that a viper can distinguish the scent trail of

a mouse it has bitten from trails left by uninjured mice.

Several features of the body form of vipers allow them to eat larger prey in relation to their own body size than can most nonvenomous snakes. Many vipers, including rattlesnakes, the jumping viper, and the African puff adder and Gaboon viper, are very stout snakes. The triangular head shape that is usually associated with vipers is a result of the outward extension of the rear of the skull, especially the quadrate bones. The wide-spreading quadrates allow bulky objects to pass through the mouth, and even a large meal makes little bulge in the stout body and thus does not interfere with locomotion.

TABLE 15.3	Components of the venoms of squamates		
Compound	**Occurrence**	**Effect**	
Proteinases	All venomous squamates, especially vipers	Tissue destruction	
Hyaluronidase	All venomous squamates	Increases tissue permeability, hastening the spread of other constituents of venom through the tissues	
L-amino acid oxidase	All venomous squamates	Attacks a wide variety of substrates and causes great tisue destruction	
Cholinesterase	High in elapids, may be present in sea snakes, low in vipers	Unknown, it is not responsible for the neurotoxic effects of elapid venom	
Phospholipases	All venomous squamates	Destroys cell membranes	
Phosphatases	All venomous squamates	Breaks down high-energy compounds such as ATP	
Basic polypeptides	Elapids and sea snakes	Blocks neuromuscular transmission	

Vipers have specialized as relatively sedentary predators that wait in ambush and can prey even on quite large animals. The other family of terrestrial venomous snakes—the cobras, mambas, and their relatives—are primarily slim-bodied snakes that actively search for prey.

Foraging Behavior and Energetics of Lizards   The activity patterns of lizards span a range from extremely sedentary species that spend hours in one place to species that are in nearly constant motion. Field observations of the tropidurid lizard *Leiocephalus schreibersi* and the teiid *Ameiva chrysolaema* in the Dominican Republic revealed two extremes of behavior. *Leiocephalus* rested on an elevated perch from sunrise to sunset and was motionless for more than 99 percent of the day. Its only movements consisted of short, rapid dashes to capture insects or to chase away other lizards. These periods of activity never lasted longer than 2 seconds, and the frequency of movements averaged 9.6 per hour. In contrast, *Ameiva* were active for only 4 or 5 hours in the middle of the day, but they were moving more than 70 percent of that time, and their velocity averaged one body length every 2 to 5 seconds.

The same difference in behavior was seen in a laboratory test of spontaneous activity: *Ameiva* was more than 20 times as active as *Leiocephalus*. In fact, the teiids were as active in exploring their surroundings as small mammals tested in the same apparatus. A xantusiid lizard tested in the laboratory apparatus had a pattern of spontaneous activity that fell approximately midway between that of the teiid and the tropidurid. Thus, a spectrum of spontaneous locomotor activity is apparent in lizards, extending from species that are nearly motionless through species that move at intermediate rates to species that are as active as mammals.

For convenience the extremes of the spectrum are frequently called sit-and-wait predators and widely foraging predators, respectively, and the intermediate condition has been called a cruising forager. Other field studies have shown that this spectrum of locomotor behaviors is widespread in lizard faunas. In North America, for example, spiny swifts (*Sceloporus*) are sit-and-wait predators, many skinks (*Eumeces*) appear to be cruising foragers, and whiptail lizards (*Cnemidophorus*) are widely foraging predators. The ancestral locomotor pattern for lizards may have been that of a cruising forager, and both sit-and-wait predation and active foraging may represent derived conditions. (A spectrum of foraging modes is not unique to lizards; it probably applies to nearly all kinds of mobile animals, including fishes, mammals, birds, frogs, insects, and zooplankton.)

The ecological, morphological, and behavioral characteristics that are correlated with the foraging modes of different species of lizards appear to define many aspects of the biology of these animals (Huey and Pianka 1981). For example, sit-and-wait predators and widely foraging predators consume different kinds of prey and fall victim to different kinds of predators. They have different social sys-

TABLE 15.4 Ecological and behavioral characteristics associated with the foraging modes of lizards. Foraging modes are presented as a continuum from sit-and-wait predators to widely foraging predators. In most cases data are available only for species at the extremes of the continuum. See the text for details.

	Foraging Mode		
Character	Sit-and-Wait	Cruising Forager	Widely Foraging
Foraging behavior			
Movements/hour	Few	Intermediate	Many
Speed of movement	Low	Intermediate	Fast
Sensory modes	Vision	Vision and olfaction	Vision and olfaction
Exploratory behavior	Low	Intermediate	High
Types of prey	Mobile, large	Intermediate	Sedentary, often small
Predators			
Risk of predation	Low	?	Higher
Types of predators	Widely foraging	?	Sit-and-wait and widely foraging
Body form			
Trunk	Stocky	Intermediate?	Elongate
Tail	Often short	?	Often long
Physiological characteristics			
Endurance	Limited	?	High
Sprint speed	High	?	Intermediate to low
Aerobic metabolic capacity	Low	?	High
Anaerobic metabolic capacity	High	?	Low
Heart mass	Small	?	Large
Hematocrit	Low	?	High
Energetics			
Daily energy expenditure	Low	?	Higher
Daily energy intake	Low	?	Higher
Social behavior			
Size of home range	Small	Intermediate	Large
Social system	Territorial	?	Not territorial
Reproduction			
Mass of clutch (eggs or embryos) relative to mass of adult	High	?	Low

Source: Based on data from L. J. Vitt and J. D. Congdon, 1978, *American Naturalist* 112:595–608; Huey and Pianka 1981; W. E. Magnusson et al., 1985 *Herpetologica* 41:324–332; Huey and Bennett 1986.

tems, probably emphasize different sensory modes, and differ in some aspects of their reproduction and life history.

These generalizations are summarized in Table 15.4 and are discussed in the following sections. However, a weakness of this analysis must be emphasized: Sit-and-wait species of lizards (at least, the ones that have been studied most) are primarily iguanians, whereas widely foraging species are mostly scincomorphs. That phylogenetic split raises the question of whether the differences we see between sit-and-wait and widely foraging lizards are really the consequences of the differences in foraging behavior, or if they are ancestral characteristics of iguanian versus scincomorph lizards. If the latter is the case, their association with different foraging modes may be misleading. In either case, however, the model presented in Table 15.4 provides a useful integration of a large quantity of information about the biology of lizards; it represents a hypothesis that will be modified as more information becomes available.

Lizards with different foraging modes use different methods to detect prey: Sit-and-wait lizards normally remain in one spot from which they can survey a broad area. These motionless lizards detect the movement of an insect visually and capture it with a quick dash from their observation site. Sit-and-wait lizards may be most successful in detecting and capturing relatively large insects like beetles and grasshoppers. Active foragers spend most of their time on the ground surface, moving steadily and poking their snouts under fallen leaves and into crevices in the ground. These lizards apparently rely largely on chemical cues to detect insects, and they probably seek out local concentrations of patchily distributed prey such as termites. Widely foraging species of lizards appear to eat more small insects than do lizards that are sit-and-wait predators. Thus, the different foraging behaviors of lizards lead to differences in their diets, even when the two kinds of lizards occur in the same habitat.

The different foraging modes also have different consequences for the exposure of lizards to their own predators. A lizard that spends 99 percent of its time resting motionless is relatively inconspicuous, whereas a lizard that spends most of its time moving is easily seen. Sit-and-wait lizards are probably most likely to be discovered and captured by predators that are active searchers, whereas widely foraging lizards are likely to be caught by sit-and-wait predators. As a result of this difference, foraging modes may alternate at successive levels in the food chain: Insects that move about may be captured by lizards that are sit-and-wait predators, and those lizards may be eaten by widely foraging predators. Insects that are sedentary are more likely to be discovered by a widely foraging lizard, and that lizard may be picked off by a sit-and-wait predator.

The body forms of sit-and-wait lizard predators may reflect selective pressures different from those that act on widely foraging species. Sit-and-wait lizards are often stout bodied, short tailed, and cryptically colored. Many of these species have dorsal patterns formed by blotches of different colors that probably obscure the outlines of the body as the lizard rests motionless on a rock or tree trunk. Widely foraging species of lizards are usually slim and elongate with long tails, and they often have patterns of stripes that may produce optical illusions as they move. However, one predator-avoidance mechanism, the ability to break off the tail when it is seized by a predator (**autotomy**), does not differ among lizards with different foraging modes (Box 15–1).

What physiological characteristics are necessary to support different foraging modes? The energy requirements of a dash that lasts for only a second or two are quite different from those of locomotion that is sustained nearly continuously for several hours. Sit-and-wait and widely foraging species of lizards differ in their relative emphasis on the two metabolic pathways that provide ATP for activity and in how long that activity can be sustained. Sit-and-wait lizards move in brief spurts, and they rely largely on anaerobic metabolism to sustain their movements. (See Chapter 4 for a discussion of aerobic and anaerobic metabolism.) These lizards quickly become exhausted when they are forced to run continuously on a treadmill, whereas widely foraging species can sustain activity for long periods without exhaustion.

These differences in locomotor behavior are associated with differences in the oxygen transport systems of the lizards: Widely foraging species of lizards have larger hearts and more red blood cells in their blood than do sit-and-wait species. As a result, each beat of the heart pumps more blood and that blood carries more oxygen to the tissues of a widely foraging species of lizard than a sit-and-wait species.

Sustained locomotion is probably not important to a lizard that makes short dashes to capture prey or to escape from predators, but sprint speed might be vitally important in both these activities. As one would predict, the sprint speed of the sit-and-wait lizards is generally greater than that of the widely foraging species.

The continuous locomotion of widely foraging species of lizards is energetically expensive. Measurements of energy expenditure of lizards in the Kalahari showed that the daily energy expenditure of a widely foraging species averaged 150 percent of that of a sit-and-wait species. However, the energy that the widely foraging species invested in foraging was more than repaid by its greater success in finding prey. The daily food intake of the widely foraging species was 200 percent that of the sit-and-wait predator. As a result, the widely foraging species had more energy available to use for growth and reproduction than did the sit-and-wait species, despite the additional cost of its mode of foraging.

BOX 15-1 Caudal Autotomy: Your Tail or Your Life

Autotomy (self-amputation) of appendages is a common predator-escape mechanism among invertebrates and vertebrates. The tail is the only appendage that vertebrates are known to autotomize, and the capacity for caudal autotomy is developed to some degree among salamanders, tuatara, lizards, and a few amphisbaenians, snakes, and rodents (Arnold 1988). In most cases autotomy is followed by regeneration of a new tail.

The caudal autotomy of squamates occurs either at distinctive fracture planes that are found in all but the four to nine anteriormost caudal vertebrae or between vertebrae. The caudal muscles are segmental, and pointed processes from adjacent segments interdigitate. The caudal arteries have sphincter muscles just anterior to each fracture site and the veins have valves. Autotomy appears to be an active process that requires contraction of the caudal muscles, bending the tail sharply to one side and initiating separation. The vertebral centrum ruptures, and the processes of the caudal muscles separate. The arterial sphincter muscles contract and the venous valves close, preventing loss of blood. An autotomized tail twitches rapidly for several minutes, and its violent writhing can distract the attention of a predator while the lizard itself scurries to safety (Figure 15–8). The tails of some juvenile skinks are bright blue, and in experiments lizards with these colorful tails were more effective at using autotomy to escape from predatory snakes than were lizards with tails that had been painted black. Of course, an autotomized tail receives no blood flow and its muscular activity is sustained by anaerobic metabolism. The anaerobic metabolic capacity of lizard tail muscles appears to be substantially greater than that of limb muscles.

The point of autotomy is normally as far posterior on the tail as possible. When the tail of a lizard is seized with forceps, autotomy usually occurs through the plane of the vertebra immediately anterior to the point at which the tail was being held, thereby minimizing the amount of tail lost. When the tail is regenerated the vertebrae are replaced by a rod of cartilage that does not contain fracture planes. Consequently, future autotomy must occur anterior to the regenerated portion of the tail. Some geckos adjust the point of autotomy according to their body temperature: Autotomy occurs closer to the body when the lizard is cold than when it is warm. When a lizard is cold it cannot run as fast as it can when it's warm, and perhaps the longer segment of tail left behind by a cold lizard occupies the predator's attention long enough to allow the lizard to reach safety.

Leaving your tail in the grasp of a predator is certainly better than being eaten, but it is not free of costs. The tail acts as a signal of status among some species of lizards, and a lizard that autotomizes a large part of its tail may fall to a lower rank in the dominance hierarchy as a result. Losing the tail also affects the energy balance of a lizard: For example, the rate of growth of juvenile lizards that have autotomized their tails is reduced while their tails are being regenerated. Many lizards store fat in the tail, and the females mobilize this energy while they are depositing yolk in eggs. Sixty percent of the total fat storage was located in the tails of female geckos (*Coleonyx brevis*). Autotomy of the tail by gravid female geckos resulted in their producing smaller clutches of eggs than lizards with tails. Some lizards, especially the small North American skink *Scincella lateralis*, eat their autotomized tails if they can, thereby recovering the lost energy.

Social Behavior

Squamates employ a variety of visual, auditory, chemical, and tactile signals in the behaviors they use to maintain territories and to choose mates. Iguanians use mainly visual signals, some gekkotans use vocalization, and scincomorphs, anguimorphs, and snakes use pheromones extensively. The various sensory modalities employed by animals have biased the amount of information we have about the behaviors of different species. Because humans are primarily visually oriented, we perceive the visual displays of other animals quite readily. The

Figure 15–8 Autotomy as a defensive mechanism. The freshly autotomized tail of a skink writhes and jerks, engaging the attention of a predatory kingsnake while the lizard escapes. In this sequence of photographs a kingsnake seizes a skink by the tail (a). The skink autotomizes its tail and runs off (b), leaving the snake struggling to swallow the wriggling tail (c). (Photographs by Benjamin E. Dial, Chapman University.)

auditory sensitivity of humans is also acute, and we can detect and recognize vocal signals that are used by other species. However, the olfactory sensitivity of humans is low and we lack a vomeronasal system, so we are unable to perceive most chemical signals used by squamates. One result of our sensory biases has been a concentration of behavioral studies on organisms that use visual signals. As a result of this focus, the extensive repertoires of visual displays of iguanian lizards figure largely in the literature of behavioral ecology, but much less is known about the chemical and tactile signals that are probably important for other lizards and for snakes.

The social behaviors of squamates appear to be limited in comparison with those of crocodilians, but many species show dominance hierarchies or territoriality. The signals that are used in agonistic encounters between individuals are often similar to those used for species and sex recognition during courtship. Parental attendance at a nest during the incubation period of eggs occurs among squamates, but extended parental care of the young is unknown.

Iguanian lizards employ primarily visual displays during social interactions. The polychrotid genus *Anolis* includes some 400 species of small to medium-size lizards that occur primarily in tropical America. Male *Anolis* have gular fans, areas of skin beneath the chin that can be distended by the hyoid apparatus during visual displays. (See color insert.) The brightly colored scales and skin of the gular fans of many species of *Anolis* are conspicuous signaling devices, and they are used in conjunction with movements of head and body.

Figure 15–9 shows the colors of the gular fans of eight species of *Anolis* that occur in Costa Rica. No two species have the same combination of colors on their gular fans, and thus it is possible to identify a species solely by seeing the colors it displays. In addition, each species has a behavioral display that consists of raising the body by straightening the fore legs (called a pushup), bobbing the head, and extending and contracting the gular fan. The combination of these three sorts of movements allows a complex display. The three movements can be represented graphically by an upper line that shows the movements of the body and head and a lower line that shows the expansion and contraction of the gular fan. This representation is called a **display action pattern.** No two display action patterns are the same, so it would be possible to identify any of the eight species of *Anolis* by seeing its display action pattern.

The behaviors that territorial lizards use for species and sex recognition during courtship are very much like those employed in territorial defense—pushups, head bobs, and displays of the gular fan. A territorial male lizard is likely to challenge any lizard in its territory, and the progress of the interaction depends on the response it receives. An aggressive response indicates that the intruder is a male and stimulates the territorial male to defend its territory, whereas a passive response

from the intruder identifies a female and stimulates the territorial male to initiate courtship. These behaviors are illustrated by the displays of a male *Anolis carolinensis* shown in Figures 15–10 and 15–11. The first response of a territorial lizard to an intruder is the assertion–challenge display shown at the top of Figure 15–10. The dewlap is extended, and the lizard bobs at the intruder. In addition the nuchal (neck) and dorsal crests are slightly raised, and a black spot appears behind the eye. The next stage depends on the sex of the intruder and its response to the challenge from the territorial male (Figure 15–11). If the intruder is a male and does not retreat from the initial challenge, both males become more aggressive. During aggressive posturing (middle panel in Figure 15–10) the males orient laterally to each other, the nuchal and dorsal crests are fully erected, the body is compressed laterally, the black spot behind the eye darkens, and the throat is swelled. All these postural changes make the lizards appear larger and presumably more formidable to the opponent. If the intruder is a receptive female, the territorial male initiates courtship (bottom panel in Figure 15–10).

The differences in color and movement that characterize the dewlaps and display action patterns of *Anolis* are conspicuous to human observers, but do the lizards also rely on them for species identification? Indirect evidence suggests that the lizards probably do use gular fan color and display action patterns for species identification. For example, examination of communities of *Anolis* that contain many species show that the differences in the colors of the gular fans and in the display action patterns is greatest for those species that encounter one another most frequently.

Pheromonal communication, mediated by the vomeronasal organ, probably occurs in several lineages of lizards, primarily scincomorphs and anguimorphs, although chemical cues may be more important for some iguanians than has been realized. A review of the subject can be found in Simon (1983). Territorial male *Sceloporus* and other phrynosomatid lizards rub secretions from their femoral glands on objects in their territories (see Mason 1992). These secretions contain protein and sometimes lipids. Exploratory behavior by lizards, including iguanians, involves touching the tongue to the substrate, and the vomeronasal organ may detect pheromones in the femoral gland secretions. In addition, the secretions absorb light strongly in the ultraviolet portion of the spectrum. Some

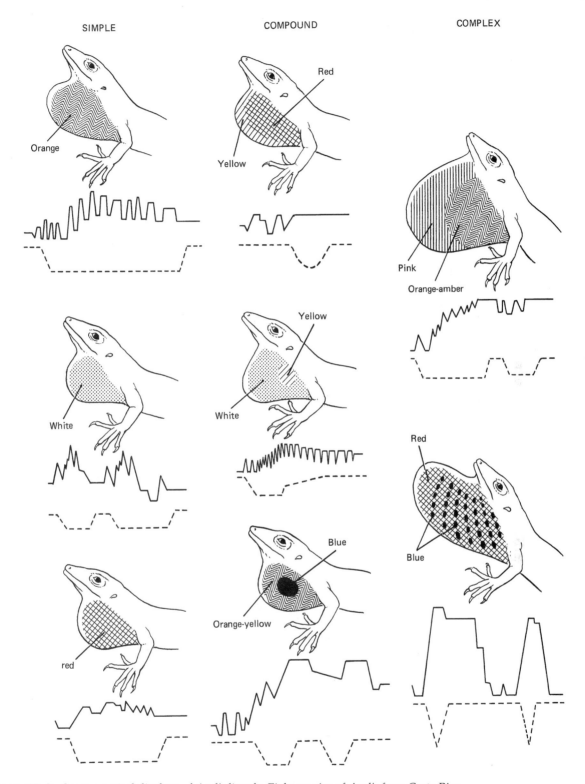

Figure 15–9 Species-typical displays of *Anolis* lizards. Eight species of *Anolis* from Costa Rica can be separated into three groups on the basis of the size and color pattern of their gular fans. *Simple* fans are unicolored, *compound* fans are bicolored, and *complex* fans are bicolored and very large. The display action pattern of each species is shown graphically beneath the drawing of the lizard. The horizontal axis is time (the duration of these displays is about 10 seconds) and the vertical axis is vertical height. Solid line shows movements of the head; dashed line indicates extension of the gular fan. (Modified from A. A. Echelle et al., 1971, *Herpetologica* 27:221–288.)

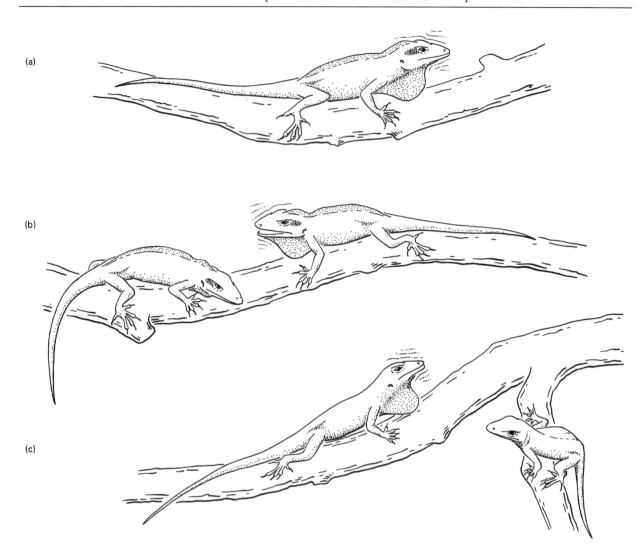

(a)

(b)

(c)

Figure 15–10 Displays by a male *Anolis carolinensis*. Top: Assertion–challenge display. Middle: Aggressive posturing between males. Bottom: Courtship. Note the extension of the dewlap, the species-typical head bob, and the absence of the dorsal and nuchal crests and the eyespot. (From D. Crews, 1978, in *Behavior and Neurology of Lizards*, edited by N. Greenberg and P. D. MacLean, U. S. Department of Health, Education, and Welfare, National Institutes of Mental Health, Rockville, MD.)

lizards are sensitive to ultraviolet light (Fleishman et al. 1993), and femoral gland secretions may be both visual and olfactory signals. Experimental studies of the use of pheromones have employed several species of North American skinks (*Eumeces*). Male and female broad-headed skinks (*E. laticeps*) can detect the cloacal odors of conspecifics, and males detect skin odors. Male skinks (but not females) distinguish between the cloacal odors of male and female conspecifics, and males will follow scent trails of females but will not follow the trails of other males. Female skinks do not follow the

scent trails of either sex. The discriminatory ability of male skinks is quite precise—they can distinguish the cloacal odors of conspecific females from the scents of females of other closely related species (Cooper and Vitt 1986).

Territoriality, the relative importance of vision compared with olfaction, and foraging behavior appear to be broadly correlated among lizards. The elevated perches from which sit-and-wait predators survey their home ranges allow them to see both intruders and prey, and they dash from the perch to repel an intruder or to catch an insect. In con-

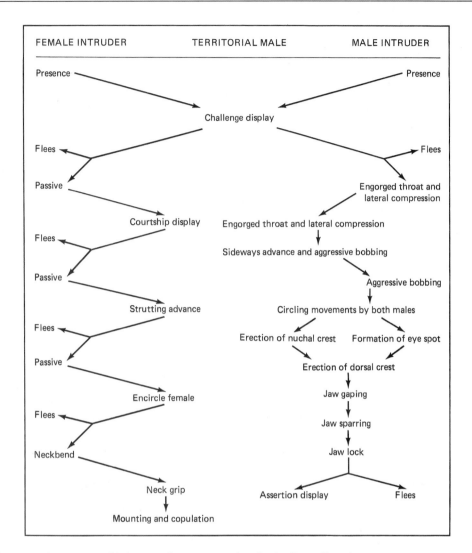

Figure 15–11   Normal sequence of behaviors for a territorial male *Anolis carolinensis* confronting an intruding male or female anole. A territorial male challenges any intruder, and the response of the intruder determines the subsequent behavior of the territorial male. (From D. Crews, 1975, *Herpetologica* 31:37–47.)

trast, widely foraging lizards are almost entirely nonterritorial, and olfaction is as important as vision in their foraging behavior. These lizards spend most of their time on the ground, where their field of vision is limited and they probably have little opportunity to detect intruders.

Reproduction and Parental Care

Squamates show a range of reproductive modes from oviparity (development occurs outside the body of the female and is supported entirely by the yolk—i.e., lecithotrophy) to viviparity (the eggs are retained in the oviducts and development is sup-

ported by transfer of nutrients from the mother to the fetuses—matrotrophy). Intermediate conditions include retention of the eggs for a time after they have been fertilized, and the production of precocial young that were nourished primarily by material in the yolk. Oviparity is assumed to be the ancestral condition, and viviparity has evolved at least 45 times among lizards and 35 times among snakes (Blackburn 1982, 1985; Shine 1985). Viviparous squamates have specialized chorioallantoic placentae, and in the Brazilian skink, *Mabuya heathi*, more than 99 percent of the mass of the fetus results from transport of nutrients across the placenta (Blackburn et al. 1984).

Oviparity A female lizard has only a certain amount of energy to devote to reproduction, and that energy can be used to produce a few large eggs (i.e., eggs with a large quantity of yolk) or several smaller eggs. All else being equal, large eggs produce large hatchlings and small eggs produce small hatchlings, so the question is, Are large hatchlings more likely to survive than small hatchlings? And if large hatchlings do survive better, is the difference in survival great enough to make up for producing fewer individual hatchlings?

This question has been addressed in studies of the side-blotched lizard, *Uta stansburiana* (Sinervo et al. 1992). Female side-blotched lizards produce several clutches annually and mature in one year. The lizards normally lay small eggs in the first clutch and larger eggs in subsequent clutches. Does that shift in egg size reflect a survival advantage for large hatchlings later in the season?

To answer that question, Sinervo and his colleagues had to compare the survival of large and small hatchlings at different times of year, but the natural variation in the size of eggs is small and it would be hard to detect differences in survival, even though a very small difference could have a significant effect in evolutionary time. To increase his chances of seeing an effect of hatchling size on survival, Sinervo created artificially small hatchlings by using a hypodermic needle and syringe to remove yolk from some eggs. In a different experiment (Sinervo and Licht 1991), he devised a method to produce giant hatchlings by surgically removing some ova from the ovary before yolk had been deposited.

In that situation, the total amount of yolk available was divided among fewer eggs, and each egg was larger than normal. These methods allowed Sinervo to produce hatchlings that ranged from 50 percent to 150 percent of the normal size (Figure 15–12).

Studies at two field sites showed that female *Uta stansburiana* could maximize the number of surviving offspring from their first clutches by producing small eggs, whereas larger eggs would maximize survival of offspring in later clutches. That change in optimum egg size as the summer progresses probably reflects a changing ecological setting for the hatchlings. Hatchlings from the first clutch of eggs emerge into a world without hatchling *Uta*—only their siblings and hatchlings from other first clutches compete with them for living space. In that situation, large body size may not confer an advantage, so a female can achieve the maximum number of surviving young by producing a large clutch of small eggs. Subsequent clutches don't have it so easy—they must establish home ranges in places that already have resident juvenile *Uta* from earlier clutches. In that situation, large hatchlings may be more likely to insert themselves successfully into the existing social system, and females achieve the maximum number of surviving young by producing a smaller clutch that contains large eggs.

In some situations the naturally occurring egg size was not the best option for a female. For example, at the Los Banos field site in 1989, the average size of eggs in natural clutches was about 0.4 grams, but the maximum number of surviving offspring would be produced by eggs that weighed

Figure 15–12 Hatchling side-blotched lizards, *Uta stansburiana*. The normal size for hatchlings (center) compared with gigantized (left) and miniaturized (right) individuals. (Photograph courtesy of Barry Sinervo.)

about 0.55 grams. In other words, naturally occurring variation was insufficient to produce eggs of the optimum size for survival.

Reintroduction of captive-bred juveniles to their natural habitats is a frequent goal of management programs for endangered species. Each captive-bred juvenile can represent thousands of hours of painstaking care, and tens or hundreds of thousands of dollars of investment. Clearly, it is desirable to maximize the chances that the juveniles will survive after they are released, and studies like Sinervo's are producing information that can be applied to management programs (Sinervo 1994). Perhaps it will be possible to use these techniques to produce hatchlings of the sex and size that will maximize the success of reintroductions (Pough 1994).

Viviparity   Viviparity is usually a high-investment reproductive strategy. Females of viviparous squamates generally produce relatively small numbers of large young, although there are exceptions to that generalization. Viviparity is not evenly distributed among lineages of squamates. Nearly half the origins of viviparity in the group have occurred in the family Scincidae, whereas viviparity is unknown in teiid lizards and occurs in only two genera of lacertids. Viviparity has advantages and disadvantages as a mode of reproduction. The most commonly cited benefit of viviparity is the opportunity it provides for a female snake or lizard to use her own thermoregulatory behavior to control the temperature of the embryos during development. This hypothesis is appealing in an ecological context, because a relatively short period of retention of the eggs by the female might substantially reduce the total amount of time required for development, especially in a cold climate. However, a test of the egg-retention hypothesis by Robin Andrews and Barbara Rose produced unexpected results (Andrews and Rose 1994). The striped plateau lizard, *Sceloporus virgatus,* is found in the Sierra Madre of Mexico and the mountain ranges of southeastern Arizona and southwestern New Mexico. Female plateau lizards retain their eggs longer than do females of many other species of *Sceloporus,* and retain their eggs still longer if the summer rainy season is late and the environment is too dry for successful egg development. Andrews and Rose found that the thermoregulatory behavior of gravid female lizards did not keep their eggs warmer than they would have been in a nest—the average body

temperature of gravid female lizards (25.4°C) was very similar to the average temperature of nest sites (25.2°C). Furthermore, eggs that were retained by females developed more slowly than eggs that were deposited in nests. Eggs that were laid at the normal time hatched on September 3d, whereas eggs that were retained for 30 days hatched on September 16th. The difference in hatching date means that hatchlings from eggs that had been retained for 30 days would have had about 2 weeks less time to feed and grow before entering hibernation. That might be a substantial handicap, because hatchling plateau lizards can increase their body mass by 40 percent in 2 weeks.

Although egg retention slows embryonic development of plateau lizards, it might accelerate development for species that live in climates where nest sites would be cold. Furthermore, the disadvantage of viviparity, in terms of its effect on reproductive output, may be lower in cold regions than in warm ones. Lizards in warm habitats may produce more than one clutch of eggs in a season, but that is not possible for a viviparous species because development takes too long. However, in a cold climate lizards are not able to produce more than one clutch of eggs in a breeding season anyway, and viviparity would not reduce the annual reproductive output of a female lizard. Phylogenetic analyses of the origins of viviparity suggest that it has evolved most often in cold climates, as this hypothesis predicts, but other origins appear to have taken place in warm climates, and more than one situation favoring viviparity among squamates appears likely.

Viviparity has costs as well as benefits. The agility of a female lizard is substantially reduced when her embryos are large. Experiments have shown that pregnant female lizards cannot run as fast as nonpregnant females and that snakes find it easier to capture pregnant lizards than nonpregnant ones. Females of some species of lizards become secretive when they are pregnant, perhaps in response to their vulnerability to predation. They reduce their activity and spend more time in hiding places. This behavioral adjustment may contribute to the reduction in body temperature seen in pregnant females of some species of lizards, and it probably reduces their rate of prey capture as well.

In general, large species of squamates produce more eggs or fetuses than do small species, and within one species large individuals often have more offspring in a clutch than do small individuals. Both phylogenetic and ecological constraints play a role in determining the number of young produced, however. All geckos have a clutch size of either one or two eggs, and all *Anolis* produce only one egg at a time. Lizards with stout bodies usually have clutches that are a greater percentage of the body mass of the mother than do lizards with slim bodies. The division between stout and slim bodies approximately parallels the division between sit-and-wait predators and widely foraging predators. It is tempting to infer that a lizard that moves about in search of prey finds a bulky clutch of eggs more hindrance than a lizard that spends 99 percent of its time resting motionless. However, some of the divisions among modes of predatory behavior, body form, and relative clutch mass also correspond to the phylogenetic division between iguanian and scincomorph lizards, and as a result it is not possible to decide which characteristics are ancestral and which may be derived.

Parthenogensis   All-female (**parthenogenetic**) species of squamates have been identified in six families of lizards and one snake. The phenomenon is particularly widespread in the teiids (especially *Cnemidophorus*) and lacertids (*Lacerta*) and occurs in several species of geckos. Parthenogenetic species are known or suspected to occur among chameleons, agamids, xantusiids, and typhlopids. However, parthenogenesis is probably more widespread among squamates than this list indicates because parthenogenetic species are not conspicuously different from bisexual species. Parthenogenetic species are usually detected when a study undertaken for an entirely different purpose reveals that a species contains no males. Confirmation of parthenogenesis can be obtained by obtaining fertile eggs from females raised in isolation, or by making reciprocal skin grafts between individuals. Individuals of bisexual species usually reject tissues transplanted from another individual because genetic differences between them lead to immune reactions. Parthenogenetic species, however, produce progeny that are genetically identical to the mother, so no immune reaction occurs and grafted tissue is retained.

The chromosomes of lizards have allowed the events that produced some parthenogenetic species to be deciphered. Many parthenoforms appear to have had their origin as interspecific hybrids. These hybrids are diploid ($2n$) with one set of chromosomes from each parental species. For example, the diploid parthenogenetic whiptail lizard, *Cnemi-*

dophorus tesselatus, is the product of hybridization between the bisexual diploid species *C. tigris* and *C. septemvittatus* (Figure 15–13). Some parthenogenetic species are triploids ($3n$). These forms are usually the result of a backcross of a diploid parthenogenetic individual to a male of one of its bisexual parental species or, less commonly, the result of hybridization of a diploid parthenogenetic species with a male of a bisexual species different from its parental species. A parthenogenetic triploid form of *C. tesselatus* is apparently the result of a cross between the parthenogenetic diploid *C. tesselatus* and the bisexual diploid species *C. sexlineatus*.

It is common to find the two bisexual parental species and a parthenogenetic species living in overlapping habitats. Parthenogenetic species of *Cnemidophorus* often occur in habitats like the floodplains of rivers that are subject to frequent disruption. Disturbance of the habitat may bring together closely related bisexual species, fostering the hybridization that is the first step in establishing a parthenogenetic species. Once a parthenogenetic species has become established, its reproductive potential is twice that of a bisexual species because every individual of a parthenogenetic species is capable of producing young. Thus, when a flood or other disaster wipes out most of the lizards, a parthenogenetic species can repopulate a habitat faster than a bisexual species.

Parental care has been recorded for more than 100 species of squamates (Shine 1988). A few species of snakes and a larger number of lizards remain with the eggs or nest site. Some female skinks remove dead eggs from the clutch. Some species of pythons brood their eggs: The female coils tightly around the eggs, and in some species muscular contractions of the female's body produce sufficient heat to raise the temperature of the eggs to about 30°C, which is substantially above air temperature. One unconfirmed report exists of baby pythons returning at night to their empty eggshells, where their mother coiled around them and kept them warm. Little interaction between adult and juvenile squamates has been documented. In captivity female prehensile-tailed skinks (*Corucia zebrata*) have been reported to nudge their young toward the food dish, as if teaching them to eat. Prehensile-tailed skinks, which occur only on the Solomon Islands, are herbivorous and viviparous.

Free-ranging baby green iguanas have a tenuous social cohesion that persists for several months after they hatch. The small iguanas move away

(a)

(b)

(c)

(d)

(e)

Figure 15–13   The apparent sequence of crosses leading to the formation of diploid and triploid unisexual species of *Cnemidophorus.* Hybridization of the bisexual diploid species (a) *C. tigris* and (b) *C. septemvittatus* produced a unisexual diploid form with half of its genetic complement derived from each of the parental species (an allodiploid). This parthenogenetic form is called *C. tesselatus* (c). Hybridization between a diploid *C. tesselatus* and a male of the bisexual species *C. sexlineatus* (d) produced a unisexual triploid form with its genetic complement derived from three different parental species (an allotriploid). This parthenogenetic triploid form is also called *C. tesselatus* (e). Thus, *C. tesselatus* consists of clones of both diploid and triploid lineages, although taxonomists will probably treat these two forms as separate species in the near future. (Photographs by C. J. Cole and C. M. Bogert, American Museum of Natural History, courtesy of C. J. Cole.)

from the nesting area in groups that may include individuals from several different nests. One lizard may lead the way, looking back as if to see that others are following. The same individual may return later and recruit another group of juveniles. During the first 3 weeks after they hatch, juvenile iguanas move up into the forest canopy and are seen in close association with adults. During this time the hatchlings probably ingest feces from the adults, thereby inoculating their guts with the symbiotic microbes that facilitate digestion of plant material (Troyer 1982). After their fourth week of life, the hatchlings move down from the forest canopy into low vegetation, where they continue to be found in loosely knit groups of two to six or more individuals that move, feed, and sleep together. This association might provide some protection from predators, and if the hatchlings continue to eat fecal material, it is another opportunity to ensure that each lizard has received its full complement of gut microorganisms.

■ Thermoregulation

The extensive repertoire of thermoregulatory mechanisms employed by ectotherms allows many species of lizards and snakes to keep body temperature within a range of a few degrees during the part of a day when they are active. Many species of lizards have body temperatures between 33 and 38°C while they are active (the **activity temperature range**), and snakes often have body temperatures between 28 and 34°C. Avery (1982) has summarized information about body temperatures of squamates in the field.

These activity temperature ranges have been the focus of much research: Field observations show that thermoregulatory activities may occupy a considerable portion of an animal's time. Less obvious, but just as important, are the constraints that the need for thermoregulation sets on other aspects of the behavior and ecology of squamates. For example, some species of lizards and snakes are excluded from certain habitats because it is impossible to thermoregulate. In temperate regions the activity season lasts only during the months when it is warm and sunny enough to permit thermoregulation; at other times of the year snakes and lizards hibernate. Even during the activity season, time spent on thermoregulation may not be available for other activities. Avery (1976) proposed that lizards in temperate regions show less extensive social behavior than do tropical lizards because thermoregulatory behavior in cool climates requires so much time.

The physiological advantages associated with a stable body temperature were discussed in Chapter 4. The body tissues of an organism are the site of a tremendous variety of biochemical reactions proceeding simultaneously and depending on one another to provide the proper quantity of the proper substrates at the proper time for reaction sequences. Each reaction has a different sensitivity to temperature, and regulation is greatly facilitated when temperature variation is limited. Thus, coordination of internal processes may be a major benefit of thermoregulation for squamates. If the temperature stability that a snake or lizard achieves by thermoregulation is important to its physiology

and biochemistry, one would expect to find that the internal economy of an animal functions best within its activity temperature range, and that is often the case. Examples of physiological processes that work best at temperatures within the activity range can be found at the molecular, tissue, system, and whole-animal levels of organization.

Organismal Performance and Temperature

How effectively does an organism carry out its normal activities at different temperatures? Does a difference in body temperature have a measurable effect on how fast a lizard can run, for example, or is running speed independent of temperature? These questions can be addressed with ecological analyses of organismal performance; that is, with measurements of the effectiveness of a process at different temperatures. Much information is available for squamates about the effects of temperature on processes as diverse as intracellular chemical reactions, recovery from disease, growth rates, and predatory success. Temperature profoundly affects the ability of squamates to carry out different activities, but not all activities are affected in parallel ways, and behavioral shifts (that is, qualitative rather than quantitative changes) are seen in some cases. Furthermore, the relationship between body temperature and physiological processes is a two-way interaction: Physiological capacities change in response to changes in body temperature, but under some conditions the sequence of cause and effect is reversed and squamates manipulate their body temperatures in response to internal conditions such as feeding status or pregnancy.

The wandering garter snake (*Thamnophis elegans vagrans*) provides examples of the effects of body temperature on a variety of physiological and behavioral functions (Stevenson et al. 1985). Wandering garter snakes are diurnal, semiaquatic inhabitants of lakeshores and stream banks in western North America. They hunt for prey on land and in water, and feed primarily on fishes and amphibians. Chemosensation is an important mode of prey detection for snakes and is accomplished by flicking the tongue. Scent molecules are transferred from the tips of the forked tongue to the epithelium of the vomeronasal organ in the roof of the mouth. The garter snakes are diurnal; they spend the night in shelters, where their body temperatures fall to ambient levels (4 to 18°C), and emerge in the morning to bask. During activity on sunny days the snakes maintain body temperatures between 28 and 32°C.

Stevenson and his associates measured the effect of temperature on the speed of crawling and swimming, the frequency of tongue flicks, the rate of digestion, and the rate of oxygen consumption of the snakes (Figure 15–14). Crawling, swimming, and tongue flicking are elements of the foraging behavior of garter snakes, and the rates of digestion and oxygen consumption are involved in energy utilization. The ability of garter snakes to crawl and swim was severely limited at the low temperatures they experience during the night when they are inactive. At 5°C snakes often refused to crawl and at 10°C they were able to crawl only 0.1 meter per second and could swim only 0.25 meter per second. The speed of both types of locomotion increased at higher temperatures. Swimming speed peaked near 0.6 meter per second at 25 and 30°C, and crawling speed increased to an average of 0.8 meter per second at 35°C. The rate of tongue flicking increased from less than 0.5 flick per second at 10°C to about 1.5 flicks per second at 30°C. The

rate of digestion increased slowly from 10 to 20°C and more than doubled between 20 and 25°C. It did not increase further at 30°C, and dropped slightly at higher temperatures. The rate of oxygen consumption increased steadily as temperature rose to 35°C, which was the highest temperature tested because higher body temperatures would have been injurious.

All five measures of performance by garter snakes increased with increasing temperature, but the responses to temperature were not identical. For example, swimming speed did not increase substantially above 20°C, whereas crawling speed continued to increase up to 35°C. The rate of digestion peaked at 25 to 30°C and then declined, but the rate of oxygen consumption increased steadily to 35°C. More striking than the differences among the functions, however, is the apparent convergence of maximum performance for all the functions on temperatures between 28.5 and 35°C. This range of temperatures is close to the body temperatures of active snakes in the field on sunny days (28 to 32°C). Anywhere within that range of body temperatures, snakes would be able to crawl, swim,

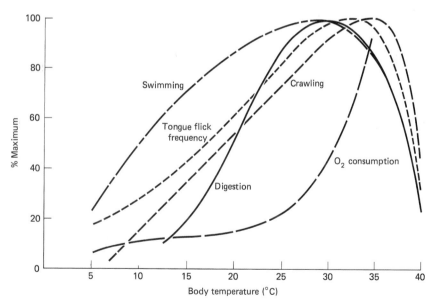

Figure 15–14 Effect of temperature on performance. The ability of a wandering garter snake, *Thamnophis elegans vagrans,* to perform many activities essential to survival depends on the body temperature of the snake. The horizontal axis shows the body temperature of the snakes and the vertical axis shows the percentage of maximum performance achieved at each temperature. (From R. D. Stevenson et al., 1985, *Physiological Zoology* 58:46–57. © 1985 by The University of Chicago. All rights reserved.)

and tongue flick at rates that are at least 95 percent of their maximum rates.

The relationship between the body temperatures of active garter snakes and the temperature sensitivity of various behavioral and physiological functions reported by Stevenson and his colleagues is probably common for squamates. That is, in most cases the body temperatures they maintain during activity are the temperatures that maximize organismal performance. However, at least two types of variation complicate the picture of squamate thermoregulation: changes in behavior that accompany changes in body temperature and changes in thermoregulation in response to the physiological status of an animal.

Behavioral Changes   A change in the body temperature of a squamate may be accompanied by a qualitative change in behavior instead of by the graded levels of performance shown by garter snakes. For example, *Agama savignyi* is an agamid lizard that lives in desert areas of the Middle East. It shows a pronounced temperature sensitivity of sprint speed: At a body temperature of 18°C it can run only 1 meter per second, but at 34°C it runs about 3 meters per second. *Agama savignyi* lives in open habitats where it may be some distance from shelters that could provide protection from predators. Clearly, the lizards are better able to run to a shelter when they are warm than when they are cool, and they display two types of defensive behavior depending on their body temperature. At body temperatures between 18 and 26°C most *A. savignyi* do not try to run from a predator; instead, they leap at the predator and try to bite. At body temperatures of 30°C or above, however, most lizards run away. This sort of qualitative shift in behavior at different body temperatures may be a widespread response among squamates to the effects of body temperature on their ability to carry out certain activities.

Effects of Nutritional Status and Bacterial Infections   Several internal states of squamates and other ectotherms influence body temperature. A thermophilic (*thermo* = heat, *philo* = loving) response after feeding is widespread: Individuals with food in the gut maintain higher body temperatures than do individuals without food. A higher body temperature accelerates digestion and increases digestive efficiency and water uptake, so a warm animal digests its food more rapidly and assimilates a higher proportion of the energy and water present in the food. Conversely, fasting animals regulate their body temperatures at low levels that reduce their metabolic rates and conserve their stored energy.

Behavioral fever is another common response of ectotherms: Individuals infected by bacteria change their thermoregulatory behavior and maintain body temperatures several degrees higher than those of uninfected controls. These behavioral fevers have been demonstrated in arthropods, fishes, frogs, salamanders, turtles, and lizards. The release of prostaglandin E_1, which acts on thermoregulatory centers of the anterior hypothalamus, appears to be the immediate cause of both the behavioral fevers of ectotherms and the physiological fevers of endotherms. Survival is enhanced by fever, apparently because bacterial growth is limited by a reduction in the availability of iron at higher temperatures.

Reproductive Status   Pregnancy affects thermoregulation by squamates. The rate of embryonic development of squamates is strongly affected by temperature, and one of the major advantages of viviparity is thought to be the opportunity it provides for the mother to control the temperature of embryos during development. The body temperatures of female squamates during pregnancy may be different from the temperatures they would normally maintain. For example, pregnant female spiny swifts (*Sceloporus jarrovi*) had an average body temperature of 32.0°C, whereas male lizards in the same habitat had an average body temperature of 34.5°C (Beuchat 1986). The female lizards changed their thermoregulatory behavior after they had given birth, and the average body temperature of postparturient female lizards was 34.5°C, like that of the males. The low body temperatures of pregnant lizards were unexpected because one can easily think of reasons why giving birth as early in the year as possible would be advantageous for the lizards.

That line of reasoning suggests that female lizards should maintain higher-than-normal body temperatures during pregnancy, or at least they should not reduce their body temperatures. Contrary to that prediction, the body temperatures maintained by pregnant squamates appear to converge toward 32°C whether the normal body temperature for the species is higher or lower. If the body temperature of pregnant female lizards is a compromise between the thermal requirements of the mother and the best temperature for embryonic development, this convergence might indicate that temperatures near 32°C are particularly favorable for embryonic development (Beuchat and Ellner 1987). Experiments have shown that surprisingly small differences in the incubation temperature of lizard and snake eggs can produce profound morphological, physiological, and behavioral differences in the hatchlings.

Temperature and the Ecology of Squamates

Squamates, especially lizards, are capable of very precise thermoregulation, and microhabitats at which particular body temperatures can be maintained may be one of the dimensions that define the ecological niches of lizards. The five most common species of *Anolis* on Cuba partition the habitat in several ways (Figure 15–15). First, they divide the habitat along the continuum, from sunny to shady: Two species (*A. lucius* and *A. allogus*) occur in deep shade in forests, one (*A. homolechis*) in partial shade in clearings and at the forest edge, and two (*A. allisoni* and *A. sagrei*) in full sun. Within habitats in the sun–shade continuum, the lizards are separated by the substrates they use as perch sites. In the forest *A. lucius* perches on large trees up to 4 meters above the ground, whereas *A. allogus* rests on small trees within 2 meters of the ground. *A. homolechis*, which does not share its habitat with another common species of *Anolis*, perches on both large and small trees. In open habitats *A. allisoni* perches more than 2 meters above the ground on tree trunks and houses, and *A. sagrei* perches below 2 meters on bushes and fenceposts.

Some species of lizards do not thermoregulate. Lizards that live beneath the tree canopy in tropical forests often have body temperatures very close to air temperature (that is, they are thermally passive), whereas species that live in open habitats thermoregulate more precisely. The relative ease of thermoregulation in different habitats may be an important factor in determining whether a species of lizard thermoregulates or allows its temperature to vary with ambient temperature.

The distribution of sunny areas is one factor that determines the ease of thermoregulation. Sunlight penetrates the canopy of a forest in small patches that move across the forest floor as the sun moves across the sky. These patches of sun are the only sources of solar radiation for lizards that live at or near the forest floor, and the patches may be too sparsely distributed or too transient to be used for thermoregulation. In open habitats sunlight is readily available, and thermoregulation is easier. The difference in thermoregulatory behavior of lizards in open and shaded habitats can be seen even in comparisons of different populations within a species. For example, *Anolis sagrei* occurs in both open and forest habitats on Abaco Island in the Caribbean. Lizards in open habitats bask and maintain body temperatures between 32 and 35°C from about 8:30 in the morning through about 5:00 in the afternoon. Lizards in the forest do not bask, and their body temperatures vary from a low of 24°C to a high of 28°C over the same period.

The task of integrating thermoregulatory behavior with foraging is relatively simple for sit-and-wait foragers such as *Anolis*. These lizards can readily change their balance of heat gain and loss by making small movements in and out of shade or between calm and breezy perch sites while they continue to scan their surroundings for prey. Widely foraging species may have more difficulty integrating thermoregulation and predation. They are continuously moving between sun and shade and in and out of the wind, and their body temperatures are affected by their foraging activity. These lizards sometimes have to stop foraging to thermoregulate, resuming foraging only when they have warmed or cooled enough to return to their activity temperature range.

Body size is yet another variable that can affect thermoregulation. An example of the interaction of body size, thermoregulation, and foraging behavior is provided by three species of teiid lizards (*Ameiva*) in Costa Rica. *Ameiva* are widely foraging predators that move through the habitat, pushing their snouts beneath fallen leaves and into holes. Three species of *Ameiva* occur together on the Osa Peninsula of Costa Rica in a habitat that extends from full sun (a roadside) to deep shade (forest). The largest of the three species, *A. leptophrys*, has an average body mass of 83 grams, the middle species, *A. festiva*, weighs 32 grams, and the smallest, *A. quadrilineata*, weighs 10 grams (Figure 15–16). The three species forage in different parts of the habitat: *A. quadrilineata* spends most of its time in the short vegetation at the edge of the road, *A. festiva* is found on the bank beside the road, and *A. leptophrys* forages pri-

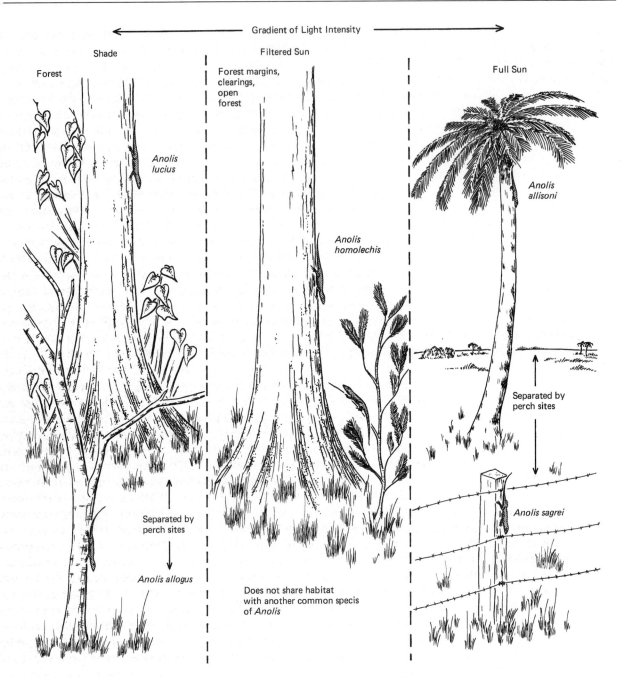

Figure 15–15 Habitat partitioning by Cuban species of *Anolis*. See text for explanation. (Based on R. Ruibal, 1961, *Evolution* 15:98–111.)

marily beneath the canopy of the forest (Figure 15–17). The different foraging sites of the three species may reflect differences in thermoregulation that result from the variation in body size.

The thermoregulatory behavior of the three species is the same: A lizard basks in the sun until its body temperature rises to 39 to 40°C, then moves through the mosaic of sun and shade as it searches for food. The body temperature of the lizard drops as it forages, and a lizard ceases foraging and resumes basking when its body temperature has fallen to 35°C. Thus, the time that a lizard can forage depends on how long it takes for its body temperature to cool from 39 or 40°C to 35°C. The rate of cooling for *Ameiva* in the shade is inversely proportional to the body size of the three

(a)

(b)

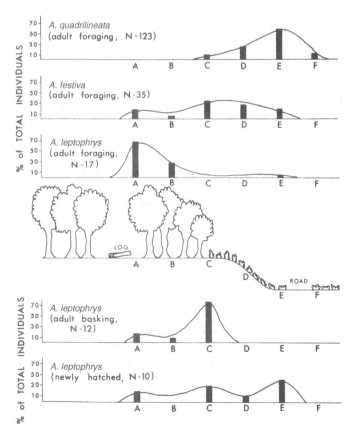

(c)

Figure 15–16 Three sympatric species of *Ameiva* from Costa Rica. (a) *Ameiva leptophrys*, which has an average adult mass of 83 grams; (b) *Ameiva festiva*, average adult mass 32 grams; (c) *Ameiva quadrilineata*, average adult mass 10 grams. ([a] Courtesy of Daniel H. Janzen, University of Pennsylvania; [b] and [c] photographed by Michael Hopiak, courtesy of the Cornell University Herpetology Collection.)

Figure 15–17 Foraging sites of three species of *Ameiva* in Costa Rica. The histograms show the number of individuals of the three species seen in each of six locations: (a) a small clearing in the forest; (b) immediately inside the forest edge; (c) outside the edge of the forest; (d) midway between the edge of the forest and open area; (e) low vegetation beside a road; (f) low vegetation in a large open area without trees. (From P. E. Hillman, 1969, *Ecology* 50:476–481.)

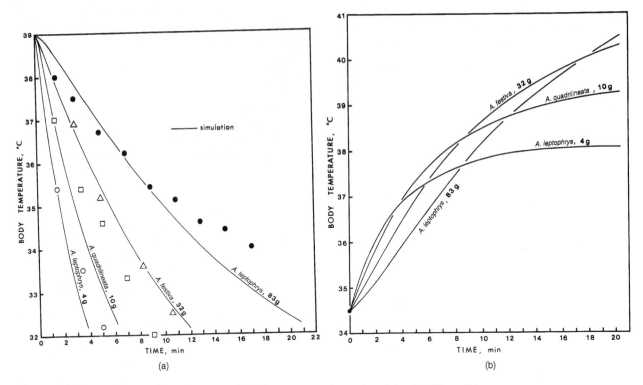

Figure 15–18 Cooling and heating rates of the three sympatric species of *Ameiva*. The solid lines are computer simulations of heating and cooling rates, and the symbols in (a) show the close correspondence of measured body temperatures to those predicted by the computer simulation. The largest species, *Ameiva leptophrys*, heats and cools more slowly than the smaller species. If it remained in the sun its body temperature would rise above 40°C. The smaller species heat and cool more rapidly than the large species and reach temperature equilibrium at lower body temperatures. ([a] From P. E. Hillman, 1969, *Ecology* 50:476–481; [b] courtesy of Peter E. Hillman.)

species: *A. quadrilineata* cools in 4 minutes, *A. festiva* in 6 minutes, and *A. leptophrys* in 11 minutes (Figure 15–18a). That relationship appears to explain part of the microhabitat separation of the three species: The smallest species, *A. quadrilineata*, cools so rapidly that it may not be able to forage effectively in shady microhabitats, whereas *A. leptophrys* cools slowly and can forage in the shade beneath the forest canopy. The species of intermediate body size, *A. festiva*, uses the habitat with an intermediate amount of shade.

The slow rate of cooling of *A. leptophrys* may explain why it is able to forage in the shade, but field observations indicate that its foraging is actually restricted to shade; it emerges from the forest only to bask. Does some environmental factor prevent *A. leptophrys* from foraging in the sun? The answer to that question may lie in the way the body temperatures of the three species increase when they are in open microhabitats. Body size profoundly affects the equilibrium temperature of

an organism in the sun. A lizard warms by absorbing solar radiation, and as it gets warmer, its heat loss by convection, evaporation, and reradiation also increases. When the rate of heat loss equals the rate of heat gain, the body temperature does not increase further. Large lizards reach that equilibrium at higher body temperatures than do small ones. Computer simulations of the heating rates of the three *Ameiva* in sun showed that *A. quadrilineata* and *A. festiva* would reach equilibrium at body temperatures of 37 to 40°C, but *A. leptophrys* would continue to heat until its body temperature reached a lethal 45°C (Figure 15–18b). This analysis suggests that *Ameiva leptophrys* would die of heat stress if it spent more than a few minutes in a sunny microhabitat, but that the two smaller species of *Ameiva* would not have that problem.

Thus, as a result of the biophysics of heat exchange, the large body size of *A. leptophrys* apparently allows it to forage in shaded habitats (because it cools slowly), but prevents it from foraging in sunny habitats (because it would over-heat). Field observations of the foraging behavior of hatchling *A. leptophrys* emphasize the importance of heat exchange in the foraging behavior of these lizards. Hatchling *A. leptophrys* forage in open habitats like *A. festiva* and *A. quadrilineata* rather than under the forest canopy like adult *A. leptophrys*. That is, the juveniles of the large species of *Ameiva* behave like adults of the smaller species, probably because of the importance of body size and heat exchange in determining the mirohabitats in which lizards can thermoregulate.

The difference in the use of various microhabitats by these three species of lizards looks, at first glance, like an example of habitat partitioning in response to interspecific competition for food. That is, because all three species eat the same sort of prey, they could be expected to concentrate their foraging efforts in different microhabitats to reduce competition. However, this analysis of the thermal requirements of the lizards suggests that interspecific competition for food is, at most, a secondary factor.

If competition for food were important, one would not expect to find hatchling *A. leptophrys* foraging in the same microhabitat as adult *A. quadrilineata*, because the similarity in size of the two lizards would intensify competition for food. The hypothesis that competition for food determines the microhabitat distribution of the animals predicts that the forms most similar in body size should be mostly widely separated in the habitat. In contrast, the hypothesis that energy exchange with the environment is critical in determining where a lizard can forage predicts that species of similar size will live in the same habitat, and that is approximately the pattern seen. Apparently, the physical environment (radiant energy) is more important than the biological environment (interspecific competition for food) in determining the microhabitat distributions of these lizards. That conclusion reflects the broad-scale ecological significance of the morphological and physiological differences between ectotherms and endotherms, a theme that is developed in Chapter 16.

■ Summary

The extant lepidosaurs include the squamates (lizards and snakes) and their sister group, the Sphenodontidae. The lepidosaurs, with more than 6800 species, form the second largest group of extant tetrapods. The two species of tuatara of the New Zealand region are the sole extant sphenodontids. They are lizardlike animals, about 60 centimeters long, with a dentition and jaw mechanism that give a shearing bite. Sphenodontids were diverse in the Mesozoic and included terrestrial insectivorous and herbivorous species as well as a marine form.

Lizards range in size from tiny geckos only 3 centimeters long to the Komodo monitor lizard, which reaches a length of 3 meters. The Iguania and Gekkota are composed largely of stout-bodied lizards and show considerable diversity of body form. The Scincomorpha and Anguimorpha are elongate and show less morphological diversity than do iguanians.

Differences in ecology and behavior parallel the phylogenetic divisions: Many iguanians are sit-and-wait predators that maintain territories and detect prey and intruders by vision. Iguanians often employ colors and patterns in visual displays during courtship and territorial defense. Many scinco-morph and anguimorph lizards are widely foraging predators that detect prey by olfaction and do not maintain territories. Pheromones are important in the social behaviors of many of these lizards.

Amphisbaenians are specialized burrowing lizards. Their skulls are solid structures that they use for tunneling through soil. Many amphisbaenians have blunt heads, and others have vertically keeled or horizontally spade-shaped snouts. The dentition of amphisbaenians appears to be specialized for nipping small pieces from prey too large to be swallowed whole. The skin of amphisbaenians is loosely attached to the trunk, and amphisbaenians slide backward or forward inside the tube of their skin as they move through tunnels with concertina locomotion.

Snakes are derived from lizards. Repackaging the body mass of a vertebrate into a serpentine form has been accompanied by specializations of the mechanisms of locomotion (serpentine, rectilinear, concertina, and sidewinding), prey capture (constriction and the use of venom), and swallowing (a highly kinetic skull).

Many squamates have complex social behaviors associated with territoriality and courtship, but parental care is only slightly developed. Fertilization is internal, and viviparity has evolved 80 or more times among squamates. Thermoregulation is another important behavior of squamates, and various activities are influenced by body temperature. The ecological niches of some lizards may be defined in part by the microhabitats needed to maintain particular body temperatures. Feeding status, pregnancy, and bacterial infections can change the thermoregulatory behavior of squamates, causing an affected individual to maintain a higher or lower body temperature than it otherwise would.

■ References

Andrews, R. M., and B. R. Rose. 1994. Evolution of viviparity: constraints on egg retention. *Physiological Zoology* 67:1006–1024.

Arnold, E. N. 1988. Caudal autotomy as a defense. Pages 235–273 in *Biology of the Reptilia*, volume 16, edited by C. Gans and R. B. Huey. Liss. New York, NY.

Auffenberg, W. 1981. *The Behavioral Ecology of the Komodo Monitor*. University Presses of Florida, Gainesville, FL.

Avery, R. A. 1976. Thermoregulation, metabolism, and social behaviour in Lacertidae. Pages 245–259 in *Morphology and Biology of Reptiles*, edited by A. d'A. Bellairs and C. B. Cox. Academic, London, UK.

Avery, R. A. 1982. Field studies of reptilian thermoregulation. Pages 93–166 in *Biology of the Reptilia*, volume 12, edited by C. Gans and F. H. Pough. Academic, London, UK.

Beuchat, C. A. 1986. Reproductive influence on the thermoregulatory behavior of a live-bearing lizard. *Copeia* 1986:971–979.

Beuchat, C. A., and S. Ellner. 1987. A quantitative test of life history theory: thermoregulation by a viviparous lizard. *Ecological Monographs* 57:45–60.

Blackburn, D. G. 1982. Evolutionary origins of viviparity in the Reptilia, I: Sauria. *Amphibia–Reptilia* 3:185–205.

Blackburn, D. G. 1985. Evolutionary origins of viviparity in the Reptilia, II: Serpentes, Amphisbaenia, and Ichthyosauria. *Amphibia–Reptilia* 6:259–291.

Blackburn, D. G., L. J. Vitt, and C. A. Beuchat. 1984. Eutherian-like reproductive specializations in a viviparous reptile. *Proceedings of the National Academy of Science USA* 81:4860–4863.

Caldwell, M. W., and M. S. Y. Lee. 1997. A snake with legs from the marine Cretaceous of the Middle East. *Nature* 386:705–709.

Cooper, W. E., Jr., and L. J. Vitt. 1986. Interspecific odour discriminations among syntopic congeners in scincid lizards (Genus *Eumeces*). *Behaviour* 97:1–9.

Daugherty, C. H., A. Cree, J. M. Hay, and M. B. Thompson. 1990. Neglected taxonomy and continuing extinctions of tuatara (Spendonod). *Nature* 347:177–179.

Diamond, J. M. 1987. Did Komodo dragons evolve to eat pygmy elephants? *Nature* 326:832.

Fleishman, L. J., E. R. Loew, and M. Leal. 1993. Ultraviolet vision in lizards. *Nature* 365:397.

Frost, D. R. and R. Etheridge 1989. A phylogenetic analysis and taxonomy of Iguanian lizards (Reptilia: Squamata). *Miscellaneous Publications of the Museum of Natural History, University of Kansas* 81:1–65.

Gillingham, J. C., C. Carmichael, and T. Miller. 1995. Social behavior of the tuatara, *Sphenodon punctatus*. *Herpetological Monographs* 9:5–16.

Greene, H. 1997. *Snakes*. University of California Press, Berkeley, CA.

Greer, A. E. 1991. Limb reduction in squamates: identification of the lineages and discussion of the trends. *Journal of Herpetology* 25:116–173.

Halpern, M. 1992. Nasal chemical senses in reptile: structure and function. Pages 423–523 in *Biology of the Reptilia*, volume 18, edited by C. Gans and D. Crews. University of Chicago Press, Chicago, IL.

Hardy, D. L., Sr. 1994. A re-evaluation of suffocation as the cause of death during constriction. *Herpetological Review* 25:45–47.

Huey, R. B., and A. F. Bennett. 1986. A comparative approach to field and laboratory studies in evolutionary biology. Pages 82–98 in *Predator–Prey Relationships*, edited by M. E. Feder and G. V. Lauder. University of Chicago Press, Chicago, IL.

Huey, R. B., and E. R. Pianka. 1981. Ecological consequences of foraging mode. *Ecology* 62:991–999.

Macey, J. R., A. Larson, N. B. Ananjeva, and T. J. Papenfuss. 1997. Evolutionary shifts in three major structural features of the mitochondrial genome among iguanian lizards. *Journal of Molecular Evolution* 44:660–674.

Mason, R. T. 1992. Reptilian pheromones. Pages 114–228 in *Biology of the Reptilia*, volume 18, edited by C. Gans and D. Crews. University of Chicago Press, Chicago, IL.

May, R. M. 1990. Taxonomy as destiny. *Nature* 347:129–130.

Pough, F. H. (editor). 1983. Adaptive radiation within a highly specialized system: the diversity of feeding mechanisms of snakes. *American Zoologist* 23:339–460.

Pough, F. H. 1994. Zoo–academic research collaboration: How close are we? *Herpetologica* 49:500–508.

Savitzky, A. H. 1980. The role of venom delivery strategies in snake evolution. *Evolution* 34:1194–1204.

Schwenk, K. 1994. Why snakes have forked tongues. *Science* 263:1573–1577.

Shine, R. 1985. The evolution of viviparity in reptiles: an ecological analysis. Pages 606–694 in *Biology of the Reptilia*, volume 15, edited by C. Gans and F. Billett. Wiley, New York, NY.

Shine, R. 1988. Parental care in reptiles. Pages 275–329 in *Biology of the Reptilia*, volume 16, edited by C. Cans and B. R. Huey. Liss, New York, NY.

Simon, C. A. 1983. A review of lizard chemoreception. Pages 119–133 in *Lizard Ecology: Studies of a Model Organism*, edited by R. B. Huey, E. R. Pianka, and T. W. Schoener. Harvard University Press, Cambridge, MA.

Sinervo, B. 1994. Experimental manipulations of clutch size and offspring size in lizards: mechanistic, evolutionary, and conservation considerations. In *Captive Management and Conservation of Amphibians and Reptiles,* edited by J. B. Murphy, J. T. Collins, and K. Adler. Contributions to Herpetology, Society for the Study of Amphibians and Reptiles. Oxford, UK.

Sinervo, B., P. Doughty, R. B. Huey, and K. Zamudio. 1992. Allometric engineering: a causal analysis of natural selection on offspring size. *Science* 258:1927–1930.

Sinervo, B., and P. Licht. 1991. Hormonal and physiological control of clutch size, egg size, and egg shape in side-blotched lizards (*Uta stansburiana*): constraints on the evolution of life histories. *Journal of Experimental Zoology* 257:252–264.

Stevenson, R. D., C. R. Peterson, and J. S. Tsuji. 1985. The thermal dependence of locomotion, tongue flicking, digestion, and oxygen consumption in the wandering garter snake. *Physiological Zoology* 58:46–57.

Troyer, K. 1982. Transfer of fermentative microbes between generations in a herbivorous lizard. *Science* 216:540–542.

Wu, X.-C., D. R. Brinkman, A. P. Russell, Z.-M. Dong, P. J. Currie, L.-H. Hou, and G.-H. Cul. 1993. Oldest known amphisbaenian from the Upper Cretaceous of Chinese Inner Mongolia. *Nature* 366:57–59.

CHAPTER
16

Ectothermy: A Low-Cost Approach to Life

Ectothermy is an ancestral character of vertebrates, but like many ancestral characters it is just as effective as its derived counterpart, endothermy. Furthermore, the mechanisms of ectothermal thermoregulation are as complex and specialized as those of endothermy. In Chapter 4 we examined the behavioral and physiological mechanisms that ectotherms use to control their body temperatures, and in Chapter 15 we considered the effect of these thermoregulatory mechanisms on the ecology and behavior of lizards and snakes. Here we consider the consequences of ectothermy in shaping broader aspects of the life-style of fishes, amphibians, and reptiles.

Ectothermal tetrapods have low energy requirements compared with endotherms, and this characteristic allows ectotherms to do things that endotherms cannot. At the level of an ecosystem, ectotherms are efficient secondary producers; that is, they convert a substantial proportion of the food they eat into new body tissues. As a result, ectotherms play an important role in energy flow through most ecosystems. As species, ectotherms display morphological and ecological specializations, such as extremely small body size, elongate body shape, and extreme sexual dimorphism, which are not feasible for endotherms. And as individuals, ectotherms can use a combination of physiological and behavioral responses to confront episodic or chronic shortages of food or water. The general conclusion from this examination is that success in difficult environments is as likely to reflect the ancestral features of a group as its derived characters.

■ Vertebrates and Their Environments

Vertebrates manage to live in the most unlikely places. Amphibians live in deserts where rain falls only a few times a year and several years may pass with no rainfall at all; lizards live on mountains at altitudes above 4000 meters where the temperature falls below freezing nearly every night of the year and does not rise much above freezing during the day.

Of course, vertebrates do not seek out only inhospitable places to live—birds, lizards, mammals, and even amphibians can be found on the beaches at Malibu (sometimes running between the feet of surfers), and fishes cruise the shore. However, even this apparently benign environment is stressful to some animals, and examination of the ways that vertebrates live in extreme environments has provided much information about how they function as organisms; that is, how morphology, physiology, ecology, and behavior interact.

In some cases elegant adaptations allow specialized vertebrates to colonize stressful habitats. More common and more impressive than these specializations, however, is the realization of how minor are the modifications of the ancestral vertebrate body plan that allow animals to endure environmental temperatures from −70 to +70°C, or water conditions ranging from complete immersion in water to complete independence of liquid water. No obvious differences distinguish animals from vastly different habitats—an Arctic fox looks very much like a desert fox, and a lizard from the Andes Mountains looks like one from the Atacama Desert. The adaptability of vertebrates lies in the combination of minor modifications of their ecology, behavior, morphology, and physiology. A view that integrates these elements shows the startling beauty of organismal function of vertebrates.

Endotherms and ectotherms react somewhat differently to many environmental factors. The essence of the endothermal approach to life is the use of energy to maintain internal homeostasis. Endotherms can regulate their body temperatures and body fluid and salt concentrations with remarkable precision in the face of extreme fluctuations in their environment. Ectotherms are also capable of remarkable homeostasis, but the general characteristic of ectotherms is low rates of energy consumption. In many cases ectotherms save energy by relaxing their limits of homeostasis, whereas endotherms expend energy to maintain homeostasis. This difference in the responses of endotherms and ectotherms to stressful environments has broad implications: By relaxing homeostasis, ectotherms are able to do things that would not be feasible for an endotherm. On the other hand, the activity of ectotherms may be curtailed for long periods during unfavorable seasons because they are not able to maintain homeostasis.

The low energy requirements of ectotherms allow them to exploit many environments in which energy is scarce seasonally or chronically. In addition, the ability of ectotherms to become torpid allows them to wait out periods when the environment may be too hot or cold or too wet or dry to permit activity. Temporary relaxation of homeostasis—allowing physiological variables to fluctuate more widely than usual—may permit organisms to occupy environments that would not otherwise be habitable.

The responses of ectotherms to stressful environments usually involve combinations of characters that include behavior and physiology as well as body structure. Patterns of life history may be modified in ways that ensure that males and females can find each other to mate, or that facilitate the development of embryos and young.

■ Heat: Ectotherms in Deserts

Deserts can be produced by various combinations of topography, air movements, and ocean currents, but whatever their cause, deserts have in common a scarcity of liquid water. That characteristic is at the root of many of the features of deserts that make them difficult places for vertebrates to live. The dry air characteristic of most deserts seldom contains enough moisture to form clouds that would block solar radiation during the day or radiative cooling at night. As a result, the daily temperature excursion in deserts is large compared with that of more humid areas. Scarcity of water is reflected by sparse plant life and a correspondingly low primary productivity in desert communities. Food shortages may be chronic and are exacerbated by seasonal shortages and unpredictable years of low production when the usual pattern of rainfall does not develop.

Not all deserts are hot; indeed, some are distinctly cold—most of Antarctica and the region of Canada around Hudson Bay and the Arctic Ocean are deserts. The low-latitude deserts north and south of the equator are hot deserts, however, and it is in these low-latitude deserts that vertebrates encounter the most difficult problems of desert life.

The scarcity of rain contributes to the low primary production of deserts and also means that sources of liquid water for drinking are usually unavailable to small animals that cannot travel long distances. These animals obtain water from the plants or animals they eat, but plants and insects have ion balances that differ from those of vertebrates. In particular, potassium is found in higher concentrations in plants and insects than it is in vertebrate tissues, and excreting the excess potassium can be difficult if water is too scarce to waste in the production of large quantities of urine.

The low metabolic rates of ectotherms alleviate some of the stress caused by scarcity of food and water, but many desert ectotherms must temporarily extend the limits within which they regulate body temperatures or body fluid concentrations, become inactive for large portions of the year, or adopt a combination of these responses. Tortoises, lizards, and anurans from deserts illustrate these phenomena.

Terrestrial Ectotherms

Terrestrial habitats in deserts are often harsh—hot by day and cold at night. Solar radiation is intense and air does not conduct heat rapidly. As a result, a sunlit patch of ground can be lethally hot, whereas a shaded area just a few centimeters away can be substantially cooler. Underground retreats offer protection from both heat and cold. The annual temperature extremes at the surface of the ground in the Mojave Desert extend from a low that is below freezing to a maximum above 50°C, but just 1 meter below the surface of the ground the annual range is only from 10 to 25°C. Desert animals rely on the temperature differences between sun and shade and between the surface and underground burrows to escape both hot and cold.

The Desert Tortoise   The largest ectothermal vertebrates in the deserts of North America are tortoises. The bolson tortoise (*Gopherus flavomarginatus*) of northern Mexico probably once reached a shell length of a meter, although predation by humans has apparently prevented any tortoise in recent times from living long enough to grow that large. The desert tortoise (*G. agassizii*) of the southwestern United States is smaller than the Bolson tortoise, but it is still an impressively large turtle (Figure 16–1). Adults can reach shell lengths approaching 50 centimeters and may weigh 5 kilograms or more. A study of the annual water, salt, and energy budgets of desert tortoises in Nevada shows the difficulties they face in that desert habitat (Nagy and Medica 1986).

Desert tortoises construct shallow burrows that they use as daily retreat sites during the summer and deeper burrows for hibernation in winter. The tortoises in the study area emerged from hibernation in spring, and aboveground activity extended through the summer until they began hibernation again in November. Doubly labeled water was used to measure the energy expenditure of free-ranging tortoises (Box 16–1).

Figure 16–2 shows the annual cycle of time spent above ground and in burrows by the tortoises, and the annual cycles of energy, water, and salt balance. A positive balance means that the animal shows a net gain, whereas a negative balance represents a net loss. Positive energy and water balances indicate that conditions are good for the tortoises, but a positive salt balance means that ions are accumulating in the body fluids faster than they can be excreted. That situation indicates a relaxation of homeostasis and is probably stressful for the tortoises. The figure shows that the animals were often in negative balance for water or energy, and they accumulated salt during much of the year. Examination of the behavior and dietary habits of the tortoises through the year shows what was happening.

After they emerged from hibernation in the spring, the tortoises were active for about 3 hours every fourth day; the rest of the time they spent in their burrows. From March through May the tortoises were eating annual plants that had sprouted after the winter rains. They obtained large amounts of water and potassium from this diet, and their water and salt balances were positive. The osmolality of the tortoises' body fluids increased by 20 percent during the spring, indicating that they were osmotically stressed as a result of the high concentrations of potassium they were ingesting. Furthermore, the energy content of the plants was not

(a)

(b)

Figure 16–1   The desert tortoise, *Gopherus agassizii*. (a) An adult tortoise; (b) a tortoise entering its burrow. (Photographs by R. Bruce Bury, U.S. Fish & Wildlife Service.)

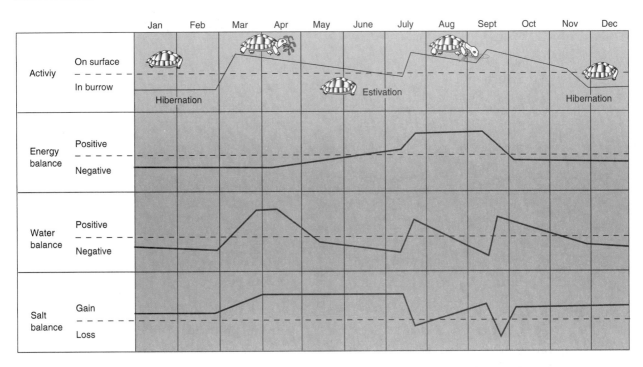

Figure 16–2   Annual cycle of desert tortoises. See text for details. (Based on Nagy and Medica 1986.)

great enough to balance the metabolic energy expenditure of the tortoises, and they were in negative energy balance. During this period the tortoises were using stored energy by metabolizing their body tissues.

As ambient temperatures increased from late May through early July, the tortoises shortened their daily activity periods to about 1 hour every sixth day. The rest of the time the tortoises spent aestivating in shallow burrows. The annual plants died, and the tortoises shifted to eating grass and achieved positive energy balances. They stored this extra energy as new body tissue. The dry grass contained little water, however, and the tortoises were in negative water balance. The osmotic concentrations of their body fluids remained at the high levels they had reached earlier in the year.

In mid-July thunderstorms dropped rain on the study site, and most of the tortoises emerged from estivation. They drank water from natural basins, and some of the tortoises constructed basins by scratching shallow depressions in the ground that trapped rain water. The tortoises drank large quantities of water (nearly 20 percent of their body mass) and voided the contents of their urinary bladders. The osmolal concentrations of their body fluids and urine decreased as they moved into positive water balance and excreted the excess salts they had accumulated when water was scarce. The behavior of

the tortoises changed after the rain: They fed every 2 or 3 days and often spent their periods of inactivity above ground instead of in their burrows.

August was dry, and the tortoises lost body water and accumulated salts as they fed on dry grass. They were in positive energy balance, however, and their body tissue mass increased. More thunderstorms in September allowed the tortoises to drink again and to excrete the excess salts they had been accumulating. Seedlings sprouted after the rain, and in late September the tortoises started to eat them.

In October and November the tortoises continued to feed on freshly sprouted green vegetation, but low temperatures reduced their activity and they were in slightly negative energy balance. Salts accumulated and the osmolal concentrations of the body fluids increased slightly. In November the tortoises entered hibernation. Hibernating tortoises had low metabolic rates and lost water and body tissue mass slowly. When they emerged from hibernation the following spring they weighed only a little less than they had in the fall. Over the entire year, the tortoises increased their body tissues by more than 25 percent, and balanced their water and salt budgets, but they did this by tolerating severe imbalances in their energy, water, and salt relations for periods that extended for several months at a time.

Doubly Labeled Water

This technique is widely employed in studies of the energy consumption of wild vertebrates because it is the only method of measuring metabolism without restraining the animal in some way. The method measures carbon dioxide production, which in turn can be used to estimate oxygen consumption. "Doubly labeled" refers to water that carries isotopic forms of oxygen and hydrogen: The oxygen atom has been replaced with its stable isotope oxygen-18 (18O), and one hydrogen atom (H) has been replaced by its radioactive form, tritium (3H). (Doubly labeled water is prepared by mixing appropriate quantities of water containing the hydrogen isotope [3HHO] with water containing the oxygen isotope [H_2 18O]. When this mixture is diluted by the body water of an animal, the concentrations of the isotopes are so low that few individual water molecules contain both isotopes.) A measured amount of doubly labeled water is injected into an animal, and allowed to equilibrate with the body water for several hours (Figure 16–3a), and then a small blood sample is withdrawn. The concentrations of tritium and oxygen-18 in the blood are measured, and the total volume of body water can be calculated from the dilution of the doubly labeled water that was injected.

After that first blood sample has been withdrawn, the animal is released and recaptured at intervals of several days or weeks. Each time the animal is recaptured a blood sample is taken and the concentrations of tritium and oxygen-18 are measured. The calculation of the amount of carbon dioxide produced by the animal is based on the difference in the rates of loss of tritium and oxygen-18. Tritium, which behaves chemically like hydrogen, is lost as water—that is, as 3HHO—whereas oxygen-18 is lost both as water (H_2 18O) and as carbon dioxide (C18OO). Thus, the decline in the concentration of tritium in the blood of the animal is a measure of the rate of water loss, and the decline in the concentration of oxygen-18 is a measure of the rates of loss of carbon dioxide and water (Figure 16–3b). The difference between decrease in concentration of tritium and oxygen-18, therefore, is the rate of loss of carbon dioxide, and this is proportional to the rate of oxygen consumption. A full description of the use of doubly labeled water for metabolic studies can be found in Nagy (1983).

Figure 16–3 Doubly labeled water. (a) The reaction of carbon dioxide and water to produce carbonic acid, and the subsequent reconversion of carbonic acid to water and carbon dioxide produce an equilibrium of 18O between H_2O and CO_2 when water labeled with the isotope is injected into a vertebrate. (b) Differential washout of hydrogen and oxygen isotopes in the body water of an animal that has been injected with doubly labeled water. (Modified from K. A. Nagy, 1988, in *Stable Isotopes in Ecological Research*, edited by J. Ehleringer, P. Rundall, and K. Nagy, Springer, New York, NY.)

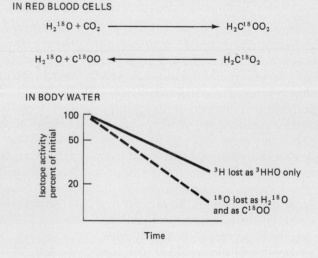

IN RED BLOOD CELLS

$$H_2^{18}O + CO_2 \longrightarrow H_2C^{18}OO_2$$

$$H_2^{18}O + C^{18}OO \longleftarrow H_2C^{18}O_2$$

IN BODY WATER

3H lost as 3HHO only

18O lost as H_2^{18}O and as C18OO

The Chuckwalla The ability to tolerate physiological imbalances is an important aspect of the ability of ectothermal vertebrates to occupy habitats where seasonal shortages of food or water occur. The chuckwalla (*Sauromalus obesus*) is an herbivorous iguanid lizard that lives in the rocky foothills of desert mountain ranges (Figure 16–4). The annual cycle of the chuckwallas, like that of the desert tortoises, is molded by the availability of water. The lizards face many of the same stresses that the tortoises encounter, but their responses are different: The lizards have nasal glands that allow them to excrete salt at high concentrations, and they do not drink rain water but instead depend on water they obtain from the plants they eat.

Two categories of water are available to an animal from the food it eats: free water and metabolic water. Free water corresponds to the water content of the food, that is, molecules of water (H_2O) that are absorbed across the wall of the intestine. Metabolic water is a by-product of the cellular reactions of metabolism. Protons are combined with oxygen during aerobic metabolism, yielding a molecule of water for every two protons. The amount of metabolic water produced can be substantial; more than a gram of water is released by metabolism of a gram of fat (Table 16.1). For animals like the chuckwalla that do not drink liquid water, free water and metabolic water are the only routes of water gain that can replace the water lost by evaporation and excretion.

Chuckwallas were studied at Black Mountain in the Mojave Desert of California (Nagy 1972, 1973). They spent the winter hibernating in rock crevices and emerged from hibernation in April. Individual

TABLE 16.1	Quantity of water produced by metabolism of different substrates	
Compound	Grams of Water/Gram of Compound
Carbohydrate	0.556
Fat	1.071
Protein	0.396 when urea is the end product
	0.499 when uric acid is the end product

lizards spent about 8 hours a day on the surface in April and early May (Figure 16–5). By the middle of May air temperatures were rising above 40°C and the chuckwallas retreated into rock crevices for about 2 hours during the hottest part of the day, emerging again in the afternoon. At this time of year annual plants that sprouted after the winter rains supplied both water and nourishment, and the chuckwallas gained weight rapidly. The average increase in body mass between April and mid-May was 18 percent (Figure 16–6). The water content of the chuckwallas increased faster than the total body mass, indicating that they were storing excess water.

By early June the annual plants had withered, and the chuckwallas were feeding on perennial plants that contained less water and more ions than the annual plants. Both the body masses and the water contents of the lizards declined. The activity of the lizards decreased in June and July: Individual lizards emerged in the morning or in the afternoon, but not at both times. In late June the chuckwallas reduced their feeding activity and in July they stopped eating altogether. They spent

Figure 16–4 Chuckwalla, *Sauromalus obesus*. (Photograph by F. Harvey Pough.)

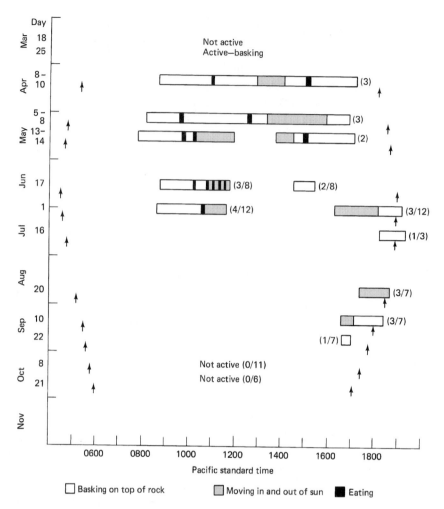

Figure 16–5 Daily behavior patterns in chuckwallas through their activity season. Arrows indicate sunrise and sunset. Numbers in parentheses for April and May indicate the number of animals whose behavior was recorded. Thereafter the fraction in parentheses indicates the number of lizards active and observed out of the number known to be present. (From Nagy 1973, *Copeia* 1973:93–102.)

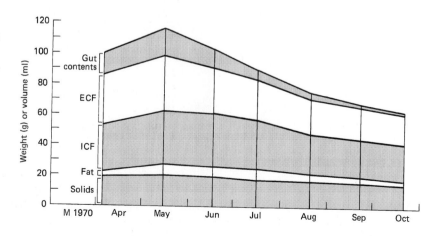

Figure 16–6 Seasonal changes in body composition of chuckwallas. The total body water is composed of the extracellular fluid (ECF; blood plasma, urine, and water in lymph sacs) and the intracellular fluid (ICF; the water inside cells). (From Nagy 1972.)

TABLE 16.2	Seasonal changes in the water balance of a 200-gram chuckwalla		
	Early May	*Late May*	*September*
Food intake (g dry mass/day)	2.60	2.86	0.00
Water content of food (g/g dry mass)	2.53	0.96	—
Water gain (g/day)			
Free water	6.56	2.74	0.0
Metabolic water	0.68	0.68	0.20
Total water gain	7.24	3.41	0.20
Water loss (g/day)	6.41	4.26	0.52
Net water flux (g/day)	+0.81	−0.84	−0.32

Source: Nagy 1972.

most of the day in the rock crevices, emerging only in the late afternoon to bask for an hour or so every second or third day. From late May through autumn the chuckwallas lost water and body mass steadily, and in October they weighed an average of 37 percent *less* than they had in April when they emerged from hibernation.

The water budget of a chuckwalla weighing 200 grams is shown in Table 16.2. In early May the annual plants it is eating contain more than 2.5 grams of free water per gram of dry plant material, and the lizard shows a positive water balance, gaining about 0.8 gram of water per day. By late May, when the plants have withered, their free water content has dropped to just under a gram of water per gram of dry plant matter, and the chuckwalla is losing about 0.8 gram of water per day. The rate of water loss falls to 0.5 gram per day when the lizard stops eating.

Evaporation from the respiratory surfaces and from the skin accounts for about 61 percent of the total water loss of a chuckwalla. When the lizards stop eating, they also become inactive and spend most of the day in rock crevices. The body temperatures of inactive chuckwallas are lower than the temperatures of lizards on the surface. As a result of their low body temperatures, the inactive chuckwallas have lower rates of metabolism: They breathe more slowly and lose less water from their respiratory passages. Also, the humidity is higher in the rock crevices than it is on the surface of the desert, and this reduction in the humidity gradient between the animal and the air further reduces evaporation. Most of the remaining water loss by a chuckwalla occurs in the feces (31 percent) and urine (8 percent). When a lizard stops eating, it also stops producing feces and reduces the amount of

urine it must excrete. The combination of these effects reduces the daily water loss of a chuckwalla by almost 90 percent.

The food plants were always hyperosmolal to the body fluids of the lizards and had high concentrations of potassium. Despite this dietary salt load, the osmotic concentrations of the body fluids of the chuckwallas did not show the variation seen in tortoises because the lizards' nasal salt glands were able to excrete ions at high concentrations. The concentration of potassium ions in the salt gland secretions was nearly 10 times their concentration in urine. The formation of potassium salts of uric acid was the second major route of potassium excretion by the lizards, and was nearly as important in the overall salt balance as nasal secretion. The chuckwallas would not have been able to balance their salt budgets without the two extrarenal routes of ion excretion, but with them they were able to maintain stable osmolal concentrations.

Both the chuckwallas and tortoises illustrate the interaction of behavior and physiology in responding to the stresses of their desert habitats. The tortoises lack salt-secreting glands and store the salt they ingest, tolerating increased body fluid concentrations until a rainstorm allows them to drink water and excrete the excess salt. Some of the tortoises constructed basins that collected rain water that they drank, whereas other tortoises took advantage of natural puddles. The chuckwallas were able to stabilize their body fluid concentrations by using their nasal glands to excrete excess salt, but they did not take advantage of rainfall to replenish their water stores. Instead, they became inactive, reducing their rates of water loss by almost 90 percent, and relying on energy stores and metabolic water production to see them through the period of drought.

Conditions for the chuckwallas were poor at the Black Mountain site during Nagy's study. Only 5 centimeters of rain had fallen during the preceding winter, and that low rainfall probably contributed to the early withering of the annual plants that forced the chuckwallas to cease activity early in the summer. Unpredictable rainfall is a characteristic of deserts, however, and the animals that live in them must be able to adjust to the consequences. Rainfall records from the weather station closest to Black Mountain showed that in 5 of the previous 10 years the annual total rainfall was about 5 centimeters. Thus, the year of the study was not unusually harsh, and conditions are sometimes even worse—only 2 centimeters of rain fell during the winter after the study. However, conditions in the desert are sometimes good. Fifteen centimeters of rain fell in the winter of 1968, and vegetation remained green and lush all through the following summer and fall. Chuckwallas and tortoises live for decades, and their responses to the boom or bust conditions of their harsh environments must be viewed in the context of their long life spans. A temporary relaxation of the limits of homeostasis in bad years is an effective trade-off for survival that allows the animals to exploit the abundant resources of good years.

Desert Amphibians Permeable skins and high rates of water loss are characteristics that would seem to make amphibians unlikely inhabitants of deserts, but certain species are abundant in desert habitats. Most remarkably, these animals succeed in living in the desert *because* of their permeable skins, not despite them. Anurans are the most common desert amphibians, but tiger salamanders are found in the deserts of North America and several species of plethodontid salamanders occupy seasonally dry habitats in California.

The spadefoot toads are the most thoroughly studied desert anurans (Figure 16–7). They inhabit the desert regions of North America, including the edges of the Algodones Sand Dunes in southern California where the average annual precipitation is only 6 centimeters and in some years no rain falls at all. An analysis of the mechanisms that allow an amphibian to exist in a habitat like that must include consideration of both water loss and gain. The skin of desert amphibians is as permeable to water as that of species from moist regions. A desert anuran must control its water loss behaviorally by its choice of sheltered microhabitats free from solar radiation and wind movement. Different species of anurans utilize different microhabitats— a hollow in the bank of a desert wash, the burrow of a ground squirrel or kangaroo rat, or a burrow the anuran excavates for itself. All these places are cooler and wetter than exposed ground.

Desert anurans spend extended periods underground, emerging on the surface only when conditions are favorable. Spadefoot toads construct burrows about 60 centimeters deep, filling the shaft with dirt and leaving a small chamber at the bottom, which they occupy. In southern Arizona the spadefoots construct these burrows in September, at the end of the summer rainy season, and remain in them until the rains resume the following July.

At the end of the rainy season when the spadefoots first bury themselves, the soil is relatively

Figure 16–7 A desert spadefoot toad, *Scaphiopus multiplicatus*. (Photograph by David Dennis.)

moist. The water tension created by the normal osmolal pressure of a spadefoot's body fluids establishes a gradient favoring movement of water from the soil into the toad. In this situation, a buried spadefoot can absorb water from the soil just as the roots of plants do. With a supply of water available, a spadefoot toad can afford to release urine to dispose of its nitrogenous wastes.

As time passes, the soil moisture content decreases and the soil moisture potential becomes more negative, until it equals the water potential of the spadefoot. At this point there is no longer a gradient allowing movement of water into the toad. When its source of new water is cut off, a spadefoot stops excreting urine and instead retains urea in its body, increasing the osmotic pressure of its body fluids. Osmotic concentrations as high as 600 mmole·[kg $H_2O]^{-1}$ have been recorded in spadefoot toads emerging from burial at the end of the dry season. The low water potential produced by the high osmolal pressure of the spadefoot's body fluids may reduce the water gradient between the animal and the air in its underground chamber so that evaporative water loss is reduced. Sufficiently high internal osmotic pressures should create potentials that would allow spadefoot toads to absorb water from even very dry soil.

The ability to continue to draw water from soil enables a spadefoot toad to remain buried for 9 or 10 months without access to liquid water. In this situation its permeable skin is not a handicap to the spadefoot—it is an essential feature of the toad's biology. If the spadefoot had an impermeable skin, or if it formed an impermeable cocoon as some other amphibians do, water would not be able to move from the soil into the animal. Instead, the spadefoot would have to depend on the water contained in its body when it buried. Under those circumstances spadefoot toads would probably not be able to invade the desert because their initial water content would not see them through a 9-month dry season.

A different pattern of adaptation to arid conditions is seen in a few tree frogs. The African rhacophorid *Chiromantis xerampelina* and the South American hylid *Phyllomedusa sauvagei* lose water through the skin at a rate only one-tenth that of most frogs. *Phyllomedusa* has been shown to achieve this low rate of evaporative water loss by using its legs to spread the lipid-containing secretions of dermal glands over its body surface in a complex sequence of wiping movements. These two frogs are unusual also because they excrete nitrogenous wastes as salts of uric acid rather than as urea. This uricotelism provides still more water conservation.

Aquatic Ectotherms in the Desert

An aquatic habitat in a desert sounds like a contradiction, but in fact several different kinds of aquatic habitats are found in deserts and some of them have distinctive faunas of fishes or amphibians. Temporary pools that are formed by heavy rains and last for a only few weeks are the breeding sites for most species of desert amphibians. The ephemeral nature of these habitats puts a premium on rapid development. Spadefoot toads, for example, can grow from an egg to metamorphosis in 2 or 3 weeks. Fishes require permanent water, and desert fishes are found in rivers, springs, and desert lakes.

Aquatic habitats in the desert have the same temperature extremes as terrestrial habitats, but there are some differences that are important to the animals living in them. Water has a much higher heat capacity than does air, so water temperature changes more slowly than does air temperature. Temperature changes from day to night are usually smaller in a pool of water than on land, but pools of water in the desert can reach lethally hot temperatures by the end of summer. Water conducts heat faster than does air, and the high heat capacity and conductance of water ensure that the body temperatures of small aquatic organisms are always close to water temperature. Aquatic organisms can regulate their body temperature by moving between areas of different water temperature.

Tadpoles   The ability of aquatic animals to select the most favorable temperatures available is shown by observations of tadpoles of the foothill yellow-legged frog, *Rana boylii* (Brattstrom 1962). The tadpoles were in a small cove with a maximum depth of about 40 cm and a shallow area that was only 10 cm deep, and they moved about in this area as temperature changed (Figure 16–8). At night (2100 hours) all the tadpoles were in the deepest part of the cove where the temperature was warmest, and they remained there until morning. During the morning the sun warmed the water in the pool, and the shallow area warmed fastest. Between 0900 and 1000 hours the tadpoles moved from the deep water into the shallow area, and by 1100 hours all of the tadpoles were in the shallows. By midday the shallow water had became too warm, and all of the tadpoles moved back into the deep part of the pool, which remained cool. The shallow parts of the cove

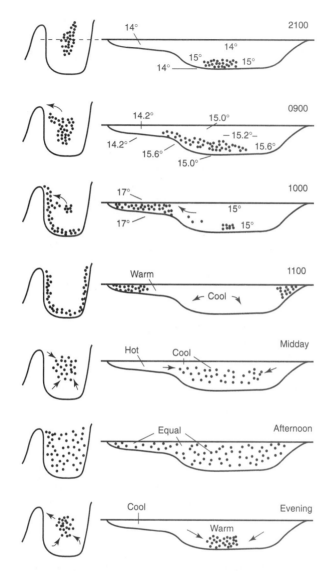

Figure 16–8 Temperature selection by tadpoles. Tadpoles of *Rana boylii* change positions in a pool of water in response to temperature changes during the day. The left column shows the view looking down on the pool, and the right column shows a cross-section of the pool at the position indicated by the dashed line in the top drawing. (Modified from Brattstrom 1962.)

cooled rapidly in the later afternoon. Water temperature was essentially the same everywhere, and the tadpoles were distributed all over the cove. As temperature continued to fall, the tadpoles moved back into the deepest part of the pool for the night.

Permanent aquatic habitats in the desert may have populations of fishes, but relatively few species can tolerate the high temperatures and high salinities that are characteristic of many of these bodies of water. Pupfish (Cyprinodontidae), minnows (Cyprinidae), and cichlids (Cichlidae) are the groups most often found in deserts. Desert lakes and springs rarely contain more than five species of fishes, and many habitats are occupied by a single species.

The stresses that desert fishes encounter depend on the habitat in which they occur. Springs, such as those at Ash Meadows in Death Valley, may be relatively large or very small. Big Spring is 15 m in diameter and 9 m deep, whereas Mexican Spring is less than 2 m in diameter and only 2 to 5 cm deep. The water in a spring usually has the same temperature and salinity year-round, but some springs are 30°C or above and others are near 20°C.

Ponds and lakes often show more seasonal variation in temperature and salinity. Some of these bodies of water are the remnants of enormous lakes that filled the desert valleys during the Pleistocene. Pyramid Lake in Nevada, for example, is a remnant of Lake Lahonton, which once covered more than 20,000 km² in California and Nevada. Former shorelines of Lake Lahonton are marked by three terraces that are now 34, 100, and 163 meters above the present lake level. Other remnants of Lake Lahonton include Honey Lake in California and Walker Lake and the Carson and Humboldt Sinks in Nevada. Similar Pleistocene lake terraces can be found in the Sahara Desert and in the deserts of the Middle East. As the Pleistocene lakes shrank, once widespread populations of fishes were isolated in the remnant bodies of water. (The Salton Sea of California has a different origin from the other lakes of the Southwest. It lies in the basin of Pleistocene Lake LaConte, but the Salton Sea was formed in 1905 when the Colorado River broke through the banks of an irrigation system and formed a lake 25 meters deep and more than 1300 km² in area.)

High temperatures, salinity, and variation in oxygen concentration make desert lakes difficult environments for fishes (Deacon and Minckley 1974). Pupfish (species of *Cyprinodon*) are widespread in these lakes and cope well with both heat and salinity. At Quitobaquito Springs in Organ Pipe National Monument, for example, desert pupfishes (*Cyprinodon macularis*) are found in shallow water at temperatures of 40 to 41°C (which is only 2 or 3°C below the lethal temperature for the fish) rather than in water of 30°C that is a few meters away. Other species of *Cyprinodon* have been found voluntarily inhabiting water with temperatures of 43 to 44°C.

Desert lakes are often characterized by high salinities as well as by high temperatures. Juvenile *Cyprinodon* can tolerate salt concentrations at least up to 90 g of dissolved salt/liter of water, which is approximately three times the concentration of seawater. Young pupfishes and large adults are slightly less tolerant of salinity than are juveniles, and eggs will not develop in salinities greater than 70 g/liter. A mosaic of salinities is often available to pupfishes because the density of water increases as the salinity increases and water masses with different salinities tend not to mix. Thus, a fish can select areas of different salinity within a habitat just as it can select areas with different temperatures.

Streams are a third habitat for desert fishes. Stream flow varies through the year, and in dry seasons surface water in intermittent streams is reduced to isolated pools separated by dry areas of the stream bed. In the rainy season, however, the stream may flow continuously and even flood. Populations of fishes in desert streams typically wax and wane in response to changes in water flow. Salt Creek in Death Valley is inhabited by Devil's Hole pupfishes (*Cyprinodon salinus*). The population increases 100-fold as water from winter rains in the Mojave Desert flows down the stream in the winter and spring, and then crashes in summer and autumn as the stream dries. Some desert fishes, such as pupfishes and the longfin dace (*Agosia chrysogaster*), penetrate far into temporary aquatic habitats during periods of heavy rain and runoff. When desert streams are close to drying up, evaporation may consume the entire flow of water during the day leaving only a damp streambed. Most species of fishes die under these conditions, but longfin daces survive beneath water-saturated mats of algae. Stream flow resumes at night when the temperature falls, and the daces emerge from beneath the algae, swimming about and feeding in a few millimeters of water. The fishes can survive in these conditions for several weeks, and if rain refills the stream they are able to return to areas of permanent water.

■ Cold: Ectotherms in Subzero Conditions

Temperatures drop below freezing in the habitats of many vertebrates on a seasonal basis, and some animals at high altitudes may experience freezing temperatures on a daily basis for a substantial part of the year. Endotherms respond to cold by increasing metabolic heat production and insulation, but ectotherms do not have those options. Instead, ectotherms show one of two responses—they avoid freezing by supercooling or synthesizing antifreeze compounds, or they tolerate freezing and thawing by using mechanisms that prevent damage to cells and tissues.

Cold Fishes

The temperature at which water freezes is affected by its osmotic concentration: Pure water freezes at 0°C, and increasing the osmotic concentration lowers the freezing point. Body fluid concentrations of marine fishes are 300 to 400 mmole·[kg H_2O]$^{-1}$, whereas seawater has a concentration near 1000 mmole·[kg H_2O]$^{-1}$. The osmotic concentrations of the body fluids of marine fishes correspond to freezing points of −0.6 to 0.8°C, and the freezing point of seawater is −1.86°C. The temperature of Arctic and Antarctic seas falls to −1.8°C in winter, yet the fishes swim in this water without freezing.

One of the early studies of freezing avoidance of fishes was conducted by P. F. Scholander and his colleagues in Hebron Fjord in Labrador (Scholander et al. 1957). In summer the temperature of the surface water at Hebron Fjord is above freezing, but the water at the bottom of the fjord is −1.73°C (Figure 16–9). In winter the temperature of the surface water falls to −1.73°C, like the bottom temperature. Several species of fishes live in the fjord, and some are bottom dwellers, whereas others live near the surface. These two zones present different problems to the fishes: The temperature near the bottom of the fjord is always below freezing, but ice is not present because ice is lighter than water and remains at the surface. Surface-dwelling fishes live in water temperatures that rise well above freezing in the summer and drop below freezing in winter, and they are also in the presence of ice.

The body fluids of bottom-dwelling fish in Hebron Fjord have freezing points of −0.8°C year round. Because the body temperatures of these fishes are −1.73°C, the fishes are supercooled. That is, the water in their bodies is in the liquid state despite the fact that it is below its freezing point. When water freezes, the water molecules become oriented in a crystal lattice. The process of crystallization is accelerated by nucleating agents that hold water molecules in the proper spatial orientation for freezing, and in the absence of nucleating agents pure water can remain liquid at −20°C. In the laboratory the fishes from the bottom of Hebron Fjord can be supercooled to −1.73°C without freezing, but if they are touched with a piece of ice, which serves as a nucleating agent, they freeze immediately. At the bottom of the fjord there is no

Figure 16–9 Water temperatures and distribution of fishes in Hebron Sound in summer and winter. The freezing point of the blood plasma of the fishes is indicated by the position of the symbol on the horizontal axis. Shallow-water fishes show a decrease of 0.7°C in the freezing point of their blood in winter, whereas deep-water fishes have the same freezing point all year. (From Scholander et al. 1957, *Journal of Cellular and Comparative Physiology* 79:39–62.)

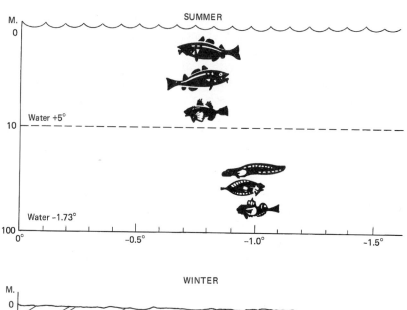

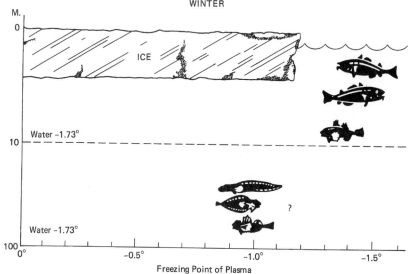

ice, and the bottom-dwelling fishes exist year round in a supercooled state.

What about the fishes in the surface waters? They do encounter ice in winter when the water temperature is below the osmotically determined freezing point of their body fluids, and supercooling would not be effective in that situation. Instead, the surface-dwelling fishes synthesize antifreeze substances in winter that lower the freezing point of their body fluids to approximately the freezing point of the seawater in which they swim.

Antifreeze compounds are widely developed among vertebrates (and also among invertebrates and plants). Marine fishes have two categories of organic molecules that protect against freezing: glycoproteins with molecular weights of 2,600 to 33,000, and polypeptides and small proteins, with molecular weights of 3,300 to 13,000 (Hew et al. 1986, Davies et

al. 1988). These compounds are extremely effective in preventing freezing. For example, the blood plasma of the Antarctic fish *Trematomus borchgrevinki* contains a glycoprotein that is several hundred times more effective than salt (sodium chloride) in lowering the freezing point. Apparently, the glycoprotein is absorbed on the surface of ice crystals and hinders their growth by preventing water molecules from assuming the proper orientation to join the ice crystal lattice.

Some terrestrial ectotherms rely on supercooling. Mountain-dwelling lizards such as Yarrow's spiny lizard (*Sceloporus jarrovi*), which lives at altitudes up to 3000 meters in western North America, are exposed to temperatures below freezing on cold nights, but sunny days permit thermoregulation and activity. These animals have osmolal concentrations of 300 mmole·[kg H_2O]$^{-1}$, which correspond to freezing points of −0.6°C, but they withstand substantially lower temperatures before they freeze. For example, spiny lizards supercooled to an average temperature of −5.5°C before they froze. At −3°C the lizards had not frozen after 30 hours. The lizards spent the nights in rock crevices that were 5 to 6°C warmer than the air temperature, and the combination of this protection and their ability to supercool was usually sufficient to allow the lizards to survive. However, a few individuals at the highest altitudes were found frozen in their rock crevices during most winters.

Frozen Frogs

Terrestrial amphibians that spend the winter in hibernation show at least two categories of responses to low temperatures. One group, which includes salamanders, toads, and aquatic frogs, buries deeply in the soil or hibernates in the mud at the bottom of ponds. These animals apparently are not exposed to temperatures below the freezing point of their body fluids, and as far as we know, they have no antifreeze substances and no capacity to tolerate freezing. However, other amphibians apparently hibernate close to the soil surface, and these animals are exposed to temperatures below their freezing points. Unlike fishes and lizards, these amphibians freeze at low temperatures, but they are not killed by freezing (Figure 16–10). These species can remain frozen at −3°C for several weeks, and they tolerate repeated bouts of freezing and thawing without damage. However, temperatures below −10°C are lethal.

Tolerance of freezing refers to the formation of ice crystals in the extracellular body fluids; freezing of the fluids inside the cells is apparently lethal. Thus, freeze tolerance involves mechanisms that control the distribution of ice, water, and solutes in the bodies of animals (Storey 1986). The ice content of frozen frogs is usually in the range 34 to 48 percent. Freezing of more than 65 percent of the body water appears to cause irreversible damage, probably because too much water has been removed from the cells.

Freeze-tolerant frogs accumulate low-molecular-weight substances in the cells that prevent intracellular ice formation. Wood frogs, spring peepers, and chorus frogs use glucose as a cryoprotectant, whereas gray tree frogs use glycerol. Glycogen in the liver appears to be the source of the glucose and glycerol. The accumulation of these substances is apparently stimulated by freezing, and is initiated within minutes of the formation of ice crystals. This mechanism of triggering the synthesis of cryoprotectant substances has not been observed for any other vertebrates or for insects.

Frozen frogs are, of course, motionless. Breathing stops, the heartbeat is exceedingly slow and irregular or may cease entirely, and blood does not circulate through frozen tissues. Nonetheless, the cells are not frozen and they have a low level of metabolic activity that is maintained by anaerobic metabolism. The glycogen content of frozen muscle and kidney cells decreases, and concentrations of lactic acid and alanine (two end products of anaerobic metabolism) increase.

The ecological significance of freeze tolerance in some species of amphibians is unclear. The four species of frogs so far identified as being freeze tolerant all breed relatively early in the spring, and shallow hibernation may be associated with early emergence in the spring. Being among the first individuals to arrive at the breeding pond may increase the

(a)

(b)

Figure 16–10   Wood frog (*Rana sylvatica*). (a) At normal temperature; (b) frozen. (Photographs courtesy of J. and K. Storey, Carleton University, Ottawa, Ontario.)

chances for a male of obtaining a mate, and it gives larvae the longest possible time for development and metamorphosis, but it also entails risks. Frequently, frogs and salamanders move across snow banks to reach the breeding ponds, and they enter ponds that are still partly covered with ice. A cold snap can lead to the entire surface of the pond freezing again, trapping some animals under the ice and others in shallow retreats under logs and rocks around the pond. Freeze tolerance may be important to these animals even after their winter hibernation is over.

■ The Role of Ectothermal Tetrapods in Terrestrial Ecosystems

Life as an animal is costly. In thermodynamic terms, an animal lives by breaking chemical bonds that were formed by a plant (if the animal is an herbivore) or by another animal (if it's a carnivore) and using the energy from those bonds to sustain its own activities. Vertebrates are particularly expensive animals because in general vertebrates are larger and more mobile than invertebrates. Big animals require more energy (i.e., food) than small ones, and active animals use more energy than sedentary ones.

In addition to body size and activity, an animal's method of temperature regulation (ectothermy, endothermy, or a combination of the two mechanisms) is a key factor in determining how much energy it uses, and therefore how much food it requires. Because ectotherms rely on external sources of energy to raise their body temperatures to the level needed for activity, ectotherms use substantially less energy than do endotherms. The metabolic rates (i.e., rates at which energy is sued) of terrestrial ectotherms are only 10 to 14 percent of the metabolic rates of birds and mammals of the same body size. The lower energy requirements of ectotherms mean that they need less food than would an endotherm of the same body size.

Body size is another major difference between ectotherms and endotherms that is directly related to their mode of temperature regulation and affects their roles in terrestrial ecosystems. Ectotherms are smaller than endotherms, partly because the energetic cost of endothermy is very high at small body sizes. As body mass decreases the mass specific cost of living (energy per gram) for an endotherm increases rapidly, becoming nearly infinite at very small body sizes (Figure 16–11). This is a finite world, and infinite energy requirements are just not

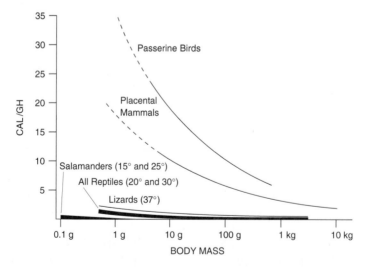

Figure 16–11 Resting metabolic rate as a function of body size for terrestrial vertebrates. (This semilogarithmic presentation emphasizes the dramatic increase in mass-specific metabolic rate at small body sizes—compare it with the log–log graph in Figure 4–13.) Metabolic rates for salamanders are shown at 15 and 25°C as the lower and upper limits of the darkened area, and data for all reptiles combined are shown at 20 and 39°C. The curve for anurans falls within the all-reptiles area, and the relationship for nonpasserine birds is similar to that for placental mammals. Dotted portions of the lines for birds and mammals show hypothetical extensions into body sizes below the minimum for adults of most species of birds and mammals. (From F. H. Pough 1980, *American Naturalist* 115:92–112. Reprinted by permission of the University of Chicago Press. © 1980 by The University of Chicago.)

feasible. Thus, energy requirements, among other factors, apparently set a lower limit to the body size that is possible for an endotherm. The mass specific energy requirements of ectotherms also increase at small body sizes, but because the energy requirements of ectotherms are about one-tenth those of endotherms of the same body size, an ectotherm can be about an order of magnitude smaller than an endotherm. A mouse-size mammal weighs about 20 grams, and few adult birds and mammals have body masses less than 10 grams. The very smallest species of birds and mammals weigh about 3 grams, but many ectotherms are only one-tenth that size (0.3 gram). Amphibians are especially small—20 percent of the species of salamanders and 17 percent of the species of anurans have adult body masses less than 1 gram, and 65 percent of salamanders and 50 percent of anurans are smaller than 5 grams. Squamates are generally larger than amphibians, but 8 percent of the species of lizards and 2 percent of snakes weigh less than 1 gram. The largest amphibians and squamates weigh substantially less than 100 kilograms, whereas more than 10 percent of the species of extant mammals weigh 100 kilograms or more (Figure 16–12).

Body shape is another aspect of vertebrate body form in which ectothermy allows more flexibility than does endothermy. An animal exchanges heat with the environment through its body surface, and the surface area of the body in relation to the mass of the body (the surface/mass ratio) is one factor that determines how rapidly heat will be gained or lost. Small animals have higher surface/mass ratios than large ones, and that is why endothermy becomes increasingly expensive at progressively smaller body sizes. Metabolic rates of small endotherms must be high enough to balance the high rates of heat loss across their large body surface areas.

Similarly, body shapes that increase surface/mass ratios have an energy cost that makes them disadvantageous for endotherms. There are no elongate endotherms, whereas elongate body forms are widespread among fishes (true eels, moray eels, pipefishes, barracudas, and many more), amphibians (all caecilians and most salamanders, especially the limbless aquatic forms), and reptiles (many lizards and all snakes). Dorsoventral or lateral flattening is another shape that increases surface/mass ratio. There are no flat endotherms, but flat fishes are common (dorsoventral flattening—skates, rays, flounders; laterally flattening—many coral reef and freshwater fishes) and some reptiles are flat (dorsoventral flattening—aquatic turtles, especially soft-shelled turtles,

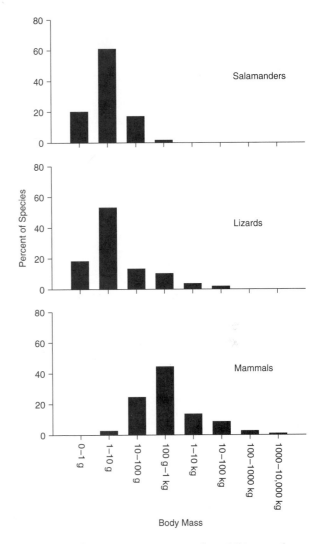

Figure 16–12   Adult body masses of amphibians and reptiles. (Based on data in Pough 1983; and R. M. May 1988, *Science* 241:1441–1449.)

horned lizards; laterally flattening—many arboreal lizards, especially chameleons). Small body sizes and specialized body forms allow ectotherms to fill ecological niches that are not available to endotherms.

The amount of energy required by ectotherms and endotherms is not the only important difference between them; equally significant is what they do with that energy once they have it. Endotherms expend more than 90 percent of the energy they take in to produce heat to maintain their high body temperatures. Less than 10 percent, often as little as 1 percent, of the energy a bird or mammal assimilates is available for net conversion (that is, increasing the species' biomass by growth of an individual or production of young). Ectotherms do not rely on

TABLE 16.3	Efficiency of biomass conversion by ectotherms and endotherms. These are net conversion efficiencies calculated as (energy converted/energy assimulated) X100.

Ectotherms		Endotherms	
Species	Efficiency	Species	Efficiency
Red-backed salamander *Plethodon cinereus*	48	Kangaroo rat *Dipodomys merriami*	0.8
Mountain salamander *Desmognathus ochrophaeus*	76–98	Field mouse *Peromyscus polionotus*	1.8
Panamanian anole *Anolis limifrons*	23–28	Meadow vole *Microtus pennsylvanicus*	3.0
Side-blotched lizard *Uta stansburiana*	18–25	Red squirrel *Tamiasciurius hudsonicus*	1.3
Hognose snake *Heterodon contortrix*	81	Least weasel *Mustela rixosa*	2.3
Python *Python curtus*	6–33	Savanna sparrow *Passericulus sandwichensis*	1.1
Adder *Vipera berus*	49	Marsh wren *Telmatodytes palustris*	0.5
Average of 12 species	50	Average of 19 species	1.4

Source: Pough 1980.

metabolic heat. The solar energy they use to warm their bodies is free in the sense that it is not drawn from their food. Thus, most of the energy they ingest is converted into the biomass of their species. Values of net conversion for amphibians and reptiles are between 30 and 90 percent (Table 16.3).

As a result of that difference in how energy is used, a given amount of chemical energy invested in an ectotherm produces a much larger biomass return than it would have from an endotherm. A study of salamanders in the Hubbard Brook Experimental Forest in New Hampshire showed that, although their energy consumption was only 20 percent that of the birds or small mammals in the watershed, their conversion efficiency was so great that the annual increment of salamander biomass was equal to that of birds or small mammals. Similar comparisons can be made among lizards and rodents in deserts. (For details, see Pough 1980, 1983.)

Small amphibians and squamates occupy key positions in terms of energy flow through an ecosystem: Because these animals are so small, they can capture tiny insects and arachnids that are too small to be eaten by birds and mammals. Because they are ectotherms, they are efficient at converting the energy in the food they eat into their own body tissues. As a result, the small ectothermal vertebrates in terrestrial ecosystems can be viewed as repackaging energy into a form that avian and mammalian predators can exploit. In other words, when a shrew or a bird searches for a meal in the Hubbard Brook Forest, they most abundant vertebrate prey it will find is salamanders. In this context, frogs, salamanders, lizards, and snakes occupy a position in terrestrial ecosystems that is important both quantitatively (in the sense that they constitute a substantial energy resource) and qualitatively (in that ectotherms exploit food resources that are not available to endotherms).

In a very real sense small ectotherms can be thought of as living in a different world from that of endotherms. As we saw in the case of the three species of *Ameiva* lizards in Costa Rica (Chapter 15), interactions with the physical world may be more important in shaping the ecology and behavior of small ectotherms than are biological interactions such as competition. In some cases these small vertebrates may have their primary predatory and competitive interactions with insects and arachnids rather than with other vertebrates. For example, orb-web spiders and *Anolis* lizards on some Caribbean islands are linked by both predation (adult lizards eat spiders and spiders may eat hatchling lizards) and competition (lizards and spiders eat many of the same kinds of insects). The competitive relationship between these distantly related animals was demonstrated by experiments: when lizards were removed from experimental plots the abundance of insect prey increased and the spiders consumed more prey and survived longer than in control plots with lizards present (Schoener and Spiller 1987).

Thus, ectothermy and endothermy represent fundamentally different approaches to the life of a terrestrial vertebrate. An appreciation of ectotherms and endotherms as animals requires understanding the functional consequences of the differences between them. Ectothermy is an ancestral character of vertebrates, but it is a very effective way of life in modern ecosystems. The following section extends this evolutionary perspective by considering examples of ectotherms that live in particularly demanding habitats and the ancestral and derived characteristics that allow them to do so.

■ Summary

Ectotherms do not use chemical energy from the food they eat to maintain high body temperatures. The results of that ancestral vertebrate characteristic are far reaching for extant ectothermal vertebrates, and ectotherms and endotherms represent quite different approaches to vertebrate life.

Because of their low energy requirements, ectotherms can colonize habitats in which energy is in short supply. Ectotherms are able to extend some of their limits of homeostasis to tolerate high or low body temperatures, and high or low body-water contents when doing so allows them to survive in difficult conditions.

When food is available, ectotherms are efficient at converting the energy it contains into their own body tissues for growth or reproduction. Net conversion efficiencies of ectotherms average 50 percent of the energy assimilated compared with an average of 1.4 percent for endotherms.

Ectotherms can be smaller than endotherms because their mass-specific energy requirements are low, and many ectotherms weigh less than a gram, whereas most endotherms weigh more than 10 grams. As a result of this difference in body size, many small ectotherms, such as salamanders, frogs, and lizards, eat prey that is too small to be consumed by endotherms. The efficiency of energy conversion by ectotherms and their small body sizes lead to a distinctive role in modern ecosystems, one that is in many respects quite different from that of terrestrial ectotherms. Understanding these differences is an important part of understanding the organismal biology of terrestrial ectothermal vertebrates.

■ References

Brattstrom, B. H. 1962. Thermal control of aggregation behavior in tadpoles. *Herpetologica* 18:38–46.

Davies, P. L., C. L. Hew, and G. L. Fletcher. 1988. Fish antifreeze proteins: physiology and evolutionary biology. *Canadian Journal of Zoology* 66:2611–2617.

Deacon, J. E., and W. L. Minckley. 1974. Desert fishes. Pages 385–488 in *Desert Biology*, volume 2, edited by G. W. Brown, Jr. Academic, New York, NY.

Hew, C. L., G. K. Scott, and P. L. Davies. 1986. Molecular biology of antifreeze. Pages 117–123 in *Living in the Cold: Physiological and Biochemical Adaptation*, edited by H. C. Heller, X. J. Musacchia, and L. C. H. Wang. Elsevier, New York, NY.

Nagy, K. A. 1972. Water and electrolyte budgets of a free-living desert lizard, *Sauromalus obsesus. Journal of Comparative Physiology* 79:39–62.

Nagy, K. A. 1973. Behavior, diet and reproduction in a desert lizard, *Sauromalus obsesus. Copeia* 1973:93–102.

Nagy, K. A. 1983. The doubly labeled water (3HH18O) method: a guide to its use. *UCLA Publication 12-1417.* University of California, Los Angeles, CA.

Nagy, K. A., and P. A. Medica. 1986. Physiological ecology of desert tortoises in southern Nevada. *Herpetologica* 42:73–92.

Pough, F. H. 1980. The advantages of ectothermy for tetrapods. *The American Naturalist* 115:92–112.

Pough, F. H. 1983. Amphibians and reptiles as low-energy systems. Pages 141–188 in *Behavioral Energetics: Vertebrate Costs of Survival*, edited by W. P. Aspey and S. I. Lustick. Ohio State University Press, Columbus, OH.

Schoener, T. W., and D. A. Spiller. 1987. Effect of lizards on spider populations: manipulative reconstruction of a natural experiment. *Science* 236:949–952.

Scholander, P. F., L. Van Dam, J. W. Kanwisher, H. T. Hammel, and M. S. Gordon. 1957. Supercooling and osmoregulation in Arctic fish. *Journal of Cellular and Comparative Physiology* 49:5–24.

Storey, K. B. 1986. Freeze tolerance in vertebrates: biochemical adaptation of terrestrially hibernating frogs. Pages 131–138 in *Living in the Cold: Physiological and Biochemical Adaptations*, edited by H. C. Heller, X. J. Musacchia, and L. C. H. Wang. Elsevier, New York, NY.

PART 4 Terrestrial Endotherms: Birds and Mammals

Birds and mammals are the vertebrates with which people are most familiar, partly because many species are large and diurnal and partly because birds and mammals have colonized nearly every terrestrial habitat on Earth. The success of birds and mammals in many habitats is related to their endothermy, which allows them to be active at night and in cold weather. These are conditions in which terrestrial ectotherms find it difficult or impossible to thermoregulate and, consequently, they are inactive.

Flight dominates the biology of birds: Most of the morphological features of birds are directly or indirectly related to the requirements of flight, and many of the distinctive aspects of their behavior and ecology stem from the mobility that flight provides. Migration, for example, is a particularly avian characteristic because, of all the terrestrial vertebrates, birds are best able to move long distances.

No one feature of mammals characterizes the group and dominates its biology as flight does for birds, but sociality comes close. Many features of the biology of mammals are related to their interactions with other individuals of their species, ranging from the period of dependence of young on their mother to lifelong alliances between individuals that affect their social status and reproductive success in a group.

Humans differ from other vertebrates in the extent to which they have come to dominate all of the habitats of Earth, and in their effects, direct and indirect, on other vertebrates. In this portion of the book we explore the evolution of birds and mammals, the adaptive zones opened to them by their distinctive characteristics, and the origin and radiation of humans as an example of vertebrate evolution.

CHAPTER
17

Characteristics of Birds: Specializations for Flight

The linear progression of a book does not lend itself to following the simultaneous evolution of several different phylogenetic lineages. At this point we must turn our attention back to the conditions in the middle of the Mesozoic that were described in Chapter 14 and consider the diversification of another group of diapsids, the birds, from their origin in or before the Jurassic. *Archaeopteryx* is the oldest fossil of a bird that is known, but by the time it lived in the Jurassic it was probably an archaic relic that existed contemporaneously with more derived birds. The debate about the role of flight in the origin of birds was described in Chapter 13. Despite our uncertainty about the route by which birds took to the air, the demands of flight have clearly shaped many aspects of the morphology of birds. In this chapter we consider the relationships between the body forms of birds and the physical and biological requirements of flight.

■ Birds as Flying Machines

In some respects birds are variable: Beaks and feet are specialized for different modes of feeding and locomotion, the morphology of the intestinal tract is related to dietary habits, and wing shape reflects flight characteristics. Despite that variation, however, the morphology of birds is more uniform than that of mammals, and much of this uniformity is a result of the specialization of birds for flight.

Consider body size as an example: Flight imposes a maximum body size on birds. The muscle power required to take off increases by a factor of 2.25 for each doubling of body mass. That is, if species B weighs twice as much as species A, it will require 2.25 times as much power to fly at its minimum speed. If the proportion of the total body mass allocated to flight muscles is constant, the muscles of a large bird must work harder than the muscles of

a small bird. In fact, the situation is still more complicated because the power output is a function of both muscular force and wing beat frequency. Large birds have lower wing beat frequencies than small birds for mechanical and aerodynamic reasons. As a result, if species B weighs twice as much as species A, it will develop only 1.59 times as much power from its flight muscles, although it needs 2.25 times as much power to fly. Therefore, large birds require longer takeoff runs than small birds, and ultimately a body mass is reached at which any further increase in size would move a bird into a realm in which its flight muscles were not able to provide enough power to take off.

Calculations of this maximum size from aerodynamic principles suggest that it lies near 12 kilograms, and that estimate corresponds reasonably well with the observed body masses of birds. The mute swan weighs about 12 kilograms, and the trumpeter swan is about 17 kilograms. The largest flying bird known was a giant condor that had a wingspan estimated to be 7 meters and a possible body mass of 20 kilograms. Large pterosaurs also had body masses estimated to be in the region of 20 kilograms.

Flightless birds are spared the mechanical constraints associated with producing power for flight, but they still do not approach the body sizes of mammals. The largest extant bird is the flightless ostrich, which weighs about 150 kilograms, and the largest bird known, one of the extinct elephantbirds, weighed an estimated 450 kilograms. In contrast, the largest mammal, the blue whale, weighs more than 135,000 kilograms. If one restricts the comparison to quadrupedal, terrestrial mammals, the elephant weighs some 5000 kilograms.

The structural uniformity of birds is seen even more clearly if their body shapes are compared with those of other diapsids such as the dinosaurs. There are no quadrupedal birds, for example, nor any with horns or bony armor. Even those species of birds that have become secondarily flightless retain many ancestral characters and the constraints that are associated with them. In this chapter we consider the body form and function of birds, especially in relation to the requirements of flight.

■ Feathers and Flight

Feathers develop from pits or follicles in the skin, generally arranged in tracts or **pterylae**, which are separated by patches of unfeathered skin, the **apteria** (Figure 17–1). Some species—such as ratites, penguins, and mousebirds—lack pterylae, and the feathers are uniformly distributed over the skin.

For all their structural complexity, feathers are remarkably simple and uniform in chemical com-position. More than 90 percent of a feather consists of beta keratin, a protein related to the keratin of scales and to the hair and horn of mammals. About 1 percent of a feather consists of lipids, about 8 percent is water, and the remaining fraction consists of small amounts of other proteins and pigments, such as melanin. The colors of feathers are produced by structural characters and pigments (see the color insert).

Basic Types of Feathers

Ornithologists usually distinguish five types of feathers: (1) contour feathers, including typical body feathers and the flight feathers (remiges and rectrices); (2) semiplumes; (3) down feathers of several sorts; (4) bristles; and (5) filoplumes. **Contour feathers** (Figure 17–2) include a short, tubular base, the **calamus**, which remains firmly implanted within the follicle until molt occurs. Distal to the calamus is a long, tapered **rachis**, which bears closely spaced side branches called **barbs**, the lowermost of which externally mark the division between calamus and rachis. The barbs on either side of the rachis constitute a surface called a **vane.** Vanes may be symmetrical or asymmetrical. The proximal portions of the vanes of a feather have a downy or plumulaceous texture, being soft, loose, and fluffy. This gives the plumage of a bird its excellent properties of thermal insulation. The more distal portions of the vanes have a pennaceous or sheetlike texture—firm, compact, and closely knit. This exposed part provides an airfoil, protects the downy undercoat, sheds water, reflects or absorbs solar radiation, and may have a role in visual or auditory communication. The barbules are structures that maintain the pennaceous character of the feather vanes. They are arranged in such a way that any physical disruption to the vane is easily corrected by the bird's preen-

Figure 17–1 Feather tracts of a typical songbird.

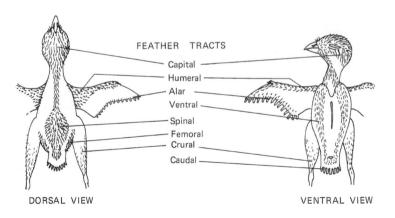

FEATHER TRACTS

Capital
Humeral
Alar
Ventral
Spinal
Femoral
Crural
Caudal

DORSAL VIEW   VENTRAL VIEW

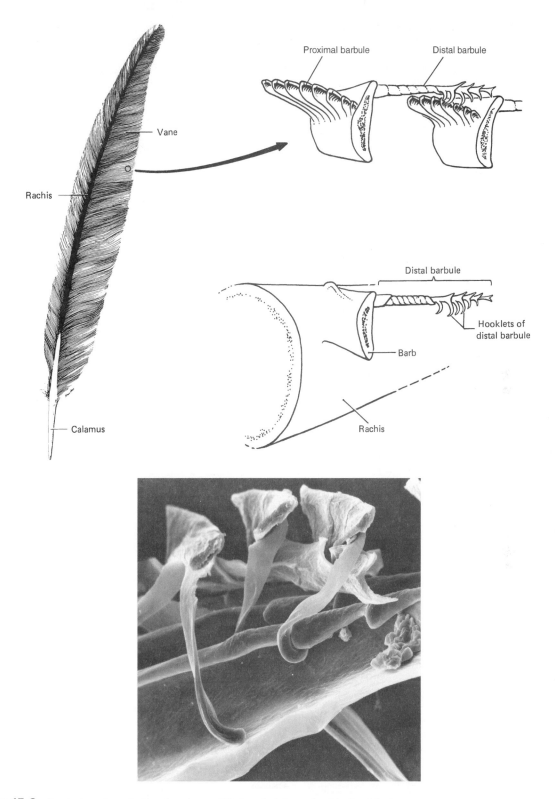

Figure 17–2 Typical contour feather (a wing quill) showing its main structural features. The inset and electron micrograph show details of the interlocking mechanism of the proximal and distal barbules. (From A. M. Lucas and P. R. Stettenheim, 1972, *Avian Anatomy and Integument*, Agriculture Handbook 362, United States Department of Agriculture, Washington, DC; and H. E. Evans, 1982, in *Diseases of Cage and Aviary Birds*, 2d edition, edited by M. L. Petrak, Lea & Febiger, Philadelphia, PA. Photograph by Alan Pooley.)

Figure 17–3 A red-tail hawk, showing the extreme development of slotting in the outer primaries. (Photograph © Fred Tilly/Leonard Rue Enterprises, Photo Researchers, Inc.)

ing behavior, in which the bird realigns the barbules by drawing its slightly separated bill over them.

The **remiges** (wing feathers, singular **remex**) and **rectrices** (tail feathers, singular **rectrix**) are large, stiff, mostly pennaceous contour feathers that are modified for flight. For example, the distal portions of the outer primaries of many species of birds are abruptly tapered or notched, so that when the wings are spread the tips of these primaries are separated by conspicuous gaps or slots (Figure 17–3). This condition reduces the drag on the wing and, in association with the marked asymmetry of the outer and inner vanes, allows the feather tips to twist as the wings are flapped and to act somewhat as individual propeller blades (see Figure 17–6).

Semiplumes are feathers intermediate in structure between contour feathers and down feathers. They combine a large rachis with entirely plumulaceous vanes and can be distinguished from down feathers by the fact that the rachis is longer than the longest barb (Figure 17–4). Semiplumes are mostly hidden beneath the contour feathers. They provide thermal insulation and help to fill out the contour of a bird's body.

Down feathers of various types are entirely plumulaceous feathers in which the rachis is shorter than the longest barb or entirely absent. Down feathers provide insulation for adult birds of all species. In addition, natal down, which is structurally simpler than adult down, provides an insulating covering on many birds at hatching or shortly thereafter. Natal downs usually precede the development of the first contour feathers, and down feathers are associated with apteria (the spaces between the contour feather tracts). Definitive downs are those that develop with the full body plumage. Uropygial gland downs are associated with the large sebaceous gland found at the base of the tail in most birds. The papilla of the gland usually bears a tuft of modified, brushlike down feathers that aid in transferring the

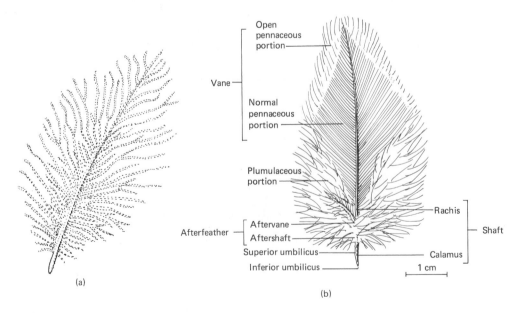

Figure 17–4 Comparison of a semiplume (a) and body contour feather (b).

oily secretion from the gland to the bill to provide waterproof dressing to the plumage.

Powder down feathers, which are difficult to classify by structural type, produce an extremely fine white powder composed of granules of keratin. The powder, which is shed into the general plumage, is nonwettable and is therefore assumed to provide another kind of waterproof dressing for the contour feathers. All birds have powder down, but it is best developed in herons.

Bristles are specialized feathers with a stiff rachis and barbs only on the proximal portion or none at all (Figure 17–5). Bristles occur most commonly around the base of the bill, around the eyes, as eyelashes, and on the head or even on the toes of some birds. The distal rachis of most bristles is colored dark brown or black by melanin granules. The melanin not only colors the bristles but also adds to their strength, resistance to wear, and resistance to photochemical damage. Bristles and structurally intermediate feathers called semibristles screen out foreign particles from the nostrils and eyes of many birds; they also act as tactile sense organs and possibly as aids in the aerial capture of flying insects,

as, for example, the long bristles at the edges of the jaws in nightjars and flycatchers.

Filoplumes are fine, hairlike feathers with a few short barbs or barbules at the tip (Figure 17–5). In some birds, such as cormorants and bulbuls, the filoplumes grow out over the contour feathers and contribute to the external appearance of the plumage, but usually they are not exposed. Filoplumes are sensory structures that aid in the operation of other feathers. Filoplumes have numerous free nerve endings in their follicle walls, and these nerves connect to pressure and vibration receptors around the follicles. Apparently, the filoplumes transmit information about the position and movement of the contour feathers via these receptors. This sensory system probably plays a role in keeping the contour feathers in place and adjusting them properly for flight, insulation, bathing, or display.

Colors and Patterns

The colors of feathers are determined by a combination of pigments and structural characteristics, and the effects can be spectacular. Colors and patterns play important roles in the social behavior of birds and in their ability to avoid detection by predators. In addition, dark melanin pigments strengthen feathers and are often found in areas of high wear, such as the tips of the wings of seabirds.

Three types of pigments are widespread in birds. Dark colors are produced by melanin—eumelanins produce black, gray, and dark brown, whereas phaeomelanins are responsible for reddish brown and tan shades. Carotenoid pigments are responsible for most red, orange, and yellow colors (see the color insert). Birds obtain these pigments from their diet, and in some cases the intensity of color can be used to gauge the fitness of a prospective mate (see Chapter 18). Porphyrins are metal-containing compounds chemically similar to hemoglobin and liver bile pigments. Ultraviolet light causes porphyrins to emit a red fluorescence. Porphyrins are destroyed by prolonged exposure to sunlight, so they are most conspicuous in new plumage.

Structural colors result from reflection of specific wavelengths of light by tiny particles of melanin in the cells on the surface of feather barbs. Blue is produced by very small particles that reflect the shortest wavelengths, whereas some greens are produced by slightly larger particles of melanin. Structural colors can be combined with pigments—green parakeets combine a structural blue with a yellow

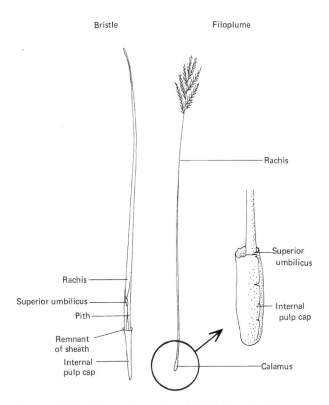

Figure 17–5   Comparison of a bristle (left) and a filoplume (right).

carotenoid, and blue parakeets have a gene that blocks formation of the carotenoid. That gene is a simple recessive, so two blue parakeets can produce only blue offspring.

Iridescent colors, such as those on the heads and throats of hummingbirds and in the eye-shaped patterns on a peacock's tail, result from interference of light waves reflected from the outer and inner surfaces of hollow structures. The hue of the iridescent color depends on the distance between the reflecting surfaces, and the intensity of the color depends on how many layers of reflective structures the feathers contain. Hummingbirds, for example, have 7 to 15 layers of hollow melanin platelets in the barbules of the feathers. Perception of interference colors depends on the angle of view—color is visible when light is being reflected toward the eye of a viewer, but the feathers appear black when they are viewed from a different angle. As a result, iridescent colors flash on and off as a bird changes its position.

■ Aerodynamics of the Avian Wing Compared with Fixed Airfoils

Unlike the fixed wings of an airplane, the wings of a bird function both as an airfoil (lifting surface) and as a propeller for forward motion. The avian wing is admirably suited for these functions, consisting of a light, flexible airfoil (Figure 17–6). The primaries, inserted on the hand bones, do most of the propelling when a bird flaps its wings, and the secondaries along the arm provide lift. Removal of flight feathers from the wings of doves and pigeons shows that when only a few of the primaries are pulled out, the bird's ability to fly is greatly altered, but a bird can still fly when as much as 55 percent of the total area of the secondaries has been removed.

A bird also has the ability to alter the area and shape of its wings and their positions with respect to the body. These changes in area and shape cause corresponding changes in velocity and lift that allow a bird to maneuver, change direction, land, and take off. Moreover, a bird's wing is not a solid structure like a conventional airfoil such as an airplane wing, but allows some air to flow through and between the feathers.

Obviously, the aerodynamic properties of a bird's wing in flight—even in nonflapping flight—are vastly more complex than those of a fixed wing on an airplane or glider. Nevertheless, it is instructive to consider a bird's wing in terms of the basic performance of a fixed airfoil. (See Norberg 1985

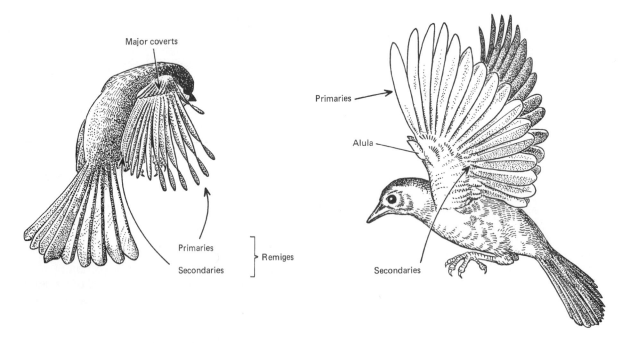

Figure 17–6 Drawings from high-speed photographs show the twisting and opening of the primaries during flapping flight. (From A. C. Thompson, 1964, *A New Dictionary of Birds*, McGraw-Hill, New York, NY.)

and Rayner 1988 for reviews.) Although a bird's wing actually moves forward through the air, it is easier to think of the wing as stationary with the air flowing past. The flow of air produces a force, which is usually called the **reaction**. It can be resolved into two components: the **lift**, which is a vertical force equal to or greater than the weight of the bird, and the **drag**, which is a backward force opposed to the bird's forward motion and to the movement of its wings through the air.

When the leading end of a symmetrically streamlined body cleaves the air, it thrusts the air equally upward and downward, reducing the air pressure equally on the dorsal and ventral surfaces. No lift results from such a condition. There are two ways to modify this system to generate lift. One is to increase the **angle of attack** of the airfoil, and the other is to modify its surface configuration.

When the contour of the dorsal surface of the wing is convex and the ventral surface is concave (a **cambered airfoil**), the air pressure against the two surfaces is unequal because the air has to move farther and faster over the dorsal convex surface relative to the ventral concave surface (Figure 17–7). The result is reduced pressure over the wing, or lift. When the lift equals or exceeds the bird's body weight, the bird becomes airborne. The camber of the wing varies in birds with different flight characteristics and also changes along the length of the wing. Camber is greatest close to the body and decreases toward the wing tip. This change in camber is one of the reasons why the proximal part of the wing generates greater lift than the distal part.

If the leading edge of the wing is tilted up so that the angle of attack is increased, the result is increased lift up to an angle of about 15 degrees, the **stalling angle**. This lift results more from a decrease in pressure over the dorsal surface than from an increase in pressure below the airfoil. If the smooth flow of air over the wing becomes disrupted, the airflow begins to separate from the wing because of the increased air turbulence over the wing. The wing is then stalled. Stalling can be prevented or delayed by the use of slots or auxiliary airfoils on the leading edge of the main wing. The slots help to restore a smooth flow of air over the wing at high angles of attack and at slow speeds. The bird's **alula** has this effect, particularly during landing or take-off (Figure 17–7). Also, the primaries act as a series of independent, overlapping airfoils, each tending to smooth out the flow of air over the one behind.

Another characteristic of an airfoil has to do with wing tip vortexes—eddies of air resulting from outward flow of air from under the wing and inward flow from over it. This is **induced drag**. One way to reduce the effect of these wing tip eddies and their drag is to lengthen the wing so that the tip vortex disturbances are widely separated and there is proportionately more wing area where the air can flow smoothly. Another solution is to taper the wing, reducing its area at the wing tip where induced drag is greatest. The ratio of length to width is called the **aspect ratio**. Long, narrow wings have high aspect ratios and high lift-to-drag (L/D) ratios. High-performance sailplanes and albatrosses, for example, have aspect ratios of 18:1 and L/D ratios in the range of about 40:1.

Wing loading is another important consideration. This is the mass of the bird divided by the wing area. The lighter the loading, the less is the power needed to sustain flight. Small birds usually have lighter wing loading than do large birds, but wing loading is also related to specializations for powered versus soaring flight. The comparisons in Table 17.1 illustrate both of these trends. Small species such as hummingbirds, barn swallows, and mourning doves have lighter wing loading than large species such as the peregrine, golden eagle,

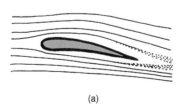
(a)

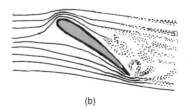
(b)

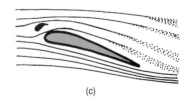
(c)

Figure 17–7 Diagram of airflow around a cambered airfoil. At a low angle of attack (a) the air streams smoothly over the upper surface of the wing and creates lift. When the angle of attack becomes steep (b), air passing over the wing becomes turbulent, decreasing lift enough to produce a stall. A wing slot (c) helps to prevent turbulence by directing a flow of rapidly moving air close to the upper surface of the wing.

TABLE 17.1	Wing loading of some North American birds		
Species	Body Mass (g)	Wing Area (cm²)	Wing Loading (g/cm²)
Ruby-throated hummingbird	3.0	12.4	0.24
Barn swallow	17.0	118.5	0.14
Mourning dove	130.0	357.0	0.36
Peregrine falcon	1,222.5	1,342.0	0.91
Golden eagle	4,664.0	6,520.0	0.71
Mute swan	11,602.0	6,808.0	1.70

Source: E. L. Poole, 1938, Auk 55:511–517.

and mute swan; yet the 3-gram hummingbird, a powerful flier, has a heavier wing loading than the more buoyant, sometimes soaring barn swallow, which is more than five times heavier. Similarly, the rapid-stroking peregrine has a heavier wing loading than the larger, often soaring golden eagle.

Flapping Flight

Flapping flight is remarkable for its automatic, unlearned performance. A young bird on its maiden flight uses a form of locomotion so complex that it defies precise analysis in physical and aerodynamic terms. The nestlings of some species of birds develop in confined spaces such as burrows in the ground or cavities in tree trunks in which it is impossible for them to spread their wings and practice flapping before they leave the nest. Despite this seeming handicap, many of them are capable of flying considerable distances on their first flights. Diving petrels may fly as far as 10 kilometers the first time out of their burrows. On the other hand, young birds reared in open nests frequently flap their wings vigorously in the wind for several days before flying—especially large birds such as albatrosses, storks, vultures, and eagles. Such flapping may help to develop muscles, but it is unlikely that these birds are learning to fly; however, a bird's flying abilities do improve with practice for a period after it leaves the nest.

There are so many variables involved in flapping flight that it becomes difficult to understand exactly how it works. A beating wing is flexible and porous and yields to air pressure, unlike the fixed wing of an airplane. Its shape, wing loading, camber, sweepback, and the position of the individual feathers all change remarkably as a wing moves through its cycle of locomotion. This is a formidable list of variables, and it is no wonder that flapping flight has not yet fully yielded to explanation in aerodynamic terms; however, the general properties of a flapping wing can be described (see Figure 17–8).

We can begin by considering the flapping cycle of a small bird in flight. A bird cannot continue to fly straight and level unless it can develop a force or thrust to balance the drag operating against forward momentum. The flapping of the wings, especially the wing tips (primaries), produces this thrust, whereas the inner wings (secondaries) are held more nearly stationary with respect to the body, and generate lift. It is easiest to consider the forces operating on the inner and outer wing separately. Most of the lift, and also most of the drag, comes from the forces acting on the inner wing and body of a flying bird. The forces on the wing tips derive from two motions that have to be added together. The tips are moving forward with the bird, but at the same time they are also moving downward relative to the bird. The wing tip would have a very large angle of attack and would stall if it were not flexible. As it is, the forces on the tip cause the individual primaries to twist as the wing is flapped downward (see Figure 17–6) and to produce the forces diagrammed in Figure 17–8c.

The forces acting on the two parts of the bird combine to produce the conditions for equilibrium flight shown. The positions of the inner and outer wings during the upstroke (dotted lines) and downstroke reveal that vertical motion is applied mostly at the wing tips (Figure 17–8a). Thus, the inner wing (the secondaries) acts as if the bird were gliding to generate the forces shown in Figure 17–8b, and the outer wing generates the force shown in part c.

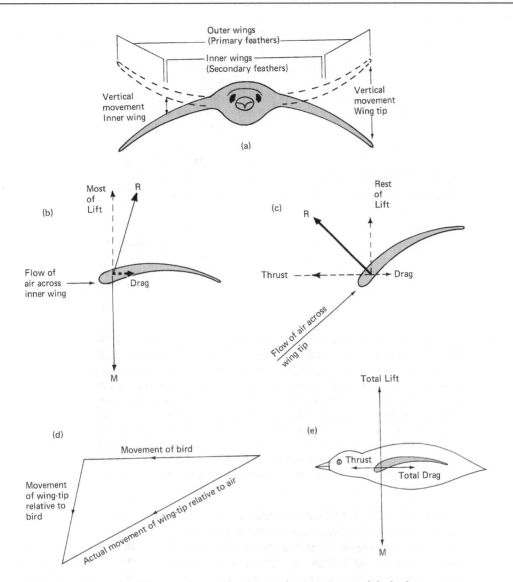

Figure 17–8 Generalized diagrams of forces acting on the inner and outer wings and the body of a bird in flapping flight. M, gravitational force; R, resultant force. See text for explanation.

Most of the lift to counter the pull of gravity (M) is generated by the inner wing and body. Canting of the wing tip (the primaries) during the downstroke (Figure 17–8c) produces a resultant force (R) that is directed forward. The movement of the wing tip relative to the air is affected by the forward motion of the bird through the air (Figure 17–8d). As a result of this motion and the canting of the wing tips during the downstroke, the flow of air across the primaries is different from the flow across the secondaries and the body (Figure 17–8e). When flight speed through the air is constant, the forces acting on the inner wing and the body and on the outer wing combine to produce a set of summed vectors in which thrust exceeds total drag and lift at least equals the body mass.

As the wings move downward and forward on the downstroke, which is the power stroke, the trailing edges of the primaries bend upward under air pressure, and each feather acts as an individual propeller biting into the air and generating thrust. Contraction of the **pectoralis major**, the large breast muscle, produces the downstroke during level flapping flight. During this downbeat, the thrust is greater than the total drag, and the bird accelerates. In small birds, the return stroke, which is upward and backward, provides little or no thrust and is mainly a passive recovery stroke. The bird decelerates during the recovery stroke.

For larger birds with slower wing actions, the time of the upstroke is too long to spend in a state of deceleration. A similar situation exists when any bird takes off: It needs thrust on both the downstroke and the upstroke. Thrust on the upstroke is produced by bending the wings slightly at the wrists and elbow and by rotating the humerus upward and backward. This movement causes the upper surfaces of the twisted primaries to push against the air and to produce thrust as their lower surfaces did in the downstroke. In this type of flight the wing tip describes a rough figure eight through the air. As speed increases the figure-eight pattern is restricted to the wing tips.

A powered upstroke results mainly from the contraction of the **supracoracoideus**, a deep muscle underlying the pectoralis major and attached directly to the keel of the sternum. It inserts on the dorsal head of the humerus by passing through the foramen triosseum, formed where the coracoid, furcula, and scapula join (Figure 17–9). In most species of birds the supracoracoideus is a relatively small, pale muscle with low myoglobin content, easily fatigued. In species that rely on a powered upstroke for fast, steep takeoffs; for hovering; or for fast aerial pursuit, the supracoracoideus is relatively larger. The ratio of weights of the pectoralis major and the supracoracoideus is a good indication of a bird's reliance on a powered upstroke; such ratios vary from 3:1 to 20:1. The total weight of the flight muscles is also indicative of the extent to which a bird

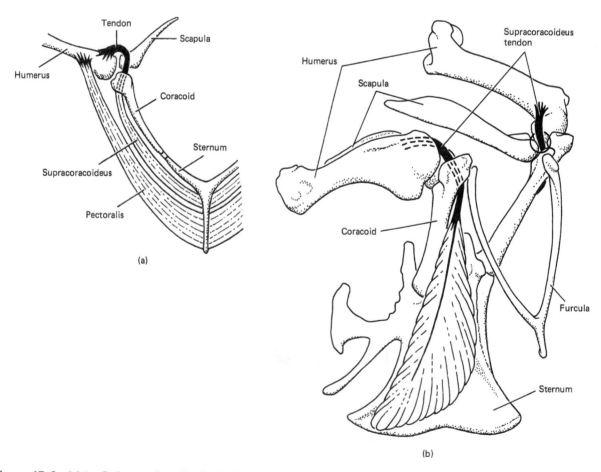

Figure 17–9   Major flight muscles of birds. (a) Cross section through the sternum of a bird showing the relationships of the pectoralis major and supracoracoideus muscles; (b) frontal and lateral view of the sternum and pectoral girdle of a bird showing the insertion of the supracoracoideus muscle through the supracoracoid foramen onto the dorsal head of the humerus. The foramen is formed by the articulation of the furcula, coracoid, and scapula.

depends on powered flight. Strong fliers such as pigeons and falcons have breast muscles comprising more than 20 percent of body weight, whereas in some owls, which have very light wing loading, the flight muscles make up only 10 percent of total weight.

A flying bird increases its speed by increasing the amplitude of its wing beats, but the frequency of wing beats remains nearly constant at all speeds during level flight. Large birds have slower wing beat frequencies than those of small birds, and strong fliers usually have slower beat frequencies than those of weak fliers. The frequency of respiration of many birds during flight appears to have a constant relationship to the wing beat frequency. Some birds, especially those that have low wing beat frequencies, breathe once per wing beat cycle, whereas birds with high wing beat frequencies have breathing cycles that span several wing beats. In general, inspiration appears to occur during or at the end of a wing upstroke, with expiration at the end of a downstroke.

Wing Structure and Flight Characteristics

Wings may be large or small in relation to body size, resulting in light wing loading or heavy wing loading. They may be long and pointed, short and rounded, highly cambered or relatively flat; and the width and degree of slotting are additional important characteristics.

Depending on whether a bird is primarily a powered flier or a soaring form, the various segments of the wing (hand, forearm, upper arm) are length-ened to different degrees. Hummingbirds have very fast, powerful wing beats, requiring maximum propulsive force from the primaries. The hand bones of hummingbirds are longer than the forearm and upper arm combined. Most of the flight surface is formed by the primaries, and hummingbirds have only six or seven secondaries. Frigate birds are marine species with long, narrow wings specialized for powered flight as well as for gliding and soaring. All three segments of the forelimb are about equal in length. The soaring albatrosses have carried lengthening of the wing to the extreme found in birds: The humerus or upper arm is the longest segment, and there may be as many as 32 secondaries in the inner wing (Figure 17–10).

Ornithologists recognize four structural and functional types of wings (Figure 17–11). Seabirds, particularly those such as albatrosses and shearwaters that rely on **dynamic soaring**, have long, narrow, flat wings lacking slots in the outer primaries. Some albatrosses have aspect ratios of 18:1 and lift-to-drag ratios similar to those of high-performance sailplanes. Dynamic soaring is possible only where there is a pronounced vertical wind gradient, with the lower 15 or so meters of air being slowed by friction against the ocean surface. Furthermore, dynamic soaring is feasible only in regions where winds are strong and persistent, such as in the latitudes of the Roaring Forties. This is where most albatrosses and shearwaters are found. Starting from the top of the wind gradient, an albatross glides downwind with great increase in ground speed (kinetic energy). Then, as it nears the surface, it turns and gains altitude while gliding into the

Figure 17–10 Wing proportions. Comparison of the relative lengths of the proximal, middle, and distal elements of the wing bones of a hummingbird (top), frigate bird (middle), and albatross (bottom) drawn to the same size.

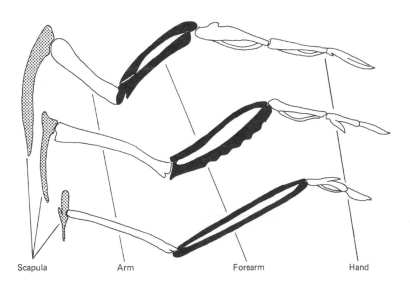

Scapula   Arm   Forearm   Hand

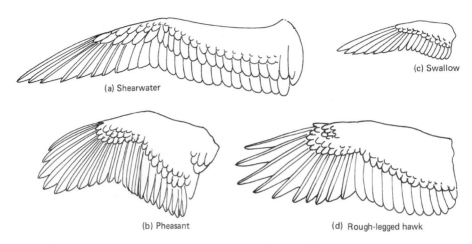

Figure 17–11 Comparison of four basic types of bird wings. (a) Dynamic soaring; (b) elliptical; (c) high aspect ratio; (d) high lift.

wind. Because the bird flies into wind of increasing speed as it rises, its loss of airspeed is not as great as its loss of ground speed, and consequently it does not stall until it has mounted back to the top of the wind gradient, where the air velocity becomes stable. At that point, the bird has converted much of its kinetic energy to potential energy and it turns downwind to repeat the cycle.

Birds that live in forests and woodlands where they must maneuver around obstructions have **elliptical wings**. These wings have a low aspect ratio, tend to be highly cambered, and usually have a high degree of slotting in the outer primaries. These features are generally associated with slow flight and a high degree of maneuverability. Although some species with elliptical wings, notably upland gamebirds such as pheasants and grouse, have fast take-off speeds, they maintain rapid flight only for short distances.

Many birds that are aerial foragers, make long migrations, or have a heavy wing loading that is related to some other aspect of their lives, such as diving, have **high aspect ratio** wings. These wings have a flat profile (little camber), and often lack slots in the outer primaries. In flight they show the swept-back attitude of jet fighter plane wings. All fast-flying birds have converged on this form.

The slotted **high lift** wing is a fourth type. It is associated with static soaring typified by vultures, eagles, storks, and some other large birds. This wing has an intermediate aspect ratio between the elliptical wing and the high aspect ratio wing, a deep camber, and marked slotting in the primaries. When the

bird is in flight, the tips of the primaries turn markedly upward under the influence of air pressure and body weight. Static soarers remain airborne mainly by seeking out and gliding in air masses that are rising at a rate faster than the bird's sinking speed. Hence, a light wing loading and maneuverability (slow forward speed and small turning radius) are advantageous. Broad wings provide the light wing loading, and the highly developed slotting enhances maneuverability by responding to changes in wind currents with changes in the positions of individual feathers instead of movements of the entire wing. A bird cannot soar in tight spirals at high speed, and flying slowly with enough lift to prevent stalling requires a high angle of attack. The deeply slotted primaries apparently make the combination of low speed and high lift possible. The distal, emarginated portion of each primary produces lift by acting as a separate high aspect ratio airfoil set at a high angle of attack. This design reduces induced drag.

In regions where topographic features and meteorological factors provide currents of rising air, static soaring is an energetically cheap mode of flight. By soaring rather than flapping, a large bird the size of a stork can decrease by a factor of 20 or more the energy required for flight per unit of time, whereas the saving is only one-tenth as much for a small bird such as a warbler. It is little wonder, then, that most large land birds perform their annual migrations by soaring and gliding as much of the time as possible, and some condors and vultures cover hundreds of kilometers each day soaring in search of food.

■ Body Form and Flight

Many aspects of the morphology of birds appear to have been molded by aerodynamic forces. (See Raikow 1985 and Rayner 1988 for reviews.) Feathers, for example, provide lift and streamlining during flight. Feathers are light, yet they are strong and resilient for their weight. Of course, flying is not the only function of feathers—they also provide the insulation necessary for endothermy and their colors and shapes function in crypsis and display.

Structural modifications can be seen in several aspects of the structure of birds. The avian skeleton is not lighter in relation to the total body mass of a bird than is the skeleton of a mammal of similar size, but the distribution of mass is different. Many bones are air filled (pnuematized), and the skull is especially light, but the leg bones of birds are heavier than those of mammals. Thus, the total mass of the skeleton of a bird is similar to that of a mammal, but more of a bird's mass is concentrated in its hindlimbs.

Characteristics of some of the organs of birds reduce body mass. For example, birds lack urinary bladders, and most species have only one ovary (the left). The gonads of both male and female birds are usually small; they hypertrophy during the breeding season and regress when breeding has finished.

Power-producing features are equally important components of the ability of birds to fly. The pectoral muscles of a strong flier may account for 20 percent of the total body mass. The power output per unit mass of the pectoralis major of a turtledove during level flight has been estimated to be 10 to 20 times that of most mammalian muscles. Birds have large hearts and high rates of blood flow and complex lungs that use crosscurrent flows of air and blood to maximize gas exchange and to dissipate the heat produced by high levels of muscular activity during flight. The brains of birds are similar in size to the brains of rodents, and the forebrain and cerebellum are well developed. Birds rely heavily on visual information and the optic lobes are especially large. The sense of smell is not well developed in most birds and the olfactory lobes are correspondingly small.

Streamlining

Birds are the only vertebrates that move fast enough in air for wind resistance and streamlining to be important factors in their lives. Many passerine birds are probably able to fly 50 kilometers per hour or even faster when they must, although their normal cruising speeds are lower. Ducks and geese can fly at 80 or 90 kilometers per hour, and peregrine falcons reach speeds as high as 200 kilometers per hour when they dive on prey. Fast-flying birds have many of the same structural characters as those seen in fast-flying aircraft. Contour feathers make smooth junctions between the wings and the body and often between the head and body as well, eliminating sources of turbulence that would increase wind resistance. The feet are tucked close to the body during flight, further improving streamlining.

At the opposite extreme, some birds are slow fliers. Many of the long-legged, long-necked wading birds, such as spoonbills and flamingos, fall in this category. Their long legs trail behind them as they fly and their necks are extended. They are far from streamlined, although they may be strong fliers.

Skeleton and Muscles

The hollow, air-filled (pneumatic) bones of birds (Figure 17–12) are probably an ancestral character of the archosaur lineage, not a derived character of birds. Not all birds have pneumatic bones. In general, pneumatization of bones is better developed in large birds than in small ones. Diving birds (penguins, grebes, loons) have little pneumaticity, and the bones of diving ducks are less pneumatic than those of nondivers.

The distribution of pneumaticity among the bones of the skeleton also varies. The skull is pneumatic in nearly all birds, although the kiwi, a flightless bird, lacks air spaces in the skull. The sternum, pectoral girdle, and humerus are pneumatic and are part of a system of interconnected air sacs that allow a one-way flow of air through the lungs (discussed in the following section). Pneumaticity extends through the rest of the appendicular skeleton of some birds, even into the phalanges.

Except for the specializations associated with flight, the skeleton of a bird is very much like that of a small, bipedal archosaur (Figure 17–13). The pelvic girdle of birds is elongated, and the ischium and ilium have broadened into thin sheets that are firmly united with a **synsacrum**, which is formed by the fusion of 10 to 23 vertebrae. The long tail of ancestral diapsids has been shortened in birds to about five free caudal vertebrae and a **pygostyle** formed by the fusion of the remaining vertebrae. The pygostyle supports the tail feathers (rectrices). The thoracic vertebrae are joined by strong ligaments that are often ossified. The relatively immo-

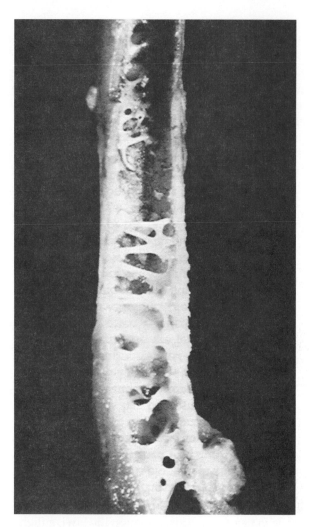

Figure 17–12   The hollow bones of birds are reinforced by struts. (Courtesy F. Harvey Pough.)

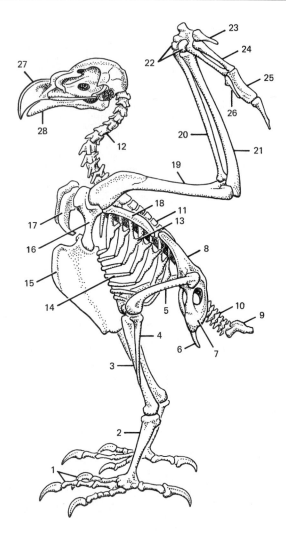

Figure 17–13   Skeleton of an eagle. **1,** Toes; **2,** tarsus; **3** and **4,** tibiotarsus formed by the fused tibia **(3)** and fibula **(4)**; **5,** femur; **6,** pubis; **7,** ischia; **8,** ilium; **9,** pygostyle; **10,** caudal vertebrae; **11,** thoracic vertebrae; **12,** cervical vertebrae; **13,** uncinate process of rib; **14,** sternal rib; **15,** sternum; **16,** coracoid; **17,** furcula; **18,** scapula; **19,** humerus; **20,** radius; **21,** ulna; **22,** carpal bones; **23,** first digit; **24,** metacarpal; **25,** second digit; **26,** third digit; **27,** upper mandible; **28,** lower mandible. (From J. Dorst, 1974, *The Life of Birds,* Columbia University Press, New York, NY.)

bile thoracic vertebrae, the synsacrum, and the pygostyle in combination with the elongated, rooflike pelvis produce a nearly rigid vertebral column. Flexion is possible only in the neck, at the joint between the thoracic vertebrae and the synsacrum, and at the base of the tail. The rigid trunk is balanced on the legs. The femur projects anteriorly and its articulation with the tibiotarsus and fibula is close to the center of gravity of the bird.

The wings are positioned above the center of gravity. The sternum is greatly enlarged compared with other vertebrates, and (except in flightless birds) it bears a keel from which the pectoralis and supracoracoideus muscles originate (Figure 17–9). Strong-flying birds have well-developed keels and their flight muscles are large. The scapula extends posteriorly above the ribs and is supported by the

coracoid, which is fused ventrally to the sternum. Additional bracing is provided by the clavicles, which, in most birds, are fused at their distal ends to form the **furcula** (wishbone).

The relative size of the leg and flight muscles of birds is related to their primary mode of locomotion. Flight muscles comprise 25 to 35 percent of the total body mass of strong fliers such as hummingbirds and swallows. These species have small legs and the leg muscles account for as little as 2 percent of the body mass. Predatory birds such as hawks and owls use their legs to capture prey. In these species the flight muscles make up about 20 percent of the body mass and the limb muscles are 10 percent. Swimming birds—ducks and grebes, for example—have an even division between limb and flight muscles, and the combined mass of these muscles may be 30 to 60 percent of the total body mass. Birds such as rails, which are primarily terrestrial and run to escape from predators, have limb muscles that are larger than their flight muscles.

Muscle fiber types and metabolic pathways also distinguish running birds from fliers. The familiar distinction between the light meat and dark meat of a chicken reflects those differences. Fowl, especially domestic breeds, rarely fly, but they are capable of walking and running for long periods. The dark color of the leg muscles reveals the presence of myoglobin in the tissues and indicates a high capacity for aerobic metabolism in the limb muscles of these birds. The white muscles of the breast lack myoglobin and have little capacity for aerobic metabolism. The flights of fowl (including wild species such as pheasants, grouse, and quail) are of brief duration and are used primarily to evade predators. The bird uses an explosive takeoff, fueled by anaerobic metabolic pathways, followed by a long glide back to the ground. Birds that are capable of strong sustained flight have dark breast muscles with high aerobic metabolic capacities.

The skulls of most birds consist of four bony units that can move in relation to each other. This skull kinesis is important in some aspects of feeding. The upper jaw flexes upward as the mouth is opened, and the lower jaw expands laterally at its articulation with the skull (Figure 17–14). The flexion of the upper and lower jaws increases the bird's gape in both the vertical and horizontal planes and probably assists in swallowing large items.

Heart, Lungs, and Gas Exchange

The heart of birds is composed of morphologically distinct left and right atria and ventricles. The separation of the ventricle into left and right halves is an archosaurian character that is seen in crocodilians as well as in birds. However, birds lack the capacity possessed by crocodilians to shunt blood between the pulmonary and systemic circulation. In birds, as in mammals, the blood must flow in series through the two circuits.

The respiratory system of birds is unique among extant vertebrates (Figure 17–15). The air sacs that

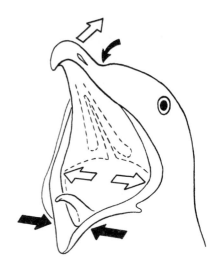

Figure 17–14 Skull and jaw kinesis. A yawning herring gull (*Larus argentatus*) shows the kinetic movements of the skull and jaws that occur during swallowing. White arrows show the positions of outward flexion and black arrows show inward flexion. (From P. Bühler, 1981, in *Form and Function in Birds*, volume 2, edited by A. S. King and J. McLelland, Academic, New York, NY.)

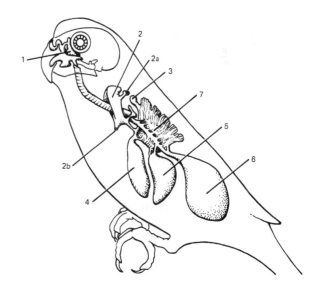

Figure 17–15 The lung and air sac system of the budgerigar. (Only the left side is shown.) **1,** Infraorbital sinus; **2,** clavicular air sac; **2a,** axillary diverticulum to the humerus; **2b,** sternal diverticulum; **3,** cervical air sac; **4,** cranial thoracic air sac; **5,** caudal thoracic air sac; **6,** abdominal air sacs; **7,** parabronchial lung. (From H. E. Evans, 1982, in *Diseases of Cage and Aviary Birds*, 2d edition, edited by M. L. Petrak, Lee & Febiger, Philadelphia, PA.)

occupy much of the dorsal part of the body and extend into the pneumatic spaces in many of the bones provide a system in which airflow through the lungs is unidirectional instead of tidal (in and out) as it is in mammalian lungs. The air sacs are poorly vascularized, and gas exchange occurs only in the parabronchial lung. The combined volume of the air sacs is about nine times the volume of the parabronchial lung itself. The flow of air through this extensive respiratory system may help to dissipate the heat generated by high levels of muscular activity during flight.

Air flows through the parabronchial lung in the same direction during both inspiration and exhalation (Figure 17–16). During inspiration the volume of the thorax increases, drawing air through the bronchus and into the posterior thoracic and abdominal air sacs and the parabronchial lung. Simultaneously, air from the parabronchial lung is drawn into the clavicular and anterior thoracic sacs. On expiration the volume of the thorax decreases, air from the posterior thoracic and abdominal sacs is forced into the parabronchial lung, and air from the clavicular and thoracic sacs is forced out through the bronchus.

Gas exchange takes place in a network of tiny, blind-end air capillaries that intertwine with equally fine blood capillaries. Airflow and blood flow pass in opposite directions, and the capillary pairs compose a crosscurrent exchange system. This arrangement is more effective at exchanging lung gases than is the mammalian lung, and the efficiency of gas exchange in the parabronchial lung may allow birds to breathe at higher altitudes than mammals (Box 17–1). Birds do sometimes penetrate to very high altitudes, either as residents or in flight. For

example, radar tracking of migrating birds shows that they sometimes fly as high as 6500 meters, the alpine chough lives at altitudes around 8200 meters on Mount Everest, and bar-headed geese pass directly over the summit of the Himalayas at altitudes of 9200 meters during their migrations.

Vocalization is a second function of the respiratory systems of many vertebrates, including birds. However, the vocal organ of birds, the **syrinx** (plural syringes), is unique. The syrinx lies at the base of the trachea where the two bronchi diverge. Several of the cartilaginous rings that support the trachea and bronchi are modified and surrounded by muscles. The anatomy of the syrinx varies among birds—some are purely tracheal, some involve both the trachea and the bronchi, and others are purely bronchial. Two membranes are associated with the syrinx, one in the base of each bronchus. Songbirds have five to nine (usually seven) pairs of syringeal muscles, parrots and lyrebirds have three pairs, falcons have two, and most other birds have only a single pair of syringeal muscles. Storks, vultures, ratites, and most pelicans lack syringeal muscles.

The mechanism of avian song production is an area of controversy. One view holds that sound is produced by vibration of the syringeal membranes and that modulations of that sound are the result of changes in the vibration of the membranes (Greenewalt 1968, 1969). An alternative hypothesis maintains that pulsatile activity of the abdominal muscles and resonance in the trachea are important in modulating the amplitude and frequencies produced by the syringeal membranes (Gaunt et al. 1982, Nowicki 1987). A recent study suggests that it is not the syringeal membranes that vibrate, but

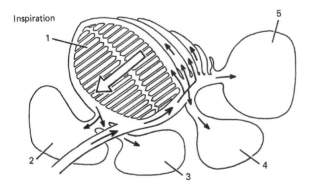 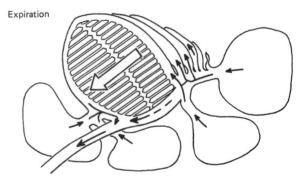

Figure 17–16 Pattern of airflow during inspiration and expiration. Note that air flows through the parabronchial lung during both phases of the respiratory cycle. **1,** Parabronchial lung; **2,** clavicular air sac; **3,** cranial thoracic air sac; **4,** caudal thoracic air sac; **5,** abdominal air sacs. (From P. Scheid, 1982, in *Avian Biology*, volume 6, edited by J. R. King and K. C. Parkes, Academic, New York, NY.)

BOX 17–1   High-Flying Birds

Birds regularly fly at altitudes higher than human mountain climbers can ascend without using auxiliary breathing apparatus, and the ability of birds to sustain activity at high altitudes is a result of the morphological characteristics of their pulmonary systems. Mammals have difficulty breathing at high altitudes because of the low oxygen pressure in the air. The atmosphere is most dense at the surface of the earth (where the entire weight of the atmosphere is pressing down on it), and it becomes increasingly less dense at higher altitudes. At sea level atmospheric pressure is 760 millimeters of mercury (760 torr in the units of the International System). The composition of dry air by volume is 79.02 percent nitrogen and other inert gases, 20.94 percent oxygen, and 0.04 percent carbon dioxide. These gases contribute to the total atmospheric pressure in proportion to their abundance, so the contribution of oxygen is 20.94 percent of 760 torr, or 159.16 torr. The pressure exerted by an individual gas is called the partial pressure of that gas. The rate and direction of diffusion of gas between the air in the lungs and the blood in the pulmonary capillaries is determined by the difference in the partial pressures of the gas in the blood and in the lungs. Oxygen diffuses from air in the lungs into blood in the pulmonary capillaries because oxygen has a higher partial pressure in the air than in the blood, whereas carbon dioxide diffuses in the opposite direction because its partial pressure is higher in blood than in air.

At higher altitudes the atmospheric pressure is lower. At 7700 meters, the atmospheric pressure is only 282 torr, and the partial pressure of oxygen in dry air is about 59 torr. As a result of the low atmospheric pressure at this altitude the driving force for diffusion of oxygen into the blood is small. (The actual pressure differential is reduced even below this figure because air in the lungs is saturated with water, and water vapor contributes to the total pressure in the lungs. The vapor pressure of water at 37°C is 47 torr. Thus, the partial pressure of oxygen in the lungs is 20.94 percent $\times$ (282 $-$ 47 torr = 49 torr.)

The tidal ventilation pattern of the lungs of mammals means that the partial pressure of oxygen in the pulmonary capillaries can never be higher than the partial pressure of oxygen in the expired air. The best that a tidal ventilation system can accomplish is to equilibrate the partial pressures of oxygen in the pulmonary air and in the pulmonary circulation. In fact, failure to achieve complete mixing of the gas within the pulmonary system means that oxygen exchange falls short even of this equilibration, and blood leaves the lungs with a partial pressure of oxygen slightly lower than the partial pressure of oxygen in the exhaled air. The cross-current blood flow system in the parabronchial lung of birds ensures that the gases in the air capillaries repeatedly encounter a new supply of deoxygenated blood (Figure 17–17, left side of diagram).

When blood enters the system (on the left side of the diagram), it has the low oxygen pressure of mixed venous blood (P_v). The blood entering the leftmost capillary is exposed to air that has already had much of its oxygen removed farther upstream. Nonetheless, the low oxygen pressure of the mixed venous blood ensures that even in this part of the parabronchus, oxygen uptake can occur. Blood flowing through capillaries farther to the right

rather the medial and lateral labia (Goller and Larsen 1997).

■ Feeding, Digestion, and Excretion

The digestive systems of birds show some differences from those of other vertebrates, although the distinctions are less pronounced than the differences in the respiratory systems. With the specialization of the forelimbs as wings, which largely precludes their having any role in prey capture, birds have concentrated their predatory mechanisms in their beaks and feet. The absence of teeth prevents birds from doing much processing of food in the mouth, and the gastric apparatus takes over some of that role.

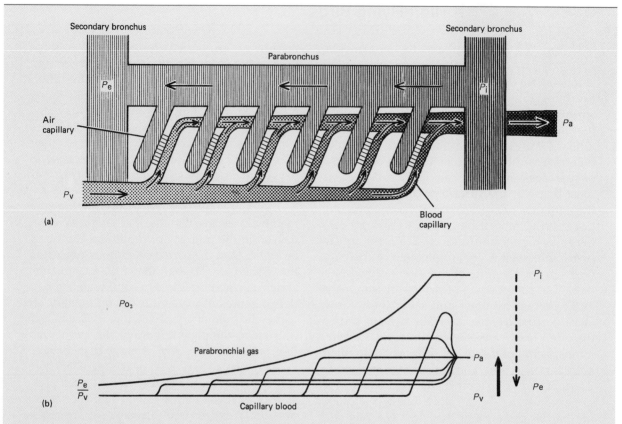

Figure 17–17 Diagram of gas exchange in a cross-current lung. Air flows from right to left in this diagram and blood flows from left to right. P_e = oxygen pressure in the air exiting the parabronchus, P_v = oxygen pressure in the mixed venous blood entering the blood capillaries, P_a = oxygen pressure in the blood leaving the blood capillaries, P_i = oxygen pressure in the air entering the parabronchus. Top: General pattern of air and blood flow through the parabronchial lung. Bottom: Diagrammatic representation of cross-current gas exchange. (From P. Scheid, 1982, in *Avian Biology*, volume 6, edited by J. R. King and K. C. Parkes, Academic, New York, NY.)

in the diagram is exposed to higher partial pressures of oxygen in the parabronchial gas and takes up correspondingly more oxygen. The oxygen pressure of the blood that flows out of the lungs (P_a) is the result of mixing of blood from all the capillaries. The oxygen pressure of the mixed arterial blood is higher than the partial pressure of oxygen in the exhaled air.

The Esophagus and Crop

Birds often gather more food than they can process in a short period, and the excess is held in the esophagus. Many birds have a **crop**, an enlarged portion of the esophagus that is specialized for temporary storage of food. The crop of some birds is a simple expansion of the esophagus, whereas in others it is a unilobed or bilobed structure (Figure 17–18). An additional function of the crop is transportation of food for nestlings. When the adult returns to the nest it regurgitates the material from the crop and feeds it to the young. In doves and pigeons the crop of both sexes produces a nutritive fluid (crop milk) that is fed to the young. The milk is produced by fat-laden cells that detach from the squamous epithelium of the crop and are suspended in an aqueous

Figure 17–18 Anterior digestive tract of birds. (a) The relationship among the parts. The relative sizes of the proventriculus and gizzard vary in relation to diet. Carnivorous and fish-eating birds like the great cormorant have a relatively small crop (b) and gizzard (c), whereas seed eaters and omnivores like the peafowl have a large crop (d) and muscular gizzard (e). (From J. McLelland, 1979, *Form and Function in Birds*, edited by A. S. King and J. McLelland, Academic, London, UK.)

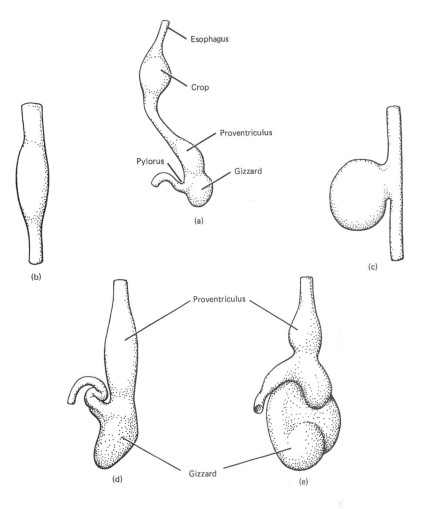

fluid. Crop milk is rich in lipids and proteins, but contains no sugar. Its chemical composition is similar to that of mammalian milk, although it differs in containing intact cells. The proliferation of the crop epithelium and the formation of crop milk is stimulated by prolactin, as is the lactation of mammals. A nutritive fluid produced in the esophagus is fed to hatchlings by greater flamingos and by the male emperor penguin.

The hoatzin, a South American bird, is the only avian species known to employ foregut fermentation (Figure 17–19). Hoatzins are herbivorous—green leaves make up more than 80 percent of the diet. More than a century ago, naturalists observed that hoatzins smell like fresh cow manure, and a study of the crop and lower esophagus revealed that volatile fatty acids are the source of the odor (Grajal et al. 1989). Bacteria and protozoa like those found in the rumen of cows break down the plant cell walls, and bacterial extracts from the hoatzin's crop were as effective as those from a cow's rumen in digesting plant material. Volatile fatty acids produced by the process of fermentation are absorbed by the gut.

The Gastric Apparatus

The form of the stomachs of birds is related to their dietary habits. Carnivorous and piscivorous (fish-eating) birds need expansible storage areas to accommodate large volumes of soft food, whereas birds that eat insects or seeds require a muscular organ that can contribute to the mechanical breakdown of food. Usually, the gastric apparatus of birds consists of two relatively distinct chambers, an anterior glandular stomach (**proventriculus**) and a posterior muscular stomach (**gizzard**). The proventriculus contains glands that secrete acid and digestive enzymes. The proventriculus is especially large in species that swallow large items such as fruit or fish intact (Figure 17–18).

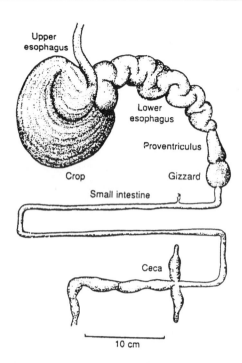

Figure 17–19   The digestive tract of the hoatzin. The muscular crop and the anterior esophagus are greatly enlarged. Cornified ridges on the inner surface of the crop probably grind the contents of the crop, reducing the particle size. This process is analagous to a cow chewing its cud, but has the advantage that mechanical procesing and fermentation occur in the same structure. (From A. Grajal, S. D. Strahl, R. Parra, M. G. Dominguez, and A. Neher, 1989, *Science* 245:1236–1238.)

The gizzard has several functions, including storage of food while the chemical digestion that was begun in the proventriculus continues, but its most important function is the mechanical processing of food. The thick, muscular walls of the gizzard squeeze the contents, and small stones that are held in the gizzards of many birds help to grind the food. In this sense the gizzard is performing the same function that is performed by the teeth of mammals. The pressure that can be exerted on food in the gizzard is intense. A turkey's gizzard can grind up two dozen walnuts in as little as 4 hours, and can crack hickory nuts that require 50 to 150 kilograms of pressure to break under experimental conditions.

The Intestine, Ceca, and Cloaca

The small intestine is the principal site of chemical digestion as enzymes from the pancreas and intestine break down the food into small molecules that can be absorbed across the intestinal wall. The mucosa of the small intestine is modified into a series of folds, lamellae, and villi that increase its surface area. The large intestine is relatively short, usually less than 10 percent of the length of the small intestine. Passage of food through the intestines of birds is quite rapid: Transit times for carnivorous and fruit-eating species are in the range of a few minutes to a few hours. Passage of food is slower in herbivores and may require a full day. Birds generally have a pair of ceca at the junction of the small and large intestines. The ceca are small in carnivorous, insectivorous, and seed-eating species, but they are large in herbivorous and omnivorous species such as cranes, fowl, ducks, geese, and the ostrich. Symbiotic microorganisms in the ceca apparently ferment plant material.

The cloaca temporarily stores waste products while water is being reabsorbed. The precipitation of uric acid in the form of urate salts frees water from the urine, and this water is returned to the bloodstream. Species of birds that have salt-secreting glands can accomplish further conservation of water by reabsorbing some of the ions that are in solution in the cloaca and excreting them in more concentrated solutions through the salt glands (Chapter 4). The mixture of white urate salts and dark fecal material that is voided by birds is familiar to anyone who has washed an automobile.

■ The Hindlimbs and Locomotion

Unlike most tetrapods, birds usually are specialized for two or more different modes of locomotion: bipedal walking or swimming with the hindlimbs and flying with the forelimbs.

Walking, Hopping, and Perching

Terrestrial locomotion may involve walking or running, supporting heavy bodies, hopping, perching, climbing, wading in shallow water, or supporting the body on insubstantial surfaces such as snow or floating vegetation. We will consider cursorial adaptations first, because birds evolved from bipedal dinosaurs and because the principles of cursorial adaptation have been well worked out in the quadrupedal mammals. Modifications usually associated with running in quadrupeds are (1) a progressive increase in the lengths of the distal limb elements relative to the proximal ones, (2) a decrease in the area of the foot surface that makes contact with the ground, and (3) a reduction in the number of toes. All three of these cursorial trends are expressed to varying degrees in running birds; however, problems of balance are more critical for bipeds than for quadrupeds, and these problems may have restricted the evolution among bipeds of some of the cursorial adaptations found in quadrupeds.

Because the center of gravity must lie over the feet of a biped to maintain balance, a reduction in the surface area in contact with the ground can be achieved only by some sacrifice in stability. No bird has reduced the length and number of toes in contact with the ground to the extent that the hoofed mammals have, but the large, fast-running ostrich has only two toes on each foot and many other cursorial species have only the three forward-directed toes in contact with the ground (Figure 17–20).

Weight-bearing characteristics such as large, heavy leg bones arranged in vertical columns as supports of great body mass are well known in large mammals such as elephants. No surviving birds show specializations of this kind, but these features are seen in some of the large, flightless terrestrial birds of earlier times. The extinct elephant-birds (Aepyornithiformes) of Madagascar and moas (Dinornithiformes) of New Zealand were herbivores that evolved on oceanic islands in the absence of large carnivorous mammals and survived there until contact with humans in the post-Pleistocene period (Figure 17–21). The giant, carnivorous *Diatryma* (Gruiformes) and related species were successful continental forms in the Americas until the appearance of large mammalian carnivores. Among the large, flightless terrestrial birds, only some of the fleet-footed cursors such as the rheas and ostrich have managed to survive in the presence of large placental carnivores.

Hopping, a succession of jumps with the feet moving together, is a special form of pedal locomotion found mostly in perching, arboreal birds. It is most highly developed in the passerines, and only a few nonpasserine birds regularly hop. Many passerines cannot walk, and hopping is their only mode of terrestrial locomotion. Some groups of passerines have a more terrestrial mode of existence and these birds possess a walking gait as well as the ability to hop. Larks, pipits, starlings, and grackles are examples. The separation between walking and hopping passerines cuts across families. For example, in the family Corvidae, the ravens, crows, and rooks are walkers, whereas the jays and magpies are hoppers.

The most specialized avian foot for perching on branches is one in which all four toes are free and mobile, of moderate length, and with the hind toe well developed, lying in the same plane as the forward three, and opposable to them (**anisodactyl**). Such a foot produces a firm grip and is highly developed in the passerine birds. The **zygodactylous** condition, with two toes forward and opposable to two extending backward is characteristic of birds such as parrots and woodpeckers, which climb or perch on vertical surfaces.

The tendons that flex the toes of a perching bird can lock the foot in a tight grip so that the bird does

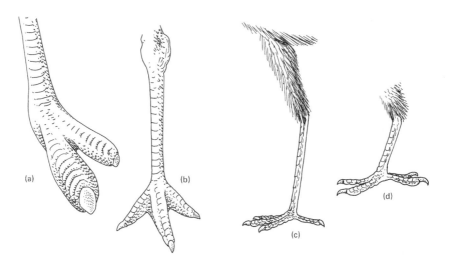

Figure 17–20 Avian feet with various specializations for terrestrial locomotion. (a) Ostrich, with only two toes; (b) rhea, with three toes; (c) secretary bird, with a typical avian foot; (d) roadrunner, with zygodactyl foot. (Not drawn to scale.)

Figure 17–21 Large, flightless, terrestrial birds. (a) elephantbird of Madagascar and (b) *Diatryma*, compared with (c) the cursorial ostrich.

not fall off its perch when it relaxes or goes to sleep. The plantar tendons, which insert on the individual phalanges of the toes, slip in grooves and sheaths that are positioned anterior to the knee joint and posterior to the ankle joint in such a way that the weight of the resting bird tightens the tendons and curls the toes around the perch. Thus, muscular contraction is not required to hold the toes closed. Furthermore, the tendons lying underneath the toe bones have hundreds of minute, rigid, hobnaillike projections that mesh with ridges on the inside surface of the surrounding tendon sheath. The projections and ridges lock the tendons in place in the sheaths and help to hold the toes in their grip around the branch.

Climbing

Birds climb on tree trunks or other vertical surfaces by using their feet, tails, beaks, and, rarely, their forelimbs. Several distantly related groups of birds have independently acquired specializations for climbing and foraging on vertical tree trunks. Species such as woodpeckers and woodcreepers, which use their toes as supports, begin foraging near the base of a tree trunk and work their way vertically upward, head first, clinging to the bark with strong feet on short legs. The tail is used as a prop to brace the body against the powerful pecking exertions of head and neck, and the pygostyle and free caudal vertebrae in these species are much enlarged and support strong, stiff tail feathers. A

similar modification of the tail is found in certain swifts that perch on cave walls and inside chimneys.

Nuthatches and similarly modified birds climb on trunks and rock walls in both head-upward and head-downward directions while foraging, and in these species, which do not use their tails for support, the claw on the hallux is larger than those on the forward-directed toes, and is strongly curved.

Although a few nestling birds clamber about with their wings, only the young hoatzin of South America has evolved a special modification of the forelimbs for climbing. Hoatzins take a long time to begin to fly—60 to 70 days. Until they can fly, they clamber through vegetation using large claws on the first and second digits of the wing that are moved by special muscles. Later in life the claws fall off, and the wing of the adult assumes a typical avian condition, but even the adults are weak fliers and they continue to use their wings to help in climbing among the dense branches of their tropical, swampy habitat. These characteristics of hoatzins may be related to their herbivorous diet. The large crop associated with foregut fermentation of plant material takes up a great deal of space in the trunk, and the sternum is reduced. As a result, there is less area for attachment of flight muscles than in other birds of the same size.

Swimming on the Surface

Although no birds have become fully aquatic like the ichthyosaurs and cetaceans, nearly 400 species are specialized for swimming. Nearly half of these aquatic species also dive and swim under water.

Modifications of the hindlimbs are the most obvious avian specializations for swimming. Other changes include a wide body that increases stability in water, dense plumage that provides buoyancy and insulation, a large preen gland, producing oil that waterproofs the plumage, and structural modifications of the body feathers that retard penetration of water to the skin. The legs are near the rear of a bird's body where the mass of leg muscles interferes least with streamlining and where the best control of steering can be achieved.

The feet of aquatic birds are either webbed or lobed (Figure 17–22). Webbing between the three forward toes (palmate webbing) has been independently acquired at least four times in the course of avian evolution. Totipalmate webbing of all four toes is found in pelicans and their relatives.

Lobes on the toes have evolved convergently in several phylogenetic lines of aquatic birds. There are two different types of lobed feet. Grebes are unique in that the lobes on the outer sides of the toes are rigid and do not fold back as the foot moves forward. A grebe rotates its foot 90 degrees so that the inner side points forward, the toes with their lobes slicing through the water like knife blades for an efficient recovery stroke with minimum drag. A simpler mechanism for the recovery stroke occurs in all the other lobe-footed swimmers where the lobes are flaps that fold back against the

toes during forward movement through water and flare open to present a maximum surface on the backward stroke.

Diving and Swimming Under Water

The transition from a surface swimming bird to a subsurface swimmer has occurred in two fundamentally different ways: either by further specialization of a hindlimb already adapted for swimming or by modification of the wing for use as a flipper under water. Highly specialized foot-propelled divers have evolved independently in grebes, cormorants, loons, and the extinct Hesperornithidae. All these families except the loons include some flightless forms (Figure 17–23). Wing-propelled divers have evolved in the Procellariiformes (the diving petrels), the Sphenisciformes (penguins), and the Charadriiformes (auks and related forms). Only among the waterfowl are there both foot-propelled and wing-propelled diving ducks, but none of these species is as highly modified for diving as specialists such as the loons or auks. The water ouzels or dippers are passerine birds that dive and swim under water with great facility using their small, round wings, but they lack any other morphological specializations.

Other morphological, behavioral, and physiological modifications are important in the evolution of diving birds, such as buoyancy and oxidative metabolism under water. Diving birds overcome

Figure 17–22 Webbed and lobed feet of some aquatic birds. (a) Duck, showing partial webbing; (b) cormorant, showing totipalmate webbing. The lobed foot of a grebe showing how it is rotated during a stroke: (c) position of toes during backward power stroke in side view; (d) front view; (e) side view of the rotated foot during the forward recovery stroke. (From R. T. Peterson, 1978, *The Birds*, 2d edition, Time-Life Books, New York, NY.)

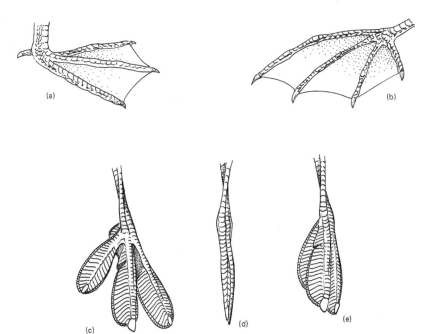

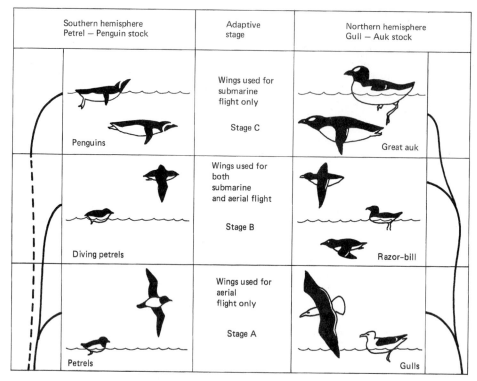

Figure 17–23 Parallel evolution of swimming and diving birds in the Southern Hemisphere (Procellariiformes and Sphenisciformes) and the Northern Hemisphere (Charadriiformes). (From R. W. Storer, 1971, in *Avian Biology*, volume 1, edited by D. S. Farner and J. R. King, Academic, New York, NY.)

buoyancy by reducing the volume of their air sacs, having bones with reduced pneumaticity, expelling air from their plumage before submerging, and in the case of some penguins, by swallowing small stones that act as ballast. Like other diving air breathers, birds constrict their peripheral blood flow, reduce heart rate, and otherwise lower their metabolic rate while under water. They also tend to have a large blood volume with a high oxygen-carrying capacity and muscles that are especially rich in myoglobin, they are able to tolerate high carbon dioxide levels in blood, and they can obtain considerable energy from anaerobic metabolism. These features allow diving times from 1 to 3 minutes, with a maximum recorded survival time of 15 minutes.

■ The Sensory Systems

A bird moves rapidly through three-dimensional space and requires a continuous flow of sensory information about its position and the presence of obstacles in its path. Vision and hearing are the senses best suited to provide this sort of information on a rapidly renewed basis, and birds have well-developed visual and auditory systems. Their predominance is reflected in the brain: The optic lobes are large and the tectum is an important area for processing visual and auditory information. Olfaction is relatively unimportant for most birds and the olfactory lobes are small. The cerebellum, which coordinates body movements, is large. The cerebrum is less developed in birds than it is in mammals and is dominated by the corpus striatum. Many aspects of the behavior of birds are relatively stereotyped in comparison with the more plastic behavioral responses of mammals, and that difference may reflect the greater development of the neopallium of mammals.

Vision

The eyes of birds are large—so large that the brain is displaced dorsally and caudally and in many species the eyeballs meet in the midline of the skull.

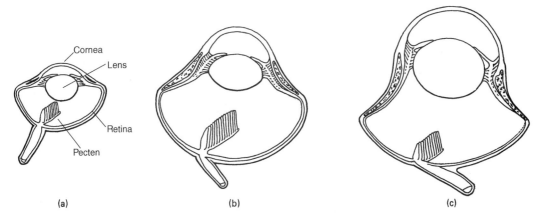

Figure 17–24 Variation in the shape of the eye of birds. (a) Flat, typical of most birds; (b) globular, found in most falcons; (c) tubular, characteristic of owls and some eagles.

The eyes of some hawks, eagles, and owls are as large as the eyes of humans. In its basic structure the eye of a bird is like that of any other vertebrate, but the shape varies from a flattened sphere to something approaching a tube (Figure 17–24). An analysis of the optical characteristics of birds eyes suggests that these differences are primarily the result of fitting large eyes into small skulls. The eyes of a starling are small enough to be contained within the skull, whereas the eyes of an owl bulge out of the skull. An owl would require an enormous, unwieldy head to accommodate a flat eye like that of a starling. The tubular shape of the owl's eye allows it to fit into a reasonable size skull.

Although the basic structures of vertebrate eyes are similar (Chapter 3), the methods of focusing vary (Figure 17–25). Mammalian eyes have spherical lenses that account for most of the bending of light rays that focuses them on the retina. The focus is adjusted to accommodate nearby or distant objects by contracting or relaxing muscles within the ciliary body that change the shape of the lens. In birds, both the cornea and the lens contribute to focus, and accommodation is produced by changing the curvature of both structures. Muscles within the ciliary body change the shape of the lens, and a second set of muscles that are associated with the cornea change its curvature.

The pecten is a conspicuous structure in the eye of birds (Figure 17–24). It is formed exclusively of blood capillaries surrounded by pigmented tissue and covered by a membrane; it lacks muscles and nerves. The pecten arises from the retina at the point where the nerve fibers from the ganglion cells of the retina join to form the optic nerve. In some

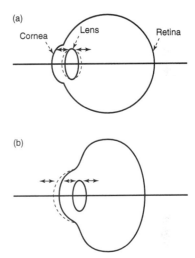

Figure 17–25 Accommodation mechanisms of vertebrate eyes. (a) Mammalian eye: contraction and relaxation of muscles associated with the ciliary bodies change the shape of the lens—more spherical for close vision, flatter for distant objects. (b) Bird eye: in addition to the change in shape of the lens, a second set of muscles anchored around the corneal margin change the curvature of the cornea. (Modified from G. R. Martin, 1987, *Nature* 328:383.)

species of birds the pecten is small, but in other species the pecten extends so far into the vitreous humor of the eye that it almost touches the lens. The function of the pecten remains uncertain after 200 years of debate. Possible functions for the pecten in vision have been proposed (reduction of glare, a mirror to reflect objects above the bird, production of a stroboscopic effect, a visual reference point), but none seems very likely. The pecten is formed largely by blood capillaries, and its highly vascularized structure suggests that it may provide nutrition for the retinal cells and help to remove metabolic waste products that accumulate in the vitreous humor.

Oil droplets are found primarily in the cone cells of the avian retina, as they are in other vertebrates. The droplets range in color from red through orange and yellow to green; red droplets occur only in birds and turtles. Different color oil droplets are associated with various types of cone cells, and these cells are localized in different areas of the retina. For example, the central dorsal part of the retina of the pigeon has a predominance of photoreceptors with red droplets and the ventral and lateral parts of the retina have cells with yellow droplets. The oil droplets act as filters, absorbing some wavelengths of light and transmitting others. The function of the oil droplets is unclear and is certainly complex because the various colors of droplets are combined with different kinds of photoreceptor cells and different visual pigments. Birds like gulls, terns, gannets, and kingfishers that must see through the surface of water have a preponderance of red droplets. Aerial hawkers of insects (swifts, swallows) have predominantly yellow droplets.

Hearing

In birds, as in other diapsids, the columella and its cartilaginous extension, the extracolumella, transmit vibrations of the tympanum to the oval window of the inner ear. The cochlea of birds has the same basic structure as that of other vertebrates (Chapter 3), but it appears to be specialized for fine distinctions of the frequency and temporal pattern of sound. The cochlea of a bird is about one-tenth the length of the cochlea of a mammal, but it has about ten times as many hair cells per unit of length. The space above the basilar membrane (the scala vestibuli) is nearly filled in birds by a folded, glandular tegmentum. This structure may damp sound waves, allowing the ear of a bird to respond very rapidly to changes in sounds.

The openings of the external auditory meatus are small, only a few millimeters in diameter in most birds, and are covered with feathers that may ensure laminar airflow across the opening during flight. The columellar muscle inserts on the columella. On contraction this muscle draws the columella away from the oval window, decreasing the sound energy transmitted to the inner ear. This mechanism may protect the ear against the noise of wind during flight and it may also help to tune the auditory system. In starlings contraction of the columellar muscle increases the effect of the middle ear as a filter for sounds of different frequencies. The sounds that most readily pass the filter are those in the range of greatest auditory sensitivity, which, in most birds, corresponds to the frequency range of their own vocalizations.

Localization of sounds in space can be difficult for small animals such as birds. Large animals localize the source of sounds by comparing the time of arrival, intensity, or phase of a sound in their left and right ears, but none of these methods is very effective when the distance between the ears is small. The pneumatic construction of the skulls of birds may allow them to use sound that is transmitted through the air-filled passages between the middle ears on the two sides of the head to increase their directional sensitivity. If this is true, internally transmitted sound would pass from the middle ear on one side to the middle ear on the other side and reach the *inner* surface of the contralateral tympanum. Here it would interact with the sound arriving on the external surface of the tympanum via the external auditory meatus. The vibration of each tympanum would be the product of the combination of pressure and phase of the internal and external sources of sound energy, and the magnitude of the cochlear response would be proportional to the difference in pressure across the tympanic membrane.

The sensitivity of the auditory system of birds is approximately the same as that of humans, despite the small size of birds' ears. Most birds have tympanic membranes that are large in relation to the size of the head. A large tympanic membrane enhances auditory sensitivity, and owls (which have especially sensitive hearing) have the largest tympani relative to their head size among birds. Sound pressures are amplified during transmission from the tympanum to the oval window of the cochlea because the area of the oval window is smaller than the area of the tympanum. The reduction ratio for birds ranges from 11 to 40. High ratios suggest sensitive hearing, and the highest values are found in owls; songbirds have intermediate ratios (20 to 30). (The ratio is 36 for cats and 21 for humans.) The inward movement of the tympanum as sound waves strike it is opposed by air pressure within the middle ear, and birds show a variety of features that reduce the resistance of the middle ear. The middle ear is continuous with the dorsal, rostral, and caudal air cavities in the pneumatic skulls of birds. In addition to potentially allowing sound waves to be transmitted to the contralateral ear, these interconnections increase the volume of the middle ear and reduce its stiffness, thereby allowing the tympanum to respond to faint sounds.

Owls are acoustically the most sensitive of birds. At frequencies up to 10 kilohertz (10,000 cycles per second), the auditory sensitivity of an owl is as great as that of a cat. Owls have large tympanic membranes, large cochleae, and well-developed auditory centers in the brain. Some owls are diurnal, others crepuscular (active at dawn and dusk), and some are entirely nocturnal. In an experimental test of their capacities for acoustic orientation, barn owls were able to seize mice in total darkness (Konishi 1973). If the mice towed a piece of paper across the floor behind them, the owls struck the rustling paper instead of the mouse, showing that sound was the cue they were using.

A distinctive feature of many owls is the facial ruff that is formed by stiff feathers. The ruff acts as a parabolic sound reflector, focusing sounds with frequencies above 5 kilohertz on the external auditory meatus and amplifying them by 10 decibels. The ruffs of some owls are asymmetric, and that asymmetry appears to enhance the ability of owls to locate prey. When the ruffs were removed from the barn owls in Konishi's experiments, the owls made large errors in finding targets.

Asymmetry of the aural system of owls goes beyond the feathered ruff. The skull itself is markedly asymmetric in many owls (Figure 17–26), and these are the species with the greatest auditory sensitivity (Norberg 1977). The asymmetry ends at the external auditory meatus; the middle and inner ears of owls are bilaterally symmetric. The asymmetry of the external ear openings of owls assists with localization of prey in the horizontal and vertical axes (Norberg 1978). The time at which sounds are received by the two ears can indicate the horizontal direction of the source, and owls are capable of detecting differences of a few hundredths of a millisecond in the arrival times of a sound at the left and right ears. The vertical direction of a sound source can be determined by the differential sensitivity of the two ears to sounds coming from above and below the level of the owl. The soft tissue and feathers surrounding the face of an owl produce a situation of reversed asymmetry in which the actual directional sensitivity of the ears is the reverse of

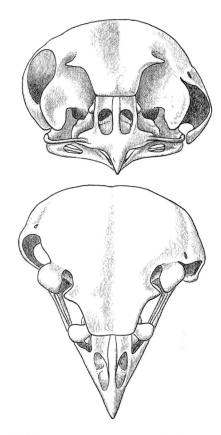

Figure 17–26 The skulls of many owls show pronounced asymmetry in the position of the external auditory meatus that assists in localization of sound. (From Norberg 1978.)

what would be expected from examination of the skull. The left ear, which opens low on the side of the head, is most sensitive to sounds that originate *above* the level of the owl's head, and the right ear is sensitive to sounds coming from *below* the level of the head. This auditory asymmetry applies only to sounds with frequencies above 6000 hertz; sensitivity to lower frequencies is bilaterally symmetrical.

Olfaction

The sense of smell is well developed in some birds and poorly developed in others; a review of the olfactory systems of birds can be found in Bang and Wenzel (1985). The size of the olfactory bulbs is a rough indication of the sensitivity of the olfactory system. Relatively large bulbs are found in ground nesting and colonial nesting species, species that are associated with water, and carnivorous and piscivorous species of birds. Some birds use scent to locate prey. The kiwi, for example, has nostrils at the tip of its long bill and finds earthworms underground by smelling them. Turkey vultures follow airborne odors of carrion to the vicinity of a carcass, which they then locate by sight. Sponges soaked in fish oil and placed on floating buoys attracted shearwaters, fulmars, albatrosses, and petrels even in the dark.

Olfaction probably plays a role in the orientation and navigation abilities of some birds. The tube-nosed seabirds (albatrosses, shearwaters, fulmars, and petrels) nest on islands, and when they return from foraging at sea they approach the islands from downwind. Homing pigeons use olfaction (as well as other mechanisms) to navigate (Ioalè et al. 1990). The well-developed nasal bulbs of colonial nesting species of birds suggest the possibility that olfaction is used for social functions such as recognition of individuals, but this has never been demonstrated.

Other Senses

Birds use a variety of cues for navigation, and many of these are extensions of the senses we have discussed into regions beyond the sensitivity of mammals. For example, birds can detect polarized light when it falls on the area of the retina that normally receives skylight, but other parts of the retina cannot detect polarization. Ultraviolet light (light with a wavelength of less than 400 nanometers) is not detected by most mammals, but pigeons are more sensitive to ultraviolet light in the region of 350 nanometers than they are to light at any wavelength in the visible part of the spectrum.

Some birds are sensitive to very small differences in air pressure. Experiments showed that pigeons were able to detect the difference in air pressure between the ceiling and floor of a room, and a pigeon flying upward at a rate of 4 centimeters per second would be able to detect a change in its altitude of 4 millimeters. This sensitivity may be useful during flight, and may also play a role in allowing birds to anticipate changes in weather patterns that are important in the timing of migration.

Another kind of sensory information that may tell birds about the weather is infrasound—very-low-frequency sounds (less than 10 cycles per second) that are produced by large-scale movements of air. Thunderstorms, winds blowing across valleys, and other geophysical events produce infrasound that is propagated over thousands of miles. The lower-frequency limit of human hearing is around 20 hertz, but birds can hear well into the region of infrasound. Pigeons, for example, can detect frequencies as low as 0.05 hertz (3 cycles per *minute*).

The magnetic field of the earth provides a cue that could be used for orientation if an animal were able to perceive it, and considerable evidence suggests that birds are able to detect magnetic fields. The orientation of several species of birds during their migratory periods can be adjusted in predictable ways by placing them in an artificial magnetic field. The mechanism by which the magnetic field is detected is not known, but deposits of magnetite recently described in the heads of pigeons may be involved (Wiltschko and Wiltschko 1988).

■ Summary

Feathers are the distinguishing character of birds, and flight is the distinctive mode of avian locomotion. In many respects the morphology of birds is shaped by the demands of flight. Flapping flight is a more complicated process than flight with fixed wings like those of aircraft, but it can be understood in aerodynamic terms. Feathers compose the aerodynamic surfaces responsible for lift and propulsion during flight and they also provide streamlining. There are many variations and specializations within the four basic types of wings, but in general high speed and elliptical wings are used in flapping flight, whereas high aspect ratio and high-lift wings are used for soaring and gliding. The hollow bones of birds, probably an ancestral character of the

archosaur lineage, combine lightness and strength. The air sacs, some of which fill several of the pneumatic bones, create a one-way flow of air through the lung that enhances oxygen uptake, and the air sacs probably also help to dissipate the heat produced by muscles during flight.

Some parts of the skeletons of birds are light in relation to the sizes of their bodies, and some of this lightness has been achieved by modification of the skull. Several skull bones that are separate in other diapsids are fused in birds, air sacs are extensively developed, and teeth are absent. The function of teeth in processing food has been taken over by the muscular gizzard, which is part of the stomach of birds. The gizzard is well developed in birds that eat hard items such as seeds and it may contain stones that probably assist in grinding food. Vision is the primary sense for most birds, and visual capacities extend to detection of ultraviolet and polarized light. Hearing is also important and the auditory system of birds is capable of very precise discriminations of the frequencies and temporal patterns of sound. Sensitivity extends downward to include sounds with frequencies lower than 10 cycles per second. Sensitivity to magnetism has been demonstrated for several species of birds, but the mechanisms involved are unknown. Olfactory sensitivity is variably developed among birds: Some species use scent to locate food and for navigation, but other species appear not to use olfaction at all.

■ References

Bang, B. G., and B. M. Wenzel. 1985. Nasal cavity and olfactory system. Pages 195–225 in *Form and Function in Birds*, volume 3, edited by A. S. King and J. McLelland. Academic, London, UK.

Gaunt, A. S., S. L. L. Gaunt, and R. M. Casey. 1982. Syringeal mechanics reassessed: evidence from *Streptopelia*. *Auk* 99:474–494.

Goller, F. and O. N. Larsen. 1997. A new mechanism of sound generation in songbirds. *Proceedings of the National Academy of Sciences, USA.* 94:14787–14791.

Grajal, A. S., D. Strahl, R. Parra, M. G. Dominguez, and A. Neher. 1989. Foregut fermentation in the hoatzin, a Neotropical leaf-eating bird. *Science* 245:1236–1238.

Greenewalt, C. H. 1968. *Bird Song: Acoustics and Physiology.* Smithsonian Institution Press. Washington, DC.

Greenewalt, C. H. 1969. How birds sing. *Scientific American* 221:126–139.

Ioalè, P., M. Nozzolini, and F. Papi. 1990. Homing pigeons do extract directional information from olfactory stimuli. *Behavioral Ecology and Sociobiology* 26:301–306.

Konishi, M. 1973. How the owl tracks its prey. *American Scientist* 61:414–424.

Norberg, R. Å. 1977. Occurrence and independent evolution of bilateral ear asymmetry in owls and implications for owl taxonomy. *Philosophical Transactions of the Royal Society of London* B280:375–408.

Norberg, R. Å. 1978. Skull asymmetry, ear structure and function, and auditory localization in Tengmalm's owl, *Aegolius funereus* (Linné). *Philosophical Transactions of the Royal Society of London* B282:325–410.

Norberg, U. M. 1985. Flying, gliding, and soaring. Pages 129–158 in *Functional Vertebrate Morphology*, edited by M. Hildebrand, D. M. Bramble, K. F. Liem, and D. B. Wake. Harvard University Press, Cambridge, MA.

Nowicki, S. 1987. Vocal tract resonances in oscine bird sound production: evidence from birdsongs in a helium atmosphere. *Nature* 325:53–55.

Raikow, R. J. 1985. Locomotor system. Pages 57–147 in *Form and Function in Birds*, volume 3, edited by A. S. King and J. McLelland. Academic, London, UK.

Rayner, J. M. V. 1988. Form and function in avian flight. Pages 1–66 in *Current Ornithology*, volume 5, edited by R. J. Johnston. Plenum, New York, NY.

Wiltschko, W., and R. Wiltschko. 1988. Magnetic orientation in birds. Pages 67–121 in *Current Ornithology*, volume 5, edited by R. F. Johnston. Plenum, New York, NY.

CHAPTER
18

The Ecology and Behavior
of Birds

In the preceding chapter we examined the functional relationships among structural characteristics of birds and the physical and biological requirements of flight. In this chapter we consider some of the consequences of flight for the biology of birds. We have stressed mobility as a basic characteristic of vertebrates, and the ability to fly gives birds extraordinary mobility. Long-distance migration is perhaps the most conspicuous option offered to birds by their capacity to fly, and navigation over long distances requires a range of mechanisms that operate under different circumstances.

A second characteristic of birds is diurnality; most species are active only by day. We know that diurnality is not necessarily related to flight, because bats are nocturnal, but the diurnal activity of birds has made them popular and accessible subjects for biological field studies. Two important areas of modern biology, optimal foraging theory and the behavioral ecology of mating systems, have drawn heavily on studies of birds for data that can be generalized to other vertebrates. Both types of studies emphasize the role of behavior in enhancing the fitness of individuals; and the study of reproductive biology, in particular, includes examples in which individual fitness may be maximized by cooperating with other individuals. These altruistic behaviors are normally directed toward relatives of the individual engaging in the behavior, as predicted by the theory of inclusive fitness explained in Chapter 1.

■ The Evolution of Birds

The fossil record of birds, which begins with *Archaeopteryx* in Jurassic sediments from Germany, is extensive and has been the subject of several reviews (Martin 1983a,b; Olson 1985; Cracraft 1986; Lockley et al. 1992). Fossils of true flying birds are known from Cretaceous deposits in Europe, Asia, and North and South America, and 22 extant orders of birds can be traced back to the Cretaceous.

Early Birds

Archaeopteryx was probably a late-surviving relict that was contemporaneous with more typically avian birds. It had teeth, claws on the fingers, and a long tail. If it were not for the presence of feathers, *Archaeopteryx* could readily be classified as a small dinosaur. However, several lines of evidence suggest that *Archaeopteryx* was capable of flight (Chapter 13): Its skeletal proportions were similar to those of some extant flying birds, the number of primaries and secondaries were identical to those of extant birds, the asymmetry of its flight feathers is like that seen in extant flying birds, and the furcula was large. The seventh specimen of *Archaeopteryx* reveals a feature not visible in the fossils previously known—a retangular sternum that was probably associated with strong flight muscles. On balance, these characteristics are consistent with the view that *Archaeopteryx* was a flying bird (Martin 1983b; Rayner 1988). Nonetheless, *Archaeopteryx* probably could not land in trees because it retained a primitive foot structure that would not have allowed it to seize a branch. It seems likely that *Archaeopteryx* made running landings as modern chickens do.

Our knowledge of the early evolution of birds after *Archaeopteryx* has increased enormously since 1980 with the discovery of more fossil birds than had been unearthed in the entire previous century (Figure 18–1). Several important discoveries have been made at the Early Cretaceous Las Hoyas site in Spain. *Iberomesornis* had a pectoral girdle that was more derived than that of *Archaeopteryx*, with strut-like coracoids, a furcular process, and an ulna that

was longer than the humerus. In addition, the tail was reduced to a series of free vertebrae and a pygostyle. The foot had curved claws and an opposable hallux (i.e., a rearward-pointing toe). This foot structure allows modern birds to perch, because as the legs bend a ligament curls the toes tightly around a branch. The presence of recurved claws and a hallux in Early Cretaceous birds such as *Iberomesornis* suggests that they were able to land in trees.

A group of birds known as Enantiornithes (opposite birds), first discovered in Argentina and now known from six continents, flourished between 140 million and 70 million years ago. *Sinornis* (Figure 18–2), from the Early Cretaceous of China, was the size of a sparrow and the largest enantornithine discovered so far. *Enantiornis* from Argentina, was the size of a turkey vulture. Most enantiornithines were small to medium size and probably lived in trees, but some had long legs and were probably wading birds and others had powerful claws like modern hawks.

Enantiornithines continued the trends seen in *Iberomesornis*. *Sinornis* had a vertebral column that

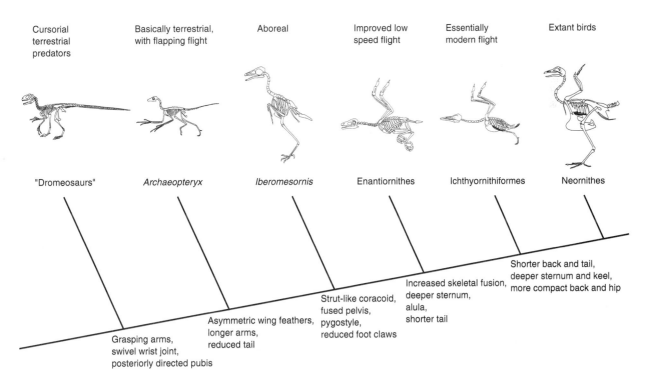

Figure 18–1 Evolution of specializations for flight.

Figure 18–2 *Sinornis,* bird from Early Cretaceous lake bed deposits in China. (From P. C. Sereno and R. Chenggang, 1992, *Science* 255:845–848. © AAAS 1992.)

contained only 11 dorsal vertebrae, compared with 14 for *Archaeopteryx.* The short trunk and tail shifted the center of mass toward the forelimbs, as in extant birds, rather than toward the hindlimbs, as in cursorial terrestrial archosaurs, and many of the derived characters of enantiornithines are associated with flight (Sereno and Chenggang 1992, Sanz et al 1996). For example, the wrist could bend backward sharply, as in extant birds, so the wing could be tucked against the body and the sternum developed a deep keel. The alula, which increases maneuverability in slow-speed flight, is first seen in an enantiornithine from Las Hoyas, *Eoavulavis* (= dawn bird with an alula).

Gobipteryx, an enantiornithine known from skulls found in Late Cretaceous deposits in Mongolia, is unique among Cretaceous birds in lacking teeth. In the same deposits that yielded fossils of adult *Gobipteryx,* the Polish Mongolian Expedition found fossilized eggs, some of which contained well-preserved skeletons with skulls very like those of adult *Gobipteryx.* The skeletons of these embryos were well developed, and it is likely that the chicks were precocial at hatching (i.e., able to walk and to find their own food).

Two flightless birds are known from the Late Cretaceous, *Patagopteryx* and the remarkable

Mononykus olecranus. Mononykus means "one claw," and refers to the peculiar structure of the forelimb, which is short and ends in a stout claw (Altangerel et al. 1993a,b). In other respects, *Mononykus* shows derived features of birds, including a keeled sternum, a fibula that was reduced to a small spike of bone, and fused metacarpals.

In addition to these fossils, an abundance of fossilized feather impressions and tracks indicates that by the Early Cretaceous birds inhabited both the Northern and Southern hemispheres. The differences among the fossil species known—flying and flightless birds and a foot-propelled diver—combined with the wide geographic distribution of birds in the Cretaceous suggest that more of the evolution of birds took place in the Jurassic than has previously been appreciated. Avian evolution is an area of lively controversy, and views of the phylogenetic history of birds are likely to change substantially as additional material is studied.

The Ichthyornithiformes were flying birds with a well-developed keel on the sternum and short backs and tails, but they retained teeth. Several species of *Ichthyornis* have been named, mostly on the basis of differences in size. In general, ichthyornithiforms were the size of gulls and terns, and like these extant birds they may have flown far out to sea.

Another group of Late Cretaceous birds, the Hesperornithiformes, were flightless, foot-propelled swimmers and divers. A fossil from England, *Enaliornis*, establishes the presence of hesperornithiforms in the Early Cretaceous and they were a diverse group by the Late Cretaceous. The hesperornithiforms were medium-size to large flightless birds that were specialized for foot-propelled diving (Figure 18–3). The body and neck were elongate, the sternum lacked a keel, and the bones were not pneumatic. Teeth remained in the maxilla and dentary. Feathers preserved with two specimens of *Parahesperornis* were plumulaceous and the birds may have had a furry appearance somewhat like that of the extant kiwis. The feet were placed far posteriorly on the body (a position that is characteristic of many foot-propelled diving birds) and the toes had lobes like those seen in extant grebes. The femur and tibiotarsus were locked in place and could not be rotated under the body. As a result, hesperornithiforms would not have been able to walk on land and probably pushed themselves along by sliding on their stomachs. The lateral placement of the feet would have made it possible for hesperornithiforms to exert force directly backward during swimming and diving without an upward component that would have tended to drive them toward the surface. Pachyostosis (an increased density of bone) gave hesperornithiforms a high specific gravity that would have facilitated diving. Coprolites (fossilized feces) found in association with *Hesperornis* and *Baptornis* contain the remains of small fishes.

The Evolution of Derived Orders and Families of Birds

Modern birds, the Neornithes, began to diversify during the last part of the Cretaceous, replacing the Enantiornithes as the predominant avian forms. An analysis that combined information from DNA and fossils has identified 22 extant avian lineages that had separated in the Cretaceous and survived the Cretaceous/Tertiary extinction (Cooper and Penny 1997). This Cretaceous radiation encompassed a wide variety of birds, including flightless forms (rhea, ostrich, and moa), wading birds (ibis, rail), freshwater and marine birds (duck, loon, grebe, gull, albatross, shearwater, tropicbird, and frigate bird), predatory birds (owl, osprey), and terrestrial and arboreal forest birds (tinamou, chicken, chachalaca, wren, and three lineages of parrots).

A major radiation of avian families occurred during the Cenozoic (Feduccia 1995, 1996). The Eocene was the epoch of greatest diversification of birds. More surviving families arose in that period

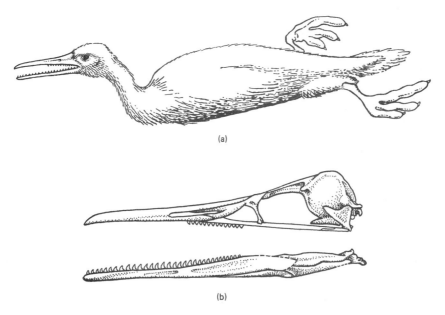

(a)

(b)

Figure 18–3   The hesperornithiforms were flightless, toothed birds. (a) Restoration of *Hesperornis*; (b) skull of *Parahesperornis*. Note the teeth in the maxilla and dentary bones. ([a] From A. Feduccia, 1980, *The Age of Birds*, Harvard University Press, Cambridge, MA; [b] from Martin 1983.)

than at any other time. Most of these families consist of additional water birds and nonpasserine forest dwellers. A second radiation occurred in the Miocene and included a few additional families of water birds, but mostly land-dwelling passerines that were adapted to drier, less forested environments. Most families of birds had evolved by the end of the Miocene, and many still-existing genera and some species were present by the Pliocene. Birds formed complex ecological communities by the middle of the Cenozoic (Warheit 1992).

Phylogeny of Extant Birds

Phylogenetic relationships among extant birds are poorly known and are the subject of continuing controversy. Several views of these relationships and the difficulties inherent in their study can be found in reviews by Cracraft (1986), Olson (1985), Sibley et al. (1988), Raikow (1985), Houde (1986, 1987), and Sibley and Ahlquist (1990).

The lack of consensus about the phylogeny of extant birds makes it impossible to provide a cladogram that represents a widely accepted hypothesis of evolutionary relationships. Charles Sibley and his colleagues (Sibley et al. 1988, Sibley and Ahlquist 1990) have presented a cladistic analysis based on comparisons of DNA. Their classification of passerine birds has been well received, but their analysis of the relationships of nonpasserine birds is more controversial and provides a good example of some of the difficulties in reconstructing phylogeny solely by molecular methods.

One of the major controversies in bird phylogeny centers on the relationships of a group of flightless birds known as ratites. Extant ratites include ostriches (Africa), rheas (South America), emus and cassowaries (Australia), and kiwis (New Zealand). All these land masses were part of the southern supercontinent Gondwana, and it has been suggested that the ratites arose from a single flightless ancestor that was widely distributed on Gondwana. By this hypothesis the ratites form a monophyletic group and their current geographic distribution reflects the breakup of Gondwana in the late Mesozoic and early Cenozoic.

An alternative view proposes that the similarities of extant ratites are ancestral characters that were found in many lineages of birds. The ratites and another group of birds, the tinamous of Central and South America, share a paleognathous palatal structure. This palate is characterized by long prevomers that extend posteriorly to articulate with the palatines and pterygoids and by large basipterygoid processes that articulate with the pterygoids. The paleognathus palate is distinguished from the neognathus palate that is characteristic of other birds. Paleognathous palatal characters are seen in toothed birds such as *Hesperornis* and in the Cretaceous toothless bird *Gobipteryx*, and they are present in early stages of the embryonic development of neognathus birds. Thus, the paleognathus condition of ratites and tinamous could have evolved by neoteny from a neognathus form. This possibility means that the paleognathus birds are not necessarily a monophyletic lineage. Furthermore, the discovery of birds related to ostriches in Paleocene and Eocene deposits in North America and Europe casts doubt on the assumption that the current distribution of ratites is the result of events associated with the breakup of Gondwana (Houde 1986).

The phylogeny and zoogeography of ratites are of considerable significance in current biochemical studies of the phylogeny of birds, because Sibley and Ahlquist based the calibration of the DNA molecular clock on the assumption that the separation of the lineages of ratites was caused by the breakup of Gondwana. If the ratites do represent two or more independent origins, or if the origins of some ratites were in the Northern Hemisphere rather than in Gondwana, the calibration of the DNA clock is erroneous and conclusions about relationships among other groups of birds that were based on that calibration are weakened.

The most commonly used classification of birds derives from Storer (1971). Because it is the system used by most references, we present it in Table 18.1.

■ Birds as Model Organisms

Birds might almost have been designed as the ideal vertebrate animals for biologists to study. They are diverse (about 9700 species), widespread, conspicuous, and largely diurnal. Most birds are visually oriented, and respond to stimuli such as colors, patterns, and movements that humans also are able to perceive. A worldwide corps of amateur ornithologists has helped to assemble the huge amount of information we have about the life history and population ecology of birds.

Studies of birds have contributed to our understanding of vertebrates, especially in areas such as

| | Approximate Number of | | |
Classification	Families	Species	Geographic Region
Palaeognathae			
Tinamiformes (tinamous)	1	47	Neotropics
Rheiformes (rheas)	2	2	Neotropics
Struthioniformes (ostriches)	1	1	Africa
Casuariiformes (emus and cassowaries)	2	4	Australia, New Guinea
Dinornithiformes (kiwis)	1	3	New Zealand
Neognathae			
Podicipediformes (grebes)	1	21	Worldwide
Sphenisciformes (penguins)	1	17	Southern Hemisphere
Procellariiformes (albatrosses, shearwaters, petrels)	4	115	Worldwide
Pelecaniformes (tropic birds, boobies, gannets, cormorants, pelicans, frigatebirds)	6	67	Worldwide
Anseriformes (screamers and waterfowl)	2	161	Worldwide
Phoenicopteriformes (flamingos)	1	5	Worldwide, except Australia
Ciconiiformes (herons, bitterns, whale-head storks, storks, ibises, spoonbills)	5	120	Worldwide
Falconiformes (condors, hawks, eagles, kites, falcons, caracaras)	5	311	Worldwide
Galliformes (curassows, guans, chachalacas, megapodes, guineafowl, pheasants, quail, grouse, turkeys)	5	258	Worldwide
Gruiformes (rails, coots, sungrebes, kagu, sunbittern, roatelos, buttonquails, cranes, limpkins, trumpeters, seriemas, bustards)	11	213	Worldwide
Charadriiformes (shorebirds, plovers, sandpipers, gulls, jaegers, skuas, skimmers, terns, auks, murres, puffins, sandgrouses)	19	366	Worldwide
Gaviiformes (loons)	1	5	New World, Eurasia
Columbiformes (doves, pigeons)	1	310	Worldwide
Psittaciformes (parrots)	3	358	Pantropical and Australia
Coliiformes (mousebirds)	1	6	Africa
Musophagiformes (turacos)	1	23	Africa
Cuculiformes (cuckoos, hoatzin)	6	143	Worldwide
Strigiformes (owls)	2	186	Worldwide
Caprimulgiformes (nightjars, poorwills, frogmouths, oilbirds)	5	113	Worldwide
Apodiformes (swifts, hummingbirds)	3	422	Worldwide
Trogoniformes (trogons, quetzals)	1	39	Pantropical except Australasia
Coraciiformes (kingfishers, todies, motmots, bee-eaters, rollers, hoopoes, hornbills)	10	218	Worldwide
Piciformes (jacamars, barbets, honeyguides, toucans, woodpeckers)	8	410	Worldwide
Passeriformes (perching birds, including the songbirds)			
Tyranni (broadbills, pittas, asities, New Zealand wrens, tyrant flycatchers, cotingas, manakins, woodcreepers, ovenbirds, antbirds, tapaculos)	15	1138	Pantropical
Passeres			
Crows and related forms	31	1113	Worldwide
Thrushes and related forms	7	611	Worldwide
Nuthatches, wrens, and related forms	14	1168	Worldwide
Larks, sparrows, finches, wood warblers, tanagers, blackbirds, and related forms	17	1651	Worldwide

Source: Based on F. B. Gill, 1995, *Ornithology*, 2d edition, Freeman, New York, NY.

ecology, morphology, and behavior (Konishi et al. 1989). These topics reveal fascinating examples of the interdependence of structure and function that emphasize the importance of broadly integrative studies in organismal biology. In this chapter we focus on aspects of feeding, reproduction, and behavior.

Divergence and Convergence in Feeding

Birds show morphological, physiological, and behavioral specializations associated with feeding on diverse sources of food. Modifications of the beak and tongue are often associated with dietary specializations.

Beaks and Tongues   The presence of a horny beak in place of teeth is not unique to birds—we have noted the same phenomenon in turtles, rhynchosaurs, dinosaurs, pterosaurs, and the dicynodonts—but the diversity of beaks among birds is remarkable. The range of morphological specializations of beaks defies complete description, but some categories can be recognized (Figure 18–4).

Insectivorous birds such as warblers, which find their food on leaf surfaces, usually have short, thin, pointed bills that are adept at seizing insects, whereas aerial sweepers such as swifts, swallows, and nighthawks, which catch their prey on the wing, have short, weak beaks and a wide gape. Kinesis of the lower jaw substantially increases the gape of the nightjar; the distance between the two rami of the lower jaw increases from 12.5 millimeters when the mouth is closed to 40 millimeters when it is opened. Stiff feathers at the corners of the mouth further increase the insect-trapping area.

It is always the case that one can find exceptions to generalizations about the correspondence between morphology and behavior, and the bills of insectivorous birds reveal many of these. For example, some hornbills use their heavy, simitar-shaped beaks to pick up termites and small insects from the ground, and flycatchers, which snap up insects in flight, have hooked beaks.

Many carnivorous birds, such as gulls, ravens, crows, and roadrunners, use their heavy pointed beaks to kill their prey, but most hawks, owls, and eagles kill prey with their talons and employ their

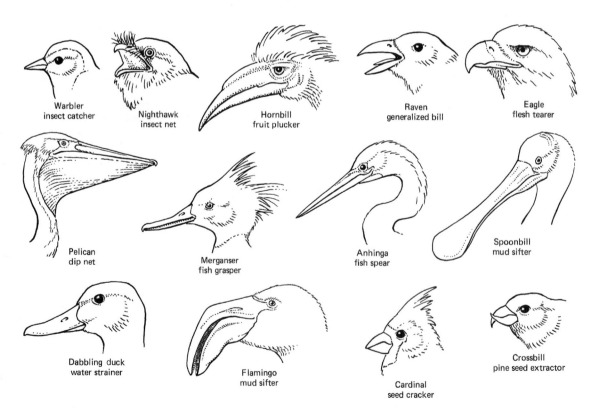

Figure 18–4 Examples of specializations of the beaks of birds.

beaks to tear off pieces small enough to swallow. Falcons stun prey with the impact of their dive, and then bite the neck of the prey to disarticulate the cervical vertebrae. The true falcons (the genus *Falco*) have a structure called a tomial tooth that aids in the process. This tooth actually is a sharp projection from the upper mandible that matches a corresponding notch on the bottom mandible. Shrikes, a group of predatory passerine birds that employ neck biting to kill prey, also have a tomial tooth. Fish-eating birds such as cormorants and pelicans have beaks with a sharply hooked tip that is used to seize fish, and mergansers have long, narrow bills with a series of serrations along the sides of the beak, in addition to a hook at the tip. Darters and anhingas have harpoonlike bills that they use to impale fishes. The massive beak and jaw apparatus of the gigantic predatory bird *Diatryma* may have been used to kill and dismember prey (Box 18–1).

Spoonbills have flattened bills with broad tips that they use to create currents that lift prey into the water column where it can be seized. Many aquatic birds strain small crustaceans or plankton from water or mud with bills that incorporate some sort of filtering apparatus. Dabbling ducks have bills with horny lamellae that form crosswise ridges and their tongues also have horny projections. The tongue and bill are densely invested with sensory corpuscles and form a filter system that allows ducks to scoop up a billfull of water and mud, filter out the prey, and allow the debris to escape. Flamingos have a similar system. The bill of a flamingo is sharply bent and the anterior part is held in a horizontal position when the flamingo lowers its head to feed. The lower jaw of a flamingo is smaller than the upper jaw, and it is the upper jaw that moves during feeding while the lower jaw remains motionless. (This reversal of the usual vertebrate pattern is possible because of the kinetic skull of birds.)

Seeds contain the energy and nutrients that plants have invested in reproduction, and seeds are usually protected by hard coverings (husks) that must be removed before the nutritious contents can be eaten. Specialized seed-eating birds use one of two methods to husk seeds before swallowing them. One group holds the seed in its beak and slices it by making fore-and-aft movements of the lower mandible, whereas birds in the second group hold the seed against ridges on the palate and crack the husk by exerting an upward pressure with their robust lower mandible. After the husk has been opened, both kinds of birds use their tongues to remove the contents. Other birds have different specializations for eating seeds: Crossbills extract the seeds of conifers from between the scales of the cones, using the diverging tips of their bills to pry the scales apart. Woodpeckers, nuthatches, and chickadees may wedge a nut or acorn into a hole in the bark of a tree and then hammer at it with their sharp bills until it cracks.

The production of fruits is a strategy of seed dispersal for plants, and birds are important dispersal agents. The bright colors of many fruits advertise their presence or ripeness and attract birds that eat them. The pulp surrounding the seed is digested during its passage through the bird's intestine, but the seeds are not damaged. The birds may discard the seed before eating the pulp, or the seeds may pass through the gut to be voided with the feces. In some cases the chemical or mechanical stress of its passage through the digestive system of a bird facilitates subsequent sprouting by the seed. Fruit-eating birds do not have to penetrate a hard covering, but the very size of the fruit may make it hard to swallow. Skull kinesis can be important for fruit eaters; the widening of the gape as the mouth opens may allow them to swallow large items.

Many birds use their beaks to probe for hidden food. Long-billed shorebirds probe in mud and sand to locate worms and crustaceans. These birds display a form of skull kinesis in which the flexible zone in the upper jaw has moved toward the tip of the beak, allowing the tip of the upper jaw to be lifted without opening the mouth (Figure 18–6). This mechanism enables long-billed waders to grasp prey under the mud.

Tongues are an important part of the food-gathering apparatus of many birds. Woodpeckers drill holes into dead trees and then use their long tongues to investigate passageways made by wood-boring insects. The tongue of the green woodpecker, which extracts ants from their tunnels in the ground, extends four times the length of its beak. The hyoid bones that support the tongue are elongated and housed in a sheath of muscles that passes around the outside of the skull and rests in the nasal cavity (Figure 18–7). When the muscles of the sheath contract, the hyoid bones are squeezed around behind the skull, and the tongue is projected from the bird's mouth. The tip of a woodpecker tongue has barbs that impale insects and allow them to be pulled

BOX 18–1 Giant Predatory Birds

One does not usually think of birds as being frightening, although some eagles have wingspans of 2 meters or more. However, the extinction of dinosaurs at the end of the Mesozoic left empty the adaptive zone that had been filled by bipedal carnivores, and giant flightless birds appear to have filled this role from the Paleocene until the Pleistocene (Marshall 1994).

The earliest of these dinosaur analogs were the diatrymas (terror cranes), which are known from Paleocene and Eocene deposits in North America and Europe. The diatrymas were 2 meters tall and had massive legs and toes with enormous claws. The head was huge—nearly as large as that of a horse—and had an enormous, hooked beak (Figure 18–5). A mechanical analysis of the feeding apparatus of *Diatryma* suggests that the birds were equipped to be ferocious predators: "Whatever *Diatryma* ate, it could bite it hard" (Witmer and Rose 1991). Indeed, the skull and jaws of *Diatryma* show the thick mandibular rami and evidence of massive adductor muscles. These features are unlike those of any extant bird (perhaps fortunately for us), but they are seen in hyenas where they are associated with the ability to crush bones. Perhaps *Diatryma*, like hyenas, was a scavenger as well as a predator and was able to crush bones to eat the marrow inside.

South America was isolated from the northern continents in the early Cenozoic, and another lineage of giant predatory birds, the phorusrachids, evolved on that continent. The phorusrachids, which were 1.5 to 2.5 meters tall, were more lightly built than the diatrymas and were probably faster runners. Like the diatrymas, the phorusrachids had huge beaks and powerful claws. Phorusrachids are known from South America from the Oligocene to the end of the Pliocene; they disappeared about the time of the great faunal interchange between North and South America. However, a phorusrachid is known from Pleistocene deposits in Florida, apparently representing a genus that moved north across the Central American land bridge.

Figure 18–5 A terror crane, *Diatryma*, attacking a primitive hoofed mammal.

Figure 18–6   Skull kinesis. Long-billed wading birds that probe for worms and crustaceans in soft substrates can raise the tips of the upper bill without opening their mouth. (From P. Béhler, 1981, in *Form and Function in Birds*, volume 2, edited by A. S. King and J. McLelland, Academic, New York, NY.)

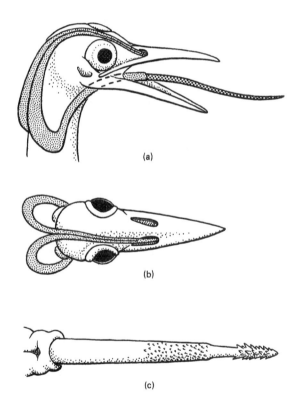

(a)

(b)

(c)

Figure 18–7   Hyoid apparatus of a woodpecker. The tongue itself is about the length of the bill, and it can be extended well beyond the tip of the beak by muscles that move the elongated hyoid apparatus. The detail of the tongue shows the barbs on the tip that impale prey.

from their tunnels. Nectar-eating birds such as hummingbirds and sunbirds also have long tongues and a hyoid apparatus that wraps around the back of the skull. The tip of the tongue of nectar-eating birds is

divided into a spray of hair-thin projections, and capillary force causes nectar to adhere to the tongue.

Dietary Specializations

The morphology of birds' bills is sometimes closely correlated with methods of prey capture or dietary specialization. For example, the spoonbills, Platalea, are related to storks and herons. Like their relatives, spoonbills feed on aquatic animals including fishes, amphibians, and crayfishes, but they differ from storks and herons in bill structure and in feeding methods.

Storks and herons have long, pointed bills. They locate prey visually while wading in shallow water, and they seize prey items in their open bills. This method of hunting depends on being able to see individual prey items under water, and a heron may extend its wings, shading a patch of water to reduce the reflection from the water's surface. Spoonbills also hunt in this way, but they have a second method of capturing prey that is effective even in murky water (Weihs and Katzir 1994).

Spoonbills take their name from the shape of their beak, which is broadened from side to side, especially near the tip (Figure 18–8). The dorsal surface of the beak is curved, and the ventral surface is flat. In clear water a spoonbill wades forward slowly, seizing prey in its beak just as a heron does. In murky water, however, a spoonbill uses a different method of foraging, sweeping its beak through the water just a few centimeters above the bottom. The curved profile of the bill creates a vortex in the water that pulls small objects, including prey animals, off the bottom and up into the water column where they are seized on the next sweep.

Bill morphology can affect the choice of food items on a very fine scale. The African black-bellied finch, *Pyrenestes ostrinus*, includes individuals with two different types of bills—large and small (Smith 1987). There is no sexual dimorphism in bill size, and no evidence of assortative mating. That is, a large-billed individual is equally likely to be male or female, and is equally likely to mate with an individual of the opposite bill morph. A mixed pair produces young with large and small bills, but no intermediates.

Finches are seed eaters, and bill size affects the ease with which they can eat different kinds of seeds. The African black-bellied finch eats the seeds of different species of sedges, and a range of seed sizes is available. Individuals of the large-billed morph are able to crack hard seeds more rapidly

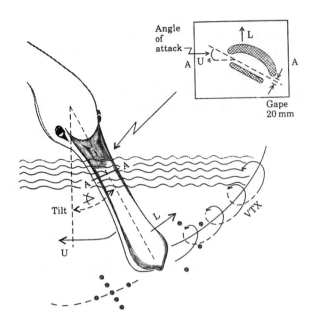

Figure 18–8   Feeding mechanism of the spoonbill. When a spoonbill sweeps its beak through the water, the curved upper surface and flat lower surface create vortex currents (shown by spiraling arrows marked VTX) that lift prey from the bottom. In this drawing the bill is being swept from right to left (indicated by the arrow marked U). The sweeping motion generates a lift (L). The line A–A indicates the position of the cross section of the beak shown in the inset. (From D. Weihs and G. Katzir, 1994, *Animal Behaviour* 47:649–654; courtesy of D. Weihs and G. Katzir.)

than small-billed individuals can, but small-billed birds consume soft seeds more rapidly than large-billed individuals can. These differences in seed handling time are reflected in the diets of the two morphs. Large-billed individuals are nearly three times as likely as small-billed birds to have hard seeds in their crop, and small-billed birds are three times as likely to have soft seeds (Figure 18–9). Thus, both bill morphs of *Pyrenestes ostrinus* specialize on the sizes of seeds they can consume most effectively.

Foraging Behavior of Birds: The Concept of Optimization

Refined morphological specializations, such as the correspondence of beak shapes and diet, demonstrate such appropriate design that we are intuitively led to hypothesize the existence of similar perfection in physiological and behavioral adaptations to the environment. A general hypothesis is implicit in much of modern biology—that over evolutionary

time, natural selection has favored organisms with genotypes providing them with characteristics that solve environmental problems in an optimal way for survival and reproduction. In the past quarter century this general hypothesis has seen vigorous testing and modification, in large part by ecologists working with **optimal foraging theory** (OFT) (Krebs et al. 1983, Stephens and Krebs 1987). Numerous other possible optimalities have been investigated, primarily those involving behavioral characteristics of animals, all borrowing from economics the procedures of cost/benefit analysis. However, the concept of optimization in biology remains controversial, and OFT is criticized by some ecologists as strongly as it is defended by others (Pierce and Ollason 1987, Stearns and Schmid–Hempel 1987).

The technique of OFT allows us to compare the predictions of a theoretical model to actual observations in the natural world. If the model and nature resemble one another, we have probably correctly considered the essential elements of the organism's adaptations in constructing the model; if they do not match well, the nature of the mismatch is a guide to other factors that must be considered. OFT has been used to investigate what animals feed on, where they go to feed, and how they search for food. It is possible to describe the rules animals use to make decisions to eat one food item and ignore another, or to hunt here and not there.

Most food resources used by birds occur in patches, and the food supply within a patch generally diminishes with time (seeds become depleted or insects take evasive action after becoming aware of a foraging predator). A foraging bird must decide how long to feed in one patch before moving to the next, taking into account that no food intake at all occurs when it is traveling between patches.

Theoretically a forager should behave as though it estimates the average rate of its food intake in the environment in which it is feeding and compares its current rate of food intake with the average, including the cost of moving from one patch to another. When the rate of food capture in a patch falls to the environmental average, it is time to switch. This hypothesis is known as the **marginal value theorem** (Figure 18–10). The graph shows the rate of prey capture for a predator foraging in patches where the prey density is high or low. As the bird continues to forage in a patch, the rate of prey capture decreases. After a period of feeding (t_1 or t_2) the rate of prey capture in the patch will have decreased until it equals the average capture

Figure 18–9 Dimorphism in bill size and diet of the African black-bellied seed eater. (a) The two bill morphs, large and small. (b) The small-billed morph takes longer than the large-billed morph to eat hard seeds, but eats soft seeds faster than the large-billed morph can. (c) The small-billed morph is most likely to have soft seeds in its crop, whereas the large-billed morph is most likely to have hard seeds. (Based on Smith 1987, *Nature* 329:717–719.)

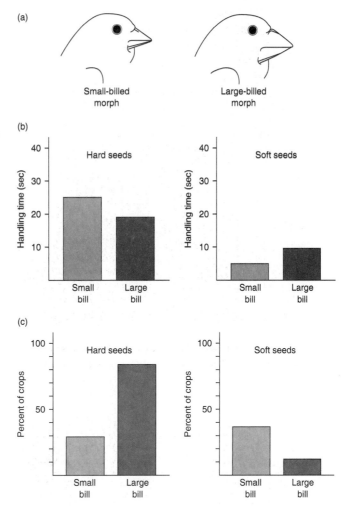

rate for the entire habitat, shown by the dotted horizontal line. Optimal foraging theory predicts that a predator will move to a new patch when its capture rate has dropped to the average for the habitat. The graph shows that a predator behaving in that manner will forage longer (t_2) in a patch where prey is abundant than in a patch where prey is scarce (t_1), thereby maximizing its energy intake during the time it spends foraging.

Most field studies of this hypothesis have been unsuccessful because the researcher has little way of knowing the food abundance in a patch. On the other hand, laboratory tests of foraging have been rewarding. By creating patches with known prey numbers and varying not only those numbers but the time required to change patches, researchers have shown that there is a remarkable correspondence between the predictions of the model and the behavior of foraging birds.

What food to eat depends on the net energy content of the food after the energy costs of search and handling (the energy required to husk or kill) have been subtracted. OFT assumes that it is advantageous for a predator to maximize its energy intake per unit of time (Figure 18–11). The rate of energy intake for prey of different sizes depends on both the energy content of the prey and the time it takes to handle (subdue and swallow) the prey item. Large prey individuals contain more energy than small individuals, but they also require longer handling times. The graph shows this relationship for a wagtail eating dungfly larvae. Larvae that are 7 millimeters long provide the greatest energy return per second of handling time. Because food patches in nature are composed of several types of edible material, a foraging organism must decide whether to eat an item or ignore it. Optimal foraging theory predicts that a low net energy item should be

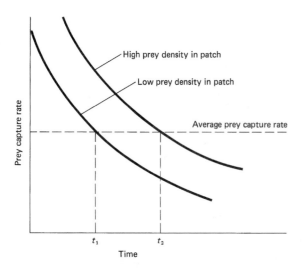

Figure 18–10 The marginal value theorem of optimal foraging. As a forager captures prey it reduces the density of prey. To maximize its rate of prey capture, a forager should move to a new patch when the rate of prey capture in its current patch falls to the average rate for the habitat. Thus, a forager will spend longer in patches that initially have high prey density than in those with low initial prey density.

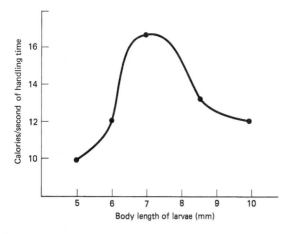

Figure 18–11 Rate of energy intake for prey of different sizes. In this example prey of intermediate size yield the greatest energy intake per second of handling time. (Data from N. B. Davies, 1977, *Journal of Animal Ecology* 46:37–57.)

rejected if the predator could expect to find an energetically superior tidbit soon after rejecting the lower-quality item. Even if a feeding patch is rich in inferior food items, theoretically they should be completely ignored if there is a greater net energy gain from rejecting them in favor of some higher-

quality item also in the patch. However, when high-quality items are scarce, the wise forager eats what is at its bill.

These predictions of what prey should be eaten and what should be ignored are excellent beginnings for laboratory experiments, and they have also been tested successfully in the field. J. D. Goss–Custard (1977) studied the European redshank (*Tringa totanus*). These sandpipers feed on polychaete worms by probing in estuarine intertidal mud with their long bills. Such habitats often contain large numbers of several species of these worms but little else that appeals to a redshank. Goss–Custard was able to study redshanks where only two species of worm occurred in significant numbers, a large species with a patchy distribution and a ubiquitous small species. As food items for the redshank these two species seem to differ only in the greater quantity of nutritious flesh in the larger species. The rate at which large worms were captured increased as the density of large worms in a patch increased (Figure 18–12a). When the rate of capture of large worms was low the birds ate many small worms, but they ignored small worms when they were able to capture large worms (Figure 18–12b). That is, they ignored less profitable prey items (small worms) when more profitable prey items (large worms) were readily available. As the rate of capture of large worms increased the redshanks became more and more selective no matter what the density of small worms was, as the theoretical predictions indicate they should.

Not all studies of the prey optimization of foragers have matched theoretical predictions. Several of these inconsistencies can be resolved by recognizing that energy content is not the only value of food. Nutritional characteristics also affect the value of a given food. Trace nutrients or the relative proportions of carbohydrate, fat, and protein may add to the value of a food item, or toxins may detract from its value.

Perhaps the greatest value of OFT has been in sharpening our perspective of the trade-offs necessary in adaptation to the complex environments in which animals live. However, the skepticism about OFT expressed by Pierce and Ollason (1987) is shared by many ecologists. Few behaviors match our simplistic models; animals must make compromises among simultaneous and conflicting demands. Adaptations also may be greatly affected by phylogenetic constraints. These complications must be

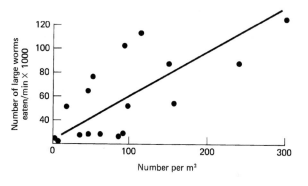
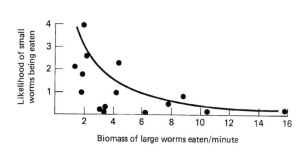

Figure 18–12   Optimal foraging in action. Redshanks feeding on polychaete worms illustrate the behavior expected from an optimally foraging predator. (Data from Goss–Custard 1977.)

remembered when the results of OFT studies appear to demonstrate that animals are behaving optimally.

■ Social Behavior and Reproduction

Vision and hearing are the major sensory modes of birds as they are of humans, and one result of this correspondence has been the important role played by birds in behavioral studies. Most birds are active during the day, and they are relatively easy to observe. A tremendous amount of information has been accumulated about the behavior of birds under natural conditions, and this background has contributed to the design of experimental studies in the field and in the laboratory.

The activities associated with reproduction are among the most complex and conspicuous behaviors of birds, and much of our understanding of the evolution and function of the mating systems of vertebrates is derived from studies of birds. Classic work in avian ethology, such as Konrad Lorenz's studies of imprinting and Niko Tinbergen's demonstration of innate responses of birds to specific visual stimuli, has formed a basis for current studies of behavioral ecology.

Vocalization and Visual Displays   Birds use colors, postures, and vocalizations for species, sex, and individual identification. Studies of birdsong have contributed greatly to our understanding of communication by vertebrates, and important general concepts such as species specificity in signals and innate predisposition to learning were first developed in studies of birdsong. Studies of the neural basis of song are leading to a close integration of

behavior and neurobiology. (See Konishi 1985 for a review.)

Birdsong has a specific meaning that is distinct from a birdcall. The song is usually the longest and most complex vocalization produced by a bird. In many species songs are produced only by mature males, and only during the breeding season. Song is a learned behavior that is controlled by a series of song control regions (SCRs) in the brain. During the period of song learning, which occurs early in life, new neurons are produced. These neurons connect a part of the SCR that is associated with song learning to a region that sends impulses to nerve cells that control the vocal muscles (Nordeen and Nordeen 1988). Thus, song learning and song production are closely linked in male birds.

The SCRs are under hormonal control, and in many species of birds the SCRs of males are larger than those of females and have more and larger neurons and longer dendritic processes (Nottebohm and Arnold 1976). The vocal behavior of female birds varies greatly across taxonomic groups: In some species females produce only simple calls, whereas in other species the females engage with males in complex song duets. The SCRs of females of the latter species are very similar in size to those of males (Table 18.2). The function of the SCR in female birds of species in which females do not vocalize has been unclear, but recent experiments suggest that it plays a role in species recognition. When the SCR of female canaries was inactivated, the birds no longer distinguished the vocalizations of male canaries from those of sparrows.

A birdsong consists of a series of notes with intervals of silence between them. Changes in frequency (frequency modulation) are conspicuous

| TABLE 18.2 | Sexual dimorphism in the song control regions of the brains of birds. The average ratio of the volumes of five SCRs in males compared with females (male:female) parallels the difference in the sizes of the song repertories of males and females. |

	Zebra Finch	Canary	Chat	Bay Wren	Buff-Breasted Wren
SCR volume ratio	4.0:1.0	3.1:1.0	2.3:1.0	1.3:1.0	1.3:1.0
Song repertoire	Males only	Males very much greater than females	Males much greater than females	Males the same as females	Males the same as females

Source: Modified from E. A. Brenowitz, A. P. Arnold, and R. N. Levin, 1985, *Brain Research* 343:104–112.

components of the songs of many birds, and the avian ear may be very good at detecting rapid changes in frequency (Chapter 17). Birds often have more than one song type, and some species may have repertoires of several hundred songs.

Birdsongs identify the particular species of bird that is singing, and they often show regional dialects. These dialects are transmitted from generation to generation as young birds learn the songs of their parents and neighbors. In the indigo bunting, one of the best studied species, song dialects that were characteristic of small areas persisted up to 15 years, which is substantially longer than the life of an individual bird (Payne et al. 1981). Birdsongs also show individual variation that allows birds to recognize the songs of residents of adjacent territories and to distinguish the songs of these neighbors from those of intruders. Male hooded warblers remember the songs of neighboring males and recognize them as individuals when they return to their breeding sites in North America after spending the winter in Central America (Godard 1991).

The songs of male birds identify their species, sex, and occupancy of a territory. Territorial males respond to playbacks of the songs of other males with vocalizations, aggressive displays, and even attacks on the speaker. These behaviors repel intruders, and broadcasting recorded songs in a territory from which a territorial male has been removed delays the occupation of the vacant territory by a new male.

Visual displays are frequently associated with songs; for example, a particular body posture that displays colored feathers may accompany singing. Male birds are often more brightly colored than females and have feathers that have become modified as the result of sexual selection. In this process, females mate preferentially with males that have certain physical characteristics. As a result of that response by females, those physical characteristics contribute to the reproductive fitness of males, even though they may have no useful function in any other aspect of the ecology or behavior of the animal. The colorful speculum on the secondaries of male ducks, the red epaulets on the wings of male red-winged blackbirds, the red crowns on kinglets, and the elaborate tails of male peacocks are familiar examples of specialized areas of plumage that are involved in sexual behavior and display.

Conspicuous or aerodynamically cumbersome feathers can make a male bird vulnerable to capture by visually guided predators, and the bright colors and special adornments of the breeding season are often discarded for a more sober, even cryptic, appearance during the rest of the year. Thus, the male African standard-wing nightjar has specially elongated and flagged second primaries that are used in flight displays during courtship, but these feathers probably slow the male's flight and make it easier for an aerial predator to capture him (Figure 18–13). As soon as courtship is over, the male bites off the projecting parts of the feathers, leaving the stubs in the wings. The pattern of molting is so arranged that the primaries are not replaced until just before the next breeding season. This pattern of molting differs from that of all other caprimulgids and from that of female standard-wing nightjars. The usual pattern for caprimulgids is to begin molt in the spring with the outermost primary, and to move sequentially through the primaries to the tenth, and this is the pattern followed by the female standard-wing nightjar. In the case of the males, however, molt begins in the center of the wing with the fifth and sixth primaries and ends with the tenth and the stump of the second. That

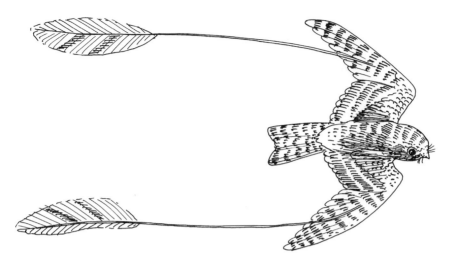

Figure 18–13   Male standard-wing nightjar. The elongated second primaries are used in an aerial courtship display.

sequence leaves just enough time for the second primary to grow to its full length at the beginning of the next courtship season.

It has been suggested that the bright colors and other adornments of male birds may be an indication of good nutritional status, of resistance to parasites, or of the ability to evade predators. If these visual signans really do correlate with the quality of a male, they could provide a basis for females to evaluate the merits of several potential mates (Hamilton and Zuk 1982, Slagsvold and Lifjeld 1992). This hypothesis, which is refered to as "truth in advertising," has been tested for several species of birds and does seem to apply in some cases. The tail of a male peacock (*Pavo cristatus*) is a classic example of a sexually selected trait, and female peafowl mate preferentially with males that have long tails with many eyes. Cutting out some of the eyespots from a male peacock's tail reduces its success in attrracting females. A study of peafowl showed that chicks sired by males whose tails have many eyes grow faster than chicks sired by males with smaller tails and had higher survival under seminatural conditions (Petrie 1994).

Some species of birds use brightly colored objects to attract females; male bowerbirds, for example, decorate their bowers with feathers from other birds, shells, or shiny bits of glass and metal. A particularly dramatic example of this behavior is provided by Archbold's bowerbird (*Archboldia papuensis*) of New Guinea (Frith and Frith 1990). Blue is an especially popular color for bowerbird ornaments, and male *Archboldia* collect the display plumes from the male King of Saxony bird of paradise (*Pteridophora alberti*). During the mating season, the male bird of paradise grows a single long feather from above each eye. These plumes look like thin wires with squares of blue plastic fastened to them at intervals. The Friths found that the bowers of several *Archboldia* were decorated with three to six *Pteridophora* plumes, which occupied a central position in the bower mat. When the Friths moved the plumes to the edges of the bower, the bower owner promptly returned them to their conspicuous location.

Vocalizations are not the only sounds that birds use in courtship; nonvocal sounds are produced by the feathers of some species. The drumming of male grouse in the spring is a familiar example of a nonvocal sound that plays a role in courtship. Sounds are often produced as a by-product of the beating of a bird's wings in flight, and only slight modification in the shapes of primaries or tail feathers is needed to produce the characteristic whistling and buzzing sounds made by certain kinds of ducks, bustards, and hummingbirds when they fly. Such sounds may be used in territorial advertisement or as individual location signals among birds flying at night or in heavy fog. Other species of birds have undergone more specific modification of their flight feathers to produce sounds used in displays. Among the tropical American manakins one finds not only narrowed and stiffened primaries involved in the production of sounds during displays, but also secondaries with thickened, clublike shafts that apparently act like castanets to produce clicks when the wings are moving (Figure 18–14).

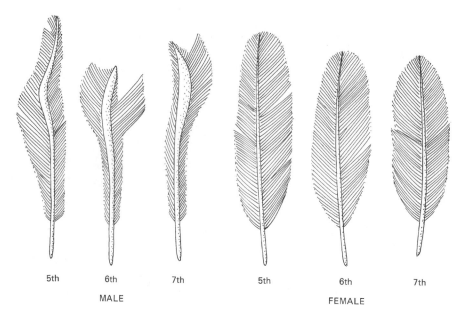

5th   6th   7th   5th   6th   7th

MALE   FEMALE

Figure 18–14 Sound-producing feathers. Secondaries of the male (left) and female (right) South American manakin. The shafts of the male's feathers are thickened and produce sounds when the wings are moved in display.

Other species, including goatsuckers, owls, doves, and larks, clap their wings together in flight, producing characteristic sounds associated with courtship or territorial defense.

Mating Systems and Parental Investment

The mating systems of vertebrates are believed to reflect the distribution of food, breeding sites, and potential mates. These resources affect individuals of the two sexes differently, and some types of resource distributions give one sex the opportunity to achieve multiple matings by controlling access to the resources. Studies of birds have contributed very largely to the development of theories of sexual strategies (Emlen and Oring 1977, Oring 1982).

The energy cost of reproduction for males of most species of vertebrates is probably lower than the cost for females. Sperm are small and cheap to produce compared with eggs that must supply the nutrients required for embryonic development. Furthermore, a male does not necessarily have any commitment beyond insemination, whereas a female must at least carry the eggs until they are deposited, and often is involved in brooding eggs and caring for the young as well. Courtship and territorial displays may be energetically expensive (see Chapter 11), but even if that is generally true, most male vertebrates can

potentially mate more often than females. A male is ready to mate again very quickly after inseminating a female, but a female must ovulate and yolk a new clutch of eggs before she can attempt a second mating. Because of this disparity in the costs of reproduction for males and females, the routes to maximizing reproductive success may be different for the two sexes. For males the most productive strategy may be to mate with as many females as possible, whereas a female may maximize her success by devoting time to careful choice of the best male and to care of her young.

The extent to which males can achieve multiple matings depends on ecological conditions and especially on the availability of food and nest sites, which are the resources most needed by females. Theoretically, a male could increase his opportunities to mate by defending these resources—excluding other males and mating with all the females in the area. His ability to do that will depend on the spatial distribution of resources. If food and nest sites are more or less evenly distributed through the habitat, it is unlikely that a male could control a large enough area to monopolize many females. Under those conditions, all males will have access to the resources and to the females. On the other hand, if resources are clumped in space with barren areas between the patches, the females will be forced to aggregate in the resource patches and it will be possible for a male to monopolize several females by defending a patch. Males that are able to defend good patches should attract more females than males defending patches of lower quality.

The temporal distribution of breeding females is also important in determining the potential for a male to achieve multiple matings. A male can mate with only one female at a time, so an important consideration is the number of receptive females relative to the number of breeding males at any moment. If the actual ratio of males to females in a population is 1:1 and if all the females became receptive at the same time, there would be one receptive female for each breeding male. In that situation, males have little opportunity to monopolize a large number of females and the variance in mating success among males will be low. That is, most males will mate with one female and relatively few males will have no matings or more than one mating. On the other hand, if females become receptive over a period of weeks, the number of breeding males at any given time will be larger than the number of females. In that situation it is possible for one male to mate with many females over the course of the breeding season. As the competition between males for mates increases, the variation in reproductive success of individual males increases and sexual selection is likely to become more intense. These are the elements that contribute to determining the mating strategies of males and females.

Social vertebrates exhibit one of two broad categories of mating systems—monogamy or polygamy. Monogamy (*mono* = one, *gamy* = marriage) refers to a pair bond between a single male and a single female. The pairing may last for part of a breeding season, an entire season, or for a lifetime. Polygamy (*poly* = many) refers to a situation in which an individual has more than one mate in a breeding season. Polygamy can be exhibited by males, females, or both sexes. In polygyny (*gyn* = female) a male mates with more than one female, whereas in polyandry (*andr* = male) a female mates with two or more males. Promiscuity is a mixture of polygamy and polyandry in which both males and females mate with several different individuals.

Monogamy is the dominant social system of birds. Both parents in monogamous mating systems usually participate in caring for the young, and 93 percent of the species of birds that produce altricial young (which require extensive parental care) are monogamous compared with 83 percent monogamy among species with precocial young.

Promiscuity is the second most common mating system for birds, accounting for 6 percent of the extant species of birds. Two percent of the species of birds are polygynous and only 0.4 percent are polyandrous. Despite their relative rarity, promiscuous, polygynous, and polyandrous species of birds have been extensively studied because these unusual mating systems can reveal much about the mechanisms of sexual selection and evolution.

Monogamy Monogamy occurs in so many species of birds in so many different ecological conditions that no one mechanism is likely to explain its prevalence. Resource distribution and the degree of parental care appear to be two factors that are frequently important in monogamy. When nest sites and food are evenly distributed through a habitat, a male or female cannot control access to these resources. If neither sex has the opportunity to monopolize additional members of the opposite sex by controlling resources, monogamy is the reproductive strategy that maximizes the fitness of individuals. When the territory quality of one male is much like that of all other males, a female can probably maximize her reproductive success by pairing with an unmated male. Perhaps a more important incentive for monogamy for many species of birds is the need for attendance by both parents to raise a brood to fledging (i.e., leaving the nest). Dramatic examples include situations in which continuous nest attendance by one parent is necessary to protect the eggs or chicks from predators while the other parent forages for food. This situation is commonly observed in seabirds that nest in dense colonies that sometimes include mixtures of two or more species. In the absence of an attending parent, neighbors raid the nest and kill the eggs or chicks. The male and female alternate periods of nest attendance and foraging, and some species engage in elaborate displays when the parents switch duties (Figure 18–15). A third situation that could make monogamy advantageous would be a sex ratio that deviates widely from 1:1. When one sex is in short supply, individuals of that sex may be the resource that individuals of the other sex defend. For example, female ducks suffer higher mortality than males and the sex ratios of ducks are biased toward males. As a result of the shortage of female ducks, competition between males for mates is intense. A male duck pairs with a female several months

Figure 18–15 Nest exchange display of northern gannets. (Photograph by Mary Tremaine, courtesy of the Cornell Laboratory of Ornithology.)

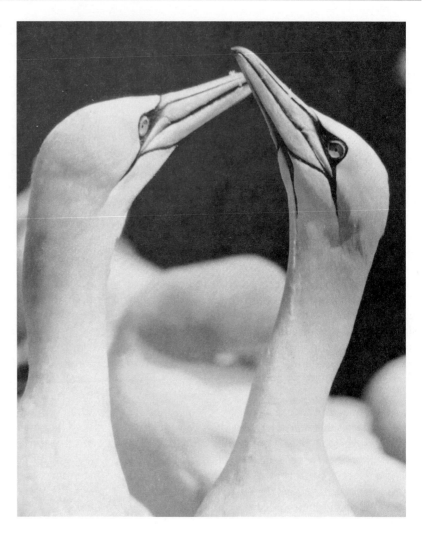

before the breeding season begins and defends her against other males.

Polygyny   When an individual male can control or gain access to several females, the male can increase his reproductive success by mating with more than one female. In **resource defense polygyny** males control access to females by monopolizing critical resources such as nest sites or food that have patchy distributions. A male that stakes out its territory in a high-quality patch can attract many females. For this system to work, a female must benefit from mating with a male that already has one mate. That is, the reproductive fitness of a female must be greater as a secondary mate on a high-quality territory than it would be as a primary mate on a territory of lower quality. Red-winged blackbirds are a familiar example of resource defense polygyny (Orians 1980). Male blackbirds arrive at their

marshy breeding areas before females and compete for territories. When the females arrive, they have a choice among a variety of territories of different quality, each defended by a male blackbird. A female should choose to mate polygynously if the difference in quality of the territories is large enough so that she will raise more young than she would by mating monogamously with a male on a poorer territory.

In **male dominance polygyny** males are not defending females, nor are they defending a resource that females require. Instead, males compete for females by establishing patterns of dominance or by demonstrating their quality through displays. This type of reproductive system is typical of situations in which the male is not involved in parental care and no potential exists for controlling resources or mates. Birds with precocial young in rich habitats often show male dominance polygyny, although this mating system is not limited to such species. The sizes of male territories in male dominance polygyny and the degree of aggregation of males are not set directly by the resources in the habitat, as is the case with resource defense polygyny. Instead, the distribution of males is determined by the sizes of the home ranges of females. Aggregations of many males in a small area are called **leks**. The prairie chicken of western North America is a well-studied lekking species (Wiley 1973). During the breeding season male prairie chickens congregate in traditional lek sites. Each male occupies a small territory (from 13 to 100 square meters in area) in the lek, and within this territory performs a courtship display that includes elaborate postures (Figure 18–16). Two colorful sacs that are outgrowths from the esophagus are filled with air and project through the breast feathers. Air is expelled from these sacs with a popping sound. Females visit the leks and copulate with a single male. The central sites appear to be the most favored and the 10 percent of the males in the most central sites obtain 75 percent of the matings.

Male Incubation and Polyandry   Incubation and care of the young by both parents is considered to be the ancestral condition for birds, and it occurs in the vast majority of the extant species of birds. However, biparental care is not always required, and situations in which it is possible for one parent to care for the eggs and young allow the development of the polygynous mating strategies we have

discussed. Males of polygynous species of birds do not participate in parental care, and all the tasks of incubation and rearing the young are performed by the female. Less commonly it is the female that is emancipated and the male that assumes parental responsibilities. The rarity of this situation probably reflects the relative parental investments of the two sexes. A male bird can leave a newly laid clutch of eggs and breed again as soon as he locates a receptive female, whereas a female who leaves her nest must ovulate and yolk a new clutch of eggs before she can obtain a second breeding. Thus, a female has more to lose by abandoning her eggs than does a male.

Despite the imbalance of energy investment in reproduction by males and females, there are a few situations in which the ability of a female bird to increase her fitness by multiple breedings equals or exceeds that of males, and these are the cases in which polygamy is balanced between males and females (promiscuity) or favors females (polyandry). Several species of charadriiforms show this pattern of breeding, including jacanas, stints, sandpipers, and phalaropes.

In polyandrous mating systems females control or gain access to multiple males. **Resource defense polyandry**, like its counterpart resource defense, polygyny, is based on the ability of one sex to control access to a resource that is critical for the other sex. This pattern of breeding among birds seems to be typical of situations in which the cost of each reproductive effort for the female is low (because

Figure 18–16   Male greater prairie chicken displaying on a lek. (Photograph by Mary Tremaine, courtesy of the Cornell Laboratory of Ornithology.)

food is abundant and a clutch contains only a few small eggs) and the probability of successful fledging is small. Spotted sandpipers (*Actitis macularia*) provide an example of this mating strategy (Oring 1982). Predation on sandpiper nests is high, and the resource that female sandpipers control is replacement clutches for males that have lost their clutches to predators. Male spotted sandpipers form territories and incubate the eggs. A female spotted sandpiper mates with a male and remains in his territory at least until she has laid three eggs. After that, she may move away to breed with other males, leaving parental care to the male, or she may remain in the territory. If she remains she may or may not participate in parental care. A female that has moved away and bred with other males may return and breed again with the original male if their first clutch is destroyed.

The conspicuousness of birds and the relative ease with which they can be studied has made them a mainstay of sociobiological research. The diversity of avian mating systems and the correlations between ecological conditions and certain types of mating systems have contributed largely to our current understanding of vertebrate behavior. Recent work has begun to emphasize the roles of individual experience and of lability of breeding systems. If environmental conditions determine the relative advantages of different mating systems, how should organisms respond to variation in these conditions? One possible response is a flexible mating system that responds in ecological time to changes in ecological conditions. Investigation of the short-term causes and consequences of variation in avian mating systems is emerging as an area of increasing importance for both ornithologists and behaviorists (Oring 1982).

Oviparity, Nesting, and Brooding Eggs

Elaborate and diverse behaviors are associated with egg laying and parental care. Nest preparation by birds runs the gamut from nothing more than the fairy tern's selection of a branch on which it balances its egg, to the multiroom communal nests of weaver birds, which are used by generation after generation. Incubation provides heat for the development of eggs and the presence of a parent is a deterrent to many predators. However, some birds leave their eggs for periods of days while they forage, and brood parasites deposit their eggs in the nests of other species of birds and play no role in brooding or rearing their young.

Oviparity In contrast to the diversity of mating strategies of birds, their mode of reproduction is limited to laying eggs. No other group of vertebrates that contains such a large number of species is exclusively oviparous. Why is this true of birds?

Constraints imposed on birds by their specializations for flight are often invoked to explain the failure of birds to evolve viviparity, but those arguments are not particularly convincing when one remembers that bats have successfully combined flight and viviparity. Furthermore, flightlessness has evolved in at least 15 families of birds, but none of these flightless species has evolved viviparity.

Oviparity is presumed to be the ancestral reproductive mode for diapsids, and it is retained by both extant groups of archosaurs, the crocodilians and the birds. However, viviparity has evolved nearly 100 times in the other major lineage of extant diapsids, the lepidosaurs (Chapter 15), so the capacity for viviparity is clearly present in diapsids. A key element in the evolution of viviparity among lizards and snakes appears to be the retention of eggs in the oviducts of the female for some period before they are deposited. This situation occurs when the benefits of egg retention outweigh its costs. For example, the high incidence of viviparity among snakes and lizards in cold climates may be related to the ability of a female ectotherm to speed embryonic development by thermoregulation. A lizard that basks in the sun can raise the temperature of eggs retained in her body, but after the eggs are deposited in a nest the mother no longer has any control over their temperature and rate of development. Birds are endotherms and brood their eggs, thereby controlling their temperature after the eggs are laid. Thus egg retention provides no thermoregulatory advantage for a bird.

Broad aspects of the biology of birds may create an unfavorable balance of costs and benefits of egg retention, thereby making it unlikely that any lineage of birds would take the first step in an evolutionary process that has repeatedly led to viviparity among snakes and lizards. If birds are viewed as being specialized for the production of one relatively large egg at a time and for complex egg incubation and parental care, the potential advantages of egg retention are greatly diminished and the costs of decreased fecundity and increased risk of maternal mortality are increased (Blackburn and Evans 1986). Perhaps it is this balance of costs and benefits rather than any single factor that is responsible for the retention of the ancestral reproductive mode by all extant birds. The same line of reasoning probably can be applied to crocodilians, which construct nests and care for their young, and it can be extended with caution to speculations about the reproductive mode of dinosaurs.

Nesting   Construction of nests is an important aspect of avian reproduction because nests provide protection for the eggs from such physical stresses as heat, cold, and rain and from predators. Bird nests range from shallow holes in the ground to enormous structures that represent the combined efforts of hundreds of individuals over many generations (Figure 18–17). The nests of passerines are usually cup-shaped structures composed of plant

(a)

(b)

(c)

(d)

Figure 18–17 Diversity of bird nests. Some nests are no more than shallow depressions, whereas other birds build elaborate structures. The piping plover (a), like many shorebirds, lays its eggs in a depression scraped in the soil, whereas the bald eagle (b) constructs an elaborate nest that is used year after year. Coots (c) build floating nests, and the Australian mallee fowl (d) scrapes together a pile of sand in which it buries its eggs. Heat from the sun warms the eggs, and the male mallee fowl adds and removes sand to keep the temperature stable. ([a] © Allan D. Cruickshank from National Audubon Society/Photo Researchers, Inc.; [b] © Joan Baron/The Stock Market; [c] © Bruce W Heinemann/The Stock Market; [d] © Jen and Des Bartlett/Photo Researchers, Inc.)

materials that are woven together. Swifts use sticky secretions from buccal glands to cement material together to form nests, and grebes, which are marsh-dwelling birds, build floating nests from the buoyant stems of aquatic plants. A review of bird nests can be found in Collias and Collias (1984).

Most birds nest individually, but some lineages are exceptions: Only 16 percent of passerines nest in colonies, but 98 percent of seabirds are colonial nesters (Wittenberger and Hunt 1985, Kharitonov and Siegel–Causey 1988). Nesting colonies of some species of penguins, petrels, gannets, gulls, terns, and auks contain hundreds of thousands of individuals. Colonies are smaller in most other groups of birds; colonies of herons, storks, doves, swifts, and passerines contain a few tens of nests. Colonial nesting offers advantages and disadvantages. A colony is a concentration of potential prey that may attract predators, but the density of nesting birds may provide a degree of protection. In many colonies the nests are located two neck lengths apart, and an intruder is menaced from all sides by snapping beaks. Centrally placed nests may be better protected against predators than nests on the periphery of the colony.

Mixed colonies of two or more species of seabirds occur, but at least some of these may be transitional situations in which one species is in the process of displacing the other. For example, on the eastern coast of North America the greater black-backed gull (*Larus marinus*) is extending its range southward, apparently in response to the abundance of food available in garbage dumps. As it moves south, it is invading the breeding colonies of herring gulls (*Larus argentatus*). Great black-backed gulls, which are larger than herring gulls and breed earlier in the year, appear to be displacing herring gulls from some of their traditional breeding sites.

Incubation   The megapodes, known as mound birds, bury their eggs in sand or soil and rely on heat from the sun or rotting vegetation for incubation, and the Egyptian plover buries its eggs in sand, but all other birds are believed to brood their eggs using metabolic heat. Some species of birds begin incubation as soon as the first egg is laid and others wait until the clutch is complete. Starting incubation immediately may protect the eggs, but it means that the first eggs in the clutch hatch while the eggs that were deposited later are still developing, forcing the parents to divide their time between incubation and gathering food for the hatchlings.

Furthermore, the eggs that hatch last produce young that are smaller than their older nestmates and these young probably have less chance of surviving to fledge. Most passerines, as well as ducks, geese, and fowl, do not begin incubation until the next-to-last or last egg has been laid.

Prolactin, secreted by the pituitary gland, suppresses ovulation and induces brooding behavior, at least in those species of birds that wait until a clutch is complete to begin incubation. The insulating properties of feathers that are so important a feature of the thermoregulation of birds become a handicap during brooding when it is necessary for the parent to transfer metabolic heat from its own body to the eggs. Prolactin plus estrogen or androgen stimulates the formation of brood patches in female and male birds, respectively. These brood patches are areas of bare skin on the ventral surface of a bird. The feathers are lost from the brood patch and blood vessels proliferate in the dermis, which may double in thickness and give the skin a spongy texture. Not all birds develop brood patches, and in some species only the female has a brood patch, although the male may share in incubating the eggs. Ducks and geese create brood patches by plucking the down feathers from their breasts; they use the feathers to line their nests. Some penguins lay a single egg that they hold on top of their feet and cover with a fold of skin from the belly, which envelops the egg as it rests on the bird's feet.

The temperature of eggs during brooding is usually maintained within the range 33 to 37°C, and some eggs can withstand periods of cooling when the parent is off the nest (see Drent 1975 for details). Tube-nosed seabirds (Procellariiformes) are known for the long periods that adults spend away from the nest during foraging. Fork-tailed storm petrels (*Oceanodroma furcata*) lay a single egg in a burrow or rock crevice. Both parents participate in incubation, but the adults forage over vast distances and both parents may be absent from the nest for periods of hours or even for several days at a time. The mean period of parental absence was 11 days (during an incubation period that averaged 50 days) for storm petrels studied in Alaska, and eggs were exposed to ambient temperatures of 10°C while the parents were away. Experimental studies showed that storm petrel eggs were not damaged by being cooled to 10°C every 4 days (Vleck and Kenagy 1980). The pattern of development of chilled eggs was like that of eggs incubated continuously at 34°C, except that each day of chilling added about one day to the total time required for the eggs to hatch.

Parent birds turn the eggs as often as several times an hour during incubation, and individual eggs are moved back and forth between the center and the edge of the clutch. Temperature variation exists within a nest, and shifting the eggs about may ensure that they all experience approximately the same average temperature. In addition, turning the eggs may help to prevent premature fusion of the chorioallantoic membrane with the inner shell membrane. Embryos attain a stable orientation during incubation—that is, the same side is usually uppermost. This position is dictated by the asymmetric distribution of embryonic mass, and the process of turning the egg allows the embryo to assume its equilibrium position. Apparently this mechanism assures that when the chorioallantoic and inner shell membranes fuse (approximately midway through incubation), the embryo is in a position that will facilitate hatching.

Incubation periods are as short as 10 to 12 days for some species and as long as 60 to 80 days for others. In general, large species of birds have longer incubation periods than small species, but ecological factors also contribute to determining the length of the incubation period. The effect of parental absence in slowing development has already been mentioned, and the amount of time a parent is absent may depend on its foraging success. A high risk of predation may favor rapid development of the eggs. Among tropical tanagers, species that build open-topped nests near the ground are probably more vulnerable to predators than are species that build similar nests farther off the ground. The incubation periods of species that nest near the ground are short (11 to 13 days) compared to those of species that build nests at greater heights (14 to 20 days). Species of tropical tanagers with roofed-over nests have still longer incubation periods—17 to 24 days.

The inorganic part of eggshells contains about 98 percent crystalline calcite, $CaCO_3$, and the embryo obtains about 80 percent of its calcium from the eggshell. An organic matrix of protein and mucopolysaccharides is distributed through the shell and may serve as a support structure for the growth of calcite crystals. Eggshell formation begins in the isthmus of the oviduct. Two shell membranes are secreted to enclose the yolk and albumen, and carbohydrate and water are added to the albumen by a process that involves active

transport of sodium across the wall of the oviduct followed by osmolal flow of water. The increased volume of the egg contents at this stage appears to stretch the egg membranes taut. Organic granules are attached to the egg membrane, and these **mammillary bodies** appear to be the sites of the first formation of calcite crystals (Figure 18–18). Some crystals grow downward from the mammillary bodies and fuse to the egg membranes, and other crystals grow away from the membrane to form cones. The cones grow vertically and expand horizontally, fusing with crystals from adjacent cones to form the palisade layer. Changes in the ionic composition of the fluid surrounding the egg during shell formation lead to an increase in the concentrations of magnesium and phosphorus and a change in the pattern of crystallization in the surface layers of the shell.

The eggshell is penetrated by an array of pores that allow oxygen to diffuse into the egg and carbon dioxide and water to diffuse out (Figure 18–19). Pores occur at the junction of three calcite cones, but only 1 percent or less of those junctions form pores; the rest are fused shut. Pores occupy about 0.02 percent of the surface of an eggshell. The morphology of the pores varies in different species of birds: Some pores are straight tubes, whereas others

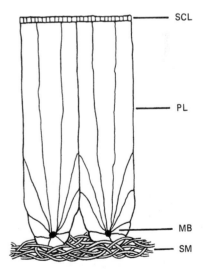

Figure 18–18 Diagram of the crystal structure of an avian eggshell. Crystallization begins at the mammillary bodies (MB) and crystals grow into the outer shell membrane (SM) and upward to form the palisade layer (PL). Changes in the chemical composition of the fluid surrounding the growing eggshell are probably responsible for the change in crystal form in the surface crystalline layer (SCL). (From Carey 1983.)

Figure 18–19 A diagram of the structure of an eggshell. Pore canals penetrate the calcified region, allowing oxygen to enter and carbon dioxide and water to leave the egg. The gases are transported to and from the embryo via blood vessels in the chorioallantoic membrane. (*Source:* Frank B. Gill, 1990. *Ornithology*, Freeman, New York, NY.)

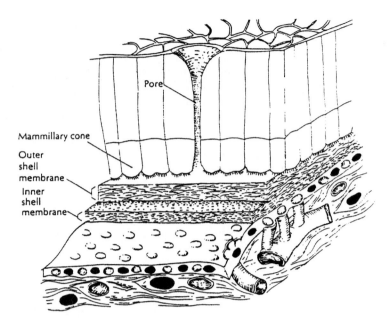

are branched. The openings of the pores on the surface of the eggshell may be occluded to varying degrees with organic or crystalline material. Additional information about the structure and function of avian eggs can be found in Carey (1983).

Water evaporates from an egg during development and the loss of water creates an air cell at the blunt end of the egg. The embryo penetrates the membranes of this air cell with its beak 1 or 2 days before hatching begins, and ventilation of the lungs begins to replace the chorioallantoic membrane in gas exchange. Pipping, the formation of the first cracks on the surface of the eggshell, follows about half a day after penetration of the air cell, and actual emergence begins half a day later. Shortly before hatching, the chick develops a horny projection on its upper mandible. This structure is called the egg tooth, and it is used in conjunction with a hypertrophied muscle on the back of the neck (the hatching muscle) to thrust vigorously against the shell. The egg tooth and hatching muscle disappear soon after the chick has hatched. In those species of birds that delay the start of incubation until all the eggs have been laid, an entire clutch nears hatching simultaneously. Hatching may be synchronized by clicking sounds that accompany breathing within the egg, and both acceleration and retardation of individual eggs may be involved. A low-frequency sound produced early in respiration, before the clicking phase is reached, appears to retard the start of clicking by

advanced embryos. That is, the advanced embryos do not begin clicking while other embryos are still producing low-frequency sounds. Subsequently, clicking sounds or vocalizations from advanced embryos appear to accelerate late embryos. Both effects were demonstrated by Vince (1969) in experiments with bobwhite quail eggs. She found that she could accelerate the hatching of a late egg by 14 hours when she paired it with an early egg that had started incubation 24 hours sooner, and the presence of the late egg delayed hatching of the early egg by 7 hours.

Parental Care

The ancestral form of reproduction in the archosaur lineage appears to consist of the deposition of eggs in a well-defined nest site, attendance at the nest by one or both parents, hatching of precocial young, and a period of association between the young and one or both parents. All the crocodilians that have been studied conform to this pattern, and evidence is increasing that at least some dinosaurs remained with their nests and young.

Extant birds follow these ancestral patterns, but not all species produce precocial young. Instead, hatchling birds show a spectrum of maturity that extends from precocial young that are feathered and self-sufficient from the moment of hatching to altricial forms that are naked and entirely depen-

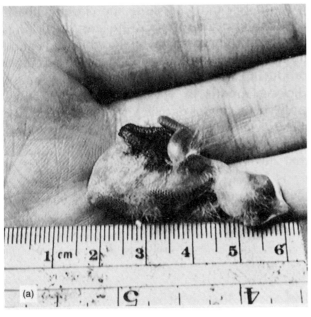
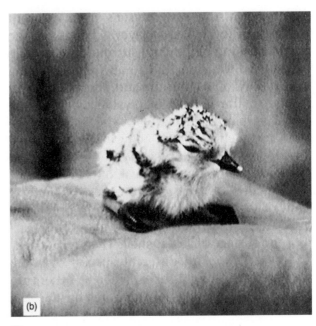

(a)   (b)

Figure 18–20   Altricial and precocial chicks. Altricial chicks (a) such as that of the tree swallow (*Tachycinta bicolor*) are entirely naked when they hatch and unable even to stand up. Precocial species (b) such as the snowy plover (*Charadius alexandrinus*) are covered with down when they hatch and can stand erect and even walk. The plover in this photograph has just hatched; it retains the egg tooth on the tip of its bill, whereas the tree swallow chick is 5 days old. The dark color on the leg of the swallow is ink, used to identify individual hatchlings for a study of parental care. (Courtesy of Professor David Winkler and Chris Swarth.)

dent on their parents for food and thermoregulation (Figure 18–20 and Table 18.3). The most precocial birds at hatching are the megapodes, and these show the most ancestral form of nesting, burying their eggs in nests made from mounds of soil and vegetation very much like those of crocodilians. Newly hatched megapodes scramble to the surface already feathered and capable of flight. Most precocial birds are covered with down at hatching and can walk, but are not able to fly.

The distinction between precocial and altricial birds extends back to differences in the amount of yolk originally in the eggs and includes differences in the relative development of organs and muscles at hatching, and the rates of growth after hatching (Table 18.4). Robert Ricklefs (1979) has proposed that the physical maturity of tissues at hatching, especially skeletal muscles, can be used to subdivide the growth patterns of birds. Mature tissues may not be capable of rapid growth, and these mature tissues may set the limits to the growth of

other tissues. Ricklefs emphasized the relationship between mode of development and food supply, and David Winkler and Jeffrey Walters (1983) have pointed to a strong phylogenetic influence on development modes. Most differences in developmental mode occur between orders, not within them, even when species within an order differ substantially in their ecology.

After altricial young have hatched they are guarded and fed by one or both parents. Adults of some species of birds carry food to nestlings in their beaks, but many species swallow food and later regurgitate it to feed the young. Hatchling altricial birds respond to any disturbance that might signal the arrival of a parent at the nest by gaping their mouths widely. The sight of an open mouth appears to stimulate a parent bird to feed it, and the young of many altricial birds have brightly colored mouth linings. Ploceid finches have covered nests, and the mouths of the nestlings of some species are said to have luminous spots that have been likened

TABLE 18.3	Maturity of birds at hatching

Precocial: eyes open, covered with feathers or down, leave nest after 1 or 2 days
1. Independent of parents: megapodes
2. Follow parents, but find their own food: ducks, shorebirds
3. Follow parents and are shown food: quail, chickens
4. Follow parents and are fed by them: grebes, rails

Semiprecocial: eyes open, covered with down, able to walk but remain at nest and are fed by parents: gulls, terns

Semialtricial: covered with down, unable to leave nest, fed by parents
1. Eyes open: herons, hawks
2. Eyes closed: owls

Altricial: eyes closed, little or no down, unable to leave nest, fed by parents: passerines

Source: Modified from M. M. Nice, 1962, *Transactions of the Linnaean Society of New York* 8:1–211.

TABLE 18.4	Comparison of altricial and precocial birds
Amount of yolk in eggs	precocial > altricial
Amount of yolk remaining at hatching	precocial > altricial
Size of eyes and brain	precocial > altricial
Development of muscles	precocial > altricial
Size of gut	altricial > precocial
Rate of growth after hatching	altricial > precocial

to beacons showing the parents where to deposit food in the gloom of the nest.

The duration of parental care is variable: The young of small passerines leave the nest about 2 weeks after hatching and are cared for by their parents for an additional one to three weeks. Larger species of birds such as the tawny owl spend a month in the nest and receive parental care for an additional 3 months after they have fledged, and the young of the wandering albatross requires a year to become independent of its parents.

Nest Helpers

A peculiar feature of the reproductive biology of more than 200 species of birds is the existence of nest helpers that provide care to offspring that are not their own. Most examples of nest helpers occur in Australia or the tropics, and few are known from Europe or North America. The mating systems of species with helpers vary from monogamy (the most common situation) through species with multiple breeders of either sex. Most species that have nest helpers are territorial, but some are colonial. Helper systems are characterized by regular involvement of the helpers in feeding and care of the young. Helpers defer their own breeding for one or more years while they assist in raising the offspring of other birds.

The peculiarity of helper systems lies in the expenditure of time and energy by helpers in caring for young that are not genetically their own. This altruistic behavior would appear to reduce the fitness of helpers, and that paradox has stimulated many studies. The concept of **kin selection** has contributed substantially to understanding helper systems. Stated in simplified form, this hypothesis proposes that an individual can increase its fitness by providing assistance to a related individual because relatives share alleles of common descent, and these alleles (not individuals) are the units of inheritance. Thus, the **inclusive fitness** of an individual consists of (1) its own reproductive success, plus (2) the additional reproductive success of relatives that results from the altruistic behavior of the individual multiplied by the fraction of alleles shared with each relative, minus (3) any decrease in the reproductive success of the individual that results from its altruistic behavior.

The hypothesis of kin selection predicts that nest helpers will be related to the individuals they help, and this is often the case. For example, almost 50 percent of the cases of nest helpers among Florida scrub jays involved birds helping their own parents, and 25 percent involved birds helping a parent and a stepparent. Birds helping their own siblings accounted for 20 percent of the nest helpers, and less than 5 percent of the examples involved helping entirely unrelated individuals (Woolfenden 1975, 1981). However, this pattern is not universal, and other examples of nest helpers involve more complicated genetic relationships among the participants, including cases where the helpers are unrelated to the individuals they help.

Nest helpers do help; nests with helpers almost always fledge more young than nests without helpers. Thus, kin selection could produce some benefit to the helpers, but why would the helpers not increase their fitness still more by breeding themselves? In other words, why *do* helpers help? Also, why do helpers *ever* help nonrelatives?

Studies of these questions have stimulated much discussion and various points of view; a summary can be found in Oring (1982). Several general hypotheses have been proposed:

1. A shortage of breeding territories, nest sites, or potential mates may make it difficult for young birds to breed. Helping to raise younger siblings may be the best way to mark time until an opportunity to breed presents itself.
2. Becoming a nest helper may be a way to gain access to a territory and, eventually, to a mate.
3. Some components of parental care are learned by experience, and birds that act as helpers for one or more breeding seasons may fledge more young when they do reproduce as a result of the experience they have gained.

These hypotheses are not mutually exclusive—they all may apply to some species—and hypotheses 2 and 3 suggest that some advantage could be gained from helping even unrelated individuals.

■ Imprinting, Learning, and Captive Husbandry

The process known as imprinting has played a prominent role in studies of bird behavior. Imprinting is a special kind of learning that occurs only during a restricted period in ontogeny called the critical period. Once imprinting is established, it is permanent and cannot be reversed. A flock of geese were imprinted on the famous ethologist Konrad Lorenz. The geese followed Lorenz around as if he were a mother goose.

The young of precocial bird species learn the characteristics that identify their parents in the hours immediately after hatching. Young ducks, for example, will imprint on an object that moves and makes a noise. Normally this object would be a parent, but in experimental situations young ducks will imprint on other animals (including humans) or on inanimate objects such as a ticking clock that is trundled along on a cart.

Most birds learn their own species' song early in life by hearing a parent bird sing. Studies of zebra finches show that the song-learning interval corresponds to a period during which new neurons are rapidly incorporated into the song control region of the brain. The images and vocalizations that birds learn early in life form the basis for their social and reproductive behavior as adults. Birds that are cross-fostered by adults of a different species, particularly males, subsequently attempt to mate with the foster parent's species, and birds that are hand-reared by humans identify their keepers as sexual partners when they are adults.

The confusion of species-identification by birds that have imprinted on a foster parent or a keeper can be disastrous for programs in which endangered species are reared in captivity and then released. Young birds must recognize appropriate mates if they are to establish a breeding population, and captive-rearing programs go to great lengths to ensure that the young birds are properly imprinted. Hatchling California condors, for example, are reared in enclosed incubators and fed by a technician who inserts her hand into a rubber glove modeled to look like the head of an adult condor (Figure 18–21a).

Still more training may be necessary to produce captive-reared young that can survive after they have been released. The bald ibis (Figure 18–21b) is an example of how complicated a process this can be. The geographic range of the bald ibis once extended from the Middle East and North Africa north to Switzerland and Germany, but the wild population has dwindled to fewer than 300 birds in a reserve in Morocco. Bald ibises flourish in captivity, and there are more than 800 captive individuals. This species seems ideal for reintroduction—it is prolific, and its disappearance from the wild seems to have been caused by human predation rather than by pollution or loss of habitat. Yet two attempts to establish populations by releasing captive-reared birds have failed.

The reason for the failures seems to have been the absence of normal social behaviors in the captive-reared birds. Bald ibises are social birds with extended parental care, and it seems that juveniles learn appropriate behaviors from adults. For some

Figure 18–21 Captive husbandry of endangered species of birds. (a) A hatchling California condor in its incubator with the model condor head used to feed it. (b) A bald ibis. (Photographs: [a] Ron Garrison, The Zoological Society of San Diego; [b] David Hosking/Photo Researchers, Inc.)

(a)

(b)

reason, this did not occur in captivity. An attempt is now underway to instruct young bald ibises in these social skills—human foster parents are hand-rearing the birds, teaching them to find their way to fields where they can forage, to recognize predators and other dangers such as automobiles, and to engage in mutual preening, which is an important social behavior.

This example illustrates the importance of basic biological information to applied programs in organismal biology, such as captive husbandry and reintroduction. Organisms are enormously complicated, and successful management of endangered species requires integrating information about their ecology, physiology, and behavior.

■ Migration and Navigation

The mobility that characterizes vertebrates is perhaps most clearly demonstrated in their movements over enormous distances. These displacements, which may cover half the globe, require both endurance and the ability to navigate. Other vertebrates migrate, even over enormous distances, but migration is best known among birds.

Migratory Movements of Birds

Migration is a widespread phenomenon among birds—about 40 percent of the bird species in the Palearctic are migratory, and an estimated total of some 5 billion birds migrate from the Palearctic every year. Migrations often involve movements over thousands of kilometers, especially in the case of birds nesting in northern latitudes, some marine mammals, sea turtles, and fishes. Short-tailed shearwaters, for example, make an annual migration between their breeding range in southern Australia and the North Pacific that requires a round-trip of more than 30,000 kilometers (Figure 18–22).

Data accumulated from recaptures of banded birds have established the origins, destinations, and migratory pathways for many species. A remarkable feature of most of these migrations is their relatively recent origin: Migrations are responses to

seasonal changes in the availability of resources. These variations in the resource base are, in turn, the result of seasonal cycles in the climate, and worldwide patterns of climate have changed frequently during the past 2 million years. Current avian migratory patterns are probably no more than 15,000 years old (Moreau 1972).

Many birds return each year to the same migratory stopover sites, just as they may return to the same breeding and wintering sites year after year. Migrating birds may be concentrated at high densities at certain points along their traditional migratory routes. For example, species that follow a coastal route may be funneled to small points of

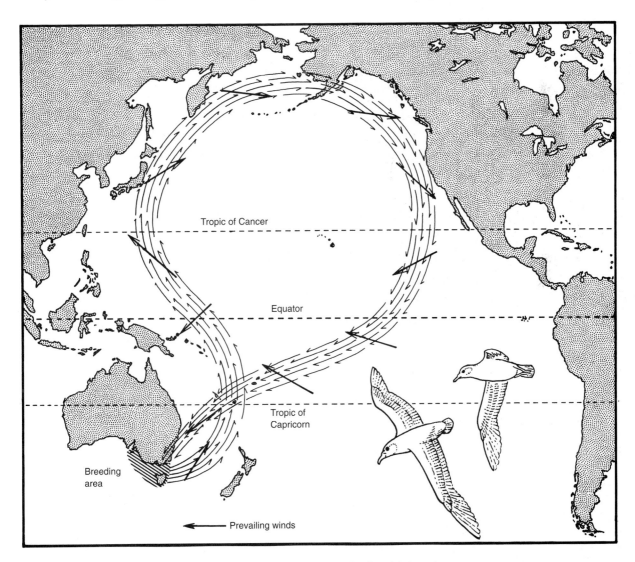

Figure 18–22 The migratory path of the short-tailed shearwater. As this species migrates from its Australian breeding area to its northern range it takes advantage of the prevailing winds in the Pacific region to reduce the energy cost of migration. (From A. J. Marshall and D. L. Serventy, 1956, *Proceedings of the Zoological Society of London* 127:489–510.)

land, such as Cape May, New Jersey, from which they must initiate long overwater flights. At these stopovers, migrating birds must find food and water to replenish their stores before they venture over the sea, and they must also avoid the predators that congregate at these sites. Development of coastal areas for human use has destroyed many important resting and refueling stations for migratory birds. The destruction of coastal wetlands has caused serious problems for migratory birds on a worldwide basis. Loss of migratory stopover sites may remove a critical resource from a population at a particularly stressful stage in its life cycle.

The Advantages of Migration   The high energy costs of migration must be offset by energy gained as a result of moving to a different habitat. The normal food sources for some species of birds are unavailable in the winter, and the benefits of migration for those species are starkly clear. Other species may save energy mainly by avoiding the temperature stress of northern winters. In other cases the main advantage of migration may come from breeding in high latitudes in the summer when the long days provide more time to forage than the birds would have if they remained closer to the equator.

Competition between species may also play a role in migration. Direct evidence of competition for food resources is lacking, but indirect evidence was provided by a study of birds that migrate between the Neotropics and North America (Cox 1968). The extent of differentiation of the beak is considered to be a measure of the difference in feeding niches of birds. Birds that have bills of different sizes and shapes are usually assumed to be exploiting different sources of food even when they forage in the same place, whereas birds with bills of the same size and shape are assumed to eat the same kinds of food and must forage in different habitats to avoid competition. During the breeding season, when food requirements are high, competition should be more intense between species with bills of similar shape than between species with bills of different shapes. Cox compared the bill morphology of resident and migrant tropical birds: If competition is irrelevant to migration, the similarity of bill shape should be the same for resident and migrant species. If competition is important in determining migration, one would predict that species with similar bill shapes would migrate, because they are less able to separate their feeding niches ecologically.

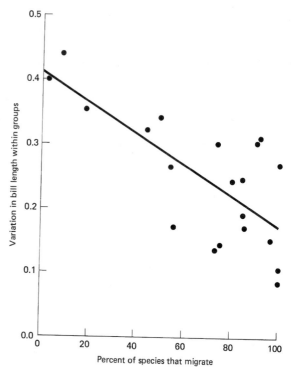

Figure 18–23   Beak morphology and migration. There is an inverse relationship between the amount of variation in beak length within a group of birds and the percentage of species in that group that migrate to North America during the breeding season. Variation in beak length is expressed as coefficient of variation for each group. (Data from Cox 1968.)

Cox found that variation in bill form was greatest in resident tropical birds, and decreased as the proportion of migratory species in a group increased (Figure 18–23). This result is consistent with the predictions of the hypothesis that competition is an important force in migration. Cox proposed that species of birds that are not ecologically separated by bill morphology avoid competition for food during the breeding season by migrating northward.

Physiological Preparation for Migration   Migration is the result of a complex sequence of events that integrate the physiology and behavior of birds. Fat is the principal energy store for migratory birds, and birds undergo a period of heavy feeding and premigratory fattening (**Zugdisposition**, migratory preparation) in which fat deposits in the body cavity and subcutaneous tissue increase tenfold, ultimately reaching 20 to 50 percent of the nonfat body mass. Fat is metabolized rapidly when migration begins, and many birds migrate at night and eat during the day. Even diurnal migrants divide the day into periods of migratory flight (usually early in the day) and periods of feeding. In addition, pauses of several days to replenish fat stores are a normal part of migration. *Zugdisposition* is followed by **Zugstimmung** (migratory mood), in which the bird undertakes and maintains migratory flight. In caged birds, which are prevented from migrating, this condition results in the well-known phenomenon of **Zugunruhe** (migratory restlessness).

Preparation for migration must be integrated with environmental conditions, and this coordination appears to be accomplished by the interaction of internal rhythms with an external stimulus. Day length is the most important cue for *Zugdisposition* and *Zugstimmung* for birds in north temperate regions. Northward migration in spring is induced by increasing day length (Figure 18–24). The direction in which migratory birds orient during *Zugunruhe* depends on their physiological condition. In this experiment, the photoperiod was manipulated to bring one group of indigo buntings into their autumn migratory condition at the same time that a second group of birds was in its spring migratory condition. When the birds were tested under an

artificial planetarium sky, the birds in the spring migratory condition oriented primarily in a north-easterly direction (Figure 18–24b), whereas birds in the fall migratory condition oriented in a southerly direction (Figure 18–24c). Dark circles show the mean nightly headings pooled for several observations for each of six birds in the spring migratory condition and five birds in the fall condition.

After breeding, many species of birds enter a refractory period in which they are unresponsive to long day lengths, their gonads regress to the non-breeding condition, and they molt. Decreasing photoperiods in autumn may accelerate the southward migration. Many birds are again refractory to photoperiod stimulation for several weeks after the autumnal migration and require an interval of several weeks of short photoperiods before they can again be stimulated by long photoperiods.

Underlying the responses of birds to changes in day length is an endogenous (internal) rhythm. This circannual (about a year) cycle can be demonstrated by keeping birds under constant conditions. Fat deposition and migratory restlessness coincide in most species and alternate with gonadal develop-

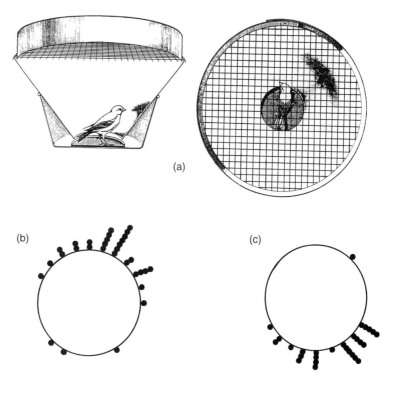

Figure 18–24 Direction in which migratory birds orient during *Zugunruhe*. (a) The birds were tested in circular cages that allow a view of the sky. The bird stands on an ink pad, and each time it hops onto the sloping wall it leaves a mark on the blotting paper that lines the cage. (b) In spring, the birds oriented toward the north, and (c) in autumn toward the south. (Source: [a] Illustration by Adolph E. Brotman from "The Stellar-Orientation System of a Migratory Bird" by Stephen T. Emlen, in *Scientific American*, August 1975, pp. 102–111; reprinted with permission; [b,c] data from S. T. Emlen, 1969, *Science* 165:716–718.)

(a)

(b)

(c)

SPRING CONDITION

AUTUMN CONDITION

ment and molt as they do in wild birds. When the rhythms are free running (that is, when they are not cued by external stimuli), they vary between 7 and 15 months. In other words, the birds' internal clocks continue to run, but in the absence of the cue normally provided by changing day length the internal rhythms drift away from precise correspondence with the seasons.

Orientation and Navigation

The seasonal migrations of vertebrates that cover thousands of kilometers and, especially, their ability to return regularly to the same locations, year after year, pose an additional question—How do they find their way? Various hypotheses propose mechanisms to explain how animals navigate on these journeys and the explanations fall into two general categories: (1) Long-distance migration is an extension of the tendency to explore territory beyond the local home range, learning to recognize landmarks as one goes along or, (2) the ability to home through unfamiliar territory results from an internal navigation system. There are no clear answers, but experiments reveal that many vertebrates can find their way home when they are displaced and that a number of different mechanisms and sensory modalities are involved. A general review of bird migration and navigation can be found in Alerstam (1990).

The homing pigeon has become a favorite experimental animal for studies of navigation. As long as people have raised and raced pigeons, it has been known that birds released in unfamiliar territory vanish from sight flying in a straight line, usually in the direction of home. How do pigeons accomplish this feat? There is no complete answer yet, but experiments have shown that navigation by homing pigeons (and presumably by other vertebrates as well) is complex and is based on a variety of sensory cues. On sunny days pigeons vanish toward home and return rapidly to their lofts. On overcast days vanishing bearings are less precise and birds more often get lost. These observations led to the idea that pigeons use the sun as a compass.

Of course, the position of the sun in the sky changes from dawn to dusk. That means that a bird must know what time of day it is to use the sun to tell direction, and this time-keeping ability requires some sort of internal clock. If that hypothesis is correct, it should be possible to fool a bird by shifting its clock forward or backward. For example, if one

turns on the lights in the pigeon loft 6 hours before sunrise every morning for about 5 days, the birds will become accustomed to that artificial sunrise, and at any time during the day they will assume that the time is 6 hours later than it actually is. When these birds are released they will judge direction by the sun, but their internal clocks will be wrong by 6 hours. As a consequence of that error, the birds should fly off on courses that are displaced by 90° from the correct course for home. Clock-shifted pigeons react differently under sunny and cloudy skies, indicating that pigeons have at least two mechanisms for navigation (Figure 18–25). Each dot in these plots shows the direction in which a pigeon vanished from sight when it was released in the center of the large circle. The home loft is straight up in each diagram. The solid bar extending outward from the center of each circle is the average vector sum of all the individual vanishing points. When they are able to see the sun, control birds that have been kept on the normal photoperiod orient predominantly in the direction of home (Figure 18–25a). Birds that have had their photope-

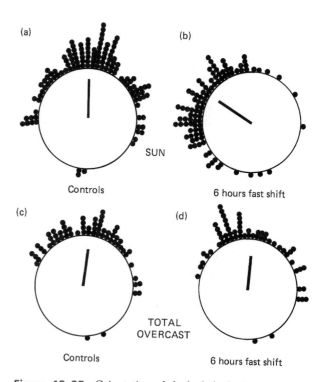

Figure 18–25 Orientation of clock-shifted pigeons under sunny and cloudy skies. The line shows the average direction chosen by the birds. (From W. T. Keeton, 1969, *Science* 165:922–928.)

riods shifted 6 hours fast disappear on bearings westward of the true direction of home (Figure 18–25b). However, when the sun is obscured by clouds, the birds cannot use it for navigation and must rely on other mechanisms. Under these conditions both control and clock-shifted birds orient correctly toward home (Figure 18–25c, d).

Polarized light is another cue vertebrates use to determine directions. In addition, some vertebrates have been shown to detect ultraviolet light and to sense extremely low-frequency sounds, well below the frequencies humans can hear. Those sounds are generated by ocean waves and air masses moving over mountains and can signal a general direction over thousands of kilometers, but their use as cues for navigation remains obscure. The senses that have been shown to be involved in navigation by pigeons do not end here. Pigeons can also navigate by recognizing airborne odors as they pass over the terrain. Even magnetism is implicated: On cloudy days pigeons wearing small magnets on their heads have their ability to navigate disrupted, but on sunny days magnets have no effect. When it is clear, pigeons apparently rely on their sun compass and magnetic cues are ignored.

Results of this sort are being obtained with other vertebrates as well, and lead to the general conclusion that a great deal of redundancy is built into navigation systems. Apparently, there is a hierarchy of useful cues. For example, a bird that relies on the sun and polarized light to navigate on clear days could switch to magnetic direction sensing on heavily overcast days. For both conditions, it might use local odors and recognition of landmarks as it approaches home.

Many birds migrate only at night. Under these conditions a magnetic sense of direction might be important (Able and Able 1990, 1993; Wiltschko et al. 1993). Several species of nocturnally migrating birds use star patterns for navigation. Apparently, each bird fixes on the pattern of particular stars and uses their motion in the night sky to determine a compass direction. As is the case for sun compass navigation, an internal clock is required for this sort of celestial navigation, and artificially changing the time setting of the internal clock produces predictable changes in the direction in which a bird orients.

Despite numerous studies the complexities of navigation mechanisms of vertebrates are far from being fully understood and much controversy surrounds some hypotheses. The built-in redundancy of the systems makes it difficult to devise experiments that isolate one mechanism. When it is deprived of the use of one sensory mode, an animal is likely to have one or several others it can use instead. This redundancy itself, and the remarkable sophistication with which many vertebrates navigate, show the importance of migration in their lives.

■ Summary

The fossil record reveals that birds radiated in the Jurassic. *Archaeopteryx*, the earliest fossil bird known, was probably a late-surviving relict that was contemporaneous with more advanced birds. It retained a large number of ancestral characters and, except for the presence of feathers, was very like a small dinosaur. True flying birds were widespread and diverse by the Cretaceous. Extant families of birds had evolved by the end of the Eocene.

The ecology and behavior of birds are directly influenced by their ability to fly. The mobility of birds allows them to exploit food supplies that have patchy distributions in time and space and to feed and reproduce in different areas. Migration is the most dramatic manifestation of the mobility of birds, and some species travel tens of thousands of kilometers in a year. Migrating birds use a variety of cues for navigation, including the position of the sun, polarized light, the Earth's magnetic field, and infrasound.

Many of the complex social behaviors of birds are associated with reproduction, and birds have contributed greatly to our understanding of the relationship between ecological factors and the mating systems of vertebrates. All birds are oviparous, perhaps because egg retention is the first step in the evolution of viviparity and the specializations of the avian way of life do not make egg retention advantageous for birds. Monogamy, with both parents caring for the young, is the most common mating system for birds, but polygyny (a male mating with several females) and polyandry (a female mating with several males) also occur.

■ References

Able, K. P., and M. A. Able. 1990. Calibration of the magnetic compass of a migratory bird by celestial rotation. *Nature* 347:378–380.

Able, K. P., and M. A. Able. 1993. Daytime calibration of magnetic orientation in a migratory bird requires a view of skylight polarization. *Nature* 364:523–525.

Alerstam, T. 1990. *Bird Migration.* Cambridge University Press, Cambridge, UK.

Altangerel, P., M. A. Norell, L. M. Chiappe, and J. M. Clark. 1993a. Flightless bird from the Cretaceous of Mongolia. *Nature* 362:623–626.

Altangerel, P., M. A. Norell, L. M. Chiappe, and J. M. Clark. 1993b. Correction: flightless bird from the Cretaceous of Mongolia. *Nature* 363:188.

Blackburn, D. G., and H. E. Evans. 1986. Why are there no viviparous birds? *American Naturalist* 128:165–190.

Carey, C. 1983. Structure and function of avian eggs. Pages 69–103 in *Current Ornithology,* volume 1, edited by Richard F. Johnston. Plenum, New York, NY.

Collias, N. E., and E. C. Collias. 1984. *Nest Building and Bird Behavior.* Princeton University Press, Princeton, NJ.

Cooper, A., and D. Penny. 1997. Mass survival of birds across the Cretaceous-Tertiary boundary: molecular evicence. *Science* 275:1109–1113.

Cox, G. W. 1968. The role of competition in the evolution of migration. *Evolution* 22:180–192.

Cracraft, J. A. 1986. The origin and early diversification of birds. *Paleobiology* 12:383–399.

Drent, R. 1975. Incubation. Pages 333–420 in *Avian Biology,* volume 5, edited by D. S. Farner, J. R. King, and K. C. Parkes. Academic, Orlando, FL.

Emlen, S. T., and L. W. Oring. 1977. Ecology, sexual selection, and the evolution of mating systems. *Science* 197:215–223.

Feduccia, A. 1995. Explosive evolution in Tertiary birds and mammals. *Science* 267:637–638.

Feduccia, A. 1996. *The Origin and Evolution of Birds.* Yale University Press, New Haven, CT.

Frith, C. B., and D. W. Frith. 1990. Archbold's bowerbird *Archboldia papuensis* (Ptilonorhynchidae) uses plumes from King of Saxony bird of paradise *Pteridophora alberti* (Paradisaeidae) as bower decoration. *Emu* 90:136–137.

Godard, R. 1991. Long-term memory of individual neighbors in a migratory songbird. *Nature* 350:228–229.

Goss–Custard, J. D. 1977. Optimal foraging and size selection of worms by redshank, *Tringa totanus. Animal Behaviour* 25:10–29.

Hamilton, W. D., and M. Zuk. 1982. Heritable true fitness and bright birds: a role for parasites? *Science* 218:384–387.

Houde, P. 1986. Ostrich ancestors found in the Northern Hemisphere suggest new hypothesis of ratite origins. *Nature* 324:563–565.

Houde, P. 1987. Critical evaluation of DNA hybridization studies in avian systematics. *Auk* 104:17–32.

Kharitonov, S. P., and D. Siegel–Causey. 1988. Colony formation in seabirds. Pages 223–272 in *Current Ornithology,* volume 5, edited by R. F. Johnston. Plenum, New York, NY.

Konishi, M. 1985. Birdsong: from behavior to neuron. *Annual Review of Neurosciences* 8:125–170.

Konishi, M., S. T. Emlen, R. E. Ricklefs, and J. C. Wingfield. 1989. Contributions of bird studies to biology. *Science* 246:465–472.

Krebs, J. R., D. W. Stephens, and W. J. Southerland. 1983. Perspectives in optimal foraging. Pages 165–216 in *Perspectives in Ornithology,* edited by A. H. Brush and G. A. Clark, Jr. Cambridge University Press, Cambridge, UK.

Lockley, M. G., S. Y. Yang, M. Matsuka, F. Fleming, and S. K. Lim. 1992. The track record of Mesozoic birds: evidence and implications. *Philosophical Transactions of the Royal Society (London) Series B* 336:113–134.

Marshall, L. G. 1994. Terror birds of South America. *Scientific American* 270(2):90–95.

Martin, L. D. 1983a. The origin and early radiation of birds. Pages 291–338 in *Perspectives in Ornithology,* edited by A. H. Brush and G. A. Clark, Jr. Cambridge University Press. Cambridge, UK.

Martin, L. D. 1983b. The origin of birds and of avian flight. Pages 105–129 in *Current Ornithology,* volume 1, edited by Richard F. Johnston. Plenum, New York, NY.

Moreau, R. E. 1972. *The Palearctic–African Bird Migration Systems.* Academic, New York, NY.

Nordeen, K. W., and E. J. Nordeen. 1988. Projection neurons within a vocal motor pathway are born during song learning in zebra finches. *Nature* 334:149–151.

Nottebohm, F., and A. P. Arnold. 1976. Sexual dimorphism in vocal control areas of the songbird brain. *Science* 194:211–213.

Olson, S. L. 1985. The fossil record of birds. Pages 79–238 in *Avian Biology,* volume 8, edited by D. S. Farner, J. R. King, and K. C. Parkes. Academic, Orlando, FL.

Orians, G. H. 1980. *Some Adaptations of Marsh-Nesting Blackbirds.* Princeton University Press, Princeton, NJ.

Oring, L. W. 1982. Avian mating systems. Pages 1–92 in *Avian Biology,* volume 6, edited by D. S. Farner, J. R. King, and K. C. Parkes. Academic, New York, NY.

Payne, R. B., W. L. Thompson, K. L. Fiala, and L. L. Sweany. 1981. Local song traditions in indigo buntings: cultural transmission of behavior patterns across generations. *Behaviour* 77:199–221.

Petrie, M. 1994. Improved growth and survival of offspring of peacocks with more elaborate trains. *Nature* 371:598–599.

Pierce, G. J., and J. G. Ollason. 1987. Eight reasons why optimal foraging theory is a complete waste of time. *Oikos* 49:111–118.

Raikow, R. J. 1985. Problems in avian classification. Pages 187–212 in *Current Ornithology,* volume 2, edited by Richard F. Johnston. Plenum, New York, NY.

Rayner, J. M. V. 1988. The evolution of vertebrate flight. *Biological Journal of the Linnean Society* 34:269–287.

Ricklefs, R. E. 1979. Adaptation, constraint, and compromise in avian postnatal development. *Biological Review* 54:269–290.

Sanz, J. L., L. M. Chiappe, B. P. Perez-Moreno, A. D. Buscalioni, J. J. Moratalla, F. Ortega, and F. J. Poyato-Ariza. 1996. A new Lower Cretaceous bird from Spain: Implications for the evolution of flight. *Nature* 382:442–445.

Sereno, P. C., and R. Chenggang. 1992. Early evidence of avian flight and perching: new evidence from the Lower Cretaceous of China. *Science* 255:845–848.

Sibley, C. G., and J. E. Ahlquist. 1990. *Phylogeny and Classification of Birds.* Yale University Press, New Haven, CT.

Sibley, C. G., J. E. Ahlquist, and B. L. Monroe. 1988. A classification of the living birds of the world, based on DNA–DNA hybridization studies. *Auk* 105:409–423.

Slagsvold, T., and J. T. Lifjeld. 1992. Plumage color is a condition-dependent sexual trait in male pied flycatchers. *Evolution* 46:825–828.

Smith, T. B. 1987. Bill size polymorphism and intraspecific niche utilization in an African finch. *Nature* 329:717–719.

Stearns, S. C., and P. Schmid–Hempel. 1987. Evolutionary insights should not be wasted. *Oikos* 49:118–125.

Stephens, D. W., and J. R. Krebs. 1987. *Foraging Theory.* Princeton University Press, Princeton, NJ.

Storer, R. W. 1971. Classification of birds. Pages 1–18 in *Avian Biology*, volume 1, edited by D. S. Farner, J. R. King, and K. C. Parkes. Academic, New York, NY.

Vince, M. A. 1969. Embryonic communication, respiration, and the synchronization of hatching. Pages 233–260 in *Bird Vocalizations*, edited by R. A. Hinde. Cambridge University Press, Cambridge, UK.

Vleck, C. M., and G. J. Kenagy. 1980. Embryonic metabolism of the fork-tailed storm petrel: physiological patterns during prolonged and interrupted incubation. *Physiological Zoology* 53:32–42.

Warheit, K. L. 1992. A review of the fossil seabirds from the Tertiary of the North Pacific: plate tectonics, paleoceanography, and faunal change. *Paleobiology* 18:401–424.

Weihs, D., and G. Katzir. 1994. Bill sweeping in the spoonbill, *Platalea leucordia:* evidence for a hydrodynamic function. *Animal Behaviour* 47:649–654.

Wiley, R. H. 1973. Territoriality and non-random mating in the sage grouse, *Centrocercus urophasianus. Animal Behaviour Monographs* 6:87–169.

Wiltschko, W., U. Munro, H. Ford, and R. Wiltschko. 1993. Red light disrupts magnetic orientation of migratory birds. *Nature* 364:525–527.

Winkler, D. W., and J. R. Walters. 1983. The determination of clutch size in precocial birds. Pages 33–68 in *Current Ornithology*, volume 1, edited by Richard F. Johnston. Plenum, New York, NY.

Witmer, L. M., and K. D. Rose. 1991. Biomechanics of the jaw apparatus of the gigantic Eocene bird *Diatryma:* implications for diet and mode of life. *Paleobiology* 17:95–120.

Wittenberger, J. F., and G. L. Hunt, Jr. 1985. The adaptive significance of coloniality in birds. Pages 1–78 in *Avian Biology*, volume 8, edited by D. S. Farner, J. R. King, and K. C. Parkes. Academic, Orlando, FL.

Woolfenden, G. E. 1975. Florida scrub jay helpers at the nest. *Auk* 92:1–15.

Woolfenden, G. E. 1981. Selfish behavior by Florida scrub jay helpers. Pages 257–260 in *Natural Selection and Social Behavior,* edited by R. D. Alexander and D. W. Tinkle. Chiron, New York, NY.

CHAPTER
19

The Synapsida and the Evolution of Mammals

We must backtrack to the end of the Paleozoic (Chapters 9 and 10) to find the origins of the final lineage of vertebrates, the synapsids. The synapsids actually had their first radiation (pelycosaurs) and second radiation (therapsids) in the Paleozoic, before the radiations of the diapsids we have already discussed. However, the third radiation of the synapsid lineage (mammals) reached its peak in the Cenozoic. Nonetheless, through the late Paleozoic and early Mesozoic the synapsid lineage was becoming increasingly mammallike and mammals and dinosaurs both appeared on the scene in the Late Triassic.

In Chapter 4 we discussed the paradox of the origin of endothermy. Endothermic thermoregulation has two components: a high metabolic rate that produces heat and insulation that retains the heat in the body. Neither characteristic confers an advantage without the prior existence of the other. We suggested that the solution of the paradox might lie in the evolution of high rates of metabolism for some purpose other than thermoregulation. One possible benefit of a high rate of metabolism would be to enhance the locomotor endurance of synapsids. It is gratifying to see in the fossil record just the sorts of structural change in the skeleton of synapsids that might be expected to accompany an increasingly active form of locomotion and foraging. The three groups of extant mammals—monotremes, marsupials, and placentals—had evolved by the late Mesozoic, and they were accompanied by several groups of mammals that are now extinct.

■ The Origins of Synapsids

Synapsids include mammals and their extinct ancestors (see Figure 19–1), commonly called mammallike reptiles. The term synapsid is often used incorrectly to refer just to the extinct nonmammalian forms, but it in fact includes all amniotes descended from a common ancestor with the synapsid type of temporal fenestration (see Chapter 10). "Mammallike reptile" is an appealing term for the ancestors of mammals, yet it is a misleading one

in a way, and is no longer used in technical publications. The term is misleading because, as we saw in Chapter 10, mammals are not the descendants of any animals closely related to modern reptiles, and to think of them as some sort of large, peculiar lizardlike beast would indeed be inaccurate. In this chapter we will stick with the more correct, if less evocative, term nonmammalian synapsid.

The synapsid lineage was the first group of amniotes to radiate widely in terrestrial habitats. During the Late Carboniferous and the entire

Permian, synapsids were the most abundant terrestrial vertebrates, and from the Early Permian into the Triassic they were the top carnivores in the food web. Most synapsids were medium to large-size animals, weighing between 10 and 200 kilograms, with a few weighing as much as a ton (e.g., *Moschops*, see Figure 19–6 later). Most of the synapsid lineages disappeared by the Late Triassic, and the surviving forms (represented only by mammals past the Middle Jurassic) were considerably smaller, mostly under a kilogram in body mass.

Chapter 10 discusses the features of synapsids in comparison with other amniote groups. Synapsids are distinguished by the synapsid type of temporal fenestra, plus a few other skull features. Judging from the distribution of characters states in living amniotes, all synapsids probably retained the more primitive tetrapod features of an eye with poor color vision (suggesting a mainly nocturnal existence), a glandular skin without the type of hard beta keratin typical of reptiles, and the inability to excrete uric acid (suggesting perhaps an oviparous mode of reproduction). The more primitive skin type suggests that synapsids never had the type of scaly covering typical of modern reptiles. Changes in the structure of the skull and skeleton of nonmammalian synapsids, and their probable relation to metabolic status and the evolution of the mammalian condition, are described later in Figure 19–11.

■ Primitive Nonmammalian Synapsids: the Pelycosaurs

Pelycosaurs are best known as the sailbacks of the late Paleozoic, although only a minority of them actually possessed sails. The best-known pelycosaur is probably *Dimetrodon* (Figures 19–2, 19–3, 19–4), an animal frequently mislabeled as a dinosaur in a variety of books, packages of plastic toys, and so on. Pelycosaurs contain the ancestry of the more derived synapsids, including the mammals. They thus represent a paraphyletic assemblage, and in theory should be termed something cumbersome like "nontherapsid synapsids." However, they were a unique group while they lived in the Late Carboniferous and the Permian, and had morphological and ecological features that made them quite distinctive from the more derived therapsids. Pelycosaurs were basically generalized amniotes, albeit with some of their own specializations, and none

showed any evidence of a tendency to have an increased metabolic rate (see Figure 19–11).

The most primitive pelycosaurs were the Early Permian eothyridids, which were small (cat-size) and probably insectivorous. More derived, larger forms, although still fairly generalized, were the varanopsids and the ophiacodontids. The ophiacodontids are the oldest known pelycosaurs, though not the most primitive. They appear to have been semiaquatic fish eaters. Their heads were long and slender and each jaw contained 40 or more small, sharp teeth (Figure 19–2a).

More derived Permian pelycosaurs include larger, specialized herbivores and carnivores. The herbivores, with their diet distinguished by the possession of blunt, peglike teeth, belong to two main lineages. The caseids, with their peculiarly pointed, tipped-forward rostrum (Figure 19–2d) were related to the primitive eothyridids, and were known from the middle portion of the Permian. The edaphosaurids were more derived in various ways, were limited to the Early Permian, and were related to the carnivorous sphenacodonts that contained the ancestry of more derived synapsids. Both edaphosaurids and caseids had barrel-shaped bodies, as evidenced from the ribcages, and surprisingly small heads (Figure 19–3).

The sphenacodonts, mainly large, carnivorous forms with large sharp teeth (Figures 19–2b and 19–3c) were known from the entire Permian. An enlarged caninelike tooth in the maxillary bone is one of the key features linking them to more derived synapsids. Additional derived features include an arched palate, which was the first step toward the development of a separation of the mouth and nasal passages seen in some therapsids and in mammals, and the reflected lamina of the angular bone becomes more prominent in therapsids and assumes an important role in the evolution of the mammalian middle ear (see Box 19–1, later).

A remarkable feature of some edaphosaurids and sphenacodontids was the elongation of the neural spines of the trunk region into the well-known pelycosaur sail (Figure 19–4). These sails must have been evolved independently in the two groups, as they are absent from more primitive sphencodonts and their immediate relatives (Hopson 1994). Sphenacodontid spines are smooth, while edaphosaurid spines had horizontal projections, rather like stubby yards on the masts of a square-rigged sailing ship. Marks of blood vessels on the spines indicate that the tissue they sup-

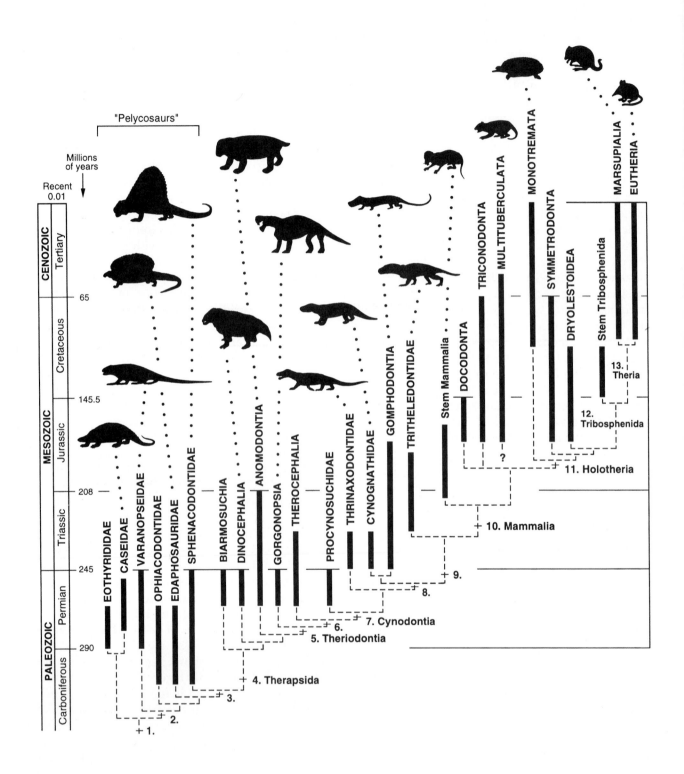

ported was heavily vascularized, and fossils of *Dimetrodon* usually have the spines aligned like pickets in a fence, including spines that have been broken and then healed in place, suggesting that in life the spines were covered by connective tissue and a web of skin that held the spines in place after death. There is no evidence of any degree of sexual dimorphism in the possession of these sails, so it is unlikely that they were devices evolved primarily for display as, for example, antelope horns.

A *Dimetrodon* 3 meters long had spines that rose as much as 1.5 meters above the vertebrae and supported a crest of skin that may have been a temperature-regulating device. Sailbacked synapsids probably relied on absorbing solar energy to raise their body temperatures to optimal activity levels, just as living reptiles do. The potential blood flow through the sails, indicated by the extent of vascularization, so greatly exceeds any reasonable metabolic requirement for such a tissue that it seems likely that the animals shunted blood through the crest in response to their thermoregulatory requirements (Haack 1986; Tracy et al. 1986). In the morning a *Dimetrodon* could orient its body perpendicular to the sun's rays and allow a large volume of blood

to flow through the sail where the blood would be warmed by the sun and the heat carried back into the animal's body. When a *Dimetrodon* was warm enough, blood flow through the sail could be restricted, and the heat would be retained within the body.

■ More Derived Nonmammalian Synapsids: the Therapsids

From the mid-Permian to the Late Triassic there was a flourishing fauna of more derived synapsids that are grouped under the general name of therapsids (Kemp 1982, 1988a; Hotton 1991; Hopson and Barghusen 1986; Hopson 1991, 1994). (Note that the strictly correct name here should be "nonmammalian therapsids," because, as these animals include the ancestors of mammals, the term therapsid includes both these beasts *and* mammals.) Therapsids all had modifications suggesting an increase in metabolic rate over the more primitive pelycosaurs (see Figure 19–11), and thus are often portrayed as possessing hair. They were all fairly heavy-bodied, large-headed, stumpy-legged forms,

1. Synapsida: Lower temporal fenestra present. 2. Eupelycosauria: Snout deeper than it is wide, frontal bone forming a large portion of the margin of the orbit. 3. Sphenacodontia: A reflected lamina on the angular bone, retroarticular process of the articular bone turned downward. 4. Therapsida: Temporal fenestra enlarged, upper canine plus the bone containing it (the maxilla) enlarged, limb bones more slender, limbs held more underneath body (indicated by inturned heads of femur and humerus), shorter feet. 5. Theriodontia: Coronoid process on dentary, flatter skull with wider snout. 6. Eutheriodontia: Temporal fossa completely open dorsally. 7. Cynodontia: Postcanine teeth with anterior and posterior accessory cusps and small cusps on the inner side, partial bony secondary palate, masseteric fossa on dentary and bowing out of zygomatic arch (evidence for the presence of a masseter muscle), lumbar ribs reduced or lost, distinct calcaneal heel. 8. Eucynodontia: Dentary greatly enlarged, postdentary bones reduced, phalangeal formula of 2-3-3-3-3. 9. Loss of postorbital

bar, at least incipient contact between dentary and squamosal bones. 10. Mammalia. Dentary-squamosal jaw articulation, double-rooted, precisely occluding postcanine teeth, and specializations of the portion of the skull housing the inner ear. ("Stem Mammalia" is a paraphyletic assemblage of Late Triassic and Jurassic genera, including [listed from more primitive to more derived] *Adelobasileus, Sinoconodon, Megazostrodon,* and *Morganucodon*.) 11. Holotheria: Reversed triangles molar pattern. 12. Tribosphenida. Tribosphenic molars. ("Stem Tribosphenida" is a paraphyletic assemblage of Early Cretaceous genera, including [listed from more primitive to more derived] *Aegialodon, Pappotherium,* and *Holoclemensia,* plus others. The somewhat more primitive *Vincelestes* might also be included in this grouping.) 13. Theria. Details of braincase structure, and many features of the soft anatomy (see Chapter 21). (Based on M. J. Benton, 1997, *Vertebrate Paleontology,* 2d edition, HarperCollins Academic, London, UK; Hopson 1994.)

Figure 19–1   Phylogenetic relationships of the Synapsida. This diagram shows the probable relationships among the major groups of synapsids. The dotted lines indicate interrelationships only, and are not indicative of times of divergence or of the presence of the taxon unrecorded in the fossil record. The numbers indicate derived characters that distinguish the lineages.

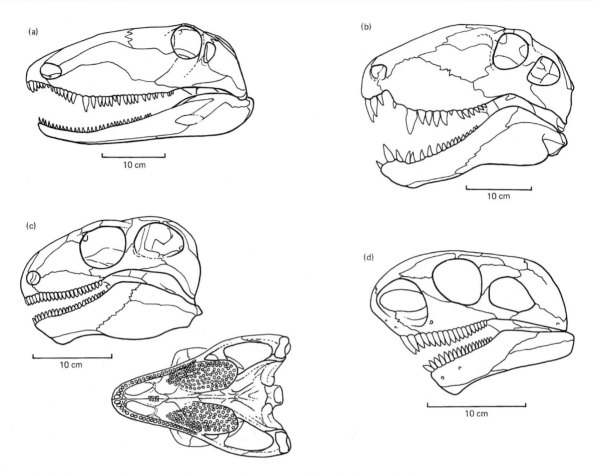

Figure 19–2 Form of skulls among pelycosaurs. Piscivorous (fish-eating) forms had long, narrow skulls with multiple sharp teeth (a, *Ophiacodon*, an ophiacodontid); carnivores had more robust skulls, with shorter jaws, and fewer, larger dagger-like teeth (b, *Dimetrodon*, a sphenacodontid). Herbivores *Edaphosaurus*, an edaphosaurid (c) and *Cotylorhynchus*, a caseid (d) had short, broad skulls with peglike teeth. Note the palatal teeth of *Edaphosaurus*, a typical feature of ancient large, nonmammalian herbivores, also seen in diapsids like rhynchosaurs (Chapter 13). (Modified from A. S. Romer, 1966, *Vertebrate Paleontology*, 3d edition, University of Chicago Press, Chicago, IL.)

and the image of this body form combined with incipient hairiness prompted the cartoonist Larry Gonick (1990) to declare them too ugly to survive. Figure 19–5 illustrates the skulls of a diversity of therapsids.

Like the earlier pelycosaurs, therapsids radiated into herbivorous and carnivorous forms. Some of the herbivorous therapsids were large, heavy-bodied, slow-moving animals (Figures 19–6, 19–7), some of which may have congregated in herds as ungulates (hoofed mammals) do today. Other herbivorous forms were small and superficially rather like rodents. The carnivorous therapsids included large, ferocious-appearing animals (Figure 19–8), which may have played an ecological role similar

to that of big cats today, smaller ones (Figure 19–9) which may have been more foxlike, and rabbit-size forms that were probably insectivorous. There were numerous different lineages of therapsids. One of them, the cynodonts, we hold as especially important because this was the group that gave rise to mammals. While cynodonts were highly derived therapsids, other therapsid lineages could be considered equally derived in their own particular fashion (e.g., the dicynodonts, with their adaptations for herbivory).

Therapsids were known from a wider biogeographical range than pelycosaurs. Pelycosaurs have been found primarily in deposits in North America and in Russia, parts of the world that were near the

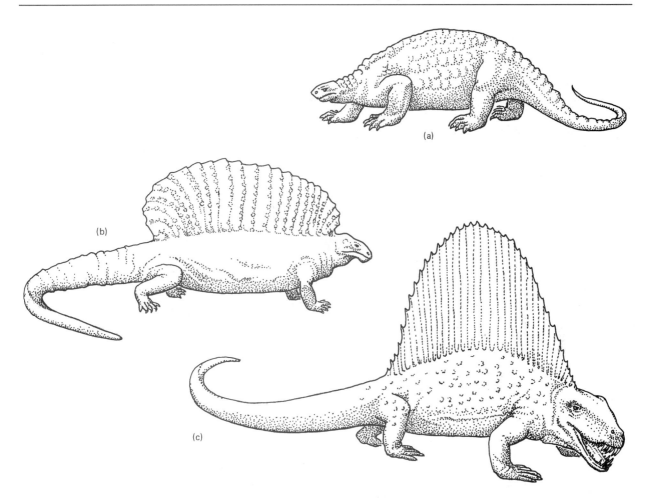

Figure 19–3   Body forms of herbivorous and carnivorous pelycosaurs. (a) *Cotylorhynchus*, a caseid; (b) *Edaphosaurus*, an edaphosaurid; (c) *Dimetrodon*, a sphenacodontid.

paleoequator at that time (Chapter 9). Late Permian therapsids were found farther afield, becoming particularly common in deposits in southern Africa, a region that had been under glaciation in the Carboniferous. Latest Permian and Triassic therapsids are known from all over Gondwana, as well as from the Northern Hemisphere (Parrish et al. 1986). The radiation of therapsids into more southern, colder climes has been held as one piece of evidence suggestive of their having a higher metabolic rate than the pelycosaurs. There also appears to be a profound difference in the types of terrestrial ecosystems inhabited by therapsids. The pelycosaur-dominated communities of the Late Carboniferous and Early Permian were still rooted in aquatic ecosystems, while the later therapsid-dominated faunas had terrestrial plants as their trophic base (Olson 1986).

The therapsids were the dominant large land mammals in the Late Permian, sharing center stage only with the large herbivorous pararreptilian pareiasaurs. The transition from the Permian to the Triassic was a period of great extinction, actually greater in magnitude than the better-known extinction of many diapsids (including dinosaurs) at the end of the Mesozoic. The known genera of tetrapods represented by fossils dropped from 200 in the Late Permian to 50 in the Early Triassic. The pattern of extinction was not regular; some old groups persisted while seemingly more derived forms disappeared. Among the herbivorous therapsids, only the tusked dicynodonts survived into the Triassic in abundance. The most derived groups of carnivorous therapsids, the therocephalians and the cynodonts, survived the Permo–Triassic transition and diversified in the Early Triassic. But other vertebrate groups also diversified in the Triassic, most notably the diapsid eureptiles (see Chapter 10 and Chapter 13). Rhynchosaurs took on the role of

Figure 19–4 *Dimetrodon grandis.* (Neg. #315862, photograph by Julius Kirschner, Courtesy of the Department of Library Services, American Museum of Natural History.)

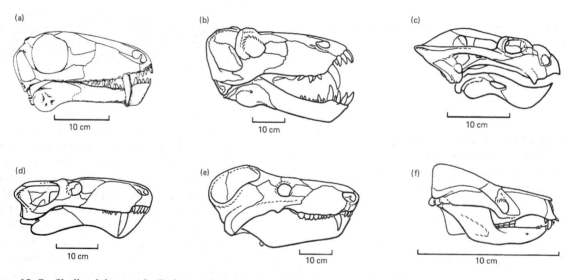

Figure 19–5 Skulls of therapsids. Early carnivores such as (a) the biarmosuchian *Biarmosuchus* and (b) the dinocephalian *Titanophoneus* had skulls that resemble those of sphenacodontid pelycosaurs. The herbivorous dicynodonts (c, *Dicynodon*) had lost most or all incisors and cheek teeth, retaining only the tusklike canines. The jaws were probably covered by a horny beak, as in turtles. Later carnivores such as gorgonopsids (d, *Scymnognathus*) and cynognathid cynodonts (e, *Cynognathus*) were carnivores specialized for attacking large prey. The tritylodontid cynodonts (f, *Oligokyphus*) were omnivores or herbivores with a very rodentlike dentition, including a lack of canines and a diastema between the incisors and cheek teeth. (Modified from A. S. Romer, 1966, *Vertebrate Paleontology*, 3d edition, University of Chicago Press, Chicago, IL; and R. L. Carroll, 1988, *Vertebrate Paleontology and Evolution*, Freeman, New York, NY.)

large herbivores, while primitive archosaurs played both herbivorous and carnivorous roles (Benton 1983). Therapsids became an increasingly minor component of the terrestrial fauna during the Triassic, with near extinction at its end. Only three groups of therapsids, the true mammals and the mammallike tritylodontids and tritheledontids, all small-size forms, survived into the Jurassic.

Early, More Primitive Therapsids

Therapsids such as the very primitive dog-size *Biarmosuchus* of the Late Permian (Figure 19–5a) differed from sphenacodontid pelycosaurs in several ways that appear to be related to increasing specialization as predators (Hopson 1994). The larger temporal fenestra allowed for an origin of the external adductor muscles from the skull roof, the upper canines were longer, and the entire skull was more rigid than it was in pelycosaurs. The postcranial skeleton of therapsids also showed changes from the sphenacodontid condition—the pectoral and pelvic girdles were less massive, and the limbs more slender. The shoulder joint appears to have allowed more freedom of movement of the forelimb (see Figure 19–11).

Slightly more derived therapsids were the Late Permian dinocephalians. The earliest forms, like *Titanophoneus* (Figure 19–5b), were carnivorous, from dog-size up to 3 meters in length. Dinocephalians had interdigitating upper and lower incisors that would have permitted the animal to tear off bite-size pieces of flesh. Some later forms were herbivorous. Some, like *Moschops* (Figure 19–6), were huge (bison-size), nearly 3 meters long and more than 1.5 meters at the shoulder. These herbivorous dinocephalians show a thickening of the roof of the skull that may indicate head-butting behavior associated with intraspecific combat. *Moschops* had a skull roof 10 centimeters thick. This bony shield would have transmitted the force of impact around the sides of the skull to the occipital condyle, which was directly in line with the shield (Barghusen 1975). Thus the impact would be transmitted along the neck and dissipated by the massive shoulders and trunk.

Later, More Derived Therapsids

Dinocephalians flourished in the early part of the Late Permian, but had disappeared before the end of that period. Other herbivorous therapsids that appeared at the same time persisted until the Late Triassic. These were the anomodonts, that were in many respects the most successful of all therapsids. In the Late Permian they dominated terrestrial faunas in diversity and in the number of specimens found as fossils. The most diverse and lasting of the anomodonts were the animals known as dicynodonts (King 1990).

A distinctive feature of dicynodonts was the extreme specialization of the skull for an herbivorous diet. In most forms all of the marginal teeth were lost, except for the upper canines, which were retained as a pair of tusks (Figure 19–5c, 19–7). The jaws are presumed to have been covered with a horny beak like that of turtles. A beak has some advantages over teeth as a structure for grinding plant material. Unlike a row of teeth, a horny beak can provide a continuous cutting surface, and it can be replaced continuously as it is worn away. The structure of the jaw articulation of dicynodonts permitted extensive fore-and-aft movement of the lower jaw, shredding the food between the two cutting plates. Dicynodonts diversified into a variety of ecological types. The marmot-size *Diictodon* apparently had marmotlike burrowing habits: it had clawed feet, wear on its tusks suggesting grubbing for roots, and has been found preserved coiled up in burrows (Hotton 1991). The pig-size *Lystrosaurus*, known from all over Gondwana, as well as China and Russia in the Early Triassic, may have had a hippolike semiaquatic life-style (see Figure 19–7).

The more derived carnivorous therapsids of the Late Permian and Triassic, the major predators, were carnivorous therapsids or theriodonts—gorgonopsians, therocephalians, and cynodonts. Theriodonts are characterized by the development of the **coronoid process** of the dentary, an upstanding flange near the back of the lower jaw that provided additional area for the insertion of the adductor musculature (see Figure 19–10, later). This process would additionally provide a lever arm for the action of the jaw muscles, perhaps important in these initially carnivorous therapsids. Accompanying changes in the skull roof opened the temporal fossa completely in the therocephalians and cynodonts, providing still more space for jaw muscles.

Gorgonopsians were lightly built animals the size of coyotes or wolves (e.g., *Lycaenops*, Figure 19–8), known from the Late Permian. Their canine teeth were long and blade-like, with serrated margins, and the incisors were well developed (Figure 19–5d). The postcanine teeth were small and gor-

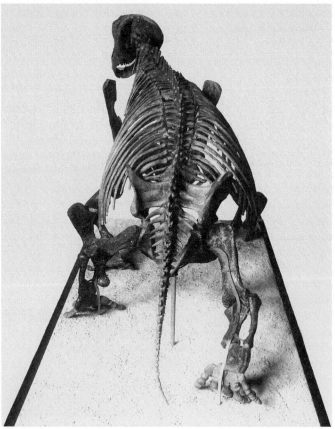

Figure 19–6 The dinocephalian therapsid *Moschops capensis* (AMNH 5552). Note the thick skull roof and the massive neck, shoulder girdle, and forelimbs—the limbs now held underneath the body—and the expanded ribcage indicative of the large gut volume of a herbivorous animal. ([upper] Neg #39137, and [lower] Neg #39140, Photos by Anderson, Courtesy of the Department of Library Services, American Museum of Natural History.)

Figure 19–7 A reconstruction of the Early Triassic dicynodont therapsid *Lystrosaurus*. (By Gregory Paul, from King, 1990.)

Figure 19–8 The gorgonopsian therapsid *Lycaenops ornatus* (AMNH 2240). The hindlimbs appear to have been carried nearly vertically, but the forelimbs extended outward from the body. ([upper] Neg #319862, and [lower] Neg #319863, Photo by Logan and Rota, Courtesy of the Department of Library Services, American Museum of Natural History)

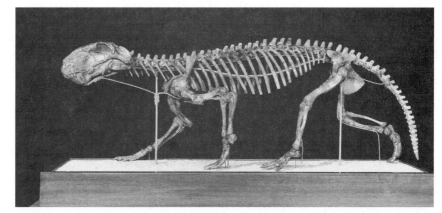

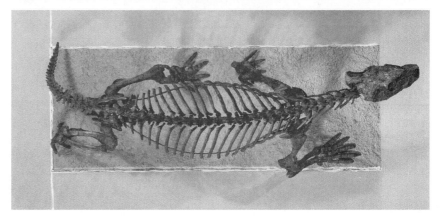

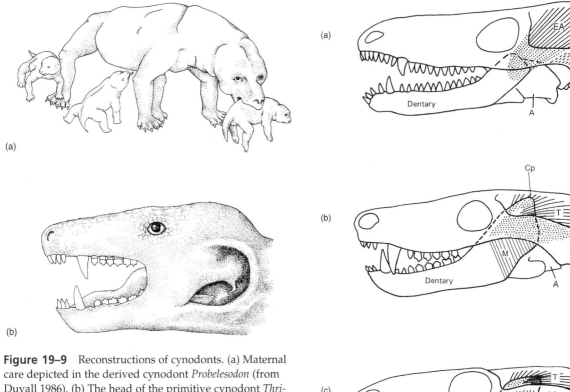

(a)

(b)

Figure 19–9 Reconstructions of cynodonts. (a) Maternal care depicted in the derived cynodont *Probelesodon* (from Duvall 1986). (b) The head of the primitive cynodont *Thrinaxodon*, showing the probable appearance of the ear region (Modified from Allin and Hopson 1992).

gonopsians probably used the anterior teeth to kill and tear chunks of flesh from their prey. Therocephalians were also known from the Late Permian, and survived into the Middle Triassic. Some were larger predators, like the gorgonopsids, while others were small and perhaps insectivorous. Later therocephalians paralleled the cynodonts in the acquisition of a complete bony secondary palate and complex postcanine teeth for masticating food (Hopson 1994).

The Most Derived Therapsids: the Cynodonts

Cynodonts appeared in the Late Permian, had their heyday in the Triassic, and were mostly extinct by the end of that period, although two nonmammalian lineages (the tritylodontids and the tritheledontids) persisted into the Jurassic. Of course, one could consider that cynodonts have persisted as mammals to the present day, and so these extinct beasts should more properly be termed nonmammalian cynodonts. A marked reduction in body size characterized the cynodont lineages, especially

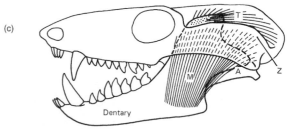

Figure 19–10 Cynodont skulls and jaw musculature. In cynodonts the dentary bone increased in size relative to the other bones of the lower jaw. In addition there was the development of a new jaw-closing muscle, the masseter, which inserted on the outside of dentary in a depression termed the masseteric fossa. The masseter was derived from the external adductor muscle, and the remaining part of that muscle is now termed the temporalis. A, angular bone; CP, coronoid process; EA, external adductor muscle; M, masseter muscle; T, temporalis muscle; Z, zygomatic arch. (a) Protocynodont condition; (b) *Thrinaxodon*, a primitive cynodont; (c) *Probelesodon*, a derived cynodont. (Modified from Kemp 1982.)

among carnivorous forms. Some early cynodonts were as big as large dogs, and this size was retained by some later herbivorous forms. But by the Middle Triassic, the carnivorous cynodonts had skulls only 70 millimeters long, about the size of a rabbit, and in the latest Triassic the total body length of the earliest mammals was less than 100 millimeters, about the size of a shrew.

Basal cynodonts (e.g., *Procynosuchus* and *Thrinaxodon*) were probably insectivorous. They had multicusped cheek teeth (that is, with small accessory cusps anterior and posterior to the main cusp) but no cutting blades for slicing flesh. Derived cynodonts of the late Early and early Middle Triassic included both carnivorous and herbivorous forms. The carnivores include the Early or Middle Triassic cynognathids, the Middle Triassic chiniquodontids, and the Late Triassic to Early Jurassic tritheledontids. These animals had well-developed canine teeth and incisors, like the earlier groups of carnivorous therapsids, and bladelike postcanines (see Figure 19–5e). Traces of wear on the surface of the postcanine teeth of *Cynognathus* indicate that serrations on the cusps of the teeth produced a tearing and cutting action. This arrangement would have allowed cynognathids to use the cheek teeth to cut off bite-size pieces of meat, and perhaps to slice the chunks into smaller pieces before they were swallowed. Herbivorous cynodonts (Gomphodontia) include the larger (dog-size) Early Triassic diademodontids and Middle Triassic transversodontids, and the mainly smaller (rodent-size) Late Triassic to Middle Jurassic tritylodontids (see Figure 19–5f). Gomphodonts had expanded teeth with blunt cusps forming opposing grinding and cutting surfaces on upper and lower teeth. As in dicynodonts, the lower jaw was apparently pulled backward into occlusion with the upper jaw.

The sculptured surfaces of the bones forming the upper and lower jaws suggest the presence of blood vessels and skin glands, with the inference that cynodonts (and also therocephalians) had a mammallike muzzle and lips, perhaps with whiskers (Hotton 1991). An enlarged infraorbital foramen, the hole under the eye through which the sensory nerves from the snout pass back to the brain, also supports the notion of a more mobile, sensitive muzzle. Cynodonts and therocephalians also had evidence for possession of turbinates, scroll-like bones in the nasal passages that warm the incoming air and help to prevent respiratory water loss (Hillenius 1992).

The Tritheledontidae, known from the Late Triassic of Argentina and the Early Jurassic of South Africa, may be the lineage most closely related to mammals. *Diarthrognathus,* the best-known form, possessed the mammalian dentary-squamosal jaw joint and its skull and teeth showed derived mammalian characters. The postcranial skeleton of *Diarthrognathus* has not been described, but it is essentially identical to that of early mammals (J. A. Hopson, personal communication). Furthermore, tritheledontids are the only cynodonts known in which the teeth were covered with prismatic enamel like that of mammals. On the other hand, the tritylodontids also had a very mammallike postcranial skeleton, and some researchers (e.g., Kemp 1982, 1983, 1988b; Rowe 1988) consider them to be the sister group of mammals. Others (e.g., Hopson and Barghusen 1986, Hopson 1994) consider tritylodontids to be more closely related to the gomphodonts, concluding that specialized adaptations of the skull and teeth for herbivory arose only once within the cynodonts. The main problem with identifying the sister group of mammals is that many aspects of morphology show extreme convergence. Specialists differ in their opinions about which characters are homologous and which are convergent, and these differences of interpretation lead to different phylogenies.

■ Evolutionary Trends in Synapsids

The synapsid lineage crossed a physiological boundary as the animals moved from ectothermy to endothermy, and this change was accompanied by changes in ecology and behavior. Physiology, ecology, and behavior do not fossilize directly, but some of the changes that were occuring in metabolism, ventilation, and locomotion can be traced indirectly via changes in the skull and the axial skeleton.

Skeletal Modifications and their Relationship with Metabolic Rate

Numerous changes in the skull and skeleton of synapsids can be observed over evolutionary time. One way to interpret these changes is to map them onto a phylogeny that considers the mammalian condition as the inevitable evolutionary outcome of synapsid evolution, and to congratulate the organisms for achieving ever-more mammalianlike status. However, there is no simple foresight in evolution: The changes in the skeleton that were occurring were not simply directed toward some mammalian condition, but rather reflected an increasing level of metabolic rate. Some of the most obvious changes are shown in Figure 19–11.

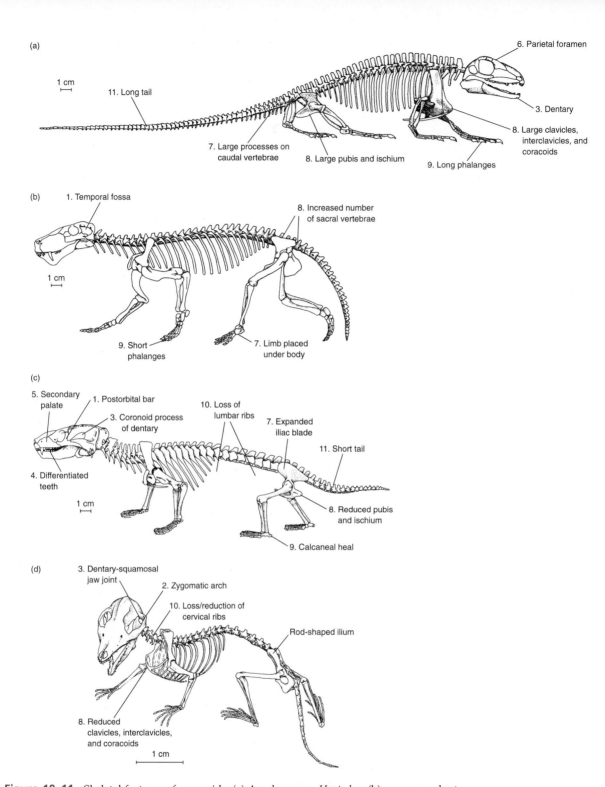

Figure 19–11 Skeletal features of synapsids. (a) A pelycosaur, *Haptodus*; (b) a noncynodont therapsid, *Lycaenops*; (c) a cynodont therapsid, *Thrinaxodon*; (d) an early mammal, *Megazostrodon*. [a] From Currie, P. J. 1977. A new haptodine sphenacodont (Reptila, Pelycosauria) from the Upper Pensylvanian of North America. *Journal of Paleontology* 51[5]:927–942. [b] From Colbert, E. H. 1948. The mammal-like reptile *Lyaenops*. *Bulletin of the American Museum of Natural History*, 89, pp. 353–404. [c] From F. A. Jenkins, Jr., 1970. Cynodont postcranial anatomy and the "Prototherian" level of mammalian organization. *Evolution* 24:230–252. Fig. 2. [d] From F. A. Jenkins, Jr., and F. R. Parrington, 1976, *Philosophical Transactions of the Royal Society (London) Series B* 273:387–431.

Metabolic rate does not directly show on the skeleton, but features associated with a higher metabolic rate may indeed be apparent. Animals with high metabolic rates require greater amounts of food and oxygen per day, so any changes suggesting improvements in the rate of feeding or respiration may indicate metabolic rate increase. Only animals with high metabolic rates are capable of sustained activity (Bennett and Ruben 1979). Thus indicators of greater levels of activity may also reflect higher metabolic rates.

The numbers of the features listed refer to the numbers on Figure 19–11. (1) The size of the temporal fenestra: A larger fenestra is indicative of a greater volume of jaw musculature, and hence implies more food eaten per day. Small in pelycosaurs, it suggests a fairly small size of jaw-closing musculature. An increasingly larger opening in more derived synapsids, along with an increasing tendency to enclose the braincase with dermal bone, results in a distinct **temporal fossa** for the origin of a larger volume of jaw musculature; the external adductor now passes through the fenestra to originate from the lateral surface of the skull roof. In the mammal the fossa is enlarged further with the loss of the postorbital bar, so that the the orbit is confluent with the temporal fossa.

(2) The condition of the lower temporal bar: A bar bowed out from the skull behind the orbit indicates the presence of a **masseter muscle**, originating from this bony bar and inserting on the lower jaw, again suggesting more food processing. The temporal bar lies very close to the upper border of the lower jaw in pelycosaurs and noncynodont therapsids, indicating that no part of the jaw musculature could have inserted on the outside of the lower jaw. In cynodonts and mammals the bar is bowed outward, forming the **zygomatic arch**, and suggestive of the presence of a masseter muscle. A corresponding fossa on the dentary in these animals also indicates the presence of this muscle.

(3) The lower jaw and jaw joint: Changes reflect the increased compromise between food processing and hearing in synapsids, as explained later. The lower jaw in pelycosaurs resembles the general amniote condition. The tooth-bearing portion, the **dentary**, takes up only about half of the jaw. By the level of cynodonts, the dentary has greatly expanded, and the postdentary bones have been reduced in size, and in mammals the dentary now forms a new jaw joint with the skull.

(4) The teeth: greater specialization of the dentition reflects an increased emphasis on food processing. The teeth of pelycosaurs are **homodont**; that is, they are virtually all the same size and shape, with no evidence of regionalization of function. In more derived synapsids the teeth become increasingly **heterodont**; that is, differentiated as to size, form, and function, although actual mastication with precise occlusion of the cheek teeth is a mammalian feature. All therapsids have the teeth differentiated into incisors, canines, and postcanine teeth, and in cynodonts these postcanine teeth may be complex. Mammals have reduced the number of tooth replacements to two (**diphyodonty**), have the postcanine teeth further differentiated into premolars (replaced) and molars (not replaced), and have the lower teeth set closer together than the uppers indicative of chewing with a rotary jaw motion.

(5) Development of a secondary palate: A secondary palate allows for breathing and eating at the same time, and also helps to bolster the skull against stresses from increased amounts of food processing (Thomason and Russell 1986). No secondary palate is apparent in pelycosaurs. An incipient, incomplete one is present in some noncynodont therapsids, and a complete one is present in derived cynodonts and in mammals (dicynodont therapsids evolved a secondary palate convergently). Mammals also have merged the originally double nasal opening into a single median one, probably reflecting an increase in the size of the nasal passages and a higher rate of respiration.

(6) Presence of a parietal foramen: A hole in the skull for the pineal eye reflects control of temperature regulation by behavioral means (Hotton 1991). It is present in pelycosaurs and in most therapsids, lost within cynodonts (and, convergently, in some therocephalians).

(7) Limb position: Limbs placed more underneath the body (**upright posture**) are reflective of a higher level of activity, resolving the conflict between running and breathing (see later discussion). Pelycosaurs have the sprawling limb posture typical of primitive amniotes. All therapsids show some degree of development of an upright posture, with mammals having the most derived condition. Also in therapsids evidence can be seen, in the expanded iliac blade and the development of the greater trochanter of the femur, of a switch to the gluteal type of hindlimb musculature typical of mammals. In pelycosaurs, large processes on the

caudal vertebrae suggest the retention of the more primitive amniote method of limb retraction using the caudofemoralis. (It is the gluteals that give mammals their rounded rear ends.)

(8) Shape of the limb girdles: The primitive amniote condition, with large ventral components to the limb girdles, reflects a sprawling posture, with a supportive undercarriage. With a more upright posture, more of the weight passes directly through the limbs. Pelycosaurs have large clavicles, interclavicles and coracoids in the pectoral girdle, and large pubes and ischia in the pelvic girdle. Therapsids have more lightly build girdles with the reduction of the ventral elements and the expansion of the dorsal ones, such as the iliac blade. Therapsids also show an increase in the number of sacral vertebrae from the two or three of pelycosaurs to four or more. Mammals have a very reduced pubis and a rod-shaped ilium, probably reflecting a change in muscle positioning and muscle forces generated with the change in the vertebral column and the adoption of a bounding gait (see [10] and later discussion) (Bramble and Jenkins 1989).

(9) Shape of the feet: Long-toed feet indicate feet used more as holdfasts, typical of a sprawling gait. Short-toed feet indicate feet used more as levers, with a more upright posture. Pelycosaurs have long toes (and fingers), with the primitive phalangeal formula of 2-3-4-5-3/4. All therapsids and mammals have shorter feet, with derived cynodonts and mammals having a phalangeal formula of (2-3-3-3-3) (count this on your own hands!) A distinct **calcaneal heel** is seen in cynodonts and mammals, providing a lever arm for a greater degree of push-off from the gastrocnemius muscle. Mammals also have an opposable big toe.

(10) The form of the vertebral column: The loss of the lumbar ribs suggests the presence of a diaphragm, indicative of a higher rate of respiration (see later discussion). Lumbar ribs are present in pelycosaurs and noncynodont therapsids, absent from mammals, and reduced or absent in cynodonts. With the complete loss of the lumbar ribs, mammals have evolved distinctive differences between the thoracic and lumbar vertebrae, indicative of the mammalian mode of bounding locomotion with dorso-ventral flexion. Mammals have also reduced or lost the ribs on the cervical vertebrae, and restricted the number of neck vertebrae to seven.

(11) The tail: A long tail, as in pelycosaurs, reflects locomotion conducted primarily by axial movements, as in the primitive amniote condition. A shorter tail, as in most therapsids and mammals, reflects a more upright posture where limb propulsion is more evident than axial flexion. A more slender tail base in these animals is also indicative of the switch in limb retractor muscles (see [7] above).

Evolution of Jaws and Ears

As in the primitive condition for tetrapods and bony fishes (Chapter 3), the original synapsid condition of the lower jaw was for a tooth-bearing dentary occupying the anterior jaw half, with a variety of bones (known collectively as **postdentary** bones) forming the posterior half. The jaw articulation was between the **articular** in the lower jaw and the **quadrate** in the skull. A trend within cynodonts was to enlarge the size of the dentary and to decrease the size of the postdentary bones. This trend was probably related to the increase in the volume of jaw adductor musculature, which inserted onto the dentary (Figure 9–11). In the most derived cynodonts a condylar process of the dentary grew backward, and eventually contacted the squamosal bone of the skull. In mammals and some very derived cynodonts this contact between the dentary and the squamosal formed a new jaw joint, the **dentary-squamosal** jaw joint. In these derived cynodonts, and also in the earliest mammals, this new jaw joint coexisted along with the old one, but in later mammals the dentary-squamosal jaw joint is the sole one. The bones forming the old jaw joint are now part of the middle ear (Box 19–1).

The bare facts of the transition have been known for a century or so, but the evolutionary interpretation of these facts has changed over time. Originally it was assumed that the lizardlike middle ear, with the stapes alone forming the auditory ossicle, was the primitive condition for all tetrapods, and hence the one possessed by the early synapsids. We now have good evidence that an enclosed middle ear evolved separately in modern amphibians and amniotes, and probably at least three times convergently within amniotes (see Chapter 3 and Chapter 10). But prior to this information it was assumed that, with the transition to mammals, an originally single-boned middle ear was transformed into a three-boned one. (This evolutionary scenario also carried the tacit assumption that the mammalian condition of both ear bones and jaw articulation was somehow superior to that of other tetrapods.) The change in jaw morphology was not assumed to

BOX 19–1 **The Evolution of the Mammalian Middle Ear**

More than a century ago embryological studies demonstrated that the malleus and incus of the middle ear of mammals were homologous with the articular and quadrate bones that formed the ancestral jaw joint of gnathostomes, and of all nonmammalian vertebrates. More recently the transition has been traced in fossils from its beginning in basal synapsids through therapsids to early mammals (Allin 1975; Crompton 1985; Allin and Hopson 1992). The first indication of a mammalian type of middle ear is seen in the sphenacodontid pelycosaurs. These animals have a structure called the "reflected lamina" on the angular bone of the lower jaw, which is believed, at least in later synapsids, to have housed a tympanum (eardrum). In therapsids, the stapes, which acted as a skull brace in primitive amniotes, now has an articulation with the quadrate, resembling the incus/stapes articulation of mammals (Hotton 1991). (Remember that a stapes [hyomandibular]–quadrate articulation is actually the primitive gnathostome condition.) Thus these early synapsids were using their jaw joint to hear with as well as to form the jaw hinge.

The transition from the nonmammalian to the mammalian condition can be visualized by comparing the posterior half of the skull of *Thrinaxodon*, a fairly primitive cynodont (Figure 19–12a), with that of *Didelphis*, the Virginia opossum (Figure 19–12b). The reflected lamina was probably the principal support of the tympanic membrane, and vibrations were transmitted to the stapes via the articular and quadrate. The mammalian jaw joint is formed by the dentary and squamosal bones. The tympanum and middle ear ossicles lie behind the jaw joint and are much reduced in size, but they retain the same relation to each other as they had in cynodonts. The lower jaw of a fetal mammal viewed from the medial side shows that the angular (tympanic), articular (malleus), and quadrate (incus) develop in the same positions they have in the cynodont skull (Figure 19–12c). The homologue of the angular, the tympanic bone, supports the tympanum of mammals. The retroarticular process of the articular bone is the manubrium of the malleus, and the ancestral jaw joint persists as the articulation between the malleus and incus.

Figure 19–12 Anatomy of the back of the skull and the middle ear bones of synapsids. (a) *Thrinaxodon*, a cynodont; (b) *Didelphis*, the Virginia opossum; (c) embryonic mammal. (From A. W. Crompton and F. A. Jenkins, Jr., 1979, pages 59–73 in *Mesozoic Mammals: The First Two-Thirds of Mammalian History*, edited by J. A. Lillegraven, Z. Kielan-Jaworowska, and W. A. Clemens, University of California Press, Berkeley, CA.)

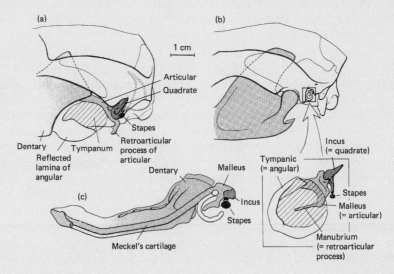

have a direct connection with the change in the ears. Rather, it was assumed that once a new jaw joint was formed, the left over bones became incorporated into the middle ear.

If you think about it, there are some problems with this story. Even if it were true that a dentary-squamosal jaw joint *was* somehow superior, how could you explain the millions of years of cynodont evolution during which the dentary is still enlarging prior to contacting the skull? Did those earlier cynodonts know that their descendants would one day make a better jaw joint out of this bone? Why is a quadrate-articular jaw articulation an inherently weak one? It appears to work well enough in other vertebrates (noone has ever accused *Tyrannosaurus rex* of having a weak jaw!). And why disrupt a perfectly functional middle ear to insert some extra bones, which happen to be going spare? Even if a three-boned middle ear is ultimately superior, there would be a period of adjustment to a new condition that would probably be suboptimal.

These questions were addressed, and solved, by Edgar Allin (1975). He came up with the revolutionary (for the time, but in retrospect merely sensible!) suggestion that the chain of bones that make up the middle ear of mammals had been used for hearing all along in synapsids (at least since the level of derived pelycosaurs, see Box 19–1). This system would be clumsy perhaps, using the same set of bones for two functions, but a variety of different types of auditory setups have evolved within tetrapods—the standard lizard condition is well known, but by no means universal. This mode of hearing would serve the early synapsids perfectly adequately; the only problem would come in the more derived ones, when increasing metabolic demands required a greater volume of jaw musculature and greater use of the jaw in feeding, with concomitant greater stresses on the jaw joint. Allin interpreted the evolutionary history of the jaw in cynodonts as representing an *evolutionary conflict* between functions.

An initial evolutionary step would be to enlarge the dentary bone and to transfer all the jaw muscle insertions to this bone. This would isolate the auditory postdentary bones somewhat from the feeding apparatus, and also allow them to become smaller, as befits auditory ossicles. Note that the reason that older workers had interpreted the jaw of synapsids as weak is because the postdentary bones remained loose and wobbly, and did not fully fuse up with one another and with the dentary as in many other tetrapods. However, given Allin's interpretation, there was a very good reason for these bones *not* to fuse up: if they had done so they would have compromised their role as vibrating auditory ossicles. In progressively more derived cynodonts the dentary increased further in size. Finally, once the dentary was large enough to contact the squamosal in the skull, the opportunity was presented for this contact to be formed into a new jaw joint, freeing up the original jaw joint from its old function, and allowing it to be devoted entirely to the function of hearing. A classic example of an evolutionary intermediate is provided by the tritheledontid *Diarthrognathus*. This animal gets its name from its double jaw joint (*di* = two, *arthro* = joint, *gnath* = jaw). It has both the ancestral articular-quadrate joint and, next to it, the mammalian dentary-squamosal articulation. These postdentary bones are still retained in a groove in the lower jaw in the earliest mammals, and it is possible that their final incorporation into a fully enclosed middle ear occurred convergently to a certain extent in monotremes, multituberculates, and therians (Allin and Hopson 1992).

Since Allin devised the above evolutionary scenario, other researchers have added to the story and refined it. Crompton (Crompton and Parker 1978, Crompton 1985) emphasized the role of the masseter muscle that first appeared in cynodonts. In mammals the masseter can move the lower jaw laterally and, acting in concert with the pterygoideus muscle on the inside of the lower jaw, can be thought of as holding the lower jaw in a supportive sling. Crompton interpreted the evolution of the masseter muscle as helping to relieve stresses at the jaw joint by this slinglike action, and so helping to resolve the conflict between jaw use and hearing. Bramble (1978) pointed out that, while a fully formed masseter might act in this fashion, a small, incipient one at its evolutionary appearance would not perform a slinglike role. He suggested that a small, forwardly directed masseter would counteract the backward pull of the enlarged temporalis, which otherwise might act to dislocate the jaw when the animal bit down hard on something. He also interpreted a preadaptive role for the condylar process of the dentary that eventually forms the new jaw joint. This process increases in size in cynodonts, but its initial function, prior to the formation of a new jaw joint, had never been deciphered. Bramble's biomechanical analysis of jaw function interprets the initial function of this structure as preventing rotatory dislocation between the dentary and the postdentary bones during biting. Finally Tim Rowe (1996) considered that the final separation of the middle ear bones from the lower jaw in true mammals is correlated with an increase in the size of the mammalian neocortex, dislocating these bones from their original position during embryonic development with the expansion of the brain.

Locomotion and the Evolution of Upright Posture

Early tetrapods must have moved with lateral undulations of the trunk, as do salamanders and lizards today, with the axial musculature contributing significantly to locomotion (see Chapter 3). A potential problem with this is that the hypaxial muscles that aid in rib ventilation in amniotes are also used in locomotion to a certain extent, meaning that an animal like a lizard cannot breathe and run simultaneously (Carrier 1987). For an ectothermic tetrapod, with fairly low levels of activ-

ity and low demands for oxygen, this does not present a problem. Besides, short bursts of speed are initially powered by anaerobic respiration in all vertebrates, even in ourselves (Bennett and Ruben 1979). A problem only presents itself if the animal requires extended periods of sustained locomotion. But evolutionary history, as exemplified by the skeletal anatomy, suggestive of active, fast-running animals, tells us that this must have become a problem in both synapsid and archosaurian lineages. That is, with increasing levels of activity, there developed an *evolutionary conflict* between running and breathing, similar to the conflict that we have just considered between jaw use and hearing.

Figure 19–13 illustrates the problem. In addition to the conflict in muscle use, the side-to-side bending of the lizard's rib cage pushes the air from one lung into the other, and interferes with the ventilation in and out of the mouth. The immediate solution to this problem is to devise a means of locomotion that involves the primary use of the limbs, with the trunk held relatively rigid. In

Figure 19–13   The effect of axial bending on lung volume of a running lizard (seen from above) and a galloping dog (seen from the side). The bending axis of the thorax of the lizard is between the right and left lungs. As the lizard bends laterally, the lung on the concave (left) side is compressed and air pressure in that lung increases (shown by +) while air pressure in the lung on the convex (right) side is reduced (shown by −). Air may be pumped between the lungs (arrow), but little or no air will move in or out of the animal. In contrast, the bending axis of the thorax of a galloping mammal is dorsal to the lungs. As the vertebral column bends, the volume of the thoracic cavity decreases, and pressure in both lungs rises (shown by +), pushing air out of the lungs (arrow). When the vertebral column straightens, the volume of the thoracic cavity increases, pressure in the lungs falls (shown by −), and air is pulled into the lungs (arrow). (From Carrier 1987, *Paleobiology* 13:326–341.)

lizards (indeed in all eureptiles, see Chapter 10) the hindlimbs are longer that the forelimbs, giving the animal the opportunity to run bipedally, a behavior seen in a number of lizards today. Bipedal locomotion involves only the hindlimbs, without movements of the trunk, thus resolving this conflict. Archosaurian eureptiles show an increased tendency toward bipedality, and early dinosaurs and birds are obligate bipeds. The synapsid lineage was never much prone to bipedality (with the exception of a few derived therian mammals, such as humans and kangaroos). Instead synapsids obtain an upright posture by bringing their limbs more underneath the trunk, meaning that the propulsion from the limbs will have less of a bending effect on the trunk (Carrier 1987). (Archosaurs also adopt an upright posture along with their bipedality.) The initial change from a sprawling to a more upright posture is seen in the first therapsids (Figure 19–11).

Further refinements to this situation come with true mammals, which have the capacity for dorsoventral flexion of the vertebral column and which adopt a bounding type of fast gait (see Chapter 3). This type of spinal flexion is only possible once the lumbar ribs have been lost or reduced, as first seen in cynodonts, where this reduction may be associated with the acquisition of a muscular diaphragm. Living mammals use the diaphragm, in addition to the ribs, to inhale air into the lungs, and experimental work on living animals (cutting the nerves leading to the diaphragm) shows that this structure is especially important in obtaining additional oxygen during activity (Ruben et al. 1987). The bounding gait of mammals now allows respiration and locomotion to work together in a *synergistic* fashion, rather than in a conflicting one. The inertial movements of the viscera (especially the liver), modulated by contractions of the diaphragm, help to force air in and out of the lungs with each bounding stride (Figure 19–13) (Bramble and Carrier 1983). We have little direct experience of this basic mammalian condition: our bipedal locomotion has led to a complete decoupling of locomotion and ventilation, just as in archosaurs. But an appreciation of this condition helps to explain certain features of locomotion in quadrupedal mammals. For example, a galloping horse will increase its speed by increasing its stride length rather than its stride frequency, so as to avoid interference with the rhythm of lung ventilation.

Evolution of the Nasal and Palatal Regions

We have been considering various skeletal features in synapsids that might be clues to their metabolic status. One structure that might be considered as a sure sign of endothermy is the presence of nasal turbinate bones—thin, scroll-like bones seen today in the living endothermic vertebrates, birds and mammals (Ruben 1995). The maxillary turbinates, in particular, are important in conserving water during respiration: the naso- and ethmo-turbinates are more concerned with olfaction (Figure 19–14).

High rates of ventilation, as demanded by an endothermic metabolism, present a problem for air-breathing vertebrates: The tissues of the lungs where gas exchange takes place are extremely thin because gas must be exchanged very rapidly (via diffusion, see Chapter 3), and they are therefore susceptible to drying. To minimize water loss, the inhaled air must be warmed to lung temperature and saturated with water vapor before it reaches the gas-exchange surfaces. This process occurs as the air passes over warm, moist surfaces in the nasal passages. During exhalation water is again conserved by condensing out on the turbinates, which are relatively cooler than the air expired from the lungs. The higher the rate of ventilation, the more elaborate are the structures a vertebrate needs to conserve respiratory water loss. Lizards have low rates of ventilation, and the simple walls of their nasal passages are adequate to treat the air before it reaches their lungs. Birds and mammals have much higher rates of ventilation than lizards, and require structures that increase the surface area of the nasal passages. Although these fragile turbinate bones do not usually fossilize, the ridges where they attach in the nasal passages *do* preserve, and these are found both in therocephalians and cynodonts, suggesting mammalian-like rates of respiration in these animals (Hillenius 1992).

There are also other fundamental differences between living mammals and reptiles in the mouth and pharyngeal regions. The secondary palate of mammals, seen also in cynodonts, separates completely the nasal passages from the mouth. This structure is indicative of a higher metabolic rate in a variety of ways; as previously discussed, it reflects both increased oral food processing and the need to eat and breathe at the same time.

Mammals can form fleshy seals against this bony hard palate with the tongue and with the epiglottis, effectively isolating the functions of breathing and

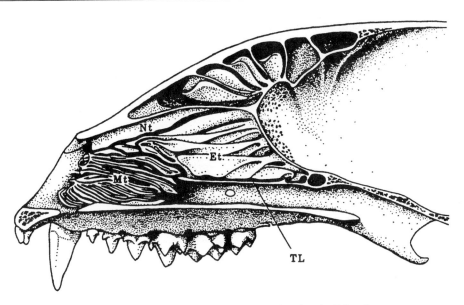

Figure 19–14   The snout of a raccoon showing the nasal passages and turbinals. Eth, ethmo-turbinal; Mt, maxilloturbinal; Nt, nasoturbinal; TL, transverse lamina, separating respiratory turbinates (maxilloturbinals) from the olfactory turbinates. (From Hillenius 1992.)

swallowing (Smith 1992; Crompton 1995). New-born mammals make use of these seals to enable suckling on the nipple without ceasing to breathe through the nose. Adult humans have lost the seal that allows for this action, with the movement of the larynx more ventrally in early childhood, which makes us more liable to choke on our food, and also enables us to breathe through the mouth as well through the nose. But we retain the more anterior seal: This is what stops you from swallowing water when you gargle. This mammalian pharyngeal anatomy is also important for our mode of swallowing a discrete, chewed bolus of food, rather than shoving large items wholesale down the gullet (like a snake swallowing a mouse) (see also discussion in Chapter 21, and Figure 21–2). Changes in the bony anatomy of the palate and surrounding areas suggest that these functions came into place only with the most derived cynodonts, suggesting that this type of swallowing, and the capacity for suckling, are fundamentally mammalian attributes (Crompton 1995).

■ The First Mammals

Living mammals today are characterized by two salient features: hair and mammary glands (*mamma* = breast, from which structure mammals

get their name). Neither of these features is directly preserved in the fossil record, although we will argue that we can infer at what point in synapsid evolution these features were acquired. We have, in fact, already argued that at least some cynodonts had a higher metabolic rate than the other therapsids, and if they were indeed endothermic then it is likely that they possessed hair for insulation. Another feature typical of most living mammals is viviparity, giving birth to live young rather than laying eggs. However, we know that this was not a feature of the earliest mammals as some living primitive mammals, the **monotremes** (the platypus and echidna of Australia and New Guinea), still lay eggs. How, then, can we define where in synapsid evolutionary history we should start to apply the term mammal?

Traditionally the acquisition of a dentary-squamosal jaw joint was used to define the first fossil mammal, as only mammals possess this type of jaw joint today. Later evidence revealed that some animals we would still classify as derived cynodonts, such as *Diarthrognathus*, also possessed a dentary-squamosal jaw articulation, while retaining the old quadrate-articular one. On the other hand, some of the earliest mammals also retained this old jaw joint as well. In practice, it has always been pretty easy to determine an early mammal. They are tiny, a couple of orders of magnitude smaller than cynodonts (of a body mass of less than 100 g, shrew-size), whereas the smallest cynodonts would have weighed about a kilogram, the size of a rabbit, with the exception of some smaller tritylodontids. But did this transition to a very small body size really signify a biological shift into a different type of adaptive zone that we can clearly signify as mammalian?

The traditional point of mammalian transition is marked not only by this jaw joint but also by some derived features of the skull, indicative of an enlargement of the brain and inner ear regions, and also by postcanine teeth with divided roots (Hopson 1994). Other workers (e.g., Rowe 1988) would prefer to limit the term Mammalia to those animals bracketed by the interrelationships of surviving mammals (i.e., to taxa at node 11 and above in Figure 19–1). However, we will argue later for the traditional division between mammals and cynodonts to represent some real biological transitions, including the evolution of lactation and suckling.

Features of the Earliest Mammals

The oldest well-known mammals are ones like the earliest Jurassic (about 210 million years ago) *Morganucodon* (also known as *Eozostrodon*) from Wales (Figure 19–15a). Good skull and skeletal material is known of early mammals like this one and similar beasts, such as *Megazostrodon* from South Africa (Figure 19–11d). A somewhat older possible mammal is *Adelobasileus* (about 225 million years old), known only from an isolated braincase from the Late Triassic of Texas. Another Early Jurassic mammal is the Chinese *Sinoconodon*, known from a skull that appears to be much more primitive than that of *Morganucodon*. Most of our information about mammals comes from their teeth. At their small size, the fragile bones do not easily preserve, but the harder, enamel-containing teeth are more likely to fossilize. Fortunately, mammalian teeth turn out to be very informative about their owners' life-style.

Mammals are diphyodont: that is, they only have two sets of replacing teeth (like our milk teeth and permanent teeth) and the molars are not replaced at all, but only erupt fairly late in life. Our last molars are our wisdom teeth, so-called because they erupt at the age (late teens) by which time we supposedly have attained wisdom. Mammals also have molars with precise occlusion that is produced by an interlocking arrangement of the upper and lower teeth. We can determine this in fossils because the teeth

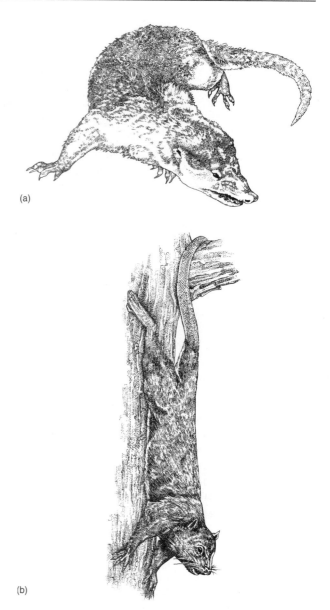

(a)

(b)

Figure 19–15 Reconstructions of early mammals. (a) The Early Jurassic mammal *Morganucodon* (modified from drawing by Marianne Collins in C. M. Janis, 1993, in *The Book of Life*, edited by S. J. Gould, Norton, New York.) (b) The early Tertiary multituberculate *Ptilodus* (modified from drawing by L. L. Sadler in Jenkins and Krause 1983.)

show distinct wear facets produced from tooth to tooth abrasion, showing that the teeth always meet in the same consistent manner. Precise occlusion makes it possible for the cusps on the teeth to cut up food very thoroughly, creating a large surface area for digestive enzymes to act on, and thereby promoting rapid digestion. Only mammals thoroughly chew, or masticate, their food in this fashion. The cheek teeth of mammals also are set in an alternating fashion, such that each upper occludes with two lowers (and, likewise, each lower occludes with two uppers). In addition, the lower jaws of mammals are set together more closely than are the upper jaws, a condition termed anisognathy. These features lead us to infer that the basic mammalian pattern of jaw movement was now in place. Reptiles move their jaw in a simple up-and-down fashion, and their lower jaws are the same distance apart as the uppers. Mammals move their jaws in a rotary fashion, chewing only on one side of the jaw at a time (Figure 19–16). As mammals only have two sets of teeth per lifetime, their teeth must now be made more durable, and a distinctive mammalian feature is teeth with more durable, prismatic enamel (Grine et al. 1979).

We can also deduce some features of the nonbony anatomy of the earliest mammals from a comparison of the monotremes with the more derived living mammals, the therians (marsupials and pla-

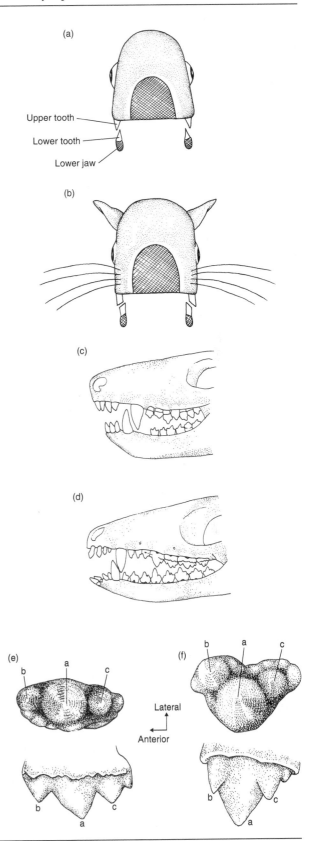

Figure 19–16 Occlusion and molar form in cynodonts and early mammals. (a) Cross-sectional view through the muzzle of a cynodont. The lower teeth and the upper teeth are the same distance apart (isognathy) and the jaw movement is a simple vertical up-and -down one. (b) Cross-sectional view through the muzzle of a mammal. The lower teeth are closer together than the upper ones, because of a narrower lower jaw (anisognathy), and the jaw movement is a rotatory one with chewing on only one side of the jaw at any one time. (c) Side view of the jaws of a cynodont (*Thrinaxodon*). The postcanine teeth all look similar (and are replaced continually), and are arranged so each tooth in the upper jaw lines up with one in the lower jaw. (d). Side view of the jaws of a mammal (*Morganucodon*). The postcanine teeth are now divided into simple premolars (replaced one) and more complex molars (not replaced), and the upper and lower molars are offset so that they interdigitate on occlusion (each tooth in the upper jaw meshes with two in the lower jaw, and vice versa). (e) Schematic upper molar of *Morganucodon* in occlusal ("tooth's eye") and lateral view, representing the original mammalian pattern (similar to that of cynodonts). The three main cusps are set in a straight line. (f) Schematic upper molar of *Kuehneotherium* in occlusal and lateral view, representing the more derived holotherian pattern. The arrangements of the cusps is triangular, with the major cusp set more medially (in the uppers, more laterally in the lowers), to effect the "reversed triangles" pattern of occlusion. (Modified from Krause 1982, *Paleobiology* 8:265–281, Fig. 7. Reprinted by permission.)

centals). We have already deduced that the earliest mammals must have laid eggs. Monotremes have a more primitive ear than therians: their cochlea in the inner ear is not highly coiled (we can actually see that this was also the case in preserved braincases of the earliest mammals), and they lack a pinna, or external ear. Thus it is likely that the earliest mammals were also pinnaless, even though this makes them look rather nonmammalian in reconstruction (Figure 19–15a). Although monotremes produce milk, their mammary glands lack nipples, and so these were also probably lacking in the earliest mammals. Monotremes, although endothermic, have a metabolic rate lower than that of therians, lack effective sweat glands and are not good at evaporative cooling: early mammals were probably similar.

The only thing that monotremes are not good for is for deductions about the behavior and ecology of the earliest mammals. Monotremes are relatively large mammals, and specialized in their habits (Chapter 21). The earliest mammals were small and, to judge from their teeth, insectivorous. By analogy with small, insectivorous marsupials and placentals today, they were probably nocturnal, and solitary in their behavior, with the mother-infant bond being the only strong social bond. We do know from preserved braincases that early mammals had large olfactory lobes, indicating the importance of the sense of smell, and proportionally larger cerebral hemispheres than even the derived cynodonts (Kielan–Jaworowska 1986). Early mammals may have been capable of much more sophisticated sensory processing than were cynodonts (Jerison 1973).

The Evolution of Lactation

There are two main questions about the evolution of the typically mammalian feature of lactation. First, when did it originate, and is it coincident with the point that we consider as the cynodont-mammal transition? Second, how did lactation arise in the first place. That is, how did milk and the mammary gland itself evolve?

Caroline Pond (1977) has argued that the precise occlusion and diphyodonty are indicative of the presence of lactation in early mammals. She points out that precise occlusion would not work with the multiply erupting system of tooth replacement (polyphyodonty) seen in living reptiles and in nonmammalian synapsids, as only a fully erupted tooth occludes properly with its counterpart in the

other half of the jaw. Thus diphyodonty must have *preceded* precise occlusion in evolution. But how could an animal come to evolve the condition of diphyodonty? This could occur only if it was fed milk during its early life, so that the jaw could grow while it had no need of teeth, and permanent teeth could erupt in a near adult-size jaw. Thus, if an animal has precise occlusion and diphyodonty, it must have first evolved lactation.

Pond's hypothesis allows us to infer that the earliest mammals lactated, but had they inherited this feature from the cynodonts? We saw earlier that the type of palatal anatomy that would allow suckling is only present in the most derived cynodonts. Another clue comes from the juveniles of some of the herbivorous cynodonts. While juvenile herbivorous mammals have flat grinding teeth, like those of their parents, the teeth of juvenile herbivorous lizards are sharp and pointed. Young lizards require more protein than the adults, and have a juvenile diet of insects, modifying both diet and tooth type as they mature. Herbivorous juvenile mammals obtain their higher protein requirements from their mother's milk. If the juvenile cynodonts received milk, their teeth should look like those of the adults, but in fact they look like the teeth of insectivorous lizards. Thus we can be fairly sure that these babies were not suckled (Hopson 1973). Note that this does not mean that cynodonts did not have parental care. Obviously, parental care would have to be in place before lactation could evolve. Parental care would be essential for an endotherm, to ensure the proper thermal environment for juveniles and the developing young.

Thus we have some fairly strong evidence to suggest that lactation came in with the origin of mammals. But how did the whole system evolve in the first place? Mammary glands cannot be specifically derived from any of the specialized skin glands (e.g., sweat glands) seen in living mammals, but they do appear to be rather closely linked to the type of glands associated with hair (sebaceous glands) (see Chapter 21). Thus they probably had the primitive ability to secrete small amounts of organic materials, as do these glands in mammals today (Blackburn 1991). One suggestion for the evolution of lactation is that these glands originally secreted substances (aggregating pheromones) signaling the offspring to recognize their mother, and to congregate with her (Figure 19–9a) (Duvall 1986).

An evolutionary scenario related specifically to the properties of milk was advanced by Blackburn et al. (1989). They noted that all milk contains proteins that are related to the lysozyme enzymes that attack bacteria: Even human milk has antimicrobial properties. They suggested that the original use of milk might have been for protection against microorganisms of the eggs in a nest. Attack of the eggs by microorganisms might be a more critical problem for an endotherm, incubating the young in a warm, bacteria-friendly nest. Once a secretion of this type had evolved, any evolutionary change to a more copious, more nutritive secretion accidentally ingested by the young could only have been of benefit. This proto milk would initially have supplemented the egg yolk, and then later supplanted it.

What is the evolutionary advantage of lactation for mammals? Lactation allows for the production of offspring to be separated from seasonal food supply. Unlike birds, which must lay eggs only when there is the appropriate food supply for the fledglings (spring and summer), mammals can store food as fat and convert it into milk at a later date. Provision of food in this manner by the mother alone also means that she does not have to be dependent on paternal care to rear her young, again unlike birds, which must form offspring-caring pair bonds, one to sit with the young and keep them warm, and one to search for food. Finally, lactation makes viviparity less strenuous on the mother. In viviparous lizards the mass of the litter may be up to 50 percent of the mass of the mother, while in mammals it never exceeds around 20 percent. Mammals can use the strategy of lactation to give birth to relatively immature young, unable to fend for themselves (baby lizards are already developed enough to fend for themselves and are not fed by the mother). This means that the mammalian mother is not so encumbered by the process of viviparity, an encumbrance that might be even more burdensome to an endotherm, needing to frequently forage for food, than to a less active ectotherm like a lizard.

The Radiation of Mesozoic Mammals

The Cenozoic is usually termed the Age of Mammals. While it is true that mammals were small and basically verminlike until the end of the Cretaceous, the period of radiation of Mesozoic mammals still represents two-thirds of the total of mammalian history. Mesozoic mammals were diverse taxonomically, but fairly homogenous in adaptive morphotype. They were all of fairly small body size: many were shrew size and none was bigger than a pre-sent-day opossum (weighing 2 to 3 kg). Their teeth reveal mainly insectivorous diets with some omnivory, but these mammals were too small to be predatory carnivores or herbivores with a highly fibrous diet. Although it is unlikely that there was ever direct competition between mammals and dinosaurs (scenarios of mammals causing dinosaur extinction by eating their eggs notwithstanding!), it is yet true that mammals did not diversify into larger-bodied forms with more varied diets until the dinosaurs' extinction. The presence of dinosaurs must in some way have been preventing the radiation of mammals into a broader variety of adaptive niches.

There were two major periods of mammalian diversification during the Mesozoic. The first, spanning the Jurassic to Early Cretaceous, produced an early radiation of forms that in the main did not survive past the Mesozoic: morgonucodonts, docodonts, triconodonts, symmetrodonts, dryolestids, and the like (Figure 19–1). These early mammals are fascinating to students of early mammal history, but we will not discuss them in more detail here. (For an extensive review see Lillegraven et al. 1979.) The second radiation, commencing in the Early Cretaceous, was comprised of more derived mammals. The first true therian mammals with tribosphenic molars (see later) are known from the Early Cretaceous, and mammals definitely identifiable as marsupials and placentals are known from later in the period. The earliest known monotremes are also Early Cretaceous in age, but must have been a separate lineage through at least most of the Jurassic. One diverse group that spans both time periods, and also persists into the Cenozoic, is the rodentlike multituberculates (see later). But here again, although primitive multituberculates appeared in the Jurassic, the emergence of the more derived forms from the initial radiation is also in the Early Cretaceous. Changes in other aspects of the terrestrial ecosystem are also apparent at this time. The Early Cretaceous marks the time of the initial radiation of the angiosperms, the flowering plants. Among other tetrapods, the Cretaceous dinosaur faunas were distinctively different from earlier ones, and snakes made their first appearance.

Very early in mammalian history, as early as the earliest Jurassic, there was a difference observable in the types of molar teeth and patterns of occlusion. The primitive type, exemplified by *Morganucodon*, is to have the three main molar cusps in a more-or-less straight line. The more derived type, exemplified by the contemporaneous *Kuehneotherium*, is to shift the principal, middle cusp so that the teeth assume a triangular form in occlusal (food's eye) view (Figure 19–16). The apex of the triangle formed by the upper tooth points inward, while that of the lower tooth points outward, forming an intermeshing relationship termed **reversed triangle** occlusion. The upper triangle is known as the trigon and the lower one as the trigonid. The longer sides of these triangular teeth result in a greater amount of available area for shearing action, and the teeth also interdigitate in a more complex fashion than do the teeth of more primitive mammals. The lineage that includes *Kuehneotherium*, and all other more derived mammals used to be called Theria, but that term has now been restricted to the groups formed by marsupials and placentals. The term Holotheria has been suggested for this more inclusive group by Jim Hopson (1994) (see Figure 19–1).

A further dental complication is seen in later (Early Cretaceous) holotheres is the development of the **tribosphenic molar**. The group of mammals possessing tribosphenic molars is termed the Tribosphenida, and includes the Theria (Figure 19–1). This type of molar adds a new cusp, the protocone, to the trigon in the uppers, which occludes against a basined addition to the lowers called the talonid (Figure 19–17). The tribosphenic molar adds the function of crushing and punching to the original tooth, that acted mainly to cut and shear. The possession of this tooth presumably reflects a greater diversity of dietary items taken.

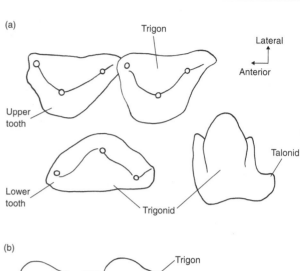

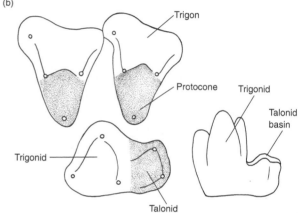

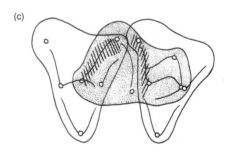

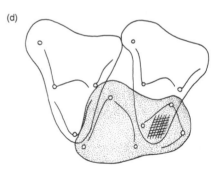

Figure 19–17 Morphology of a tribosphenic molar. (a) Schematic occlusal view of reversed triangle molars of a nontherian holotherian mammal. The lower molar is also illustrated in side view. (b) Similar view of the tribosphenic molars of a therian. The new portions (the protocone in the uppers and the basined talonid in the lowers) are shaded. Parts (c) and (d) show the action of the lower molars in occlusion with the uppers: The lower molar is shaded, and areas of tooth contact are crosshatched. (c) Initial contact between the teeth at the start of occlusion. The cusps of the trigonid produce a shearing action along the side of the cusps of the back of the trigon of the anterior upper tooth and the front of the trigon of the posterior upper tooth. (d) Mortar-and-pestle action of the molars at the end of the occlusal power stroke. The protocone (= the pestle of the combination) fits into the basin formed between the cusps in the trigonid (the mortar).

Multituberculates—the "Rodents of the Mesozoic"

A very important radiation of early mammals was of the **multituberculates** (multis), a group sometimes known as the subclass Allotheria (= other mammals). They were a very long-lived group, known from the Late Jurassic to the early Cenozoic (late Eocene). They are known almost entirely from the Northern Hemisphere: Only recently has a Gondwanan radiation been recognized in South America and Madagascar (Krause et al. 1997). Multis get their name from their molars, which are broad, multicusped (or multituberculed) teeth specialized for grinding rather than shearing. Wear on the teeth indicates that they moved their lower jaw backwards while bringing their teeth into occlusion (Krause 1982). Their teeth and jaw movements were rather similar to the tritylodontids, the lineage of cynodonts that survived into the Jurassic, and the radiation of the multis may have something to do with their demise. The teeth and jaw movements were also similar to those of rodents, except rodents move their lower jaws *forward* into occlusion (Figure 19–18).

Multis probably occupied an adaptive niche similar to that of rodents, small terrestrial and semiarboreal omnivores. Some multis were rather squirrellike: The structure of their ankle bones shows that they could rotate their foot backward to descend trees head first, like a squirrel, and their caudal vertebrae indicate a prehensile tail (Jenkins and Krause 1983) (Figure 19–15b). These squirrel-like multis also had the specialty of an enlarged lower posterior premolar that formed a shearing blade, perhaps used to open hard seeds (Figure 19–18a). Other multis were more terrestrial, and rather wombatlike. The extinction of multis in the Eocene was probably due to competition with the rodents, which first appeared in the late Paleocene (Krause 1986).

We know nothing definite of the mode of reproduction of multis, but there are some clues. Multituberculate fossils are fairly common, but no associated eggs have been found. Their very narrow pelvis suggests that they did not lay eggs, but may have given birth to immature young, as do marsupials (Chapter 21). If multis are indeed less closely related to therians than are monotremes (Figure 19–1, and discussion later), their viviparity

Figure 19–18 Comparison of the skulls and jaws of (a) a multituberculate (*Ptilodus*) and (b) a rodent (*Hapalomys*). The cusps on the molars of the multituberculate are concave anteriorly on the uppers and concave posteriorly on the lowers, indicating retraction of the mandible during chewing. The cusps on the molars of the rodent are concave posteriorly on the uppers and concave anteriorly on the lowers, indicating protraction of the mandible during chewing. Black areas are exposed dentine, stippled areas are worn enamel, clear areas are unworn enamel, and dashed lines are valleys between cusps. (From D. W. Krause, 1982, *Paleobiology* 8:265–281, Fig. 7. Reprinted by permission.)

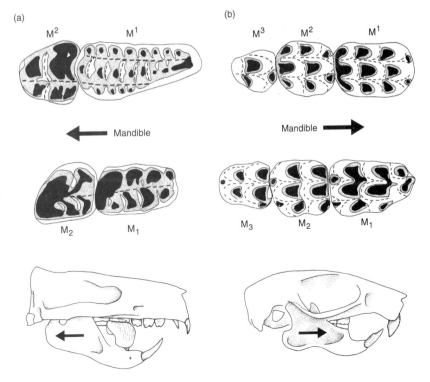

would have to have been an independent evolution of the condition from the situation in therians. A lineage most likely cannot return to egg-laying once its members have become viviparous, as the shell glands and so on, are lost. So this hypothesis of the phylogenetic position of the monotremes implies that the common ancestor of monotremes and therians was oviparous.

Basal Mammalian Interrelationships

There are three major lineages of mammals that survived the Mesozoic, the multituberculates, the monotremes, and the therians. Multis and monotremes were originally seen as being very distantly related to therians. Living monotremes are primitive in a variety of ways, not only because of their egg-laying habits, and were once even considered to be an independent radiation from the cynodonts. The teeth of multis are so different from those of other early mammals that they, too, were thought to have a very early offshoot from the main lineage. Living monotremes are toothless as adults, and so the characters of dental anatomy (on which much of mammalian phylogeny is based) cannot easily be used to evaluate their relationships.

The phylogenetic position of the monotremes was reassessed with the discovery of a single jaw of a fossil form (*Steropodon*) from the Early Cretaceous of Australia (Archer et al. 1985). How did these researchers know that this tooth belonged to a monotreme if living monotremes are toothless? Teeth are found in the juveniles of the present-day platypus, but these are replaced by horny plates in the adult. A few molars are known from an adult Miocene form. The distinctive nature of these teeth enabled the recognition of the monotreme nature of *Steropodon*, but its more fully formed teeth were sur-prisingly also clearly triangular in shape. The shape of these teeth suggests that monotremes are actually holotheres, rather than an offshoot of a more primitive type of mammal (Kielan–Jaworowska et al. 1987), although the primitive nature of their shoulder girdle means that they must have branched off before the symmetrodonts, known from the Early Jurassic (Hu et al. 1997) (Figure 19–1).

The position of the multis within the Mammalia is more controversial. Multis have a rather derived, therianlike shoulder girdle (see Chapter 21), which until fairly recently was considered to have been an independent evolution within this group. More recently certain researchers, generating cladograms based primarily on postcranial characters, have asserted that this feature actually links multis with more derived holotheres, with the suggestion that they are even more closely related to therians than are monotremes (Rowe 1988). Multituberculates have a clavicle (collar bone) that can pivot on the sternal area to allow a degree of shoulder mobility, a condition more derived than in the shoulder girdle of monotremes. They share this character not only with therians, but also with more primitive holotheres such as symmetrodonts (Hu et al. 1997).

In contrast, Zofia Kielan-Jaworowska (1997), who has spent a lifetime studying these critters, considers multis to be very primitive, perhaps related to triconodonts, as we suggest here (Figure 19–1). She bases her opinion on the very primitive nature of the foot, pelvis, brain, and inner ear, with the conclusion that the derived nature of the shoulder girdle must represent convergence between multis and therians. The phylogenetic position of multis is an area of active debate and controversy; better fossil material of early (Jurassic) multis would greatly help to resolve their relationships to other mammals.

■ Summary

The synapsid lineage is characterized by a single lower temporal fenestra on each side of the skull. The first synapsids were the pelycosaurs of the Late Carboniferous and Early Permian, including the familiar sailbacks. Many pelycosaurs were large animals, and some may have weighed as much as 250 kilograms. The most derived pelycosaurs, the sphenacodonts, had several more mammalianlike features, including the beginnings of a three-boned middle ear. The earliest therapsids were more derived in possessing an upright posture, limbs more designed for propulsion, and a greater volume of jaw musculature. The most derived therapsids, the Triassic cynodonts, had many features indicative of endothermy, including turbinate bones in the nose, a secondary palate, and a reduction of the rib cage indicative of the presence of a diaphragm. Many of the features of the cynodont skull that changed over their history can be understood in the context of an evolutionary conflict between chewing and hearing, as some of the bones of the mammalian middle ear formed the original synapsid jaw joint.

The first mammals of the Jurassic had teeth which were only replaced once, and that precisely interlocked to masticate the food. Their skeleton suggests that by this time they had developed the typically mammalian bounding gait. A substantial reduction in body size accompanied the evolution of the first mammals: they were only 100 millimeters long and probably weighed less than 50 grams. We can deduce quite a lot about the probable biology of these early mammals, not just from the skeletal remains, but also from considering the biology of the living monotremes and primitive therians. By inference from patterns of tooth replacement we can conclude that lactation evolved with the earliest mammals. Milk itself may have been evolved for its antimicrobial properties in the nests of oviparous mammals.

The radiation of Mesozoic mammals was mainly one of small insectivorous or omnivorous forms. Mammals did not diversify larger, more specialized forms until the Cenozoic, after the extinction of the dinosaurs. Multituberculates, specialized omnivores, were an important rodentlike Mesozoic lineage that only became extinct in the early Cenozoic with the origin of true rodents. The modern groups of mammals, monotremes and therians (marsupials and placentals), can trace their origin back to the Early Cretaceous, a time of evolutionary turnover not only in mammals, but also in other tetrapods and in plants. The relationships of these major groups of mammals to one another, and to the earlier Mesozoic radiation, is the subject of current controversy.

■ References

Allin, E. F. 1975. Evolution of the mammalian middle ear. *Journal of Morphology* 147:403–437.

Allin, E. F., and J. A. Hopson. 1992. Evolution of the auditory system in Synapsida ("mammal-like reptiles" and primitive mammals) as seen in the fossil record. Pages 587–614 in *The Evolutionary Biology of Hearing*, edited by D. B. Webster, R. R. Fay, and A. N. Popper. Springer-Verlag, New York, NY.

Archer, M., T. F. Flannery, A. Ritchie, and R. E. Molnar. 1985. First Mesozoic mammal from Australia—an early Cretaceous monotreme. *Nature* 318:363–366.

Barghusen, H. R. 1975. A review of fighting adaptations in dinocephalians (Reptilia, Therapsida). *Paleobiology* 1:295–311.

Bennett, A. F., and J. A. Ruben. 1979. Endothermy and activity in vertebrates. *Science* 206:649–654.

Benton, M. J. 1983. Dinosaur success in the Triassic: a noncompetitive evolutionary model. *Quarterly Review of Biology* 58:29–55.

Blackburn, D. G. 1991. Evolutionary origins of the mammary gland. *Mammal Review* 21:81–96.

Blackburn, D. G., V. Hayssen, and C. J. Murphy. 1989. The origins of lactation and the evolution of milk: a review with new hypotheses. *Mammal Review* 19:1–26.

Bramble, D. M. 1978. Origin of the mammalian feeding complex: models and mechanisms. *Paleobiology* 4:271–301.

Bramble, D. M., and F. A. Jenkins, Jr. 1989. Structural and functional integration across the reptile-mammal boundary. Pages 133–146 in *Complex Organismal Functions: Integration and Evolution in Vertebrates*, edited by D. B. Wake and G. Roth. Wiley, New York.

Bramble, D. M., and D. R. Carrier 1983. Running and breathing in mammals. *Science* 262:235–240.

Carrier, D. R. 1987. The evolution of locomotor stamina in tetrapods: circumventing a mechanical constraint. *Paleobiology* 13:326–341.

Crompton, A. W. 1985. Origin of the mammalian temporomandibular joint. Pages 1–18 in *Development of Temporomandibular Joint Disorders*, edited by D. S. Carlson, J. McNamara, and K. A. Ribbens. Monograph 16, Craniofacial Growth Series. University of Michigan Press, Ann Arbor, MI.

Crompton, A. W. 1995. Masticatory function in nonmammalian cynodonts and early mammals. Pages 55–75 in *Functional Morphology in Vertebrate Paleontology*, edited by J. J. Thomason. Cambridge University Press, Cambridge, UK.

Crompton, A. W., and P. Parker. 1978. Evolution of the mammalian masticatory apparatus. *American Scientist* 66:192–210.

Duvall, D. 1986. A new question of pheromones: aspects of possible chemical signaling and reception in the mammal-like reptiles. Pages 219–238 in *The Ecology and Biology of Mammal-Like Reptiles*, edited by N. Hotton III, P. D. MacLean, J. J. Roth, and E. C. Roth. Smithsonian Institution Press, Washington, DC.

Gonick, L. 1990. *The Cartoon History of the Universe*, volumes 1–7. Doubleday, New York, NY.

Grine, F. E., E. S. Vrba, and A. R. I. Cruickshank. 1979. Enamel prisms and diphyodonty: linked apomorphies of Mammalia. *South African Journal of Science* 75:114–120.

Haack, S. C. 1986. A thermal model of the sailback pelycosaur. *Paleobiology* 12:450–458.

Hillenius, W. J. 1992. The evolution of nasal turbinates and mammalian endothermy. *Paleobiology* 18:17–29.

Hopson, J. A. 1973. Endothermy, small size, and the origin of mammalian reproduction. *American Naturalist* 107:446–452.

Hopson, J. A. 1991. Systematics of the nonmammalian Synapsida and implications for patterns of evolution in synapsids. Pages 635–693 in *Origins of the Higher Groups of Tetrapods,* edited by H.-P. Schultze and L. Trueb. Cornell University Press, Ithaca, NY.

Hopson, J. A. 1994. Synapsid evolution and the radiation of non-eutherian mammals. Pages 190–219 in *Major Features of Vertebrate Evolution,* edited by D. R. Prothero and R. M. Schoch. Short Courses in Paleontology No. 7. Paleontological Society and University of Tennessee Press, Knoxville, TN.

Hopson, J. A., and H. R. Barghusen. 1986. An analysis of therapsid relationships. Pages 83–106 in *The Ecology and Biology of Mammal-Like Reptiles,* edited by N. Hotton III, P. D. MacLean, J. J. Roth, and E. C. Roth. Smithsonian Institution Press, Washington, DC.

Hotton, N., III. 1991. The nature and diversity of synapsids: prologue to the origin of mammals. Pages 598–634 in *Origins of the Higher Groups of Tetrapods,* edited by H.-P. Schultze and L. Trueb. Cornell University Press, Ithaca, NY.

Hu, Y., Y. Wang, Z. Luo, and C. Li. 1997. A new symmetrodont mammal from China and its implications for mammalian evolution. *Nature* 390:137–142.

Jenkins, F. A., Jr., and D. W. Krause. 1983. Adaptations for climbing in North American multituberculates (Mammalia). *Science* 220:712–715.

Jerison, H. J. 1973. *Evolution of Brain and Intelligence.* Academic, New York, NY.

Kemp, T. S. 1982. *Mammal-like Reptiles and the Origin of Mammals.* Academic, London, UK.

Kemp, T. S. 1983. The relationships of mammals. *Zoological Journal of the Linnaean Society* 77:353–384.

Kemp, T. S. 1988a. Interrelationships of the Synapsida. Pages 1–22 in *The Phylogeny and Classification of the Tetrapods,* volume 2, edited by M. J. Benton. Clarendon, Oxford, UK.

Kemp, T. S. 1988b. A note on the Mesozoic mammals, and the origin of therians. Pages 23–29 in *The Phylogeny and Classification of the Tetrapods,* volume 2, edited by M. J. Benton. Clarendon, Oxford, UK.

Kielan-Jaworowska, Z. 1986. Brain evolution in Mesozoic mammals. Pages 21–34 in *Vertebrates, Phylogeny, and Philosophy,* edited by K. M. Flanagan and J. A. Lillegraven. Contributions to Geology, Special Paper 3. University of Wyoming, Laramie, WY.

Kielan-Jaworowska, Z. 1997. Characters of multituberculates neglected in phylogenetic analyses of early mammals. *Lethaia* 29:249–266.

Kielan-Jaworowska, Z., A. W. Crompton, and F. A. Jenkins, Jr. 1987. The origin of egg-laying mammals. *Nature* 326:871–873.

King, G. 1990. *The Dicynodonts: A Study in Paleobiology.* Chapman & Hall, London, UK.

Krause, D. W. 1982. Jaw movement, dental function, and diet in the Paleocene multituberculate *Ptilodus. Paleobiology* 8:265–281.

Krause, D. W. 1986. Competitive exclusion and taxonomic displacement in the fossil record: the case of rodents and multituberculates in North America. *Contributions to Geology,* University of Wyoming, Special Paper 3:95–117.

Krause, D. W., G. V. R. Prasad, W. von Koenigswald, A. Sahni, and F. E. Grine. 1997. Cosmopolitanism among Late Cretaceous mammals. *Nature* 390:504–507.

Lillegraven, J. A., Z. Kielan-Jaworowska, and W. A. Clemens. 1979. *Mesozoic Mammals: the First Two-Thirds of Mammalian History.* University of California Press, Berkeley, CA.

Olson, E. C. 1986. Relationships and ecology of the early therapsids and their predecessors. Pages 47–60 in *The Ecology and Biology of Mammal-Like Reptiles,* edited by N. Hotton III, P. D. MacLean, J. J. Roth, and E. C. Roth. Smithsonian Institution Press, Washington, DC.

Parrish, J. M., J. T. Parrish, and A. M. Ziegler. 1986. Permian–Triassic paleogeography and paleoclimatology and implications for therapsid distribution. Pages 109–131 in *The Ecology and Biology of Mammal-Like Reptiles,* edited by N. Hotton III, P. D. MacLean, J. J. Roth, and E. C. Roth. Smithsonian Institution Press, Washington, DC.

Pond, C. M. 1977. The significance of lactation in the evolution of mammals. *Evolution* 31:177–199.

Rowe, T. 1988. Definition, diagnosis, and origin of Mammalia. *Journal of Vertebrate Paleontology* 8:241–264.

Rowe, T. 1996. Coevolution of the mammalian middle ear and neocortex. *Science* 273:651–654.

Ruben, J. A. 1995. The evolution of endothermy in mammals and birds: from physiology to fossils. *Annual Review of Physiology* 57:69–95.

Ruben, J. A., A. F. Bennett, and F. L. Hisaw. 1987. Selective factors in the origin of the mammalian diaphragm. *Paleobiology* 13:54–59.

Smith, K. K. 1992. The evolution of the mammalian pharynx. *Zoological Journal of the Linnean Society* 104:313–349.

Thomason, J. J., and A. P. Russell. 1986. Mechanical factors in the evolution of the mammalian secondary palate. *Journal of Morphology* 189:199–213.

Tracy, C. R., J. S. Turner, and R. B. Huey. 1986. A biophysical analysis of possible thermoregulatory adaptations in sailed pelycosaurs. Pages 195–206 in *The Ecology and Biology of Mammal-like Reptiles,* edited by N. Hotton III, P. D. MacLean, J. J. Roth, and E. C. Roth. Smithsonian Institution Press, Washington, DC.

CHAPTER
20

Geography and Ecology of the Cenozoic

The role of Earth history in shaping the evolution of vertebrates is difficult to overestimate. The positions of continents have affected climates and the ability of vertebrates to migrate from region to region. The geographical continuity of Pangaea in the late Paleozoic and early Mesozoic allowed tetrapods to migrate freely across continents, and the faunas were fairly similar in composition across the globe. However, by the late Mesozoic Pangaea no longer existed as a single entity. Epicontinental seas extended across the centers of North America and Eurasia, and the southern continents were separating from the northern continents and from one another. This isolation of different continental blocks resulted in the isolation of their contained tetrapod faunas, and limited the possibility for migration. As a result, tetrapod faunas became progressively regionalized. Distinct regional differences were apparent in the dinosaur faunas of the late Mesozoic, and have been a prominent feature of Cenozoic mammalian faunas.

Continental drift in the late Mesozoic and early Cenozoic moved the northern continents that had formed the old Laurasia (North America and Eurasia) from their early Mesozoic near-equatorial position into higher latitudes. This different latitudinal distribution of continents, plus other resultant changes such as changes in patterns of ocean currents, resulted in a higher-latitude cooling trend in the later Cenozoic. With the formation of the Arctic ice cap some 5 million years ago this cooling led to a series of ice ages that began in the Pleistocene and continue to the present. We are currently living in a relatively ice-free interglacial period. Both the fragmentation of the landmasses and the changes in climate during the Cenozoic have been important factors in the evolution of mammals.

■ Continental Geography During the Cenozoic

The breakup of Pangaea in the Jurassic was initiated by the movement of North America to open the ancestral Atlantic Ocean. Rifts began to open in Gondwana, and India moved northward on its separate oceanic plate (Figure 20–1), eventually to coalesce with Eurasia. The collision of the Indian and Eurasian plates in the mid-Cenozoic produced the Himalayas, the highest mountain range in today's world.

South America, Antarctica, and Australia separated from Africa during the Middle and Late Cretaceous, but maintained connections with one another into the early Cenozoic (Figure 20–1). In the

581

Figure 20–1 Continental positions in the late Paleocene and early Eocene. An epicontinental sea, the Turgai Straits (crosshatching) extended across Eurasia. Dashed arrows show the direction of continental drift, and solid arrows indicate the major land bridges mentioned in the text.

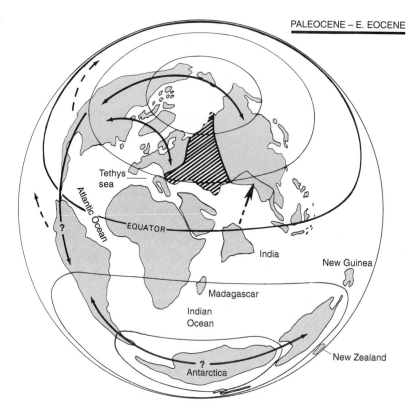

PALEOCENE – E. EOCENE

middle to late Eocene, Australia separated from Antarctica and, like India, drifted northward. (Note that New Guinea, today an island north of Australia separated from the mainland continent by a shallow sea, is actually a part of the Australian continental block, and was in direct land contact with Australia for much of Earth's history.) Intermittent land connections between South America and Antarctica were retained until the middle Cenozoic via the Scotia Island arc. Mammal faunas are known from Antarctica in the late Eocene, bearing strong resemblances to those from South America. New Zealand rifted from Australia sometime in the middle Mesozoic, apparently too early in the history of mammalian diversification to carry with it its own endemic component of mammals. Although New Zealand has many other endemic tetrapods—most notably the primitive diapsid reptile *Sphenodon* (the tuatara)—its only endemic mammal is a bat, which evidently reached the island by flying over from Australia.

In the Northern Hemisphere a land bridge between Alaska and Siberia—the trans-Bering Bridge—broadly connected North America to Asia at high but relatively ice-free latitudes (Figure 20–1). Intermittent connections also persisted between eastern North America and Europe via Greenland and Scandinavia from the Cretaceous to the early Eocene. However, migrations of mammals between North America and Europe via this route appear to have been prominent only during the early Eocene. The connection apparently broke during the Eocene, and continued migrations between North America and the Old World must have occurred via the Bering land bridge linking Siberia and Alaska. Other tectonic movements also influenced Cenozoic climates. For example, the uplift of mountain ranges such as the Rockies, the Andes, and the Himalayas in the middle Cenozoic cast rain shadows along their western flanks, resulting in the replacement of woodlands by grasslands.

Continental Movements and Vegetational Changes

An appreciation of the fact that the major landmasses were moving away from the equatorial region and toward the poles is the key to understanding the changes in climatic conditions that accompanied the radiation of Cenozoic mammals. The passage of landmasses over the polar region, Antarctica in the early Cenozoic and Greenland in the later Cenozoic, allowed the formation of polar ice caps, culminating in the periods of glaciation (ice ages) of the Pleistocene. The story of Cenozoic mammal evolution is also the story of the temperate regions of the higher latitudes becoming cooler and drier with accompanying changes in vegetation (for example, the replacement of lush tropical-like forests with woodland and grassland).

The warm and humid conditions typical of the Jurassic and Early to Middle Cretaceous changed toward the end of the Cretaceous when widespread moderate cooling took place. Yet the world of the early Cenozoic still reflected the hothouse world of the Mesozoic: tropicallike forests were found in high latitudes, and even within the Arctic circle. A mammalian fossil assemblage from the early Eocene of Ellesmere Island (Canada) shows the presence of mammals resembling (although not closely related to) the tree-dwelling primates and flying lemurs of present-day southeast Asia. The peak of climatic warming in the higher latitudes occurred around the early–middle Eocene boundary (Figure 20–2). From this high point, the higher-latitude regions started to cool, with a rather precipitous drop in mean annual temperature in the latest Eocene, plunging the Earth into the start of the colder world of the later Cenozoic.

What caused this dramatic change in the earth's temperatures? Present studies of continental movements and the reconstruction of ancient ocean currents indicate that the middle Eocene was the time when Australia broke away from Antarctica and Greenland broke away from Norway. Cold polar-bottom water was formed with the isolation of landmasses over the poles, and ocean circulation carried the cold water toward the equator, cooling the temperate latitudes. The Antarctic ice cap probably formed by the end of the Eocene, although the Arctic ice cap did not form until some 30 million years later.

Following a rather cool Oligocene, temperatures started to rise in higher latitudes in the early Miocene, reaching a second peak in the middle Miocene (but nowhere near as high as in the early Eocene). The Miocene world was in general drier than during the Eocene, and the combination of warmth and dryness promoted the spread of grasslands and the evolution of mammals adapted to a savanna type of habitat. Miocene vegetational changes, and the expansion of grass at the expense of other plants, may also have been related to decreasing global levels of atmospheric carbon dioxide (Cerling et al. 1997). Grass plants are capable of switching to a different biochemical pathway for photosynthesis (the C_4 pathway), which is more efficient in conditions of low carbon dioxide. Most other plants cannot use this pathway. The cause of low levels of carbon dioxide may have been the uplift of the Himalayas, where mountain uplift resulted in increased chemical weathering, absorbing carbon dioxide from the atmosphere (Raymo and Ruddiman 1992).

This Miocene warming may be due to the opening of Drake's Passage between Antarctica and South America, which isolated the cold polar water around Antarctica. However, expansion of the Antarctic ice cap in the late Miocene once again brought cooling to the higher latitudes, a trend that has persisted to the present day with occasional remissions.

Note that changes in the diversity of mammals paralleled changing temperatures at higher latitudes throughout the Cenozoic, with peaks seen in the mid-Eocene and mid-Miocene (Figure 20–2). This pattern makes sense when we think of today's world, in which a much greater diversity of mammals exists in the tropical forests than in the temperate woodlands. It may seem paradoxical that the diversity appears to be greater at the mid-Miocene peak than at the warmer mid-Eocene peak. Several phenomena probably contribute to this paradox. Some of these factors may be artifacts of the fossil record, whereas others probably represent real ecological differences. First, there is the Pull of the Recent. That is, the nearer we get to the present day, the less likely it is that fossils have been eroded and lost forever, so the *apparent* diversity of fossils in young deposits is greater than in old ones. Second, there were more large mammals in the Miocene than there had been in the Eocene, and large teeth and bones have a greater chance of preservation than small ones, again biasing the fossil record. Finally, the changing Cenozoic climates had produced a fractionation of habitat types by the Miocene. Tropical forests were still found at the equator, but other kinds of habitats (such as woodland and grassland) were found at higher latitudes, and these diverse habitats probably supported a great diversity of mammals.

■ The Pleistocene Ice Ages

The extensive episodic continental glaciers that characterize the Pleistocene were events that had not been a feature of the world since the Paleozoic. These ice ages had an important influence not only

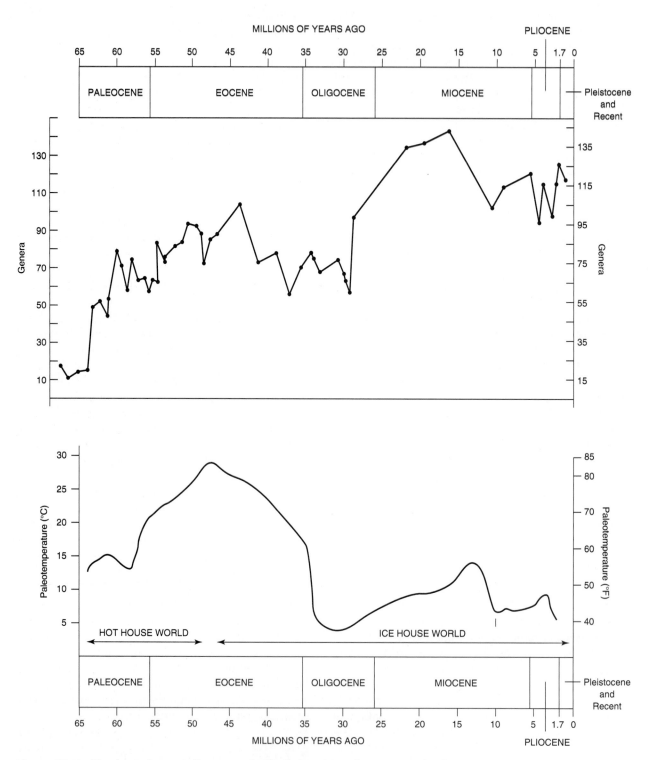

Figure 20–2   Numbers of mammalian genera in North America and mean annual paleotemperatures in the North Sea during the Cenozoic. Note that the peaks in total genera and in temperature substantially coincide. (Modified from R. K. Stucky, 1990, *Current Mammalogy* 2:375–432; and Janis 1993.)

on Cenozoic mammal evolution in general, but also on our own evolution and even on our present civilizations. The world can still be considered to be in the grip of an ice age, but at the present time we inhabit a warmer, interglacial, period.

For example, at present the volume of ice on earth constitutes about 26 million cubic kilometers. During glacial episodes in the Pleistocene there could be as much as 77 million cubic kilometers of ice, perhaps even more. An enormous volume of water was, and still is, locked up in glaciers and polar ice caps. The melting of the glaciers of the last glacial episode at the end of the Pleistocene, around 10 thousand years ago, caused the sea level to rise by about 140 meters (almost half the height of the Empire State Building) to its present relatively stable condition. If the present-day glaciers were to melt, sea level would rise at least another 50 meters, submerging most of the world's coastal cities. No wonder present-day environmentalists are concerned about the possibilities of global warming caused by human activities!

Today glaciers cover 10 percent of the earth's land surface, mostly in polar regions but also on high mountains. At times in the Pleistocene an ice mass that was probably between 3 and 4 kilometers thick covered as much as 30 percent of the land, and extended southward in North America to 38°N latitude (southern Illinois, Figure 20–3). A similar ice sheet covered northern Europe. However, the area covering much of Alaska, Siberia, and Beringia (Pleistocene land which is now underwater as the Bering Straits) was free of ice cover, and housed a biome known as the Mammoth Steppe or the steppe-tundra. This environmental type is unknown today, and was obviously much more productive than present-day high-latitude habitats, as it contained a mammalian faunal assemblage that rivaled the diversity of modern African savanna faunas (Guthrie 1990). This fauna mixed mammals now absent from higher latitudes, such as lions and rhinos, with animals that persist in Arctic latitudes today, such as reindeer and musk ox.

These continental glaciers advanced and retreated several times during the Pleistocene. (The Southern Hemisphere was less affected because the southern continental landmasses were further from the poles than the northern ones at this time, as they are today.) There were four major episodes of glaciation, as shown in Figure 20–3, but we now know that many (perhaps 20 or more) minor ones were interspersed among these major ones.

Continental glaciation had a greater effect on world climates than just ice covering the high latitudes. Although popular books depict mammoths struggling to free themselves from ice, glaciers advance slowly enough for animals to migrate toward the equator, although problems may occur if routes are blocked by mountain ranges or seaways. Drying of the ice-free portions of the Earth due to the volume of water tied up in glaciers was at least as important for mammalian evolution as the glaciers themselves. Many of the equatorial areas that today are covered by lowland rain forests were then much drier, even arid. Even today's relatively mild interglacial period is apparently colder and drier than other interglacial periods in the Pleistocene. For example, remains of hippos are found in what is now the Sahara Desert, and hippos were known in England during the last interglacial period.

With each glacial episode the forests in the Amazonian and Congo basins contracted into several isolated refugia separated by savannas. During interglacial periods, the forests again spread over the basins, and the savannas contracted and were fractionated. As a result of these alternating expansions and contractions, plant and animal populations were repeatedly isolated and remixed. During isolations one species might be separated into several populations. The effect of glaciation on equatorial aridity, and the resultant contraction of moist habitats, may explain the high species diversity that now exists in these areas (Terborgh 1992).

What caused these episodes of glaciation? A long-standing theory suggests that the amount of solar radiation impinging on the Earth (solar insolation) varies enough to affect the Earth's climate. In the 1930s the Yugoslavian astronomer Milutin Milankovitch proposed that episodes of glaciation are initiated by the fortuitous (or perhaps unfortunate!) combination of several small variations of the passage of the Earth's orbit around the sun, and the relative position of the Earth to the sun. Three cycles interact here, each with its own characteristic periodicity (time elapsed between the extremes of the cycle): (1) the Earth's elliptical orbit around the sun (with a periodicity of 100,000 years); (2) the tilt of the Earth's rotational axis (with a periodicity of 40,000 years); and (3) the precession (wobble) of Earth's rotational axis (with a periodicity of 26,000 years (Imbrie and Berger 1984).

Each of these orbital properties produces different effects. Change in tilt and precession modify the

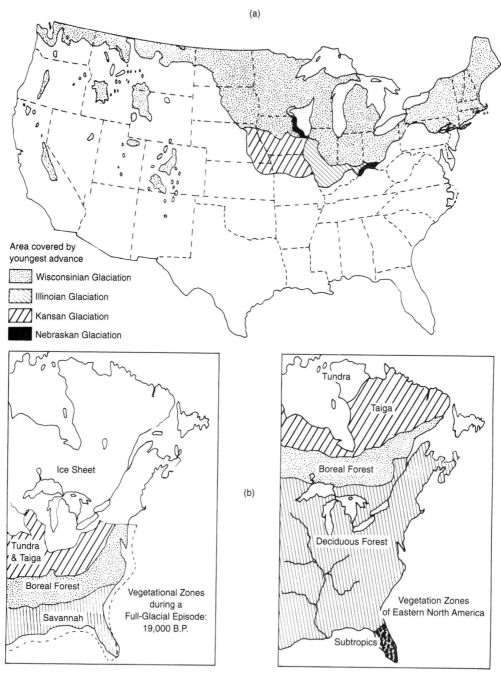

Figure 20–3 Pleistocene glaciation. (a) Extent of glaciation in North America. Several advances of the continental glacier are shown. In the west montane glaciers advanced and retreated. The major episodes of glaciation, named in North America for the southern extent of the ice sheets, are listed in order from youngest (the Wisconsinian, commencing approximately 100,000 years ago) to the oldest (the Nebraskan, commencing approximately 1.30 million years ago). (b) Effect of glacial periods on the position of biomes in North America. Biomes are shifted southward during periods of glacial advance (left), and extend northward during interglacial periods like the present (right). Note that, in addition to shifting biomes, entire types of habitats may appear and disappear. There is no savanna habitat today in the southeastern United States, and there was no subtropical habitat in Florida during the last full glacial episode.

distribution of sunlight with respect to season and latitude, but not total global insolation, whereas changes in the Earth's orbit result in minute changes in global insolation. Normally these properties are cycling out of phase, like discordant keys played on a piano, but every so often they line up together like notes making a chord. Milankovitch suggested that the critical factor that leads to a glacial episode is a change in the amount of summer insolation at high latitudes. It appears that glacial episodes get their start not from the world as a whole getting colder year round, but from cool summers that prevent the melting of winter ice. In contrast, the winters during glacial periods may have been warmer than those of the present day.

It is important to realize that these Milankovitch cycles must have been in existence throughout Earth's history. However, in the Cenozoic it was only after the formation of the Arctic ice cap in the Pleistocene (possibly as early as the Pliocene) that there existed sufficient buildup of polar ice to plunge the Northern Hemisphere into an ice age.

■ Biogeography of Cenozoic Mammals

As the geography of the world changed during the Cenozoic to assume its present character, so the types of mammals changed to fit the changing patterns of climate and vegetation. Following their origin in the latest Triassic, and their persistence through the Mesozoic at small body size and low levels of morphological diversity, mammals diversified in the Cenozoic. Thus the Cenozoic is commonly known as the Age of Mammals, even though the time elapsed since the start of the Cenozoic represents only about a third of the time spanned by the total history of mammals. The radiation of mammals is almost certainly related to the extinction of the dinosaurs, which left the world free of large-size tetrapods, providing a window of opportunity for other groups. Large terrestrial birds, including carnivorous forms (now all extinct) and herbivores like the ostrich also diversified, and in the early Cenozoic there was a modest radiation of terrestrial crocodiles in the Southern Hemisphere.

The radiations of mammals took place in two major waves, one in the continuing hothouse world of the early Cenozoic and one more adapted to the later Cenozoic ice house. We call the first wave of mammals archaic types, a pejorative term that really refers to our own perspective from the comfort of the Recent. Archaic mammals are those that did not leave members of their lineages surviving until the present day. Members of most present-day orders did not make their first appearance until the Eocene, but there are some notable exceptions, most importantly the orders Carnivora (first known from the early Paleocene) and Rodentia (first known from the late Paleocene). The early archaic mammalian faunas have a very different aspect from the ones that followed. They appear to have been composed mainly of small to medium-size generalized mammals with a predominance of arboreal over terrestrial types. Larger, specialized predators, and herbivores with teeth suggestive of a completely herbivorous (rather than omnivorous) diet did not appear until the late Paleocene. It may be the case that forests bounced back so successfully after the extinction of herbivorous dinosaurs that they dominated terrestrial habitats, so that it was not until the climatic changes of the Eocene produced more diverse habitats that larger-size mammals began to radiate into the terrestrial niches that they occupy today (reviewed in Janis 1993).

During the early Cenozoic the continents had not moved as far from their equatorial positions as they are today, but the major landmasses were perhaps more isolated than at present. Australia had broken free from the other southern continents by the mid-Eocene, but North and South America did not come into contact until the Pliocene. India, having broken away from Africa in the Mesozoic, did not make contact with Asia until the Miocene, when its impact resulted in the uplift of the Himalayan mountain ranges. Africa, floating northward, did not make contact with Eurasia until the late Oligocene or early Miocene, closing off the original east–west expanse of the Tethys Sea to form the now-enclosed Mediterranean basin. Europe was divided from Asia by a north–south epicontinental sea, the Turgai Straits (the remnants of which can be seen in existing bodies of water such as the Black Sea) until the Eocene/Oligocene boundary (see Figure 20–1).

The radiation of mammals was concurrent with this fractionation of the continental masses. Various mixtures of the basal mammalian stocks were isolated on different continents, and hence from one another. This apparent movement and separation of ancestral stocks from one another, by the Earth's physical processes rather than by their own movements, is termed **vicariance**. Some of the difference in the distribution of present-day mammals (for example, the isolation of the monotremes in Australia and New Guinea) can be ascribed to what we would term **vicariance biogeography**.

Other patterns of mammal distribution can be explained by **dispersal**, which reflects movements of the animals themselves, usually by the relatively slow (in biological time, but not in geological time) spread of populations rather than the long-distance movements of individual animals. The presence of marsupials in Australia apparently represents a dispersal event from South America via Antarctica in the early Cenozoic, although the subsequent isolation of Australia may play a role in the extent of their diversification there. Dispersal can result in extinctions as well as radiations. For example, when the Turgai Straits dried up, mammals that had previously inhabited Asia flooded into Europe and some uniquely European mammals (mainly archaic types) became extinct. This episode of Eocene/Oligocene extinctions was so dramatic that it is known as the Grand Coupure (the Great Dying).

Today the mammals of the Northern Hemisphere (Holarctica) and of Africa, Madagascar, South America, and Australia are strikingly different from one another. These four geographic groupings fall into three major faunal provinces: (1) a Laurasian fauna, including Africa, consisting almost exclusively of placentals; (2) a South American, or New World tropical fauna, containing a mixture of placentals and marsupials; and (3) an Australian fauna, containing monotremes, marsupials, and a sprinkling of placentals.

However, the fauna of Africa used to be even more distinct from the fauna of the rest of Holarctica before Africa collided with Eurasia in the Oligocene/Miocene. For example, a diversity of hyraxes, which now survive only as small rodent-like forms (Figure 20–4q), assumed ecomorphological roles taken today by antelope and pigs. Similarly, the South American fauna was more distinct from that of Holarctica before South America was connected with North America in the Pliocene (as we discuss later). Even the North American fauna was much more distinct from that of the rest of Holarctica for most of the Cenozoic than it is today. Much of the present North American fauna (e.g., deer, bison, and rodents such as voles) crossed over from Eurasia in the Pliocene and Pleistocene via the Bering land bridge. Today only Madagascar and Australia retain distinctly different faunas. It is unfortunate that we have so little

fossil evidence from the early Cenozoic of India, as it, too, must have harbored a distinctive early mammalian fauna.

■ Convergent Evolution of Mammalian Ecomorphological Types

The term ecomorphology describes the way in which an animal's form (its morphology) is adapted to affect its behavior in its environment (its ecology). The separate evolution of different basic mammalian stocks on different continents is strikingly illustrated by the convergent evolution of ecomorphs in Cenozoic mammals. Figure 20–4 shows examples of convergence. Specialized running herbivores include the extinct litopterns (Figure 20–4a) of South America, the Holarctic artiodactyl antelope (Figure 20–4b) of Eurasian origin, and the perissodactyl horses (Figure 20–4c) (most of the evolution of which took place in North America), which are all are strikingly similar in many aspects (see also Figure 20–5). Even the Australian marsupials such as the kangaroo (Figure 20–4d) demonstrate convergences in jaws, teeth, and feeding behavior to these placental herbivores, although of course they are hoppers rather than runners. Convergent evolution also took place among large-bodied, slower-moving herbivores. Compare, for example, the rhino perissodactyls, which originated in Eurasia (Figure 20–4e), the elephants, which originated in Africa (Figure 20–4f), the extinct notoungulates of South America (Figure 20–4g), and the extinct marsupial diprotodontids of Australia (Figure 20–4h).

The carnivorous mammals show similar convergences. For example, the true wolf (Figure 20–4i) in Holarctica, the recently extinct marsupial wolf or thylacine (Figure 20–4j) in Australia, and the extinct marsupial borhyaenids (Figure 20–4k) in South America have similar body morphology and tooth form, although only the true wolves have the long legs that distinguish fast-running predators. Similar types of intercontinental convergences, again involving both marsupials and placentals, occurred with a carnivorous ecomorph that does not exist today, that of the saber-toothed catlike predator.

Mammals specialized for feeding on ants and termites (myrmecophagy) include the giant anteater in South America (Figure 20–4l), the aardvark in Africa (Figure 20–4m), the pangolin in tropical Asia and Africa (Figure 20–4n), and the spiny anteater (a

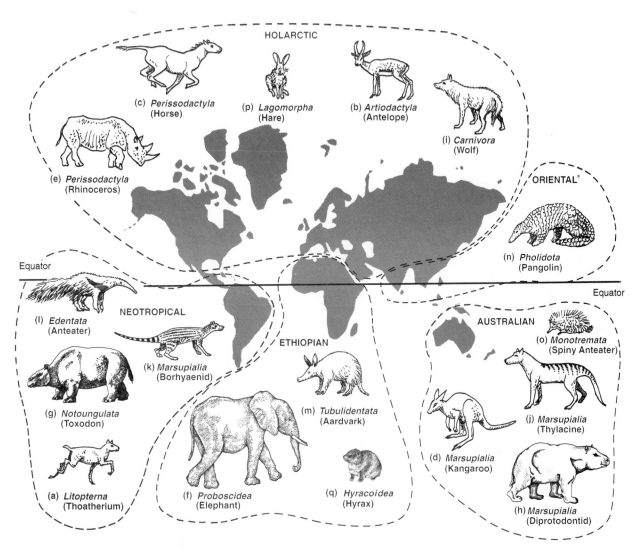

Figure 20–4 Radiation and convergence of mammals evolving in isolation during the Cenozoic. Mammals are illustrated with the landmasses on which they probably originated. Mammals of Northern Hemisphere origin are grouped as Holarctic. The major biogeographical regions of the world today are illustrated. Our current convention, rather reflective of the historical patterns of colonization by Europeans, is to call the American continents the New World, and the other continents (including Australia) the Old World. The northern continents, North America and northern Eurasia, can be grouped together as Holarctica; they can be further subdivided into the Nearctic (North America, including Greenland), and the Palaearctic (Europe and northern Asia, including Asia Minor). India and southeast Asia fall within the tropics, and together are termed the Oriental region. Africa (including Madagascar) forms the Ethiopian or African region. The Ethiopian and Oriental regions are sometimes grouped together as the Old World tropics, or Paleotropics. South and Central America form the Neotropical region, or New World Tropics. Finally Australia and associated islands (including New Guinea, Tasmania, and New Zealand) make up the Australian region.

Figure 20–5 Convergence between unrelated mammals from isolated continents to a fibrous herbivorous diet and a cursorial (running-adapted) lifestyle. South American litopterns (left) and North American (Holarctic) equid perissodactyls (horses) (right) (not to scale). (a) Reconstructions of the Miocene South American litoptern *Diadiaphorus* and a Miocene North American three-toed horse, *Hypohippus*; (b) skeletons of *Diadiaphorus* and *Hypohippus*; (c) occlusal surface of the cheek teeth of *Diadiaphorus* and comparable developments in the Oligocene horse *Miohippus*; (d) frontal view of the left hind feet of the three-toed forms *Diadiaphorus* and the horse *Protohippus* from the Miocene; (e) frontal views of the hind foot of the Miocene one-toed litoptern *Thoatherium* and the Pleistocene one-toed horse *Equus*. These litopterns reached this degree of limb specialization much earlier than the horses, which did not show similar reduction of the toes until millions of years later.

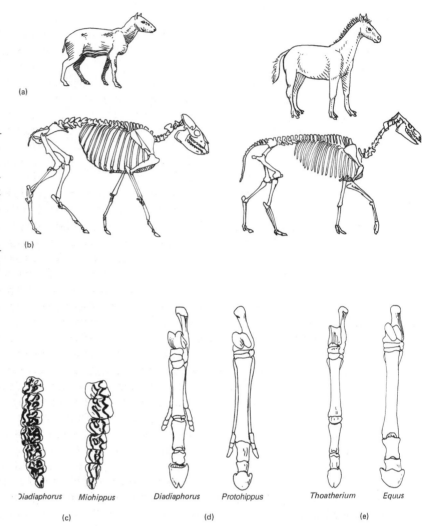

Diadiaphorus   Miohippus

(c)

Diadiaphorus   Protohippus

(d)

Thoatherium   Equus

(e)

monotreme) in Australia (Figure 20–4o). Ants and termites are social insects and employ group defense. They often build impressive earthen nests containing thousands of individuals, some of which are strong-jawed soldiers. The convergent myrmecophagous specializations of these unrelated or distantly related mammals include a reduction in the number and size of teeth, changes in jaw and skull shape and strength, and forelimbs modified for digging (see Figure 21–23). Some mammals with a carnivorous ancestry have adopted a myrmecophagous lifestyle and show similar, though less extensive, specializations. These species include a marsupial anteater, the Australian numbat, and an African hyena, the aardwolf.

Other examples of convergent evolution of ecomorphs abound, such as burrowing moles or molelike animals or gliders. Molelike forms include the true moles of Holarctica, the mole rats (rodents) and golden moles (not closely related to true moles) of Africa, and the marsupial moles of South America (extinct) and Australia. Gliding forms include the flying squirrels of the Northern Hemisphere and the marsupial flying phalangers in Australia (see Figure 20–6), plus the flying lemurs (not true primates) of southeast Asia and a completely different type of flying squirrel in Africa. Sometimes similar forms evolved under what appear to be much less isolated conditions. Thus hares and rabbits (Figure 20–4p) evolved in Holarctica where other small herbivores, the rather closely related rodents, also occurred. The rodentlike animals of Africa are the hyraxes (Figure 20–4q), which had a much greater diversity of sizes and body forms in the past, and are actually related to elephants (see Chapter 21).

■ Early Cenozoic Distribution of Mammalian Types

As discussed in Chapter 19, there are three major groups (subclasses) of mammals: the Theria, including the placentals (Eutheria) and the marsupials (Metatheria); the monotremes, the primitive egg-laying mammals; and the multituberculates, the now-extinct rather rodentlike mammals that were predominant in the Mesozoic and survived until the late Eocene. At the start of the Cenozoic these mammals were all small and fairly unspecialized. The marsupials appear to have been omnivorous and arboreal, like modern opossums, while the placentals were mostly shrewlike terrestrial "proteutherians" or basal ungulates ("condylarths") (both are paraphyletic assemblages) from which most extant mammals have evolved.

The origin of the marsupials appears to have been in South America, while that of the placentals was in Asia. Both marsupials and placentals were known in North America in the Late Cretaceous. Multituberculates were primarily Northern Hemisphere residents, but a distinct southern branch, the gondwanatheres, has now been identified, known from the Cretaceous of South America, Africa, and Madagascar (Krause et al. 1997). Monotremes were probably originally Australian in origin, but a fossil monotreme was recently found in Patagonia, at the tip of South America (Pascual et al. 1992). It is not clear if this animal represents a limited dispersal from Australia (across Antarctica) or the remnants of an earlier, unrecorded, Gondwanan fauna that spread across the southern continents.

It used to be thought that the more derived mammals with tribosphenic molars (including therians, see Chapter 19) were initially a Northern Hemisphere radiation, perhaps originating subsequent to the splitting of North America and Eurasia from Gondwana. However, fragmentary fossils with tribosphenic molars have recently been described from both South America and Australia (Rich et al. 1997). Thus there is the suggestion that late Mesozoic mammalian faunas were more cosmopolitan than was previously thought, and that the apparent distribution at the start of the Cenozoic was not simply due to vicariance following the breakup of Pangaea.

Marsupials are considered today as the quintessential Australian mammals. Yet their origin appears to have been in South America, where they survive today as opossums and their relatives (although the diversity of South American marsupials was much greater in the past, including a radiation of large carnivorous forms, the borhyaenids). The dispersal of marsupials to Australia is discussed later. However, it is seldom appreciated that during the Cenozoic marsupials dispersed not only across the southern continents but also across the northern ones. Marsupials are known from the Eocene and/or Oligocene of Europe, Asia and northern Africa (summarized by Benton 1985), but apparently they were never particularly numerous or diverse there. Their mid-Cenozoic extinction in that part of the world may just be a part the extinction of many archaic mammals that took place at that time. There is no need to invoke a complex scenario of competition with placentals.

The present-day North America native marsupial, the common opossum *Didelphis virginiana*, is a recent (Pleistocene) immigrant from South America. Opossums have been noted to still be moving north in recent historical times, first recorded in Canada in the 1950s (Peterson 1966). There is no evidence that opossums are in any competition with local North American placental mammals; at least, not with those that lack a driving license.

Cenozoic Mammals of the Southern Continents

Most of us are aware that the mammals of Australia differ from those of Asia, Europe, Africa, and North America. The mammals of South America also differ from those of the Northern Hemisphere, but less so than do the Australian mammals (Keast 1972). These two continents provide particularly clear examples of the effects of biogeographical isolation, as does the island of Madagascar.

Cenozoic Isolation of Australia   The mammalian fauna of Australia has always been composed almost entirely of marsupials (and monotremes) rather than placentals (Rich and van Tets 1985). The earliest marsupial fossils currently known from Australia are of early Eocene age, and there are abundant and diverse remains from the Miocene onward. South America, Antarctica, and Australia were still close together in the late Mesozoic and early Cenozoic, and Australia was probably populated by marsupials that moved from South America across Antarctica, which was warm and moist until about 35 million years ago (Kerr 1987, Eaton 1993, Janis 1993). Marsupial fossils from the Cretaceous are known from Peru and Bolivia in South America, and a fossil South American marsupial was found in Eocene deposits in Antarctica in 1982.

Once marsupials reached Australia, they enjoyed the advantages of long-term isolation, and a radiation of diverse types followed. Kangaroos and wallabies, the wombats and koala, possums and phalangers, marsupial mice and marsupial moles, bandicoots, and the probably extinct marsupial (or Tasmanian) wolf evolved to fill a variety of niches with food habits ranging from complete herbivory to carnivory (Archer and Clayton 1984, Archer et al. 1991). Figure 20–6 illustrates a diversity of Australian marsupials and notes their convergences with northern placentals. Note that the possums and phalangers are a diverse radiation of arboreal mammals

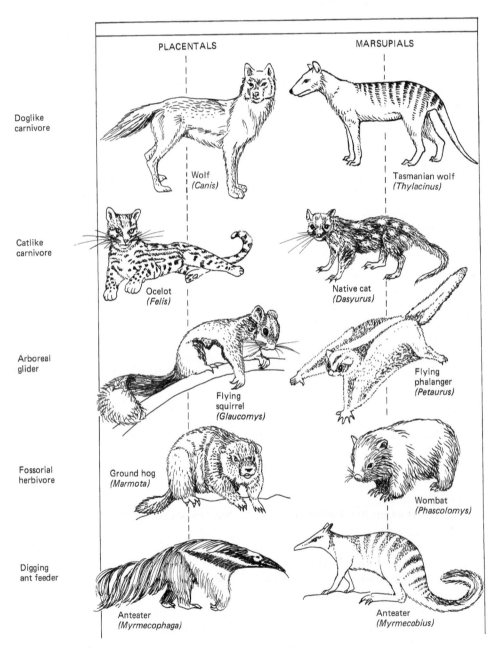

Figure 20–6 Convergences in body form and habits between placental and marsupial mammals. (From G. G. Simpson, G. S. Pittendrigh, and L. H. Tiffany, 1957, *Life*, Harcourt, Brace, Jovanovich, New York, NY.)

that are convergent not only with rodents like squirrels, but also with primates. A particularly striking example of convergence exists between the aye-aye of Madagascar (a lemur, a type of primitive primate, see Chapter 24) and the striped possum of the York Peninsula of northeastern Australia. Both are specialists on prying wood-boring insects out from under tree bark, and both have chisellike incisors and have elongated one of their fingers to act as a probe. Perhaps even more interestingly, Madagascar and Australia are the only places in the world that lack woodpeckers, a bird with similar dietary habits.

The early Eocene fauna of Australian mammals was to reveal a remarkable discovery: As well as a number of marsupial species it preserved single molar of a condylarthlike (primitive ungulate) placental, similar to forms known from the early Cenozoic of North America (Godthelp et al. 1992). This suggested that marsupials did not make the journey across Antarctica alone, but that they were accompanied by at least one type of placental. This placental evidently became extinct, as other terrestrial placentals are unknown in Australia until the late Miocene. This animal rather turns the tables on the supposed marsupial inferiority in the presence of placentals (see also discussion in Chapter 21). The only other placentals known in the early Cenozoic of Australia are bats. Their affinities appear to be with the bats of Asia, which suggests that they flew across to Australia via quite a different route (Archer et al. 1991).

Rodents founded colonies in Australia by island-hopping from southeast Asia in the late Miocene and on several occasions since. Australian rodents are an interesting endemic radiation today; they are ultimately related to the mouse/rat group of Eurasian rodents, but have evolved into some unique Australian forms such as the small jerboa-like hopping mice and the large (otter-size) water rats. However, this radiation apparently had surprisingly little overall effect on the Australian marsupials. A far greater threat has been the prehistoric invasion by humans and dogs (dingos), and the recent historical introduction of domestic mammals such as rabbits and cats. The Tasmanian wolf and Tasmanian devil, both carnivorous marsupials, are so named because of their relict distribution on this island in historical times; both animals were known from mainland Australia prior to the arrival of dingos. Today numerous other mainland forms are threatened or endangered by humans and their introduction of northern placentals.

Madagascar Madagascar is an island situated off the coast off East Africa (Figure 20–1). It apparently separated from Africa in the mid-Mesozoic, and its present-day mammalian fauna represents subsequent immigration. However the source of these immigrants, whether from the African mainland, or from Asia (the source of the present-day indigenous people) remains in debate. The best-known endemic mammals of Madagascar are the lemurs, a radiation of primitive primates known nowhere else in the world (see Chapter 24). Diverse as today's lemurs are, their diversity was much greater in the recent past. As recently as a few thousand years ago there was a big diversity of much larger (up to gorilla-size) forms that appeared to parallel the radiation of the great apes among the anthropoid primates. Some of these forms were arboreal, resembling orangutans or giant koalas, and some were terrestrial, resembling the extinct ground sloths of South America. Some smaller extinct terrestrial forms resembled the African baboons. The extinction of these giant lemurs appears to be related to the arrival of humans a couple of thousand years ago, but it seems unlikely that these people hunted or otherwise deliberately slaughtered the lemurs. The evidence points to habitat destruction, possibly resulting from the importing of cattle to the island, probably aided and abetted by the climatic changes at the end of the Pleistocene during which savanna spread at the expense of tropical forests (Dewar 1984).

The other native Madagascan mammals belong to the orders Carnivora and Insectivora. The native insectivores are the tenrecs, which in basic form resemble a large shrew, but have diversified into hedgehoglike spiny forms, and also into molelike burrowers and otterlike swimmers. The carnivores are viverrids, related to the mainland civets and genets. The most remarkable of these is the fossa (*Cryptoprocta ferox*), an animal a little larger than a big house cat, which, in the absence of true cats, has basically evolved to become one. Although it is more stockily built than true cats, with shorter, more muscular legs that reflect its more arboreal habits, its skull is virtually indistinguishable from that of a cat.

South American Mammals and the Great American Interchange The paleontological record of South America is extensive and shows a history of connection, separation, and reconnection to North America. The effects of these geological events can be traced in the changing fauna of South American mammals. South America was isolated from North America by a seaway between Panama and the northwestern corner of South America from the Late Jurassic until the late Cenozoic. In the Pliocene, about 2.5 million years ago, the Panamanian land bridge was established between North and South America and animals from the two continents were free to mix for the first time in more than 100 million years (Marshall et al. 1982, Marshall 1988). Faunal interchange by island hopping or rafting commenced in the late Miocene as the two American landmasses drew ever nearer to each other. This event, the Great American Interchange (GAI), is a spectacular example of the effects of dispersal and faunal intermingling between two previously separated land masses (Stehli and Webb 1985) (see Figure 20–7 for the cast of characters involved).

Superficially the mammals moving from North America to South America appear to have been more numerous and to have fared better than those moving in the opposite direction, and for many years the interchange was viewed as an example of the competitive superiority of Northern Hemisphere mammals. However, with reconsideration of the available evidence, a different interpretation is preferred today. Before discussing the GAI in more detail, first we need to consider the diversity of mammals that inhabited South America prior to the interchange.

Three major groups of mammals can be distinguished in South America prior to the GAI: early inhabitants, known from the Paleocene, evolving in situ or originating from North America; Eocene/Oligocene colonizers, probably arriving by rafting from Africa; and late arrivals, arriving by island-hopping from North America across an island arc linking the two continents in the latest Miocene (Patterson and Pascual 1972).

The earliest inhabitants were the marsupials, edentates, and condylarths (archaic ungulates). Equally important were the groups of North American mammals that failed to colonize South America at this time, notably insectivorans, carnivorans, and rodents. We have no explanation of why these groups did not succeed in populating South America, but their absence is important because it left adaptive zones open and marsupials radiated into them during the isolation of South America in the early Cenozoic.

For example, some marsupials (argyrolagids) evolved hopping rodentlike forms resembling kangaroo rats or jerboas, while others (borhyaenids) evolved into a variety of large carnivorous types. All the borhyaenids were relatively short-legged animals that probably stalked or ambushed their prey rather than pursuing it (Figure 20–4k). Most of these marsupials were extinct by the time of the GAI in the Pliocene, with the exception of a type of borhyaenid (*Thylacosmilus*), which was strikingly similar to the saber-toothed cats of the Northern Hemisphere. The adaptive zone for large cursorial predators in early Cenozoic South America was apparently occupied by the psilopterids and phorusrachids, flightless birds standing 1.5 meters or taller (Marshall 1994).

The edentates are placentals known only from South America prior to the Pliocene (although some possible relatives are known from the Paleocene of China and the Eocene of Europe). Present-day edentates comprise armadillos (also known from Central America and the southern United States), tree sloths, and anteaters (both also known from Central America). The past diversity of edentates was considerably greater, with the presence of two additional main groups: the armadillo-related glyptodonts, cow-size beasts encased in a turtlelike carapace of dermal bone (see Chapter frontispiece figure); and ground sloths, ranging from the size of a large dog to the size of a rhino (see Figure 20–7a).

The third group of early colonizers of South America was the condylarths and their descendants, the unique endemic South American ungulates. These animals radiated into several orders, many of them containing extremely large animals. The main ungulate lineages, and the ones that survived up to the time of the GAI, were the litopterns and the notoungulates. Litopterns were more gracile, more cursorial forms, and were in general rather ponylike (Figure 20–4a, 20–5a), or were larger and rather camellike. Notoungulates were of stockier build, and mainly diverged into smaller rodentlike or hyraxlike forms, or larger, rhinolike forms (Figure 20–4g, 20–7g). Unfortunately, all these endemic ungulates are now extinct. Many forms became extinct during the Miocene, well before the GAI, probably as a result of climatic changes following the uplift of the Andean mountains. The rain shadow that this range cast on much of the continent would have resulted in the changing of woodlands into grasslands. Indeed, much of the original diversity of the South American mammal fauna was extinct by the time of the GAI, and

Figure 20–7 The mammalian taxa involved in the Great American Interchange. A dagger (†) indicates taxa that are now extinct. Moving from South America to North America were edentates such as (a) ground sloths†, (b) glyptodonts†, (c) armadillos, and (d) anteaters; rodents such as (e) porcupines and (f) capybaras (known today only from Central America); (g) notoungulates†; and (h) opossums. Moving from North America to South America were carnivores such as (i) cats (e.g. ocelots, leopards), (j) dogs (e.g. foxes, maned wolf), (k) bears (the spectacled bear), (l) mustelids (e.g. weasels, skunks, and otters), and (m) procyonids (racoons, coatis, etc., first appearing in the late Miocene); artiodactyls such as (n) deer (e.g., brocket deer and pampas deer), (o) camelids (llamas and vicunas), and (p) peccaries; perissodactyls such as (q) tapirs and (r) horses (now locally extinct in South America); (s) proboscideans (gomphotheres†); and a variety of small mammals such as (t) squirrels, (u) voles, (v) rabbits, and (w) shrews. (Modified from L G. Marshall et al., 1982, *Science* 215:1351–1357; and Marshall 1988.)

so competition with northern immigrants cannot be invoked for their demise.

The later arrivals in South America were all placental mammals. Arriving some time in the late Eocene or early Oligocene were the caviomorph rodents (guinea pigs and their relatives, such as capybaras and Patagonian hares) and platyrrhine primates (New World monkeys). The caviomorph rodents diversified in the Miocene and Pliocene to include the largest rodents that have ever lived. *Telicomys*, a dinomyid (= terrible mouse), was the size of a small rhinoceros, and even today the pig-size capybara is extremely large for a rodent. The late Miocene arrivals were the procyonid carnivores (raccoons, coatis, and their relatives). At this time, just prior to the GAI proper with the establishment of a land bridge, some small types of ground sloths also migrated in the opposite direction, from South America to North America.

What happened when the establishment of the Panamanian land bridge in the Pliocene allowed these two very different faunas to mix? Some animals from North America moved southward, and rather fewer South American forms moved northward (see Figure 20–7). (Note that this apparent discrepancy in the numbers of immigrants is nullified if one considers that North America has a greater land area than South America, and hence potentially a greater diversity of mammalian taxa to donate [Marshall et al. 1982]). On each continent the newcomers and the native fauna appeared to coexist; for the most part the immigrants enriched the existing fauna rather than displacing it. However, a later disparity exists. Although Pleistocene extinction affected the largest mammals on both continents, the southern immigrants to North America were more profoundly affected than North American forms in South America. Today about half the generic diversity of South American mammals consists of forms with a North American origin (although some notable northern immigrants to South America are now extinct there, for example, horses and the elephant-related gomphotheres). The southern species that persist in North America are mostly confined to Central America and the southern United States (opossums and porcupines being notable exceptions).

The key to understanding the apparent greater success of the immigrants to South America lies in an understanding of the biogeography, particularly in the fact that the equator and the tropical belt fall within South America (Webb 1991; Vrba 1992). Thus

at times of climatic stress, such as during glacial periods, South America will harbor a greater diversity of equable habitats than North America, and fewer extinctions might be expected. Vegetational changes associated with climatic changes obviously also played a role. It is thought that the Isthmus of Panama had some savannalike habitats linking North and South America during the Pliocene, acting as a corridor allowing for the movement south of mammals like horses and deer and the movement north of mammals like glyptodonts and notoungulates. By the Pleistocene this corridor was evidently closed for migration of savanna-adapted mammals, possibly because of the encroachment of tropical forests. Mammals that only arrived in North America in the Pleistocene, such as bison and mammoths, never made it down into South America. If this corridor remained occupied by tropical forest vegetation in the late Pleistocene, more tropically adapted southern mammals such as ground sloths and glyptodonts would have been trapped in North America when their habitat disappeared, perhaps contributing to their extinction. However the late Pleistocene extinctions affected many large mammals in both North and South America (see later discussion), immigrants and endemics alike.

A final point of consideration in the GAI is that counts of who moved where, when, usually only consider species known from the fossil record (as in Figure 20–7). Because tropical habitats rarely preserve fossils, we have little information about the fossil history of Central America. Yet the large diversity of opossumlike marsupials, edentates, monkeys, and caviomorph rodents in Central America today can only have come from South America. Some of the other Central American mammals, traditionally considered as northern taxa, such as cats like ocelots and pumas, and ungulates like brocket deer and tapirs, may also have evolved into their present form in South America and reimmigrated back into North America. Because of our present-day political boundaries, we often forget that Central America is part of North America, not South America! A proper tally of the immigrants from South America to Central America is necessary before we can write the final chapter on the GAI.

■ Cenozoic Extinctions

The best-known extinction of the Cenozoic is probably the one at the end of the Pleistocene, although this was by no means the extinction of greatest overall magnitude. The Pleistocene extinction appears dramatic because of the extinction of the megafauna, the diversity of large (over 20 kg in body mass) mammals. This included many very large mammals that are now totally extinct, such as glyptodonts and ground sloths in North and South America, mammoths in Holarctica and Africa, and diprotodontids in Australia. It also included many larger and exotic forms of more familiar mammals, such as the saber-toothed cats of Holarctica and Africa, the Irish elk, cave bears and woolly rhinos of Eurasia, and the oversized kangaroos in Australia.

There is much debate about the cause of these extinctions. The main extinctions occurred at the end of the last glacial period, some 10,000 years ago. (Surprisingly enough, animals appear to be more vulnerable to extinction when the climate changes from glacial to interglacial, rather than the other way around, probably because the former event appears to occur with greater rapidity.) Thus climatic change would be an obvious explanation. However, many scientists have queried the fact that it is only the end of the last glacial period, rather than any of the previous ones, that brought with it such magnitude of extinctions. They would attribute part if not all of the blame to the spread of modern humans and modern hunting techniques, which was concurrent with that time period (see summary of debates in Martin and Klein 1984).

About 30 percent of mammal genera became extinct at the end of the Pleistocene, which is of approximately the magnitude of the other major Cenozoic extinctions, during the late Eocene and the late Miocene. However, the two latter extinctions differ in several critical ways. In both the Eocene and Miocene mammals of all body sizes were affected (not just large ones), and other organisms, both terrestrial and marine, also experienced profound extinctions. These other extinction events did not occur in the late Pleistocene.

The late Eocene extinctions were associated with the dramatic fall in higher-latitude temperatures (Figure 20–2). Higher-latitude forests turned to temperate woodlands, with the accompanying disappearance of mammals adapted to these tropical-like forests. This included not only a diversity of archaic mammals but also some early more modern types, such as higher-latitude primates and early horses (*Hyracotherium* and relatives). The early Cenozoic diversity of amphibians and reptiles in higher latitudes was also greatly reduced during the late Eocene.

The late Miocene extinctions were associated again with falling higher-latitude temperatures, but also with global drying and perhaps in response to vegetational changes following a fall in atmospheric levels of carbon dioxide, as discussed previously. Cooling and changes in ocean currents at the end of the Miocene resulted in intermittent cutting off of the flow of the Mediterranean Sea through the Straits of Gibraltar around 5 to 6 million years ago. During this time the entire Mediterranean basin dried up and refilled several times, an event known as the Messinian salinity crisis. The major extinctions in the late Miocene were of browsing mammals (including a large diversity of browsing horses), which suffered habitat loss as the savanna woodlands turned into open grasslands and prairie. North America was especially hard hit by the climatic events of the late Miocene, because of its relatively high latitudinal position. In the middle Miocene the Great Plains of North America had a mammalian fauna resembling that of present-day East African savannas, and rivaling it in taxonomic diversity (although the animals were largely unrelated; for example there was a diversity of camels rather than of antelope). By the end of the Miocene the large mammal fauna was around two-thirds of its previous generic diversity, and the majority of browsing forms were extinct, reflecting a drier, less productive type of environment.

Thus the climatic events of the Cenozoic have resulted in a number of extinctions, but also in a number of diversifications and radiations. The fauna of today is considerably more diverse than that of the early Cenozoic, at least in terms of types of mammalian ecomorphs. While tropicallike forest habitats are no longer found within the confines of the Arctic circle, this habitat is retained within the equatorial belt, and with it many animals reminiscent of the Eocene types of high-latitude forests, such as prosimian primates and mouse deer (primitive ruminant artiodactyls). The increased diversity of habitats has resulted in increased diversity of types of mammalian ecomorphs. Some of these mammals reflect present-day climatic extremes, such as polar bears in the Arctic and camels in the deserts. Others just reflect the vast tracts of habitats that are run of the mill today but that did not exist during the early Cenozoic, such as the deer and pigs in the temperate woodlands, and the horses (or zebras) and antelope on the prairie and the savannas.

■ References

Archer, M., and G. Clayton (editors). 1984. *Vertebrate Zoogeography and Evolution in Australasia*. Hesperian, Carlisle, Australia.

Archer, M., S. J. Hand, and H. Godhelp. 1991. *Riversleigh*. Reed Books, Balgowish, Australia.

Benton, M. J. 1985. First marsupial fossil from Asia. *Nature* 318:313.

Cerling, T. E., J. M. Harris, B. J. MacFadden, M. G. Leaky, J. Quade, V. Eisenmann, and J. R. Ehleringer. 1997. Global vegetation change through the Miocene/Pliocene boundary. *Nature* 389:153–158.

Dewar, R. E. 1984. Extinctions in Madagascar: the loss of the subfossil fauna. Pages 574–593, in *Quaternary Extinctions*, edited by P. S. Martin and R. G. Klein. University of Arizona Press, Tucson, AZ.

Eaton, J. G. 1993. Marsupial dispersal. *National Geographic Research and Exploration* 9:436–443.

Godthelp, H., M. Archer, and R. Cifelli. 1992. Earliest known Australian Tertiary mammal fauna. *Nature* 356:514–516.

Guthrie, R. D. 1990. *Frozen Fauna of the Mammoth Steppe*. University of Chicago Press, Chicago, IL.

Imbrie, J., and A. Berger (editors). 1984. *Milankovitch and Climate Change*. Elsevier, Amsterdam, Netherlands.

Janis, C. M. 1993. Tertiary mammal evolution in the context of changing climates, vegetation, and tectonic events. *Annual Review of Ecology and Systematics* 24:467–500.

Keast, A. L. 1972. Comparisons of contemporary mammal faunas of southern continents. Pages 433–501 in *Evolution, Mammals, and Southern Continents*, edited by A. Keast, F. C. Erk, and B. Glass. State University of New York Press, Albany, NY.

Kerr, R. A. 1987. Ocean drilling details steps to an icy world. *Science* 236:912–913.

Krause, D. W., G. V. R. Prasad, W. von Koenigswald, A. Sahni, and F. E. Grine. 1997. Cosmopolitanism among Late Cretaceous mammals. *Nature* 390:504–507.

Marshall, L. G. 1988. Land Mammals and the Great American Interchange. *American Scientist* 76:380–388.

Marshall, L. G. 1994. The terror birds of South America. *Scientific American* 270(2):90–95.

Marshall, L. G., S. D. Webb, J. J. Sepkoski, and D. M. Raup. 1982. Mammalian evolution and the great American interchange. *Science* 215:1351–1357.

Martin, P. S., and R. G. Klein. 1984. *Quaternary Extinctions*. University of Arizona Press, Tucson, AZ.

Pascual, R., M. Archer, E. Ortiz Jaureguizar, J. C. Prado, H. Godhelp, and S. J. Hand. 1992. First discovery of monotremes in South America. *Nature* 256:704–706.

Patterson, B., and R. Pascual. 1972. The fossil mammal fauna of South America. Pages 274–309, in *Evolution, Mammals and Southern Continents*, edited by A. Keast, F. C. Erk, and B. Glass. State University of New York Press, Albany, NY.

Peterson, R. L. 1966. *The Mammals of Eastern Canada*. Oxford University Press, Oxford, UK.

Raymo, M. E., and W. F. Ruddiman. 1992. Tectonic forcing of late Cenozoic climate. *Nature* 359:117–122.

Rich, P. V., and G. F. van Tets. 1985. *Kadimakara, Extinct Vertebrates of Australia*. Pioneer Design Studio, Lilydale, Australia.

Rich, T. H., P. Vickers-Rich, A. Constantine, T. F. Flannery, L. Kool, and N. van Klaveren. 1997. A tribosphenic mammal from the Mesozoic of Australia. *Science* 278:1438–1442.

Stehli, F. S., and S. D. Webb (editors). 1985. *The Great American Interchange*. Plenum, New York, NY.

Terborgh, J. 1992. *Diversity and the Tropical Rainforest*. Scientific American Library, New York, NY.

Vrba, E. S. 1992. Mammals as a key to evolutionary theory. *Journal of Mammalogy* 73:1–28.

Webb, S. D. 1991. Ecogeography and the Great American Interchange. *Paleobiology* 17:266–280.

CHAPTER
21

Characteristics of Mammals

Cenozoic mammals are a highly diverse group of organisms, adapted to a wide variety of lifestyles and displaying a large amount of ecomorphological diversity. As discussed in Chapter 20, much of the diversity seen among Cenozoic therian mammals (marsupials and placentals) reflects the isolation of different groups of mammals on different continental land masses; many of these ecomorphological types evolved convergently on different continents. The changing climates of the Northern Hemisphere during the course of the Cenozoic also resulted in a wider diversity of mammals adapted to new habitats, such as grasslands and tundra. Although the majority of mammals alive today are placentals, an understanding of mammal diversity and adaptations requires an understanding of how placentals differ from marsupials, and also how therians differ from monotremes.

■ Features Shared by All Mammals

Mammals are perceived as the dominant terrestrial animals of the Cenozoic, but their species diversity (around 4400 species) is less than half that of birds (around 9100 species), and considerably less than that of lepidosaurian reptiles (around 5600 species). Mammal species diversity is in fact about the same as that of amphibians (around 4300 species), animals often considered as primitive tetrapods (although, of course, they have been evolving separately from their Paleozoic ancestors for the same length of time as have mammals). Almost half of present-day mammalian species diversity is represented by rodents (around 1800 species). The diversity of non-rodent placental mammals (around 2300 species) is considerably less than that of frogs (around 3800 species) or lizards (around 3000 species), and even slightly less than the diversity of snakes (around 2500 species).

Mammals do, of course, include the largest living terrestrial and aquatic vertebrates (the blue whale, at around 120 tons, is the largest animal ever known). And perhaps mammals have cornered the market on morphological diversity; no other vertebrate taxon has forms as different from each other as a whale is from a bat, and even among strictly terrestrial forms there is a tremendous morphological difference between, say, a mole and a giraffe. But it is salutary to consider that mammals do not rise above other vertebrates when some measures of evolutionary success, such as species diversity, are considered. Figure 21–1 illustrates the diversity of the major extant groups of mammals.

We saw in Chapter 19 that mammals were derived from a group of cynodonts, the tritheledontids, in the Late Triassic. The basic features that distinguish mammals from other amniotes were discussed in Chapter 19, as was the evolution of milk and lactation. The females of all mammalian species lactate, caring for their young with the production of milk. In Chapter 19 we argued that lactation was shared by all mammals, living and fossil, but was not a feature of cynodonts. Mammary glands are entirely absent from the males of marsupials, but are present, and potentially functional, in male monotremes and placentals (Tyndale-Biscoe and Renfree 1987). There have been examples of human males producing milk under certain circumstances, and recently a species of

fruit bat has been identified in which the male actually produces milk. It has long been a mystery why male mammals retain mammary glands but do not lactate themselves (see Daly 1979); indeed, breast cancer affects a good number of human males, as well as females.

Although all mammals lactate, only therians (marsupials and placentals) have nipples so that the young can suck directly from the breast, rather than from the mother's fur. (However, monotremes have specialized beaks that seem quite unsuited for suckling, and it is tempting to speculate that nipples might have been secondarily lost in this lineage.) Note, however, that the mammae (breasts) of

---

1. Theria: Mammary glands with nipples, viviparity with loss of eggshell, digastric muscle used in jaw opening, anal and urogenital openings separate in adults, spiraled cochlea, scapula with supraspinous fossa, and numerous features of skull and dentition. **2.** Metatheria: Dentition essentially monophyodont (P3 is only tooth replaced), development of chorioallantoic membrane suppressed, pseudovaginal canal present at parturition, and various detailed features of skull, dentition (inc. upper molars with wide styler shelves), and ankle joint. **3.** Ameridelphia: Sperm paired in epididymis. **4.** Australidelphia: Details of dentition and ankle joint (also supported by biochemical data). **5.** Syndactylous foot (digits 2 and 3 enclosed in a common skin sheath), W-shaped outer border (ectoloph) of upper molars. **6.** Eutheria: Egg shell membrane lost, intrauterine gestation prolonged with suppression of estrus cycle, corpus callosum connects cerebral hemispheres, ureters pass lateral to Mullerian ducts, fusion of Mullerian ducts into a median vagina, penis simple (not bifid at tip), plus details of dentition (inc. upper molars with narrow styler shelves). **7.** Edentata: Details of skull anatomy, sacrum strongly fused to pelvis, tooth development suppressed with loss of anterior teeth and enamel poorly developed or absent. **8.** Epitheria: Stirrup-shaped stapes, plus some skull features. **9.** Glires: Details of skull anatomy. **10.** Details of skull anatomy, first pair of incisors lost, second pair of incisors large and ever-growing, details of placenta formation. **11.** Insectivora: details of skull anatomy, simplification of the hindgut with the loss of the cecum, reduction of pubic symphysis in pelvis. **12.** Archonta: Pendulous penis, plus details of ankle structure. **13.** Marked elon-

gation of forelimbs, flight membrane between fingers, plus details of skull anatomy. **14.** Ferae (also includes the extinct order Creodonta): Restriction of carnassial shearing teeth to the posterior part of the dentition, bony laminar separating cerebrum from cerebellum in brain, plus details of ankle joint. **15.** Ungulata: Bunodont dentition, reduced canines, astragalus with short robust head. **16.** Paenungulata: Styloglossus tongue muscle bifurcate, details of structure of skull, wrist bones, and placenta. (Modified from information from the following sources: L. G. Marshall, J. A. Case, and M. O. Woodburne, 1990, Phylogenetic relationships of the families of marsupials, *Current Mammalogy* 2, 433–505, M. J. Novacek, 1990, M. J. Novacek, Morphology, paleontology, and the higher clades of mammals, *Current Mammalogy* 2, 507–543, 1994, The radiation of placental mammals, pages 220–237 in *Major Features of Vertebrate Evolution*, edited by D. R. Prothero and R. M. Schoch, Short Courses in Paleontology No. 7, The Paleontological Society, University of Tennessee Press, Knoxville, TN, D. R. Prothero, 1993, Ungulate phylogeny: molecular vs. morphological evidence, pages 173–181, in *Mammal Phylogeny, Placentals*, edited by F. S. Szalay, M. J. Novacek, and M. C. McKenna, Springer-Verlag, New York, A. R. Wyss and J. J. Flynn, 1993, A phylogenetic analysis and definition of the Carnivora, pages 32–52 in *Mammal Phylogeny, Placentals*, edited by F. S. Szalay, M. J. Novacek, and M. C. McKenna, Springer-Verlag, New York, M. S. Springer, M. Westerman, and J. A. W. Kirsch, 1994, Relationships among orders and families of marsupials based on 12S Ribosomal DNA sequences and the timing of marsupial radiation, *Journal of Mammalian Evolution* 2:85-115.)

Figure 21–1 Phylogenetic relationships of extant mammalian orders. This diagram shows the probable relationships among living therian mammals. Dotted lines show interrelationships only, and are not indicative of the times of divergence of or the unrecorded presence of taxa in the fossil record. Numbers indicate derived characters that distinguish the lineages.

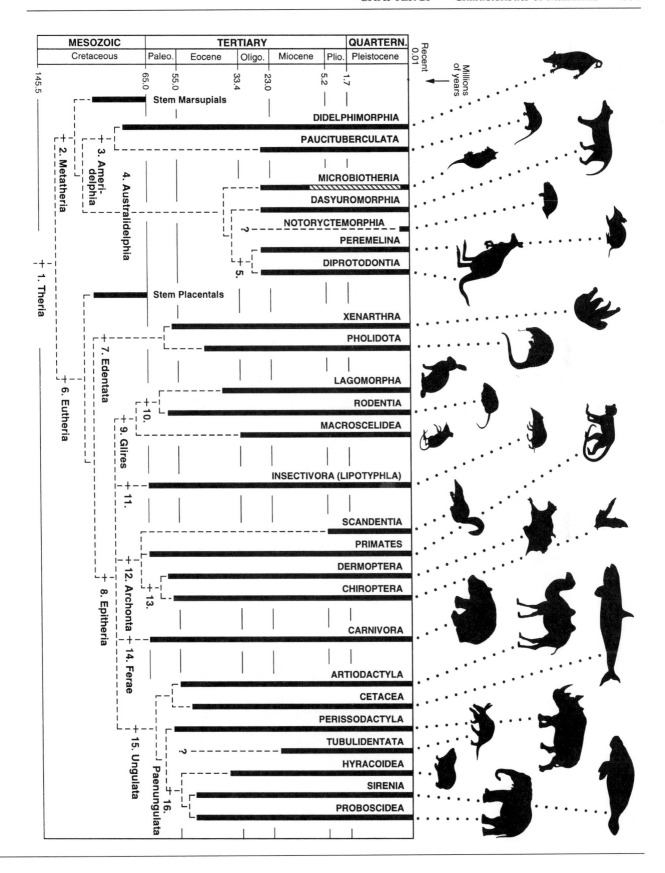

MESOZOIC	TERTIARY					QUARTERN.
Cretaceous	Paleo.	Eocene	Oligo.	Miocene	Plio.	Pleistocene

Millions of years

Recent 0.01

145.5 65.0 55.0 33.4 23.0 5.2 1.7

Stem Marsupials

DIDELPHIMORPHIA

PAUCITUBERCULATA

MICROBIOTHERIA

DASYUROMORPHIA

NOTORYCTEMORPHIA

PEREMELINA

DIPROTODONTIA

Stem Placentals

XENARTHRA

PHOLIDOTA

LAGOMORPHA

RODENTIA

MACROSCELIDEA

INSECTIVORA (LIPOTYPHLA)

SCANDENTIA

PRIMATES

DERMOPTERA

CHIROPTERA

CARNIVORA

ARTIODACTYLA

CETACEA

PERISSODACTYLA

TUBULIDENTATA

HYRACOIDEA

SIRENIA

PROBOSCIDEA

1. Theria
2. Metatheria
3. Ameri-delphia
4. Australidelphia
5.
6. Eutheria
7. Edentata
8. Epitheria
9. Glires
10.
11.
12. Archonta
13.
14. Ferae
15. Ungulata
16. Paenungulata

monotremes and marsupials share some similarities (probably primitive mammalian features). Mammary hairs are present in both, and the mammae develop from areola patches confined to the abdominal region. In placentals these mammary hairs are absent, and the mammae develop from mammary lines that form along the entire length of the abdomen (Renfree 1993).

The Evolution of Mammalian Suckling

The ability to suckle is a unique mammalian feature. The mammalian pharynx is very different from that of other amniotes; we discussed in Chapter 3 how mammals, unlike other vertebrates, not only masticate their food but swallow a discrete bolus of food with a distinct swallowing reflex. Mammals are also able to form tight seals within the pharynx to prevent fluids in the mouth from entering the stomach or lungs in an uncontrolled fashion (Smith 1992); it is a seal of this type (the back of the tongue against the anterior portion of the soft secondary palate) that enables you to gargle without accidentally swallowing the mouthwash (see Figure 21–2). A second seal, between the epiglottis and the back of the soft palate, is present in most mammals but is lost in humans after the neonatal stage, when the larynx moves posteriorly and ventrally. This change in the position of the larynx is probably essential for our capacity for complex speech (see Chapter 24). The use of these seals can also be seen in the behavior of baleen whales,

Figure 21–2 Cross sectional views of the oral and pharyngeal regions. (a) Lizard. (b) Mammal. (Modified from R. Collin and C. M. Janis, 1997, in *Ancient Marine Reptiles*, edited by J. M. Callaway and E. L. Nicholls, Academic Press, New York, NY.)

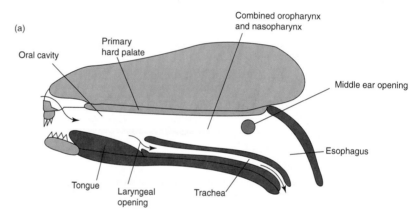

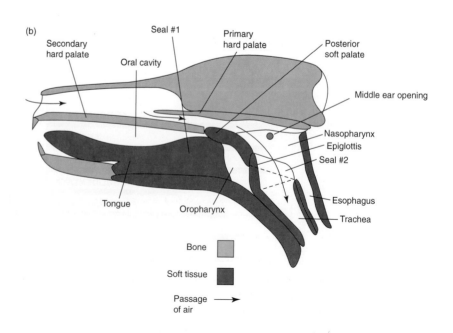

which take in a large mouthful of water and then strain it out through the baleen plates to filter out the plankton. The absence of these seals in other tetrapods may explain why Mesozoic marine reptiles, such as ichthyosaurs (see Chapter 13) never adopted this whalelike mode of filter feeding (Collin and Janis 1997). Filter-feeding fish, such as the whale shark, entrap food particles on the gills with the through passage of water, and so do not need these types of mouth seals.

Mammalian pharyngeal seals were probably evolved within the context of the mammalian type of swallowing, and bony evidence for the soft tissue restructuring of the pharynx is evident in the most mammallike cynodonts (Crompton 1995). However, pharyngeal seals are also essential for mammalian suckling. With the anterior seal applied, depression of the tongue draws milk into the mouth. The application of the second seal not only prevents milk from entering the nose, but also allows milk to pass around the larynx as it flows into the esophagus; in this way the nasal passages can remain in contact with the trachea, and the infant can suckle and breathe at the same time.

Another characteristic feature of mammals is the possession of facial muscles, lacking in other vertebrates (Figure 21–3). These muscles make possible our varieties of facial expressions, but they were probably first evolved in the context of suckling, for mobile lips and cheeks to enable the young to suck. The facial muscles are homologous with the neck constrictor muscles (constrictor colli) of other amniotes; we can tell this because of the pattern of cranial nerve innervation (see Chapter 3) both type of muscles being innervated by cranial nerve VII. There is some evidence that the acquisition of facial muscles may have occurred somewhat differently in various mammal lineages, as monotremes extend a different portion of the constrictor colli muscle into the face during development than do therians, and they lack mobile lips. There is a great deal of difference in the elaboration of these muscles in different mammals. Most mammals do not have highly expressive faces. However, it is not just primates that are capable of facial expressions. Horses use their lips in feeding, and are incidentally capable of quite a wide variety of expressions. This is why Mr. Ed (the television talking horse) seems plausible to us, whereas that role could never be played by a cow. All mammals with well-developed facial muscles display similar expressions for similar emotions, even though the smile as an expression of pleasure or greeting is a uniquely human feature

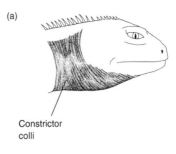

(a)

Constrictor colli

(b)

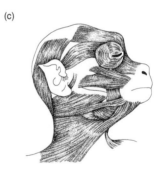

(c)

Figure 21–3 Muscles of facial expression. (a) Lizard, no muscles of facial expression. (b) Rodent, moderate development of muscles of facial expression. (c) Monkey, extensive development of muscles of facial expression. (Modified from K. V. Kardong, 1998, *Vertebrates: Comparative Anatomy, Function, Evolution*, 2nd ed. Wm. C. Brown, Dubuque, IA.)

(possibly modified from the appeasement grimace of apes). A sneer is as instantly recognizable on the face of a dog or a horse as it is on a person. This is perhaps surprising, as these different mammals must have elaborated their facial muscles independently from ancestors with little capacity for facial expression.

The Mammalian Integument

In many ways the outside covering of mammals is the key to their unique way of life. We have emphasized that endothermy is an energetically expensive process, and much of the ability of mammals to live in harsh climates is attributable to properties of their integument. The variety of mammalian integuments is enormous. Some small rodents have an exceedingly delicate epidermis only a few cells thick. Human epidermis varies from a few dozen cells thick over much of the body to over a hundred cells thick on the palms and soles. Elephants, rhinoceroses, hippopotamuses, and tapirs were once classified together as pachyderms (*pachy* = thick, *derm* = skin) because their epidermis is several hundreds of cells thick. The texture of the external surface of the epidermis varies from smooth (in fur-covered skins and the hairless skin of cetaceans) to rough, dry, and crin-

kled (many hairless terrestrial mammals). The tail of opossums and many rodents is covered by epidermal scales similar to those of lizards.

Figure 21–4 illustrates the typical structure of mammalian skin. Note that while mammalian skin is like that of other vertebrates in basic form, with epidermal, dermal, and hypodermal layers (see Chapter 3), there are also a number of unique components. Mammalian skin has typically growing, replaceable hair, lubricant- and oil-producing sebaceous glands, and apocrine and eccrine glands that secrete volatile substances, water, and ions. There are also a number of typically mammalian structures derived from the keratinous layer of the epidermis, including nails, claws, hoofs, and horns. Sensory nerve endings include free nerve endings

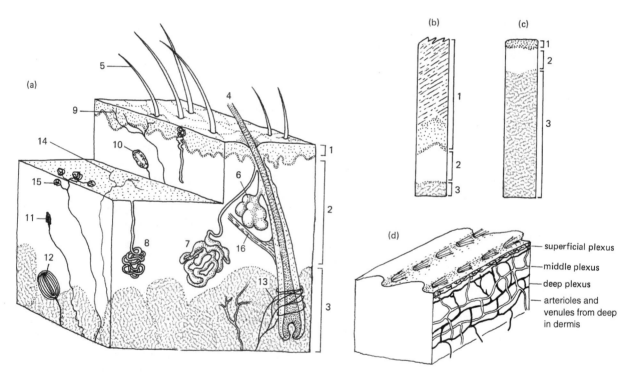

Figure 21–4   Structure of mammalian skin. (a) Composite of skin and appendages showing: (1) layers and surface configuration of the epidermis, (2) the relatively cell-poor dermis, (3) the hypodermis rich in subcutaneous fat cells, (4) guard hairs, (5) undercoat or wool hairs, (6) sebaceous gland, (7) apocrine gland, (8) sweat gland, (9) free nerve endings, (10) beaded nerve nets around blood vessels, (11) Meissner's corpuscles, (12) Pacinian corpuscles, (13) nerve terminals around a hair follicle, (14) heat, (15) cold receptors, and (16) Erector pili muscle. (b) Thick epidermis of the skin on the sole of the human foot. (c) Thin, hairy skin and subcutaneous tissue from the human thigh (numbering as in part a). (d) Canine skin showing three of the vascular plexuses involved in thermoregulation. Note also the numerous hair shafts emerging from a single hair follicle complex, a characteristic of furred mammals. (Modified from various sources, especially A. W. Ham and D. W. Cormack, 1973, *Histology*, 8th edition, Lippincott, Philadelphia, PA; and R. J. Harrison and E. W. Montagna, 1973, *Man*, 2d edition, Appleton-Century-Crofts, New York, NY.)

(probably pain receptors), beaded nerve nets around blood vessels, Meissner's corpuscles (touch receptors), Pacinian corpuscles (pressure receptors), nerve terminals around hair follicles, and warmth and cold receptors. Vascular plexuses (intertwined blood vessels) of the skin are involved in thermoregulation.

Hair   Hair has a variety of functions in a mammal, including camouflage, communication, and sensation via vibrissae (= whiskers), but its basic function is insulation. Fur consists of closely placed hairs, often produced by multiple hair shafts arising from a single complex root. Its insulating effect depends on its ability to trap air within the fur coat, and this is proportional to the length of the hairs. Prominent features of the pelage of extant mammals are its growth, replacement, color, and mobility. A hair is composed of keratin, and grows from a deep invagination of the germinal layer of the epidermis called the hair follicle (Figure 21-4). The color of hair depends on the quality and quantity of melanin injected into the forming hair by melanocytes at the base of the hair follicle, and the color patterns of mammals are built up by the colors of individual hairs.

Because exposed hair is nonliving, it wears and bleaches. Replacement occurs by growth of an individual hair or by **molting,** in which old hairs are replaced. Most mammals have pelage that grows and rests in seasonal phases, and molting usually occurs only once or twice a year. Erection of the hairs is accomplished by the erector pili muscles that attach midway along the hair shaft (see Figure 21-4). Cold stimulates a general contraction of the erector pili via the sympathetic nerves, as do other stressful conditions such as fear and anger. Hair erection increases the depth of the pelage, and thus traps a larger volume of air. A curious side effect noticeable in near-naked mammals such as humans are the dimples (goose pimples) on the skin's surface over the insertion of contracted erector pili muscles. Hair erections can serve for communication as well as for thermoregulation, a warning of fear or anger, as seen in the display of a puffed up cat, or in the raised hackles of a dog.

Glandular Structures   Secretory structures of the skin develop from the epidermis. There are three major types of skin glands in vertebrates: **sebaceous glands, apocrine glands**, and **eccrine glands**.

With the exception of the eccrine glands, skin glands are associated with hair follicles, and the secretion in all of them is under neural and hormonal control. A full component of these skin glands is found in monotremes as well as in therians, and thus may be assumed to be a basic feature of all mammals (Blackburn 1991). The common sweat glands of humans do not appear to be a primitive mammalian feature. Indeed, most mammals do not thermoregulate by secreting fluid from skin glands for evaporative cooling; for example, dogs pant to keep cool, and kangaroos lick their forearms. The capacity to cool off by copious sweating is a peculiarly human trait, seen elsewhere only to a certain extent in some large ungulates such as horses, where sweating is largely associated with activity, not heat load alone.

Sebaceous glands are found over the entire body surface, and produce an oily secretion, sebum, that lubricates and waterproofs the hair and skin. Sheep lanolin, our own greasy hair, and the grease spots that the family dog leaves on the wallpaper where it curls up in the corner are all sebaceous secretions. Apocrine glands have a restricted distribution in most mammals, and their secretions appear to be used in chemical communication. In humans apocrine glands are found in the armpit and pubic regions—these are the secretions which we usually try to mask with deodorant. In some other mammals, such as large ungulates, these glands are scattered over the body surface and may be used in evaporative cooling.

Many mammals have specialized scent glands, which may be modified from either sebaceous or apocrine glands. Sebaceous glands secrete a more viscous substance, usually employed to mark objects, while apocrine glands produce more volatile substances that may be released into the air as well as placed on objects. Scent marking is used to indicate the identity of the markee and to define territories. Scent glands are usually placed on areas of the body that can easily applied to objects, such as the face, chin, or feet. Domestic cats are often seen to rub their face and chin to mark objects, or their owners. Many carnivorans have anal glands so that scents can be deposited along with the urine and feces.

In contrast with sebaceous and apocrine glands, eccrine glands produce a secretion that is mainly watery, with little organic content. In most mammals eccrine glands are restricted to the soles of the feet and other areas that contact environmental surfaces, such as prehensile tails. Here their function is to improve adhesion or to enhance tactile perception. They are found over the body surface only in primates, especially in humans, where they function as sweat glands, secreting copious amounts of fluid for evaporative cooling. Thermoregulatory sweating has evolved convergently within mammals, as different glands are involved in different groups; eccrine glands in humans and apocrine glands in ungulates. In humans sweat glands may act in conjunction with nearby apocrine glands, contributing to odor production under conditions of stress and excitement.

Mammary glands have a more complex, branching structure than other skin glands. They have features in common in terms of structure, body distribution, and chemical composition of secretion with both apocrine and sebaceous glands. Their evolution may have occurred with the formation of a new type of skin gland that contained properties of both of these glands, as they resemble both types of glands and cannot be fully homologised with either one alone (Blackburn 1991).

Claws, Nails, and Hooves   Some integumentary appendages are involved in locomotion, offense, defense, or display. Claws, nails, and hoofs are accumulations of keratin that protect the terminal phalanx of the digits (Figure 21–5). Claws are the primitive condition; a derived condition of claws is seen in catlike carnivores, whose retractable claws avoid wear from the ground during locomotion, and are maintained sharp for predatory functions. The hoof, characteristic of ungulates, is illustrated by that of the horse. The fingernails of humans and other primates is a simpler structure than either the retractable claw or the hoof, but was derived from ancestral claws.

■ The Major Lineages of Mammals

Traditionally, the class Mammalia has been divided into three subclasses: **Allotheria** (multituberculates, now extinct), **Prototheria** (monotremes), and **Theria** (marsupials, infraclass **Metatheria**, and placentals, infraclass **Eutheria**). This classification does not really take into account the large diversity of Mesozoic mammals (see Chapter 19). The original concept of Theria formerly included those extinct mammals that we would now term holotheres, and the Prototheria included such non-holotherian mammals as triconodonts and docodonts, before it

was realized that monotremes were actually considerably more derived mammals; the "Prototheria" as originally defined is not monophyletic (see Chapter 19). However, these three subclasses do reflect basic divisions in body plans between those mammals surviving into the Cenozoic (bearing in mind that Cenozoic mammals represent only the final third of total mammalian history, see Chapter 20).

Differences between Therians and Nontherians

The multituberculates were discussed in Chapter 19, and are not further considered here. Therians are distinguished from monotremes by a number of features. Some obvious ones, already considered in Chapter 19, are the features of giving birth to young (as opposed to egg-laying), and the possession of a more derived type of cheek tooth, the tribosphenic molar. (The differences in reproduction between different types of mammals is considered later in this chapter.) Therians also have a cochlea in the inner ear with at least two and a half coils, an external ear (pinna), and mammae with nipples. They also have several distinctive features of the postcranial skeleton; in the ankle joint and especially in the shoulder region (see later).

No mammal retains the jaw opening muscle of non-mammalian tetrapods, the depressor mandibulae. This muscle inserted onto the retroarticular process of the articular bone in the lower jaw, which in mammals has been transformed into the malleus of the middle ear (see Chapter 19). Therian mammals have a new muscle called the **digastric** (*di* = two, *gaster* = belly), so named because it primitively consists of two separate portions, which are innervated by different cranial nerves (the anterior portion by nerve V and the posterior by nerve VII). The new muscle in monotremes is the detrahens muscle, which is innervated entirely by cranial nerve V, and also lies above the ear canal (the digastric lies below it). This difference in jaw opening muscles has led to speculation that the final incorporation of the articular into the middle ear happened independently in monotremes and therians.

All mammals have a specialized ankle joint, known as a crurotarsal joint. The upper ankle bones of amniotes are rather specialized bones called the **astragalus**, which articulates primarily with the tibia, the major shin bone, and the **calcaneum**, which articulates with the smaller fibula. In the primitive amniote condition, which is retained in most other living amniotes, the plane of move-

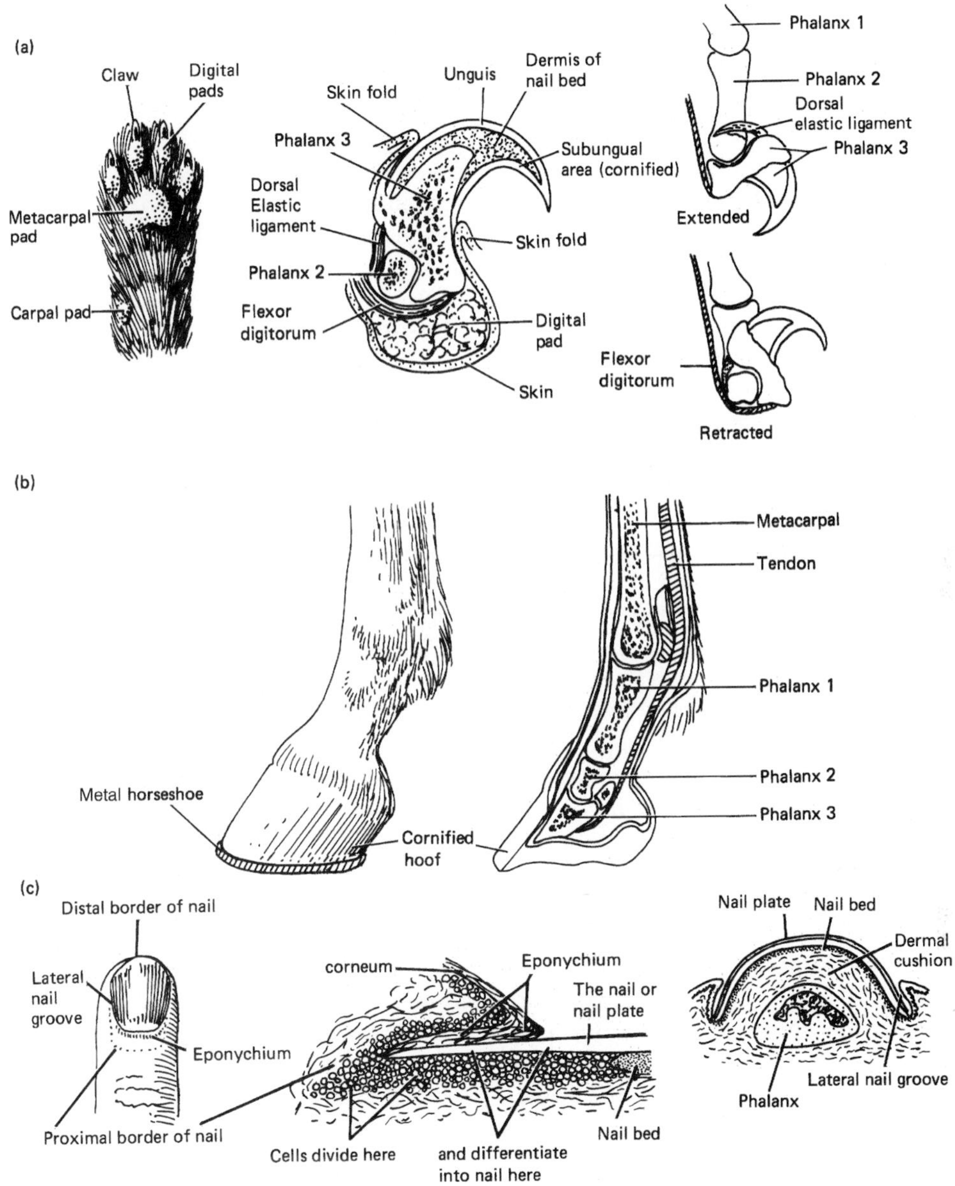

Figure 21–5 Skin appendages associated with terminal phalanges. (a) Retractable claws. Left: Hair and thick epidermal pads associated with the base of the claws. Center: Cross section of a claw showing its close relationships with the blood vessels, dermis, and bone of the third (terminal) phalanx. Right: Claw retraction mechanism characteristic of cats. (b) The hoof of a horse. Left: Normal appearance of the hoof of a shod horse. (Horse shoes are devices used to minimize wear of the hoof on unnaturally (human produced) hard and abrasive surfaces.) Right: Longitudinal section of lower foot showing relationship of phalanges to hoof. (c) The human nail. Left: Distinct regions on a nail correspond to the regional specializations of the epidermis associated with the nail (Center). Right: A cross section of the end of a finger shows the close association of the nail with the dermis and terminal phalanx of the digit.

ment in the ankle joint is a mesotarsal one, between the upper and lower rows of ankle bones. The mammalian ankle joint is between the tibia and the astragalus. Rather than the astragalus and the calcaneum lying side by side, as in other amniotes, the astragalus is superimposed on top of the calcaneum, and the calcaneum is extended posteriorly into the **calcaneal heel**, serving as an attachment for the major calf muscle, the gastrocnemius. The beginning of this specialized ankle joint is seen in some cynodonts, but its fully derived condition, with complete superposition of the astragalus on the calcaneum, is not seen until therians (see Figure 21–6e). This more derived condition creates an ankle joint that functions better as a hinge joint, with the calcaneal heel serving as a lever arm for the gastrocnemius. This ankle joint probably made improved forms of locomotion possible in therians, such as running and hopping.

The therian shoulder girdle is also extremely derived. Monotremes have the derived mammalian form of pelvis, with a compact pubis and ischium and a rod-shaped, forwardly pointing ilium (see Chapter 19), but their shoulder girdle is more reminiscent of the typically reptilian condition. Monotremes retain large ventral bony components, anterior and posterior coracoid and interclavicle bones, and lack a **scapular spine** (see Figure 21–6a, c). Therians have reduced the ventral elements of the shoulder girdle, and expanded the scapula. The anterior coracoid and the interclavicle are lost, the posterior coracoid is fused to the scapula as a little remnant nubbin (the coracoid process), and the clavicle (if present) is usually a slender bone linking the scapula to the sternum. The scapula is larger, and more expanded dorsally, with the addition of a scapular spine. In fact, it is not the spine itself that is the new feature; the fact that the articulation of the clavicle is now with a projection the base of the scapular spine (the acromion process) indicates that this spine is homologous with the old anterior border of the scapula. It is the portion in front of the spine (the supraspinous fossa) that is the new addition (see Figure 21–6b, d). Along with these bony changes, the shoulder musculature has been reorganized (see later discussion on mammalian locomotion).

Differences between Marsupials and Placentals

Therian mammals are more derived than more primitive mammals (represented only by monotremes today, but by a much greater diversity in the Mesozoic) not only in their patterns of reproduction, but also in their sensory acuity (coiled cochlea and pinna), their capacity for food processing (tribosphenic molars), and their locomotory ability (derived features of the shoulder girdle and the ankle joint). Although there are numerous differences between marsupials and placentals in their reproductive biology, as will be discussed later in the chapter, there are few major differences in their anatomy.

A couple of differences can be seen in the brain. Marsupials lack the **corpus callosum** seen in placentals, a nerve tract that connects the two hemispheres and is important in transferring information between the two brain halves. However, marsupials have enlarged another tract present in all amniotes, the anterior commissure, to serve this purpose. The diprotodontid marsupials (e.g., kangaroos), arguably the most intelligent marsupials, have a unique nerve tract, the fasciculus aberrans, paralleling the development of the placental corpus callosum (Parker 1977). Another difference is that marsupials lack the anastomosing capillary network of blood vessels to the surface of the brain seen in placentals, but instead have a series of structures termed end arteries (Lillegraven et al. 1987), the functional significance of which is not clear.

A few distinguishing features in the skull and dentition can be used to tell a marsupial apart from a placental, although not all of these features apply to the earliest Mesozoic forms, nor even to all living marsupials. (Mesozoic marsupials are distinguished from placentals by details of molar form.) For example, marsupials characteristically have an inflected angle to the dentary bone (at the pterygoideus muscle insertion) that is lacking in placentals, and their nasal bones abut against the frontals with a flared, diamond shape in contrast to the rectangular shape of the placental nasals (see Figure 21–7). Placentals may also have an elaboration of bone around the ear region, the **auditory bulla**, that may aid in increasing auditory acuity. Marsupials usually lack a bulla, or they may possess a small one, but in this case it is formed from a different bone from the one in placentals. Herbivorous placentals may have a postorbital bar (see Figure 21–19), but this is never seen in marsupials. During ontogeny, placentals replace all their teeth except for the molars, while marsupials replace only the last premolar (although this feature cannot be determined from an adult skull).

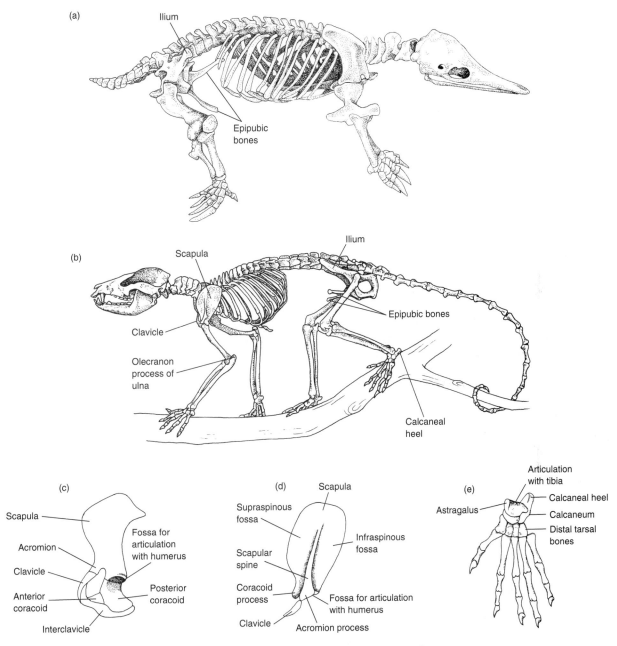

Figure 21–6 Skeletal differences between monotremes and therians. (a) Skeleton of a monotreme, the echidna *Tachyglossus*. (b) Skeleton of a therian, the opossum *Didelphis*. (c) Monotreme shoulder girdle (left girdle in lateral view). (d) Therian shoulder girdle (left girdle in lateral view). (e) Therian foot and ankle (left foot in anterior view). (Modified from E. Rogers, 1986, *Looking at Vertebrates*, Longman, Harlow, UK, and W. F. Walker, Jr. and K. F. Liem, 1994, *Functional Anatomy of the Vertebrates: an Evolutionary Perspective*, 2nd. ed., Saunders, Fort Worth, TX.)

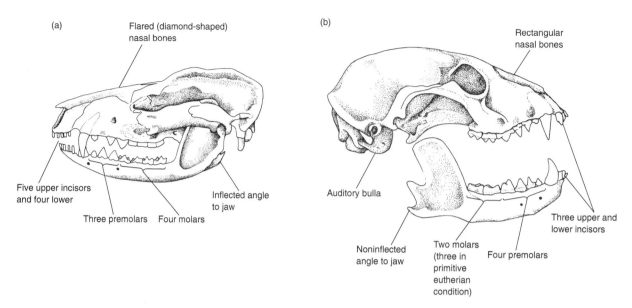

Figure 21–7 Skull differences between placentals and marsupials. (a) Marsupial, the opossum *Didelphis*. (b) Placental, the raccoon *Procyon*. (Modified from T. E. Lawlor, 1979, *Handbook to the Orders and Families of Living Mammals*, Mad River Press, Eureka, CA.)

Marsupials also differ from placentals in their **dental formula**, or numbers of different types of teeth. The maximum number of teeth usually seen in placentals is three upper and lower incisors on each side (making 12 incisors in total), one upper and lower canine (four in total), four upper and lower premolars (16 in total), and three upper and lower molars (12 in total). Many placentals have fewer teeth than this (for example, humans have lost a pair [an upper and lower set] of incisors and two pairs of premolars from each side, so we have a total of only 32 teeth instead of the primitive placental component of 44), but they rarely have more. The exceptions are mammals with highly specialized diets, such as armadillos and dolphins, where supernumerary teeth are added and the difference between different types of teeth is usually modified or lost. In contrast, marsupials have a different dental formula, with a maximum (on each side) of five upper and four lower incisors, three (rather than four) upper and lower premolars, and four (rather than three) upper and lower molars.

In the postcranial skeleton marsupials can be distinguished from placentals primarily by the possession of **epipubic bones** projecting forward from the pubis (see Figure 21–6b) (although there are also some detailed differences in other areas, such as the form of the ankle bones, that would be apparent only to a specialist). It used to be thought that epipubic bones were a unique feature of marsupials,

supporting the pouch. However, not all marsupials possess pouches; epipubic bones are also present in monotremes, and as more postcranial skeletons of Mesozoic mammals have become known it has become apparent that these bones are a primitive mammalian feature, lost in placentals. Epipubic bones may well play a role in pouch support in marsupials, or in the support of the young attached to the nipples, especially as they are larger in females than in males, but they cannot have been evolved specifically for this purpose (White 1989). The original function of these bones in mammals appears now to be the insertion of various muscles (e.g., the rectus abdominus) that would have been affected by the reduction of the large pubo-ischiatic plate of the cynodont pelvic girdle (see Chapter 19). Epipubic bones are vestigial in the thylacine (marsupial wolf), and were lost entirely in the extinct doglike borhyaenid marsupials. The fact that these two types of marsupials are the only ones that appear to have been quadrupedal runners (as opposed to the bipedal hopping mode of fast locomotion in other marsupials) also implies a role of these bones in musculature support and attachments.

The loss of epipubic bones in placentals probably relates to the fact that they are rigid components of the abdominal wall that would interfere with the expansion of the abdomen during pregnancy (Lillegraven 1969). It has also been claimed that the bacculum (penis bone) seen in certain placentals is homologous with these epipubic bones, suggesting that they were transformed in function rather than entirely lost (Jellison 1945). However, it now appears that complete loss of epipubic bones (in their original capacity), although true of all living placentals, was not the case in some early fossil forms, as a placental bearing these bones has recently been described from the Late Cretaceous of Mongolia (Novacek et al. 1997).

Mammalian Ordinal Diversity

The orders of living therian mammals are listed in Tables 21–1 and 21–2, and the interrelationships of these orders is shown in Figure 21–1.

Monotremes   Monotremes are grouped in the infraorder Ornithodelphia, order Monotremata. There are two families. The Ornithorhynchidae (= *bird-billed*) contains the platypus, a semiaquatic animal with a body mass of about 2 kilograms, feeding on aquatic invertebrates in the streams of eastern Australia. The family Tachyglossidae (= *fast-tongued*) contains two types of spiny anteaters or echidnas (with body masses of 5 - 10 kg); the short-nosed echidna of Australia, which eats mainly ants and termites, and the long-nosed echidna of New Guinea, which includes more earthworms in its diet (see Figure 21–8). Monotremes may have originally had a wider distribution over Gondwana (see Chapter 20), but although quite a few monotreme fossils are known, ranging from a lower jaw from the Cretaceous to the giant echidna of the Pleistocene, there is as yet no indication that monotremes ever comprised a much greater adaptive diversity of eco-morphological types than is seen today.

Monotremes are primitive mammals in a number of ways, not just in their egg-laying habits, as previously discussed. However, their rather sprawling stance, reminiscent of the reptilian condition, may reflect life-style adaptations (swimming or digging) more than a truly primitive condition. Monotremes also have some of their own unique specializations: a bill or beak that can sense electromagnetic signals put out by the muscles of other animals (useful for sensing prey underwater or in a termite nest) and, in the male platypus, a spur on the hind leg attached to a venom gland, that can be used to poison rivals or predators (although a similar type of spur has been noted in some fossil nontherian mammals).

TABLE 21.1	Classification of extant marsupial orders and approximate numbers of families and species (note that different researchers may recognize different numbers of families within an order)	
Classification	*Families/Species*	*Major Examples*
Cohort Ameridelphia		
Didelphimorphia	1/77	Opossums; 20 g to 6 kg; Neotropical region (plus one North American species).
Paucituberculata	1/5	Caenolestids or rat opossums; 15 to 40 g; Neotropical region.
Cohort Australidelphia		
Microbiotheria	1/1	The monito del monte; ~25 g; Neotropical region.
Dasyuromorphia	3/60	Marsupial mice, native cats, Tasmanian devil, Tasmanian wolf (thylacine), marsupial anteater (numbat); 5 g to 20 kg; Australian region.
Notoryctemorphia	1/1	Marsupial mole; 50 g; Australian region.
Peramelina	2/21	Bandicoots and bilbies; 100 g to 5 kg; Australian region.
Diprotodontia	9/110	Possums, flying phalangers, cuscuses, honey possum (noolbender), koala, wombats, potoroos, wallabies, kangaroos. 12 g to 90 kg; Australian region; possums and wallabies introduced into New Zealand by humans.

Sources: L. G. Marshall, J. A. Case, and M. O Woodburne, 1990, *Current Mammalogy* 2:433-505; T. A. Vaughan, 1986, *Mammalogy*, 3d edition, Saunders College, Philadelphia. R. M. Nowak and J. L. Paradiso, 1991, *Walker's Mammals of the World*, 5th edition, Johns Hopkins University Press, Baltimore, MD. See Chapter 20 for an explanation of geographical regions.

Classification	Species	Major Examples
Grandorder Edentata		
Xenarthra	3/30	Anteaters, sloths, armadillos; 20 g to 33 kg; Neotropical region (plus some armadillos in southern USA).
Pholidota	1/7	Pangolins (scaly anteaters); 2 to 33 kg; Ethiopian and Oriental regions.
Grandorder Glires		
Lagomorpha	2/69	Rabbits, hares, pikas; 180 g to 7 kg; worldwide except Antarctica, introduced in Australia by humans.
Rodentia	29/1814	Rats, mice, squirrels, guinea pigs, capybara; 7 g to over 50 kg; worldwide except Antarctica.
Macroscelidea	1/15	Elephant shrews; 25 to 500 g; Ethiopian region with one species in Morocco and Algeria.
Grandorder Insectivora		
Insectivora (= Lipotyphla)	6/390	Hedgehogs, moles, shrews, tenrecs; 2 g to 1 kg; worldwide except Australia and Antarctica (although only a single species of shrew is known from South America, a Pleistocene immigrant).
Grandorder Archonta		
Scandentia	1/16	Tree shrews; 400 g; Oriental region.
Primates	9/235	Lemurs, monkeys, apes, humans; 85 g to over 275 kg; primarily Oriental, Ethiopian, and Neotropical regions, humans are now worldwide.
Dermoptera	1/2	Flying lemurs; 1 to 2 kg; Oriental region.
Chiroptera	15/986	Bats; 4 g to 1.4 kg; worldwide (including New Zealand) except Antarctica.
Grandorder Ferae		
Carnivora	12/274	Dogs, bears, raccoons, weasels, hyaenas, cats, sea lions, walruses, seals (these last three are often assigned to the suborder Pinnipedia); 70 g to 760 kg, some marine forms over 100 kg; worldwide.
Grandorder Ungulata		
Artiodactyla	10/213	Even-toed ungulates: Swine, hippopotamuses, camelids, deer, giraffe, antelope, sheep, cattle; 2 to 2500 kg; worldwide except Antarctica (introduced into Australia and New Zealand by humans).
Cetacea	9/80	Porpoises, dolphins, sperm whales, baleen whales; 20 to 120,000 kg; worldwide in oceans and in some rivers and lakes in Asia, South America, northern America and Eurasia.
Perissodactyla	3/17	Odd-toed ungulates: Horses, tapirs, rhinoceroses; 150 to 3600 kg; Worldwide except Antarctica (horses introduced by humans into North America and Australia).
Tubulidentata	1/1	Aardvark; 64 kg; Ethiopian region.
Hyracoidea	1/7	Hyraxes (= conies or dassies); 4 kg; Ethiopian region and Asia Minor.
Proboscidea	1/2	Elephants and fossil relatives; 4500 to 7000 kg; Ethiopian and Oriental regions.
Sirenia	2/4	Dugongs, manatees; 140 to over 1000 kg; coastal waters and estuaries of all tropical and subtropical oceans except the eastern Pacific (in the Atlantic drainage they enter rivers).

Source: J. A. Hopson, 1970, *Journal of Mammalogy* 51:1–9; M. C. McKenna, 1975, in *Phylogeny of the Primates*, edited by W. P. Luckett and F. S. Szalay, Plenum, New York, NY; T. A. Vaughan, 1986, *Mammalogy*, 3d edition, Saunders College, Philadelphia; J. F. Eisenberg, 1981, *The Mammalian Radiations*, University of Chicago Press, Chicago, IL; R. M. Nowak and J. L. Paradiso, 1991, *Walker's Mammals of the World*, 5th edition, Johns Hopkins University Press, Baltimore, MD; S. Anderson and J. K. Jones, Jr., 1984, *Orders and Families of Recent Mammals of the World*, Wiley–Interscience, New York, NY; M. J. Novacek and A. R. Wyss, 1987, *Cladistics* 2:257–287. See Chapter 20 for explanation of geographical regions.

(a)

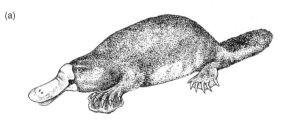

(b)

(c)

Figure 21–8   Diversity of living monotremes. (a) The duck-billed platypus, *Ornithorhynchus anatinus.* (b) The short-nosed echinda (Australia), *Tachyglossus aculeatus.* (c) The long-nosed echidna (New Guinea), *Zaglossus bruijni.* (Modified from J. Z. Young 1981, *The Life of Vertebrates* [3rd ed.], Clarendon Press, Oxford, in part.)

Marsupials   Marsupials traditionally have been considered as a single order, **Marsupialia**, but more recent researchers have claimed that they can be divided into a minimum of four groupings that are equivalent in morphological and genetic diversity to placental orders; one current scheme is shown in Table 21–1, and Figure 21–9 illustrates the diversity of living marsupials.

There is a fundamental split in the interrelationships of living marsupials into the Ameridelphia of

the New World and the Australidelphia of (mainly) Australia. A third group, now extinct and possibly more primitive than either of these living groups, was the Deltatheroidea of the Late Cretaceous of Asia. The most primitive living marsupials are the **didelphids** (opossums) of South America, including the common opossum as a recent (Pleistocene) immigrant to North America. The order Didelphimorpha includes didelphoids (didelphids plus related extinct forms, such as the Northern Hemisphere marsupials of the early Cenozoic) and some extinct Cretaceous forms. Present-day South American opossums are quite a diverse group of small to medium-size marsupials, mainly arboreal or semiarboreal omnivores, including animals such as the herbivorous woolly opossum and the otterlike yapok (Figure 21–9). The other Ameridelphian order is the Paucituberculata, the **caenolestids** or rat opossums, small, terrestrial, shrewlike forms (Figure 21–9). A much greater diversity of didelphoids existed in the past, including jerboalike hopping argyrolagids, molelike forms, and a large radiation of carnivorous doglike forms, the borhyaenoids. Borhyaenoids appear to be the sister group to didelphoids rather than actually being included within that group (Muizon et al. 1997).

The one remaining type of South American marsupial is the monito del monte, a tiny mouselike animal living in the montane forests of Chile and Argentina (Figure 21–9). This animal belongs to the family Microbiotheriidae, a family that was until quite recently thought to have been extinct since the early Miocene. The monito del monte itself was thought to be a type of didelphid, until molecular studies showed it to cluster with the Australian marsupials (Kirsch et al. 1991). This interrelationship was borne out by further anatomical studies, and today most researchers regard this animal as a distant relict of the stock of originally South American marsupials that migrated across Antarctica to Australia in the early Cenozoic (Luckett 1994, Springer et al. 1994). Some recent molecular studies also suggest that the caenolestids are more closely related to the Australian marsupials than are the didelphids (Springer et al. 1997a).

The other Australidelphia fall into three major orders. The **dasyurids** are carnivorous forms: the marsupial cats (Figure 20–6) and marsupial mice (which would better be termed marsupial shrews, as they are carnivorous and insectivorous rather than omnivorous). Some larger dasyurids include the dogsize Tasmanian devil (Figure 21–9d), and the

Tasmanian (marsupial) wolf or thylacine (Figure 20-6 and Chapter heading figure). The thylacine has reportedly been extinct since the 1930s, but there are occasional claims for its continued existence from purported sightings or footprint evidence. Both these Tasmanian animals were known from mainland Australia before the arrival of humans and their placental true dogs, the dingoes. The marsupial anteater (the numbat) (Figure 20-6) is included with the dasyurids in the order Dasyuromorphia. The marsupial mole (Figure 21–9e) (in its own order Notoryctemorphia) may be distantly related to this grouping (Luckett 1994).

The **peramelids** comprise the bandicoots and bilbies (Figure 21–9f). These animals look rather like rabbits, especially the long-eared bilbies, but they are insectivorous rather than herbivorous. Peramelids share with the final group a condition of the hind feet known as syndactyly, where the second and third toes are reduced in size and enclosed within the same skin membrane (so that they appear to be a single toe in outer view). The syndactylous toes serve as a grooming structure. Some researchers consider this morphological feature to link peramelids and diprotodontians (Luckett 1994) as shown in Figure 21–1, but other evidence, especially from molecular studies, suggests that peramelids are more primitive than other Australidelphia, and that the condition of syndactyly is convergent (Springer et al. 1994).

The largest group of marsupials is the **diprotodontians**. This lineage comprises herbivorous or omnivorous forms today, although the recently extinct marsupial lion *Thylacoleo* appears to represent a return to carnivory within this group from a herbivorous ancestry. *Thylacoleo* shows some interesting adaptations: coming from a herbivorous ancestry it had lost its canines, but modified the incisors into canine-like teeth. Diprotodontians are so called because all of them have modified their lower incisors into a pair of forward-projecting, rather rodentlike teeth (*Di* = two, *proto* = first, *dont* = tooth).

There are three major radiations within the diprotodontians; phalangeroids, phascolarctoids, and macropodoids. Phalangeroids represent an arboreal radiation of rather primatelike animals, comprising gliding forms (Figure 20–6), including six families of possums, phalangers, ring tails, and cuscuses. There is some evidence that the family containing the diminutive honey possum (or noolbenger) (Figure 21–9g), the only nectar-eating mammal that is not a bat, falls outside of the monophyletic grouping that unites the other possums (Luckett 1994). Phascolarctoids or vombatiformes include the arboreal koala and the terrestrial, burrowing wombats (Figure 20–6). The marsupial lion may be related to these animals,—perhaps the source behind the Australian legend of the marsupial drop bear, which supposedly drops from trees to savage unsuspecting passersby (primarily gullible tourists)! Extinct phascolarctoids include the cow to bison-size diprotodontids, which looked like giant wombats and may have been grazers on the Plio-Pleistocene savannas. Macropodoids include the small, omnivorous rat kangaroos (or potaroos) (Figure 21–9i), and the larger, herbivorous true kangaroos (including wallabies and tree kangaroos). The largest kangaroos today have a body mass of about 90 kg, but larger ones (up to twice that size) existed in the Pleistocene, including a radiation of one-toed, short-faced browsing sthenurine kangaroos, now all extinct. Sthenurine kangaroos could perhaps be the source of legends of giant bunnies in the interior of

Figure 21–9 Diversity of living marsupials. (a) The common North American opossum, *Didelphis virginiana* (Didelphidae: Didelphimorphia). (b) The shrew opossum, *Lestoros inca* (Caenolestidae: Paucituberculata). (c) The monito-del-monte, *Dromiciops australis* (Microbiotheriidae: Microbiotheria). (d) The Tasmanian devil, *Sarcophilus harrisii* (Dasyuridae: Dasyuromorphia). (e) The marsupial mole, *Notoryctes typhlops* (Notoryctidae: Notoryctemorphia). (f) The bilbey, or rabbit-eared bandicoot, *Macrotis lagotis* (Thylacomyidae: Peramalina). (g) The honey possum, *Tarsipes rostratus* (Tarsipedidae, Phalangeroidea, Diprotodontia). (h) The koala, *Phascolarctos cinereus* (Phascolarctidae, Phascolartoidea, Diprotodontia). (i) The long-nosed potoroo (rat kangaroo), *Potorous tridactylus* (Macropodidae, Macropodoidea, Diprotodontia). (Modified from D. MacDonald, 1984, *The Encyclopedia of Mammals*, Facts on File Publications, in part.)

Australia, as they had stouter forearms than modern kangaroos and, as arid-adapted animals, may have had larger ears.

Placentals   Placental mammals can be grouped into a number of distinct taxa, but the relationships of these groups remains obscure. Neither current morphological nor molecular data can provide a better resolution of mammalian relationships than that shown in Figure 21–1, which suggests that the diversification of these groups from some ancestral stock occurred rapidly in the Late Cretaceous or earliest Cenozoic.

The current scheme of dividing placental mammals into a variety of subgroups, termed grandorders, was devised by Malcolm McKenna (McKenna 1975). Insectivores are often considered to be primitive mammals, and many older texts display phylogenies suggesting that they are somehow the basal stock from which other placentals were derived. However, although modern insectivores such as shrews may superficially resemble ancestral placental mammals, especially in their body size, their diet, and their nocturnal, relatively solitary behavior, in terms of their phylogenetic position among the array of modern mammals they are no more primitive than any others. There were a number of insectivorous mammals in the early Cenozoic that were probably not closely related to modern insectivores, or even to one another: they are loosely grouped as the "Proteutheria."

The **Edentata** (order Xenarthra: sloths, anteaters, and armadillos) (Figures 20–6, 21–10a) appears to be the earliest surviving branch off the main placental stem. Pangolins (order Pholidota) may be included in this grouping, or may be more closely related to carnivorans (Novacek 1994). The other placentals can be grouped as the Epitheria, although the reality of this grouping separate from the Edentata has been challenged (Gaudin et al. 1996). The order **Insectivora** comprises one of the grandorders in this group. The current grouping of insectivorans includes only what used to be called the subgroup Lipotyphla within the order: shrews, moles, hedgehogs, and tenrecs (Figure 21–10b). Various other forms, such as tree shrews and elephant shrews, are now recognized as belonging to different orders within different grandorders. Elephant shrews (Figure 21–10c) (order Macroscelidea, so-named because of their trunklike nose) are grouped in the **Glires**, along with the rodents and rabbits (although this position is controversial, and some researchers consider elephant shrews to be closer to the ungulates, see McKenna 1987).

Tree shrews (order Scandentia) (Figure 21–21) were once thought to be primitive primates. This is now no longer believed to be true, but they are grouped with the primates, bats, and dermopterans (flying lemurs) (Figure 21–10e) in the grandorder **Archonta**. There has been much debate about whether bats are truly a monophyletic radiation; various similarities of the brain and visual system have led some researchers to suggest that the larger, diurnal fruit bats (suborder Megachiroptera) are more closely related to primates than they are to the smaller, nocturnal insectivorous bats (suborder Microchiroptera) (Pettigrew, 1986, 1991). If this were true, it would imply that flight had evolved twice within mammals, independently within both types of bats. However, reanalysis of the data suggests that the grouping of primates and fruit bats depends on primitive characters, features of the visual system that would be lost in the nocturnal microbats which rely on echolocation rather than vision (Baker et al. 1991).

The only order in the grandorder **Ferae** today is the **Carnivora**, mammals that are primitively generalized carnivores (living carnivorans such as civets and genets probably look much like their early Cenozoic ancestors), but also today contains secondarily omnivorous forms, or even herbivores, such as the panda bear. The Carnivora also includes other bears, dogs, weasels, skunks, raccoons, cats, hyenas, and one of the three living groups of secondarily aquatic mammals, the **pinnipeds** (seals, sea lions, and walruses). Pinnipeds are related to bears, and first appeared in the late Oligocene. Pinnipeds were once thought to be derived from different groups within the Carnivora, but are now considered to represent a monophyletic radiation (Wyss and Flynn 1993). An important extinct order in the Ferae was the Creodonta, whose members took the role of the large-size predators in the early Cenozoic.

The largest grandorder, both in terms of numbers of species and in the size of its members, is the **Ungulata**, or hoofed mammals (hooves are terminal appendages made out of keratin, see Figure 21–5). Hooves are the major feature uniting the ungulates on morphological grounds. However, the grouping of all ungulates into a single clade, as shown in Figure 21–1, is not always supported by molecular evidence; in particular, the subungulates (elephants, hyraxes, etc.) tend to cluster together in a different part of the mammalian tree from the other ungulates (e.g., Springer et al. 1997a).

One of the surprises in the revisions of mammalian interrelationships over the past couple of decades has been the realization that whales and dolphins (order **Cetacea**) are actually related to the living artiodactyls (even-toed ungulates), despite their carnivorous diets. This relationship is supported both by molecular and morphological data (Novacek 1992, 1994). Early Cenozoic ungulates are grouped together in the paraphyletic assemblage "Condylarthra." Not all condylarths were herbivorous: several types were omnivorous, and one group, the mesonychids, were carnivorous. There is good fossil evidence that mesonychids are the group that gave rise to whales (Thewissen 1994). Sirenians (sea cows and dugongs), the sister group of proboscideans, are a second radiation of aquatic mammals from within the Ungulata, although these mammals are all herbivorous. A third radiation of aquatic ungulates, the desmostylians (more semi-aquatic forms, related to the sirenians), is now extinct.

The **Artiodactyla**, or even-toed ungulates, is the most diverse ungulate order today, comprising pigs, hippos, camels, giraffes, deer, and bovids (cattle and antelope). This present-day diversity is mainly due to the Plio-Pleistocene expansion of the family Bovidae. Even in the comparatively recent past, the numbers of **Perissodactyla** (odd-toed ungulates; horses, rhinos, and tapirs [Figure 21–10g]), and **Proboscidea** (elephants and their relatives) was much greater than it is today. This change in predominance of ungulate diversities is better explained by climatic changes than by competition (Janis 1989). Mammals related to elephants include sirenians, hyraxes (Figure 21–10i), and possibly the aardvark. There were also several orders of ungulates that radiated in South America, discussed in Chapter 20, that are now entirely extinct.

Some recent molecular studies have resulted in controversy about the interrelationships of mammals. There are claims that whales should actually be included within the Artiodactyla, perhaps as close relatives to hippos, rather than being the sister group of artiodactyls among living mammals (Graur and Higgins 1994, Gatesy et al. 1996). However, there are problems with analyzing and interpreting these molecular data when it is not possible to obtain equivalent data from the wide variety of extinct possible relatives (Theodor and Mahoney 1997), and most morphologists and paleontologists

remain skeptical of this claim. Another recent molecular study claims that all the endemic African mammals are closely related to each other (Springer et al. 1997b). Morphological studies have long clustered together proboscideans, hyraxes, and sirenians, and although aardvark relationships are a bit of a mystery some studies have grouped them here as well (Novacek 1992, 1994). However, this new study would also cluster not only elephant shrews (which have been considered problematical) but also golden moles (which have never been considered as other than regular insectivorans) with these African ungulates. It remains to be seen how the traditional morphologists will address this claim.

Evolution of Horns in Ungulates

Horns and antlers are characteristic of many large ungulates (Bubenik and Bubenik 1990). Their primary roles appear to be social recognition, sexual display, and jousting between males, although they may also be used for defense (see Chapter 23). Figures 21–11 illustrates a variety of types of mammalian cranial appendages (the proper collective term for horns, antlers, etc.). Modern rhinos are unlike other horned ungulates (today all ruminant artiodactyls; deer, giraffes, and bovids): their horns are formed entirely of keratin and are found in both males and females (although some extinct rhinos had bony horns that were present in males only). Rhino horns also tend to be midline in structure and found on the nose region, whereas the horns of ruminants are paired and formed over the eyes (although single horns on the nose or on the back of the head, in addition to the paired horns over the eyes, are known in some fossil artiodactyls).

Although the horns of ruminant artiodactyls appear rather similar, they are not homologous in their mode of growth, and appear to have evolved independently within different ruminant lineages. This hypothesis is strengthened by the existence of animals such as the Chinese water deer, a perfectly good deer but one that lacks antlers entirely, suggesting that antlers evolved within the deer (family Cervidae), separately from the horns of bovids or the ossicones of giraffes. The evolution of ruminant horns appears to be tied in with their socioecology. The body size, diet and habitat preference of present-day antelope is rather tightly correlated with their type of social behavior: solitary, territorial, or herd-forming (see Chapter 23). The evolution of ruminant horns can be understood in the context of

changing Cenozoic habitats, which in turn led to changes in diet, body size, behavior, and morphology (Janis 1982).

Ruminants first appear in the fossil record in the late Oligocene, when they are small, hornless animals with teeth suggestive of a diet of fruit and young leaves, much like the present-day mouse deer or chevrotains (family Tragulidae) (see Figure 21–10h), which inhabit the tropical forests of Asia and Africa. By the early Miocene the Eurasian woodlands where these animals lived became more seasonal, and more open in structure, which resulted in a different distribution of food resources. The ruminants responded by becoming somewhat larger (goatsize rather than rabbitsize), and evolving teeth more capable of eating fibrous vegetation. As discussed later, a small ruminant would not be able to cope with a fibrous diet in any case. This new diet, in the new habitat, enabled the ruminants to adopt a new type of social behavior, that of territoriality in the males defending a patch of resources to attract females, moving from a monogamous type of mating system to a polygynous one. Previously, ruminant social behavior was probably like that of the mouse deer, solitary or pair-bonding, and defending an individual home range only. This opportunity for defending territories that could attract roving bands of females could have produced intense male-male competition over territorial boundaries and resulted in the evolution of horns (or equivalent structures). (Note that horns act as devices of ritual display and stylized combat, and may actually reduce the incidence of injury during male-male interactions.)

The above explanation is of course a historical scenario; we will never be able to know for certain what actually happened. However, evidence for this scenario is as follows: Horns (or their equivalents) appear in different families of ruminants at about the same point in time, in correlation with a change in habitat and an increase in body size, corresponding to an ecomorphological shift that in present-day ruminants is associated with a change in behavior from a solitary life-style to one involving grouping among females and territorial conflict among males. Thus, this scenario makes good sense in terms of what we know about the variations in behavior of living animals with factors such as habitat, body size, and diet. Ruminant horns appear to have evolved in males initially, as in the early members of all horned ruminant lineage there are both horned and hornless (presumed female) individuals. The faillure of horns to evolve in ungulates such as camels and horses can be explained in part by the fact that they evolved in North America, where the pattern of vegetational change was somewhat different. Additionally, hindgut fermenters like horses are less efficient feeders than ruminants (see later discussion), and so may always require a home range area that is too large to defend as a territory (as is also true for larger, grazing ruminants, where the females may now have horns as well).

■ Mammalian Reproduction

All mammals have an early embryonic ball of cells (blastocyst) that has two distinct layers; the inner cell layer differentiates into the embryo and the outer layer forms the **trophoblast**. The trophoblast is a precocious differentiation of extraembryonic tissue specialized for obtaining nutrition in the uterus, for producing hormones to signal the state of pregnancy to the mother, and (in therians) for helping the embryo implant to the uterine wall. It is

---

Figure 21–10 Diversity of living placentals. (a) Two-toed sloth, *Choloepus didactylus* Megalonychidae, Xenarthra, Edentata). (b) Common tenrec, *Tenrec ecaudatus* (Tenrecidae, Insectivora, Insectivora). (c) Golden-rumped elephant shrew, *Rhynchocyon chrysopygus* (Macroscelididae, Macroscelidea, Glires). (d) Naked mole rat, *Heterocephalus glaber* (Bathyergidae, Rodentia, Glires). (e) Flying lemur, *Cynocephalus volans* (Cynocephalidae, Dermoptera, Archonta). (f) The spotted hyaena, *Crocuta crocuta* (Hyaenidae, Carnivora, Ferae). (g) The Asiatic tapir, *Tapirus indicus* (Tapiridae, Perissodactyla, Ungulata). (h) The African water chevrotain, *Hyemoschus aquaticus* (Tragulidae, Artiodactyla, Ungulata). (i) The rock hyrax, *Procavia capensis* (Procaviidae, Hyracoidea, Ungulata). (Modified from D. MacDonald, 1984, *The Encyclopedia of Mammals*, Facts on File Publications, in part.)

often stated that the trophoblast is found in placentals only, but this is incorrect. Placentals do have a greater apparent distinction between the inner and outer cell layers than do monotremes and marsupials, however (Tyndale-Biscoe and Renfree 1987). Additionally, all mammals share the feature of a glandular uterine epithelium (**endometrium**) that can secrete materials to nourish intrauterine young when stimulated by the hormone progesterone.

An obvious reproductive difference between the two extant subclasses is that monotremes lay eggs (oviparity) and that all other living mammals give

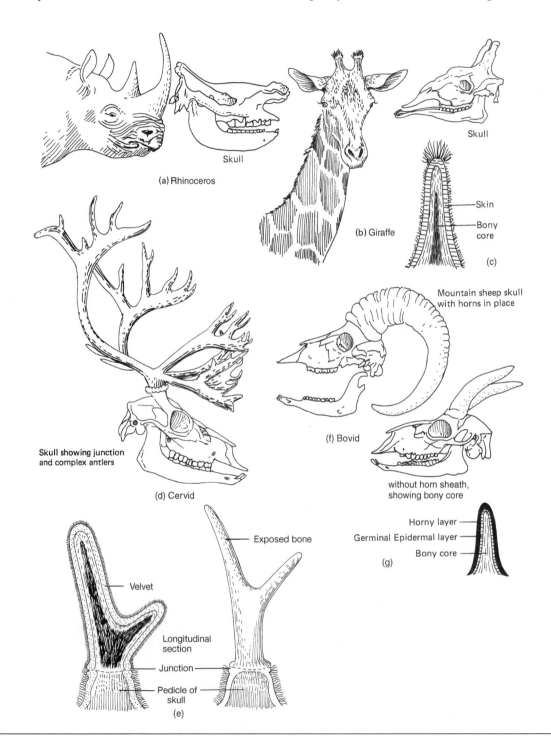

(a) Rhinoceros

Skull

(b) Giraffe

Skull

Skin

Bony core

(c)

Mountain sheep skull with horns in place

(f) Bovid

Skull showing junction and complex antlers

(d) Cervid

without horn sheath, showing bony core

Horny layer

Germinal Epidermal layer

Bony core

(g)

Exposed bone

Velvet

Longitudinal section

Junction

Pedicle of skull

(e)

birth to live young (viviparity). However, all mammals share the feature of the formation of a **corpus luteum**, a hormone-secreting structure formed in the ovary from the follicular cells remaining after the egg is shed (although this structure is also found in other amniotes). Hormones secreted by the corpus luteum are essential for the establishment and at least the initial maintenance of pregnancy.

The egg-laying mode of monotremes is most likely the primitive mammalian condition; egg-laying is primitive for amniotes. With the evolution of viviparity the uterine glands that add the shell and other egg components are lost. Thus it seems highly likely that, once a lineage has become dedicated to viviparity, it would be impossible to return to oviparity. However, the reproductive biology of monotremes is quite unlike that of other living oviparous amniotes, as is discussed later (although it is impossible to determine if monotremes perhaps retain the primitive amniote reproductive mode).

Another reproductive difference between the mammalian subclasses is in the testes. Therians usually have testes descended into a scrotum during development, whereas monotremes are like other amniotes in having testes which are retained within the abdomen (as are ovaries). Not all placentals have descended testes, however. For example, whales, elephants, and hyraxes have abdominal testes. The scrotum is probably homologous in marsupials and placentals, despite the fact that it differs in position (Renfree 1993). The scrotum is situated in front of the penis in marsupials and in some placentals. Considering the fact that all marsupials retain a close opposition of urogenital and alimentary openings (see Figure 21–12), it would not be possible for a marsupial to put the scrotum behind the penis without also putting it behind the anus,

which would probably be a developmental impossibility. With the further separation of the urogenital and alimentary tracts in placentals there is now a perineal area where the scrotum can be positioned. Presumably the testes are more protected in this postpenile position; however, some placentals, such as rabbits, have a prepenile scrotum, perhaps a retained primitive condition.

Reproductive Mode of Monotremes

The reproductive tract of monotremes retains the primitive amniote condition (see Chapter 3). The two oviducts remain separate, and do not fuse in development, except at the base where they are conjoined with the urethra from the bladder to form the urogenital sinus (see Figure 21–12a). The oviducts swell to form a uterus where the fertilized egg is retained (only the left oviduct is functional in the platypus). In all mammals the eggs are fertilized in the anterior portion of the oviduct, the Fallopian tube, before they enter the uterus. The ovaries of monotremes are bigger than those of therians, and as egg-layers they provide the embryo with a large amount of yolk. However, the eggs of monotremes are much smaller at ovulation than those of similarly-sized reptiles or birds. Monotremes exhibit matrotrophy: the amount of yolk provided is not sufficient to sustain the young until hatching, and the eggs are retained in the uterus and are nourished by maternal secretions before the shell is secreted, and during this time the egg also increases in size (Tyndale-Biscoe and Renfree 1987). The egg shell is leathery, like that of lizards, rather than the calcareous shell of birds. Hatchling monotremes have a birdlike egg tooth that they use to open the shell.

Figure 21–11 Mammalian cranial appendages. (a) Rhinoceros with nasal horn made of keratin. Horns are found in both males and females. (b) Giraffe with ossicones. (c) Structure of giraffid ossicone: the bony core is formed from a separate bone in development that fuses with the skull, and the entire structure is covered with skin. Ossicones are found in both male and female giraffes (d) Cervid (deer, a caribou) with antlers. Antlers are the only cranial appendages that are branched or forked, and that are shed annually. (e) Detail of a simple antler, showing the growing structure covered with skin (" in velvet") left, and the fully-grown structure where the skin has been shed and naked bone is exposed (right). The junction between antler and pedicle demarcates the line where the antler is shed. Antlers are found in the males alone except in caribou and reindeer. (f) Bovid (sheep) with horns. Horns are composed of a bony horn core (lower) covered with a keratin sheath (upper). The bony portions of both horns and antlers represent outgrowths from the frontal bone. (e) Cross-sectional detail of developing bovid horn.

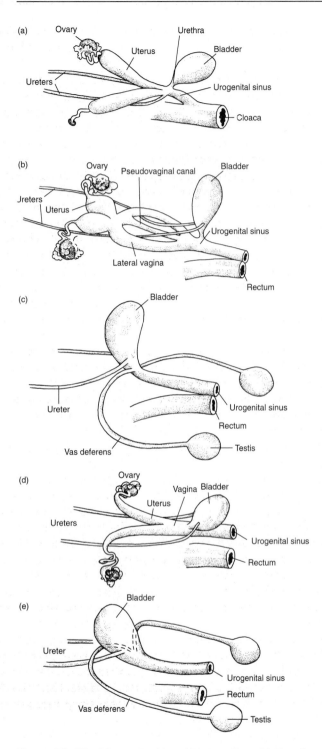

Figure 21–12 Mammalian reproductive tracts. (a) Female monotreme (platypus). (b) Female marsupial. (c) Male marsupial. (d) Female placental. (e) Male placental. (Modified from M. B. Renfree, 1993, in *Mammal Phylogeny*, edited by F. S. Szalay, M. J. Novacek, and M. C. McKenna, Springer Verlag, New York, NY.)

Not only do monotremes retain the egg in the uterus for a long period of time, but the young hatch relatively rapidly after the egg is laid. The young are hatched at an undeveloped, almost embryonic stage (see Figure 21–13a). In the platypus the egg is incubated for 12 days, but brooding of the young by the mother continues for a further 16 weeks. The platypus usually lays a single egg in a burrow while echidnas lay one or two eggs and keep them in a ventral pouch which resembles, but is probably not homologous with, the pouch of marsupials. All monotremes have a low reproductive rate, and reproduce no more than once a year (Vaughan 1986).

Reproductive Mode of Therians

All therians possess a placenta, which is formed from the extraembryonic membranes of the fetus (see Chapter 10 for a description of the extraembryonic membranes of all amniotes). In some placentals (e.g., higher primates and some rodents) the placenta is highly invasive into the uterine lining, so much so that the fetal and maternal blood systems are separated only by a layer or two of tissues. In the majority of placentals, however, there are six distinct layers separating fetal and maternal blood. There is much variety in the form of the mammalian placenta as well as the types of placentation that we will not elaborate on here (see Mossman 1987 for more detail).

It is often stated that placentals differ from marsupials in the possession of a **chorioallantoic placenta**—that is, a placenta derived from the combination of the chorionic and allantoic amniote membranes. In contrast, marsupials are said to have a more primitive type of **yolk sac placenta** (the yolk sac being the embryonic membrane that is common to all vertebrates). However, the differences in types of placentas represent differences in developmental timing, not differences in possession of structures. All therians possess an initial yolk sac placenta, which may persist after the later chorioallantoic placenta has appeared (see Figure 21–14). While the yolk sac placenta is the only one usually seen in marsupials, some marsupials, most notably bandicoots, but also koalas and wombats to a certain extent, show a transitory chorioallantoic placenta near the end of gestation (Sharman 1976) (see Figure 21–15). The echidna also shows an elaboration of the chorioallantoic membrane within the egg

Figure 21–13 Mammalian neonates.
(a) Monotreme (echidna). (b) Marsupial (opossum). (c) Altricial placental
(rat). (d) Precocial placental (cow).
(Modified from M. Griffiths, 1968,
Echidnas, Pergamon Press, Oxford, UK,
and Nowak and Paradiso.)

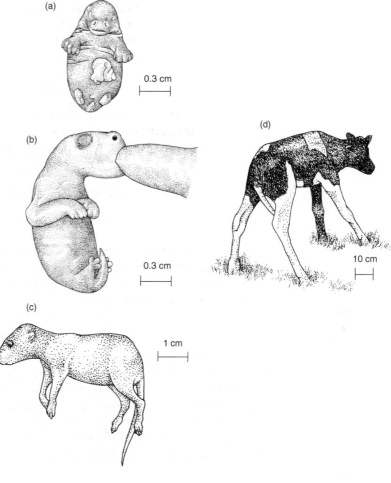

Figure 21–14 Mammalian placental
structure. Two types of placental structures as seen in a transitional stage of
an implanted embryo of a cat. Both a
yolk sac and a chorioallantoic placenta
are present at this stage. The chorioallantoic placenta grows outward and
takes over the function of the earlier-
forming yolk sac placenta. (Modified
after W. W. Ballard, 1964, *Comparative
Anatomy and Embryology*, Ronald Press,
New York, NY.)

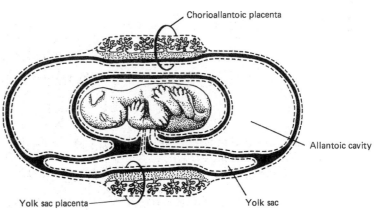

after laying (Tyndale-Biscoe and Renfree 1987). Of
course, all other egg-laying amniotes show an elaboration of the chorioallantoic membrane in development, as it is used for respiration within the egg
(see Chapter 10). The development of the marsupial
chorioallantoic membrane actually appears to have
been *suppressed*.

The use of the penis to pass urine as well as
sperm also appears to be a derived therian feature.
Note, however, that a bifid (forked) glans of the
penis is seen in monotremes and in most marsupials, as opposed to the single glans of placentals.

In all therians the ureters enter the base of the
bladder, rather than the cloaca or urogenital sinus as

Figure 21–15 Types of placentation in marsupials and placentals. (a) Egg-laying monotreme. (b) Dasyurid: the allantois reaches the chorion and then retreats from it without forming a placental structure. (c) Bandicoot: a complex chorioallantoic placenta is formed at the close of gestation and the yolk sac placenta remains functional until the young are born. (d) Possums and kangaroos: The allantois may grow to a large size but remains enshrouded in the folds of the yolk sac wall. (e) Koala and wombat: The allantois reaches the chorion forming an apposed chorioallantoic placenta. (f) Placental: yolk sac placenta is short-lived, and a complex chorioallantoic placenta is the functional one for most of the gestation. Key: 1 = vascular yolk sac placenta; 2 = non-vascular yolk sac placenta; 3 = syncytialized yolk sac placenta; 4 = apposed chorioallantoic placenta; 5 = syncytialized chorioallantoic placenta; Ac = allantoic cavity; EC = extraembryonic coelom; S = shell; YC = yolk sac cavity. (Modified from G. B. Sharman, 1976, in *Reproduction in Mammals, 6: The Evolution of Reproduction*, edited by C. R. Austin and R. V. Short, Cambridge University Press, Cambridge, UK.)

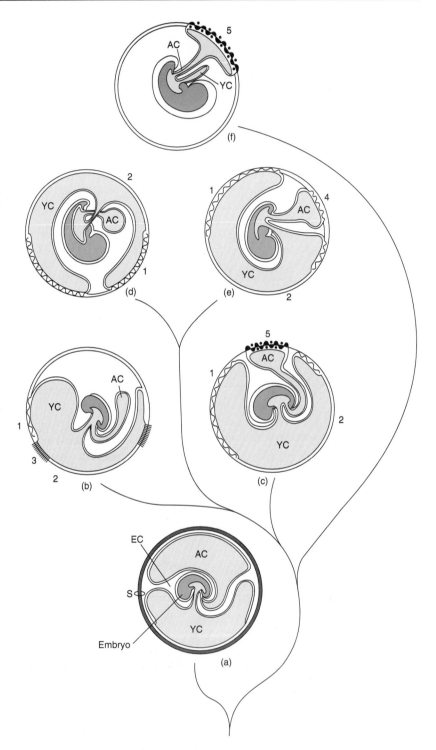

in other animals, and in the female, the oviducts are fused in the midline to a lesser or greater extent anterior to the urogenital sinus. However, both these features apparently evolved convergently in marsupials and placentals (see later). It may seem an odd feature of design that the ureters would not enter the bladder in vertebrates. However, it should be remembered (see Chapter 3) that while some type of tube draining the kidney is a feature of all vertebrates, a bladder is a tetrapod invention, as an outpocketing of the cloaca. Backwashing of the urine from the cloaca into the bladder may be a good enough design for most vertebrates; indeed, the bladder is lost in many nonmammalian amniotes, including most lepidosaurs and birds. However, in a viviparous mammal this arrangement might lead to backwashing of urine into the uterus, perhaps making a repositioning of the ureters adaptive at this evolutionary juncture (Renfree 1993).

In all therians parturition (giving birth) and lactation are under the control of hormones produced by the pituitary and hypothalamus, often with complicated feedback control loops. Hormone production by the embryo also plays a key role. The female may bear one or many young per litter. Single young are seen in both large and small mammals, but few larger mammals have large litters (although carnivorans tend to have largish litters while ungulates of a similar size have twins or a single young). In litter-producing mammals the young may be born in a single litter (semelpary), or in several litters spread over the mother's lifetime (iteropary).

Specializations of Placentals   In placentals the ureters pass laterally around the developing reproductive ducts to enter the bladder. This arrangement enables the oviducts of females to fuse in the midline for much of their length anteriorly to the urogenital sinus (Figure 21–12d), and also results in the vasa deferentia (the male reproductive tracts, singular = vas deferens) of the males looping around the ureters in their passage from the scrotum to the urogenital sinus (Figure 21–12e). All placentals have a single, midline vagina, but not all have the single median uterus seen in humans; most placentals have a uterus that is bipartite for some or all of its length, which may also occur as a developmental abnormality in humans.

In most placentals the urogenital sinus and the alimentary canal have separate openings with an external space between them, the perineum (edentates and some insectivorans are the exceptions here, with a more marsupiallike condition). The separation of female urogenital openings into distinct external urethral and vaginal openings is seen only in primates and some rodents.

The corpus luteum (or the corpora lutea, if more than one egg has been shed) is maintained for a longer period than one **estrus cycle** (the normal reproductive cycle of growth, maturation, and release of an egg) by hormones secreted by the pituitary and/or the placenta. (In humans and some other higher primates the estrus cycle is called the **menstrual cycle**, as it is associated with a periodic shedding of the uterine endometrial lining not seen in other mammals.) The maintenance of the corpus luteum allows placentals to retain the young in the uterus for a period greater than a single estrus cycle, in contrast to the marsupial condition (Renfree 1993). The length of the time of gestation is correlated with body size, larger placentals having longer gestation periods. All evidence of the egg shell has been lost.

Placentals may be born in a highly altricial state (i.e., poorly developed, as in many rodents and insectivorans), in which they are only slightly more developed than some marsupial young, or in more developed stages extending to a highly precocial state (i.e., well developed, as in most ungulates) in which the young can run within a few hours of birth (see Figure 21–13). All placentals, however precocial, still require a period of lactation for the transfer of essential antibodies from the mother as well as for nutrition. However, the period of lactation in placentals is relatively short in comparison with other mammals, usually shorter than the period of gestation.

Specializations of Marsupials   In marsupials the ureters pass medial to the developing reproductive ducts to enter the bladder. This arrangement prevents the oviducts of the females from fusing in the midline, at least more posteriorly, but means that the vasa deferentia of the males do not have to loop around the ureters (Figure 21–12c). The female reproductive tract consists of two lateral vaginae that unite medially anteriorly, from which point the two separate uteri diverge. The lateral vaginae are for the passage of sperm only. Birth of the young is through a midline structure, the median vagina or **pseudovaginal canal**, which develops at the first parturition (Figure 21–12b).

Although there is hormonal feedback from the embryonic trophoblast to the pituitary and hypothalamus alerting the mother to the state of pregnancy and influencing the secretory activity of the uterus, marsupials do not maintain the corpus luteum and the young are ejected at the end of the estrus cycle. The length of gestation in marsupials is relatively independent of body size (although the total time taken to rear the young is not). In contrast to placentals, marsupials retain direct evidence of their oviparous ancestry; a transient shell membrane is apparent, and some neonates have an egg tooth (Tyndale-Biscoe and Renfree 1987).

When the young are born, they must make their way from the vagina to attach themselves to a nipple to complete their development. Most, but not all, marsupials enclose these nipples within a pouch. A pouch is absent in some dasyurids (marsupial mice, etc.) and some didelphids (opossums). The primitive mode appears to be the one seen in macropodids (kangaroos, etc.), in which the young climbs up to the pouch unaided, and the forelimbs are considerably more developed than the hindlimbs at this point in time to aid with the climb. The mother adopts a distinct sitting birth posture at parturition (see Figure 21–16a, b), and licks a path from the vagina to the pouch, but does not otherwise aid the young in its journey. Marsupial neonates are evidently equipped with an instinct to climb in an antigravity fashion, straight upward. The condition in some dasyurids and didelphids, where even more highly altricial young are ejected directly into the pouch (or mammary area, if pouchless) at birth and the young are passive in this process, is probably the derived one within marsupials (Renfree 1993).

The amount of time that marsupial young spend developing while attached to the nipple greatly exceeds the time of gestation. Lactation also continues for some time after the young have become sufficiently mature to detach from the nipple. This is when we typically see the pouched young, such as in the kangaroo baby or joey, which may be observed to hop in and out of the pouch. Although the composition of the milk also varies during pregnancy in placentals, there is a still more marked variation in marsupials (and also in monotremes). The first milk is more dilute and more protein rich, while the later milk is more concentrated and richer in fats. In some kangaroos asynchronous lactation has been observed; an immature pouch young attached to the nipple can exist concurrently with a more mature, independent pouch young, and the mother produces different kinds of milk at the appropriate nipples (Renfree 1993) (see Figure 21–16c). The control and regulation of this is unclear, but presumably some feedback loop, such as the amount of time spent suckling, is involved.

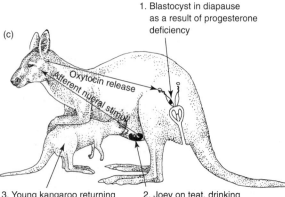

1. Blastocyst in diapause as a result of progesterone deficiency

Oxytocin release

Afferent nueral stimulus

3. Young kangaroo returning to drink low-protein, high-fat milk

2. Joey on teat, drinking high protein low-fat milk, and inhibiting corpus luteum via suckling stimulus

Figure 21–16   Birth posture and embryonic diapause in kangaroos. (a) Birth posture of red kangaroo. (b) Birth posture of gray kangaroo. (c) Red kangaroo with three different young at three different stages of development. (Modified from G. B. Sharman, 1976, in *Reproduction in Mammals, 6: The Evolution of Reproduction*, edited by C. R. Austin and R. V. Short, Cambridge University Press, Cambridge, UK. and R.V. Short, 1972, in *Reproduction in Mammals, 2: Reproductive Patterns*, edited by C. R. Austin and R. V. Short, Cambridge University Press, Cambridge, UK.)

The Primitive Therian Condition   Given the fact that the young of both monotremes and marsupials are highly altricial, this is probably the primitive condition for mammals in general, and also for therians. Altricial young may be adaptive for small, endothermic vertebrates. These young are essentially ectothermic as neonates (newborns), with a correspondingly low metabolic rate; parental brooding keeps them warm, and because of their low metabolic rate a high proportion of the food provided by the parents is converted into body tissue (Hopson 1973). Of course, the production of such altricial young, whether from eggs or by live birth, is dependent on the existence of lactation and parental care, and so is likely to be a derived mammalian feature rather than one inherited from cynodonts (see Chapter 19).

Viviparity was probably a feature of the earliest therians. The specializations of the reproductive anatomy of marsupials and placentals cannot be derived from each other; they must represent separate evolutionary histories in each group. Possibly the adoption of viviparity in the common ancestor of marsupials and placentals stimulated the migration of the ureters to the base of the bladder separately in the two types of mammals, with different consequences for the subsequent possible morphologies of the reproductive tracts. The early therians of the Cretaceous period were small animals, less than a kilogram in body mass, and are likely to have had the life-history features shared by small living therians: short life span, several litters produced in rapid succession (or a single large litter), and a short gestation period. Some fetal placentals show evidence of mouth seals—tissue that develops around the lateral margins of the mouth of neonatal marsupials to aid in attachment to the nipples. This feature might be taken to suggest that an attachment to a nipple is a primitive therian feature. However, a pouch is definitely a derived feature of marsupials, as previously discussed. Indeed, a pouch may even have been evolved independently on different occasions within marsupials, as it is absent in many primitive marsupials, and differs in form in different derived lineages.

Another reproductive feature that may be primitive for therians is the capacity for **embryonic diapause**. This is the maintenance of the embryo in a state of suspended animation prior to implantation, and it enables the mother to space out successive litters and to disassociate the time of mating and fertilization from the inception of gestation. This system is particularly well developed in kangaroos (see Figure 21–16c), and so has often been perceived as a derived marsupial feature. However, embryonic diapause is seen in a wide variety of placentals as well as marsupials, and is likely to be a primitive therian trait.

Some Extreme Reproductive Specializations   Numerous interesting reproductive specializations exist among the diversity of living placentals. Among the most bizarre are those seen in the naked mole rat (*Heterocephalus glaber*) (Jarvis 1981) (see Figure 21–10d) and the spotted hyena (*Crocuta crocuta*) (Frank 1996) (see Figure 21–10f).

Naked mole rats are found in arid areas in sub-Saharan Africa, and live as underground burrowers feeding on plant roots and tubers. They are eusocial, a type of social system otherwise seen only in social insects such as ants, termites, and bees. Like these insects, animals within a colony are closely related but, unlike the insects, they are all diploid in chromosomal structure. The mole rats live in colonies of up to 40 individuals where there is only one breeding female, the queen. The queen somehow hormonally suppresses the breeding of the other female members of the colony, and produces one to four litters per year with up to two dozen young in each litter. Other colony members are divided into three social castes: the smaller frequent workers that engage in cooperative burrowing and feed the community; the infrequent workers (also small) whose role is similar, but who appear to do only about 25% of the work of the other workers; and the larger nonworkers that only care for the young. All the males produce sperm, but only the nonworkers are large enough to successfully copulate with the queen. If the queen dies, one of the faster-growing infrequent worker females may become the new queen. The adaptive advantages of this social structure may relate to sharing energy costs and reducing metabolic rates (as they huddle together for warmth) in conditions of sparse food supply and long periods of seasonal aridity.

Spotted hyenas, found in the African savannas, are the only hyenas that regularly hunt in packs, and they also have females with masculinized genitalia. For many years it was mistakenly thought that these hyenas were hermaphrodites. The clitoris is so enlarged that it resembles a male penis (complete with the capacity for erection), and the labia are fused to form a structure resembling a scrotum. Various adaptive hypotheses have been proposed for these features, but it is unlikely that the appearance of the external genitalia themselves is adaptive. Rather, it appears that the advantage is that high levels of androgens are advantageous for females because they cause aggressive behavior, in an ecological situation (perhaps recently encountered in evolution) where food is short and more aggressive females and their offspring obtain more than their share of food during communal predation. These high levels of testosterone would have the side effect of masculinizing the females' genitalia during development. Although hyena females may use their genitalia for behavioral display, there are clearly many disadvantages to this condition; all the functions of the original urogenital sinus must now be transmitted through this penislike structure. Thus female hyenas must not only urinate through the enlarged clitoris, they must also copulate and give birth through this structure. Perhaps unsurprisingly there is a high incidence of mortality among females giving birth for the first time.

Are Placentals Reproductively Superior to Marsupials?

It used to be considered that the marsupial mode of reproduction was inferior to that of placentals. This conclusion was based primarily on the reasoning that marsupials had been unable to compete with placentals except in Australia, where they had evolved in isolation (but see Chapter 20 for a discussion of the fallacies of this type of argumentation). It was claimed that marsupials were unable to maintain the young in the uterus past one estrus cycle because the mother was unable to recognize the condition of pregnancy, due to the lack of the evolution of hormonal feedback between the developing young and the maternal brain. But we now know that hormonal feedback of this nature does, in fact, exist in marsupials even though they lack the extended gestation of placentals. It has also been argued that the lack of midline fusion of the oviducts in marsupials would make it impossible for them to carry large young to full term. However, many placentals have uteri that are completely separate without evidence of midline fusion; separate uteri are seen, for example, in cows, which no-one would accuse of giving birth to small young. It seems more likely that, rather than the marsupial reproductive mode being some primitive therian condition or an inferior version of the placental condition, marsupials and placentals evolved different but essentially equal reproductive strate-

gies. Marsupials capitalized on the development of a pouch and extended postgestation lactation, while placentals capitalized on the prolongation of intrauterine life (Renfree 1993).

In the past couple of decades an alternative viewpoint of marsupial reproduction has developed; that is, that marsupial reproduction may be superior under some conditions (e.g., Kirsch 1977, Parker 1977). For example, kangaroos have been observed to eject pouch young while fleeing predators (actually, humans chasing them in cars, there are no native pursuit predators in Australia), and it has been suggested that this could provide an adaptive advantage. In this type of situation the marsupial mother, freed from the burden of carrying her young, could escape to breed again, whereas in the case of a pregnant placental both mother and young would perish.

An alternative advantage has been proposed concerning the fact that it takes a marsupial longer to produce a young to full independence (i.e., the end of lactation) than a placental of similar body size (this is in part because the transfer of nutrients via the milk is less efficient than across the placenta). Both marsupial and placental mothers invest a comparable amount of resources in their young, but at any given body size it takes a marsupial about half as long again from the time of conception to the time of weaning as it does for a placental (Lillegraven et al. 1987). It has been argued that the slower rate of resource investment in marsupials to the developing young means that, should the young die prematurely at some point in the process, the marsupial has invested less up to that point in time than the placental, and so has lost less overall.

For example, imagine that a marsupial and a placental both conceive a litter in March, and then experience a sudden dry spell in June, resulting in the death of the young. The placental, who had been investing more food to develop the litter more rapidly, might be worse off than the marsupial, who had not devoted so many resources to its young. At this point in time, the marsupial might have more reserves left (e.g., stored fat supply) to conceive again immediately, whereas the placental would not. This feature of marsupial reproduction has been proposed as being adaptive in arid, unpredictable climates, such as those found in Australia, where a sudden drought might disrupt the ability to provide the young with sufficient resources for survival.

One critical problem with these arguments, and with other similar ones, is that they consider only the case of present-day mammals. But in considering the possible evolutionary reasons for the development of marsupial or placental reproductive strategies, we must consider them at the time of divergence, back in the Early Cretaceous. The ability to dump the pouch young if pursued is unlikely to be adaptive for a small mammal having but a single litter per lifetime (as seen in many extant dasyurids). Likewise, harsh, arid climates were not a feature of the Cretaceous. Australia did not develop its arid interior until the late Cenozoic, and marsupials did not even reach Australia until early Cenozoic. As previously discussed, in the small primitive therians, these reproductive strategies were likely to represent perfectly good, if different, modes of achieving the same goal.

Is there any feature of marsupial reproduction that would make their potential adaptive diversity different from placentals at the point in the Cenozoic when mammals became larger and diversified into a greater variety of ecomorphological types? The lack of marsupial species diversity (about six percent that of placentals) has been pointed to as an example of evolutionary inferiority but, as a result of historically contingent factors, marsupials have had less land area to evolve on during the later Cenozoic, and so would be expected to have produced a lesser diversity of species (Kirsch 1977). The disappearance of much of the original marsupial diversity in South America has also been used as evidence of marsupial inferiority, but the South American native placentals have suffered a similar loss. Marsupials also have a low diploid chromosome number, which has been claimed to limit their capacity for evolutionary variability (Lillegraven 1979), but low chromosome numbers may also be seen among placentals, even if the average number is greater.

One ecomorphological mode that is probably impossible for a marsupial to achieve is that of a fully aquatic mammal, such as a whale, because of carrying altricial young in a pouch where they would be unable to breathe air. There is one semiaquatic marsupial, the South American yapok, which seals up its pouch on underwater forays, but in general marsupials have avoided aquatic situations. It is also hard to imagine a marsupial giving birth under water in the fashion of a whale,—the tiny neonates would probably be swept away by currents before they could reach the pouch. True

flight has not been evolved by any marsupial, but flight has evolved only once among placentals, so this could just be a matter of chance. In contrast, placentals have evolved semiaquatic and fully aquatic forms numerous times in parallel, and the relative absence of this mode of life among marsupials may represent a genuine constraint.

The mode of marsupial birth might limit the size of the adults. There are no marsupials with a body mass greater than around 90 kg today, and in the past only a very few were larger than this. The biggest were the bison-size diprotodontids—no marsupial ever reached the size of a rhino or an elephant. The birth posture (see Figure 21–16) might be difficult to adopt for a large animal, and the neonate would have a much greater absolute distance to climb to reach the nipples (Lillegraven 1979). It has also been suggested that the need for marsupials to have well-developed forelimbs with large claws at birth (in order to climb up to the pouch) has somehow constrained the possibilities of later morphological adaptations of those limbs. This may limit the formation of flippers or wings, although as discussed earlier there are other reasons for the absence of aquatic or flying marsupials. It might also limit the type of cursorial (running-adapted) morphologies seen in ungulate placental mammals (see later description), where the number of digits has been reduced to one or two. This might explain why the marsupial ungulate-equivalents, the kangaroos, hop with specialized hind legs but retain rather unspecialized fore legs, in contrast to the running placentals which specialize both fore and hind legs.

Lillegraven et al. (1987) argued for a placental advantage in the elevation of basal metabolic rates, which would be especially advantageous at small body sizes. They claimed that high metabolic rates of placentals enable an increased rate of intrauterine development, and hence the capacity for greater reproductive output and reproductive turnover. Increased intrauterine development would also shorten the period necessary for lactation, a more expensive process to the mother than gestation (because of the less efficient transfer of nutrients). An increased metabolic rate would not aid in increasing the rapidity of marsupial development due to their commitment to a prolonged period of lactation. The prolonged period of intrauterine development may also be essential for the evolution of the large brain seen in some, but by no means all, placentals. Thus although the marsupial mode of reproduction may not be adaptively inferior overall, the placental mode may enable placentals to diversify in certain ways that are not an option for marsupials.

■ Adaptations for Feeding

We saw in Chapter 19 that mammals have a number of specialized features of the skull and teeth. Inherited from their cynodont ancestors was a differentiated dentition (incisors, canines, and postcanine teeth), with the original external adductor musculature mass split into masseter and temporalis muscles. The presence of the masseter muscle gives mammals their characteristic ability to move their jaws sideways when chewing. The earliest mammals showed the further division of the postcanine teeth into premolars and molars, and the condition of diphyodonty, where the teeth are replaced only once (except for the molars, which are not replaced). Finally, therian mammals share the derived feature of tribosphenic molars, teeth which add grinding and crushing functions to the original mammalian dental function of shearing.

The mastication of food is exceedingly important for mammals. As endotherms they rely on mastication to reduce the particle size of swallowed food to speed up the digestive processes. Birds manage to be endothermic without teeth, of course, but they have a gizzard within the digestive tract to grind up their food (Chapter 17). Some other amniotes show evidence of mastication, for example some herbivorous dinosaurs. But all mammals masticate their food, not just herbivores and, as previously described, all mammals have a distinct swallowing reflex whereby they ingest a discrete bolus of finely chewed food. The mammal tongue, important in both oral food processing and in swallowing, also has a unique system of intrinsic muscles. Also important in this process are the muscular cheeks, whose muscles are derived from the uniquely mammalian set of facial muscles earlier described.

Dentition

Mammalian teeth are formed like those of other vertebrates, and have a thecodont type of rooting in the jaw bone (see Chapter 3). A typical mammalian molar is shown in Figure 21–17a. The mammalian dental formula was described earlier, in the context of differences between marsupials and pla-

centals. Mammals usually use their incisors to seize food, their canines to stab prey items, premolars to initially break down food via piercing and crushing, and their molars to finely break down the food via mastication. The ancestral form of the tribosphenic molar has a triangular (trituberular) crown (Figure 21–17d).

The incisors of mammals that gnaw, such as rodents and rabbits, may be enormously enlarged and grow continuously throughout life. Rodent incisors have enamel only on the anterior surface; because the enamel is the hardest part of the tooth it wears more slowly than the dentine behind it, producing a self-sharpening chisel edge (see Figure 21–17b, c).

Canines are often lost in herbivores, which have no need to subdue their food items, but they may be retained in modified form. The tusks of pigs and walruses are modified canines (but the tusks of elephants are modified incisors). Ruminant artiodactyls incorporate the lower canine into the incisor row, so that they appear to have a total of eight lower incisors (the upper incisors are replaced by a horny pad). Male horses may have small, apparently functionless canines, but these are rarely seen in females. Upper canines are generally larger in male primates than in females, even slightly so in humans. Hornless ruminants, such as the mouse deer (Figure 21–10h), may retain large upper canines in the male for fighting and display.

The molars and premolars are usually different in form. Primitively premolars are single-cusped slicing or puncturing teeth, while molars are three-cusped (or more) teeth for more thorough food processing. In many herbivores the entire postcanine tooth row is used for general mastication, and the premolars become modified to resemble the molars (molarized). This condition can be seen in ruminant artiodactyls to a certain extent, and especially in horses where all the postcanine teeth appear identical.

Omnivorous and fruit-eating mammals have reduced the originally pointy cusps of their molars to rounded, flattened structures, more suitable for crushing and pulping than for piercing and shearing. They also add a fourth cusp to the upper molars, and increase the size of the talonid basin in the lower molars, so that these teeth now appear square in form (quadrituberular), rather than triangular. These teeth are called **bunodont** (*buno* = a hill or mound) in reference to the rounded cusps (Figure 21–17e). We have bunodont molars, as do

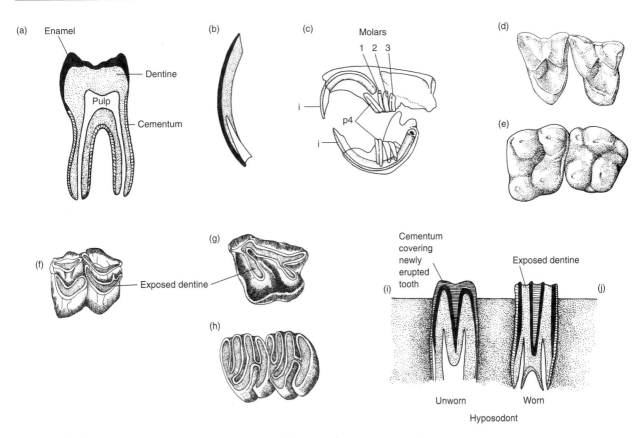

Figure 21–17   The structure of mammalian teeth. (a) Sectioned mammalian molar showing general dental form. (b) Sectioned rodent ever-growing incisor, showing enamel on anterior surface only. (c) Sectioned rodent skull, showing ever-growing incisors, and ever-growing (hypselodont) cheek teeth. (d) Tritubercular upper molar, as found in the primitive mammalian condition. (e) Bunodont, quadritubercular upper molars, as found in omnivorous mammals. (f) Selenodont upper molar of a deer. (g) Lophodont upper molar of a rhino. (h) Multilophed upper molars of a rodent. (i) Sectioned unworn hypsodont molar, showing covering of cementum. (j) Worn hypsodont molar, showing sharp enamel ridges interspersed with softer areas of dentine and cementum. (Modified from various sources, including C. M. Janis and M. Fortelius, 1988, *Biological Reviews* 63:197-230, and T. A. Vaughan, 1986, *Mammalogy*, 3rd. edition, Saunders, Philadelphia, PA.)

most other primates, and other omnivores such as pigs and raccoons.

Herbivorous mammals are derived from omnivorous ones (see Figure 21–18). Herbivores need the molars to grind up flat, fibrous food rather than to pulp and crush the food in the function of the bunodont molars of omnivores. In order to effect this grinding they have molars in which the simple cusps of the bunodont form of tooth have been run together into ridges, or **lophs**. These lophed molars are designed to function best after some initial wear, when the enamel has been worn off the top of the ridges to reveal the underlying dentine, so that each ridge then consists of a pair of sharp

enamel blades lying either side of the intervening dentine (see Figure 21-17 f, g, h, j). When these teeth occlude and the jaws move sideways the food encounters multiple sets of flat, shearing blades, in a manner analogous to cheese moving over a cheese grater.

Different lineages of herbivorous mammals have evolved these lophed teeth convergently, and we use different terminologies to describe them. The teeth of perissodactyls (and also hyraxes) have straight lophs that run predominantly in a lateral to medial direction across the teeth; these teeth are termed **lophodont** (Figure 21–17g). The teeth of ruminant artiodactyls have crescentic lophs that run

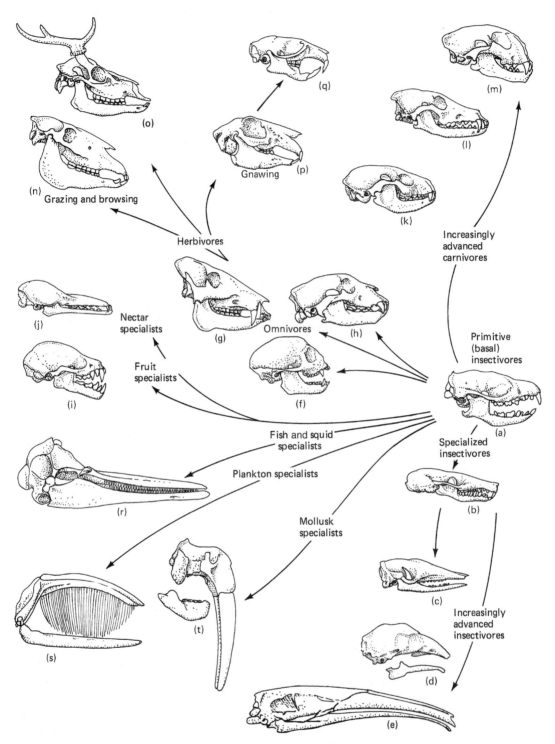

Figure 21–18 Feeding specializations of the teeth and skulls of mammals: (a) hedgehog, (b) mole, (c) armadillo, (d) anteater, (e) giant anteater, (f) marmoset, (g) peccary, (h) bear, (i) fruit-eating bat, (j) nectar-eating bat, (k) raccoon, (l) coyote, (m) mountain lion, (n) horse, (o) deer, (p) jackrabbit, (q) woodrat, (r) porpoise, (s) right whale, (t) walrus. See text for details.

in a predominantly anterior to posterior direction across the teeth; these teeth are termed **selenodont** (Figure 21–17f). There is probably no significant difference in the function of these teeth, their difference in form merely reflects difference in ancestry. Among other herbivorous mammals, kangaroos and rabbits have a form of lophodont molars; koalas a form of selenodont molars; and wombats, rodents, warthogs, and elephants a highly complex form of molars termed multi-lophed or lamellar (Figure 21–17h) (Janis and Fortelius 1988).

All herbivorous mammals face a similar problem with their teeth, that of dental durability. Durability of the dentition is not an issue for most vertebrates, which continually replace their teeth. But all mammals have inherited the condition of diphyodonty (a single set of replacement teeth) from their original ancestor. Diphodonty was probably essential for precise occlusion in early mammals (see discussion in Chapter 19), but it presents a problem in that the adult dentition must now last a lifetime. Herbivores face a particular problem in that vegetation is more abrasive than other forms of food, especially grass which contains silica in its cell wall.

There are a variety of ways in which herbivorous mammals render their dentition more durable (Janis and Fortelius 1988). In the manatee (a sirenian) and in the narbelek (a rock wallaby), the normal mode of bringing in the molars from the back of the jaw is tricked into making a continual supply of molars that replace the worn teeth, which then drop out of the front of the jaw. Elephants do something similar, although they have not added extra teeth. Instead, they make each molar enormous, the size of the entire original tooth row, and bring in a total of six molars (three milk molars and three permanent molars) one at a time during an animal's lifetime. However, the most common mode of making the molars more durable is to make them high crowned or **hypsodont** (Figure 21–17 i, j). The opposite of hypsodont, the primitive default mode for teeth, is low crowned or **brachydont**.

Hypsodont cheek teeth look like regular teeth when you see them in the jaw, but you can't see the division at the base between the crown and the root as with brachydont teeth. The crowns of the teeth have been extended into the depth of the jaw bones, and the skull may be highly modified to accommodate this. This condition can be seen in the very deep lower jaw, the deep cheek region, and the posteriorly moved orbit of the horse (Fig-

ure 21–18n).These modifications provide room to accommodate the very high-crowned cheek teeth. Hypsodont teeth also extend the layer of cementum, a bonelike material, which in most mammals only covers the root and the base of the crown (Figure 21–17a) so that it covers the entire tooth (Figure 21-17i). This is done for mechanical reasons; the high lophs of the teeth must be laid down during tooth development, before the tooth erupts. Without cementum acting as filler, the individual lophs would be like tall free-standing blades once the tooth had erupted, liable to fracture. As the animal ages and wears down the teeth, the teeth push up from the base to provide a continuous occlusal surface, much like the way that lead pushes out of an mechanical pencil.

Most hypsodont mammals have a finite amount of tooth crown, and when the tooth is worn out the animals can no longer eat (although it will normally have died of natural causes long before this event). However, some mammals have molars in which the roots do not close, and the tooth is functionally ever-growing or **hypselodont**. For a variety of reasons, this appears to be an option primarily for small mammals (Janis and Fortelius 1988). Hypselodont molars are seen most commonly in rabbits and some rodents, and are also present in wombats, dugongs, and sloths (in the latter case it is the root that is continually growing, not the crown).

Craniodental Specializations in Mammals

Figure 21–18 shows a variety of mammalian skulls arranged according to trophic specializations. The hedgehog (Figure 21–18a) shows the generalized insectivorous condition that can be taken to represent the primitive mammalian mode. The opossum (Figure 21–7a) is also a good example. The molars of generalized mammals retain usually the primitive triangular shape, with pointed individual cusps, that are useful for puncturing insect cuticle.

Mammals that are specialized myrmecophages (*myrme* = ant, *phago* = to eat) tend to elongate the jaws and progressively reduce the teeth (shown in the trajectory from the armadillo to the giant anteater in Figure 21–18). In addition to long snouts, they also have enlarged salivary glands and highly elongated tongues. Myrmecophageous mammals usually specialize on ripping apart termite mounds, and have digging adaptations for this purpose (see later description). Reduction of the teeth is also seen in mammals that specialize on nectar (e.g. some bats, Figure 21–18j).

Aquatic fish-eating or squid-eating mammals such as porpoises and dolphins (Figure 21–18r) have highly elongate jaws where the anterior-most teeth have been lost and the remaining teeth are single-cusped and pointed in form, and greatly increased in number. Their skulls and teeth have become convergent with other aquatic carnivorous tetrapods such as ichthyosaurs and crocodiles. Seals show some modifications in the same direction, but retain a full complement of anterior teeth. The baleen whales (mysticetes) have replaced their teeth with sheets of a fibrous, stiff, hornlike epidermal derivative known as baleen which extend downward from the upper jaw (Figure 21–18s). These whales filter-feed, using the baleen to strain planktonic organisms from the water. The walrus (Figure 21–18t) feeds on mollusks, and its postcanine teeth are flat for crushing their shells (the enormous canine tusks are used mainly for display).

Differences Between Carnivores and Herbivores

The basic mode of mammalian mastication is best understood by considering the difference between carnivorous and herbivorous mammals (see Figure 21–19). All mammals use a combination of masseter, temporalis, and pterygoideus muscles to close the jaws, and the digastric (in therians) and hypobranchial muscles (see Chapter 3) to open the jaw. But the balance of the muscles used, especially in jaw closing, and the shape of the skulls, reflects the different demands of masticating flesh and masticating vegetation. The temporalis is situated so that it has a better mechanical advantage at initiating jaw closure at moderate to large gapes, when the incisors and canines are likely to be used. Thus a large temporalis is typical of carnivores, which employ force with their canines to kill and subdue prey. The masseter is situated so that its line of action creates forces closer to the back of the tooth row, and also to move the jaw sideways. Thus a large masseter is typical of herbivores, which grind up their fibrous food using lateral jaw movements and complex molars.

Carnivorous mammals (and most generalized mammals, like the opossum [Figure 21–7a]) have a fairly large temporalis muscle and a large coronoid process of the jaw for its insertion. The temporal fossa on the skull is also large for the origin of this muscle, and a sagittal crest along the midline of the

skull may increase the area of origin of the temporalis. The masseter muscle is of moderate size. The jaw joint is on the same level as the tooth row, as in the primitive mammalian condition. This position of the jaw joint results in the teeth coming into contact sequentially with jaw closing, like the blades of a pair of scissors—a design well-suited for teeth that primarily cut and shear (see Figure 21–19b).

An additional specialization of mammals in the order Carnivora is in the dentition. A pair of teeth, the last premolar in the upper jaw and the first molar in the lower jaw, have been modified into set of tightly shearing blades, the **carnassials** (Figure 21–19f). Carnivorous mammals also have specialized modifications of the jaw joint (the postglenoid process) to prevent the strong temporalis muscle from dislocating the lower jaw. They also tend to have a high occipital (back of the head) region, reflecting extensive musculature linking the head to the neck. This musculature is probably important for resisting struggling prey. The extinct saber-toothed carnivores had extremely high occipital regions.

The skull of herbivorous mammals is more modified than that of carnivorous ones, which is closer to the primitive mammalian type in many respects. Herbivores must have skulls and teeth modified to grind up tough, resistant food, and also have modifications of the digestive system to aid in coping with a diet of plant matter. Plant food is much more abundant than animal food and it does not run away, but the energy content of plant material is generally lower than that of animal tissues. The protein content of leaves and stems is usually low, and the protein is enclosed by a tough carbohydrate cell wall. Although specialized teeth can rupture the leaves and expose the cells, only enzymes (cellulases) can break through the cellulose protecting the cytoplasm. However, no multicellular animal has the ability to synthesize cellulases. Thus the efficient use of plants as food requires indirect attack on the cell walls by enzymes produced by microorganisms that live as symbionts in the guts of herbivorous animals. Several different types of mammals have independently evolved chambers within the digestive tract to house symbiotic microorganisms that convert the cellulose and lignin of plant cell walls into digestible nutrients (see Box 21–1).

Herbivorous mammals have increased the size of the masseter and reduced the size of the temporalis in comparison with the primitive mammalian condition. These differences in musculature are reflected in the increased size of the angle of the lower jaw (for the insertion of the masseter), and the reduced size of the coronoid process and temporal fossa. The jaw joint has been shifted so that it is offset from the tooth row, and is situated higher up on the skull. This offsetting of the jaw joint means that the part of the jaw between the tooth row and the joint can act as a sort of handle, increasing the moment arm for the action of the masseter muscle, and allowing the teeth to be occluded simultaneously for grinding rather than sequentially (much as the offset handle of a cooking spatula allows you to apply the entire blade of the spatula to the bottom of the frying pan while keeping your hand above pan's rim) (see Figure 21–19d). Some herbivorous dinosaurs also had offset jaw joints, but in this case the jaw joint was below the level of the tooth row. It is the offsetting of the jaw joint from the tooth row that is the important mechanical feature, not whether the joint is above or below the row.

Herbivores also usually have elongated snouts, resulting in a gap between the cheek teeth and the incisors called the **diastema**. (If horses did not have a diastema, we would not be able to put a bit in their mouths.) The actual function of the diastema is uncertain. It may allow extra space for the tongue to manipulate food, or it may just be a reflection of the elongation of the jaw for other reasons. A long jaw enables the animal to select food with its incisors without poking its eye on the vegetation; note that herbivores that can use their hands to select food, such as monkeys, rodents and even kangaroos, have shorter faces than most ungulates. Many herbivorous placental mammals also ossify the cartilaginous partition at the back of the orbit, to form a bony **postorbital bar**. Herbivores usually have a fairly low occipital region as they do not need to have extensive head-on-neck movements. An exception is pigs, which root with their snout and have extensive musculature linking the back of the head to the neck.

Many rodents have a highly specialized type of food processing. Their upper and lower tooth rows are the same distance apart (isognathous), rather than the condition in most mammals where the lower tooth rows are closer together than the uppers (see Chapter 19). This derived condition in rodents is combined with a rounded jaw condyle, which allows forward and backward jaw movement and the insertion of a portion of the masseter muscle far forward on the skull, so that the lower jaw can be pulled forward into occlusion (Figure

21–19e). This jaw apparatus allows rodents to chew on both sides of the jaw at once, presumably a highly efficient mode of food processing. Note that this mode of chewing can be achieved only with flattened, lamellar teeth (Figure 21–17h), as the high ridges of other types of teeth would prevent this jaw motion. Elephants, which also possess lamellar teeth, chew in a somewhat similar manner, but they have obviously evolved this capacity convergently with the rodent condition, and the musculature arrangement is different.

■ Adaptations for Locomotion

As we saw in Chapter 3, the specialized rapid mammalian gait is the bound, leaping from the hind feet to the fore feet with flexion of the backbone. The tree shrew illustrated in Figure 21–21 provides a good example of the skeletal structure of a small, generalized mammal adapted for a mixture of terrestrial and arboreal locomotion (**scansorial**), and shows how the bounding gait appears in a small mammal of this type. Bounding is an asymmetric gait: that is, the movements of the two feet of a diagonal pair (fore and hind) are unevenly spaced in time. Other mammalian gaits, such as the walk and the trot, are symmetrical—the movements of the two feet of a pair are evenly spaced in time. During bounding (and also during cantering and galloping, the modified versions of bounding employed by larger mammals) the hind limb are used together to launch the animal into the air, and it lands on its front feet.

The tree shrew illustrates the mode in which the limbs and back are flexed during locomotion in small mammals. In larger mammals the limbs are held in a less flexed position and the back is less arched, due to the increased stress experienced on the bones by larger animals (Biewener 1989). A mammal the size of a horse stands and moves with relatively stiff, straight legs, and gallops rather than bounds (there is no period of leaping through the air with all four legs outstretched in the gallop) (see Figure 21–21c). In a mammal the size of an elephant, the legs are virtually pillarlike and the fastest gait is a rapid walk (see Chapter 3).

Asymmetric gaits permit coupling of locomotion and respiration (the exact opposite of the problem initially facing early tetrapods in fast locomotion, see Chapter 19). As the animal leaps off the hind legs, the liver and other viscera are pushed back-

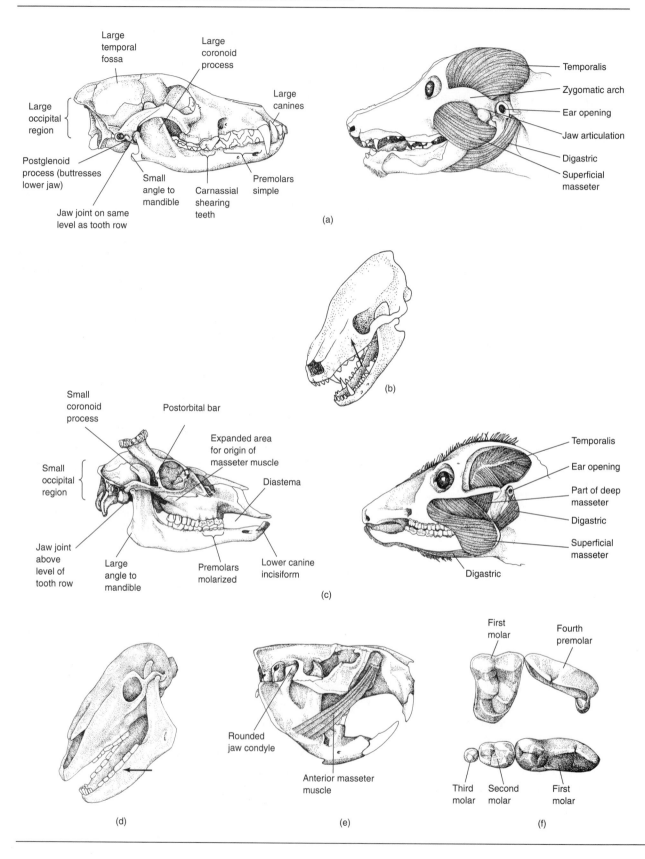

Large temporal fossa

Large coronoid process

Large canines

Large occipital region

Postglenoid process (buttresses lower jaw)

Small angle to mandible

Carnassial shearing teeth

Premolars simple

Jaw joint on same level as tooth row

Temporalis

Zygomatic arch

Ear opening

Jaw articulation

Digastric

Superficial masseter

(a)

(b)

Small coronoid process

Postorbital bar

Expanded area for origin of masseter muscle

Diastema

Small occipital region

Jaw joint above level of tooth row

Large angle to mandible

Premolars molarized

Lower canine incisiform

Temporalis

Ear opening

Part of deep masseter

Digastric

Superficial masseter

Digastric

(c)

Rounded jaw condyle

Anterior masseter muscle

First molar

Fourth premolar

Third molar

Second molar

First molar

(d)

(e)

(f)

wards, helping with the expansion of the thorax in inspiration. When the animal lands on its fore legs the viscera are pushed forward onto the diaphragm, helping with expiration (see Figure 19–13). This locomotor/respiratory coupling in mammals means that a breath is taken at each stride (Bramble and Jenkins 1989). With our bipedal gait we no longer have this advantage, and our breathing is decoupled from our locomotion. A side effect of this is, however, that big mammals must breathe at a rate that is quite rapid during locomotion. If you ride a galloping horse you may notice that the horse is taking a breath every stride, breathing out when the forelimbs hit the ground, but you actually breathe much less frequently than that, about once for every three or four horse strides. It is not known if this coupling imposes any kind of limitation on large, cursorial mammals.

The earliest mammals had already lost the lumbar ribs, a condition inherited from their cynodont ancestors, and so potentially had the ability for this bounding type of motion. However, it seems likely that the type of bounding seen in the tree shrew was not evolved until the appearance of therians, with their distinctive modifications of the shoulder girdle (see later). All mammals share a derived type of pelvis, with the reduction of the pubo-ischiadic plate of cynodonts, and the streamlining of the broad ilium to a forward-pointing, rod-shaped one (see Figure 19–11 and Figure 21–6). This may reflect the realigning of the hip muscles to enhance propulsive thrust, and a repositioning of the limbs closer together to better allow for an asymmetric bounding gait (Bramble and Jenkins 1989). Thus, some sort of asymmetrical gait may have been present in the earliest mammals.

Shoulder Specializations of Therian Mammals

A locomotor specialization of therian mammals is seen in the reduction of the elements of the shoulder girdle so that only the scapula and (sometimes) the clavicle remain (see earlier discussion and Figure 21–6). This reduction or loss of the ventral elements of the original girdle allows the scapula to move as an independent limb segment around its dorsal border, probably adding to the length of the stride during bounding and contributing to the shock-absorbing capacity of the front limbs. This change in shoulder morphology would allow more independent movement of the forelimbs and may be important for nonlocomotory use of the forelimbs in therians, such as feeding and grooming (Bramble and Jenkins 1989). The shoulder musculature has also been reorganized to reflect this change in function (Figure 21–22). A muscle that originally protracted the humerus on the shoulder girdle, the supracoracoideus, has been modified into two new muscles, the infraspinatus and supraspinatus, that may help to stabilize the limb on the shoulder girdle during bounding. (The supracoracoideus became modified in a different fashion in birds to form a wing elevator, see Chapter 17.) Additionally some of the hypaxial wall muscles have become modified into the serratus and rhomboideus muscles, running between the scapula and the axial skeleton. These muscles, together with the trapezius and pectoralis muscles found in other tetrapods, hold the limb girdle in a muscular **scapular sling**. This muscle arrangement probably also aids with scapular mobility during locomotion and cushions the impact of the weight of the body landing on the front limbs during bounding. The mammalian type of bounding gait may be dependent on this modification of the shoulder girdle anatomy and musculature (Bramble and Jenkins 1989).

Adaptations for Specialized Forms of Locomotion

The basic form of mammalian locomotion is the bounding and scrambling of small, scansorial mammals such as tree shrews and squirrels. However, larger mammals are usually modified for

Figure 21–19 Craniodental differences between carnivorous and herbivorous mammals. (a) Carnivore skull and musculature (a dog). (b) Action of carnivore jaws. (c) Herbivore skull and musculature (a deer). (d) Action of herbivore jaws. (e) Rodent skull and musculature (beaver). (f) Carnivore carnassial shearing teeth (in a coyote). (Modified from E. Rogers, 1986, *Looking at Vertebrates*, Longman, Harlow, UK, and T. A. Vaughan, 1986, *Mammalogy*, 3rd. edition, Saunders, Philadelphia, PA.)

BOX 21–1 Herbivores, Microbes, and the Ecology of Digestion

The many separate evolutions of fermentative digestion among vertebrates have resulted in distinctly different solutions to the problems posed by plants as food (Janis 1976). Horses and other perissodactyls are examples of **hindgut (monogastric)** fermenters. These have a simple stomach and have enlarged both the colon (the large intestine) and the cecum (Figure 21–20, left). Other hindgut fermenters include elephants, hyraxes, New World howler monkeys, wombats, koalas, rabbits, and many rodents. Some degree of hindgut fermentation is probably a primitive vertebrate character: it is known among birds, lizards, turtles, and fishes, as well as omnivorous and carnivorous mammals such as humans and dogs.

Cows and other ruminant artiodactyls are examples of **foregut (ruminant)** fermenters, in which the nonabsorptive forestomach is divided into three chambers that store and process food, followed by a fourth chamber in which digestion occurs (Figure 21–20, right). Ruminants are so called because they ruminate, or chew the cud (see below). Camels resemble other ruminants in many respects, but have only three-chambered stomachs (the omasum is lacking). A simpler type of foregut fermentation, without extensive stomach division or cud-chewing, is found in many other mammals, including Old World colobine monkeys, kangaroos, hippos, and some rodents.

Hindgut fermenters chew their food thoroughly, fracturing the plant cell walls with their teeth so that the cell contents are released. These cell contents are then processed and absorbed in the stomach and small intestine. The cellulose of the plant cell wall is not digested until it reaches the cecum and colon, where it is attacked by the symbiotic microorganisms. Cellulose is fermented to form substances known as volatile fatty acids, which are absorbed through the walls of the cecum and colon.

Some small hindgut fermenters, such as rabbits and rodents, ferment the food largely in the cecum, and do not absorb much of the initial products of fermentation. Instead they rely on **coprophagy**, re-eating the first set of feces that are produced and recycling the nutrients. This digestive strategy would probably not work for a larger animal, which would not so easily be able to contort itself to ingest the feces as they emerge from the anus.

Ruminant foregut fermenters do not need to chew their food as thoroughly on initial mastication, as the cell walls will be chemically disrupted in the stomach. Ruminants do not have such extensive modifications of the skull and teeth as do hindgut fermenters (compare the skull of the horse [Figure 21–18n] and the deer [Figure 21–18o]). The food is initially retained in the two front chambers of the stomach, the **rumen** and the reticulum. Here microorganisms break down the cellulose, and the food is repeatedly regurgitated and rechewed (chewing the cud). The limitation of passage from the reticulum to the third compartment, the omasum, is based on the particle size of the digested food. Thus this rechewing of the food acts in part to regulate the reduction of particle size and the passage of the food out of the fermentation chambers into the omasum (the function of which is not entirely clear), and the abomasum (the true stomach). As most or all of the cellulose has been broken down and absorbed before the true stomach, the digestive process of ruminants from this point on is like that of most other mammals. However, there may be a small amount of additional fermentation later on, in the moderately enlarged cecum.

Distinct advantages and disadvantages are associated with each of the two kinds of fermentative digestion. Foregut fermentation can be extremely efficient because the microorganisms attack the plant material *before* it reaches the small intestine, where most absorption takes place. In contrast, the food has already passed the small intestine of a hindgut fermenter before it is mixed with microorganisms in the cecum and colon, although if the teeth have done their work most of the cell contents have been digested and absorbed by this point. But this prestomach digestion can also be disadvantageous for ruminants. Not only is the cellulose fermented, but so are all the other food components, including free sugars and protein.

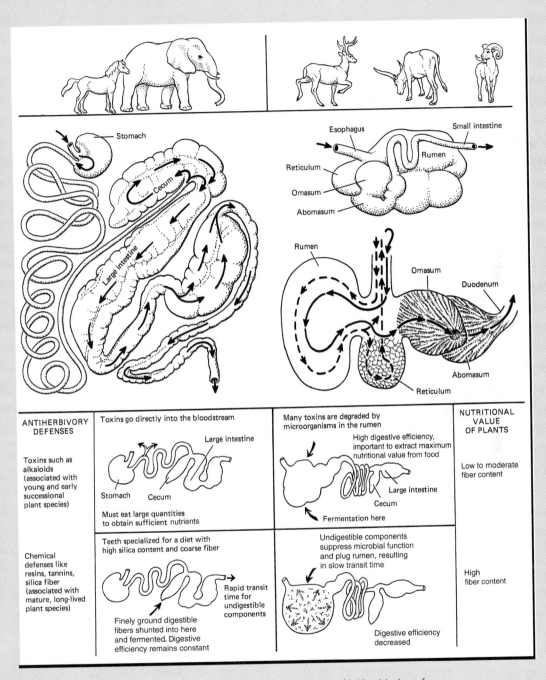

ANTIHERBIVORY DEFENSES	Toxins go directly into the bloodstream	Many toxins are degraded by microorganisms in the rumen	NUTRITIONAL VALUE OF PLANTS
Toxins such as alkaloids (associated with young and early successional plant species)	Large intestine / Stomach / Cecum / Must eat large quantities to obtain sufficient nutrients	High digestive efficiency, important to extract maximum nutritional value from food / Large intestine / Cecum / Fermentation here	Low to moderate fiber content
Chemical defenses like resins, tannins, silica fiber (associated with mature, long-lived plant species)	Teeth specialized for a diet with high silica content and coarse fiber / Rapid transit time for undigestible components / Finely ground digestible fibers shunted into here and fermented. Digestive efficiency remains constant	Undigestible components suppress microbial function and plug rumen, resulting in slow transit time / Digestive efficiency decreased	High fiber content

Figure 21–20 Hindgut and ruminant foregut digestive systems. (Left) The hindgut fermenting system. Fermentation occurs in the enlarged cecum and colon (large intestine). (Right) The ruminant system, showing the four-chambered stomach.

This protein fermentation actually ends up being beneficial to the ruminant, as they engage in a process termed **nitrogen cycling**. Microorganisms ferment the protein into ammonia, which is then taken via the circulation to the liver where it is converted to urea. This urea is transported by the circulatory system to the rumen, where it is used by the microorganisms for their own growth. Surplus microorganisms overflow from the fermentation chambers into the abomasum, where they are digested. Thus all the protein that the ruminant ever actually gets to digest is microbial protein. An advantage of this system is that the microorganisms make all of the essential amino acids needed in the diet; a ruminant can be more limited in its selection of plant species than a hindgut fermenter, who must find all of its essential amino acids by eating a variety of plant sources.

An additional advantage of foregut fermentation is the role microorganisms in the rumen play in detoxifying chemical compounds that would be harmful to a vertebrate. A hindgut fermenter receives no such benefit and must absorb plant toxins into its bloodstream and transport them to its liver for detoxification.

On the other hand, a hindgut fermentation system processes material rapidly whereas ruminants process food more slowly. Food moves through the gut of a horse in 30 to 45 hours, compared to 70 to 100 hours for a cow. Hindgut fermentation works well with food that has relatively high concentrations of fiber, because a large volume of food can be processed rapidly. The system is not efficient at extracting energy from the cellulose, but by processing a large volume of food rapidly a horse can obtain a large quantity of energy from the cell contents in a short time. In contrast, a ruminant foregut system is slow because food cannot pass out of the rumen until it has been ground into very fine particles. Ruminants do not do well on diets that contain high levels of fiber because this slows the passage rate of the food even further, and the animal can literally starve to death with a stomach full of food. Ruminants are very efficient at extracting maximum amounts out of the cellulose of food of moderate fiber content, but they cannot process highly fibrous food as can hindgut fermenters.

These differences in digestive physiology are reflected in the ecology of foregut and hindgut fermenters. Hindgut fermenters can survive on very low-quality food such as straw as long as it is available in large quantities. Consequently, the feral horses in the American west can survive on land too poor for cattle to graze; these ruminants (cattle) are unable to process the low-quality food fast enough to subsist. In contrast, hindgut fermenters cannot survive so well in areas where the absolute quantity of food is limiting. Ruminants are the main herbivores in places like the Arctic and deserts, where the food is of moderately good quality, but severely limited in quantity, so that it best supports an animal which can make the most efficient use of its dietary intake. Ruminants also have an advantage in desert conditions because of their nitrogen cycling. Because this cycle uses some of the waste urea from other sources, less urea needs to be excreted by the kidneys and so less water needs to be used to produce the urine. Ruminants are better able to go without water for a few days than are perissodactyls, and ruminants are more typically found in arid habitats. Ruminants may have come to be the dominant herbivores in the later Cenozoic because the increased seasonality resulted in vegetation where it was easier for a selective feeder to make a living (Janis 1989).

more specialized forms of locomotion, because larger animals experience the world differently from smaller ones because of physical size and scaling effects. We do not have room here for an extensive discussion of these effects. However, you can perhaps appreciate some of the differences of effects of body size by considering the fact that a mouse falling out of a second story window would be unharmed, whereas you would certainly break some bones in such a fall, and an elephant would be killed outright. Bigger animals must be more cautious in their behavior and are more specialized in their adaptations.

Figure 21–23 contrasts the adaptations of running (**cursorial**) mammals and digging (**fossorial**) mammals. (Adaptations of mammals for climbing

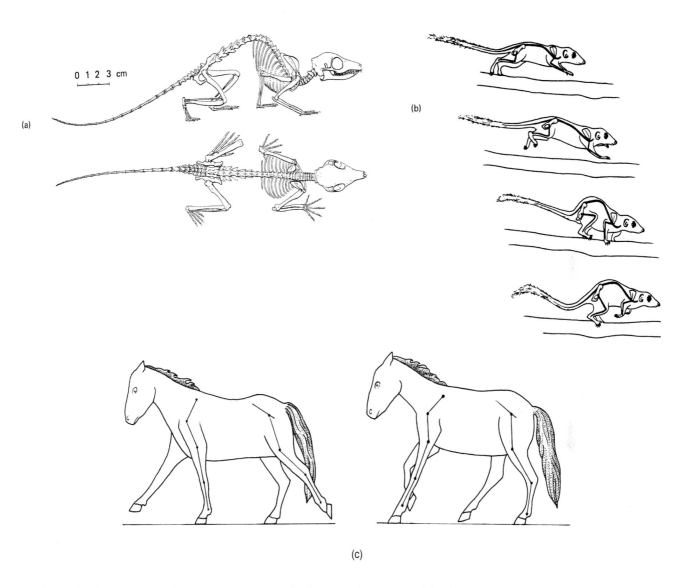

Figure 21–21   Gait and locomotion in mammals. (a) Skeleton of tree shrew (*Tupaia glis*) in typical posture with flexed limbs and quadrupedal stance. (b) Sequential phases of the bounding run in a tree shrew. Note the relatively flexed limbs and mobile back. (c) Sequential phases of the gallop in a horse. Note the relatively straight limb angles and immobile back. (Modified from F. A. Jenkins, Jr. (editor), 1974, *Primate Locomotion,* Academic, New York, NY., and A. A. Biewener, 1989, *BioScience* 39:776–783.)

can be seen in the primates discussed in Chapter 24.) Cursorial mammals need to maximize their stride length, and have thus elongated their legs. The cost of locomotion is in the number of strides it takes to travel a given distance, and so a long-legged mammal will cover it in fewer strides than a shorter-legged one. Long legs also provide a long outlever arm for the major locomotor muscles, such as the triceps in the forelimb and the gastrocnemius in the hindlimb. This provides an arrangement that favors speed of motion. Imagine using a ruler resting on a pencil to flip a coin at the ruler's tip into the air: you'd be able to flip the coin faster if most of the ruler was on the side of the coin, and only a short portion was on the other side of the

pencil for you to use as a lever. This is similar to the limb set-up in Figure 21–23b, left, where the olecranon process is the short lever arm (the part of the ruler that you would push down on), and the whole limb from the elbow on down is the long lever arm (the part of the ruler on which the coin is balanced.)

However, cursorial mammals have made their legs long by elongating only certain portions of the limb, not by elongating each segment. They elongate primarily the lower portions of the limb, the radius and ulna (in the forelimb) or the tibia and fibula (in the hindlimb) and the metapodials. The humerus and femur are not elongated, nor are the phalanges. Contrast this with our long hindlimbs,

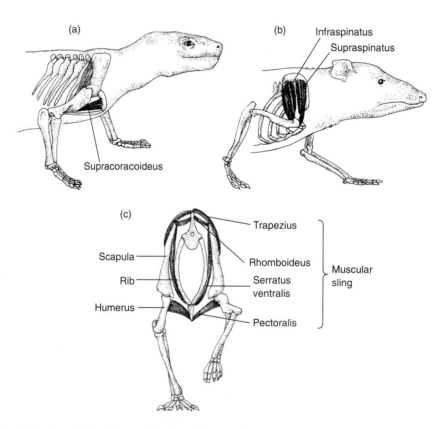

Figure 21–22 Specializations of shoulder girdle musculature. (a) The shoulder girdle and musculature in a cynodont (the condition in monotremes is similar). (b) The shoulder girdle and musculature in a therian mammal (opossum). (c) The scapular sling of a therian mammal, viewed from the front. (Modified from K. V. Kardong, 1998, *Vertebrates: Comparative Anatomy, Function, Evolution*, 2nd ed., Wm. C. Brown, Dubuque, IA. Reprinted by permission of McGraw-Hill Companies.)

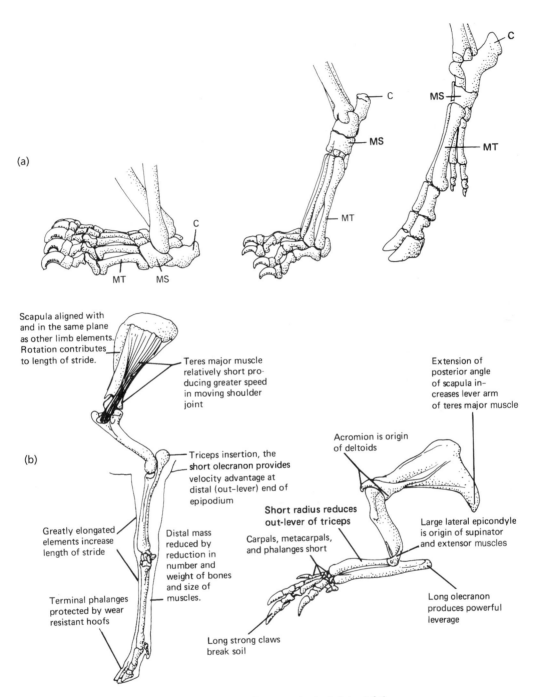

Figure 21–23 Contrasting specializations of the limbs of mammals. (a, left to right) Plantigrade (a beaver), digitigrade (a dog), and unguligrade (a pig) postures. C, calcaneum; MS, mesopodial (tarsal) elements; MT, metapodial elements. (b) The skeletal elements of the left forelimb of a deer (cursorial) and the armadillo (fossorial) compared. (From various sources, including M. Hildebrand, 1988, *Analysis of Vertebrate Structure*, 3d edition, Wiley, New York, NY.)

where the femur is elongated but the whole foot is short. Along with this limb lengthening is a change in foot posture, from the primitive, flat on the ground **plantigrade** posture (as in ourselves) to a tip-toed **digitigrade** foot posture as in dogs and cats (Figure 21–23a). Ungulates go even further with this type of foot posture and adopt an **unguligrade** stance, which would be equivalent to a ballerina standing on point. Lengthening the lower portion of the limb also allows the muscles to be bunched up high, and attached to long elastic tendons that insert distally; there is almost no muscle in a horse's leg below the wrist (the horse's so-called knee joint) or the ankle (the hock). These tendons allow storage of elastic energy during locomotion and contribute to locomotor efficiency.

Other cursorial modifications include ones that restrict the motion of the limb to a fore-and-aft plane, so that most of the thrust on the ground contributes to forwards movement. The clavicle is reduced or lost, and the wrist and ankle bones are relatively immobile. (Note how easily you can turn your hand at the wrist so that your palm faces upwards; a dog can't do that and a horse has almost no ability to rotate this joint.) The number of digits may also be reduced, perhaps to lighten the weight of the limb so that it can be accelerated and stopped more easily during striding (the higher position of the muscles also results in a ligher lower limb). Carnivores often lose digit 1, but otherwise compress the digits together rather than reduce them in number. Artiodactyls reduce or lose digits 1, 2 and 5, becoming effectively four-toed like a pig (see Figure 21–23a, right), or two-toed like a deer (see Figure 21–23b, left). Perissodactyls lose digits 1 and 5, and reduce digits 2 and 4, becoming three-toed like a rhino, or single-toed like a horse (see Figure 20–5).

A fossorial limb is designed in almost exactly the opposite fashion from the cursorial one, here maximizing power at the expense of speed. In this case the thought experiment with the ruler would be in using it to lever up a heavy object; now you would want to put the short end of the ruler under the object, and have a long lever arm at the other end for you to push down on, as with a crow bar. Fossorial mammals acheive this mechanical design in the forelimb with a long olecranon process (the lever arm for the insertion of the triceps) and a relatively short forearm (Figure 21–23b, right). Stout claws and large projections for attachments of strong muscles are also a general feature of the limbs of diggers.

Evolution of Cursorial Adaptations in Mammals

No early Cenozoic (Paleocene) mammal showed cursorial specializations, and early members of the Carnivora and the ungulate orders of the Eocene were also fairly unspecialized. However, during the later Cenozoic we find these mammals becoming larger, and also with a more cursorial form of limb morphology. Although the majority of living carnivores are ambush predators that do not pursue their prey for more than a few yards, we do have a number of pursuit predators that hunt in groups, such as wolves and spotted hyenas. Cheetahs pursue their prey but are not pack hunters. Lions hunt in groups, but do not pursue their prey for a long distance.

Given this difference between ancient and more modern mammals, it has long been assumed that the cursorial adaptations of ungulates and carnivores must have arisen in the context of predator-prey relationships. Longer legs would have given a carnivore a little more speed to pursue the herbivore, resulting in selection for ungulates with longer legs to make a faster getaway. But this evolutionary scenario is not supported by the fossil record. One would expect ungulates and carnivores to have evolved their longer limbs in a coevolutionary, lockstep fashion, but this is not the case. Ungulates evolved their longer limbs and other cursorial specializations in the early Miocene, some 20 million years before the fossil record yields evidence of carnivores built like present-day pursuit predators in the Pliocene (Janis and Wilhelm 1993).

Why, then, did ungulates evolve cursorial adaptations if not to flee predators? It appears that all of the limb modifications that make a mammal a faster runner will also make it more efficient at slower gaits, such as the walk and the trot. The early Miocene is the time when habitats in the higher latitudes started to turn from productive woodlands to less productive grasslands, meaning that ungulate would now have to forage further each day for food. Cursorial adaptations may actually have evolved to boost stamina at slower speeds, in the context of traversing a home range to obtain food, with the capacity for fast running being an unexpected benefit. Even the highly cursorial pack-hunting carnivores may have originally evolved their limb morphologies for stamina, perhaps following migratory herds in the highly seasonal habitats that first appeared in the Pliocene.

A final unresolved issue is why ungulates appear to be more cursorially-adapted than carnivores. A horse has a more elongated legs and a more derived foot stance than a dog, and additionally has lost all of the toes but one and has much more restricted movement at the limb joints. Yet there is no evidence that a horse can run faster or longer than a dog; if this was true, foxhunting on horseback with hounds would be impossible. Perhaps the limbs of carnivores are subject to multiple selection pressures because they must use their forelimbs to aid in killing and digging. One might expect that if carnivores had fewer limb modifications for fast running than ungulates that they would show more extensive modifications of other systems, such as the heart and the lungs, but fast-running ungulates also have enlarged hearts and lungs. The answer may lie in the digestive physiology of ungulates. The gut and gut contents of an ungulate may comprise up to 40 percent of the total body mass. Thus, for any given body weight, an ungulate has proportionally less muscle mass than a carnivore of the same size, as so much of its mass is composed of the gut. It may be the case that ungulates have to be more modified in the skeleton than carnivores to compensate for this difference in relative muscle mass in proportion to total body weight.

■ Mammalian Brain and Sensory Systems

The basic structure of vertebrate nervous systems and the regions of the generalized vertebrate brain are covered in Chapter 3. The brain of living mammals is distinctive in the enlargement of the area of the telencephalon called the **neopallium**. As discussed in Chapter 10, mammals differ from other amniotes in their poor color vision, and most living mammals are much more dependent on hearing and olfaction than on vision, both for perceiving their environment and for communication.

The Evolution of Mammalian Brain Size

Both mammals and birds have brains that are several times the size of those of ectothermic tetrapods, although some later Cenozoic mammals have evolved especially large brains, with this trend occurring in parallel among a variety of mammalian lineages. Although we tend to think of the tendency to evolve a large brain as a natural outcome of mammalian evolution, it is not at all clear what (if any) the adaptive advantage has been to mammals. Large brains do appear to be associated with complex social behavior. Pack-hunting carnivores are bigger-brained than solitary ones, for example. The deteriorating climates of the later Cenozoic (see Chapter 20) may have produced conditions where smarter mammals may have had an adaptive advantage, but it should not be forgotten that many small-brained mammals survived these conditions as well.

Evaluating how brainy an animal is can be problematical. For a start, the size of brains scales with negative allometry: that is, larger animals have proportionally smaller brains for their size than small animals. The reason for this negative scaling is not known, but may be related to the fact that absolutely more brain tissue is not needed to work a bigger body. For example, if we were to suppose that 200 nerve cells in the brain were necessary to power the right hind leg of a mouse, there is no reason to suppose that more cells would be necessary to power the leg of an elephant. Of course, larger animals have brains that are absolutely larger than smaller ones, they are just not quite as large as one would predict for their size, all other things being equal. (People often forget this difference in size; for example, when they claim that the brains of dolphins are just as big as human brains, implying equivalent intelligence, forgetting that most dolphins are much bigger than humans and so would be expected to have a large brain anyway.)

To get around the effect of body size, the size of brains is usually estimated in relative terms. One such estimate is the **encephalization quotient (EQ)**, a measure of the actual brain size in relation to the expected brain size for an animal of that body mass (Jerison 1973). The average EQ of an extant (non-primate) mammal is 0.5. Insectivores, rodents, and marsupials mostly have EQ values of less than one, while primates and whales have values of greater than one (great apes have values of around 3, while humans have a value of around 8). Some carnivorans and ungulates (e.g., dogs, cats, horses, and elephants) also have EQ values of greater than one.

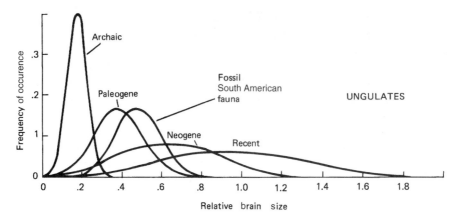

Figure 21–24 Changes in the relative brain size of ungulates during the Cenozoic. Species are from the Northern Hemisphere unless otherwise stated. The Paleogene includes the Paleocene through the Oligocene epochs, the Neogene the Miocene through the Pleistocene epochs. (After H. J. Jerison, 1973, *Evolution of the Brain and Intelligence,* Academic, New York, NY. Also see L. B. Radinsky, 1978, *American Naturalist,* 112:815–831.)

Figure 21–24 shows a plot of the changes of EQs of ungulates over time, and plots for other mammalian orders would have similar shapes, if not similar absolute values. An important thing to notice is that, while the average brain size has increased over time and the ungulates that have the largest brains are among the ones found today, there are still living ungulates whose brains are as small as some of the early Cenozoic forms. There has been an increase in the range of brain sizes, rather than an overall trend for the brains of all mammals to increase in size.

Vision

It is a common misconception that mammals other than primates are color blind. While a retina comprised mainly of rods is probably the primitive mammalian condition, as seen in many extant small, nocturnal mammals such as insectivorans, all mammals, even monotremes, have some cones in their retinas. Thus it is likely that at least a rudimentary ability to distinguish color is present in all mammals, possibly inherited from their ancestry with other amniotes. Some diurnal mammals, such as squirrels, have retinas that are densely packed with cones and the ability to distinguish colors is clearly present in many other mammals, including dogs, cats, and horses (Jacobs 1993).

What is the adaptive advantage of color vision? Color vision is probably useful only to a diurnal animal where the eye can function at relatively high light intensities. Color allows increased perception of contrast, enhancing the visibility of an object from its surroundings. Color also has significance for determining food choice, such as fruit ripeness, and for social signals, such as dimorphic coloration, or blushing in humans.

Only Old World apes and monkeys share with humans the capacity for trichromatic color vision—i.e., having cones containing visual pigments with three different absorption spectra, rendering the eye sensitive to three different wavelengths of light (in us, corresponding to the colors red, green, and blue) (Jacobs 1993). Other mammals appear to have only two visual pigments, giving them dichromatic color vision similar to (but probably not identical with) humans with red-green color blindness.

Hearing

Audition has several advantages as a distance sense compared with vision and olfaction. Sound is not readily blocked by obstacles in the environment (as is light), and it is transmitted more directionally and much faster than odors. The therian mammalian ear shows the importance of audition, especially in therians with the extensively coiled cochlea in the inner ear and the pinna or outer ear. The combined effect of these specialized structures is exceptional frequency discrimination, broad sensitivity to various intensities of sound, and precision of directionality. Cranial casts of early mammals show that auditory areas of the brain were large.

Many mammals are more sensitive than humans to one or another sensory modality: The olfactory sensitivity of dogs is probably the most familiar example of the sensory capacity of a mammal that exceeds our own. Equally impressive is the use that bats and cetaceans have made of hearing as a distance sense for navigation and location of prey. An examination of echolocation illustrates the way in which a sensory capacity that is ancestral for mammals can be elaborated and how environment and phylogeny interact.

Several derived mammals emit sounds above 20 kilohertz (20,000 cycles per second), called **ultrasound** because it is above the range of normal human sensitivity (the 10 octaves between 20 hertz and 20 kilohertz). Elephants emit sounds below this range (**infrasound**) in connection with group movements and reproductive receptivity. When infant rodents stray outside their nest, they emit ultrasounds that stimulate adults to retrieve them. Some adult rodents, a few marsupials, dermopterans, pinnipeds, many insectivores, microchiropteran bats, and odontocete cetaceans emit such sounds throughout their life as part of a sound-based distance sensing system of **echolocation.**

The most thoroughly studied echolocating mammals are the microchiropteran bats and the toothed cetaceans (e.g., dolphins), which use this sensory modality to locate prey under conditions where vision would not be appropriate. (The types of whales whose songs you can buy on records are the filter-feeding baleen whales, which do not produce ultrasound, probably because they do not need to target moving prey.) Bats hunt for insects at night, and toothed whales hunt for fish and other marine animals in murky waters. The high-frequency sounds emitted bounce back off from surrounding objects, including prey items, and the sound received back in the animal's ear can translate these reflected sound waves into information about spatial relationships. We ourselves have a certain capacity to use sound to form a picture of our surroundings. Imagine that you open a door onto a darkened room, and yell "Hello": you could easily distinguish between an empty room and one that was full of furniture just by the echo of your own voice. Blind people, of course, have greatly increased their sensitivity to being able to use sound to determine spatial relationships in their environment.

Bats and cetaceans differ in their production and reception of ultrasound because they operate in different media. In some ways bats are less specialized than cetaceans, because air is the original medium for the sensory modality of hearing. Bats produce a stream of ultrasounds from their larynx, which is enlarged but is not greatly modified from the general mammalian condition. The sounds are emitted through the mouth or the nose, which often have highly complex folds and flaps to concentrate the sound, giving microchiropteran bats their typically gargoyle-like faces (see Figure 21–25). In contrast the megachiropteran fruit bats, which do not echolocate, have rather foxlike faces, and these bats are often known as "flying foxes." (Ironically, it is these harmless fruit bats that usually play the role of microchiropteran vampire bats in horror movies, because of their large size and carnivoran-appearing faces.) The external ears of microchiropteran bats are also large and complexly-shaped to receive the ultrasound.

Cetaceans produce clicks that are of much higher frequency (i.e., with shorter sound waves) than those emitted by bats because a given frequency of sound travels as a longer wave in water than in air (because of the acoustical properties of water) and short sound waves are important for the detection of small objects. The ultrasound is not produced through the larynx as there is only a limited amount of air in the lungs that cannot be refilled underwater. Instead sound is produced in the nasal passages and focused through an oil-filled body on the forehead called the melon (see Figure 21–26). There is also a problem with the reception of sound in water. The middle ear of mammals is designed to transduce sound to the inner ear with an air/air interface and an air/fluid interface where the auditory ossicles the inner ear at the eardrum; it does not work well underwater. Additionally the body tissues absorb sound from the water and can interfere with sound reception in the inner ear. To solve these problems the cetaceans isolate the inner ear from the rest of the skull with special sound-absorbing tissues, and sound is transmitted to the inner ear directly via a fat body that runs alongside of the lower jaw (Norris 1974, Au 1993).

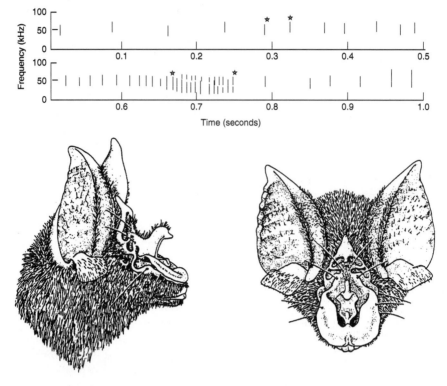

Figure 21–25 Bat echolocation sounds and modifications of the nose to broadcast them. The sound spectrograph analysis is of the frequency-modulated (FM) pulses emitted by the little brown bat, *Myotis lucifugus*, during an interception maneuver. Frequency in kilohertz is plotted against time during the continuous 1-second record. Filled stars indicate typical loud pulses near the time of detection of the target; open stars indicate the onset and completion of the terminal buzz just before capture of prey. (After M. S. Gordon et al., 1982, *Animal Physiology, Principles and Adaptations*, 4th edition, Macmillan, New York, NY.)

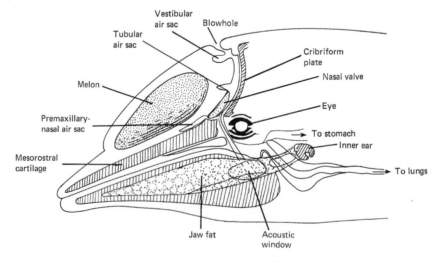

Figure 21–26 Proposed odontocete echolocation. Sound production and reception apparatus shown for the bottle-nosed dolphin (*Tursiops*). Sound produced by air shuttled between air sacs through the nasal valve is focused by the oil of the melon into a forwardly directed beam. Some sound may also be guided by the mesorostral cartilage. Returned sound is channeled through the mandibular (jaw) fat bodies and especially the acoustic window on the lower jaw to the otherwise isolated and fused middle and inner ears. (Modified after K. S. Norris, 1966, in *Evolution and Environment,* edited by E. T. Drake, Peabody Museum Centenary Volume, Yale University, New Haven, CT.)

Summary

All mammals share a number of uniquely derived features. Lactation is the most obvious mammalian feature, and the mammalian features of facial muscles and pharyngeal seals may have arisen in the evolution of suckling. All mammals have hair and a variety of skin glands used for hair lubrication and waterproofing, olfactory communication, and thermoregulation. Mammary glands evolved from these types of skin glands.

The major groups of living mammals are monotremes and therians (marsupials and placentals). Therians are not only more derived than monotremes in their mode of reproduction (viviparity as opposed to egg-laying), but are also more derived in their teeth, and in several features of the skeleton and musculature, especially the anatomy of the shoulder girdle. The more mobile scapula of therians may allow for a greater range of locomotory behaviors. Only a few dental and skeletal differences distinguish marsupials and placentals, although they are quite distinct in their mode of reproduction and the anatomy of their reproductive tracts. Marsupials give birth to very immature young which complete their development attached to the nipples, usually, but not always, enclosed in a pouch. Placentals give birth to more mature young, and have a shorter period of lactation than marsupials. The marsupial mode of reproduction has often been considered inferior to the placental one, but the differences may just reflect their separate evolutionary histories, with neither method being inherently superior to the other.

Cenozoic mammals have diversified into a variety of feeding types, reflected in different anatomies of their skulls and dentitions. The skulls and teeth of herbivores are in general more specialized than those of omnivores and carnivores, as fibrous plant material is more difficult to chew, and is more abrasive to the teeth. Vegetation is also more difficult to digest than other diets, and many herbivores have evolved a symbiotic association with microorganisms in their guts, which ferment the plant fiber and aid in its chemical break-down. The primitive mammalian mode of locomotion is probably some sort of bounding. With the radiation of larger mammals in the Cenozoic, more specialized types of locomotion evolved. One specialized type of limb design is that possessed by cursorial (running) mammals, involving the elongation of the legs, a change in foot posture, restriction of the range of motion, and sometimes loss of digits. The popular notion that carnivores and herbivores evolved long legs in a coevolutionary fashion over time, in a predator-prey arms race, is not supported by the fossil record.

Many mammals have evolved larger brains over the course of the Cenozoic, including ungulates, carnivorans, and whales as well as primates, but many small-brained mammals persist today. Contrary to the popular notion that nonprimate mammals are color blind, some sort of color vision probably characterizes all mammals, but only Old World monkeys and apes share with humans the capacity for trichromatic color vision. Hearing was probably always a highly important mammalian sense, and the capacity to emit and perceive ultrasound (echolocation) may well be a primitive mammalian capacity. The sensory modality of echolocation is best developed in microchiropteran bats and in toothed whales such as dolphins.

References

Au, W. W. L. 1993. *The Sonar of Dolphins*. Springer, New York, NY.

Baker, R. J., M. J. Novacek, and N. B. Simmons. 1991. On the monophyly of bats. *Systematic Zoology* 40:216–231.

Blackburn, D. G. 1991. Evolutionary origins of the mammary gland. *Mammal Review* 21:81–96.

Biewener, A. A. 1989. Mammalian terrestrial locomotion and size. *BioScience* 39 (11):776-783.

Bramble, D. M. and F. A. Jenkins, Jr. 1989. Structural and functional integration across the reptile-mammal boundary: the locomotor system. Pages 133–146 in *Complex Organismal Functions: Integration and Evolution in Vertebrates*, edited by D. B. Wake and G. Roth. John Wiley, Chichester, UK.

Bubenik, G. A., and A. B. Bubenik. 1990. *Horns, Pronghorns, and Antlers*. Springer, New York, NY.

Collin, R. and C. M. Janis 1997. Morphological constraints on tetrapod feeding mechanisms. Why were there no suspension-feeding marine reptiles? Pages 451–466 in *Ancient Marine Reptiles*, edited by J. M. Callaway and E. L. Nicholls. Academic Press, New York, NY.

Crompton, A. W. 1995. Masticatory function in nonmammalian cynodonts and early mammals. Pages 55–75 in *Functional Morphology in Vertebrate Paleontology*, edited by J. J. Thomason. Cambridge University Press, Cambridge, UK.

Daly, M. 1979. Why don't male mammals lactate? *Journal of Theoretical Biology* 78:325-345.

Frank, L. G. 1996. Female masculinzation in the spotted hyena: endocrinology, behavioral ecology, and evolution. Pages 78–131 in *Carnivore Behavior, Ecology, and Evolution*, volume 2, edited by J. L. Gittleman. Comstock Publishing Associates, Ithaca, NY.

Gatesy, J., C. Hayashi, M. A. Cronin, and P. Arctander. 1996. Evidence from milk casein genes that cetaceans are close relatives of hippopotamid artiodactyls. *Molecular Biology and Evolution* 13:954–963.

Gaudin, T. J., J. R. Wible, J. A. Hopson, and W. D. Turnbull. 1996. Reexamination of the morphological evidence for the cohort Epitheria (Mammalia, Eutheria). *Journal of Mammalian Evolution* 3:31–79.

Graur, D. and D. G. Higgins. 1994. Molecular evidence for the inclusion of cetaceans within the order Artiodactyla. *Molecular Biology and Evolution* 11:357–364.

Hopson, J. A. 1973. Endothermy, small size, and the origin of mammalian reproduction. *American Naturalist* 107:446–452.

Jacobs, G. H. 1993. The distribution and nature of colour vision among the mammals. *Biological Reviews* 68:413–471.

Janis, C. M. 1976. The evolutionary strategy of the Equidae and the origins of rumen and cecal digestion. *Evolution* 30:757–774.

Janis, C. M. 1982. Evolution of horns in ungulates: ecology and paleoecology. *Biological Reviews* 57:261–318.

Janis, C. M. 1989. A climatic explanation for patterns of evolutionary diversity in ungulate mammals. *Palaeontology* 32:463–481.

Janis, C. M., and M. Fortelius. 1988. On the means whereby mammals achieve increased functional durability of their dentitions, with special reference to limiting factors. *Biological Reviews* 63:197–230.

Janis, C. M. and P. B. Wilhelm. 1993. Were there mammalian pursuit predators in the Tertiary? Dances with wolf avatars. *Journal of Mammalian Evolution* 1:103–126.

Jarvis, J. U. M. 1981. Eusociality in a mammal: Cooperative breeding in the naked mole rat. *Science* 212: 571–573.

Jellison, W. L. 1945. A suggested homolog to the os penis or bacculum of mammals. *Journal of Mammalogy* 26:146–147.

Jerison, H. J. 1973. *Evolution of the Brain and Intelligence*. Academic Press, New York, NY.

Kirsch, J. A. 1977. The six percent solution: Second thoughts on the adaptedness of the Marsupialia. American Scientist 65:276–288.

Kirsch, J. A. W., A. W. Dickerman, O. A. Reig, and M. S. Springer. 1991. DNA hybridization evidence for the Australian affinity of the American marsupial *Dromiciops australis*. *Proceedings of the National Academy of Sciences* 88:10465–10469.

Lillegraven, J. A. 1969. Latest Cretaceous mammals of upper part of Edmonton Formation of Alberta, Canada, and review of marsupial-placental dichotomy in mammalian evolution. *University of Kansas Paleontological Contributions* 50:1–122.

Lillegraven, J. A. 1979. Reproduction of Mesozoic mammals. Pages 259–276 in *Mesozoic Mammals*, edited by J. A. Lillegraven, Z. Kielan-Jaworowska, and W. A. Clemens. University of California Press, Berkeley, CA.

Lillegraven, J. A., S. D. Thompson, B. K. McNab, and J. L. Patton. 1987. The origin of eutherian mammals. *Biological Journal of the Linnean Society* 32:281–336.

Luckett, W. P. 1994. Suprafamilial relationships within Marsupialia: resolution and discordance from multidisciplinary data. *Journal of Mammalian Evolution* 2:255–283.

McKenna, M. C. 1975. Toward a phylogenetic classification of the Mammalia. Pages 21–46 in *Phylogeny of the Primates*, edited by P. Luckett and F. S. Szalay. Plenum Press, New York, NY.

McKenna, M. C. 1987. Molecular and morphological analysis of higher level mammalian interrelationships. Pages 53–93 in *Molecules and Morphology in Evolution*, edited by C. Patterson. Cambridge University Press, Cambridge, UK.

Mossman, H. W. 1987. *Vertebrate Fetal Membranes*. Rutgers University Press, New Brunswick, NJ.

Muizon, C. de, R. L. Cifelli, and R. C. Paz. 1997. The origin of the dog-like borhyaenoid marsupials of South America. *Nature* 389:486–489.

Norris, K. S. 1974. *The Porpoise Watcher*. George J. McLeod, Toronto, Canada.

Novacek, M. J. 1992. Mammalian phylogeny: shaking the tree. *Nature* 356:121–125.

Novacek, M. J. 1994. The radiation of placental mammals. Pages 220–237 in *Major Features of Vertebrate Evolution*, edited by D. R. Prothero and R. M. Schoch. Short Courses in Paleontology No. 7, The Paleontological Society, University of Tennessee Press, Knoxville, TN.

Novacek, M. J., G. W. Rougier, J. R . Wible, M. C. McKenna, D. Dashzeveg, and I. Horovitz. 1997. Epipubic bones in eutherian mammals from the Late Cretaceous of Mongolia. *Nature* 389:483–486.

Parker, P. 1977. An ecological comparison of marsupial and placental patterns of reproduction. Pages 273-286 in *The Biology of Marsupials*, edited by B. Stonehouse and D. Gilmore. MacMillan Press, London, UK.

Pettigrew, J. D. 1986. Flying primates? Megabats have the advanced pathway from eye to midbrain. *Science* 231:1304–1306.

Pettigrew, J. D. 1991. Wings or brain? Convergent evolution in the origins of bats. Systematic Zoology 40:199–216.

Renfree, M. B. 1993. Ontogeny, genetic control, and phylogeny of female reproduction in monotreme and therian mammals. Pages 4–20 in *Mammal Phylogeny, Mesozoic Differentiaion, Multiberculates, Monotremes, Early Therians, and Marsupials*, edited by F. S. Szalaly, M. J. Novacek, and M. C. McKenna. Springer Verlag, New York, NY.

Sharman, G. B. 1976. Evolution of viviparity in mammals. Pages 32–70 in *Reproduction in Mammals, 6: The Evolution of Reproduction*, edited by C. R. Austin and R. V. Short. Cambridge University Press, Cambridge, UK.

Smith, K. K. 1992. The evolution of the mammalian pharynx. *Zoological Journal of the Linnean Society* 104:313–349.

Springer, M. S., A. Burk, J. R. Kavanagh, V. G. Waddell, and M. J. Stanhope. 1977a. The interphotoreceptor retinoid binding protein gene in therian mammals: Implications for higher level relationships and evidence for loss of function in the marsupial mole. *Proceedings of the National Academy of Sciences* 94:13754–13759.

Springer, M. S., G. C. Cleven, O. Madsen, W. W. de Jong, V. G. Waddell, H. M. Amrine, and M. J. Stanhope. 1997b.

Endemic African mammals shake the phylogenetic tree. *Nature* 388:61–64.

Springer, M. S., M. Westerman, and J. A. W. Kirsch. 1994. Relationships among orders and families of marsupials based on 12S Ribosomal DNA sequences and the timing of marsupial radiation. *Journal of Mammalian Evolution* 2:85–115.

Theodor, J. M., and M. J. Mahoney. 1997. Why do molecules and morphology conflict? Examination of the artiodactyl-cetacean relationship. *Journal of Vertebrate Paleontology* 17 (suppl. to no. 3): p. 80A.

Thewissen, J. G. M. 1994. Phylogenetic aspects of cetacean origins. *Journal of Mammalian Evolution* 2:157–184.

Tyndale–Biscoe, C. H., and M. B. Renfree. 1987. *Reproductive Physiology of Marsupials*. Cambridge University Press, Cambridge, UK.

Vaughan, T. A. 1986. *Mammalogy*, 3rd. edition. Saunders, Philadelphia, PA.

Wyss, A. R., and J. J. Flynn. 1993. A phylogenetic analysis and definition of the Carnivora. Pages 17–50 in *Mammal Phylogeny, Placentals*, edited by F. S. Szalaly, M. J. Novacek, and M. C. McKenna. Springer Verlag, New York, NY.

CHAPTER 22

Endothermy: A High-Energy Approach to Life

Endothermy is a derived character of mammals and birds. The two lineages evolved endothermy independently, but the costs and benefits are the same for both. Endothermy is a superb way to become relatively independent of many of the stresses of the physical environment, especially cold. Birds and mammals can live in the coldest habitats on Earth, provided that they can find enough food. That qualification expresses the major problem of endothermy: It is energetically expensive. Endotherms need a reliable supply of food. As a result, the conspicuous interactions of endotherms are often with their biological environment—predators, competitors, and prey—rather than with the physical environment as is often the case for ectotherms. Because energy intake and expenditure are important factors in the daily lives of endotherms, calculations of energy budgets can help us to understand the consequences of some kinds of behavior.

When all efforts at homeostasis are inadequate, endotherms have two more methods of dealing with harsh conditions: (1) Birds and large species of mammals can migrate to areas where conditions are more favorable. (2) Many species of small mammals and some birds can become torpid. This response, a temporary drop in body temperature, conserves energy and prolongs survival at the cost of abandoning the benefits of homeothermy.

■ Costs and Benefits

Endothermy has both benefits and costs compared to ectothermy. On the positive side, endothermy allows birds and mammals to maintain high body temperatures when solar radiation is not available or is insufficient to warm them—at night, for example, or in the winter. The thermoregulatory capacities of birds and mammals are astonishing; they can live in the coldest places on Earth. On the negative side, endothermy is energetically expensive. We have pointed out that the metabolic rates of birds and mammals are nearly an order of magnitude greater than those of amphibians and reptiles. The energy to sustain those high metabolic rates comes from food, and endotherms need more food than do ectotherms.

Of course, a host of other differences distinguish the ecology and behavior of endotherms and ectotherms, and these also can be considered costs or benefits of the different methods of thermoregulation. In this chapter we concentrate on how endotherms use energy, the ways in which endotherms thermoregulate in cold and in hot environments, and how endotherms control their water gains and losses. These topics are intimately related, because the high metabolic rates of endotherms are associated with more precise homeostatic control of their internal environment than is necessary for many ectotherms. For example, rising body temperature can be countered by evaporative cooling (sweating or panting), but too much evaporative cooling depletes water stores and leads to other problems. Body size plays a large role in determining the stresses to which endotherms are subjected and the responses that are possible for them.

The same sorts of habitats that are stressful for ectotherms (Chapter 16) are also difficult for endotherms, although not always for the same reasons. Cold temperatures, for example, make ectothermal thermoregulation difficult or impossible and may present a risk of freezing. Endotherms have sufficient insulation and thermogenic (heat-producing) capacity to survive low temperatures, but they need a plentiful and regular supply of food to do that. Indeed, their high energy requirements appear to shape several aspects of the biology of endotherms, such as the relationship among body size, diet, and home range discussed in the next chapter. The role that energy gain and use play in the day-to-day lives of endotherms can be illustrated by an energy budget.

■ Energy Budgets of Vertebrates

An understanding of the costs of living can be obtained by constructing an energy budget for an animal. An energy budget, like a financial budget, shows income and expenditure but uses units of energy as currency. The energy costs of different activities can be evaluated by converting the energy intake (food) and loss (metabolism, feces, and urine) to a common unit of measurement. We will use kilojoules (kJ) for these calculations. (One kJ equals 0.24 kilocalories. The kilocalorie is the unit called Calories on labels showing nutritional content of packaged foods.) This quantitative approach to the study of ecology and behavior offers the promise of understanding some of the reasons why animals behave as they do.

A Daily Energy Budget: The Vampire Bat

Studies of vampire bats (*Desmodus rotundus*) by Brian McNab (1973) have revealed a clear-cut relationship between energy intake, energy expenditure, and the species' geographic range. These bats of the suborder Microchiroptera inhabit the Neotropics and are specialized to feed exclusively on blood. Their daily pattern of activity is simple: They spend about 22 hours in their caves, fly out at night to a feeding site, and return after they have fed. Typically, a vampire flies about 10 kilometers round-trip at 20 kilometers per hour to find a meal. Thus, a bat spends half an hour per day in flight. The remaining time outside the cave may be spent in feeding.

The vampire's food is convenient for energetic calculations because of the relatively constant caloric content of blood. The information needed to construct an energy budget is the following:

> I = ingested energy (blood). The blood a bat drinks must provide the energy needed for all of its life processes: maintenance, activity, growth, and reproduction.

> E = excreted energy. As in any animal, not all of the food ingested is digested and taken up by the bat. The energy contained in the feces and urine is lost.

> $I–E$ = assimilated energy. This is the energy actually taken into the bat's body.

> M = metabolism. This can be subdivided into M_i (metabolism while the bat is inside the cave) and M_o (nonflight metabolism while the bat is outside the cave).

> A = cost of activity, a half hour of flight per day.

> B = biomass increase. This term is the profit a bat shows in its energy budget. It may be stored as fat or used for growth or for reproduction (production of gametes, growth of a fetus, or nursing a baby).

In its simplest form, the energy budget is

$$\text{energy in} = \text{energy out} \pm \text{biomass change}$$

The biomass term appears as ± because an animal metabolizes some body tissues when its energy expenditure exceeds its energy intake. (This is what every dieter hopes to do to lose weight.) Translating this general equation into the terms defined gives

$$I - E = M_i + M_o + A + B$$

All these terms can be measured and expressed as kilojoules per bat per day (kJ/bat·day). These calculations are based on McNab's studies and apply to a Brazilian vampire bat weighing 42 g.

Ingested energy: In a single feeding a vampire can consume 57 percent of its body mass in blood, which contains 4.6 kJ/g. Thus the ingested energy is

$$42 \text{ g} \times 57\% \times 4.6 \text{ kJ/g blood} = 110.1 \text{ kJ}$$

Excreted energy: A vampire excretes 0.24 g urea in the urine plus 0.95 g of feces daily. Urea contains 10.5 kJ/g and the feces contain 23.8 kJ/g. Thus the excreted energy is

$$0.24 \text{ g urea} \times 10.5 \text{ kJ/g} + 0.95 \text{ g feces} \times 23.8 \text{ kJ/g} =$$

$$2.5 \text{ kJ} + 22.6 \text{ kJ} = 25.1 \text{ kJ}$$

Assimilated energy: The energy the bat actually assimilates from blood equals the energy ingested (110.1 kJ) minus that excreted (25.1 kJ). Thus a vampire's energy intake is 85.0 kJ/day:

$$110.1 \text{ kJ} - 25.1 \text{ kJ} = 85.0 \text{ kJ}$$

Metabolism: In a tropical habitat, 20°C is a reasonable approximation of the temperature a bat experiences both inside and outside the cave. While at rest in the laboratory at 20°C a vampire's metabolic rate is 3.8 cm³ O₂/g·hr. The terms for metabolism can be calculated and converted to joules using the energy equivalent of oxygen (20.1 J/cm³ O₂):

$$M_i = 42 \text{ g} \times 3.8 \text{ cm}^3 \text{ O}_2/\text{g·hr} \times 20.1 \text{ J/cm}^3 \text{ O}_2$$

$$\times 22 \text{ hr/day} = 70.6 \text{ kJ}$$

$$M_o = 42 \text{ g} \times 3.8 \text{ cm}^3 \text{ O}_2/\text{g·hr} \times 20.1 \text{ J/cm}^3 \text{ O}_2$$

$$\times 1.5 \text{ hr/day} = 4.8 \text{ kJ}$$

Activity: The metabolism of a bat flying at 20 km/hr is 11.4 cm³ O₂/g·hr. The cost of the round trip from the cave to the feeding site is

$$A = 42 \text{ g} \times 11.4 \text{ cm}^3 \text{ O}_2/\text{g·hr} \times 20.1 \text{ J/cm}^3 \text{ O}_2 \times 0.5 \text{ hr}$$

$$= 4.8 \text{ kJ}$$

Biomass change: The quantities calculated so far are fixed values that the bat cannot avoid. The biomass change is a variable value. If the assimilated energy is greater than the fixed costs, this energy profit can go to biomass increase. Fixed costs that exceed the assimilated energy are reflected as a loss of biomass. For the situation described there is an energy profit:

$$I - E = M_i + M_o + A \pm B$$

$$110.1 \text{ kJ} - 25.1 \text{ kJ} = 70.6 \text{ kJ} + 4.8 \text{ kJ} + 4.8 \text{ kJ} \pm B$$

$$B = 4.8 \text{ kJ/bat·day}$$

These calculations show that vampires can live and grow under the conditions assumed. What happens if we change some of the assumptions? McNab points out that the northern and southern limits of the geographic range of vampires conform closely to the winter isotherms of 10°C (Figure 22–1). That is, the minimum temperature outside the cave during the coldest month of the year is 10°C; the bats do not occur in regions where the minimum temperature is lower. Is this coincidence, or is 10°C the lowest temperature the bats can withstand? Calculating an energy budget for a vampire under these colder conditions provides an answer.

Caves have very stable temperatures that usually do not vary from summer to winter. We will assume that temperature remains constant at 20°C in the cave our imaginary vampires inhabit. In that case only the conditions a bat encounters outside the cave are altered. Because of limitations of stomach capacity, ingestion cannot increase beyond 57 percent of body mass, the value assumed in the previous calculation. Therefore, we need recalculate only M_o, A, and B.

Metabolism outside: At 10°C a bat must increase its metabolic rate to maintain its body temperature, and laboratory measurements indicate the resting metabolic rate increases to 6.3 cm³ O₂/g·hr:

$$M_o = 42 \text{ g} \times 6.3 \text{ cm}^3 \text{ O}_2/\text{g·hr} \times 20.1 \text{ J/cm}^3 \text{ O}_2 \times 1.5 \text{ hr}$$

$$= 8.0 \text{ kJ}$$

Activity: The cost of activity will not change, because the metabolic rate of the bat during flight (11.4 cm³ O₂/g·hr) is higher than the resting metabolic rate needed to keep it warm (6.3 cm³ O₂/g·hr). Only the term M_o changes, increasing from 4.8 to 7.9 kJ, and the sum of the energy costs becomes 83.4 kJ/bat·day.

Because the assimilated energy remains at 85.1 kJ/bat day, only 1.8 kJ is available for biomass increase. The assumptions in these calculations introduce a degree of uncertainty, and probably 1.7 kJ is not statistically different from 0 kJ. At 10°C a bat uses all its energy staying alive. Thus a vampire bat could live under those conditions, but it would have no energy surplus for growth or repro-

Figure 22–1 The geographic range of the vampire bat, *Desmodus rotundus*. The area in which vampire bats are found closely approximates the 10°C isotherm for the minimum average temperature during the coldest month of the year (dashed line) at the northern limit of its range (in Mexico) and the southern limit (in Uruguay, Argentina, and Chile). The positions of the 10°C isotherm and the altitudinal range of the bats in the Andes Mountains are not known and are indicated by question marks. (Based on B. K. McNab, 1973, *Journal of Mammalogy* 54:131–144.)

duction. If the temperature outside the cave were lower than 10°C, the bat would have a negative energy balance and would lose body mass with each meal. The agreement between our calculations and the actual geographic distribution of the bats suggests that energy may be a biologically significant factor in limiting their northward and southward spread.

Additional calculations reveal more about the selective forces that shape the lives of vampire bats. A bat's stomach can hold a volume of blood equal to 57 percent of its body mass, but a bat cannot fly with that load. The maximum flight load is 43 percent of the body mass. Before it can take off to start the flight back to its cave, therefore, a bat must reduce the weight gained from its meal. Vampires do this by rapidly excreting water. Within 2 minutes after it begins to eat, a vampire starts to emit a stream of dilute urine. Experiments reveal that a

vampire produces urine at a maximum rate of 0.24 ml per g body mass per hour. Thus in the hour and a half the bat may spend in feeding, it could excrete as much as 15 g of water—more than enough to allow it to fly (Busch 1988).

Although rapid excretion of water solves the bat's immediate problem, it introduces another. The bat is left with a stomach full of protein-rich food that will yield a large amount of urea. To excrete this urea, the bat needs water to form urine. By the time a vampire gets back to its cave it is facing a water shortage instead of a water excess. Unlike many mammals, vampires seldom drink water but depend instead on blood for their water requirements. Like other mammals adapted to conditions of water scarcity, vampire bats have kidneys capable of producing very concentrated urine to conserve water. As a result of its unusual ecology and behavior, a vampire bat can be considered to live in a desert of its own making in the midst of a tropical forest.

■ Endotherms in the Cold: The Arctic

As the energy budget for the vampire bat revealed, endotherms expend most of the energy they consume just keeping themselves warm even in the moderate conditions of tropical and subtropical climates. Nonetheless, endotherms have proven themselves very adaptable in extending their thermoregulatory responses to allow them to inhabit even arctic and antarctic regions (Bech and Reinertsen 1989, Davenport 1992). Not even small body size is an insuperable handicap to life in these areas: Redpolls and chickadees that weigh only 10 g overwinter in central Alaska.

Aquatic life in cold regions places still more stress on an endotherm. Because of the high heat capacity and conductivity of water, an aquatic animal may lose heat at 50 to 100 times the rate it would if it were moving at the same speed through air. Even a small body of water is an infinite heat sink for an endotherm; all of the matter in its body could be converted to heat without appreciably raising the temperature of the water. How, then, do endotherms manage to exist in such stressful environments?

Increased Heat Production Versus Decreased Heat Loss

There are potentially two solutions to the problems of endothermal life in cold environments and the special problems of aquatic endotherms in particular. A stable body temperature could be achieved by increasing heat production or by decreasing heat loss. On closer examination the option of increasing heat production does not seem particularly attractive. Any significant increase in heat production would require an increase in food intake. This scheme poses obvious ecological difficulties in terrestrial Arctic and Antarctic habitats where primary production is extremely low, especially during the coldest parts of the year. For most polar animals the quantities of food necessary would probably not be available, and a number of studies have shown that metabolic rates of most polar endotherms are similar to those of related species from temperate regions.

Because they lack the option of increasing heat production significantly, conservation of heat within the body is the primary thermoregulatory mechanism of polar endotherms. Insulative values of pelts from arctic mammals are two to four times as great as those from tropical mammals. In arctic species insulative value is closely related to the length of the fur (Figure 22–2). Small species such as the least weasel and the lemming have fur only 1 or 1.5 centimeters long. Presumably, the thickness of their fur is limited because longer hair would interfere with the movement of their legs. Large mammals (caribou, polar and grizzly bears, dall sheep, and arctic fox) have hair 3 to 7 centimeters long. There is no obvious reason why their hair could not be longer; apparently, further insulation is not needed. The insulative values of pelts of short-haired tropical mammals are similar to those measured for the same hair lengths in arctic species. Long-haired tropical mammals, like the sloths, have less insulation than arctic mammals with hair of similar length.

A comparison of the lower critical temperatures of tropical and arctic mammals illustrates the effectiveness of the insulation provided (Figure 22–3). **Lower critical temperature** is the environmental temperature at which metabolic heat production must rise above its basal level to maintain a stable body temperature. A number of tropical mammals have lower critical temperatures between 20 and 30°C. As air temperatures fall below their lower critical temperatures, the animals are no longer in their thermoneutral zones and must increase their metabolic rates to maintain normal body temperatures. For example, a tropical raccoon has increased its metabolic rate approximately 50 percent above its standard level at an environmental temperature of 25°C.

Arctic mammals are much better insulated; even small species like the least weasel and the lemming have lower critical temperatures in still air that are between 10 and 20°C, and larger mammals have thermoneutral zones that extend well below freezing (Chappell 1980). The arctic fox, for example, has a lower critical temperature of −40°C, and at −70°C (approximately the lowest air temperature it ever encounters) has elevated its metabolic rate only 50 percent above its standard level. Under those conditions the fox is maintaining a body temperature approximately 110°C above air temperature. Arctic birds are equally impressive. An arctic jay has a lower critical temperature below 0°C in still air and can withstand −70°C with a 150 percent increase in its metabolic rate, and an arctic gull, like the arctic

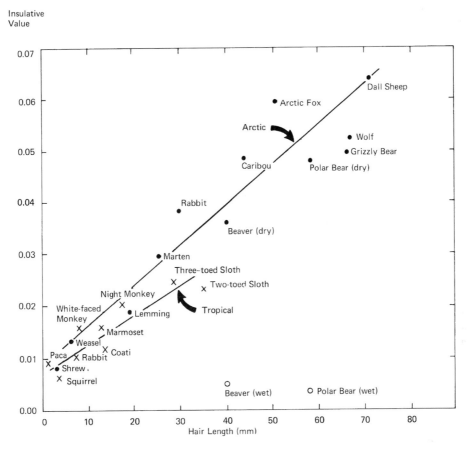

Figure 22–2   The insulative values of the pelts of arctic mammals. In air (•) the insulation is proportional to the length of the hair. Pelts from tropical mammals (×) have approximately the same insulative value as those of tropical mammals at short hair lengths, but long-haired tropical mammals like sloths have less insulation than arctic mammals with hair of the same length. Immersion in water greatly reduces the insulative value of hair, even for such semi-aquatic mammals as the beaver and polar bear (○). (Modified from P. F. Scholander et al., 1950, *Biological Bulletin* 99:237–258.)

fox, has a lower critical temperature near −40°C and can withstand −70°C with a modest increase in metabolism.

Clearly, hair or feathers can provide superb insulation for a terrestrial endotherm. These external insulative coverings are of limited value to aquatic animals, however, because when air trapped between hairs is displaced by water the coverings lose most of their insulative value. The insulation of beaver and polar bear hair falls almost to zero when it is wet (Figure 22–2). In water, fat is a far more effective insulator than hair, and aquatic mammals have thick layers of blubber. This blubber forms the primary layer of insulation; skin temperature is nearly identical to water temperature and there is an steep temperature gradient through the blub-

ber so that its inner surface is at the animal's core body temperature.

The insulation provided by blubber is so effective that pinnipeds and cetaceans require special heat-dissipating mechanisms to avoid overheating when they engage in strenuous activity, or venture into warm water or onto land. This heat dissipation is achieved by shunting blood into capillary beds in the skin outside the blubber layer and into the flippers, which are not covered by blubber. Selective perfusion of these capillary beds enables a seal or porpoise to adjust its heat loss to balance its heat production. When it is necessary to conserve energy, a countercurrent heat exchange system in the blood vessels supplying the flippers is brought into operation; when excess heat is to be dumped,

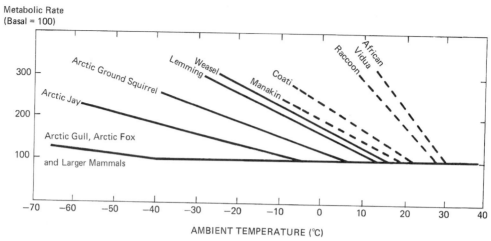

Figure 22–3   Lower critical temperatures for birds and mammals. Solid lines, arctic birds and mammals; dashed lines, tropical birds and mammals. The basal metabolic rate for each species is considered to be 100 units to facilitate comparisons among species. The metabolic rate of a species rises above its basal rate at the lower critical temperature for the species. Because of their effective insulation, arctic birds and mammals can maintain resting metabolic rates at lower environmental temperatures than tropical species, and show smaller increases in metabolism (i.e., flatter slopes) below the lower critical temperature. (Modified from P. F. Scholander et al., 1950, *Biological Bulletin* 99:237–258.)

blood is shunted away from the countercurrent system into superficial veins.

The effectiveness of the insulation of marine mammals is graphically illustrated by the problems experienced by the northern fur seal (*Callorhinus ursinus*) during its breeding season. Northern fur seals are large animals; males attain body masses in excess of 250 kg. Unlike most pinnipeds, fur seals have a dense covering of fur, which is probably never wet through. They are inhabitants of the North Pacific. For most of the year they are pelagic, but during summer they breed on the Pribilof Islands in the Bering Sea north of the Aleutian Peninsula. Male fur seals gather harems of females on the shore. Here they must try to prevent the females from straying, chase away other males, and copulate with willing females.

George Bartholomew and his colleagues have studied both the behavior of the fur seals and their thermoregulation (Bartholomew and Wilke 1956). Summers in the Pribilof Islands (which are near 57°N latitude) are characterized by nearly constant overcast and air temperatures that rise only to 10°C during the day. These conditions are apparently close to the upper limits the seals can tolerate. Almost any activity on land causes the seals to pant and to raise their hind flippers (which are abundantly supplied with sweat glands) and wave them

about. If the sun breaks through the clouds, activity suddenly diminishes—females stop moving about, males reduce harem guarding activities and copulation, and the adult seals pant and wave their flippers. If the air temperature rises as high as 12°C, females, which never defend territories, begin to move into the water. Forced activity on land can produce lethal overheating.

At that time, seal hunters herded the bachelor males from the area behind the harems inland preparatory to killing and skinning them. Bartholomew recorded one drive that took place in the early morning of a sunny day while the air temperature rose from 8.6°C at the start of the drive to 10.4°C by the end. In 90 minutes the seals were driven about 1 kilometer with frequent pauses for rest. "The seals were panting heavily and frequently paused to wave their hind flippers in the air before they had been driven 150 yards from the rookery. By the time the drive was half finished most of the seals appeared badly tired and occasional animals were dropping out of the pods [groups of seals]. In the last 200 yards of the drive and on the killing grounds there were found 16 'roadskins' (animals that had died of heat prostration) and in addition a number of others prostrated by overheating." The average body temperature of the roadskins of this drive was 42.2°C, which is 4.5°C above the 37.7°C mean body temperature of adults not under thermal stress.

Fur seals can withstand somewhat higher temperatures in water than they can in air because of the greater heat conduction of water, but they are not able to penetrate warm seas. Adult male fur seals apparently remain in the Bering Sea during their pelagic season. Young males and females migrate into the North Pacific, but they are not found in waters warmer than 14 to 15°C, and they are most abundant in water of 11°C. Their inability to regulate body temperature during sustained activity and their sensitivity to even low levels of solar radiation and moderate air temperatures probably restrict the location of potential breeding sites and their movements during their pelagic periods. Summers in the Pribilofs are barely cool enough to allow the seals to breed there. An increase in summer temperature associated with global warming might drive the seals from their traditional breeding grounds.

■ Migration to Avoid Stressful Conditions

Every environment has unfavorable aspects for some species, and these unfavorable conditions are often seasonal, especially in latitudes far from the Equator. The primary cause of migrations is usually related to seasonal changes in climatic factors such as temperature or rainfall. In turn, these conditions influence food supply and the occurrence of suitable breeding conditions.

We can consider the costs and benefits of migrating by considering two kinds of animals that represent extremes of body size. The baleen whales are the largest animals that have ever lived, and hummingbirds are among the smallest endotherms; yet both whales and hummingbirds migrate.

Whales

The annual cycle of events in the lives of the great baleen whales is particularly instructive in showing how migration relates to the use of energy and how it correlates with reproduction in the largest of all animals. Most baleen whales summer in polar or subpolar waters of either the Northern or the Southern Hemisphere, where they feed on krill or other crustaceans that are abundant in those cold, productive waters. For three or four months each

year a whale consumes a vast quantity of food that is converted into stored energy in the form of blubber and other kinds of fat. During this same time pregnant female whales nurture their unborn young, which may grow to one-third the length of their mothers before birth.

Near the end of summer the whales begin migration toward tropical or subtropical waters where the females bear their young and nurse them for a period of time before making the reverse migration. During this winter sojourn in warm waters, some of the whales also mate. The young grow rapidly on the rich milk provided by their mothers, and by spring the calves are mature enough to travel with their mothers back to arctic or antarctic waters. The calves are weaned about the time they arrive in their summer quarters. From a bioenergetic and trophic point of view the remarkable feature of this annual migration is that virtually all of the energy required to fuel it comes from ravenous feeding and fattening during the three or four months spent in polar seas. Little or no feeding occurs during migration or during the winter period of calving and nursing. Energy for all these activities comes from the abundant stores of blubber and fat.

The gray whale (*Eschrichtius robustus*) of the Pacific Ocean has one of the longest and best known migrations (Figure 22–4). The summer feeding waters are in the Bering Sea and the Chukchi Sea north of the Bering Strait in the Arctic Ocean. A small segment of the population moves down the coast of Asia to Korean waters at the end of the Arctic summer, but most gray whales follow the Pacific Coast of North America, moving south to Baja California and adjacent parts of western Mexico. They arrive in December or January, bear their young in shallow, warm waters, and then depart northward again in March. Some gray whales make an annual round-trip of at least 9000 kilometers and the adults eat little or nothing for the eight months they are away from their northern feeding grounds.

The amount of energy expended by a whale in this annual cycle is phenomenal. The basal metabolic rate of a gray whale with a fat-free body mass of 50,000 kg is approximately 979,000 kJ per day. If the metabolic rate of a free-ranging whale, including the locomotion involved in feeding and migrating, is about three times the basal rate (a typical level of energy use for mammals), the whale's average daily energy expenditure is around 2,937,000 kJ. Body fat contains 38,500 kJ/kg, so the whale's

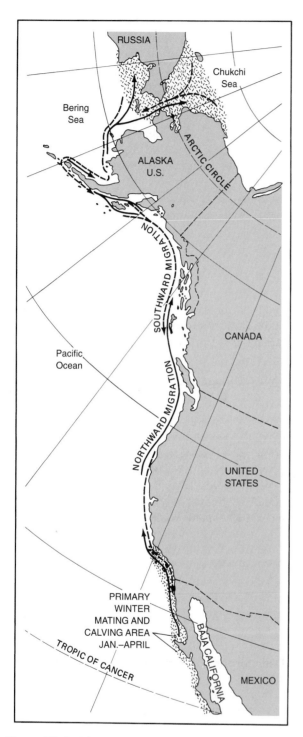

Figure 22–4 Migratory route of the gray whale between the Arctic Circle and Baja California.

daily energy expenditure is equivalent to metabolizing over 76 kg of blubber or fat per day. Assuming an energy content of 20,000 kJ/kg for krill and a 50 percent efficiency in converting the gross energy intake of food into biologically usable energy, the energy requirement for existence is equivalent to a daily intake of 294 kg of food.

In addition to satisfying its daily energy needs, a whale on the feeding grounds must accumulate a store of blubber. To live for 245 days during the migration and calving in midlatitudinal waters without eating, the whale must metabolize a minimum of 18,375 kg of fat. Accumulating that amount of fat in 120 days of active feeding in arctic waters at a conversion efficiency of 50 percent requires the consumption of 70,438 kg of krill, or 586 kg per day. The total food intake per day on the feeding grounds to accommodate the whale's daily metabolic needs plus energy storage for the migratory period would be not less than 294 + 586 = 880 kg of krill per day.

This is a minimum estimate for females because the calculations do not include the energetic costs of the developing fetus or the cost of milk production. Nor does it include the cost of transporting 20,000 kg of fat through the water. But a large whale can do all this work and more without exhausting its insulative blanket of blubber because nearly half the total body mass of a large whale consists of blubber and other fats.

Why does a gray whale expend all this energy to migrate? The adult is too large and too well insulated ever to be stressed by the cold Arctic and subarctic waters that do not vary much from 0°C from summer to winter. It seems strange for an adult whale to abandon an abundant source of food and go off on a forced starvation trek into warm waters that may cause stressful overheating. The advantage probably accrues to the newborn young, which, though relatively large, lacks an insulative layer of blubber. If the young whale were born in cold northern waters it would probably have to use a large fraction of its energy intake (milk produced from its mother's stored fat) to generate metabolic heat to regulate its body temperature. That energy could otherwise be used for rapid growth. Apparently, it is more effective, and perhaps energetically more efficient, for the mother whale to migrate thousands of kilometers into warm waters to give birth and nurse in an environment where the young whale can invest most of its energy intake in rapid growth.

Hummingbirds

At the opposite end of the size range, hummingbirds are the smallest endotherms that migrate.

Ornithologists have long been intrigued by the ability of the ruby-throated hummingbird (*Archilochus colubris*), which weighs only 3.5 to 4.5 g, to make a nonstop flight of 800 kilometers during migration across the Gulf of Mexico from Florida to the Yucatan Peninsula. For many years it seemed impossible that such a small bird with such a high resting metabolic rate could store enough energy for such a long flight.

Measurements of body fat, oxygen consumption during flight, and speed of flight have finally solved the riddle. Like most migratory birds, ruby-throated hummingbirds store subcutaneous and body fat by feeding heavily prior to migration. A hummingbird with a lean mass of 2.5 g can accumulate 2 g of fat. Measurements of the energy consumption of a hummingbird hovering in the air in a respirometer chamber in the lab indicate an energy consumption of 2.89 to 3.10 kJ per hour. Hovering is energetically more expensive than forward flight, so these values represent the maximum energy used in migratory flight. Even so, two grams of fat produces enough energy to last for 24 to 26 hours of sustained flight. Hummingbirds fly about 40 kilometers per hour, so crossing the Gulf of Mexico requires about 20 hours. Thus, by starting with a full store of fat, they have enough energy for the crossing with a reserve for unexpected contingencies such as a headwind that slows their progress. In fact, most migratory birds wait for weather conditions that will generate tailwinds before they begin their migratory flights, thereby further reducing the energy cost of migration.

■ Torpor as a Response to Low Temperatures and Limited Food

We have stressed the high energy cost of endothermy because the need to collect and process enough food to supply that energy is a central factor in the lives of many endotherms. In extreme situations environmental conditions may combine to overpower a small endotherm's ability to process and transform enough chemical energy to sustain a high body temperature through certain critical phases of its life. For diurnally active birds, long cold nights during which there is no access to food can be lethal, especially if the bird has not been able to feed fully during the daytime. Cold winter seasons usually present a dual problem for resident endotherms—the need to maintain high body temperature when environmental temperatures are low despite the seasonal scarcity of food energy. In response to such problems, some birds and mammals have mechanisms that permit them to avoid the energetic costs of maintaining a high body temperature under unfavorable circumstances by entering a state of torpor (adaptive hypothermia). By entering torpor an endotherm is giving up many of the advantages of endothermy, but in exchange it realizes an enormous saving of both energy and water. Thus, endotherms enter torpor only when they would face critical shortages of energy or water if they remained at normal body temperature.

Physiological Adjustments During Torpor

When an endotherm becomes torpid profound changes occur in a variety of physiological functions (Heller 1987). Although body temperatures may fall very low during torpor, temperature regulation does not entirely cease. In **deep torpor** an animal's body temperature drops to within 1°C or less of the ambient temperature, and in some cases (bats, for example) extended survival is possible at body temperatures just above the freezing point of the tissues. Arctic ground squirrels actually allow the temperature of parts of their bodies to supercool as low as −2.9°C (Barnes 1989). Oxidative metabolism and energy use are reduced to as little as one-twentieth of the rate at normal body temperatures. Respiration is slow, and the overall breathing rate can be less than one inspiration per minute. Heart rates are drastically reduced and blood flow to peripheral tissues is virtually shut down, as is blood flow posterior to the diaphragm. Most of the blood is retained in the core of the body. In this respect, the cardiovascular adjustments that occur during torpor are like those seen in diving animals (Jones et al. 1988).

Deep torpor is a comatose condition much more profound than the deepest sleep. Voluntary motor responses are reduced to sluggish postural changes, but some sensory perception of powerful auditory and tactile stimuli and ambient temperature changes is retained. Perhaps most dramatically, a torpid animal can arouse spontaneously from this state by endogenous heat production that restores the high body temperature characteristic of a normally active endotherm. Some endotherms can rewarm under their own power from the lowest levels of torpor, whereas others must warm passively with an increase in ambient temperature until some threshold is reached at which arousal starts.

There are varying degrees of torpor, from the deepest states of hypothermia to the lower range of body temperatures reached by normally active endotherms during their daily cycles of activity and sleep. Nearly all birds and mammals, especially those with body masses under 1 kg, undergo **circadian temperature cycles.** These cycles vary from 1 to 5°C or more between the average high-temperature characteristic of the active phase of the daily cycle and the average low-temperature characteristic of rest or sleep (Aschoff 1982). Small birds (sunbirds, hummingbirds, chickadees) and small mammals (especially bats and rodents) may drop their body temperatures during quiescent periods from 8 to 15°C below their regulated temperature during activity. Even a bird as large as the turkey vulture (about 2.2 kg) regularly drops its body temperature at night. When all these different endothermic patterns are considered together, no really sharp distinction can be drawn between torpor and the basic daily cycle in body temperature that characterizes most small to medium-size endotherms.

Body Size and the Occurrence of Torpor

Species of endotherms capable of deep torpor are found in a number of groups of mammals and birds. The echidna, platypus, and several species of small marsupials display patterns of hypothermia, but the phenomenon is most diverse among placentals, particularly among bats and rodents. Certain kinds of hypothermia have also been described for some insectivores, particularly the hedgehog, some primates, and some edentates. Deep torpor, contrary to popular notion, is not known for any of the carnivores, despite the fact that some of them den in the winter and remain inactive for long periods. Among birds, torpor occurs in some of the goatsuckers or nightjars and in hummingbirds, swifts, mousebirds, and some passerines (sunbirds, swallows, chickadees, and others). Other species, including larger ones like turkey vultures, show varying depths of hypothermia at rest or in sleep but are not in a semicomatose state of deep torpor.

Torpor and body size are closely related, especially among mammals (French 1986). The largest mammals that undergo deep torpor are marmots, which weigh about 5 kg. The limitation on body size reflects a balance between the energy expendi-

ture at normal body temperatures and during torpor and the time and energy spent in entry into torpor and in arousal. Torpor is not as energetically advantageous for a large animal as for a small one. In the first place, the energetic cost of maintaining high body temperature is relatively greater for a small animal than for a large one and, as a consequence, a small animal has more to gain from becoming torpid. Second, a large animal cools off more slowly than a small animal and does not lower its metabolic rate as rapidly.

Furthermore, large animals have more body tissue to rewarm on arousal, and their costs of arousal are correspondingly larger than those of small animals (Figure 22–5). An endotherm weighing a few grams, such as a little brown bat or a hummingbird, can warm up from torpor at the rate of about 1°C per minute, and be fully active within 30 min-

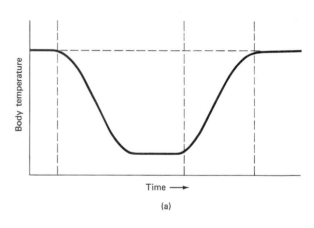

(a)

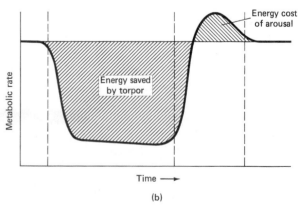

(b)

Figure 22–5 Changes in body temperature and metabolic rate during torpor. A decrease in metabolic rate (shown in part a) precedes a fall in body temperature (part b) to a new set point. An increase in metabolism produces the heat needed to return to normal body temperatures; the metabolic rate during arousal briefly overshoots the resting rate.

utes or less depending on the depth of hypothermia. A 100-gram hamster requires more than 2 hours to arouse, and a marmot takes many hours. Entrance into torpor is slower than arousal. Consequently, daily torpor is feasible only for very small endotherms; there would not be enough time for a large animal to enter and arouse from torpor during a 24-hour period. Moreover, the energy required to warm up a large mass is very great. Oliver Pearson calculated that it costs a 4-gram hummingbird only 0.48 kilojoule to raise its body temperature from 10 to 40°C. That is 1/85 of the total daily energy expenditure of an active hummingbird in the wild. By contrast, a 200 kg bear would require 18,000 kJ to warm from 10 to 37°C, the equivalent of a full day's energy expenditure. The smaller potential saving and the greater cost of arousal make daily torpor impractical for any but small endotherms.

Medium-size endotherms are not entirely excluded from the energetic savings of torpor, but the torpor must persist for a longer period to realize a saving. For example, ground squirrels and marmots enter prolonged torpor during the winter **hibernation** when food is scarce. They spend several days at very low body temperatures (in the region of 5°C), then arouse for a period before becoming torpid again. Still larger endotherms would have such large total costs of arousal (and would take so long to warm up) that torpor is not

feasible for them even on a seasonal basis. Bears in winter dormancy, for example, lower their body temperatures only about 5°C from normal levels, and metabolic rate decreases about 50 percent. Even this small drop, however, amounts to a large energy saving through the course of a winter for an animal as large as a bear. That small reduction in body temperature, combined with the large fat stores bears accumulate before retreating to their winter dens, is sufficient to carry a bear through the winter.

Energetic Aspects of Daily Torpor

Studies of daily torpor in birds have emphasized the flexibility of the response in relation to the energetic stress faced by individual birds. Susan Chaplin's work with chickadees provides an example (Chaplin 1974). These small (10- to 12-gram) passerine birds are winter residents in northern latitudes, where they regularly experience ambient temperatures that do not rise above freezing for days or weeks (Figure 22–6).

Chaplin found that in winter chickadees around Ithaca, New York, allow their body temperatures to drop from the normal level of 40 to 42°C that is maintained during the day to 29 to 30°C at night. This reduction in body temperature permits a 30 percent reduction in energy consumption. The chickadees rely primarily on fat stores they accu-

Figure 22–6 The black-capped chickadee, *Parus atricapillus.* This small bird enters torpor at night in cold climates. (Photograph © Gregory K. Scott/Photo Researchers, Inc.)

mulate as they feed during the day to supply the energy needed to carry them through the following night. Thus the energy available to them and the energy they use at night can be estimated by measuring the fat content of birds as they go to roost in the evening and as they begin activity in the morning. Chaplin found that in the evening chickadees had an average of 0.80 gram of fat per bird. By morning the fat store had decreased to 0.24 gram. The fat metabolized during the night (0.56 gram per bird) corresponds to the metabolic rate expected for a bird that had allowed its body temperature to fall to 30°C.

Chaplin's calculations show that this torpor is necessary if the birds are to survive the night. It would require 0.92 gram of fat per bird to maintain a body temperature of 40°C through the night. That is more fat than the birds have when they go to roost in the evening. If they did not become torpid, they would starve before morning. Even with torpor, they use 70 percent of their fat reserve in one night. They do not have an energy supply to carry them far past sunrise and chickadees are among the first birds to start to forage in the morning. They also forage in weather so foul that other birds, which are not in such precarious energy balance, remain on their roosts. The chickadees must reestablish their fat stores each day if they are to survive the next night.

Hummingbirds, too, may depend on the energy they gather from nectar during the day to carry them through the following night. These very small birds (4 to 10 g) have extremely high energy expenditures and yet are found during the summer in northern latitudes and at high altitudes. An example of the lability of torpor in hummingbirds was provided by studies of nesting broad-tailed hummingbirds at an altitude of 2900 meters near Gothic, Colorado (Calder and Booser 1973). Ambient temperatures drop nearly to freezing at night, and hummingbirds become torpid when energy is limiting. Calder and Booser were able to monitor the body temperatures of nesting birds by placing an imitation egg containing a temperature-measuring device in the nest. These temperature records showed that hummingbirds incubating eggs normally did not become torpid at night. The reduction of egg temperature that results from the parent bird's becoming torpid does not damage the eggs, but it slows development and delays hatching. Presumably, there are advantages to hatching the eggs as quickly as possible, and as a result brooding hummingbirds expend energy to keep themselves and their eggs warm through the night, provided that they have the energy stores necessary to maintain the high metabolic rates needed.

On some days bad weather interfered with foraging by the parent birds, and as a result they apparently went into the night with insufficient energy supplies to maintain normal body temperatures. In this situation the brooding hummingbirds did become torpid for part of the night. One bird that had experienced a 12 percent reduction in foraging time during the day became torpid for 2 hours, and a second that had lost 21 percent of its foraging was torpid for 3.5 hours. Thus, torpor can be a flexible response that integrates the energy stores of a bird with environmental conditions and biological requirements such as brooding eggs (Calder 1994).

Energetic Aspects of Prolonged Torpor

Hibernation is an effective method of conserving energy during long winters, but hibernating animals do not remain at low body temperatures for the whole winter. Periodic arousals are normal, and these arousals consume a large portion of the total amount of energy used by hibernating mammals (French 1986). An example of the magnitude of the energy cost of arousal is provided by Lawrence Wang's study of the Richardson's ground squirrel (*Spermophilus richardsonii*, Figure 22–7) in Alberta, Canada (Wang 1978).

Figure 22–7   Richardson's ground squirrel, *Spermophilus richardsonii*. (Photograph by Gail R. Michener, Univerity of Lethbridge, Alberta.)

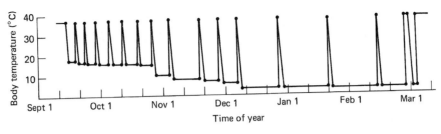

Figure 22–8   Record of body temperature during a complete torpor season for a Richardson's ground squirrel. Torpor cycles are initially short and become longer as winter progresses, then shorten again as spring approaches. (From L. C. H. Wang, 1978, *Strategies in Cold: Natural Torpidity and Thermogenesis*, edited by L. C. H. Wang and J. W. Hudson, Academic, New York, NY.)

The activity season for ground squirrels in Alberta is short: They emerge from hibernation in mid-March and adult squirrels reenter hibernation 4 months later, in mid-July. Juvenile squirrels begin hibernation in September. When the squirrels are active they have body temperatures of 37 to 38°C, and their temperatures fall as low as 3 to 4°C when they are torpid. Figure 22–8 shows the body temperature of a juvenile male ground squirrel from September through March; periods of torpor alternate with arousals all through the winter. Hibernation began in mid-September with short bouts of torpor followed by rewarming. At this time the temperature in the burrow was about 13°C. As the winter progressed and the temperature in the burrow fell, the intervals between arousals lengthened and the body temperature of the torpid animal declined. By December, January, and February the burrow temperature had dropped to 0°C and the periods between arousals were 14 to 19 days. In late February the periods of torpor became shorter, and in early March the squirrel emerged from hibernation.

A torpor cycle consists of entry into torpor, a period of torpor, and an arousal (Figure 22–9). Entry into torpor began shortly after noon on February 16, and 24 hours later the body temperature had stabilized at 3°C. This period of torpor lasted until late afternoon on March 7, when the squirrel started to arouse. In 3 hours the squirrel warmed from 3 to 37°C. It maintained that body temperature for 14 hours, and then began entry into torpor again.

These periods of arousal account for most of the energy used during hibernation (Table 22–1). The energy costs associated with arousal include the cost of warming from the hibernation temperature to 37°C, the cost of sustaining a body temperature

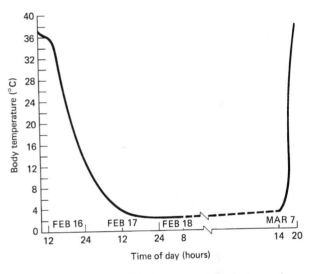

Figure 22–9   Record of body temperature during a single torpor cycle for a Richardson's ground squirrel. (From L. C. H. Wang, 1978, *Strategies in Cold: Natural Torpidity and Thermogenesis*, edited by L. C. H. Wang and J. W. Hudson, Academic, New York, NY.)

of 37°C for several hours, and the metabolism above torpid levels as the body temperature slowly declines during reentry into torpor. For the entire hibernation season the combined metabolic expenditures for those three phases of the torpor cycle account for an average of 83 percent of the total energy the squirrel uses.

Surprisingly, we have no clear understanding of why a hibernating ground squirrel undergoes these arousals that increase its total winter energy expenditure nearly fivefold. Ground squirrels do not store food in their burrows, so they are not using the periods of arousal to eat. They do urinate during arousal, and it is possible that some time at a

TABLE 22.1	Use of energy during different phases of the torpor cycle by Richardson's ground squirrel			
	Percentage of Total Energy per Month			
Month	*Torpor*	*Warming*	*Intertorpor Homeothermy*	*Reentry*
July	8.5	17.2	56.5	17.8
September	19.2	15.2	49.9	15.7
November	20.8	23.1	43.1	13.0
January	24.8	24.1	40.0	11.1
March	3.3	14.0	76.4	6.3
Average for season	16.6	19.0	51.6	12.8

Source: L. C. H. Wang, pages 109–145 in *Strategies in Cold: Natural Torpidity and Thermogenesis,* edited by L. C. H. Wang and J. W. Hudson, Academic, New York, NY.

high body temperature is necessary to carry out physiological or biochemical activities such as resynthesizing glycogen, redistributing ions, or synthesizing serotonin. Arousal may also allow a hibernating animal to determine when environmental conditions are suitable for emergence. Whatever their function, the arousals must be important because the squirrel pays a high energy price for them during a period of extreme energy conservation.

■ Endotherms in the Heat: Deserts

Hot, dry areas place a more severe physiological stress on endotherms than do the polar conditions we have already discussed. The difficulties endotherms encounter in deserts result from a reversal of their normal relationship to the environment. Endothermal thermoregulation is most effective when an animal's body temperature is higher than the temperature of its environment. In this situation heat flow is from the animal to its environment, and thermoregulatory mechanisms achieve a stable body temperature by balancing heat production and heat loss. Very cold environments merely increase the gradient between an animal's body temperature and the environment. The example of arctic foxes with lower critical temperatures of −40°C illustrates the success that endotherms have had in providing sufficient insulation to cope with enormous gradients between high core body temperatures and low environmental temperatures.

In a desert the gradient is not increased; it is reversed. Desert air temperatures can climb to 40 or 50°C during summer, and the ground temperature may exceed 60 or 70°C. Instead of losing heat to the environment, an animal is continually absorbing heat, and that heat plus metabolic heat must somehow be dissipated to maintain the animal's body temperature in the normal range. It can be a greater challenge for an endotherm to maintain its body temperature 10°C below the ambient temperature than to maintain it 100°C above ambient.

Evaporative cooling is the major mechanism an endotherm uses to reduce its body temperature. The evaporation of water requires approximately 2400 kJ/kg. (The exact value varies with temperature.) Thus, evaporation of a liter of water dissipates 2400 kJ, and evaporative cooling is a very effective mechanism as long as an animal has an unlimited supply of water. In a hot desert, however, where thermal stress is greatest, water is a scarce commodity and its use must be carefully rationed. Calculations show, for example, that if a kangaroo rat were to venture out into the desert sun, it would have to evaporate 13 percent of its body water per hour to maintain a normal body temperature. Most mammals die when they have lost 10 to 20 percent of their body water, and it is obvious that, under desert conditions, evaporative cooling is of limited utility except as a short-term response to a critical situation.

Unable to rely on evaporative cooling, endotherms have evolved a number of other responses that have allowed a diverse assemblage of birds and mammals to inhabit deserts. The mechanisms they use are complex and involve combinations of ecological, behavioral, morphological, and physiological mechanisms that act together to enhance the effectiveness of the entire system. As a start toward unraveling some of these complexities, we can categorize three major classes of responses of endotherms to desert conditions as follows:

Relaxation of Homeostasis—Some endotherms have relaxed the limits of homeostasis. They manage to survive in deserts by tolerating greater ranges of variation in characters such as body temperature or body water content than normal.

Avoidance—Other endotherms manage to avoid desert conditions by behavioral means. They live in deserts but are rarely exposed to the full stress of desert life.

Specializations—Physiological mechanisms such as torpor in response to shortages of food or water and a reduced standard metabolic rate (and, consequently, a reduction in the amount of metabolic heat an animal must dissipate) are combined with behavior by some desert organisms.

Relaxation of Homeostasis: Large Mammals in Hot Deserts

Large animals, including humans, have specific advantages and disadvantages in desert life that are directly related to body size. A large animal has nowhere to hide from desert conditions. It is too big to burrow underground, and few deserts have vegetation large enough to provide useful shade to an animal much larger than a jackrabbit. On the other hand, large body size offers some options not available to smaller animals. Large animals are mobile and can travel long distances to find food or water, whereas small animals may be limited to home ranges only a few meters or tens of meters in diameter. Large animals have small surface/mass ratios and can be well insulated. Consequently, they absorb heat from the environment slowly. A large body mass gives an animal a large thermal inertia; that is, it can absorb a large amount of heat before its body temperature reaches dangerous levels.

The Camel The dromedary camel (*Camelus dromedarius*) is the classic large desert animal (Figure 22–10). There are authentic records of journeys in excess of 500 kilometers, lasting two or three weeks, during which the camels did not have an opportunity to drink. The longest trips are made in winter and spring when air temperatures are relatively low and scattered rainstorms may have produced fresh vegetation that provides a little food and water for the camels.

Camels are large animals—adult body masses of dromedary camels are 400 to 450 kg for females and up to 500 kg for males. The camel's adjustments to desert life are revealed by comparing the daily cycle of body temperature in a camel that receives water daily and one that has been deprived of water (Figure 22–11). The watered camel shows a small daily cycle of body temperature with a minimum of 36°C in the early morning and a maximum of 38°C in midafternoon. When a camel is deprived of water, the daily temperature variation triples.

Figure 22–10 Dromedary camels. In the heat of the day, most of these camels have faced into the sun to reduce the amount of direct solar radiation they receive and have pressed against each other to reduce the heat they gain by convection and reradiation. (Photograph by P. Ward/Bruce Coleman, Inc.)

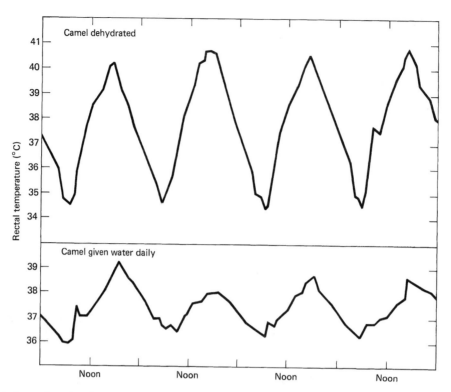

Figure 22–11   Daily cycles of body temperature of camels. A dehydrated camel (top) relaxes its control of body temperature compared to a camel with daily access to water (bottom). (From K. Schmidt–Nielsen et al., 1957, *American Journal of Physiology* 188:103–112.)

Body temperature is allowed to fall to 34.5°C at night and climbs to 40.5°C during the day.

The significance of this increased daily fluctuation in body temperature can be assessed in terms of the water that the camel would expend to prevent the 6°C rise by evaporative cooling. With a specific heat of 4.2 kJ/(kg·°C), a 6°C increase in body temperature for a 500 kg camel represents storage of 12,600 kJ of heat. Evaporation of a kilogram of water dissipates approximately 2400 kJ. Thus, a camel would have to evaporate slightly more than 5 liters of water to maintain a stable body temperature at the nighttime level; by tolerating hyperthermia during the day it can conserve that water.

In addition to the direct saving of water not used for evaporative cooling, the camel receives an indirect benefit from tolerating hyperthermia in a reduction of energy flow from the air to the camel's body. As long as the camel's body temperature is below air temperature a gradient exists that causes the camel to absorb heat from the air. At a body temperature of 40.5°C the camel's temperature is equal to that of the air for much of the day, and no net heat exchange takes place. Thus, the camel saves an additional quantity of water by eliminating the temperature gradient between its body and the air. The combined effect of these measures on water loss is illustrated by data from a young camel (Table 22–2). When deprived of water the camel

TABLE 22.2	Daily water loss of 250-kg camel			
		Water Loss (L/day) by Different Routes		
Condition	Feces	Urine	Evaporation	Total
Drinking daily (8 days)	1.0	0.9	10.4	12.3
Not drinking (17 days)	0.8	1.4	3.7	5.9

reduced its evaporative water loss by 64 percent and reduced its total daily water loss by half.

Behavioral mechanisms and the distribution of hair on the body aid dehydrated camels in reducing their heat load. In summer camels have hair 5 or 6 centimeters long on the back and up to 11 centimeters long over the hump. On the ventral surface and legs the hair is only 1.5 to 2 centimeters long. Early in the morning camels lie down on surfaces that have cooled overnight by radiation of heat to the night sky. The legs are tucked beneath the body and the ventral surface, with its short covering of hair, is placed in contact with the cool ground. In this position a camel exposes only its well-protected back and sides to the sun and places its lightly furred legs and ventral surface in contact with cool sand, which may be able to conduct away some body heat. Camels may assemble in small groups and lie pressed closely together through the day. Spending a day in the desert sun squashed between two sweaty camels may not be your idea of fun, but in this posture a camel reduces its heat gain because it keeps its sides in contact with other camels (both at about 40°C) instead of allowing solar radiation to raise the fur surface temperature to 70°C or above.

Despite their ability to reduce water loss and to tolerate dehydration, the time eventually comes when even camels must drink. These large, mobile animals can roam across the desert seeking patches of vegetation produced by local showers and move from one oasis to another, but when they drink they face a problem they share with other grazing animals: Water holes can be dangerous places. Predators frequently center their activities around water holes, where they are assured of water as well as a continuous supply of prey animals. Reducing the time spent drinking is one method of reducing the risk of predation, and camels can drink remarkable quantities of water in very short periods. A dehydrated camel can drink as much as 30 percent of its body mass in 10 minutes. (A very thirsty human can drink about 3 percent of body mass in the same time.)

The water a camel drinks is rapidly absorbed into its blood. The renal blood flow and glomerular filtration rate increase and urine flow returns to normal within a half hour of drinking. The urine changes from dark brown and syrupy to colorless and watery. Aldosterone stimulates sodium reabsorption, which helps to counteract the dilution of the blood by the water the camel has drunk.

Nonetheless, dilution of the blood causes the red blood cells to swell as they absorb water by osmosis. Camel erythrocytes are resistant to this osmotic stress, but other desert ruminants have erythrocytes that would burst under these conditions. Bedouin goats, for example, have fragile erythrocytes, and the water a goat drinks is absorbed slowly from the rumen. Goats require two days to return to normal kidney function after dehydration.

Other Large Mammals   Richard Taylor has investigated the temperature and water relations of several species of African antelope that live in arid grasslands or desert regions (Taylor 1972). These animals, which range in size from the 20 kg Thomson's gazelle and 50 kg Grant's gazelle (*Gazella thomsoni* and *G. granti*) to the 100 kg oryx (*Oryx beisa*) and 200 kg eland (*Taurotragus oryx*) use heat storage like the dromedary, but allow their body temperatures to rise considerably above the 40.5°C level recorded for the camel. Taylor recorded rectal temperatures of 45°C for the oryx and 46.5°C for the Grant's gazelle. (Thomson's gazelles, which do not penetrate into desert areas, began to pant at air temperatures above 42°C and used evaporative cooling to maintain body temperature below air temperature.)

Body temperatures above 43°C rapidly produce brain damage in most mammals, but Grant's gazelles maintained rectal temperatures of 46.5°C for as long as 6 hours with no apparent ill effects. These antelope keep brain temperature below body temperature by using a countercurrent heat exchange to cool blood before it reaches the brain. In ungulates the blood supply to the brain passes via the external carotid arteries (Figure 22–12). At the base of the brain these arteries break into a rete mirabile that lies in a venous sinus. The blood in the sinus is venous blood, returning from the walls of the nasal passages where it has been cooled by the evaporation of water. This chilled venous blood cools the warmer arterial blood before it reaches the brain. A mechanism of this sort is widespread among mammals.

Unlike the dromedary camel, antelopes are apparently independent of drinking water even during summer. Taylor suggests that one of the mechanisms that permits this independence is behavioral. The leaves of a desert shrub, *Diasperma*, are an important part of the diet of the antelopes. During the day, when air temperature is high and humidity is low, these leaves contain about 1 per-

Figure 22–12 A countercurrent heat-exchange mechanism that cools blood going to a gazelle's brain. (Modified from C. R. Taylor, 1972, in *Comparative Physiology of Desert Animals*, edited by G. M. O. Maloiy, Academic, London, UK.)

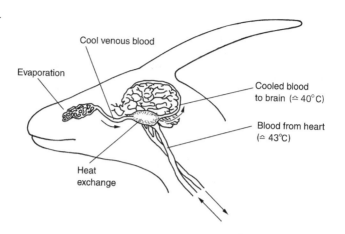

cent water by weight. They are so dry that they disintegrate into powder when they are touched. At night, however, as air temperatures fall and relative humidity increases, the leaves take up water and after 8 hours have a water content of 40 percent. If antelopes ate the leaves at night rather than in the daytime, they might obtain enough water from their food to be independent of water holes.

Large animals such as those we have discussed illustrate one approach to desert life. Too large to escape the stresses of the environment, they survive by tolerating a temporary relaxation of homeostasis. Their success under the harsh conditions in which they live is the result of complex interactions between diverse aspects of their ecology, behavior, morphology, and physiology. Only when all of these features are viewed together does an accurate picture of an animal emerge.

Birds in Desert Regions

Although birds are relatively small vertebrates, the problems they face in deserts are more like those experienced by camels and antelope than like those of small mammals. Birds are predominantly diurnal and few seek shelter in burrows or crevices. Thus, like large mammals, they meet the stresses of deserts head on and face the antagonistic demands of thermoregulation in a hot environment and the need to conserve water.

Also like large mammals, birds are mobile. It is quite possible for a desert bird to fly to a mountain range on a daily basis to reach water. For example, mourning doves in the deserts of North America congregate at dawn at water holes, some individuals flying 60 kilometers or more to reach them. The normally high and labile body temperatures of

birds give them an advantage in deserts that is not shared by mammals. With body temperatures normally around 40°C, birds face the problem of a reversed temperature gradient between their bodies and the environment for a shorter portion of each day than would a mammal. Furthermore, birds' body temperatures are normally variable, and birds tolerate moderate hyperthermia without apparent distress. These are all preadaptations to desert life that are present in virtually all birds. Neither the body temperatures nor the lethal temperatures of desert birds are higher than those of related species from nondesert regions.

The mobility provided by flight does not extend to fledgling birds, and the most conspicuous adaptations of birds to desert conditions are those that ensure a supply of water for the young. Altricial fledglings, those that need to be fed by their parents after hatching, receive the water they need from their food. One pattern of adaptation in desert birds ensures that reproduction will occur at a time when succulent food is available for fledglings. In the arid central region of Australia, bird reproduction is precisely keyed to rainfall. The sight of rain is apparently sufficient to stimulate courtship, and mating and nest building commence within a few hours of the start of rain. This rapid response ensures that the baby birds will hatch in the flush of new vegetation and insect abundance stimulated by the rain.

A different approach, very like that of mammals, has been evolved by columbiform birds (pigeons and doves), which are widespread in arid regions. Fledglings are fed on pigeon's milk, a liquid substance produced by the crop under the stimulus of prolactin. The chemical composition of pigeon's milk is very similar to that of mammalian milk; it is primarily water plus protein and fat, and it simultaneously satisfies both the nutritional requirements and the water needs of the fledgling. This approach places the water stress on the adult, which must find enough water to produce milk as well as meeting its own water requirements.

Seed-eating desert birds with precocial young, like the sandgrouse found in the deserts of Africa and the Near East, face particular problems in providing water for their young. Baby sandgrouse begin to find seeds for themselves within hours of hatching, but they are unable to fly to water holes as their parents do and seeds do not provide the water they need. Instead, adult male sandgrouse transport water to their broods. The belly feathers, especially in males, have a unique structure in which the proximal portions of the barbules are coiled into helices. When the feather is wetted, the barbules uncoil and trap water. The feathers of male sandgrouse hold 15 to 20 times their weight of water, and the feathers of females hold 11 to 13 times their weight.

Male sandgrouse in the Kalahari Desert of southern Africa fly to water holes just after dawn and soak their belly feathers, absorbing 25 to 40 milliliters of water. Some of this water evaporates on the flight back to their nests, but calculations indicate that a male sandgrouse could fly 30 kilometers and arrive with 10 to 28 milliliters of water still adhering to its feathers. As the male sandgrouse lands, the juveniles rush to him, and seizing the wet belly feathers in their beaks, strip the water from them with downward jerks of their heads. In a few minutes, the young birds have satisfied their thirst and the male rubs himself dry on the sand.

Avoiding Desert Conditions: Small Mammals in Hot Deserts

Rodents are the preeminent small mammals of arid regions. It is a commonplace observation that population densities of rodents may be higher in deserts than in moist situations. A number of features of rodent biology can be viewed as preadaptive for extending their geographic ranges into hot, arid regions. Among the most important of these preadaptations are the normally nocturnal habits of many rodents and their practice of living in burrows. A burrow provides ready escape from the heat of a desert, giving an animal access to a microenvironment within its thermoneutral zone while soil temperatures on the surface climb above 60°C. Rodents that live in burrows during the day and emerge to forage at night escape the desert heat so successfully that their greatest temperature stress may be cold. Because of the normal absence of clouds, deserts cool rapidly after sundown and many deserts are distinctly chilly at night during much of the year.

Although retreat to a burrow during the day provides direct escape from heat, it is not, by itself, a solution to the other major challenges of desert life—the chronic shortages of food and water. What the burrow does provide is the shelter and microclimate an animal needs in order to solve the other problems. We pointed out earlier that a kangaroo rat would reach its lethal limit of dehydration in less than 2 hours if it had to rely on evaporative cooling to maintain its body temperature at normal levels during the day. By retreating into its burrow, a kangaroo rat avoids that use of water. Indeed, the water savings of a burrow probably go beyond that. As a rodent in a burrow loses water by evaporation, the air in the burrow becomes humid. At the same time of day, the relative humidity of air outside the burrow may be only 20 to 30 percent. The higher humidity of burrow air reduces an animal's evaporative water loss.

A further saving is achieved in some animals (including birds and lizards in addition to mammals) by a countercurrent water recycler in the nasal passages. The air an animal exhales leaves the nares at a temperature lower than that at which it left the lungs. The phenomenon has important implications in terms of energy and water balance.

A brief consideration of the respiratory cycle illustrates the mechanism involved. As air is inhaled, it passes over moist tissues in the nasal passages. The nasal passages themselves are narrow and the wall surface area is large. As the air passes over these moist surfaces, it is warmed and humidified so that when it enters the lungs it is saturated with water at the animal's core body temperature. Temperature equilibration and saturation with water vapor are essential to protect the lungs, which are delicate structures that would be damaged if they were exposed to dry air. As the relatively dry inhaled air passes over the moist tissues of the nasal passages, evaporation cools the surfaces of the nasal passages. When the warm, saturated air from the lungs is exhaled, water from the air condenses on the cool surfaces of the nasal passages. This process of evaporation on inhalation and condensation on exhalation saves water. It must be emphasized that this countercurrent exchange of heat and energy is not an adaptation to desert life. It is an inevitable consequence of the anatomy and physiology of the nasal passages. However, a preliminary comparison of the nasal heat and water exchange of five species of rodents suggests that interspecific differences may be related to the aridity of the habitat (Welch 1984). Two desert rodents, the kangaroo rat (a heteromyid) and the Australian hopping mouse (a murid), were especially good at recovering water when they were breathing air of low humidity. In contrast, two murid rodents from moist habitats, the deer mouse and the house mouse, were good at recovering heat when they were breathing cold air.

The importance of the nasal countercurrent in water recovery can be illustrated by calculations (Table 22–3). During the day a kangaroo rat in its burrow inhales air that is at 30°C and 80 percent relative humidity. This air contains 24 mg of water per liter of air. (Saturated air, at 100 percent relative humidity, contains 30 mg of water per liter at 30°C.) The kangaroo rat must warm this air to core temperature (38°C) and add enough water to raise the relative humidity at that temperature to 100 percent. Saturated air contains 46 mg water per liter at 38°C, so the amount of water that must be evaporated in the nasal passages is 22 mg per liter of inhaled air.

Under the conditions we have assumed, a kangaroo rat exhales air at 31°C. That is, as the air travels out through the nasal passages it is cooled 7°C by contact with the walls. The exhaled air is still saturated with water, but at 31°C saturated air contains only 31 mg of water per liter instead of the 46 mg/liter it contained at 38°C. Thus, a kangaroo rat evaporates 22 mg of water per liter of air to saturate the air before it enters the lungs, and recovers 15 mg of water per liter of air on exhalation. The nasal countercurrent system reduces its respiratory water loss by nearly 70 percent from that which the kangaroo rat would experience if the air were exhaled at core body temperature. The savings amounts to 15 mg of water per liter of air under the conditions we have assumed.

The water saving achieved at night when the rat is outside its burrow is still greater. The outside air is cool (15°C) and dry (20 percent relative humidity). Consequently, the kangaroo rat must evaporate 43.5 mg of water per liter of air to bring it to saturation at core temperature. The increased evaporation cools the kangaroo rat's nose to 14.5°C, and air exhaled at this temperature contains only 12 mg of water per liter. Thus, under nighttime conditions, a kangaroo rat recovers 74 percent of the water evaporated in the nasal passages, a saving of 34 mg of water per liter of inhaled air.

Water excreted with the urine and feces is another avenue of water loss. Rodents in general have the ability to produce relatively dry feces and concentrated urine. The laboratory white rat, for example, can produce urine with twice the concentration humans can achieve. The dromedary camel has a urine-concentrating ability approximately equivalent to that of a rat, and so do dogs and cats. Desert rodents, such as kangaroo rats, sand rats, and jerboas, have urine concentrations of 3000 to 6000 mmole·kg^{-1}, and the current world champion urine concentrator appears to be the Australian hopping mouse, which can produce urine concentrations in excess of 9000 mmole·kg^{-1}. As we pointed out in Chapter 4, high urine concentrations in mammals are associated with long loops of Henle in the kidney which enhance the countercurrent multiplier function.

As a result of their low evaporative water losses and ability to concentrate urine and produce relatively dry feces, many desert rodents are completely independent of liquid water. Their water loss has been reduced to the point at which they

TABLE 22.3	Water recycled by nasal countercurrent exchange in a kangaroo rat							
	Inhaled Air				Exhaled Air			
Condition	Temperature (°C)	RH (%)	Water Content (mg/L)	Water Added (mg/L)	Temperature (°C)	RH (%)	Water Content (mg/L)	Water Recovered (mg/L)
Daytime, in burrow	30	80	24	22	31	100	31	15
Night, on surface	15	20	2.5	43.5	14.5	100	12	34

are able to obtain all the water they need from their food. Part of this water comes from water actually contained in the food, and part from the water that is produced as the food is oxidized (metabolic water, Table 16–2).

The free water content of food depends in part on the relative humidity at which it is stored. We pointed out that *Diasperma* leaves have a water content of only 1 percent during the day but absorb water at night when the relative humidity rises, and it appears to be at night that the antelope eat them. Seeds show a similar variation in water content with humidity. Knut Schmidt–Nielsen found that the barley he fed his kangaroo rats contained less than 4 percent water when it was kept at 10 percent relative humidity, but when it was stored at 76 percent relative humidity, the water content rose to 18 percent. He reported that bannertail kangaroo rats (*Dipodomys spectabilis*) may store several kilograms of plant material in their burrows, where it is exposed to the high relative humidity of the burrow atmosphere. The smaller Merriam's kangaroo rat (*D. merriami*) does not store much food in its own burrow, but sneaks into the burrows of bannertail kangaroo rats and may help itself to the food stored there. Gerbils in the Old World deserts also store seeds in their burrows. Air-dried seeds contained 4 to 7 percent water, whereas seeds taken from the gerbils' burrows contained 30 percent water. Thus, hoarding food in the burrow not only provides a hedge against food shortages but increases the amount of water available to an animal from the food.

Nocturnal activity allows some rodents to avoid the heat of the desert, but not all rodents that live in deserts are nocturnal. Ground squirrels are diurnal and are conspicuous inhabitants of deserts (Figure 22–13). They can be seen running frantically across the desert surface even in the middle of day. The almost frenetic activity of desert ground squirrels on intensely hot days is a result of the thermoregulatory problems that small animals experience under these conditions. Studies of the antelope ground squirrel (*Ammospermophilus leucurus*) at Deep Canyon, near Palm Springs, California, provide information about how the behavior of the squirrels is affected by the heat stress of the environment (Chappell and Bartholomew 1981a,b).

The heat on summer days at Deep Canyon is intense, and standard operative temperatures in the sun are as high as 70 to 75°C (Box 22–1). The squirrels are heat-stressed for most of the day. Standard operative temperature rises above the thermoneutral zone of ground squirrels within 2 hours after sunrise, and the squirrels follow a bimodal pattern of activity that peaks in midmorning and again in the late afternoon. Relatively few squirrels are active in the middle of the day. The body temperatures of antelope ground squirrels are labile, and body temperatures of individual squirrels vary as much as 7.5°C (from 36.1 to 43.6°C) during a day. The squirrels use this lability of body temperature to store heat during their periods of activity.

The high operative temperatures limit the time that squirrels can be active in the open to no more than 9 to 13 minutes. The squirrels sprint furiously

Figure 22–13 The antelope ground squirrel, *Ammospermophilus leucurus*, is a diurnal desert rodent. (Photograph by George A. Bartholomew and Mark A. Chappell, University of California at Los Angeles.)

How Hot Is It?

Measurements of environmental temperatures figure largely in studies of the energetics of animals, but the actual process of making the measurements is complicated, and no one measurement is necessarily appropriate for all purposes. Exchange of energy between animals and their environments involves radiation, convection, conduction, and evaporation. In addition, metabolic heat production contributes significantly to the body temperatures of endotherms. The thermal environment of an animal is determined by all of the routes of heat exchange operating simultaneously, and its body temperature includes the effect of metabolism as well. The question How hot is it? translates to What is the heat load for an animal in this environment? Answering that question requires integrating all the routes of energy exchange to give one number that represents the environmental heat stress. (It is easier to think of heat stress as coming from a hot environment and being represented by a risk of overheating [hyperthermia], but the same reasoning applies to a cold environment. In that situation the heat stress is loss of heat and the risk of hypothermia.)

Physiological ecologists have developed several measurements of the environmental heat stress on an organism, and Figure 22–14 illustrates four of these. The data come from a study of the thermoregulation of the antelope ground squirrel in a desert canyon in California (Chappell and Bartholomew 1981a).

The easiest measurement to make is the temperature of the air (T_a, frequently called **ambient temperature**). At Deep Canyon, California, in June air temperature rose from about 25°C at dawn to a peak above 50°C in late afternoon, and then declined. Air temperature is a factor in conductive and convective heat exchange.

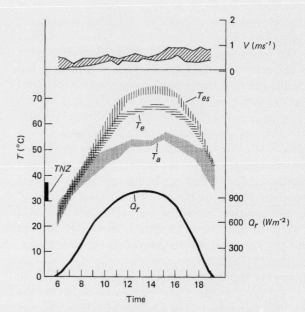

Figure 22–14 Ground-level meterological conditions in open sunlit areas at Deep Canyon, California, during June. Wind velocity (V) in meters per second, solar insolation (Q_r) in watts per square meter, effective environmental temperature (T_e) and standard operative temperature (T_{es}) in °C. The thermoneutral zone (TNZ) of ground squirrels is indicated. (From M. A. Chappell and G. A. Bartholomew, 1981, *Physiological Zoology* 54:81–93. Copyright 1981 by The University of Chicago. All rights reserved.)

An animal gains heat by conduction and convection when the air temperature is warmer than the animal's surface temperature and loses heat when the air is cooler. Conductive heat exchange is usually small, but convection can be an important component of the overall energy budget of an organism. However, the magnitude of convective heat exchange depends on windspeed as well as air temperature. Thus, measuring air temperature provides

from one patch of shade to the next, pausing only to seize food or to look for predators. They minimize their exposure to the highest temperatures by running across open areas, and seek shade or their burrows to cool off. On a hot summer day a squirrel can maintain a body temperature below 43°C (the maximum temperature it can tolerate) only by

retreating every few minutes to a burrow deeper than 60 centimeters where the soil temperature is 30 to 32°C. The body temperature of an antelope ground squirrel shows a pattern of rapid oscillations, rising while the squirrel is in the sun and falling when it retreats to its burrow (Figure 22–15). Ground squirrels do not sweat or pant; instead, only part of the information needed to assess just one of the three important routes of heat exchange. Consequently, air temperature is not a very useful measure of heat stress.

If air temperature is unsatisfactory as a measure of environmental heat load because it makes only a small contribution to the overall energy exchange, perhaps a measurement of the major source of heat is what is needed. **Solar insolation** in this arid habitat is the major source of heat stress, and the magnitude of the insolation (Q_r) can be measured with a device called a pyranometer. Solar insolation rises from 0 at dawn to about 900 watts per square meter in midday, and falls to zero at sunset. This measurement provides information about how much solar energy is available to heat an animal, but that is still only one component of the energy exchange that determines the heat stress.

The **effective environmental temperature** (T_e) combines the effects of air temperature, ground temperature, solar insolation, and wind velocity. The effective environmental temperature is measured by making an exact copy of the animal (a mannikin), equipping it with a temperature sensor such as a thermocouple, and putting the mannikin in the same place in the habitat that the real animal occupies. Taxidermic mounts are frequently used as mannikins: The pelt of an animal is stretched over a framework of wire or a hollow copper mold of the animal's body. Because the mannikin has the same size, shape, color, and surface texture as the animal, it responds the same way as the animal to solar insolation, infrared radiation, and convection. The equilibrium temperature of the mannikin is the temperature that a metabolically inert animal would have as a result of the combination of radiative and convective heat exchange. At Deep Canyon the temperatures of mannikins of antelope ground squirrels increased more rapidly than air temperatures and stabilized near 65°C from midmorning through late afternoon. The temperatures of the mannikins were 15°C higher than air temperature, showing that the heat load experienced by the ground squirrels was much greater than that estimated from air temperature alone.

Because the mannikin is a hollow shell—a pelt stretched over a supporting structure—it does not duplicate thermoregulatory processes that have important influences on the body temperature of a real animal. Metabolic heat production increases the body temperature of a ground squirrel, evaporative water loss lowers body temperature, and changes in peripheral circulation and raising or lowering the hair change the insulation. The effects of these factors can be incorporated mathematically if the appropriate values for metabolism, insulation, and whole-body conductance are known. The result of this calculation is the **standard operative temperature** (T_{es}). An explanation of how to calculate T_{es} can be found in Bakken (1980). For the ground squirrels in our example the standard operative temperature was nearly 10°C higher than the effective temperature and about 25°C higher than the air temperature. For much of the day the T_{es} of a ground squirrel in the sun at Deep Canyon was 30°C or more above the squirrel's upper critical temperature of 43°C. Similar calculations can provide values for T_{es} in other microenvironments the squirrels might occupy—in the shade of a bush, for example, or in a burrow. This is the information needed to evaluate the behavior of the squirrels to determine if their activities are limited by the need to avoid overheating.

they use this combination of transient heat storage and passive cooling in a burrow to permit diurnal activity. The strategy the antelope ground squirrel uses is basically the same as that employed by a camel—saving water by allowing the body temperature to rise until the heat can be dissipated passively. The difference between the two animals is a consequence of their difference in body size: A camel weighs 500 kg and can store heat for an entire day and cool off at night, whereas an antelope ground squirrel weighs about 100 g and heats and cools many times in the course of a day.

The tails of many desert ground squirrels are wide and flat, and the ventral surfaces of the tails

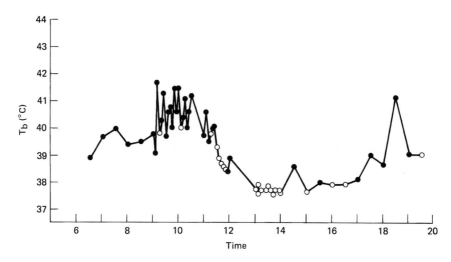

are usually white. The tail is held over the squirrel's back with its white ventral surface facing upward. In this position it acts as a parasol, shading the squirrel's body and reducing the standard operative temperature. The tail of the antelope ground squirrel is relatively short, extending only halfway up the back, but the shade it gives can reduce the standard operative temperature by as much as 6 to 8°C. The Cape ground squirrel (*Xenurus inauris*) of the Kalahari Desert has an especially long tail that can be extended forward nearly to the squirrel's head. Cape ground squirrels use their tails as parasols (Figure 22–16), and observations of the squirrels indicated that the shade may significantly extend their activity on hot days.

(a)

(b)

Figure 22–16 Cape ground squirrel (*Xenurus inauris*) using its tail as a parasol. (a) The erected tail shades the dorsal surface of the animal; (b) the tail is held over the back of a horizontal squirrel, shading its head and body. (Photographs courtesy of Albert F. Bennett, University of California at Irvine.)

The Use of Torpor by Desert Rodents

The significance of daily torpor as an energy conservation mechanism in small birds was illustrated earlier. Many desert rodents have the ability to become torpid. In most cases the torpor can be induced by limiting the food available to an animal. When the food ration of the California pocket mouse (*Perognathus californicus*) is reduced slightly below its daily requirements, it enters torpor for a part of the day. In this species even a minimum period of torpor results in an energy saving. If a pocket mouse were to enter torpor and then immediately arouse, the process would take 2.9 hours. Calculations indicate that the overall energy expenditure during that period would be reduced 45 percent compared to the cost of maintaining a normal body temperature for the same period. In this animal, the briefest possible period of torpor gives the animal an energetic saving, and the saving increases as the time spent in torpor is lengthened.

The duration of torpor is proportional to the severity of food deprivation in the pocket mouse.

As its food ration is reduced, it spends more time each day in torpor and conserves more energy. Adjusting the time spent in torpor to match the availability of food may be a general phenomenon among seed-eating desert rodents. These animals appear to assess the rate at which they accumulate food supplies during foraging rather than their actual energy balance. Species that accumulate caches of food will enter torpor even with large quantities of stored food on hand if they are unable to add to their stores by continuing to forage. When seeds were deeply buried in the sand, and thus hard to find, pocket mice spent more time in torpor than they did when the same quantity of seed was close to the surface (Reichman and Brown 1979). This behavior is probably a response to the chronic food shortage that may face desert rodents because of the low primary productivity of desert communities and the effects of unpredictable variations from normal rainfall patterns, which may almost completely eliminate seed production by desert plants in dry years.

■ Summary

Endothermy is an energetically expensive way of life. It allows organisms considerable freedom from the physical environment, especially low temperatures, but it requires a large base of food resources to sustain high rates of metabolism. Energy budgets—calculations that quantify the energy expenditures and energy returns of specific activities—can provide insights about the energy implications of many behaviors of endotherms.

Endothermy is remarkably effective in cold environments; some species of birds and mammals can live in the coldest temperatures on Earth. The insulation provided by hair, feathers, or blubber is so good that little increase in metabolic heat production is needed to maintain body temperatures 100°C above ambient temperatures. In fact, some aquatic mammals, such as northern fur seals, are so well insulated that overheating is a problem when they are on land or in water warmer than 10 or 15°C.

Endothermy is most effective when an animal is warmer than its environment. In this situation metabolism and insulation are adjusted to balance heat production and heat loss. In hot environments the usual temperature gradient is reversed—the environment is hotter than the organism—and this condition creates problems for endotherms. Evaporative cooling is effective as a short-term response to overheating, but it depletes the body's store of water and creates new problems. Small animals, nocturnal rodents for example, can often avoid much of the stress of hot environments by spending the day underground in burrows and emerging only at night when it is cool. Larger animals have nowhere to hide and must meet the stress of hot environments head-on. Camels and other large mammals of desert regions relax their limits of homeostasis when they are confronted by the twin problems of high temperatures and water shortage: They allow their body temperatures to rise during the day and fall at night. This physiological tolerance is combined with behavioral and morphological characteristics that reduce the amount of heat that actually reaches their bodies from the environment.

Mobility is an important part of the response of large endotherms to both hot and cold environments: Seasonal movements away from unfavorable conditions (migration) or regular movements between scattered oases that provide water and shade are options available to medium-size or large mammals. The great mobility of birds makes these sorts of movements feasible even for relatively small species.

When the stresses of the environment overwhelm the regulatory capacities of an endotherm and resources to sustain high rates of metabolism are unavailable, many small mammals (especially rodents) and some birds enter torpor, a state of adaptive hypothermia. During torpor the body temperature is greatly reduced and the animal becomes inert. Periods of torpor can be as brief as a few hours (nocturnal hypothermia is widespread), or can last for many weeks. Mammals that hibernate (enter torpor during winter) arouse at intervals of days or weeks, warming to their normal temperature for a few hours and then returning to a torpid condition. Torpor conserves energy at the cost of forfeiting the benefits of endothermy.

The most remarkable feature of the ability of birds and mammals to live in diverse climates is not the specializations of arctic or desert animals, remarkable as they are, but the realization that only minor changes in the basic endothermal pattern are needed to permit existence over nearly the full range of environmental conditions on Earth.

■ References

Aschoff, J. 1982. The circadian rhythm of body temperature as a function of body size. Pages 173–188 in *A Companion to Animal Physiology*, edited by C. R. Taylor, K. Johansen, and L. Bolis. Cambridge University Press, Cambridge, UK.

Bakken, G. S. 1980. The use of standard operative temperature in the study of the thermal energetics of birds. *Physiological Zoology* 53:108–119.

Barnes, B. M. 1989. Freeze avoidance in a mammal: body temperatures below 0°C in an arctic hibernator. *Science* 244:1593–1595.

Bartholomew, G. A., and F. Wilke. 1956. Body temperature in the northern fur seal, *Callorhinus ursinus. Journal of Mammalogy* 37:327–337.

Bech, C., and R. E. Reinertsen (editors). 1989. *Physology of Cold Adaptation in Birds.* Plenum, New York, NY.

Busch, C. 1988. Consumption of blood, renal function, and utilization of free water by the vampire bat, *Desmodus rotundus. Comparative Biochemistry and Physiology* 90A:141–146.

Calder, W. A. 1994. When do hummingbirds use torpor in nature? *Physiological Zoology* 67:1051–1076.

Calder, W. A., and J. Booser. 1973. Hypothermia of broadtailed hummingbirds during incubation in nature with ecological correlations. *Science* 180:751–753.

Chaplin, S. B. 1974. Daily energetics of the black-capped chickadee, *Parus atricapillus*, in winter. *Journal of Comparative Physiology* 89:321–330.

Chappell, M. A. 1980. Thermal energetics and thermoregulatory costs of small Arctic mammals. *Journal of Mammalogy* 1:278–291.

Chappell, M. A., and G. A. Bartholomew. 1981a. Standard operative temperatures and thermal energetics of the antelope ground squirrel *Ammospermophilus leucurus. Physiological Zoology* 54:81–93.

Chappell, M. A., and G. A. Bartholomew. 1981b. Activity and thermoregulation of the antelope ground squirrel *Ammospermophilus leucurus* in winter and summer. *Physiological Zoology* 54:215–223.

Davenport, J. 1992. *Animal Life at Low Temperature.* Chapman & Hall, New York, NY.

French, A. R. 1986. Patterns of thermoregulation during hibernation. Pages 393–402 in *Living in the Cold: Physiological and Biochemical Adaptations*, edited by H. C. Heller, X. J. Musacchia, and L. C. H. Wang. Elsevier, New York, NY.

Heller, H. C. (editor). 1987. Living in the cold. *Journal of Thermal Biology* 12, No. 2. (The entire issue is devoted to this topic.)

Jones, D. R., W. K. Milsom, and N. H. West (editors). 1988. The comparative physiology and biochemistry of cardiovascular, respiratory, and metabolic responses to hypoxia, diving, and hibernation. *Canadian Journal of Zoology* 66:3–200.

McNab, B. K. 1973. Energetics and distribution of vampires. *Journal of Mammalogy* 54:131–144.

Reichman, O. J., and J. H. Brown. 1979. The use of torpor by *Perognathus amplus* in relation to resource distribution. *Journal of Mammalogy* 60:550–555.

Taylor, C. R. 1972. The desert gazelle: a paradox resolved. Pages 215–217 in *Comparative Physiology of Desert Animals*, edited by G. M. O. Maloiy. *Symposia of the Zoological Society of London, No. 31.*

Wang, L. C. H. 1978. Energetic and field aspects of mammalian torpor: the Richardson's ground squirrel. Pages 109–145 in *Strategies in Cold: Natural Torpidity and Thermogenesis*, edited by L. C. H. Wang and J. W. Hudson. Academic, New York, NY.

Welch, W. R. 1984. Temperature and humidity of expired air: interspecific comparisons and significance for loss of respiratory heat and water from endotherms. *Physiological Zoology* 57:366–375.

CHAPTER
23

Body Size, Ecology, and Sociality of Mammals

We have noted the increase in brain size that has occurred during the evolution of mammals, and suggested that part of the origin of the derived features of the mammalian brain might be sought in the nocturnal habits that are postulated for Mesozoic mammals. Relying on scent or hearing instead of vision to interpret their surroundings, ancestral mammals may have experienced selection for an increased ability to associate and compare stimuli received over intervals of time. The associative capacity resulting from changes in the brain during the evolution of mammals might also contribute to more complex behavior, and the association of mother and young during nursing could provide an opportunity to modify behavior by learning.

Indeed, social behaviors and interactions between individuals play a large role in the biology of mammals. These behaviors are modified by the environment, and clear-cut relationships between energy requirements, resource distribution, and social systems can often be demonstrated. In this chapter we consider some examples of those interactions that illustrate the complexity of the evolution of mammalian social behavior. In addition, we consider the social behavior of several species of primates. The social behavior of many primates is elaborate, but not necessarily more complex than that of some other kinds of mammals, including canids. However, primates have been the subjects of more field studies than have other mammals, with the result that we know a great deal about their social behavior, its consequences for the fitness of individuals, and even a little about the way some species of primates view their own social systems.

■ Social Behavior

Sociality means living in structured groups, and some form of group living is found among nearly all kinds of vertebrates. However, the greatest development of sociality is found among mammals, and much of the biology of mammals can best be understood in the context of what sorts of groups form, the advantages of group living for the individuals involved, and the behaviors that stabilize groups.

Mammals may be particularly social animals as a result of the interaction of several mammalian characteristics, no one of which is directly related to sociality, that in combination create conditions in which sociality is likely to evolve. Thus, the relatively large brains of mammals (which presumably facilitate complex behavior and learning), long gestation periods and (for some species) continued growth of the central nervous system after birth, prolonged association of parents and young, and high metabolic rates and endothermy (with the resulting high resource requirements) may be viewed as conditions that are conducive to the development of interdependent social units (Eisenberg 1981).

Of course, not all mammals are social. Mammalian characteristics do not necessarily lead to sociality: Solitary and social species are known among marsupials and placentals. Monotremes appear to be solitary, but the three living monotreme species provide too small a sample to form a basis for speculations about the phylogenetic origins of sociality among mammals. Of course, the social behavior of mammals does not operate in a vacuum; it is only one part of the biology of a species. Social behavior interacts with other kinds of behavior (such as food gathering, predator avoidance, and reproduction), with the morphological and physiological characteristics of a species, and with the distribution of the resources in the habitat. Our emphasis in this chapter is on those interactions, and we illustrate the interrelationships of behavior and ecology with examples drawn from both predators and their prey.

The social behavior of mammals is an area of active research, and our treatment is necessarily limited. Additional information can be found in reviews by Eisenberg (1981), Wittenberger (1981), Rubenstein and Wrangham (1986), Gittleman (1989), and Caro (1994). Some interesting examples of the costs and benefits of social behavior were briefly reviewed by Lewin (1987).

■ Population Structure and the Distribution of Resources

From an ecological perspective, the distribution of resources needed by a species is usually a major factor in determining its social structure. If resources are too limited to allow more than one individual of a species to inhabit an area, there is little chance of developing social groupings. Thus, the distribution of resources in the habitat and the amount of space needed by an individual to fill its resource requirements are important factors influencing the sociality of mammals.

Most animals have a **home range**, an area within which they spend most of their time and find the food and shelter they need. Home ranges are not defended against the incursions of other individuals (an area that is defended is called a **territory**), and the value of a home range probably lies in the familiarity of an individual animal with the locations of food and shelter. Many species of vertebrates employ a type of foraging known as trap lining, in which they move over a regular route and visit specific places where food may be available. For example, a mountain lion may carefully approach a burrow where a marmot lives, beginning its stalk long before it can actually see whether the marmot is outside its burrow, and a hummingbird may return to patches of flowers at intervals that match the rate at which nectar is renewed. This kind of behavior demonstrates a familiarity with the home range and with the resources that are likely to be available in particular places.

The **resource dispersion hypothesis** predicts that the size of the home range of an individual animal will depend primarily on two factors: the resource needs of the individual, and the distribution of resources in the environment. That is, individuals of species that require large quantities of a resource such as food should have larger home ranges than individuals of species that require less food. Similarly, the home ranges of individuals should be smaller in a rich environment than in one where resources are scarce. The resource dispersion hypothesis is a very general statement of an ecological principle. It applies equally well to any kind of animal and to any kind of resource. The resources usually considered are food, shelter, and access to mates. In Chapter 18 we considered the role of monopolization of resources by individuals in relation to the mating systems of birds, and here we discuss the role of resource dispersion in relation to home range size and sociality of mammals.

Body Size and Resource Needs

Studies of mammals have concentrated on food as the resource of paramount importance in determining the sizes of home ranges. Reviews by Gittleman and Harvey (1982), Clutton–Brock and Harvey (1983), Macdonald (1983), and McNab (1983) provide additional details. Food requirements are assumed to be equivalent to energy requirements, and we discussed the relationship between energy requirements and body size in Chapter 4.

The energy consumption of vertebrates increases in proportion to body mass raised to a power that is usually between 0.75 and 1.0. If one assumes that

Figure 23–1 Home-range size of mammals as a function of body mass. The lines have slopes of 0.75 and 2.0, which illustrate allometric increases in home-range size on this double logarithmic scale. (From B. K. McNab, 1983, in Advances in the Study of Mammalian Behavior, edited by J. F. Eisenberg and D. G. Kleiman, Special Publication 7, The American Society of Mammalogists.)

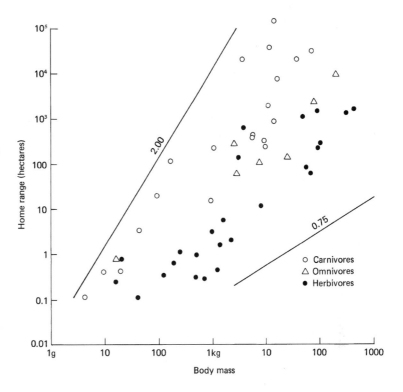

energy requirements determine home range size, one can predict that home range size will also increase in proportion to the 0.75 or 1.0 power of body mass. That prediction appears to be correct in general, but perhaps wrong in detail (Figure 23–1). That is, the sizes of the home ranges of mammals do increase with increasing body size, but the rates of increase (the slopes in Figure 23–1) are somewhat greater than expected. Home ranges appear to be proportional to body mass raised to powers between 0.75 and 2.0. This relationship between energy requirements and home range sizes suggests that energy needs are important in determining the size of the home range, but that additional factors are involved. One possibility is that the efficiency with which an animal can find and use resources decreases as the size of a home range increases. If that is true, the sizes of home ranges would be expected to increase with the body sizes of animals more rapidly than energy requirements increase with body size.

The failure of the resource dispersion hypothesis to predict the exact relationship between body size and the size of home ranges indicates that we have more to learn about how animals use the resources of their home ranges. So far we have been assuming that resources are distributed evenly throughout the home range, but that assumption overlooks

the structural complexity of most habitats. What insights can be obtained from a more realistic consideration of how mammals gather food?

The Availability of Resources

Three factors seem likely to be important in determining the availability of food to mammals: what they eat, whether their food is evenly dispersed through the habitat or is found in patches, and how they gather their food. We will consider examples of each of these factors.

Dietary Habits   Figure 23–1 shows that home range size increases with body size, and that dietary habits also affect the size of the home range. Herbivores have smaller home ranges than do omnivores of the same body size, and carnivores have larger home ranges than do herbivores or omnivores. For example, the home range of an elk (an herbivore) that weighs 100 kilograms is approximately 100 hectares. A bear (an omnivore) of the same body size has a home range larger than 1000 hectares, and a tiger (a carnivore) has a home range of more than 10,000 hectares.

The relationship between home range size and dietary habits of mammals probably reflects the abundance of different kinds of food. The grasses and leaves eaten by some herbivores are nearly ubiquitous, and a small home range provides all the food an individual requires. The plant materials (seeds and fruit) eaten by omnivores are less abundant than leaves and grasses, and different species of plants produce seeds and fruit at different seasons. Thus, a large home range is probably necessary to provide the food resources needed by an individual omnivore. The vertebrates that are eaten by carnivores are still less abundant, and a correspondingly larger home range is apparently needed to ensure an adequate food supply.

Distribution of Resources We have continued to assume that resources are evenly distributed through the habitat and that one part of a home range is equivalent to another part in terms of the availability of food. This assumption may be valid for some grazing and browsing herbivorous mammals, but it is clearly not true for mammals that seek out fruiting trees (which represent patches of food) or for any carnivorous mammal that preys on animals that occur in groups. The sizes of the home ranges of animals that use food that occurs in patches should reflect the quality of the habitat: Home ranges should be small if concentrations of food are abundant and large if concentrations of food are widely dispersed.

That relationship is well illustrated by the home ranges of arctic foxes (*Alopex lagopus*) in Iceland (Hersteinsson and Macdonald 1982). The foxes live in social groups consisting of one male and two females plus the cubs from the current year. The home ranges of the individuals of a group overlap widely with each other, and there is very little overlap between the home ranges of members of different groups. The home ranges of the foxes are located along the coast and do not extend far into the uplands (Figure 23–2). Between 60 and 80 percent of the diet is composed of items the foxes find on the shore—the carcasses of seabirds, seals, and fishes, and invertebrates from clumps of seaweed washed up on the beach. Little food is available for foxes in the uplands. The foxes concentrate their foraging on the beach during the 3 hours before low tide, which is the best time for beachcombing. The foxes approach the shore carefully, stalking along gullies. They creep out on the beach carefully, apparently looking for birds that are resting or feeding. If birds are present, the foxes stalk them. If no birds are present, the foxes search the beach for carrion.

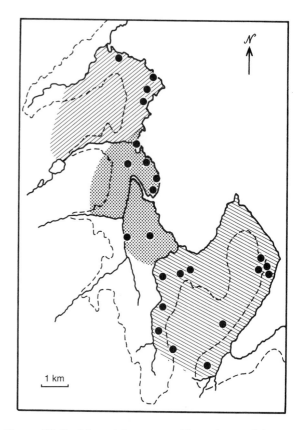

Figure 23–2 Map of the territorial boundaries of three groups of arctic foxes in Iceland. The 200-meter contour line is shown. Black dots mark the sites of dens used by the foxes. (From P. Hersteinsson and D. W. Macdonald, 1982, in Telemetric Studies of Vertebrates, edited by C. L. Cheeseman and R. B. Mitson, Symposia of the Zoological Society of London, No. 49, Academic, London, UK.)

Three groups of foxes were studied in detail, using radiotelemetry to follow the movements of individuals. The areas of the home ranges varied more than twofold, from 8.6 to 18.5 square kilometers (Table 23–1). The sizes of the home ranges were slightly more similar when only the coastline was considered: Each territory included between 5.4 and 10.5 kilometers of coastline.

The coastline was, of course, the source of most of the food the foxes were eating, but not all areas of the coastline accumulated floating objects. The distribution of food on the beaches was patchy and depended on the directions of currents. As a result, some parts of the shore were more productive than others. The length of productive coastline occupied by each group of foxes was quite similar—from 5.4 to 6.0 kilometers. Farmers in Iceland use driftwood

TABLE 23.1 Home ranges of three shrouds of arctic foxes in Iceland				
	Group 1	*Group 2*	*Group 3*	*Average*
Total area (km²)	10.3	8.6	18.5	12.5
Length of coastline (km)	5.6	5.4	10.5	7.2
Length of productive coastline (km)	5.6	5.4	6.0	5.7
Driftwood productivity (logs/year)	1800	1800	2100	1900

Source: P. Hersteinsson and D. W. Macdonald, 1982, pages 259–289 in *Telemetric Studies of Vertebrates*, edited by C. L. Cheeseman and R.B. Mitson, Symposia of the Zoological Society of London, No. 49, Academic, London, UK.

to make fence posts, and the amount of driftwood that was harvested by the farmers from the coasts in the home ranges of the three groups of foxes varied only from 1800 to 2100 logs per year. Because both driftwood and carrion are moved by currents and deposited on the beaches, the harvest of driftwood by farmers probably reflects the harvest of carrion by the foxes. Thus, the sizes of the home ranges of the three groups appear to match the distribution of their most important food resource, and the productive areas of the home ranges of the three groups are very similar despite the more than twofold difference in total areas of their home ranges.

Group Size and Hunting Success   It is readily apparent that the average size of the home range of a species of mammal can influence the social system of that species. Individuals of a species probably encounter each other frequently when home ranges are small, whereas individuals of species that roam over thousands of hectares may rarely meet. Thus, the distribution of resources in relation to the resource needs of a species is one of the factors that can set limits to the degree to which social groupings can occur. However, sociality may influence resource distribution if groups of animals are able to exploit resources that are not available to single individuals.

The influence of sociality on resource distribution may be seen among predatory animals that can hunt individually or in groups. Some species of prey are too large for an individual predator to attack, but are vulnerable to attack by a group of predators. For example, spotted hyenas (*Crocuta crocuta*) weigh about 50 kilograms. When hyenas hunt individually they feed on Thomson's gazelles (*Gazella thomsoni*, 15 kilograms) and juvenile wildebeest (*Connochaetes taurinus*, about 30 kilograms)

(Figure 23–3). However, when hyenas hunt in packs they feed on adult wildebeest (about 200 kilograms) and zebras (*Equus burchelli*, about 220 kilograms). Some species of prey have defenses that are effective against individual predators but less effective with groups of predators. For example, the success rate for solitary lions (*Panthera leo*) hunting zebras and wildebeest is only 15 percent, whereas lions hunting in groups of six to eight individuals are successful in up to 43 percent of their attacks. Groups of lions make multiple kills of wildebeest more than 30 percent of the time, but individual lions kill only a single wildebeest.

The relationship of sociality and body size of a predator to the size of its prey is shown in Figure 23–4: Social predators (defined in this study as those that hunt in groups of eight to ten individuals) attack larger prey than weakly social predators (average group sizes of 1.6 to 3.1 individuals), and these weakly social predators attack larger prey than do solitary predators (average group sizes of 1.0 to 1.3 individuals). Thus, one consequence of sociality for predatory mammals appears to be an increase in the potential food resources of an environment: Individual predators may be able to extend the range of prey species they can attack by hunting in groups.

Of course, the major disadvantage to hunting in a group is that there are more mouths to feed when a kill is made. The food requirement of a group of predators is the sum of the individual requirements of the members of the group, and the per capita amount of food obtained by hunting in a group would have to exceed that caught by a solitary hunter to make group hunting advantageous.

Packer and Ruttan (1988) have reviewed factors that could contribute to the evolution of cooperative hunting. The question is, do predators form groups *because* that allows them to hunt large prey,

(a)   (b)

(c)   (d)

Figure 23–3   Spotted hyenas. Spotted hyenas (a) may hunt individually or in packs. They prey on small animals like the Thomson's gazelle (b) when they hunt individually. When they hunt in packs, they attack larger prey such as the wildebeest (c) and zebras (d). (Photographs by Sara Cairns.)

or *must* they hunt large prey because they live in groups for some other reason? A study of lions on the Serengeti Plains suggests that the second hypothesis is correct (Packer et al. 1990). Female lions are the only female felids to live in social groups. Female lions defend a group territory and protect their cubs from other groups of female lions. The high population densities that are characteristic of lions may have favored group defense of a territory. The presence of large prey makes it possible for lions to hunt in groups, but group hunting does not increase the amount of food available per lion—a lion hunting by herself can catch as much prey as her share of a group capture. Thus, groups form because of the advantages they provide in the social structure of the population of lions on the Serengeti, and group hunting is a by-product of that social structure.

A similar interpretation has been suggested for the formation of groups of male cheetahs (Caro 1994). Male cheetahs may live alone or form permanent coalitions of two or three individuals that live and hunt together. In Caro's study, these coalitions were often composed of littermates, and a coalition was more successful in occupying a territory than was a single male. Competition for territories was intense, and territorial disputes were an important source of mortality for male cheetahs. Cheetahs hunting singly concentrated on small prey such as Thomson's gazelles, whereas coalitions attacked larger prey such as wildebeest. Overall foraging success increased with group size for male cheetahs, but Caro concluded that the benefits of a coalition in holding a territory and controlling access to females was probably more important than its effect on food intake.

Figure 23–4 Size of prey in relation to predator mass for solitary predators and for predators that hunt in small or large groups . Vertical lines connect points for species that hunt in groups of variable size. (From B. K. McNab, 1983, in Advances in the Study of Mammalian Behavior, edited by J. F. Eisenberg and D. G. Kleiman, Special Publication 7, The American Society of Mammalogists.)

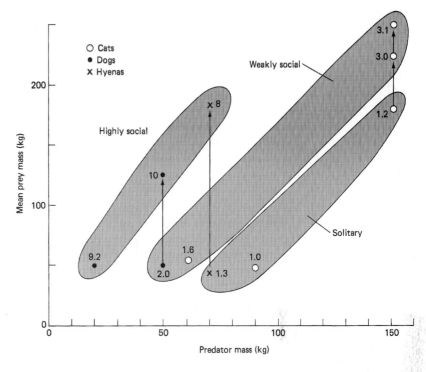

■ Advantages of Sociality

The advantages of cooperative hunting may provide a basis for sociality among some carnivorous mammals, but sociality is not limited to species of mammals that hunt in groups and the potential advantages of sociality are not confined to predatory behavior. Mammals may derive benefits from sociality in terms of avoiding predation and in reproduction and care of young.

Defenses Against Predators

One probable advantage of sociality is a reduction in the risk of predation for an individual that is part of a group compared to the risk for a solitary individual. The benefits of sociality in avoiding predation take many forms. A group of animals may be more likely to detect the approach of a predator than an individual would be, simply because a group has more eyes, ears, and noses to keep watch. Alternatively, an individual in a group may be able to devote a larger proportion of its time to feeding and less to watching for predators than a solitary individual can. Mammals that live in groups generally occur in open habitats, whereas solitary species are usually found in forests, and that relationship may reflect in part the antipredator aspects of group living. It is important to note that the benefits of sociality in predator avoidance

result from the reduction in the risk of predation for an *individual* that is part of a group, not for the species as a whole.

Sociality and Reproduction

Groupings of animals are important factors in mating systems and in care of young. In Chapter 18 we described mating systems in the context of avian biology, and most aspects of that discussion apply equally well to the mating systems of mammals. In the next section we extend the analysis by considering the specific relationships among body size, habitat, diet, antipredator behavior, and mating systems of several species of African ungulates.

The extensive period of dependence of many young mammals on their parents provides a setting in which many benefits of sociality can be manifested. Maternal care of the offspring is universal among mammals, and males of many species also play a role in parental care. Group living provides opportunities for complex interactions among adults and juveniles that involve various sorts of **alloparental behavior** (care provided by an individual that is not a parent of the young receiving the care). Collaborative rearing of young of several mothers is characteristic of lions and of many canids. Frequently, nonbreeding individuals join the mothers in protecting and caring for the young.

Among dwarf mongooses (*Helogale undulata*) this kind of behavior extends to the care of sick adults, and reports of similar behaviors exist for mammals as diverse as elephants and cetaceans. Many social groups of mammals consist of related individuals, and these helpers may increase their inclusive fitness by assisting in rearing the offspring of their kin. (See Chapter 18 for a discussion of helpers.)

■ Body Size, Diet, and the Structure of Social Systems

The complex relationships among body size, sociality, and other aspects of the ecology and behavior of herbivorous mammals are illustrated by the variation in social systems of African antelopes (family Bovidae) (Jarman 1974, Leuthold 1977, Estes 1991). The smallest species of these bovids have adult weights of 3 to 4 kilograms (the dik-diks, *Madoqua*, and some duikers, *Cephalophus*), and the largest (the African buffalo, *Syncerus caffer*) weighs 900 kilograms (Figure 23–5). The smallest species are forest animals that browse on the most nutritious parts of shrubs, live individually or in pairs, defend a territory, and hide from predators (Table 23–2). The largest species (including the 300-kilogram eland, *Taurotragus oryx*, and the African buffalo) are grassland animals that graze unselectively, live in large herds, are migratory, and use group defense to deter predators. Species with intermediate body sizes are also intermediate in these ecological and behavioral characteristics. It seems likely that the correlated variation in body size, ecology, and behavior among

(a)

(b)

(c)

Figure 23–5 The Bovidae includes species with a wide range of adult body sizes. The dik-dik (a) is among the smallest species, the impala (b) is medium-size, and the African buffalo (c) is one of the largest. ([a] Photograph by Jack Cranford, Virgina Polytechnic Institute and State University; [b,c] photograph by Sara Cairns.)

Diet Type	Examples	Body Mass (kg)	Food Habits	Group Size	Mating System	Predator Avoidance
I	Dikdik, some duikers	3–20	Highly selective browser	1 or 2	Stable pair, territorial	Hide
II	Thompson's gazelle, impala	20–100	Moderately selective browser and grazer	2 to 100	Male territorial in breeding season, temporary harems	Flee
III	Wildebeest, hartebeest	100–200	Grazers, selective for growth stage	Large herds	Nomadic, temporary harems	Flee, hide in herd, threaten predator
IV	Eland, buffalo	300–900	Grazers, unselective	Large	Male hierarchy herds	Group defense

TABLE 23.2 Correlations of the ecology and social systems of African ungulates

Source: Modified from P. J. Jarman, 1974, *Behaviour* 58:215–267.

these bovids reveals functional relationships among these aspects of their biology. How might such diverse features of mammalian biology interact?

The feeding habits of these antelope appear to provide a key that can be used to understand other aspects of their ecology and behavior. The diets of the different species are closely correlated with body size and the habitats in which the species live. In turn, those relationships are important in setting group size. The size of a group determines the distribution of females in time and space, and this is a major factor in establishing the mating system used by males of a species. Group size also plays an important role in determining the appropriate antipredator tactics for a species. Mating systems and antipredator mechanisms are central factors in the social organization of a species.

Body Size and Food Habits

Antelope are ruminants, relying on symbiotic microorganisms in the rumen to convert cellulose from plants into compounds that can be absorbed by the vertebrate digestive system. The effectiveness of ruminant digestion is proportional to body size. This relationship exists because the volume of the rumen in species with different body sizes is proportional to body mass, whereas metabolic rates are proportional to the 0.75 power of body mass. The ecological consequence of this difference in allometric slopes is illustrated in Figure 23–6: A large ruminant has proportionately more capacity to process food than does a small ruminant. As one

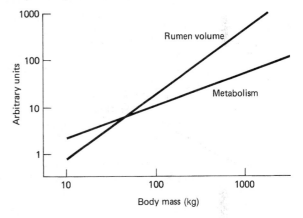

Figure 23–6 Rumen volume and energy requirements in relation to body size. Rumen volume increases in proportion to body size (an allometric slope of 1), whereas energy requirements are proportional to metabolism (an allometric slope of 0.75). Thus large species are more effective ruminants than small species. Both axes are drawn with logarithmic scales, and the scale of the vertical axis is in arbitrary units.

moves downward to animals of very small body size, the metabolic requirements become high in relation to the volume of rumen that is available to ferment plant material.

Because of this relationship, small ruminants must be more selective feeders than large ruminants. That is, a large ruminant has so much volume in its rumen that it can afford to eat large quantities of food of low nutritional value. It does not extract much energy from a unit volume of this food, but it is able to obtain its daily energy requirements by processing a large volume of food. Small ruminants, in contrast, must eat higher quality food and rely upon obtaining more energy per unit volume from the smaller volume of food that they can fit into their rumen in a day. In fact, 40 kilograms is the approximate lower limit of body size at which an unselective ruminant can balance its energy budget; species larger than 40 kilograms can be unselective grazers, whereas smaller species must eat only the most nutritious parts of plants (Van Soest 1982).

The species of antelopes in this example can be divided into four feeding categories:

Type I species are very selective grazers and browsers. They feed preferentially on certain species of plants, and they choose the parts of those plants that provide the highest-quality diet—new leaves (which have a higher nitrogen content than mature leaves) and fruit. Dik-diks and duikers fall in this category, and they have adult body masses between 3 and 20 kilograms.

Type II species are moderately selective grazers and browsers. They eat more parts of a plant than the type I species, and they may have seasonal changes in diet as they exploit the availability of fresh shoots or fruits on particular species of plants. Thomson's gazelle (*Gazella thomsoni*) and the impala (*Aepyceros melampus*) weigh 20 to 100 kilograms and have type II diets.

Type III species are primarily grazers that are unselective for species of grass, but selective for the parts of the plant. That is, they eat the leaves and avoid the stems. Hence, they are selecting for a growth stage: They avoid grass that is too short, because that limits food intake, and also avoid grass that is too long (because it has too many stems that are low-quality food). Wildebeest (*Connochaetes taurinus*) and hartebeest (*Alcelaphus buselaphus*), which weigh about 200 kilograms, are type III feeders,

Type IV species are unselective grazers and browsers. They eat all species of plants and all parts of the plant. Eland (*Taurotragus oryx*, 300 kilograms) and buffalo (*Syncerus caffer*, 900 kilograms) are type IV species.

Food Habits and Habitat

The food habits of the different species of antelope are important in determining what sorts of habitats provide the resources they need. Selective feeding operates at three levels: the vegetation type, the species and individual groups of plants, and the parts of plants eaten. The type of vegetation present largely depends on the habitat—forests contain shrubs and bushes, whereas the plains are covered with grass. The resources needed by species with type I diets are found in forests where the presence of a diversity of species with different growth seasons ensures that new leaves and fruit will be available at all times of the year. Species with type II diets are found in habitats that are a mosaic of woodland and grassland, and type III species (which are primarily grazers) are found in savanna and grassland areas. Species with type II and type III diets may move from place to place in response to patterns of rainfall. For example, wildebeest require grass that has put out fresh new growth, but that has not had time to mature. To find grass at this growth stage, wildebeest have extensive nomadic movements that follow the seasonal pattern of rain on the African plains.

Type IV feeders eat almost any kind of plant material, and they can find something edible in almost any habitat. They occupy a range of habitats, including grassland and brush, and do not have nomadic movements.

Habitat and Group Size

The habitats in which antelope feed and the types of food they eat set certain constraints on the sorts of social groupings that are possible. For example, species with type I diets live in forests and feed on scattered, distinct items. They eat an entire leaf or fruit at a bite and they must move between bites. A type I feeder completely removes the items it eats, so it changes the distribution of resources in its habitat (Figure 23–7). A second individual cannot feed close behind the first, because the food resources of an individual bush or shrub are entirely consumed by the first individual to feed there. As a result, the feeding behavior of species with type I diets makes it impossible for a group of animals to feed together. If one individual attempts to follow behind another to feed, the second animal must search to find food items overlooked by the individual ahead, and consequently it falls behind. Alternatively, it can move aside from the path of the first animal to find an area that has not already been searched. In either case, small animals in dense vegetation rapidly lose track of each other, and no cohesive group structure is maintained.

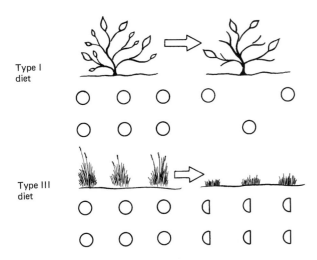

Figure 23–7 The effect of feeding by a selective browser with a type I diet and a grazer with a type III diet. (a) The browser removes entire food items, thereby changing the distribution of food in the habitat, as well as the abundance of food. (b) The grazer removes part of a grass clump, changing the abundance of food in the habitat but not its distribution. (From P. J. Jarman, 1974, *Behaviour* 58:215–267.)

Instead, type I species are solitary or occur in pairs, and the individuals of a pair are only loosely associated as they feed. A type I diet places a premium on familiarity with a home range, because a tree or bush is a patch of food that must be visited repeatedly to harvest fruit or new leaves as they appear. Also, the resources represented by the patches of food can be defended against intruders, and species of antelope with type I diets are territorial. The resources of a territory do not change very much from one season to the next, and the only seasonal variation in the group size of species with type I diets results from the presence of a juvenile in its parents' territory for part of the year.

Species with type II and type III diets are less selective than species with type I diets, and their feeding has less impact on the distribution of resources. These species do not remove all of the food resource in an area, and other individuals can feed nearby. Type III feeders, in particular, graze as they walk—taking a bite of grass, moving on a few steps, and taking another bite. This mode of feeding changes the abundance of food, but not its distribution in space, and herds of wildebeest graze together, all moving in the same direction at the same speed and maintaining a cohesive group. Rainfall is a major determinant of the distribution

of suitable food in the habitat of these species. The rainstorms that stimulate the growth of grass are erratic, and the patch sizes in which food resources occur are enormous—hundreds of square kilometers of new grass where rain fell are separated by hundreds of kilometers of old, dry grass that did not receive rain. Instead of having home ranges or territories, species with type II and type III diets move nomadically with the rains. Group sizes change as the distribution of resources changes, from half a dozen to 60 individuals for species with type II diets, and from herds of 300 or 400 to superherds of many thousands of individuals during the nomadic movements of wildebeests.

Species of bovids with type IV diets are so unselective in their choice of food that they can readily maintain large groups, and herds of buffalo number in the hundreds. Because these species can eat almost any kind of vegetation, the distribution of resources does not change seasonally and the size of the herds is stable.

Group Size and Mating Systems

The mating systems used by African antelope are closely related to the size of their social groups and the distribution of food because those are the major factors that determine the distribution of females and the potential for males to obtain opportunities to mate by controlling resources that females need. The females of species with type I diets are dispersed because the distribution of resources in the habitat does not permit groups of individuals to form. A male of a type I species can defend food resources, but individuals must disperse through the territory to feed and it is not feasible for a male to maintain a harem of females. Males of type I species pair with one female; the male defends its territory year round, the pair bond with an individual female appears to be stable, and offspring are driven out of the territory as they mature.

A group of individuals of type II species contains several males and females. The evenly distributed nature of food of these species makes it difficult for a male to monopolize resources. Only some of the males are territorial, and even this territoriality is manifested for only part of the year. A territorial male tries to exclude other males from its territory and to gather harems of females. Exclusive mating rights are achieved by holding a patch of ground and containing females within it, driving them back if they try to leave. These species have no long-term association between a male and a particular female.

Type III species are nomadic, and males establish territories only when the herd is stationary. During these periods male wildebeest hold harems of females within their territories, but the association between a male and females is broken when the herd moves on. However, mothers and their daughters maintain associations for 2 or 3 years. Unmated male wildebeest form bachelor herds with hierarchies, and individuals at the top of a bachelor hierarchy try to displace territorial males. If a territorial male is displaced, it joins a bachelor herd at the bottom of the hierarchy and must work its way up to the top before it can challenge another territorial male.

The social structure of buffalo herds differs in two respects from that of wildebeests: (1) Each herd includes many mature males that form a dominance hierarchy. The individuals near the top of the hierarchy court receptive females, but no territoriality or harem formation is seen. (2) The female membership of the herd is fixed, and this situation results in a degree of genetic relationship among all the members of a herd of buffalo. That genetic relationship among individuals creates situations in which kin selection may be a factor in the social behavior of the African buffalo.

Mating Systems and Predator Avoidance

Prey species have a variety of ways to avoid predators, but only some will work in a given situation. In general, a prey species can (1) avoid detection by a predator, (2) flee after it has been detected but before the predator attacks, (3) flee after the predator attacks, or (4) threaten or attack the predator. Body size, habitat, group size, and the mating system all contribute to determining the risk of predation faced by a species and which predator avoidance methods are most effective.

Predators usually attack prey that are the same size as the predator or smaller. Small species of animals potentially have more species of predators than do large species. Species of antelopes with type I diets are small and, consequently, they are at risk from many species of predators. Furthermore, small antelopes may not be able to run fast enough to escape a predator after it has attacked. On the other hand, these small antelopes live in dense habitats, where they are hard to see. They are cryptically colored and secretive, and they rely on being inconspicuous to avoid detection by predators. If they are pursued, they may be able to use their familiarity with the geography of their home range to avoid capture.

Groups of animals are more conspicuous to predators than are individuals, but groups also have more eyes to watch for the approach of a predator. Species of antelopes with type II diets live in small groups in open habitats, where they can detect predators at a distance. These antelopes avoid predators by fleeing either before or after the predator attacks (Box 23–1). Small predators may be attacked by the antelope, but usually only when a member of the group has been captured, and this sort of defense is normally limited to a mother protecting her young; the rest of the group does not participate.

Species of antelope in the type III diet category are large enough to have relatively few predators, and in a group they may be formidable enough to scare off a predator. Wildebeest sometimes form a solid line and walk toward a predator: This behavior is effective in deterring even lions from attacking. Many predators of wildebeest focus their attacks on calves, and defense of a calf is usually undertaken only by the mother. Much of the antipredator behavior of wildebeest depends on the similarity of appearance of individuals in the herd to each other. Field observations have shown that the individuals in a group of animals that are distinctive in their markings or behavior are most likely to be singled out and captured by predators.

One of the unavoidable events that makes a female wildebeest distinctive is giving birth to a calf, and the reproductive biology of the species has specialized features that appear to minimize the risks associated with giving birth. The breeding season and birth of wildebeests are highly synchronized. Mating occurs in a short interval, and as a consequence 80 percent of the births occur within a period of 2 or 3 weeks. Furthermore, nearly all of the births that will take place on a day occur in the morning in large aggregations of females, all giving birth at once. A female wildebeest who is slightly out of synchrony with other members of her group can interrupt delivery at any stage up to emergence of the calf's head so as to join the mass parturition. Presumably, this remarkable synchronization and control of parturition reflects the advantage of presenting predators with a homogeneous group of cows and calves rather than a group with only a few calves that could readily be singled out for attack.

BOX 23–1 **Altruism—or Taunting?**

A distinctive behavior—stotting, which consists of leaping vertically into the air—is used by some species of antelope when they are threatened by a predator. The function of stotting is unclear. It may be an alarm signal that alerts other individuals of the species to the presence of a predator, but the advantage to the individual that gives the warning is not clear. Altruistic behavior of this type is usually associated with kin selection, but the individuals in groups of antelope with type II diets are not closely related and do not show other types of altruistic behavior such as group defense of young. It has been suggested that some behaviors of prey species that had been considered to be altruistic alarm signals are really signals directed to the predator by fleet-footed prey.

Figure 23–8 Alarm signals to conspecifics or signals to a predator? The white-tail deer displays the white underside of its tail when it detects a predator. (Photograph © Stephen J. Krasemann/Photo Researchers, Inc.)

Alarm signals are given by many other kinds of vertebrates. A familiar example is the white underside of the tail of deer (Figure 23–8). A deer that sees a predator at a distance does not immediately flee but stands watching the predator. It may flick its tail up and down, exposing the white ventral surface in a series of flashes. European hares stand erect on their hind legs when a fox in the open approaches within 30 meters of the hare. In this posture, the hare is readily visible to the fox.

This kind of behavior is not limited to mammals. For example, several related species of fleet-footed lizards that live in open desert habitats have dorsal colors that blend with the substrate on which they live, and a pattern of white with black bars on the underside of the tail. These lizards stand poised for flight as a predator approaches, looking back over their shoulder at the predator. The tail is curled upward, exposing the contrasting black and white pattern on its ventral surface, and waved from side to side. Is it possible that in behaviors of this sort the prey animal is signaling to the predator that it has been detected, and to attack it will be unprofitable because the prey is ready to flee? Does the prey's behavior deter pursuit by the predator?

This intriguing hypothesis requires experimental test of the prediction that predators are less likely to attack prey individuals that engage in these behaviors than individuals that do not signal their awareness of the predator's approach. However, if the hypothesis can be supported by experiments, some puzzling examples of apparently altruistic signals can be reinterpreted as behavior that benefits the individual giving the signal (Hasson 1991).

Buffalo are formidable prey even for a pride of lions and they escape much potential predation simply as a result of their size. When buffalo are attacked, they engage in group defense, and if a calf is captured its distress cries bring many members of the group to its defense. This altruistic behavior probably represents kin selection, because the stability of the female membership of buffalo herds results in genetic relationships among the individuals.

Evolution of Social Behaviors of Antelope

It is tempting to view the continuum of increasing sociality from antelopes with type I diets through species with type IV diets as an evolutionary progression from simple social systems to complex ones. However, this view would almost certainly be wrong. The relationships among body size, diet, habitat selection, group size, mating system, and antipredator behavior form a web, not a ladder. If any one aspect of the biology of antelopes can be seen as limiting the range of possibilities for other features of their biology, body size is probably the key factor. The relationships among body size, rumen size, and metabolic requirements appear to define the four dietary types we have discussed and to determine what sorts of habitats supply the resources they require. In turn, the habitats in which different species of antelope live constrain the sizes of groups and the sorts of social systems they can exhibit.

If that is so, a progression from simple social systems to more complex ones is unlikely. Ruminant digestion is most advantageous for medium-size animals, and the first ruminants probably weighed about 100 kilograms and had diets like those of impalas and gazelles (Van Soest 1982). If dietary habits and habitat selection were important influences on the ecology and behavior of the early ruminants, it is likely that the ancestral social system was some form of temporary territoriality and harem formation. The monogamous mating system seen in dik-diks and the huge herds of buffalo sharing some degree of kinship probably both represent derived behaviors.

■ Social Systems Among Primates

The phylogenetic relationship of humans to other primates has led some biologists to assume that these are the animals that should have the most elaborate social systems, and that the study of the social systems of primates will provide information about the evolution of human behavior. Both assumptions are controversial: Increasing information indicates that complex social systems exist among many kinds of vertebrates other than primates, and interpretation of primate behavior in the context of human evolution is fraught with difficulty and must be approached cautiously. Nonetheless, some primates do have elaborate and complex social systems, and more long-term research has focused on the social systems of primates than on any other vertebrate.

The approximately 200 species of primates (Table 23–3) are ecologically diverse. They live in habitats ranging from lowland tropical rain forests, to semideserts, to northern areas that have cold, snowy winters. Some species are entirely arboreal, whereas others spend most of their time on the ground. Many are generalist omnivores that eat fruit, flowers, seeds, leaves, bulbs, insects, bird eggs, and small vertebrates, but many of the colobus (*Colobus*) and howler monkeys (*Alouatta*) are specialized folivores (leaf eaters) with sacculated stomachs in which bacteria and protozoans ferment cellulose, and some of the small prosimians and callithricid monkeys are insectivores.

R. W. Wrangham (1982) proposed that the social systems of primates can best be classified on the basis of the amount of movement of females that occurs between groups (Table 23–4). Four categories can be defined on this basis:

Female transfer systems In species with this type of social organization most females move away from the group in which they were born to join another social group. Because of this migration of females among groups, the females in a group are not closely related to each other. In contrast, males often remain with their natal groups and associations of male kin may be important elements of the social behaviors of these species of primates. Male chimpanzees, for example, cooperate in defending their territories from invasion by neighboring males. The majority of species of primates with female transfer systems live in relatively small social groups.

Nonfemale transfer systems Most females of these species spend their entire lives in the group in which they were born. Social relations among the females in a group are complex and are based on kinship. Males of these species emigrate from their natal group as adolescents and may continue to move among groups as adults. In some of these species a single male lives with a group of females until he is displaced by a new male, whereas in other species several males may be part of the group and maintain an unstable dominance hierarchy among themselves. Cooperation by several adult males may allow them to resist challenges from younger, stronger males that they would not be able to subdue if they acted as individuals. Group size is usually larger for nonfemale transfer species than for species with female transfer.

Monogamous species A single male and female form a pair, sometimes accompanied by juvenile

TABLE 23.3 Social organization of extant primates

Taxon	Social Organization
Lemuroidea	Largely solitary or monogamous pairs
Aye-aye (*Daubentonia*, 1 species)	
Lemurs (*Lemur* and 9 other genera, 18 species)	
Indri (*Indri*, 1 species)	
Sifaka (*Propithecus*, 2 species)	
Lorisoidea	Largely solitary
Bushbabies (*Galago*, 8 species)	
Lorises (*Loris*, 1 species; *Nycticebus*, 2 species)	
Potto (*Perodicticus*, 1 species)	
Angwantibo (*Artocebus*, 1 species)	
Tarsiiformes	Solitary or monogamous pairs
Tarsiers (*Tarsius*, 3 species)	
Cebidea = Platyrrhines (New World monkeys)	
Callithrichinae	Largely monogamous pairs
Goeldi's marmoset (*Callimico*, 1 species)	
Marmosets and tamarins (4 genera, 15 species)	
Cebinae = Atelinae	Monogamous pairs or small to large groups
Capuchin monkeys (*Cebus*, 4 species)	
Squirrel monkeys (*Samiri*, 2 species)	
Howler monkeys (*Alouatta*, 6 species)	
Spider monkeys (*Ateles*, *Brachyteles*, *Lagothrix*, 7 species)	
Owl monkeys (*Aotus*, 1 species)	
Uakaris (*Cacajo*, 2 species)	
Titis (*Callicebus*, 3 species)	
Sakis (*Chiropotes* and *Pithecia*, 6 species)	
Catarrhini (Old World monkeys and apes)	
Cercopithecidea	Mostly small to large groups
Cercopithecinae	
Vervet monkey, guenons, and others (*Cercopithecus*, 17 species)	
Mangabeys (*Cercocebus*, 5 species)	
Macaques (*Macaca*, 12 species)	
Baboons (*Papio*, 4 species; *Theropithecus*, 1 species)	
Colobrinae	
Colobus monkeys (*Colobus*, 7 species)	
Langurs (*Nasalis*, *Presbytis*, *Pygathrix*, *Rhinopithecus*, 20 species)	
Hominoidea (apes and humans)	
Hylobatidae	Monogamous pairs
Gibbons (*Hylobates*, 9 species)	
"Pongids"	
Orangutan (*Pongo*, 1 species)	Solitary
Gorilla (*Gorilla*, 1 species)	Small groups with a variable number of resident males
Chimpanzee (*Pan*, 2 species)	Closed social network containing several breeding males and females
Hominidae	Closed social network containing several breeding males and females
Human (*Homo*, 1 species)	

Source: Modified from B. B. Smuts et al., editors, 1987, *Primate Societies*, University of Chicago Press, Chicago, IL.

TABLE 23.4	Characteristics of the social systems of primates				
System	*Group Size*	*Number of Males in Group*	*Male Behavior*	*Example*
Female transfer	Small	One or many	Territorial, harems, sometimes male kinship groups	Chimpanzee, gorilla, howler monkeys, hamadryas baboons, colobus monkeys, some langurs
Nonfemale transfer	Large	One or several	Male hierarchy, whole group (males and females) may exclude conspecifics from food sources	Most cercopithecines: yellow baboons, mangabeys, macaques, guenon monkeys
Monogamous	Male and female, plus juvenile offspring	One	Both sexes participate in territorial defense and parental care	Gibbons, marmosets, tamarins, indri, titis
Solitary	Individual, or female plus juvenile male offspring	—	Range of male overlaps ranges of several females	Bushbabies, tarsiers, lorises, orangutans

Source: Based on R. W. Wrangham, 1982, pages 269–289 in *Current Problems in Sociobiology,* edited by King's College Sociobiology Group, Cambridge University Press, Cambridge, UK.

offspring. These species of primates show little sexual dimorphism, the sexes share parental care and territorial defense, and the offspring are expelled from the parents' territory during adolescence.

Solitary species   These live singly or as females with their infants and juvenile offspring. Male prosimians maintain territories that include the home ranges of several females and exclude other males from their territories, whereas male orangutans do not defend territories, but instead repulse other males when a female within the male's home range comes into estrus.

Three ecological factors appear to be particularly important in shaping the social systems of primates, as they are for other vertebrates:

Distribution of resources   The defensibility of food resources appears to determine whether individuals will benefit from not attempting to defend resources, defending individual territories, or form-

ing long-term relationships with other individuals and jointly defending resources.

Group size   The distribution of food in time and in space may determine how large a group can be, and whether the group can remain stable or must break into smaller groups when food is scarce.

Predation   The risk of predation may determine whether individuals can travel alone or require the protection of a group, whether the benefit of the additional protection that is provided by a large versus a small group outweighs the added competition among individuals in a large group, and whether the presence of males is needed to protect young.

Life within a group of primates is a balance between competition and cooperation (Figure 23–9). Competition is manifested by aggression. Some aggression—for example, the defense of food, rest, sleeping sites, or mates—is closely linked to resources. Other types of aggression involve establish-

(a)

(b)

Figure 23–9 Social behaviors of yellow baboons. (a) A male friend grooming a female baboon in estrus; (b) aggression among male baboons. (Photographs by Carol Saunders.)

ing and maintaining dominance hierarchies, which may be an indirect form of resource competition if high-ranking individuals have preferential access to resources.

Cooperation, too, is diverse. Grooming behavior in which one individual picks through the hair of another, removing ectoparasites and cleaning wounds, is the most common form of cooperation. Other types of cooperation include sharing food or feeding sites, collective defense against predators, collective defense of a territory or a resource within a home range, and the formation of alliances between individuals. Two-way, three-way, and even more complex alliances that function during competition within a group are common among primates.

Kinship and the concept of inclusive fitness play important roles in the interpretation of primate social behavior. A behavior must not decrease the fitness of the individual exhibiting the behavior if it is to persist in the repertoire of a species. Fitness is nearly impossible to demonstrate in wild populations, and behaviorists normally search for effects that are likely to be correlated with fitness, such as access to females (for males), interbirth interval (for females), or the probability that offspring will survive to reproductive age. Behaviors that increase these measures are assumed to increase fitness. The behaviors may directly benefit the individual displaying the behavior (personal fitness) or they may be costly to the personal fitness of the individual but sufficiently beneficial to its close relatives to offset the cost to the individual (inclusive fitness).

Social Relationships Among Primates

Four general types of relationships among individuals have been described in the social behavior of primates (For more details see Watts [1985], Richard [1985], Smuts et al. [1987], Dunbar [1988], Cheney and Seyfarth [1990], and Nishida [1990].)

Adult–Juvenile Associations Primates are born in a relatively helpless state compared to many mammals, and they are dependent on adults for unusually long periods. The relationship of a mother to her infant is variable within a species—some mothers are protective, whereas others are permissive. Permissive mothers often wean their offspring earlier than protective mothers and may have shorter intervals between the birth of successive offspring, although this relationship has not been observed in all species. The offspring of permissive mothers may suffer higher rates of mortality than the offspring of protective mothers, and the incompetence of some first-time mothers appears to lead to high mortality among firstborn offspring.

Older siblings often participate in grooming and carrying an infant, but they may also assault, pinch, and bite the infant while it is being fed or groomed by the mother. Allomaternal behavior provided by an adult female who is not the mother includes cuddling, grooming, carrying, and protecting an infant. Several factors seem to influence allomaternal behavior: Young infants are preferred to older ones, infants of high-ranking mothers receive more attention and less abuse than infants of low-ranking mothers, and siblings may participate more than unrelated females in allomaternal behavior (Nicolson 1987). Males of the monogamous New World primates participate extensively in caring for infants, carrying them for much of the day and sharing food with them, whereas the relationships of males of Old World primates with infants are more often characterized by proximity and friendly contact than by care.

Female Kinship Bonds   The females of some species of semiterrestrial Old World primates live in groups that include several males and females. This social organization is typical of yellow baboons (*Papio cynocephalus*), several species of macaques (*Macaca*), and vervet monkeys (*Cercopithecus aethiops*). Females of these species remain for their entire lives in the troops in which they were born, whereas males migrate to other troops when they mature. The role of female kinship bonds is much smaller in female transfer systems because the females in a group are not closely related.

The females within a group form a dominance hierarchy and compete for positions in the hierarchy. Related females within a group are referred to as **matrilineages**. Females consistently support their female relatives during encounters with members of other matrilineages. The supportive relationship among females within a matrilineage is an important element of the social structure of a group. For example, when their female kin are nearby, young animals can dominate older and larger opponents from subordinate matrilineages. Furthermore, high-ranking females retain their position in the hierarchy even when age or injury reduces their fighting ability. An adolescent female yellow baboon normally attains a rank in the group just below that of her mother, and this inheritance of status provides stability in the dominance relationships among the females of a group. However, the social rank of the matrilineage is not fixed: Low-ranking female yellow baboons, with their female kin, may challenge higher-ranking individuals, and if they are successful their entire matrilineage may rise in rank within the group.

The female kinship bonds are clearly important elements of the social structure of nonfemale transfer systems, but the exact contribution of the long-term relationships among females to the fitness of individual females is not clear. In some troops high-ranking females are young when they first give birth and have short interbirth intervals and high infant survival, but those correlations are not present in all

the troops that have been studied. Furthermore, female kinship bonds are manifested weakly if at all in female transfer systems, which include most species of apes and many species of monkeys.

Male–Male Alliances   Male primates in nonfemale transfer species often form dominance hierarchies, but male rank depends mainly on individual attributes and is therefore less stable than female dominance systems based on matrilineage. Young adult males, which are usually recent immigrants from another group, have the greatest fighting ability and usually achieve the highest rank. Some older males achieve stable alliances with each other that enable them to overpower younger and stronger rivals in competition for opportunities to court receptive females. These males probably achieve greater mating success by engaging in these reciprocal alliances than they would achieve on the basis of their individual ranks in the hierarchy.

Cooperative relationships among males are most common in female transfer systems, because the males of these species remain in their natal group. As a result, kin relationships exist among the males in a group. In red colobus monkeys (*Colobus badius*), for example, only males born in the group appear to be accepted by the adult male subgroup, and the membership of this subgroup can remain stable for years. Adult males spend much of their time in close proximity to each other and cooperate in aggression against males of a neighboring group. Male chimpanzees (*Pan troglodytes*) spend more time together than do females and engage in a variety of cooperative behaviors, including greeting, grooming, and sharing meat. However, this apparent cooperation is simply a way of cementing relationships that are based on intense and sometimes violent competition over females. For example, Goodall (1986) reported the systematic killing of an entire group of males by the males of a neighboring group, which then took over the females in that community.

Male–Female Friendships Among Baboons   Barbara Smuts's (1985) observations of a group of yellow baboons revealed that interactions between individual male and female baboons were not randomly distributed among members of the group. Instead, each female had one or two particular males called friends. Friends spent much time near each other and groomed each other often. These friendships lasted for months or years, including periods when the female was not sexually receptive because she was pregnant or nursing a baby. Male friends were solicitous of the welfare of their female friends and of their infants. Similar male–female friendships have been described in mountain gorillas (*Gorilla gorilla beringei*), gelada baboons (*Theropithecus gelada*), hamadryas baboons (*Papio hamadryas*), rhesus macaques (*Macaca mulatta*), and Japanese macaques (*Macaca fuscata*).

The advantage of these friendships for a female appears to lie in the protection that males provide to the females and their offspring from predators and from other members of the group. The advantage for a male of friendship with a female is less apparent. If the female's offspring had been sired by the male, protecting it would contribute to the male's fitness. However, in Smuts's study of yellow baboons, only half the friendships between males and infants involved relationships in which the male was the likely sire of the infant. The other friendships involved males that had never been seen mating with the mother of the infant. The advantage of friendship for males may depend on long-term associations with females. Smuts noted that males who participated in a friendship with a female had a significantly increased chance of mating with that female many months later when she was again receptive.

How Do Primates Perceive Their Social Structure?

The summary of primate social structures presented above represents the results of tens of thousands of hours of observations of individual animals over periods of many years. Statistical analyses of interactions between individuals—grooming sessions, aggression, defense—reveal correlations associated with factors including age, personality, kinship, and rank. Do the animals themselves recognize those relationships?

That is a fascinating but difficult question, especially with studies of free-ranging animals, but observations are accumulating that suggest that primates probably do recognize different kinds of relationships among individuals. For example, when juvenile rhesus macaques are threatened by another monkey, they scream to solicit assistance from other individuals who are out of sight. The kind of scream they give varies depending on the intensity of the interaction (threat or actual attack) and the dominance rank and kinship of their oppo-

nent. Furthermore, a mother baboon appears to be able to interpret the screams of her juvenile and to respond more or less vigorously depending on the nature of the threat her offspring faces. When tape-recorded screams were played back to the mothers, the mothers responded most strongly to screams that were given during an attack by a higher-ranking opponent, less strongly to screams that were given in response to interactions with lower-ranking opponents, and least strongly to screams that were given in interactions with relatives.

In a similar experiment with free-ranging vervet monkeys, the screams of a juvenile were played back to three females, one of whom was the mother of the juvenile. The mother responded more strongly to the screams than did the other two monkeys, as one would expect if females can recognize the voices of their own offspring. However, the other two monkeys responded to the screams by looking toward the mother, suggesting that they were able not only to associate the screams with a particular juvenile, but also to associate that juvenile with its mother.

Observations of redirected aggression also suggest that some primates classify other members of a group in terms of matrilineage and friendships. When a baboon or macaque has been attacked and routed by a higher-ranking opponent, the victim frequently attacks a bystander who took no part in the original interaction. This behavior is known as redirected aggression, and the targets of redirected aggression are relatives or friends of the original opponent more frequently than would be expected by chance. Vervet monkeys show still more complex forms of redirected aggression: They are more likely to behave aggressively toward an individual when they have recently fought with one of that individual's close kin. Furthermore, an adult vervet is more likely to threaten a particular animal if that animal's kin and one of its own kin fought earlier that same day. This sort of feud is seen only among adult vervets, suggesting that it takes time for young animals to learn the complexities of the social relationships of a group.

These sorts of observations suggest that adult primates have a complex and detailed recognition of the genetic and social relationships of other individuals in their group. Furthermore, they may be able to recognize more abstract categories, such as *relative* versus *nonrelative, close relative* versus *distant relative,* or *strong friendship bond* versus *weak friendship bond,* that share similar characteristics independent of the particular individuals involved.

■ Summary

Sociality, the formation of structured groups, is a prominent characteristic of the behavior of many species of mammals. However, social behavior is only one aspect of the biology of a species, and social behaviors coexist with other aspects of behavior and ecology, including finding food and escaping from predators.

The size and geography of an animal's home range is related to the distribution and abundance of resources, the body size of the animal, and its feeding habits. Large species have larger home ranges than small species, and for any given body size the sizes of home ranges are in the order carnivores > omnivores > herbivores.

Social systems are related to the distribution of food resources and to the opportunities for an individual (usually, a male) to increase access to mates by controlling access to resources. Dietary habits, the structural habitat in which a species lives, and its means of avoiding predators are closely linked to body size and mating systems. These aspects of biology form a web of interactions, each influencing the others in complex ways.

The social systems of primates, especially cercopithecoid monkeys, have been the subjects of field studies and more information about social behavior under field conditions is available for primates than for other mammals. The social systems of primates are complex, but not unique among mammals. Some primates are solitary or monogamous, but others live in groups and display behaviors that suggest not just recognition of other individuals, but also recognition of the genetic and social relationships among other individuals. Studies of other kinds of mammals will probably reveal similar phenomena, and understanding the behavior of mammals requires a broad understanding of their ecology and evolutionary histories.

■ References

Caro, T. M. 1994. *Cheetahs of the Serengeti Plains.* University of Chicago Press, Chicago, IL.

Cheney, D., and R. Seyfarth. 1990. *How Monkeys See the World.* University of Chicago Press, Chicago, IL.

Clutton–Brock, T. H., and P. H. Harvey. 1983. The functional significance of variation in body size among mammals. Pages 632–663 in *Advances in the Study of Mammalian Behavior,* edited by J. F. Eisenberg and D. G. Kleiman. Special Publication 7, The American Society of Mammalogists, Lawrence, KS.

Dunbar, R. I. M. 1988. *Primate Social Systems.* Cornell University Press, Ithaca, NY.

Eisenberg, J. F. 1981. *The Mammalian Radiations.* University of Chicago Press, Chicago, IL.

Estes, R. D. 1991. *The Behavior Guide to African Mammals.* University of California Press, Berkeley, CA.

Gittleman, J. L. (ed). 1989. *Carnivore Behavior, Ecology, and Evolution.* Cornell University Press, Ithaca, NY.

Gittleman, J. L., and P. H. Harvey. 1982. Carnivore home-range size, metabolic needs, and ecology. *Behavioral Ecology and Sociobiology* 10:57–63.

Goodall, J. 1986. *The Chimpanzees of Gombe.* Harvard University Press, Cambridge, MA.

Hasson, O. 1991. Pursuit-deterrent signals: communication between prey and predator. *Trends in Ecology and Evolution* 6:325–329.

Hersteinsson, P., and D. W. Macdonald. 1982. Some comparisons between red and arctic foxes, *Vulpes vulpes* and *Alopex lagopus,* as revealed by radio tracking. Pages 259–289 in *Symposia of the Zoological Society of London,* No. 49, edited by C. L. Cheesman and R. B. Mitson. Academic, London, UK.

Jarman, P. J. 1974. The social organization of antelope in relation to their ecology. *Behaviour* 58:215–267.

Leuthold, W. 1977. *African Ungulates: A Comparative Review of their Ethology and Behavioral Ecology.* Springer, New York, NY.

Lewin, R. 1987. Social life: a question of costs and benefits. *Science* 236:775–777.

Macdonald, D. W. 1983. The ecology of carnivore social behavior. *Nature* 301:379–381.

McNab, B. K. 1983. Ecological and behavioral consequences of adaptation to various food resources. Pages 664–697 in *Advances in the Study of Mammalian Behavior,* edited by J. F. Eisenberg and D. G. Kleiman, Special Publication 7, The American Society of Mammalogists, Lawrence, KS.

Nicolson, N. A. 1987. Infants, mothers, and other females. Pages 330–342 in *Primate Societies,* edited by B. Smuts, D. Cheney, R. Seyfarth, R. Wrangham, and T. Struhsaker. University of Chicago Press, Chicago, IL.

Nishida, T. (ed) 1990. *The Chimpanzees of the Mahale Mountains. Sexual and Life History Strategies.* Tokyo University Press, Tokyo, Japan.

Packer, C., and L. Ruttan. 1988. The evolution of cooperative hunting. *The American Naturalist* 132:159–198.

Packer, C., D. Scheel, and A. E. Pusey. 1990. Why lions form groups: food is not enough. *The American Naturalist* 136:1–19.

Richard, A. F. 1985. *Primates in Nature.* Freeman, San Francisco, CA.

Rubenstein, D. I., and R. W. Wrangham (editors). 1986. *Ecological Aspects of Social Evolution: Birds and Mammals.* Princeton University Press, Princeton, NJ.

Smuts, B. 1985. *Sex and Friendship in Baboons*. Aldine, Hawthorne, NY.

Smuts, B., D. Cheney, R. Seyfarth, R. Wrangham, T. Struhsaker (eds). 1987. *Primate Societies*. University of Chicago Press, Chicago, IL.

Van Soest, P. J. 1982. *Nutritional Ecology of the Ruminant*. O & B Books, Corvallis, OR.

Watts, E. S. (ed). 1985. *Nonhuman Primate Models for Human Growth and Development*. Liss, New York, NY.

Wittenberger, J. F. 1981. *Animal Social Behavior*. Duxbury, Boston, MA.

Wrangham, R. W. 1982. Mutualism, kinship, and social evolution. Pages 269–289 in *Current Problems in Sociobiology*, edited by King's College Sociobiology Group. Cambridge University Press, Cambridge, UK.

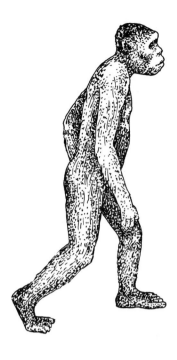

CHAPTER
24

Humans as Vertebrates

Humans are primates, and complex social systems such as those discussed in Chapter 23 are an ancestral character. The fossil record indicates that the first stone tools are at least 2.5 million years old. Tool cultures are clearly associated with the first appearance of the genus *Homo*, but may not be an exclusive characteristic of our genus. Molecular techniques of studying genetic relationships among organisms have recently been applied to human evolution and have challenged some prevailing views: The molecular studies suggest that the separation of humans from the African great apes was more recent than had been inferred from anatomical studies, and that the closest extant relatives of humans are chimpanzees.

The growth of human populations, especially in the past 50,000 years, is a unique phenomenon in the history of vertebrates. Never before has a single species so dominated the resources of the Earth. The first extinctions of other species of vertebrates that can be traced to humans may have occurred during the Pleistocene when humans first entered North America, although this hypothesis is controversial.

■ Primate Origins and Diversification

Humans have descended from arboreal ancestors that lived in early Cenozoic forests 65 million years ago. Our closest extant relatives are the chimpanzees and gorillas of Africa. What is the basis for these statements, which Darwin's Victorian contemporaries found so startling and upsetting? In the following sections we summarize the evidence and the inferences about human phylogeny and evolution.

Characteristics of Primates

Humans share many biological traits with animals variously called apes, monkeys, and prosimians.

Using the principle of homology (Chapter 1), comparative anatomy demonstrates that all of these mammals can be grouped together in the class Primates. Obvious traits that characterize primates are (1) retention of the clavicle (which is reduced or lost in many mammalian lineages) as a prominent element of the pectoral girdle; (2) a shoulder joint allowing a high degree of limb movement in all directions and an elbow joint permitting rotation of the forearm; (3) general retention of five functional digits on the fore and hind limbs; (4) enhanced mobility of the digits, especially the thumb and big toes, which are usually opposable to the other digits; (5) claws modified into flattened nails; (6) sensitive tactile pads developed on the distal ends of the digits; (7) reduced snout and olfactory apparatus with most of the skull posterior to the orbits; (8) reduction in number of teeth compared to primitive mammals but with retention of simple bunodont molar cusp patterns (see Chapter 21); (9) complex visual apparatus with high acuity, color perception, and a trend toward development of forward-directed binocular eyes; (10) large brain relative to body size, in which the cerebral cortex is particularly enlarged; (11) trend toward derived fetal nourishment mechanisms; (12) only two mammary glands (some exceptions); (13) typically, only one young per pregnancy associated with prolonged infancy and pre-adulthood; and (14) trend toward holding the trunk of the body upright leading to facultative bipedalism (Szalay and Delson 1979). It is important to understand that several of the above characteristics can be identified as trends within the primates and thus may not be apparent in more primitive members of the lineage. Nor are many of these characters unique to primates: for example, many mammals retain the clavicle, pigs have bunodont molars similar to those of primates, and many ungulates and kangaroos have only a single young per pregnancy.

Most of these traits have long been attributed to an arboreal life. All of the basic modifications of the appendages can be seen as contributions to arboreal locomotion, as can the stereoscopic depth perception that results from binocular vision as well as the enlarged brain for neuromuscular coordination between visual perception and locomotory response. Most primates are arboreal, but some have become secondarily terrestrial (baboons, for example) and humans are the most terrestrial of all. Even so, many of the traits that are most distinctively human have been said to derive from earlier arboreal specializations. However, arboreality cannot be the entire basis for these primate characteristics. Squirrels provide a telling counter example; they are arboreal but show few of the specializations seen in primates (Cartmill 1974). Although squirrels do have a clavicle and good mobility of the shoulder and elbow joint, the range of movement is not as great as that of primates. The thumbs of squirrels are greatly reduced, there is no opposability, and the remaining digits have long, sharp, recurved claws lacking tactile pads at their tips. Squirrels have large olfactory organs and snouts, laterally directed eyes, and no notable brain enlargement compared with fully terrestrial and diurnal rodents, although they do have good color vision. Squirrel life histories are typical of

small mammals: they produce large litters of fast-growing young. Nevertheless, squirrels are fully arboreal and can match or exceed the climbing skills of similar-size primates. Thus primate characteristics cannot be fully explained by an early tendency to arboreality.

Evolutionary Trends and Diversity in Primates

Table 23–3 presents a traditional classification of modern primates in the context of their social systems, and Figure 24–1 presents a simplified representation of their interrelationships. It is generally agreed that the first primates evolved from a lineage of arboreal generalized mammals not unlike the present-day tree shrews of southeast Asia (family Tupaiidae). Tree shrews have long bushy tails and rather short limbs, appearing rather like squirrels (Figure 21–21). The skull and teeth show most of the unspecialized characteristics of generalized, primitive mammals, including a long snout, tritubercular cheek teeth, laterally placed eyes, and occipital condyles located at the extreme posterior of the skull with the head carried fully out in front of the vertebral column. Tree shrews were once considered as true, primitive primates. Today they are acknowledged as close relatives within the Grandorder Archonta (see Chapter 21), but are placed in their own order, Scandentia. Nonetheless, they offer a good extant anatomical model for the basal stock of our lineage.

Plesiadapiformes   The first primatelike mammals (**Plesiadapiforms**) appear in the earliest Cenozoic. Plesiadapiforms were rather squirrellike, and ranged from around chipmunk-size to marmot-size. They comprised a number of different lineages, varying in their diets (as can be judged from their teeth) from generalized omnivores to insectivores and gum eaters (Fleagle 1988). Plesiadapiforms were most diverse in the Paleocene of North America, although they were known from across the Northern Hemisphere. Their numbers declined in the Eocene, and they were extinct by the end of this epoch. The decline in plesiadapiform diversity is coincident with the evolution and radiation of rodents in the late Paleocene, and there may well have been competition between these two lineages, leading to the eventual demise of the plesiadapiforms (Maas et al. 1988).

There is considerable debate as to whether plesiadapiforms should be considered as true primates,

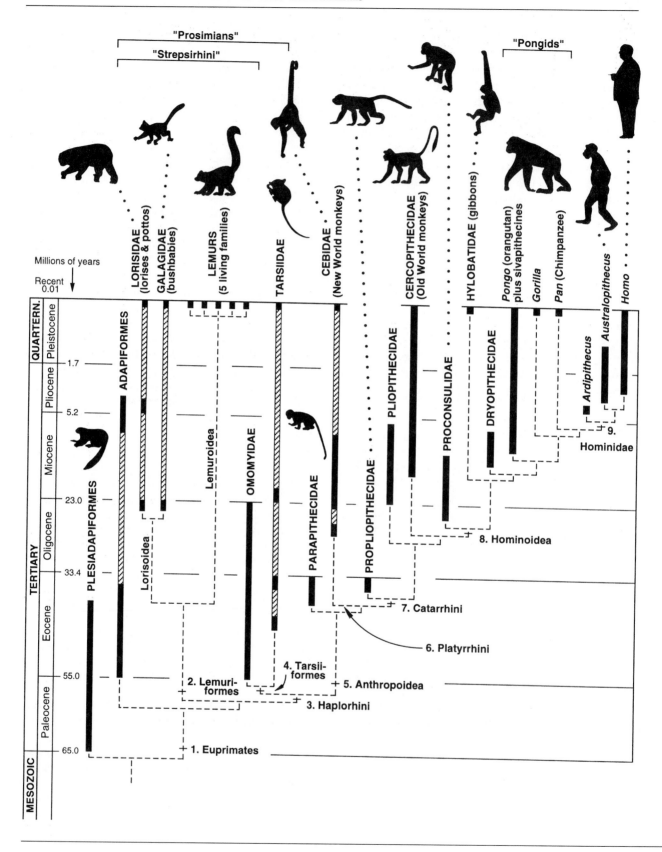

or as the sister group to primates. There is even some evidence that some types were more closely related to dermopterans (flying lemurs) than they were to true primates (Beard 1990). Plesiadapiforms shared some derived features of the teeth and skeleton with true primates. They differed in their smaller brains, their longer snout, the lack of a post orbital bar, the lack of an opposable hallux (big toe), and the specialization of rather rodentlike incisors in some forms (see Figure 24–2a). Plesiadapiforms also apparently retained claws. In contrast, all true primates have nails, with the exception of the marmosets of South America, which have secondarily reverted to having claws.

Prosimians   The first true primates (or Euprimates) are known from the early Eocene of North America, Eurasia, and northern Africa, and isolated teeth from the late Paleocene of Morocco may possibly belong to an even earlier primate (Kay et al. 1997). These early primates belong to a group that we would call "**prosimians**", which today includes the bush babies of Africa, the lemurs of Madagascar, and the lorises, pottos and tarsiers of southeast Asia

(Figure 24–3). Prosimians are in general small, nocturnal, long-snouted, and relatively small brained, in comparison with the more derived **anthropoids**, or apes and monkeys. Their diets are more generalized, and there are few specialized herbivores. However, the grouping of prosimians is a paraphyletic one, as several derived features (for example a short snout with a dry nose, rather than a wet, doglike one) link tarsiers as more closely related to the anthropoids than are the other prosimians (Figure 24-1). An alternative division of the primates is into the **Strepsirhini** (lemuroids and lorisoids) and **Haplorhini** (tarsiers and anthropoids). The Strepsirhini is paraphyletic, although living strepsirhines from a monophyletic grouping, the lemuriformes (Figure 24–1).

The Eocene prosimians were in general (but not always) larger than the plesiadapiforms, with larger brains and more obviously specialized arboreal adaptations such as relatively longer, more slender limbs. They can be grouped into two main lineages: the larger adapids, which were longer-snouted with teeth more specialized for herbivory, and the smaller omomyids, which were shorter-

1. Euprimates: Cheek teeth bunodont; a nail (instead of a claw) always present in extant forms, at least on the pollex (thumb); postorbital bar present. **2.** Lemuriformes: Grooming claw present on second toe; lower front teeth modified into a tooth comb. **3.** Haplorhini [tarsiiformes plus anthropoids]: Cranium short; orbit and temporal fossa separated ventrally by a postorbital wall; dry nose and free (rather than tethered) upper lip. **4.** Tarsiiformes: Eyes greatly enlarged. **5.** Anthropoidea (monkeys and apes): Fused frontal bones; fused mandibular symphysis; tubular external auditory meatus; lower molars increase in size posteriorly, the third only slightly larger than the second, all with five cusps, the hypoconulid small; **6.** Platyrrhini (New World monkeys): Widely spaced and rounded nostrils; contact between jugal and parietal bones on lateral wall of skull behind orbit; first two lower molars lack hypoconulids. **7.** Catarrhini (Old World monkeys and apes): Narrowly-spaced nostrils; number of premolars reduced to two; contact between frontal and sphenoid bones in lateral wall of skull; tympanic bone extents laterally to form a tubular auditory meatus (ear tube). **8.** Hominoidea (apes and humans): Lower molars with expanded talonid basin surrounded by five main cusps (the Y-5 configuration); broad palate and nasal regions; enlarged brain; broad thorax with dorsally positioned scapula; reduced lumbar region, with expanded sacrum and the absence of a tail. **9.** Hominidae (humans): Relatively small incisors and canines; short snout; ventrally-positioned foramen magnum; short, broad ilium; long legs in comparison with arms; big toe not opposable. (From J. G. Fleagle, 1988, *Primate Adaptation and Evolution*, Academic Press, New York, NY, and E. Delson and I. Tattersall, 1997, Primates, pages 93–104 in *Encyclopedia of Human Biology*, Volume 7, Academic Press, New York, NY. See discussion in the text about some newer ideas about the classification of the Hominoidea, and taxa included within the family Hominidae.)

Figure 24–1   Phylogenetic relationships of the primates. This diagram shows the probable relationships among the major groups of primates. Dotted lines show interrelationships only, and are not indicative of the times of divergence or of the unrecorded presence of taxa in the fossil record. Crosshatched bars indicate ranges of time when the taxon is known to be present, but is unrecorded in the fossil record. Numbers indicate derived characters that distinguish the lineages.

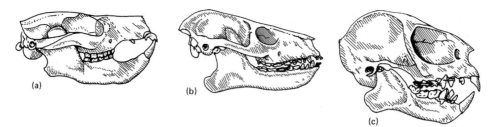

Figure 24–2 Reconstruction of fossil skulls of some early primates and primate-like mammals, showing variation in dentition with feeding habits. (a) *Plesiadapis*, a late Paleocene form, was rodentlike and questionably in the primate lineage; (b) *Notharctus*, an Eocene adapid, had teeth indicative of folivory, while (c) *Tetonius*, an Eocene omomyid form, had teeth indicative of insectivory. The large orbits of *Tetonius* clearly indicate nocturnal habits. Not to the same scale. (Modified from A. S. Romer, 1966, *Vertebrate Paleontology*, 3d edition, University of Chicago Press, Chicago, IL.)

Figure 24–3 Diversity of living prosimians. (a) Ring-tailed lemur, *Lemur catta* (Lemuridae, Lemuroidea, Lemuriformes); (b) Indri, *Indri indri* (Indriidae, Lemuroidea, Lemuriformes). (c) Aye-aye, *Daubentonia madagascarensis* (Daubentoniidae, Lemuroidea, Lemuriformes). (d) Demidoff's bush baby, *Galagoides demidovii* (Galagidae, Lorisoidea, Lemuriformes). (e) Potto, *Perodicticus potto* (Lorisidae, Lorisoidea, Lemuriformes). (f) Tarsier, *Tarsius spectrum* (Tarsiidae, Tarsiformes). (Modified from Fleagle 1988, *Primate Adaption and Evolution*, Academic Press. Reprinted by permission.)

snouted with teeth more specialized for insectivory or gum-eating (Figure 24–2). Judging by the relative orbit size, the adapids were probably diurnal, while the larger-eyed omomyids were probably nocturnal. Adapids are thought to be related to present-day lemurs and lorisoids, although they may actually be more primitive than other euprimates (see Figure 24–1), while omomyids are closer to tarsiers (Fleagle 1988, Kay et al. 1997, Delson and Tattersall 1997).

The diversification of the adapids and omomyids throughout the Northern Hemisphere reflects the tropicallike climates of the higher latitudes during the earlier part of the Eocene (see Chapter 20). With the late Eocene climatic deterioration in the temperate latitudes, primates declined and eventually disappeared from areas outside of Africa and tropical Asia. The primitive types of prosimians were largely extinct by the end of the Eocene, although some specialized forms (sivaladapids) survived into the late Miocene and early Pliocene in Asia (Fleagle 1988, Delson and Tattersall 1997). Even today, almost all nonhuman primates are restricted to the tropics. This has been true for most of the later Cenozoic, with the exception of some excursions of apes into more northern portions of Eurasia during the warming period in the late Miocene (see later).

Present-day prosimians are a moderately diverse Old World tropical radiation, first known in the fossil record from the late Oligocene of Africa (Fleagle 1988). The modern lineages are only sparsely known from the fossil record, probably because fossil preservation is rare in tropical forest habitats. The lemurs of the island of Madagascar have undergone an evolutionary diversification into five different families, including some large (raccoon-size) diurnal specialized herbivores such as the indri (*Indri indri*), and the peculiar aye-aye (*Daubentonia madagascarensis*) which uses its specialized long middle finger to probe grubs out of tree bark (Figure 24–3c). Until relatively recent times (only a couple of thousand years ago) there was a much greater variety of lemurs, including a number much larger forms. There were arboreal forms resembling giant koalas and orangutans, and terrestrial forms resembling ground sloths and baboons. It seems that the lemurs, in isolation from the rest of the world, evolved their own version of primate diversity including parallels to the anthropoid apes. Unfortunately much of this diversity is now gone,

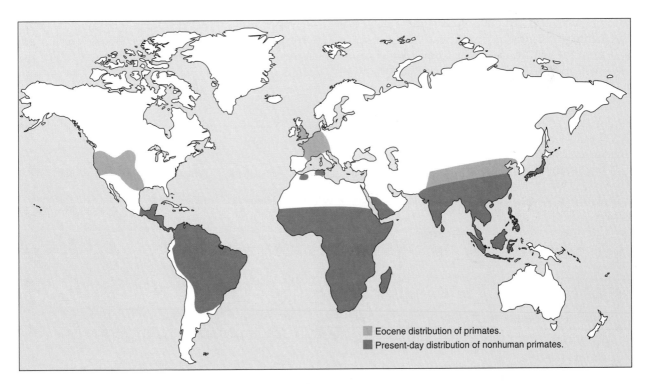

Figure 24–4   Distribution map of primates in Recent and Eocene times.

probably because of the immigration of humans to the island, and many present-day lemurs are threatened with extinction, owing to further destruction of forest habitat (Jolly 1980).

Anthropoids   Modern anthropoids are in general larger than prosimians, with larger brains and smaller olfactory lobes, and have a frugivorous (fruit-eating) or folivorous (leaf-eating) diet rather than an omnivorous or insectivorous one. They also are usually diurnal in habit, with more complex social systems, and in their locomotion are arboreal quadrupedal above-branch climbers or suspensory under-branch climbers, while prosimians are usually clinging and leaping forms. Modern anthropoids can be distinguished from prosimians by a variety of skull features that relate to being bigger brained and to having a more fibrous diet in need of more oral processing. Anthropoids possess a bony wall behind the orbit (as do tarsiers, a feature linking tarsiers and anthropoids in the Haplorhini), and have fused up the bones joining the two halves of the lower jaws and the paired frontal bones between the eyes (Figure 24–5). They also lack the grooming claw on the second toe seen in modern prosimians.

The earliest anthropoids are known from the middle Eocene, and there is considerable debate as to whether the candidate for the earliest anthropoid is a form known from Asia or from Africa (Kay et al. 1997). In either case, the earliest likely anthropoid would have been a small animal, probably insectivorous, resembling a modern tarsier. A diverse radiation of anthropoids is known from the Fayum Formation of Egypt, which spans a time range from the late Eocene to the early Oligocene. Modern anthropoids can be divided into the **Platyrrhini** (the broad-nosed New World monkeys) and the **Catarrhini** (the narrow-nosed Old World monkeys and apes). Some Fayum anthropoids, the smaller (marmoset-size), monkeylike parapithecids, represent forms more primitive than any living anthropoid. Some others, such the larger, more apelike propliopithecids, represent early catarrhines.

Platyrrhines, comprising the New World monkeys or **cebids**, first appeared in South America in the Oligocene, and have been an exclusively New World radiation. They must have somehow rafted across the Atlantic ocean to get to this continent from Africa: rodents of African origin also reached South America at around the same time (see Chapter 20). Platyrrhines are more primitive than catarrhines in their retention of three premolars in each side of the jaw, while all catarrhines have only two. Platyrrhines and catarrhines also differ in some details of the skull, especially in the ear region.

Platyrrhines can be divided into the cebines (e.g., the familiar capuchin or organ grinder monkey), the callitrichines (marmosets and tamarins), and the atelines (including specialized climbing monkeys with prehensile tails) (Figure 24–6). These groups are sometimes accorded subfamily status (within the family Cebidae, as we have followed here) and sometimes family status (within the superfamily

Figure 24–5   Cranial differences between prosimians and anthropoids. (Modified from Fleagle 1988, *Primate Adaption and Evolution*, Academic Press. Reprinted by permission.)

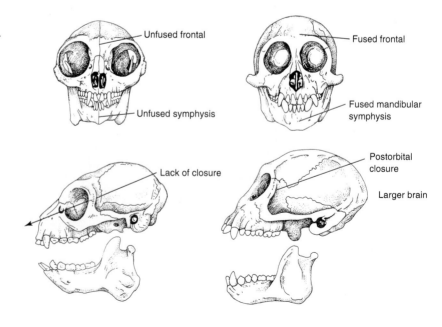

Figure 24–6 Diversity of living monkeys. (a) Pygmy marmoset, *Cebuella pygmaea* (Callitrichinae, Cebidae). (b) Squirrel monkey, *Saimiri sciureus* (Cebinae, Cebidae). (c) Spider monkey, *Ateles paniscus* (Atelinae, Cebidae). (d) Red howler monkey, *Alouatta seniculus* (Atelinae, Cebidae). (e) Pig-tailed macaque, *Macaca nemistrina* (Cercopithecinae, Cercopithecidae). (f) Savanna baboon, *Papio anubis* (Cercopithecinae, Cercopithecidae). (g) Hanuman langur, *Presbytis vetulus* (Colobinae, Cercopithecidae). (h) Red colobus, *Piliocolobus badius* (Colobinae, Cercopithecidae). (Modified from Fleagle 1988.)

Ceboidea), depending on the researcher (see Fleagle 1988). Marmosets and tamarins are small and squirrellike, and have secondarily clawlike nails on all digits except for the big toe. They have simplified molars, and while a few species are insectivorous, most are frugivores and specialists on eating the gum exudate from trees. They are also unusual among anthropoid primates in producing twins. There is no anthropoid equivalent to the marmosets in the Old World, although perhaps the bush baby prosimians are analogous in certain respects.

Cebines include squirrel monkeys and capuchins, and atelines include sakis, owl monkeys, titi monkeys, woolly monkeys, howler monkeys, and spider monkeys, the latter three types possessing a prehensile tail and having a specialized suspensory mode of arboreal locomotion. The cebid radiation paralleled that of Old World monkeys to a certain extent, although there is no terrestrial radiation equivalent to that of baboons and macaques. Neither was there ever a cebid radiation that was equivalent to the anthropoid great apes. The lack of apelike forms among the cebids is surprising when one considers that there was an evolutionary radiation of apelike forms (now all extinct) among the Madagascan lemurs. Perhaps the extensive radiation of ground sloths in South America inhibited a terrestrial radiation among the primates. However, a striking parallel does exist between the spider monkey and the gibbon (which is usually considered as a lesser ape). Both are specialized brachiators, with exceptionally long arms for swinging through the branches, and have evolved a remarkable convergence in a wrist joint modification that allows an extra degree of rotation. Spider monkeys can be distinguished from gibbons chiefly by their use of a prehensile tail as a fifth limb during locomotion (as apes, gibbons lack a tail entirely).

The catarrhines include the Old World monkeys, apes, and humans. We catarrhines have nostrils that are close together, open forward and downward, and have a smaller bony nasal opening from the skull than is the case for platyrrhines. There is a trend toward large body size in our lineage; the great apes and humans are the largest living primates, rivaled only by some of the extinct lemurs. The tail is often short or absent, and prehensile tails have never evolved. The group consists of two clades: the Old World monkeys (**Cercopithecoidea**); and the apes and humans (**Hominoidea**), the latter including the gibbons (Hylobatidae), and the great apes and humans. Humans, including

extinct genera such as *Australopithecus*, are traditionally placed in their own family, **Hominidae** (but see later discussion) (see Figure 24–1).

Present-day Old World monkeys constitute two groups, colobines and cercopithecines. Colobines are found in both Africa and Asia, including colobus monkeys, langur monkeys, proboscis monkeys, and the golden monkey. They are more folivorous than cercopithecines, and have more lophed, higher-cusped molars and a complex forestomach for fermentation of plant fiber (see Chapter 21). Colobines are primarily arboreal animals, with a long tail and hindlegs longer than the forelegs. Cercopithecines are predominately an African radiation, although the genus *Macaca* is widespread, known also from Asia (including quite high latitude places such as Japan and Tibet) and Europe (in Gibraltar, where it is known as the Barbary ape). Cercopithecines include macaques, mangabeys, baboons, guenons, and the patas monkey. They are more omnivorous or folivorous than colobines, as reflected in their broader incisors and their flatter, more bunodont molars. Cercopithecines are also more terrestrial, as reflected by their short tail and their equal-lengthed fore- and hindlimbs. They have cheek pouches for storing food, and a hand with a longer thumb and shorter fingers than colobines (Fleagle 1998) (see Figure 24–6).

The first Old World monkeys are known from the middle Miocene (Benefit and McCrossin 1997). These earliest monkeys, victoriapithecines, are more primitive than any known Old World monkey, and so form the sister group to the modern cercopithecids. Monkeys are known from a slightly later date than the first true apes, the generalized proconsulids from the early Miocene of Africa. Monkeys are actually more derived than apes in certain respects: they have teeth that are more specialized for herbivory, some have gut specializations for the fermentation of cellulose, and they are more specialized for arboreality than the generalized Miocene apes. The radiation of monkeys in the late Miocene and Pliocene was coincident with the reduction in diversity of the earlier radiation of generalized apes and apelike forms. Because we ourselves are apes, we often think of the monkeys as being the earlier, more primitive anthropoid radiation. But among the Old World anthropoids, the converse is actually true. Originally it was the apes which were the more primitive, generalized forms, and the radiation of cercopithecoid monkeys which was the more derived one in many respects, and ultimately the more successful one in terms of species diversity.

■ The Origin and Evolution of the Hominoidea

Apes and humans are placed in the Hominoidea. Hominoids are morphologically distinguished from other recent anthropoids by a pronounced widening and dorsoventral flattening of the trunk relative to body length so that the shoulders, thorax, and hips have become proportionately broader than in monkeys. The clavicles are elongated, the iliac blades of the pelvis are broad, and the sternum is a broad structure, the bony elements of which fuse soon after birth to form a single flat bone. The shoulder blades of hominoids lie over a broad, flattened back, in contrast to their lateral position next to a narrow chest in monkeys (Figure 24–7) and most other quadrupeds. The pelvic and pectoral girdles of hominoids are relatively closer together because the lumbar region of the vertebral column is short. The caudal vertebrae have become reduced to vestiges in all Recent hominoids, and normally no free tail appears postnatally. Balance in a bipedal pose is assisted by the flat thorax, which places the center of gravity near the vertebral column. These and other anatomical specializations of the trunk are common to all hominoids and help to maintain the erect postures that these primates assume during sitting, vertical climbing, and walking bipedally (Campbell 1985) (see Figure 24-8). The skulls of hominoids also differ from those of other catarrhines by their extensive formation of sinuses, hollow air-filled spaces lined with mucous membranes that develop between the outer and inner surfaces of skull bones. Chimpanzees, gorillas, and humans share the derived character of large frontal sinuses.

Diversity and Evolution of Nonhuman Hominoids

Anthropoid primates that we can call apes in the broad sense of the word have been around since the late Eocene. However, primates that can be included in a monophyletic Hominoidea date from the early Miocene, when the anthropoid lineage diverges into the hominoids and the cercopithecoids (Old World monkeys). Modern apes are a highly specialized radiation of large tropical animals. The Miocene radiation of apes was of more generalized animals, that also radiated into more temperate parts of the Old World.

Differences in the cheek teeth between hominoids and Old World monkeys are of paramount significance in the identification of fossils because many primate fossils are represented by individual teeth. The Old World monkeys have lower molars

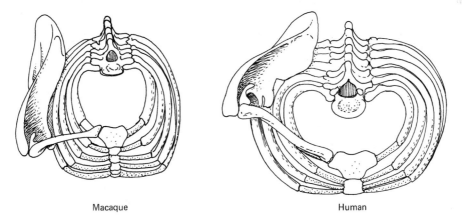

Macaque   Human

Figure 24–7   Cephalic view (i.e., from the top with the head removed) of chest and pectoral girdle (right half) of macaque (cercopithecoid monkey) and human (hominoid). Note the broader chest and the dorsal position of the scapula in the hominoid; additionally, the curvature of the ribs is greater, with the vertebral column lying more in the middle of the rib cage, closer to the center of gravity. All of these features make it more easy for a hominoid to balance in an upright position (while monkeys must bend their knees and lean forwards if balancing on their hind legs, to avoid tipping over backwards).

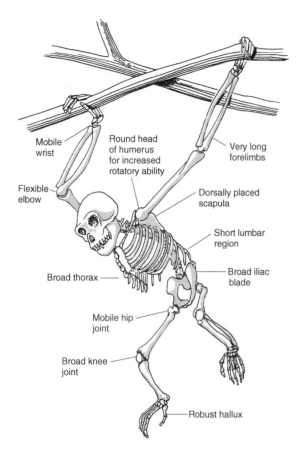

Figure 24–8 Skeleton of generalized hominoid, showing morphological adaptations for suspensory locomotion.

frequently obscured by crenulations or variations in the number of cusps. When five cusps do appear the grooves between the cusps usually resemble the letter Y, with the open part of the Y embracing the hypoconid cusp (Figure 24–9). This molar pattern, called Y-5, has persisted among hominoids for more than 20 million years (Day 1986).

Diversity of Present-day Apes

Present-day apes include the Asian gibbons (including siamangs) and orangutan and the African chimpanzees and gorilla (Figure 24–10). Traditionally, gibbons have been accorded their own family, Hylobatidae, and the other apes have been placed in the family "Pongidae." However, it is now clear that pongids represent a paraphyletic grouping (see Figure 24–1), and the official term has been abandoned (although the notion of a term to encompass the nonhuman great apes is still a useful one).

There are nine species of gibbons (genus *Hylobates*), found on the mainland and the islands of southeast Asia. They are the smallest apes, and also differ from other apes in their monogamous social system. Gibbons move through the trees most frequently by brachiation (swinging from the underside of one branch to the underside of the next using the hands to grasp the branches). They become bipedal when moving on the ground, holding their arms outstretched for balance as a tightrope walker uses a pole.

There are two subspecies of the orangutan, *Pongo pygmaeus*, one living on Borneo and one on Sumatra, although their range was greater in prehistoric times. Orangutans are around the same size as humans, and are extremely sexually dimorphic, with males being twice the weight of females. Their

(M1 and sometimes M2) with four cusps, one at each corner of a rectangular crown; the anterior pair of cusps, like the posterior pair, are each connected by a ridge. Hominoid lower molars have crowns with five cusps, but in extant humans (although not most fossil relatives) this pattern is

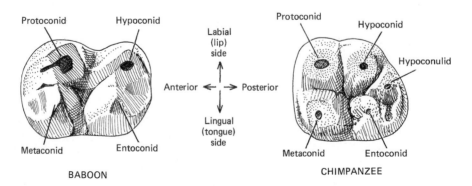

Figure 24–9 Right lower molar patterns of Old World monkey (baboon) and hominoid (chimpanzee) compared. Shading indicates low crown areas or grooves between major cusps and ridges illustrating the Y-5 configuration of hominoids.

Figure 24–10 Diversity of living apes. (a) Siamang (a type of gibbon), *Hylobates syndactylus*. (b) Orangutan, *Pongo pygmaeus*. (c) Gorilla, *Gorilla gorilla*. (d) Common chimpanzee, *Pan troglodytes*. (Modified from Fleagle 1988, in part, *Primate Adaption and Evolution*, Academic Press. Reprinted by permission.)

(a)

(b)

(c)

(d)

behavior is fairly solitary, the main groups consisting of females and their offspring. Orangutans are also arboreal but rarely swing by their arms, preferring slow quadrupedal climbing among the branches of trees, usually hanging below the branch (suspensory climbing).

Gorillas and chimpanzees live in the tropical forests of central Africa. Both African apes are more terrestrial than the Asian ones, and when on the ground locomote quadupedally by a mode termed knuckle-walking: rather than place their weight flat on the palm of the hand, as we do when we walk on all fours, they support themselves on the dorsal surface of the digits, with their hand in a similar posture to the one we adopt when knocking on a door. There are three subspecies of gorilla (*Gorilla gorilla*).

Gorillas are the largest and the most terrestrial of the apes. Like the orangutan, they are extremely sexually dimorphic in body size, but unlike the orangutan they are highly social and live in groups. There are two species of chimpanzees, the larger and more widely distributed common chimpanzee (*Pan troglodytes*), and the smaller pygmy chimpanzee or bonobo (*Pan paniscus*). Chimps are more omnivorous than the more strictly herbivorous gorillas, and are also more arboreal, exhibiting a greater degree of suspensory locomotion. They are only moderately sexually dimorphic in body size, and also live in groups. It has been suggested that the pygmy chimp is more closely related to humans than is the common chimp (Zihlman et al., 1978): if this were true, this would mean that the genus *Pan* is paraphyletic.

Although all modern hominoids can stand erect and walk to some degree on their hind legs, only humans display an erect bipedal mode of striding locomotion involving a specialized structure of the pelvis and hind limbs, thereby freeing the forelimbs from obligatory functions of support, balance, or locomotion.

Diversity of Fossil Apes

Fossil primates commonly called apes are known from the late Eocene to early Oligocene Fayum Formation of Egypt, which appears to represent a tropical forest type of environment. These primates belong to the extinct family Propliopithecidae, and include the cat-size supposed early ape *Aegyptopithecus*. However, these primates are more primitive than any living catarrhine, and predate the divergence of modern monkeys and apes. They thus cannot be classified as hominoids. These primates are considered apelike rather than monkeylike because they have low-crowned, bunodont cheek teeth, suggesting a diet of fruit and seeds, but lacking in mature leaves. Their skeletal anatomy suggests that they were primarily arboreal quadrupeds, not terrestrial but neither highly specialized for climbing (Fleagle 1988). Other apelike primates that are not true hominoids are the pliopithecids, gibbonlike forms from the middle to late Miocene of Eurasia.

The first true hominoids were the early Miocene proconsulids of East Africa. They apparently occupied primarily forested habitats (Andrews 1992). Proconsulids were generalized quadrupedal arboreal animals, ranging from the size of a small monkey to the size of a female gorilla, with bunodont molars suggesting a frugivorous diet (Fleagle 1988). By the middle Miocene more derived hominoids had diversified into a number of ecological types and had spread into Eurasia, following the general middle Miocene warming trend (see Chapter 20). As just mentioned, the more primitive pliopithecids were also found Eurasia during this warm part of the later Tertiary, and a variety of monkeys, both cercopithecines and colobines, was also known from the Eurasian late Miocene and Pliocene (Andrews et al. 1996).

The later Cenozoic Eurasian hominoids include the dryopithecids and sivapithecids, which are more closely related to the great apes and humans than are gibbons. Perhaps the best known of these fossil apes is *Sivapithecus*. This genus now includes

the animal formerly known as *Ramapithecus*, known from around 17 million years ago, and originally considered to be an ancestral hominid. Evidence from paleoclimatic studies and the nature of the other animals in the fauna suggests that these Miocene hominoids primarily occupied woodland or forest habitats (Andrews 1992).

Dryopithecids, and the related African afropithecids and kenyapithecids, were probably more primitive than any living great ape. In contrast, the sivapithecids appear to be related to the living orangutan. The size of the teeth and jaws of sivapithecids suggests animals about a meter or so in stature. The dentition of these primates, with reduced canines and thick-enameled molars, suggests to some workers that they may have fed on material that required crushing (thick enamel) and grinding (no interlocking canines to inhibit rotary chewing movements), indicative of a diet of nuts and hard fruits. (Early hominids also have thick-enameled molars, which is one of the reasons why *Ramapithecus* was originally thought to be a hominid.) The orangutan lineage also included the late Miocene to Pleistocene *Gigantopithecus* of Asia. The Pleistocene species represented the largest primate that has ever lived; at an estimated body mass of 300 kg it would have been twice the size of a gorilla. Some people have speculated that a surviving lineage of *Gigantopithecus* is behind the legends of the Yeti in Tibet, and the Bigfoot or Sasquach of northwestern North America (which presumably would have reached this continent by migrating across Beringia during the Pleistocene, as did so many other mammals at this time).

A few fossil apes, such as the European *Graecopithecus* of 10-8 million years ago, appear to belong to the same clade as the great apes plus humans (Delson and Tattersall 1997). It is notable that in numerous dental and associated cranial features it is humans who have retained the ancestral characteristics of our clade while the lineages of great apes have each derived unique specializations. Of course, humans have also evolved their own specializations independently of the various great ape lineages. It remains important to note, however, that all of the living hominoids are derived in comparison with the Mio-Pliocene ape radiation. The fact that gibbons and orangutans are placed in a less derived position on the cladogram than are humans or African apes (Figure 24–1) does not imply that earlier apes looked like these modern forms.

■ Origin and Evolution of Humans

Humans differ enough in their anatomy from the apes so that they have usually been placed in a separate family, called the Hominidae, although molecular evidence suggests a much closer intrafamilial relationship between apes and humans. The jaw in humans is shorter in association with the shortening of the muzzle, certain teeth are smaller and the entire dentition is more uniform in size and shape. In particular, the canines lie on the same occlusal plane as the incisors and cheek teeth. Apes have a prominent diastema between the canines and incisors that accommodates occlusion of the jaws, whereas in humans all the teeth touch their adjacent members (Figure 24–11). The jaws of an ape are rectangular or U-shaped, with the four incisors lying at right angles to the canines and cheek teeth, which form nearly parallel lines along the jaw's two sides. The ancestors of the hominids, and fossil hominoids such as *Sivapithecus*, had an almost V-shaped jaw. Some of the earliest hominids had a U-shaped jaw. The jaw of members of the genus *Homo* is bow-shaped, with the teeth running in a curve that is widest at the back of the mouth. The human palate is prominently arched, whereas the ape palate is flatter between their parallel rows of cheek teeth.

Various evolutionary trends within the hominids can also be identified. The articulations of the skull with the vertebral column (occipital condyles) and the foramen magnum (for the passage of the spinal cord) shifted from the ancestral position at the rear of the braincase to a position under the braincase. This change balances the skull on top of the vertebral column, in association with an upright, vertical posture of the trunk. The braincase itself became greatly enlarged in association with an increase in forebrain size. By the end of the middle Pleistocene a prominent vertical forehead developed, in contrast to the sloping foreheads of the apes. The brow

ridges and crests for muscular attachments on the skull became reduced in size in association with the reduction in size of the muscles that once attached to them. The human nose became a more prominent feature of the face, with a distinct bridge and tip.

The primate phylogenetic tree (Figure 24–1) indicates that the human, chimpanzee, and gorilla are more closely related to each other, in terms of recency of their common ancestor, than they are to orangutans or gibbons. These relationships among extant apes and humans were first determined on the basis of comparative anatomy by T. H. Huxley, who published his ideas in 1863. They have gained additional support and clarity from recent biochemical, serological, and cytological comparisons as well as from the fossil record of the earlier hominoids. The majority of studies, especially the molecular ones, support a close relationship between chimpanzees and humans, although some anatomical studies place chimpanzees and gorillas closer to each other. For example, both of these apes have the specialized type of quadrupedal terrestrial locomotion known as knuckle-walking.

The extant African apes have no known fossil record. At present we must depend on molecular studies of extant forms to gain insight into the history of our nearest surviving relatives. This evidence indicates that gorillas separated from the chimpanzee and human common ancestor between 8 and 10 million years ago. The gorillas were subsequently isolated by unknown phenomena into eastern and western populations about 3 million years ago. Sometime in the interim, perhaps as recently as 6 million years ago, chimpanzee and human lineages separated (Morell 1994). Two or possibly three species of chimpanzee exist today with geographic differences in genetic patterns similar to that found in gorillas. However, the differences in chimpanzee populations are thought to

Figure 24–11 Upper jaw of a Miocene ape (*Sivapithecus*), an orangutan (*Pongo*), and a human (*Homo*) compared.

Sivapithecus

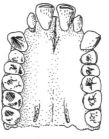

Orangutan

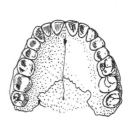

Human

have occurred more recently, between about 2.5 and 1.6 million years ago.

A surprising conclusion from the emerging discipline of molecular evolution is that humans are more closely related to the extant great apes of Africa than morphologists or paleontologists had thought (Ciochon and Corruccini 1983, Lewin 1984). For example, hybridization of nonrepeated DNA sequences of humans and chimpanzees indicate 98 percent identity. Electrophoretic measurement of genetically controlled polymorphic proteins (allozymes) in the six extant genera of hominoids show that the degree of genetic difference among human, chimpanzee, gorilla, and orangutan is no greater than that observed among species in the same genus in many other taxa of vertebrates, including most mammals. The difference between the gibbons (Hylobatidae) and other hominoids is only slightly greater than the average difference between species in the same genus among other vertebrates (Bruce and Ayala 1979). High-resolution analysis of chromosomal morphology also reveals close relatedness among the hominoids: Humans are most closely allied to chimpanzees, the gorillas are slightly more distantly related, and the orangutans still farther removed (Yunis and Prakash 1982). These sorts of data and calculations, based on the concept of the **molecular clock** (the supposedly unvarying rate of generic change within a clade over evolutionary time), suggest that *Homo* and the extinct related genus *Australopithecus* last shared a common ancestor with the African apes no more than 5 to 10 million years ago, in the late Miocene to early Pliocene. This is a much more recent split than most biologists have previously supposed, and indicates a phase of rapid evolutionary change in the lineage leading to the specialized apes (Andrews 1992).

Because of this amount of genetic relatedness between living hominoids, there has been a recent trend to readjust their higher level classification. Many taxonomists now consider the family Hominidae, which we use here in the more traditional sense to include just humans (genera *Homo*, *Australopithecus*, and *Ardipithecus*), to also include all of the great apes (i.e., those originally classified as "pongids"). Humans would now be reduced to the level of the subtribe Hominina (which also includes chimpanzees) within the subfamily Homininae (which also includes at least the gorilla) (Delson and Tattersall 1997, Lewin 1998). However, this classification is very new, and there is much dispute about

the different taxonomic levels (e.g., some researchers consider gibbons to be within the family Hominidae, others prefer to leave them as their own family Hylobatidae, as traditionally; some researchers would place orangutans in the subfamily Homininae within the newly defined family Hominidae, others would accord them their own subfamily Ponginae). For this reason, we have adhered to the traditional classification (e.g., Fleagle 1988) in this presentation, but caution readers that this area of primate taxonomy nomenclature is in a state of flux.

If this molecular time estimate is correct, a gap of only 1 to 5 million years occurs in the geological record before the first undoubted hominid fossils are found in mid-Pliocene deposits in Kenya and Ethiopia. About 8 million years ago, at the beginning of the essentially blank period for hominoid fossils in East Africa, tectonic forces split the region almost in two along a north to south feature still dramatically obvious today, the Rift Valley. New mountain boundaries and resulting changes in the ecological landscape appear to have divided an as yet unknown ancestral population of hominoids. The western population survived in moist forested lowlands and became the ancestors of the chimpanzees. The eastern population lived in the rain shadow of the new mountains where forests gave way to woodlands and woodlands to savannas. As conditions became dryer and more seasonal 2 to 3 million years ago, savannas became increasingly widespread in the rain shadow. The hominids isolated in the East became our direct ancestors (Coppens 1994).

Primitive Hominids

Although isolated fragments as old as 5.6 million years are known from Africa, they are too small to yield much information. No interpretable hominid remains older than about 3.8 million years had been discovered until recently. The earliest hominids are **australopithecines**. Despite their role in human ancestry, in terms of their biology they are best thought of as bipedal apes with a modified dentition (Lewin 1998). Microwear analysis of their teeth suggests that they were primarily fruit-eaters, perhaps including some meat in the diet, as do present-day chimpanzees. However, they were not strictly carnivorous hunters, as has been proposed for early members of the genus *Homo*. All australopithecines appear to have been at least partially arboreal. The evidence from this comes not only from their limb anatomy, but also from the anatomy of the semicircular canals in the inner ear (structures responsible for orientation and balance, see Chapter 3). Australopithecines all have an apelike pattern, suggesting the retention of apelike orientation in an arboreal environment rather than a fully terrestrial lifestyle (Spoor et al. 1996). It appears that australopithecines were able to stand and walk bipedally to

a certain extent, but were not capable active, sustained running (Lewin 1998).

The most completely known early australopithecine, and until very recently the earliest known hominid, is *Australopithecus afarensis*. This species is best known from a very substantial part of a single young adult female skeleton, known in popular literature by the nickname Lucy. Lucy was discov-

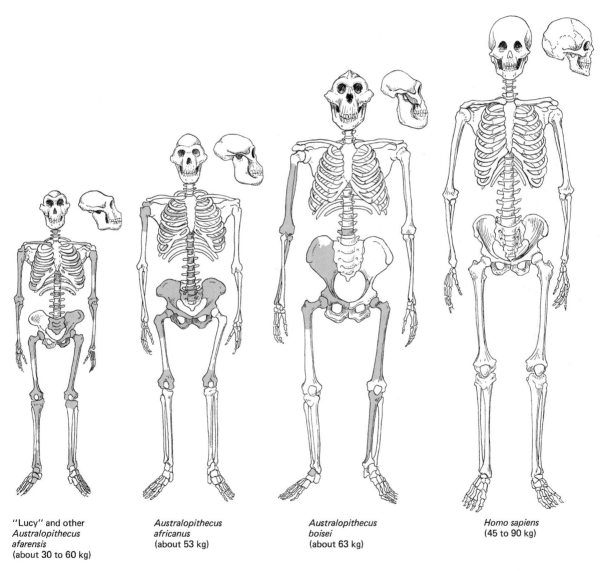

''Lucy'' and other
*Australopithecus
afarensis*
(about 30 to 60 kg)

*Australopithecus
africanus*
(about 53 kg)

*Australopithecus
boisei*
(about 63 kg)

Homo sapiens
(45 to 90 kg)

Figure 24–12   Reconstructed skeletons of four hominid species, showing relative stature and stance. Shaded portions of the postcranial skeletons of the fossils show the parts actually known from specimens. Although almost all australopithecine skulls are fragmentary, sufficient material exists to reconstruct entire skulls with fair certainty. Too little of the most ancient australopithecine (*Ardipithecus ramidus*) has been discovered to permit confident reconstruction. Note the shorter iliac blade, the less funnel-shaped rib cage, the relatively longer legs, and the shorter fingers and toes in *Homo*.

ered by Donald Johanson in the desert of the Afar plain, also in Ethiopia, not far from the Red Sea, in a deposit dated at 3.2 million years (Johanson and Edey 1981). She is an astonishing specimen in several respects. Lucy is the most complete pre-*Homo* hominid fossil ever found, consisting of more than 60 pieces of bone from the skull, lower jaw, arms, legs, pelvis, ribs, and vertebrae. Paleoanthropologists believe that she stood fully erect. Her overall body size was small. Young but fully grown when she died, Lucy was only about 1 meter tall and weighed perhaps 30 kilograms (see Figure 24–12 and the Chapter-opening figure), but other finds indicate that males of her species were larger, averaging 1.5 meters tall and 45 kilograms (McHenry 1994). Although her hip and limb clearly indicate bipedalism, detailed analysis of the fossils and reconstruction of musculature demonstrate a bipedalism different from modern humans and retention of a partly arboreal anatomy (Berge 1994). Arboreality is also be reflected in her hands and feet, with fingers and toes significantly longer and more curved than in modern humans. Lucy and her kind may have slept and taken refuge in trees, bipedalism being important in the efficient harvesting of fruits in their open forest and woodland habitat (Hunt 1994). Her teeth and lower jaw are also clearly humanlike. Her diet may have been rich in hard objects, probably fruits that would have been unevenly distributed in space and time (Andrews and Martin 1991). Unfortunately, we know little about the size and shape of Lucy's cranium. Other specimens of *A. afarensis* indicate a brain size of 380 to 450 cubic centimeters, quite close to that of modern chimpanzees and gorillas (Simons 1989, Lewin 1993).

Humanlike footprints were found by Mary Leakey and her associates at Laetoli in Tanzania, from volcanic ash beds radiometrically dated between 3.6 and 3.8 million years in age, and were probably made by *A. afarensis*, which is also known from fossils at the same site. Analysis of these footprints indicates that they do not differ substantially from modern human trails made on a similar substrate (White 1980), proving the antiquity of bipedalism in hominid ancestry, long before the acquisition of a enlarged brain.

More recently, earlier and even more primitive hominids have been discovered. A new genus of fossil hominid based on 17 specimens, all but four of them teeth, represents the remains of a form that lies close to the divergence between our closest African ape relatives and the lineage to humans (White et al. 1994, Wood 1994). *Ardipithecus ramidus* (formerly *Australopithecus ramidus*), as the fragments have been named, comes from Ethiopian sediments about 4.4 million years of age and indicative of a wooded habitat (WoldeGabriel et al. 1994). *A. ramidus* has many chimpanzeelike features, and lacks some of the derived traits shared by the next most recent fossil hominids and all later hominids. Tentative evaluation of the scant evidence, however, indicates that *A. ramidus* was bipedal (judging from the position of the foramen magnum), had a humanlike rather than apelike arm (especially the shoulder joint and elbow), and had incisiform canines with less sexual dimorphism than modern African apes, traits that are hallmarks of the human lineage.

The earliest known member of the genus *Australopithecus* is now *A. anamensis*, found by Maeve Leakey and Alan Walker in several sites in Kenya, which range in dates from as 4.2 to 3.9 million years old (Leakey et al., 1995). This hominid appears to be intermediate in anatomy between *Ardipithecus* and *Australopithecus afarensis*, with a less apelike dentition than *Ardipithecus*, and with fragments of limb bones strongly suggestive of bipedality. Its estimated body mass, around 50 kg, is larger than either of these other early hominids. Another new *Australopithecus* species, slightly younger and contemporaneous with *A. afarensis*, is *A. bahrelghazali* (Brunet et al. 1996). This hominid was found in Chad, in central Africa, in fossil site with an interpreted environment of lakeside woodland. This is the first known australopithecine to be found west of the Rift Valley, suggesting that early hominids were more widespread in Africa, and also more diverse in their habitats, than had previously been supposed.

There is controversy about the interrelationships of these early hominids. Some researchers would interpret them as an ancestor-descendant evolutionary line, with *Ardipithecus* giving rise to *Australopithecus anamensis*, which in turn gave rise to *A. afarensis*, and *A. afarensis* giving rise to both *Homo* and the later australopithecines. Others see a more bushy interrelationship between these taxa, as shown in Figure 24–13 (Lewin 1998).

The later australopithecines were distributed in East and South Africa from about 2.5 to 1 million years ago. The later australopithecines are represented by two different types: three large, robust forms with sagittal crests on the skulls and enormous grinding postcanine teeth and the proportions of a football player (often placed in their own genus *Paranthropus*); and one smaller, more delicate, gracile form, *Australopithecus africanus*, that lacked the sagittal crests and massive eye ridges of the robust forms (Johanson and Edey 1981, Delson 1987). (See Figure 24–12 and the color insert.) Although *A. africanus* was fully bipedal, it also had very robust arm bones suggesting that it may have spent even more time in trees than *A. afarensis*, and implying that it may not be in the direct evolutionary line to *Homo* (Lewin 1998). The three robust forms, *Australopithecus robustus* of South Africa and *A. aethiopicus* and *A. boisei* of East Africa, were terrestrial savanna-dwelling vegetarians, somewhat analogous in dietary habits to the forest-inhabiting gorillas. In comparison with other australopithecines their molars were big and exhibited heavy wear, suggesting a more coarse and fibrous diet. It is not known how these robust australopithecines are interrelated, or even whether they represent a single radiation from within the gracile australopithecines. The robust type of australopithecine may have arisen independently on more than one occasion.

The gracile australopithecines were primarily a early Pliocene radiation. In the late Pliocene, at around 2.5 million years ago, the hominid lineage split into two, one leading to our direct ancestors, the genus *Homo*, and the other leading to the robust australopithecines. This particular time appears to record global climatic changes. It was 2.5 million years ago when the Isthmus of Panama formed, linking North and South America. This resulted in changes in oceanic currents, as there was no longer a direct passage between Atlantic and Pacific oceans, and the modern Gulf Stream circulation probably dates from this time. There was significant global cooling, with the onset of Arctic glaciation. Paleontological evidence from both the flora and fauna of Africa suggests climatic change at this time, to a drier, more savannalike habitat; grazing antelopes increased in abundance, and new types of carnivores appeared. This environmental change may have been the trigger in changing the course of hominid evolution (Vrba et al. 1989). Thus during the late Pliocene there were two evolving lineages of hominids, early true humans and robust australopithecines. Further cooling and drying of the climate resulted in the reduction in abundance of the robust australopithecines at the start of the Pleistocene, and their extinction later in the epoch. However, had the Pleistocene climatic changes been different, such as a reversal back to a wetter and warmer regime, it might have been our ancestors who went extinct and the robust australopithecines who survived.

Derived Hominids (the genus *Homo*)

A controversial form (or forms) described from fragmentary remains, existed in East Africa from 2.4 to 1.6 million years ago (Hill et al. 1992, Tattersall 1993). The actual taxonomic status of these highly variable remains, which have been called *Homo habilis*, is much debated (Wood 1987, 1992). The remains may include a second species, *H. rudolfensis*, which was somewhat larger-brained and a more suitable ancestor for later species of *Homo*. The structure of the hand and wrist, and the long and powerful arms of both *Australopithecus* and *H. habilis'* indicate arboreal capabilities (Susman and Stern 1982). *Homo habilis* is best distinguished by its larger cranial capacity: between 500 and 750 cubic centimeters in contrast to the value of 380 to 450 cubic centimeters for *Australopithecus afarensis* (Campbell 1985, Falk 1985). *Homo habilis* also differs from *Australopithecus* in having a smaller face, and a smaller jaw and dentition, with smaller cheek teeth and larger front teeth (see Figure 24–14). However, the tooth wear was similar to that of *Australopithecus*, suggesting a similar fruit-eating diet (Lewin 1998).

Around 2 million years ago a new hominid appeared in the fossil record. *Homo erectus*, originally described as *Pithecanthropus erectus*, probably originated in East Africa, where it coexisted for at least several hundred thousand years with two of the robust australopithecines (Harris et al. 1988). *Homo erectus* was the first intercontinentally distributed hominid. It appears to have spread to Asia no later than 1.8 million years ago, and subsequently perhaps into Europe (Swisher et al. 1994). Nowadays the older African version of *H. erectus* is usually called *Homo ergaster*, with the name of *erectus* reserved for the Asian hominid. *Homo ergaster* disappeared around 1.3 million years ago, whereas *H. erectus* survived for much longer. It was originally thought that the species disappeared between 200,000 and 300,000 years ago, but recent discoveries have shown that it survived for around a quarter of million years longer. Remains from Java have been dated as being between 27 and 53 thousand years old (Swisher et al. 1996), making *H. erectus* a contemporary of the Neandertals and modern *H. sapiens*.

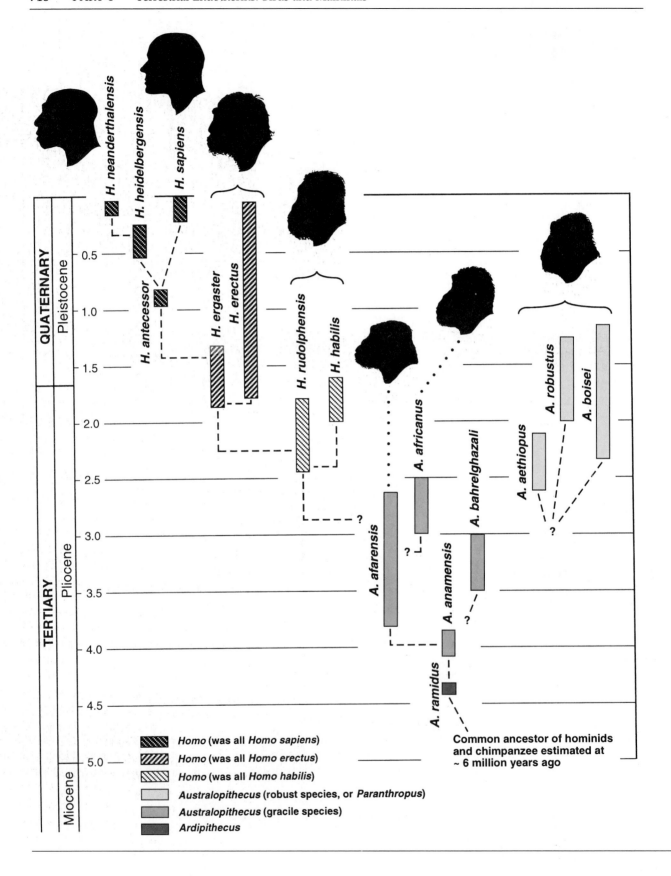

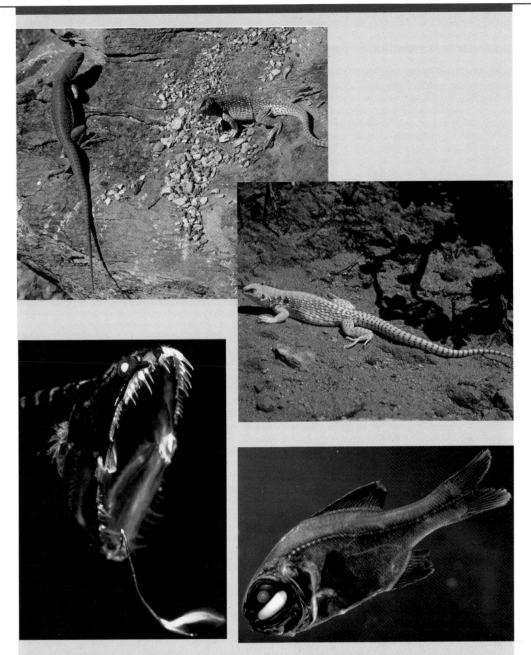

Color change is a temperature-regulating mechanism used by lizards such as the desert iguana (*Dipsosaurus dorsalis*). (Upper left) When they first emerge in the morning, desert iguanas are dark. (Upper right) By the time it has reached its activity temperature, a lizard has turned light. This color change reduces heat gained from the sun by 23 percent.

Luminescent bacteria in the light organs of fishes emit light as a by-product of their metabolism. (Lower left) A black dragonfish, *Idiacanthus*. A long barbel on the chin bears a luminous lure that is believed to attract prey close enough to be engulfed by the enormous jaws lined with sharp teeth. (Lower right) The flash-light fish, *Photoblepharon*, has a light-emitting organ under each eye. The fish can cover the organ with a pigmented shutter to conceal the light, or open the shutter to reveal it. It uses the light organ in social interactions with other flashlight fish, and in a blink-and-run defense to startle and confuse predators.

Photographs: Top left © Tom McHugh; Top right © Bucky Reeves; Bottom © Norbert Wu, DRK Inc.

Three species of salamanders form a mimicry complex in eastern North America. The red eft (*Notophthalmus viridescens*, top left) and red salamander (*Psuedotriton ruber*, top right) have skin toxins that deter predators. The red-backed salamander (*Plethodon cinereus*, middle left) is not protected by toxins, but predators confuse the erythristic form of that species (middle right) with the toxic species. The experiment described in the text used the mountain dusky salamander (*Desmognathus ochrophaeus*, bottom left) as a palatable control.

Photographs: red eft © Michael Lustbader; red salamander © Alan Blank, National Audubon Society; red-backed salamander, erythristic red-backed salamander, and mountain dusky salamander © F. H. Pough.

The gular fans of lizards are used in social displays. Color, size, and shape identify the species and sex of an individual. (All the lizards in these photographs are males.) (Top left) Carolina anole, *Anolis carolinensis*, from Florida. (Top right) knight anole, *Anolis equestris*, from Cuba. (Bottom left) *Anolis grahami* from Jamaica. (Bottom right) *Anolis chrysolepis* from Brazil.

Photographs: top left © J. H. Robinson; top right © Cosmos Blank, National Audubon Society; bottom left © Fred McConnaughey; bottom right © Jany Sauvanet.

The colors of birds result from a combination of structural characteristics and pigments. The blue of a blue jay (left) is produced by small particles in the feathers that scatter blue light back toward the viewer. The red of a cardinal and many other birds is produced by a caretenoid pigment, zoonerythrin.

 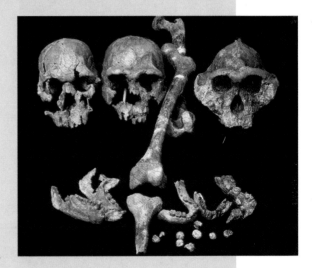

Skulls of hominids. (Left) Skulls of a gracile australopithecine (top) and a robust form. (Right) Skulls of *Homo habilis* (left), *Homo erectus* (center), and a robust australopithecine (right). Limb bones and mandibles are also shown.

Photographs: Top left © Thomas W. Martin; Top right © Stephen J. Krasemann, The National Audubon Society Collection. Skull photographs by John Reader, Science Photo Library.

Three characteristics are especially important features of *Homo erectus* and *H. ergaster*: Firstly, it was of substantially larger body size than earlier hominids (to 1.85 meters and at least 65 kilograms), with a major increase in female size that reduced sexual dimorphism. In earlier hominids males were apparently twice the size of females, whereas in *H. erectus/ergaster* the males were only about 20 or 30 percent larger than the females, comparable with our own species. The notably larger body size of males in earlier *Homo* species implies a ranging pattern in which females foraged in smaller territories than males and the probability of a polygynous mating system (McHenry 1994). The substantial increase of body size and reduction in sexual dimorphism of *H. erectus/ergaster* and subsequent forms of *Homo* imply behavioral changes. These new characteristics may be directly related to a significant increase in group mobility and ultimately to intercontinental distribution. Secondly, *H. erectus/ergaster* also had larger brains than earlier *Homo* species, with cranial capacities ranging from 775 to 1100 cubic centimeters. However, because they were also larger animals than earlier *Homo*, this difference in brain size mainly reflected larger overall body size. Finally, *Homo erectus/ergaster* was the first hominid to have a humanlike nose, with downwards-facing nostrils (Lewin 1998).

The other facial features of *H. erectus/ergaster* were primitive—a prognathous (projecting) face with relatively large teeth, almost no chin, a flat sloping forehead, prominent bony eyebrow ridges, and broad, flat nose (Figure 24–14). The skeletal proportions were similar to those of modern humans, although the femoral head was relatively smaller, but the bones were more robust, suggesting a more muscular build.

Homo erectus/ergaster represents a large change in the evolutionary history of humans. With this pair of species was recorded a number of firsts in human prehistory, including the first appearance of hominids outside of Africa, the first evidence for tool-making and the use of fire, the first evidence

of hunting and the use of home bases, and the first evidence of an extended childhood (as evidenced by patterns of tooth eruption) (Lewin 1998).

Homo ergaster is more closely related to our own species, *Homo sapiens*, than is *Homo erectus*. No derived characters have yet been defined that clearly distinguish the latest fossils assigned to *Homo ergaster* from fossils believed to be early (archaic) *Homo sapiens*. The characters used to separate the two taxa are all measurements (continuous variables), not the presence or absence of a distinctive structure. On average, *Homo sapiens* have a slightly larger brain, a thicker and more robust skull, larger teeth, and less prognathism (projection of the jaw beyond the plane of the upper face) than *Homo ergaster* or *Homo erectus*. All of these characters show overlap between the two groups; the clearest distinction is the reduction in prognathism.

The Origin of Modern Humans

The species *Homo sapiens*, as originally defined, first appeared around 500,000 years ago, and included not only the modern types of humans, which date from around 200,000 years ago, but also the Neandertals, which sometimes have been classified as the subspecies *Homo sapiens neanderthalensis*. More recent evidence, from a variety of sources, has complicated this picture. First, archaic types of *Homo sapiens*, known from both Africa and Europe, have been accorded their own species, *H. heidelbergensis*, with the term *H. sapiens* becoming reserved for modern humans, and Neandertals accorded their own species, *H. neanderthalensis*. *H. heidelbergensis* was thought to have been ancestral to both modern humans and Neandertals. However, recent analysis of ancient DNA from the bone of a Neandertal showed considerable genetic difference from modern humans, suggesting that they were not directly ancestral to modern humans nor, perhaps, quite as closely related as once thought (Kahn and Gibbons 1997). Additionally, a new hominid found 800,000 years ago in Spain has a face very like that of a

Figure 24–13   A hypothesis of the phylogenetic relationships within the Hominidae. (Based primarily on R. Larick and R. L. Ciochon, 1996, The African emergence and early Asian dispersals of the genus *Homo*, *American Scientist*, 84, 538–551, A. Gibbons, 1997, A new face for human ancestors, *Science*, 276:1331–1333, and R. Lewin, *Principles of Human Evolution: A Core Textbook*, Blackwell Scientific, Boston, MA.) See text for details of characters.

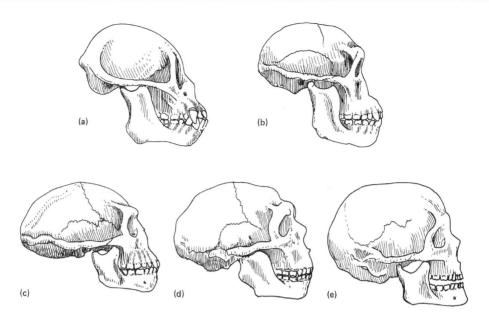

Figure 24–14 Reconstructed skulls of hominids and ancestral hominoid compared. (a) *Dryopithecus*; (b) *Australopithecus africanus*; (c) *Homo erectus*; (d) *Homo neanderthalensis*; (e) *Homo sapiens*. This series illustrates the changes seen in the acquisition of the human condition, with the relative increase in the size of the cranium and the relative decrease in the size of the face and the lower jaw. Note that while the crania of *H. neanderthalensis* and *H. sapiens* are of similar volume, that of *H. neanderthalensis* is more expanded in the back (occipital) region, while that of *H. sapiens* is more expanded in the dorsal (temporal) region.

modern human. Researchers have named this hominid *Homo antecessor*, and have nominated it as the common ancestor of Neandertals and modern humans (Gibbons 1997). *Homo heidelbergensis*, formerly termed archaic *Homo sapiens*, may actually be more closely related to the Neandertals than to modern humans (see Figure 24–13).

There has been considerable debate about the origin of *Homo sapiens*. Some workers hold to a multiregional model of human evolution. They suggest that *H. sapiens* may have evolved independently in different areas, each from an already distinctive local population of *H. erectus* (e.g., Wolpoff in Mellars and Stringer 1989). Others hold to a single, African origin for modern *H. sapiens*, implying a second wave of migrations out of Africa, replacing *H. erectus* in Asia and the Neandertals in Europe (e.g., Stringer and McKie 1996). Analysis of both fossil and modern material has not supported the multiregional hypothesis, indicating that there was most probably a single African origin for all *Homo sapiens* (Lahr 1994).

A single African origin is also supported by the Mitochondrial Eve hypothesis. This uses mitochondrial DNA, which as part of the egg cytoplasm rather than the egg nucleus is only passed to the offspring from the mother. A 1987 study by Alan Wilson analyzed the mitochondrial DNA from 147 individuals representing a large diversity of the world's races. This showed that the greatest diversity in living humans resides in Africa, leading to the conclusion of a single African origin (e.g., Wilson and Cann 1992). This study also concluded that human mitochondrial DNA can be traced back to a single human female around 200,000 years ago, and there was a bottleneck in human evolution at this time with all living humans coming from this line of descent. (Other studies have made the claim for a similar time for a human "Adam", based on divergence times for genes on the Y chromosome, which are passed only from father to son.) This argument is especially appealing as, as previously noted, the fossil record is in agreement with modern *Homo sapiens* dating from around this time. However, there has been much criticism of the original study, especially in mode of statistical analyses (Lewin 1998). Other genetic studies conclude that humans did not experience the type of evolutionary bottleneck that would be predicted by the Mitochondrial Eve story (Hey 1997).

The Neandertals

The first recognized discovery of fossils of *Homo neanderthalensis* were from the Neander Valley in western Germany in 1856. The Neandertal features first appear in fossils about 100,000 years ago. Neandertals were 1.5 to 1.7 meters tall and had receding foreheads, prominent brow ridges, and weak chins, but their brains were as large or larger than those of modern-day *Homo sapiens*. They were stone tool makers, producing tools known as the Mousterian tool industry, with a well-organized society and advancing culture.

On the average, Neandertals appear to have been much stronger than extant humans. They had short limbs with prominent attachments for massive muscles. Another striking difference between Neandertals and extant humans is the difference in the size of facial features: Neandertals had thick brow ridges, large noses, and broad midface regions. Neandertals had well-developed incisor and canine teeth, and the facial features of Neandertals may have been associated with structural modifications that supported these large teeth. The front teeth of Neandertals typically show very heavy wear, sometimes down to the roots. Were Neandertals processing tough food between their front teeth, or perhaps chewing hides to soften them as do some modern aboriginal peoples? Fossilized feces attributable to both archaic *H. heidelbergensis* and *H. neanderthalensis* ranging from 300,000 to 50,000 years ago appear to indicate an exclusively meat diet (Kurtén 1986). Of course, the sample size is small and we have no way of knowing if such habits were merely seasonal.

Neandertals probably hunted wild horse, mammoth, bison, giant deer, and woolly rhinoceros from close range: Their Mousterian-style hunting tools were of the punching, stabbing, and hacking type. Although almost all skeletal remains of Neandertals show evidence of serious injury during life, one in five persons was over 50 years old at the time of death. It was not until after the Middle Ages that historic human populations again achieved this longevity. Whether or not the Neandertals had the capacity for complex speech remains controversial (Gibbons 1992), but they were the first humans known to bury their dead, often it appears after considerable ritual. Of special importance are burials at Shanidar cave in Iraq that include a variety of plants recognized in modern times for their medicinal properties.

The emerging picture of *H. neanderthalensis* is quite different from that proposed for much of the time since their discovery in 1856, when they were portrayed as primitive savages; they now appear to have been adept hunters who probably lived in a complex society. The Neandertals vanished between 40,000 and 34,000 years ago, long after modern *Homo sapiens* appeared. Anatomically modern humans, known in southern Europe as Cro-Magnon people, are distinguished by suites of subtle skeletal features equivalent to those distinguishing modern races. It is with the Cro-Magnons that an unbroken trail of evidence and history leads to the present.

Other Theories of Human Evolution

One popular view of human evolution is that many of the features that distinguish humans from apes, especially in the skull and face, can be explained by the process of neoteny, or the evolution of a new species essentially from the juvenile form of its ancestors. We discussed the concept of neoteny in Chapter 2, in the context of the hypothesis that vertebrates evolved from a neotenic tunicate larva, so that they resemble the tadpolelike larva rather than the sedentary adult. In a similar vein, people have noted that humans bear a greater resemblance to juvenile chimpanzees than they do to adults, especially in the flatter face and the higher forehead, and have speculated that the process of neoteny have been responsible. There has been some rather flippant speculation that human features arose out of some process for the sexual selection of juvenile features; perhaps the obsession with the sexual appeal of youth is a property of our genus (Ridley 1993, Jack Sepkoski, personal communication). However, this rather appealing explanation has proven to be a rather superficial one. It has been shown that the specific features of humans that resemble those of juvenile apes come about by specific, new growth processes, not by delaying of growth as would be expected if neoteny was responsible (Shea in Jones et al., 1992).

Another theory of the uniqueness of humans is the Aquatic Ape hypothesis. This idea, first suggested by Sir Alistair Hardy in the 1960s, and further developed by Elaine Morgan in subsequent decades (e.g., Morgan 1982), proposes that humans went through an aquatic phase in their evolution. This supposed aquatic phase would link together many unique features of humans that otherwise seem to be inexplicable in the context of terrestrial evolution on the savannas, such as the deposition of subcutaneous body fat, the loss of the body hair, the breathing control necessary for speech, human profligate loss of salt in the sweat with the proliferation of eccrine glands for evaporative cooling (see Chapter 21), and even aspects of bipedal posture. The Aquatic Ape Hypothesis has been dismissed without examination by almost all anthropologists, who can rightly be criticized in this context for automatically dismissing ideas written outside of the scientific tradition. A more careful and sympathetic rebuttal of this hypothesis is performed by Langdon (1997), who points out inconsistencies and problems with the arguments without being patronizing.

■ The Evolution of Human Characteristics: Bipedality, Larger Brains, and Language

Humans are classically distinguished from other primates by three derived features: a bipedal stance and mode of locomotion, an extremely enlarged brain, and the capacity for speech and language. Here we examine the possible steps in the evolution of each of these key features.

Bipedality

The most radical changes in the hominid postcranial skeleton are associated with the assumption of a fully erect, bipedal stance in the genus *Homo*. Anatomical modifications include the S-shaped curvature of the vertebral column, the modification of the pelvis and position of the acetabulum (socket in the hip for the ball joint with the femur) in connection with upright bipedal locomotion, and the lengthening of the leg bones and their positioning as vertical columns directly under the head and trunk (see Figure 24–15). The secondary curve of the spine in humans is a consequence of bipedal locomotion, and only forms when the infant learns to walk. We have by no means perfected our spines for the stresses of bipedal locomotion, which are quite different from those encountered by quadrupeds. One consequence of these stresses is the high incidence of lower back problems in modern humans, especially with increasing age.

Humans stand in a knock-kneed position, which enables us to walk with our feet placed on the midline, and reduces rolling of the hips from side to

size. This limb position leaves some tell-tale signatures on the femur (the thigh bone), both in the articulation with the hip and with the knee joint, and this type of bony evidence can aid researchers in deducing whether or not fossil species were fully bipedal. An unfortunate consequence of this limb position is that humans, especially athletes, are rather prone to knee dislocations and torn knee ligaments. Because women have hips that are wider than those of men, their femurs are at an even more acute angle, and they are more prone to such knee injuries.

The feet of humans show drastic modification for bipedal striding locomotion, having become flattened except for a tarso-metatarsal arch with corresponding changes in the shapes and positions of the tarsals (ankle bones) and with close, parallel alignment of all five metatarsals and digits; the big toe is no longer opposable as in apes and monkeys (Figure 24–16), although it may still have had some capacity to diverge from the rest of the toes in early hominids.

It is important to emphasize that among mammals the bipedal, striding mode of terrestrial locomotion is unique to the human line of evolution and that it may have been a key change that made possible the evolution of other distinctively human traits, such as the perfection of tool-using hands, and thus indirectly probably stimulated the evolution of ever larger forebrains. What evolutionary events turned the human into an obligate terrestrial biped from ancestors that clearly were arboreal? How did our tool-using hands and our big brain with its associated implications for intelligence, derived social organization, and culture evolve?

There are almost as many hypotheses for the reasons for human bipedality as there are anthropologists! Among the reasons that have been suggested are improved predator avoidance (being able to look over tall grasses), freeing the arms for carrying objects (either for hunting or collecting foods), thermoregulation (an upright ape presents a smaller surface area to the sun's rays), and efficiency of locomotion (Lewin 1998). An obvious problem with all such hypotheses is that they are difficult to test. Although humans are extremely efficient at bipedal locomotion, especially at walking, it seems unlikely that bipedality evolved specifically for efficient, striding locomotion. Other apes are not nearly as efficient as humans at bipedal walking, but this is the evolutionary condition from which human bipedality must have commenced. That is, a proto-hominid or early hominid must have walked

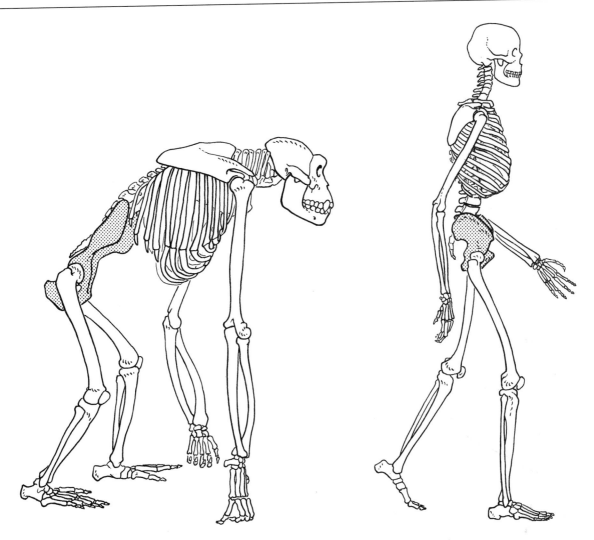

Figure 24–15 Comparison of skeletons of gorilla and human. The pelvis is shaded: note the shorter iliac blade and the change in pelvic orientation in the human. Also note the relatively longer legs, more compact feet, shorter arms, and S-shaped spinal curvature in the human. The position of the head of the human is reflected in the more ventral (versus posterior) position of the occipital condyles and foramen magnum.

bipedally in an inefficient way first, before selection could act on the skeleton to improve the efficiency. The exception to this evolutionary scenario could be if the skeletal adaptations had initially been adopted for some other function besides bipedality, incidentally preadapting hominids for bipedal locomotion. This hypothesis is partially supported inasmuch as the upright trunk of all hominoids is clearly adapted for suspensory arboreal locomotion, resulting in preadaptation for a bipedal stance. But there is no evidence that the modifications of the human pelvis, spine, and legs which are critical to bipedal locomotion were ever evolved for some other function.

An interesting window into the issue of the evolution of bipedality in humans has been opened by the recent reinterpretation of the postcranial skeleton of the Miocene ape *Oreopithecus*, known from the Italian island of Tuscany (Köhler and Moyà-Solà 1997). This animal appears to have evolved a type of bipedality convergent with the condition in hominids: it had an S-shaped spine, a pelvic girdle rather like the condition in *Australopithecus*, and a knock-kneed angle to the femur. However, the foot differed markedly from that of humans. Rather than a compact foot, with a big toe aligned with the other toes (Figure 24–16), it had a widely divergent big toe, apparently providing a broad tripodal base

Figure 24–16   Feet of extant hominoids compared, showing some skeletal parts (metatarsals for digits in I and
II and phalanges of digit I) in relation
to foot form. Note difference in arboreal specializations of gibbon and
orangutan, with the long toes and the
divergent hallux (big toe). The feet are
more specialized for terrestriality in the
chimpanzee, gorilla, and human, with
shorter toes and a less abducted position of the hallux. The human foot is
highly specialized, with its very short
toes, but very stout and straight hallux,
which is incapable of abduction.

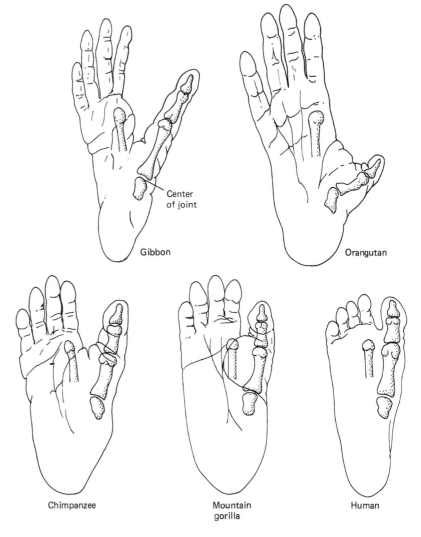

of support. This foot anatomy, in combination with
the short legs, indicates at slow shuffling gait,
rather than humanlike efficient striding, and suggests that, at least in this species, bipedality must
have evolved for some other reason besides efficient locomotion. It has been suggested that
bipedality evolved in *Oreopithecus*, an animal living
on an island insulated from predators, to increase
food-gathering efficiency.

In some respects, human bipedality may not be
such a mystery as it first appears. Because were are
most closely related to chimps and gorillas, there
has been the tendency to take their feature of
knuckle-walking as the primitive condition for the
common ancestor. But in fact it is unlikely that
knuckle-walking was primitive for hominids, and
protohominids were most likely at least semiarboreal rather than specialized for terrestrial

quadrupedal locomotion (Steudal 1996). Other
apes, such as gibbons and orangutans, tend to walk
in a clumsy bipedal stance on the ground: their
upright trunk, adapted for arboreal locomotion,
predisposes them to do this. A tendency to walk
bipedally appears to be a primitive hominoid feature, further developed in *Oreopithecus* as well as in
hominids (and perhaps also in *Gigantopithecus* if the
Bigfoot rumors are true!). It may be that it is the
chimps and gorillas who are the odd ones out
among hominoids in walking quadrupedally on
the ground.

Origins of Large Brains

Brain tissue is a metabolically expensive tissue both
to grow and to maintain. Most of the growth of the
brain occurs during embryonic development, and

requires energy input from the mother. Thus, selective pressures for larger brains can be satisfied only in an environment that provides sufficient energy, especially to the pregnant or lactating female (Foley and Lee 1991). The evolution of larger brains may have required increased foraging efficiency (in part achieved through larger female size and mobility), high-quality foods in substantial quantities (in part achieved through the use of tools and fire), and a change in life history pattern that probably exaggerated the ancestral primate character of slow rates of pre- and postnatal development (thus lowering daily energy demands and also a females' lifetime reproductive output). The origin of bipedality may be linked to the origin of large brain size and a change in the human mode of reproduction (see Box 24–1).

Origin of Speech and Language

Although other animals can produce sounds, and many mammals communicate with the use of a specific vocabulary of sounds (as anyone who has kept domestic pets is well aware of), the use of a symbolic language is a uniquely human attribute. Although some apes and chimpanzees have been taught to use some human words and form simple sentences, this is a far step from the complexity of human language. But where in human evolution did language evolve, and how can we tell this from the fossil record? The first evidence of human writing is only a few millenia old: obviously language evolved before this, but how long before?

One line of evidence comes from the study of brains. Although brains themselves do not fossilize, evidence can be obtained from endocasts, the impressions left by brains on the inside of the skull. One unique human brain feature associated with speech is an expansion on the left side of the brain called Broca's area. A similar area has been interpreted to be present in *Homo rudolfensis* and later species of *Homo* (Falk 1985, Lewin 1998). But does this mean that speech and language dates back to the start of the genus *Homo*? Certainly, trauma to this area results in damage to speech production and comprehension in present-day humans, but this does not necessarily mean that humanlike language had evolved by this point. In contrast, Alan Walker argues that controlled speech would not have been possible until a later stage than *Homo ergaster* (Walker and Shipman 1996). In this species the spinal cord in the region of the thorax is much

smaller than in modern humans. The implication is that *H. ergaster* lacked the capacity for the complex neural control of the intercostal muscles that allows modern humans to control breathing in such a way that we can talk coherently.

Even if more derived *Homo* species had evolved the capacity for language, they would not have been able to produce the range of vowel sounds that we can produce until a change in the anatomy of the pharynx and vocal tract had taken place (Lieberman 1984). The primitive position of the mammalian larynx is high up in the neck, right behind the base of the tongue. In this position the epiglottis can make a seal with the back of the pharynx, allowing for breathing and suckling to take place simultaneously (see Chapter 21). However, in adult modern humans the larynx shifts ventrally between one to two years of age, with the loss of this seal, and the creation of a much larger resonating chamber for vocalization. This change in the anatomy of the vocal tract is associated with a change in the shape of the base of the skull, so we can infer from fossil skulls when the shift in the position of the larynx occurred. Although there are some differences of opinion, a fully modern condition of the vocal tract was probably not a feature of the genus *Homo* until true *H. sapiens*.

There remain some evolutionary problems with the origin of this vocal tract trait. In losing the seal between the palate and the epiglottis, humans are especially vulnerable to choking on their food. It seems likely that this liability to choke would be a powerful selective force acting in opposition to repositioning the larynx. In addition, the death of infants from SIDS (sudden infant death syndrome) is associated with the developmental period when the larynx is in flux. It is difficult to imagine that the ability to produce a greater range of vowel sounds could counteract these antagonistic selective forces: perhaps there was another, more immediately powerful reason for repositioning the larynx.

One advantage that repositioning the larynx affords us is the ability to voluntarily breathe through our mouths. Other mammals are unable to do this. One can subdue a rambunctious horse quite easily by clamping one's hand over its nose and blocking the nasal passages. Although dogs appear to mouth breathe, their panting is actually a means of ventilatory cooling: Air is passing through the nose and out of the mouth, not in and out of the lungs as it does when we pant. Voluntary mouth breathing has an obvious importance in the pro-

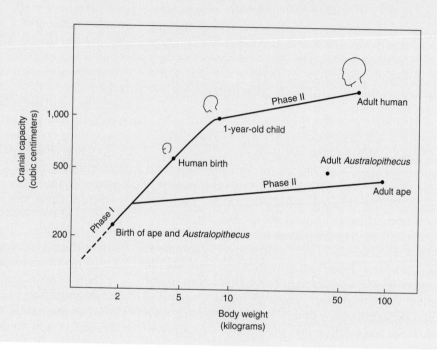

BOX 24-1 Correlation of Bipedality with Increase in Brain Size in Human Evolution

Steven Stanley (e.g., Stanley 1996) has noted that brain growth in humans is unlike that in other animals, including apes. Our large brain size is in large part due to a prolonged period of postnatal growth in the first year of life, continuing the rapid growth that occurs in utero. In contrast, brain growth slows markedly after birth in apes (Figure 24–17). The obvious hypothesis for this pattern of brain growth is that humans already

Figure 24–17 Patterns of brain growth in humans and apes. The pattern for *Australopithecus* resembled that of a living ape, such as a chimpanzee, whereas in humans the continuation of the high prenatal rate of growth through the first year of life produces a much larger brain as an adult. (Modified from S. M. Stanley, 1996, *Children of the Ice Age*, Harmony Books, New York, NY.)

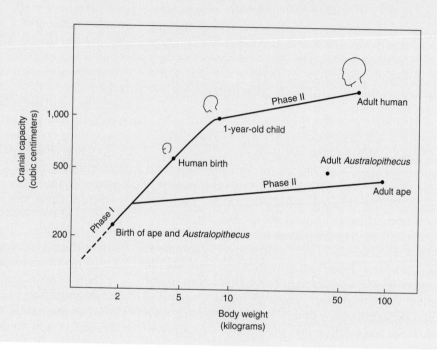

duction of speech. But perhaps a more important function of mouth breathing is apparent to anyone reading this with a bad cold: Many of us would suffocate every winter if we were unable to breathe through our mouths. It is tempting to speculate that the human capacity for at least well-enunciated speech owes its existence to a prior encounter of the species with the common cold virus (Janis 1998).

■ Origins of Human Technology and Culture

Humans are tool users and tool makers *par excellence*. Some other animals also use tools to a limited extent, usually in rather stereotyped and instinctive ways. Egyptian vultures open ostrich eggs by picking up stones in their beaks and dropping them on the shells, a Galápagos finch holds twigs and cactus spines in its beak to probe for insects in holes or under bark, both baboons and chimpanzees use sticks and stones as weapons very much in the way that ancestral humans must have done, and chimpanzees use these same types of materials as tools in obtaining food. The use of roots, wooden clubs, and stones as hammers and anvils to crack five different species of nuts may be a culturally transmitted behavior in some West African chimpanzee populations (Boesch et al. 1994).

The earliest recognized simple stone tools are found throughout East Africa and date to 2.5 to 2.7 million years ago. They are called the Oldowan culture and they continue to appear in the geological record relatively unchanged for 1 million years. For some time most paleoanthropologists believed they were made by *Homo*, not *Australopithecus* (Lewin have large enough heads to cause a problem at birth for the mothers, and so further brain enlargement must occur postnatally. However, this pattern of brain growth means that human babies are born in a particularly helpless condition, and require intensive care for the first year of life. Stanley argues that this type of brain development must have postdated the evolution of full terrestriality, and the abandoning of arboreal habits. Australopithecine infants must have been like those of modern apes, mature enough to cling to their mother's fur soon after birth, as is essential in an arboreal habitat where the female would need to use her arms and hands for climbing. Only in a fully terrestrial hominid could a helpless infant be looked after properly. Thus, whatever the reason for the evolution of the fully human type of bipedality, it must have preceded the evolution of the very large human brain. The transition to a prolonged postnatal period of brain growth probably occurred at around the evolutionary level of *Homo erectus/ergaster*. Here there is dental evidence (delayed tooth eruption) for the type of prolonged childhood typical of humans, but not of other animals, including apes (see Figure 24–18).

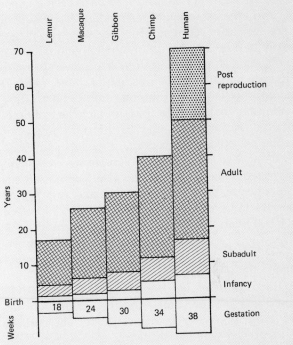

Figure 24–18 Progressive changes in the length of life phases and gestation in primates. Note the proportional increase in the length of the postjuvenile stages as gestation increases. Only humans have a significant postreproductive stage, although the stage has also occasionally been observed in chimpanzees.

1988, but see Susman 1988). Careful analysis of the structures of the modern human hand that allow the precise grasping necessary for stone tool manufacture and the evidence of these structures on the bones of the hand, especially the thumb (Susman 1994), may lead to a very different conclusion. On the basis of the only thumb morphology data available (Aiello 1994), the Oldowan tools could have been made by *Homo* or *Australopithecus robustus*, a small-brained species not generally considered in direct *Homo* ancestry. Perhaps all of the hominid species in existence 2 million years ago—both gracile and robust australopithecines and the newly emerged *Homo habilis*—might have been tool makers. Unfortunately, thumbs are rarely preserved among these fossils. It is interesting, however, that australopithecines thought to have become extinct 500,000 years before the earliest Oldowan tool finds

(*A. afarensis*) do not have the hand bone characteristics of precision grip.

Stone tools no more sophisticated than the Oldowan culture are the only tools earlier than about 1.4 million years ago. Novel tools, especially cleavers and so-called hand axes appear in East Africa about 1.4 million years ago. These later tools of *H. ergaster*, known as the Acheulean tool industry, changed very little in style for the next 1.2 million years, although the materials chosen changed and later samples have a much higher proportion of small tools than do early examples. The lack of dramatic advance in tool manufacture over this immense period is surprising, especially in light of the spread of these tools to southwest Asia and western Europe (Burenhult 1993).

Thus, one of the remarkable conclusions from paleoanthropological findings is that the use of tools, chipped stones, and possibly modified bone and antler precedes the origin of the big-brained *Homo sapiens* by at least 1.5 million years. The use of tools by ancestral hominids may have been a major factor in the evolution of the modern *Homo* type of cerebral cortex, although tool use need not necessarily be associated with brain enlargement. Once the manufacture and use of tools began to increase fitness, selective pressures might have favored neural mechanisms promoting improved crafting and use of tools (Calvin 1994). In fact, the elaborate brain of *Homo sapiens* may be the consequence of culture as much as its cause (but see Susman 1988).

By at least 750,000 years ago *Homo erectus* had perfected stone tools and had also learned to control and use, but perhaps not to make, fire. Actual hearths in caves are not widely recognized before 500,000 years ago. With fire humans could cook their food, increasing its digestibility and nutritional value and preserving meat for longer periods than it would remain usable in a raw state; they could keep themselves warm in cold weather; they could ward off predators; and they could light up the dark to see, work, and socialize. The earliest evidence of wooden throwing spears, found in association with stone tools and the butchered remains of horses, is from 400,000 years ago in Germany (Thieme 1997).

It is often assumed that much of the evolution of human tool use and culture developed in the context of humans hunting other animals. The term "Man the Hunter" was coined back in the 1960s, although numerous researchers who happen to be women have noted that there are some inherent biases with the perception that human evolution has been shaped solely by male activities. There is a strong counter-argument for the importance of the role of "Woman the Gatherer", and anthropologists have pointed out that much of our perception of human evolution as being an upwards and onwards quest have as much to do with the traditional western cultural myths of the "Hero's tale" as they do with any hard anthropological evidence (Landau 1984, Fedigan 1986). More recent examination of the archeological evidence for hunting in early hominids, such as stone tools and bones with cut marks, has reinterpreted much of these activities as due to scavenging rather than active hunting (e.g., Shipman 1986, Blumenschine and Cavallo 1992, Larick and Ciochon 1996).

Neandertal people practiced ritual burial in Europe and the Near East at least 60,000 years ago,

suggesting that religious beliefs had developed by that time. Not long afterward the cave bear became the focus of a cult in Europe. By 40,000 years ago, Cro-Magnon people began constructing their own dwellings and living in communities—things Neandertal peoples also probably did. The domestication of animals and plants, the development of agriculture, and the dawn of civilization were soon to follow.

■ Humans and the Pleistocene Extinctions of Mammals

The number of genera of Cenozoic mammals reached peaks in the Miocene and early Pleistocene. Only 60 percent of the known fossilized Pleistocene genera are living now. Extinction seems to have occurred mostly among large (over 20 kg) terrestrial mammals.

What caused the extinctions? Some researchers speculate that delayed effects of the Miocene climatic change and the coming of the ice ages were the root causes; others think that the extinctions were largely caused by another phenomenon of the Pleistocene—the evolution of hunting humans with their newly manufactured tools and social skills. The latter view has been pursued intensively by P. S. Martin at the University of Arizona (Martin and Wright 1967, Martin 1973, Mosimann and Martin 1975, Diamond 1983, Martin and Klein 1984, Stuart 1991). What types of information lead to these conclusions? The most important points in favor of human causation are that the highest rates of extinction (1) were largely a postglacial event, and (2) occurred more frequently among large mammals than among small mammals. The climatic changes in postglacial time have left a more subtle record than the human spear points found in association with mammal remains and are consequently more difficult to evaluate. It is perhaps best to attribute the faunal changes to both human and climate factors.

The Human Factor

Clearly, the high rates of mammalian extinction occurred primarily during the Wisconsin and, especially, in postglacial time (Figure 24–19). Examples of extinction are mastodons, mammoths, and ground sloths. Various camels, horses, and pronghorns also became extinct, but their remains are rarely found in association with human artifacts.

Figure 24–19   Coincidence between the extinction of North American mammals, glacial retreat, and the population of humans. Solid line represents the cumulative percentage extinction of 40 mammalian species; dashed line is the percentage of withdrawal of the late Wisconsin glaciation; histograms are arbitrary units of relative abundance of evidence for the occurrence of humans in North America. [From J. J. Hester, 1967, pages, 169–192 in P. S. Martin and H. E. Wright, Jr. (editors), *Pleistocene Extinctions: The Search for a Cause,* Yale University Press, New Haven, CT.]

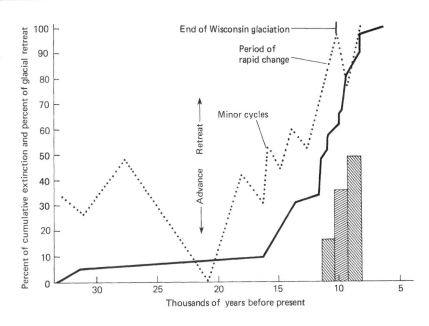

Martin contends that large mammals were preyed upon by invading nomadic humans, and archaeological data support this view. Presumably, large mammals would be more susceptible to extinction by humans than would small mammals. Many more large mammals than small ones are more threatened by extinction today, in large part because their slower reproductive rates. While a pair of rabbits can produce several dozen young a year (without even counting the grandchildren and great-grandchildren that could also be produced during that same year!), a pair of rhinos or elephants produce but a single young every 4–5 years. Thus large mammals cannot rapidly recover population numbers if challenged by losses either from hunting or climatic events, and are more vulnerable to extinction.

Dan Janzen (1983) proposed that humans had help in contributing to the megafauna demise from large contemporary carnivores. He agreed with Martin that humans migrated into an area that had abundant large herbivorous mammals and began extensive hunting. The presence of humans and their kills would have provided more carrion to the carnivores, whose population densities, Janzen pointed out, would have increased in response to the food supply. The combined predation pressure of increasing human and carnivore populations could have led to further decimation of the large herbivores. When the prey populations became critically low the nomadic hunters would have moved on and the populations of carnivores would

subsequently decline because their resource base was gone.

Norman Owen–Smith (1987) suggested that the elimination of large herbivorous mammals (megaherbivores), specifically mammoths, by humans could have had a cascading effect on smaller species because grazing by the megaherbivores was a major factor in creating and maintaining spatial diversity of habitats. Once the megaherbivores were gone, habitats would have become more uniform and this change would have been detrimental for the small herbivores that were dependent on nutrient-rich and spatially diverse habitats.

A relation can be shown between the arrival of prehistoric humans in different regions and the extinction of large herbivorous mammals. It would appear that gradually a hunting technology developed in Africa during the middle Wisconsin glaciation and then spread northward and burst into the Western Hemisphere as the late Wisconsin glacier retreated. In the New World humans were present at least 25,000 years ago (Patrusky 1980, Adovasio and Carlisle 1986) and possibly more than 40,000 years ago. Evidence of extensive hunting of mammals began in the colder north, perhaps with a new wave of humans immigrating from Asia some 13,000 years ago (Mosimann and Martin 1975). No extinction of similar proportion has occurred in Africa, where human hunting apparently evolved side-by-side with the evolution of large mammals. Extinctions in northern Eurasia were moderate, staggered in time, and occurred more than 20,000 years after the appearance of humans with advanced stone tools (Stuart 1991). Extinction of the marsupial megafauna of Australia also occurred (Gillespie et al. 1978, Martin and Klein 1984), but not until these large Australian mammals had coexisted with aboriginal humans for several thousand years. Thus, the model of overkill of large mammals by humans may not apply to megafaunal extinction in Australia.

The Climatic Factor

Could human hunters have been the primary cause of extinction of large mammals in the Pleistocene? The evidence suggests that prehistoric humans did hunt large mammals such as mammoths, but this does not necessarily mean that they caused the extinction of entire species. Many other researchers do not attribute the demise of the large mammals solely to human influence, but suggest that changing climates and their influence on habitat availability were as important as humans in producing extinctions. In their view, large mammals are more susceptible to environmental stress. Severe restrictions of forage and available water and elimination of migratory corridors to more suitable habitats would affect large mammals with their correspondingly large requirements more than smaller mammals. Thus, large North American mammals may well have been on the decline when intensive human hunting began.

Dale Guthrie (in Martin and Klein 1984) has pointed out that most climatic theories of Pleistocene extinction are too ambiguous and diffuse to account for the final extinction event, however effective they are at depicting environmental stress. In the general trend of replacement of closed-canopy forests by more open, grass-dominated steppes and savannas that began in the early Cenozoic, Guthrie sees increasing seasonality as being of primary significance. The climatic trend throughout the Cenozoic was toward a shorter growing season. At first this trend increased the mosaic patchwork of forest, scrub, and grassland over much of the world. This increasingly complex pattern of vegetation supported a large, diverse fauna.

Indeed, the spread of grasses promoted faunal diversification. Responding to the spread of grasslands, the generally large-bodied ungulates reached maximum diversity in the late Miocene and Pliocene, contributing significantly to the total number of mammalian genera known from those epochs. But as the trend continued toward seasonal extremes of temperature and aridity the diversity of vegetation declined. The flora over broad expanses of continents changed from a mosaic of plant associations to a latitudinal and altitudinal zonation of broad bands of plant communities with low diversity. The lower overall diversity of floras and greater regional homogeneity reached its maximum after the Wisconsin glacial advance. The reduction of plant diversity may have eliminated many herbivores, especially larger forms, and restricted all but a few species to limited ranges. A reduction of vegetational diversity would be expected to have a proportionally greater effect on hindgut fermenting herbivores, as these animals need to obtain a wider variety of plants in their diet (see Chapter 21). As Guthrie points out, these were precisely the types of herbivores hardest hit, at least in North America.

The postglacial period beginning 15,000 to 10,000 years ago appears to have been more stressful to large mammal faunas than the previous 2.5 million years of the Pleistocene (Stuart 1991). Shorter growing seasons mean less plant productivity to support herbivores, even in the restricted ranges where they found suitable floras. Kiltie (in Martin and Klein 1984) argues that the rapid advent of short growing seasons and heightened seasonality critically decreased the resources available to many species of large herbivorous mammals with long periods of growth to maturity and long gestation periods. These changes constituted environmental challenges to which they could not rapidly adapt physiologically or genetically. The fossil record attests to the resulting decrease in local faunal diversity, distributional ranges, and frequently to the resulting extinctions without the influence of human hunting.

Many large mammals persisted in some regions despite prehistoric human hunting pressure. In the New World camels and horses became extinct, but they survived in Eurasia and Africa. Others, like bison and elk, survived in the New World in spite of humans. The Egyptian civilization knew of mammoths, and other evidence indicates that the pharaohs and mammoths were contemporaries, although geographically widely separated (Rosen 1994). There is currently no final solution to the puzzle of Pleistocene extinctions; a combination of unique new climatic stress and human predation seems most plausible.

■ Summary

Evidence for the origin of *Homo sapiens* comes from the Cenozoic fossil record of primates and from comparative study of living monkeys, apes, and human beings. The first primatelike mammals are known from the early Paleocene, but the earliest true primates are not known until the early Eocene. These were prosimians, rather similar to the extant lemurs, and were initially known from North America as well as from the Old World. All were arboreal and some possessed somewhat larger brains in relation to body size than do most other mammals.

After the climatic deterioration of the late Eocene, primates were confined to the tropical regions until the evolution of humans. By the Oligocene two other distinct groups of higher primates had evolved: the platyrrhine monkeys of the New World tropics and the Old World catarrhine monkeys and apes. The anthropoid apes and humanlike species, including *Homo sapiens*, are grouped in the Hominoidea. Many morphological features distinguish the hominoids from other catarrhines, and enlargement of the brain has been a major evolutionary force molding the shape of the hominoid skull, especially in the later part of human evolution.

The first known hominoids occur in the early Miocene, around 25 million years ago. By the late Miocene hominoids had diversified into a number of environments and had spread widely over Africa, Europe, and Asia. A variety of hominid (human) fossils occur in late Pliocene and early Pleistocene deposits of Kenya and Ethiopia. The earliest hominids, with small cranial volumes and often heavy features of skull, tooth, and jaw, are the australopithecines are known from 4.4 to 1.2 million years ago. Australopithicines were apparently bipedal, but retained considerable arboreal habits. The earliest member of the genus *Homo* dates from around 2.5 million years ago, concurrent with the earliest stone tools are found in East Africa. *Homo* appears to be a primarily terrestrial genus, and this terrestriality may have been an important feature in the production of helpless infants whose brains continued to grow after birth. A global climatic change at around this time may have prompted the evolution both of *Homo* and of the robust australopithecines.

Homo erectus ranged across Africa and Eurasia from about 1.8 million years to 300,000 years ago. This hominid had a brain capacity approaching the lower range of *Homo sapiens*, made stone tools, and used fire. *Homo sapiens*, the only surviving species of the family Hominidae, came into existence around 200,000 years ago. By 40,000 to 60,000 years ago some populations of *Homo* had a well-organized society with a rapidly developing culture, especially obvious in their use of stone tools. The first significant human impacts on other vertebrates may have occurred in prehistoric time. Extinction of many species of large vertebrates in the late Pleistocene may be the result of hunting by humans, although other predators and changes in climate may have been additional factors.

■ References

Adovasio, J. M., and R. C. Carlisle. 1986. The first Americans, Pennsylvania pioneers. *Natural History* 95(12):20–27.

Aiello, L. C. 1994. Thumbs up for our early ancestors. *Science* 256:1540–1541.

Andrews, P. 1992. Evolution and environment in the Hominoidea. *Nature* 360:641–646.

Andrews, P., and L. Martin. 1991. Hominoid dietary evolution. *Philosophical Transactions of the Royal Society, London B* 334:199–209.

Andrews, P., T. Harrison, E. Delson, R. L. Bernor, and L. Martin. 1996. Distribution and biochronology of European and Southwest Asian Miocene catarrhines. Pages 168–207 in *The Evolution of Western Eurasian Neogene Mammal Faunas*, edited by R. L. Bernor, V. Fahlbusch, and H.-W. Mittmann. Columbia University Press, New York, NY.

Beard, K. C. 1990. Gliding behaviour and palaeoecology of the alleged primate family Paromomyidae (Mammalia, Dermoptera). *Nature* 345:340–341.

Benefit, B. R., and M. L. McCrossin. 1997. Earliest known Old World monkey skull. *Nature* 388:368–371.

Berge, C. 1994. How did the australopithecines walk? A biomechanical study of the hip and thigh of *Australopithecus afarensis*. *Journal of Human Evolution* 26:259–273.

Blumenschine, R. J., and J. A. Cavallo. 1992. Scavenging and human evolution. Scientific American 267(4):90–96.

Boesch, C., P. Marchesi, and N. Marchesi. 1994. Is nut cracking in wild chimpanzees a cultural behavior? *Journal of Human Evolution* 26:325–338.

Bruce, E. J., and F. J. Ayala. 1979. Phylogenetic relationships between man and the apes: electrophoretic evidence. *Evolution* 33:1040–1056.

Brunet, M., A. Beauvilain, Y. Coppens, E. Heintz, A. H. E. Montay, and D. Pilbeam. 1995. *Australopithecus bahrelghazali*, a new species of early hominid from Koro Toro region, Chad. *Comptes Rendues*, series II, 322:907–913.

Burenhult, G. (editor). 1993. *The First Humans (The Illustrated History of Humankind, Volume 1)*. Harper Collins, New York, NY.

Calvin, W. H. 1994. The emergence of intelligence. *Scientific American* 271(4):100–107.

Campbell, B. 1985. *Human Evolution: An Introduction to Man's Adaptations*, 3d edition. Aldine, Hawthorne, NY.

Cartmill, M. 1974. Rethinking primate origins. *Science* 1984:436–443.

Ciochon, R. L., and R. S. Corruccini (editors). 1983. *New Interpretations of Ape and Human Ancestry*. Plenum, New York, NY.

Ciochon, R. L., and J. G. Fleagle. 1987. *Primate Evolution and Human Origins*. Aldine, Hawthorne, NY.

Coppens, Y. 1994. East side story: the origin of humankind. *Scientific American* 270(5):88–95.

Delson, E. 1987. Evolution and palaeobiology of robust *Australopithecus*. *Nature* 327:654–655.

Delson, E., and I. Tattersall, 1997, Primates, pages 93–104 in *Encyclopedia of Human Biology*, Volume 7, Academic Press, New York, NY.

Diamond, J. M. 1983. Extinctions, catastrophic and gradual. *Nature* 304:396–397.

Falk, D. 1985. Hadar AL 162–28 endocast as evidence that brain enlargement preceded cortical reorganization in hominid evolution. *Nature* 313:45–47. (See also *Nature* 321:536–537, 1986.)

Fedigan, L. M. 1986. The changing role of women in models of human evolution. *Annual Review of Anthropology* 15:25–66.

Fleagle, J. G. 1988. *Primate Adaptation and Evolution*. Academic Press, San Diego.

Foley, R. A., and P. C. Lee. 1991. Ecology and energetics of encephalization in hominid evolution. *Philosophical Transactions of the Royal Society, London B* 334:223–232.

Gibbons, A. 1992. Neandertal language debate: tongues wag anew. *Science* 256:33–34.

Gibbons, A. 1997. A new face for human ancestors. *Science* 276:1331–1333.

Gillespie, R., D. R. Horton, P. Ladd, P. G. Macumber, T. H. Rich, R. Thorne, and R. V. S. Wright. 1978. Lancefield swamp and the extinction of the Australian megafauna. *Science* 200:1044–1048.

Harris, J. M., F. H. Brown, M. G. Leakey, A. C. Walker, and R. E. Leakey. 1988. Pliocene and Pleistocene hominid-bearing sites from west of Lake Turkana, Kenya. *Science* 239:27–33.

Hey, J. 1997. Mitochondrial and nuclear genes present conflicting portraits of human origins. *Molecular Biology and Evolution* 14:166–172.

Hill, A., S. Ward, A. Deino, C. Garniss, and R. Drake. 1992. Earliest *Homo*. *Nature* 355:719–722.

Hunt, K. D. 1994. The evolution of human bipedality: ecological and functional morphology. *Journal of Human Evolution* 26:183–202.

Janis, C. M. 1988. This chapter.

Janzen, D. H. 1983. The Pleistocene hunters had help. *American Naturalist* 121:598–599.

Johanson, D. C. and M. A. Edey. 1981. *Lucy, The Beginnings of Humankind*. Simon & Schuster, New York, NY.

Jolly, A. 1980. *A World Like Our Own: Man and Nature in Madagascar*. Yale University Press, New Haven, CT.

Jones, S., R. Martin, and D. Pilbeam. 1992. *The Cambridge Encyclopedia of Human Evolution*. Cambridge University Press, Cambridge, UK.

Kahn, P., and A. Gibbons. 1997. DNA from an extinct human. *Science* 277:176–178.

Kay, R. F., C. Ross, and B. A. Williams. 1997. Anthropoid origins. *Science* 275:797–804.

Köhler, M. and S. Moyà-Solà. 1997. Ape-like or hominid-like? The positional behavior of *Oreopithecus bambolii* reconsidered. *Proceedings of the National Academy of Sciences* 94:11747–11750.

Kurtén, B. 1986. *How to Deep-Freeze a Mammoth*. Columbia University Press, New York, NY.

Lahr, M. M. 1994. The multiregional model of modern human origins: a reassessment of its morphological basis. *Journal of Human Evolution* 26:23–56.

Landau, M. 1984. Human evolution as a narrative. *American Scientist* 72:262–268.

Langdon, J. H. 1997. Umbrella hypotheses and parsimony in human evolution: a critique of the Aquatic Ape Hypothesis. *Journal of Human Evolution* 33:479–494.

Larick, R. and R. L. Ciochon. 1996. The African emergence and early Asian dispersals of the genus *Homo*. *American Scientist* 84:538–551.

Leakey, M. G., C. Feikel, I. McDougall, and A. Walker. 1995. New four-million-year-old hominid species from Kanapoi and Allia Bay, Kenya. *Nature* 376:565–571.

Lewin, R. 1984. DNA reveals surprises in human family tree. *Science* 226:1179–1182.

Lewin, R. 1988. A new tool-maker in the hominid record? *Science* 240:724–725.

Lewin, R. 1993. *Human Evolution*, 3d edition. Blackwell Scientific, Boston, MA.

Lewin, R. 1998. *Principles of Human Evolution: a core textbook*. Blackwell Scientific, Boston. MA.

Lieberman, P. 1984. *The Biology and Evolution of Language*. Harvard University Press, Cambridge, MA.

Maas, M. C., D. W. Krause, and S. G. Strait. 1988. The decline and extinction of plesiadapiforms (Mammalia: ?Primates) in North America: displacement or replacement? *Paleobiology* 14:410–431.

Martin, P. S. 1973. The discovery of America. *Science* 179:969–974.

Martin, P. S., and R. G. Klein (editors). 1984. *Quaternary Extinctions, a Prehistoric Revolution*. University of Arizona Press, Tucson, AZ.

Martin, P. S., and H. E. Wright, Jr. (editors). 1967. *Pleistocene Extinctions: The Search for a Cause*. Yale University Press, New Haven, CT.

Martin, R. D. 1990. *Primate Origins and Evolution: A Phylogenetic Reconstruction*. Princeton University Press, Princeton, NJ.

McHenry, H. M. 1994. Behavioral ecology implications of early hominid body size. *Journal of Human Evolution* 27:77–87.

Mellars P., and C. B. Stringer, editors. 1989. *The Human Revolution*. Edinburgh University Press, Edinburgh, UK.

Morell, V. 1994. Will primate genetics split one gorilla into two? *Science* 265:1661.

Morgan, E. 1982. *The Aquatic Ape. A Theory of Human Evolution*. Stein and Day, New York, NY.

Mosimann, J. E., and P. S. Martin. 1975. Simulating overkill by Paleoindians. *American Scientist* 63:304–313.

Owen–Smith, N. 1987. Pleistocene extinctions: the pivotal role of megaherbivores. *Paleobiology* 13:352–362.

Patrusky, B. 1980. Pre-Clovis man: sampling the evidence. *Mosaic* 11(5):2–10.

Ridley, M. 1993. *The Red Queen: Sex and the Evolution of Human Nature.* MacMillan, New York, NY.

Rosen, B. 1994. Mammoths in ancient Egypt? *Nature* 369:364.

Simons, E. L. 1989. Human origins. *Science* 245:1343–1350.

Shipman, P. 1986. Scavenging or hunting in early hominids. *American Anthropologist* 8:27–43.

Spoor, F. et al. 1996. Evidence for a link between human semicircular canal size and bipedal behavior. *Evolutionary Anthropology* 30:183–187.

Stanley, S. M. 1996. *Children of the Ice Age,* Harmony Books, New York, NY

Steudal, K. 1996. Limb morphology, bipedal gait, and the energetics of hominid locomotion. *American Journal of Physical Anthropology* 99:345–355.

Stringer, C. B., and R. McKie. 1996. *African Exodus.* Henry Hold, New York, NY.

Stuart, A. J. 1991. Mammalian extinctions in the Late Pleistocene of northern Eurasia and North America. *Biological Reviews* 66:453–562.

Susman, R. L. 1988. Hand of *Paranthropus robustus* from member 1, Swartkrans: fossil evidence for tool behavior. *Science* 240:781–784.

Susman, R. L. 1994. Fossil evidence for early hominid tool use. *Science* 265:1570–1573.

Susman, R. L., and J. T. Stern. 1982. Functional morphology of *Homo habilis. Science* 217:931–934.

Swisher, C. C. III, G. H. Curtis, and T. Jacob. 1994. Age of the earliest known hominids in Java, Indonesia. *Science* 263:1118–1121.

Swisher, C. C. III, W. J. Rink, C. S. Antón, H. P Schwarcz, C. H. Curtis, A. Suprijo, Widiasmoro. 1996. Latest *Homo erectus* of Java: potential contemporaneity with *Homo sapiens* in Southeast Asia. *Science* 274:1870–1874.

Szalay, F. S., and E. Delson. 1979. *Evolutionary History of the Primates.* Academic, New York, NY.

Tattersall, I. 1993. *The Human Odyssey: Four Million Years of Human Evolution.* Prentice Hall, New York, NY.

Thieme, H. 1997. Lower Palaeolithic hunting spears from Germany. *Nature* 385:807–810.

Vrba, E. S., E. H. Denton, and M. L. Prentice. 1989. Climatic influence on early hominid behavior. *Ossa* 14:127–156.

Walker, A., and P. Shipman. 1996. *The Wisdom of the Bones: in Search of Human Origins.* Alfred A. Knopf, New York, NY.

White, T. D. 1980. Evolutionary implications of Pliocene hominid footprints. *Science* 208:175–176.

White, T. D., G. Suwa, and B. Asfaw. 1994. *Australopithecus ramidus,* a new species of early hominid from Aramis, Ethiopia. *Nature* 371:306–312.

Wilson, A. C., and R. L. Cann. 1992. The recent African genesis of humans. Scientific American 266(4):68–73.

WoldeGabriel, G., T. D. White, and H. Buffetaut. 1994. Ecological and temporal placement of early Pliocene hominids at Aramis, Ethiopia. *Nature* 371:330–333.

Wood, B. 1987. Who is the "real" *Homo habilis? Nature* 327(6119):187–188.

Wood, B. 1992. Origin and evolution of the genus *Homo. Nature* 355:783–790.

Wood, B. 1994. The oldest hominid yet. *Nature* 371:280–281.

Yunis, J. J., and O. Prakash. 1982. The origin of man: a chromosomal legacy. *Science* 215:1525–1530.

Zihlman, A. L., J. Cronin, D. Cramer, and V. Sarich. 1978. Pygmy chimpanzee as possible prototype for the common ancestor of humans, chimpanzees and gorillas. *Nature* 275:744–746.

Glossary

Technical terms, and some words with special biological meanings, are included in this glossary. In general, if a word is defined in the text and appears only on the page where it is defined and immediately adjacent pages, we have not attempted to define it again in the glossary. Similarly, if the definition in a standard dictionary is adequate, we have not included it here. However, certain words have slightly different meanings in different contexts. In these cases we have included the word in this glossary and limited the definition to the use of the word in this book.

abduction Movement away from the midventral axis of the body (*see also* adduction).

acetabulum Depression on the pelvic girdle that accommodates the head of the femur.

adduction Movement toward the midventral axis of the body (*see also* abduction).

allochthonous With an origin somewhere other than the region where found.

allopatry Situation in which two or more populations or species occupy mutually exclusive, but often adjacent, geographic ranges.

ammonotelic Excreting nitrogenous wastes primarily as ammonia.

amniotes Those vertebrates whose embryos possess an amnion, chorion, and allantois (e.g., turtles, lepidosaurs, crocodilians, birds, and mammals).

amphicoelous (amphicelous) In which the vertebral centrum has both the anterior and posterior surfaces concave.

anadromous Migrating up a stream or river from a lake or ocean to spawn (of fishes).

angiosperm Most advanced and recently evolved of the vascular plants, characterized by production of seeds enclosed in tissues derived from the ovary. The ovary and/or seed is eaten by many vertebrates, and the success of the angiosperms has had important consequences for the evolution of terrestrial vertebrates.

aphotic "Without light"—for example, in deep-sea habitats or caves.

apocrine gland Type of gland in which the apical part of the cell from which the secretion is released breaks down in the process of secretion (*see also* holocrine gland).

apomorphic A character that is changed from its preexisting (ancestral) condition (*see also* autapomorphy).

aposematic Device (color, sound, behavior) used to advertise the noxious qualities of an animal.

arcade Curve or arch in a structure, such as the tooth row of humans.

archaic Of a form typical of an earlier evolutionary time.

archipterygium Fin skeleton, as in a lungfish, consisting of symmetrically arranged rays that extend from a central skeletal axis.

aural Of the external or internal ear or sense of hearing.

autapomorphy An attribute unique to one evolutionary lineage of organisms.

autochthonous With an origin in the region where found.

benthic Living at the soil/water interface at the bottom of a body of water.

bilateral symmetry (bisymmetry) Characteristic of a body that can be divided into mirror-image halves.

biomass Living organic material in a habitat (available as food for other species).

biome Biogeographic region defined by a series of spatially interrelated and characteristic life forms (e.g., tundra, mesopelagic zone, tropical rain forest, and coral reef).

brachial Pertaining to the forelimb.

branchial Pertaining to the gills.

branchiomeric Referring to segmentation of structures associated with, or derived from, the ancestral pharyngeal arches (*see also* metameric).

carapace Dorsal shell, as of a turtle.

catadromous Migrating down a river or stream to a lake or ocean to spawn (of fishes).

catastrophism Hypothesis of major evolutionary change as a result of unique catastrophic events of broad geographic and thus ecologic effect.

centrum Vertebral element formed in or around the notochord (plural, centra).

cephalic Pertaining to the head.

ceratotrichia Keratin fibers that support the web of the fins of Chondrichthyes.

choana Internal nares (plural, choanae).

chondrification Formation of cartilage.

clade Phylogenetic lineage originating from a common ancestral taxon and including all descendants (*see also* grade).

cladistic Pertaining to the branching sequences of phylogenesis.

cladogram Branching diagram representing the hypothesized relationships of taxa.

cleidoic egg One independent of environment except for heat and gas (carbon dioxide, oxygen, water vapor) exchange. Characteristic of amniotes.

cline   Change in a biological character along a geographic gradient.

coelom (celom)   Body cavity, lined with tissue of mesodermal origin.

coevolution   Complex biotic interaction through evolutionary time resulting in the adaptation of interacting species to unique features of the life histories of the other species in the system.

cones   Photoreceptor cells in the vertebrate retina that are differentially sensitive to light of different wavelengths.

conspecific   Belonging to the same species as that under discussion (*see also* heterospecific).

convergent evolution   Evolution of similar characters in phyletically distantly related or unrelated forms.

cosmine   Form of dentine containing branching canals characteristic of the cosmoid scales of crossopterygian fishes and early dipnoans.

countershaded   Referring to a color pattern in which the aspect of the body that is more brightly lighted (normally, the dorsal surface) is darker colored than the less brightly illuminated surface. The effect of countershading is to make an animal harder to distinguish from its background.

cranial   Pertaining to the cranium or skull, a unique and unifying characteristic of all vertebrates.

demersal   More dense than water and therefore sinking, as in the eggs of many fishes and amphibians.

detritus   Particulate organic matter that sinks to the bottom of a body of water.

deuterostomy   Condition in which the embryonic blastopore forms the anus of the adult animal; characteristic of chordates (*see also* protostomy).

double cone   Type of retinal photoreceptor in which two cones share a single axon (*see also* cones).

durophagous   Feeding on hard material.

ecosystem   Community of organisms and their entire physical environment.

ectoderm   One of the embryonic germ layers, the outer layer of the embryo.

ectotherm   An organism that relies on external sources of heat to raise its body temperature.

edentulous   Lacking teeth.

endemism   Property of being endemic (i.e., found only in a particular region).

endoderm   Innermost of the germ cell layers of late embryos.

endotherm   An organism that relies on internal (metabolic) heat to raise its body temperature.

epicontinental sea (epeiric sea)   Sea extending within the margin of a continent.

epigenetic   Pertaining to an interaction of tissues during embryonic development that results in the formation of specific structures.

epiphysis   (1) Pineal organ, an outgrowth of the roof of the diencephalon. (2) (plural, epiphyses) Accessory center of ossification at the ends of the long bones of mammals, birds, and some squamates. When the ossifications of the shaft (diaphysis) and epiphysis meet, lengthwise growth of the shaft ceases. This process produces a determinate growth pattern.

epiphyte   Plant that grows nonparasitically on another plant.

estivation (aestivation)   Form of torpor, usually a response to high temperatures or scarcity of water.

estuarine   Pertaining to, or formed in, a region where the fresh water of rivers mixes with the seawater of a coast.

euryhaline   Capable of living in a wide range of salinities (*see also* stenohaline).

euryphagous   Eating a wide range of food items; a food generalist (*see also* stenophagous).

eurythermal   Capable of tolerating a wide range of temperatures (*see also* stenothermal).

eurytopic   Capable of living in a broad range of habitats.

extraperitoneal   Positioned in the body wall beneath the lining of the coelom (the peritoneum) in contrast to being suspended in the coelom by mesenteries.

fossorial   Burrowing through the soil.

fovea centralis   Area of the vertebrate retina containing only cone cells, where the most acute vision is achieved at high light intensities.

furcula   Avian wishbone formed by the fusion of the two clavicles at their central ends.

geosyncline   Portion of the Earth's crust that has been subjected to downward warping. Sediments frequently accumulate in geosynclines.

gestation   Period during which an embryo is developing in the reproductive tract of the mother.

gill arch   Assemblage of tissues associated with a gill; the term may refer to the skeletal structure only or to the entire epithelial muscular and connective tissue complex.

Gondwana   Supercontinent that existed either independently or in close contact with all other major continental land masses throughout vertebrate evolution until the middle of the Mesozoic and was composed of all the modern Southern Hemisphere continents plus the subcontinent of India.

grade   A level of morphological organization achieved independently by different evolutionary lineages (*see also* clade).

gymnosperms   Group of plants in which the seed is not contained in an ovary—conifers, cycads, and ginkos.

hemal arch   Structure formed by paired projections ventral to the vertebral centrum and enclosing caudal blood vessels.

hermaphroditic   Having both male and female gonads.

heterocoelus   Having the articular surfaces of the vertebral centra saddle-shaped, as in modern birds.

heterospecific   Belonging to a different species from that under discussion (*see also* conspecific).

heterosporous plants   Plants with large and small spores; the smaller give rise to male gametophytes and the larger to female gametophytes (equivalent to protogymnosperms).

heterotrophic   Capable of using only organic materials as a source of energy.

holocrine gland   Type of gland in which the entire cell is destroyed with the discharge of its contents (*see also* apocrine gland).

homologous   Referring to characters having a common origin.

homology   The fundamental similarity of individual structures that belong to different species within a monophyletic group.

hydrosphere   Free liquid water of the earth—oceans, lakes, rivers, and so on.

hyperdactyly   Increase in the number of digits.

hyperphalangy   Increase in the number of bones in the digits.

hypertrophy   Increase in the size of a structure.

hypotremate   Having the main gill openings on the ventral surface and beneath the pectoral fins as in skates and rays (*see also* pleurotremate).

inguinal   Pertaining to the groin.

interspecific   Pertaining to phenomena occurring between members of different species.

intraspecific   Pertaining to phenomena occurring between members of the same species.

isohaline   Of the same salt concentration.

isostasy   Condition of gravitational balance between segments of the Earth's crust or of return to balance after a disturbance.

isostatic movement   Vertical displacement of the lithosphere due to changes in the mass over a point or region of the earth.

isotherm   Line on a map that connects points of equal temperature.

leptocephalus larva   Specialized, transparent, ribbon-shaped larva of tarpons, true eels, and their relatives.

lithosphere   Crust of the Earth.

littoral   Pertaining to the shallow portion of a lake, sea, or ocean where rooted plants are capable of growing.

lophophorate   Pertaining to several kinds of marine animals that possess ciliated tentacles (lophophores) used to collect food (e.g., pterobranchs).

meninges   Sheets of tissue enclosing the central nervous system. In mammals these are the dura mater, arachnoid, and pia mater.

mesenteries   Membranous sheets derived from the mesoderm that envelop and suspend the viscera from the body wall within the coelom.

mesoblast   Mesodermal cell.

mesoderm   Central of three germ layers of late embryos.

metameric   Pertaining to ancestral segmentation, used in reference to serially repeated units along the body axis.

monophyletic lineage   A taxon composed of a common ancestor and all its descendants.

monophyly   Relationship of two or more taxa having a common ancestor.

morph   Genetically determined variant in a population.

morphotypic   Referring to a type of classification based entirely on physical form.

neoteny   Retention of larval or embryonic characteristics past the time of reproductive maturity (*see also* paedomorphosis and progenesis).

neural arch   Dorsal projection from the vertebral centrum that, at its base, encloses the spinal cord.

neural crest   Embryonic cells unique to vertebrate animals, associated with the neurectoderm, but subsequently widely migrating to participate in the formation of many tissues and structures that are characteristic of the subphylum.

neurocranium   Portion of the head skeleton encasing the brain.

niche   The functional role of a species or other taxon in its environment—the ways in which it interacts with both the living and nonliving elements.

occipital   Pertaining to the posterior part of the skull.

ontogenetic   Pertaining to the development of an individual organism.

operculum   Flap or plate of tissue covering the gills.

orogeny   Process of crustal uplift or mountain building.

osseous   Bony.

outgroup   Group of organisms that is related to but removed from the group under study. One or more outgroups are examined to determine which character states are evolutionary novelties (apomorphies).

paedomorphosis   Condition in which a larva becomes sexually mature without attaining the adult body form. Paedomorphosis may be achieved by neoteny or by progenesis.

palatoquadrate   Upper jaw element of primitive fishes and Chondrichthyes, portions of which contribute to the palate, jaw articulation, and middle ear of other vertebrates.

Pangaea (Pangea)   Single supercontinent that existed during the mid-Paleozoic and consisted of all modern continents apparently in direct physical contact with a minimum of isolating physical barriers.

paraphyletic   Referring to a taxon that includes the common ancestor and some but not all of its descendants.

Phanerozoic   Period since the Cambrian.

pharyngotremy   Condition in which the pharyngeal walls are perforated by slitlike openings; found in chordates and hemichordates.

photophore   Light-emitting organ.

phylogenetic   Pertaining to the development of an evolutionary lineage (*see also* ontogenetic).

physoclistic   Lacking a connection from the gut to the swim bladder in adults (of fishes).

physostomous   Having a connection between the swim bladder and gut in adults (of fishes).

piloerection   Contraction of muscles attached to hair follicles resulting in the erection of the hair shafts.

piscivorous   Fish eating.

placoid scale   Primitive type of scale found in elasmobranchs and homologous with vertebrate teeth.

plastron   Ventral shell, as of a turtle.

plate tectonics   Theory of Earth history in which the lithosphere is continually being generated from the underlying core at specific areas and reabsorbed into the core at others, resulting in a series of conveyorlike plates that carry the continents across the face of the Earth.

plesiomorphic   Pertaining to the ancestral character from which an apomorphy is derived.

pleurotremate   Having the main gill openings on sides of the body anterior to the pectoral fins as in sharks (*see also* hypotremate).

polymorphism   Simultaneous occurrence of two or more distinct phenotypes in a population.

polyphyletic   Referring to a taxon that does not contain the most recent common ancestor of all the subordinate taxa of the taxon.

portal system   Portion of the venous system specialized for the transport of substances from the site of production to the site of action. A portal system begins and ends in capillary beds.

postzygapophysis   Articulating surface on the posterior face of a neural arch.

prezygapophysis   Articulating surface on the anterior face of a neural arch.

progenesis Accelerated development of reproductive organs relative to somatic tissue, leading to paedomorphosis.

Proterozoic Later part of the Precambrian, from about 1.5 billion years ago until the beginning of the Cambrian 500 million years ago (*see also* Phanerozoic).

protostomy Condition in which the embryonic blastopore forms the mouth of the adult animal (*see also* deuterostomy).

protraction Movement away from the center of the body (*see also* retraction).

protrusible Capable of being moved away (protruded) from the body.

refugium Isolated area of habitat fragmented from a formerly more extensive biome.

rete mirabile "Marvelous net," a complex mass of intertwined capillaries specialized for exchange of heat and/or dissolved substances between countercurrent flows.

retraction Movement toward the center of the body (*see also* protraction).

rod Photoreceptor cell in the vertebrate retina specialized to function effectively under conditions of dim light.

rostrum Snout; especially an extension anterior to the mouth.

scapulocoracoid cartilage In elasmobranchs and certain primitive gnathostomes, the single solid element of the pectoral girdle.

scutes Scales, especially broad or inflexible ones.

serial Repeated, as are the body segments of vertebrates.

sinus Open space in a duct or tubular system.

sister group Group of organisms most closely related to the study taxa, excluding their direct descendants.

somite Member of a series of paired segments of the embryonic dorsal mesoderm of vertebrates.

speciose Referring to a taxon that contains a large number of species.

squamation Scaly covering of the body.

stenohaline Capable of living only within a narrow range of salinity of surrounding water; not capable of surviving a great change in salinity (*see also* euryhaline).

stenophagous Eating a narrow range of food items; a food specialist.

stenothermal Capable of living or of being active in only a narrow range of temperatures (*see also* eurythermal).

stratigraphy Classification, correlation, and interpretation of stratified rocks.

stratum Layer of material (plural, strata).

sympatry Occurrence of two or more species in the same area.

symphysis A joint between bones formed by a pad or disk of fibrocartilage that allows a small degree of movement.

symplesiomorphy Character shared by a group of organisms that is found in their common ancestor.

talonid Basinlike heel on a lower molar tooth, found in certain mammals.

tarsometatarsus Bone formed by fusion of the distal tarsal elements with the metatarsals in birds and some dinosaurs (*see also* tibiotarsus).

taxon Any scientifically recognized group of organisms.

thecodont teeth Teeth set in bony sockets in the jaw.

tibiotarsus Bone formed by fusion of the tibia and proximal tarsal elements in birds and some dinosaurs (*see also* tarsometatarsus).

troglodyte Organism that lives in caves.

trophic Pertaining to feeding and nutrition.

ureotelic Excreting nitrogenous wastes primarily as urea.

uricotelic Excreting nitrogenous wastes primarily as uric acid and its salts.

urogenital Pertaining to the organs, ducts, and structures of the excretory and reproductive systems.

vacuoles Membrane-bound spaces within cells containing secretions, storage products, and so on.

viscera Internal organs of the coelom.

visceral skeleton Skeleton primitively associated with the pharyngeal arches, uniquely derived from the neural crest cells and forming in mesoderm immediately adjacent to the endoderm lining the gut.

zygapophysis Articular process of the neural arch of a vertebra (*see also* postzygapophysis and prezygapophysis).

zygodactylous Type of foot, in which the toes are arranged in two opposable groups.

Subject Index

Author Index